Comparative Embryology
of the
Vertebrates

Comparative Embryology of the Vertebrates

by

Olin E. Nelsen, M.A., Ph.D.

Department of Zoology
University of Pennsylvania

With 2057 Drawings and Photographs
Grouped as 380 Illustrations

New York · THE BLAKISTON COMPANY, Inc. · Toronto

PRINTED IN THE UNITED STATES OF AMERICA
BY REEHL LITHO COMPANY, INC., NEW YORK, N. Y.

THIS VOLUME IS
DEDICATED RESPECTFULLY TO
MY PARENTS

Preface

A study of the comparative embryology of a group of animals such as the vertebrates when followed to its logical conclusion leads to a consideration of the comparative anatomy of the group. Students claim, and justly so, that they learn best through the association of events, things, and concepts. As applied to the study of vertebrate embryology and anatomy, the principle of learning by association means this: observations upon the adult anatomy of the various organ-systems of a particular vertebrate species when correlated with the earlier stages of embryonic development of these systems lead to a more ready perception and understanding of structural principles and relationships involved. Furthermore, when the developmental anatomy and the adult anatomy of any one species is associated with similar phenomena in other species of the vertebrate group it naturally produces a clearer understanding of the development and morphology of the group as a whole. This broad, comprehensive approach is a fundamental one and it is a requirement for the furtherance of research in vertebrate biology, whether it be on the level of cellular chemistry or the physiology of organ-systems.

An endeavor to satisfy a demand for a comprehensive approach to vertebrate development by an extension of the descriptions of the earlier phases of the embryology of several representative vertebrate species into their final stages of development, and hence into the realm of comparative anatomy, is the main purpose of this book. This goal is the greatest defense which the author can give for his effort to assemble the material and data contained herein.

On the other hand, though the book correlates comparative vertebrate embryology with comparative vertebrate anatomy, its arrangement is such that the fundamental features of comparative vertebrate embryology readily can be divorced from the intricate phases of comparative anatomy. For example, Chaps. 1–11, 20, 21, and 22 are devoted to a consideration of basic embryological principles whereas Chaps. 12–20 treat particularly the relationships of comparative embryology and comparative anatomy. A proper selection of descriptive material in Chaps. 12–20 (which may be done readily by a survey of the outline heading each chapter) added to the basic embryological data affords a basis for a thorough course in comparative vertebrate embryology.

The selection of material suggested in the previous paragraph brings forth another motive for writing this text. It has been the author's habit—one common to many other teachers—never to give a course in exactly the same way two years in succession. This procedure enlivens a course and keeps successive groups of students out of the rut of looking forward to the same identical lectures and laboratory approach year after year. As a result, in reality this book is a compilation of the different aspects of embryology presented by the author over a period of years to classes in comparative vertebrate embryology. Consequently, by the use of certain chapters and the outlines at the headings of each chapter, various facets of embryology may be presented one year while other aspects are selected the following year, and so on. Moreover, a selective procedure allows the book to be used readily for short courses in embryology as well as longer courses. For example, Chaps. 3, 5–11, and 20–22 may serve as the basis for a short course in vertebrate embryology.

Another feature of the text is the presentation of many illustrations well prepared. Illustrations are an important adjunct to the teaching of embryology. This is true especially where the teacher is burdened with the teaching of other courses and thus is handicapped by lack of time to make adequate blackboard drawings and illustrations of laboratory and lecture material. In Chaps. 3, 5–11, and 20–22, one finds illustrative material adequate to enable the student to gain an appreciation of the fundamental features of vertebrate development. Thus, this part of the book may be used extensively as a laboratory guide to the fundamental principles involved in vertebrate development.

A final aspect of the text may be mentioned, namely, the references given at the close of the chapters. References to literature are important especially in courses of embryology where small groups of students are assembled. Under these conditions the teacher often prefers to give the course on a seminar basis. With this approach, references are most valuable in the assignment of special reports and student lectures which the student later gives to the class as a whole.

Acknowledgments

The author expresses his great obligation to and appreciation for the superior artistic abilities, continual patience, and conscientious effort of Elisabeth R. Swain who executed the difficult task of preparing—with certain exceptions —the illustrations for this text. He also wishes to express his sincere thanks to Edna R. White and Julia A. Lloyd who contributed illustrations. These three artists were most exact in carrying out the author's instructions for illustrations, and also in transforming his preliminary sketches into finished drawings.

The author is indebted greatly to Wistar Institute of Anatomy and Biology, Philadelphia, for permission to redraw various illustrations from the journals published by the Wistar Institute. Appreciation similarly goes to the Carnegie Institution of Washington; The Marine Biological Laboratory, Woods Hole, Mass.; Williams and Wilkins Co., Baltimore; University of Chicago Press, Chicago; Yale University Press, New Haven; Academic Press, Inc., New York; Museum of Comparative Zoology at Harvard College; Oxford University Press, Inc., New York; Ginn and Co., Boston; W. B. Saunders Co., Philadelphia; McGraw-Hill Book Co., Inc., New York; Henry Holt and Co., Inc., New York; W. W. Norton and Co., Inc., New York; John Wiley and Sons, Inc., New York; J. B. Lippincott Co., Philadelphia; The Macmillan Co., New York and London; Knopf, Inc., New York; Appleton-Century Co., Inc., New York; Sidgewick and Jackson, Ltd., London; Cambridge University Press, England; and Columbia University Press, New York.

To his colleagues in the Department of Zoology of the University of Pennsylvania the author owes a debt of appreciation for encouragement during the writing of the manuscript, especially to Dr. J. Percy Moore, Dr. D. H. Wenrich, and Dr. L. V. Heilbrunn. Acknowledgments and appreciation go to Mrs. Anna R. Whiting, also of the Department of Zoology, and to Dr. Miles D. McCarthy of the Harrison Department of Surgical Research of the University of Pennsylvania Medical School and the Department of Zoology, Pomona College, Claremont, California, who read much of the manuscript and offered valuable suggestions. Frances R. Houston, Librarian of the University of Pennsylvania Medical School, and Elizabeth D. Thorp, Librarian of the Botany-Zoological Library of the University of Pennsylvania, deserve sincere thanks for coöperative understanding and help in securing and placing many periodicals at the author's disposal. Various students contributed clerical efforts toward the completion of this work, especially Barbara Neely Gilford, Carolyn Kerr, and Louise Mertz. Their endeavors are appreciated greatly.

Any attempt of the author to acknowledge obligations would be incomplete, indeed, without mention of the extreme readiness to serve and coöperate on the part of Dr. James B. Lackey, then Science Editor of The Blakiston Co. (presently Research Professor, School of Engineering, University of Florida), and also to Irene Claire Moore, then Assistant Manuscript Editor (presently Book Editor, United Lutheran Publication House, Philadelphia), and to W. T. Shoener, Production Manager.

THE AUTHOR

Autumn 1952
Philadelphia, Pa.

Contents

PART V

The Care of the Developing Embryo

Orientation

I. Some Definitions Relative to Embryology

The word *embryo* has various shades of meaning. In general, it is applied to the rudimentary or initial state of anything while it remains in an undeveloped or primitive condition. As used in zoology, it designates in one sense the earlier stages of the development of an animal before the definitive or adult form of the species is assumed; or, in a second sense, it signifies the entire period of prenatal existence.

The word *development* not only is used to denote the various changes evident in prenatal emergence, but also it applies to postnatal changes as well. Moreover, in the development of a particular animal it may be extended beyond the period of structural and physiological maturity to the changes involved in eventual senescence.

The developing young of viviparous animals while undergoing the later stages of development within the uterus is spoken of as a *fetus*. This term is used also, on occasion, to designate the later stages of development of oviparous species. The phrase *mammary fetus* is applied to the young of marsupial mammals such as the opossum while it remains attached to the nipple within the marsupial pouch of the mother.

The term *descriptive embryology* is applied to the method of embryological study concerned with the direct observation and description of embryological development. Up to the latter part of the last century embryology was concerned mainly with the direct observation of the changes going on in the intact embryo. However, beginning in the 1880's Wilhelm Roux and others initiated the expeimental approach in embryological study and the school of *experimental or causal embryology* was formed. In experimental embryology various parts of the developing embryo are removed, transplanted, parts are exchanged, or the environmental conditions are altered. The end sought by this method is an analysis of the respective roles played during development by different parts of the developing organism and by different environmental factors, in an endeavor to give a mechanical and functional explanation of development. One of the outstanding results of the experimental method applied to embryological study is the great body of evidence which points to the fact that in the vertebrate group one of the main processes in development (morphogenesis) is the *induction of organs and organ-systems by so-called organizer cellular areas present in certain parts of the developing embryo.* Organization of the developing body, in other words, is dependent upon a series of changes mediated by cellular groups known as organizers which appear at the correct time and locus in development.

It soon became apparent, however, that the terminology employed in experimental embryology was vague because it substituted indefinite terms such as "inductors" or "organizers" as an explanation of developmental events. The use of the word organizer means little unless one is able to describe the manner of operation of the physical and chemical substances which effect the results produced by the organizer. Consequently, embryologists with physiological and biochemical training are concerned now with the effort of determining the specific chemical factors concerned with the various processes and steps involved in development. This type of embryological study is called *biochemical* or *chemical embryology*. Chemical embryology is divisible into two main lines of attack, namely, an investigation of the chemistry of cells and cellular parts or *cytochemistry*, and a study of the chemistry of groups of cells or *histochemistry*.

II. Free-living Versus Sheltered Embryological Forms; Periods of Development

The independence of a free-living existence on the part of developing young is assumed at different stages of development depending upon the species involved. For example, in the case of the frog, the developing embryo becomes free-living at an early stage and it experiences a free-living larval existence for an extended period before its metamorphosis into the adult or definitive form of the frog. In the chick, the young undertakes a kind of free-living existence at the time of hatching or about a week after it has assumed the definitive body form. The human young, on the other hand, experiences an extensive period of fetal development for about five months in utero after it has achieved definitive body form. Moreover, it is most helpless and dependent even after birth.

Regardless of the time during its development when an animal species assumes a free-living, independent existence, it is apparent that the development of the individual as a whole may be divided into two general periods, viz., *embryonic* and *post-embryonic periods*. The *embryonic period* of development begins at fertilization of the egg and continues for a time after *definitive body form* is achieved. The end of the embryonic period may be regarded as the time of birth in viviparous forms, hatching in oviparous species, and the end of metamorphosis in free-living larval species. This is an arbitrary and, for some forms, quite comprehensive definition. Nevertheless, for comparative purposes this definition is suitable. The post-embryonic period begins at the termination of the embryonic phase of development and continues through sexual maturity into later life.

The embryonic period of development in all vertebrate species may be resolved into three distinct phases:

a. *An early embryonic period* which begins at the time when the egg starts to develop and which reaches its culmination when the embryo has attained the state of *primitive, generalized body form* (see Chaps. 10 and 11, and fig. 255).

b. *A period of transition* then follows during which the structural conditions prevalent in primitive body form are transformed into the morphology present in *definitive body form*. Definitive body form is reached *when the embryo assumes a general resemblance to the adult form of the species*. The changes described in Chaps. 12–20 are concerned to a considerable extent with this phase of development.

c. *The late embryonic period*. This phase of development comprises the changes which the embryo experiences for a time after it has achieved definitive body form. In the human embryo, it includes several months of fetal growth in the uterus, and in the chick it is of about a week's duration continuing from day 14 of incubation to the time of hatching around day 20. In the frog it is a brief period during the close, and possibly shortly after, metamorphosis.

The period of transition may be regarded as the *larval period of development*. If so conceived, two types of larval forms exist, namely (1) *free-living larval forms* such as the frog tadpole in which the body structures are adapted to a free-living existence outside of protective embryonic structures, and (2) *non-free-living larval forms* in which the larval or transitional period is passed within the confines of covering egg membranes or within the protective tissues of the female or male parent. Free-living larval forms include Amphioxus, most fishes, and amphibia, while some fishes and all reptiles, birds, and mammals may be regarded as having a protected larval existence.

III. Summary of Developmental Phenomena Associated with the Life of an Individual Vertebrate Animal

A. PERIOD OF PREPARATION

During this period the parents are prepared for reproduction and the reproductive cells or gametes are elaborated.

B. EMBRYONIC DEVELOPMENT

1. *Early embryonic period*

This period begins with fertilization of the egg and ends with the development of primitive embryonic body form with its basic conditions of the various systems. The *basic or group condition* of a particular vertebrate organ-system is that stage of development of the system when it possesses structural features common to all embryos of the vertebrate group. When the common or primitive embryonic conditions of the various systems are present, a common, basic, primitive embryonic body form also is present. Hence, all vertebrate embryos tend to pass through a stage of development in which the shape and form of the developing body resembles that of all other vertebrate species at this stage of development. This stage of body formation is known as the *primitive, embryonic body-form stage.*

2. *The larval period or period of transition*

During this phase of development, the basic conditions of the organ-systems, which are present at the end of primitive body formation, are transformed into the structural conditions present in definitive body form. At the end of this period of development the general form of the organ-systems, and of the embryo as a whole, resembles the adult morphology of the species. Hence the term: *"definitive body form."*

3. *The late embryonic period*

This part of development intervenes between the time when definitive body form is established and the episode of hatching or birth. In free-living larval species it comprises a brief period at the end of metamorphosis.

C. POST-EMBRYONIC DEVELOPMENT

Post-embryonic development may be divided into the following periods:

1. *Prepuberal period*

During this time the organ-systems grow and enlarge, and the reproductive mechanisms mature.

2. *Puberal period and the adult*

The organism now is capable of reproduction, and in size, activity, and appearance is recognized as an adult.

3. *Period of senescence and decline*

The sexual activities lessen and the organ-systems of the body may very slowly undergo regressive changes.

IV. A Classification of the Vertebrates and Related Species

A. CHARACTERISTICS OF THE PHYLUM CHORDATA

The vertebrates belong to the phylum *Chordata.* This phylum is characterized by three main features which appear in the early embryo, viz., (1) a *dorsally situated nerve cord* which in most instances is hollow or tube-like; (2) a dorsally placed *notochordal or median skeletal axis* located always immediately ventral to the nerve cord, and (3) a complicated anterior portion of the digestive tract known as the *pharynx*. The pharyngeal area of the digestive tract is composed of a series of paired skeletogenous arches known as the *visceral or branchial arches,* between which are found the *branchial pouches* and *branchial furrows or grooves.*

B. MAJOR DIVISIONS OF THE PHYLUM

The entire phylum *Chordata* may be divided into the *lower chordates* and the *higher chordates.*

Lower Chordata (Acraniata)

Subphylum: Hemichordata

These are small, soft-bodied animals living along the shores of the sea, and in some instances to considerable depths into the sea. Dorsal and ventral nerve cords are present in the class *Enteropneusta* or the "tongue worms." The notochord is a short structure confined to the anterior end. Gill slits are present.

Subphylum: Urochordata (Tunicata)

These forms inhabit the sea from the polar regions to the equator, and from the shores outward to considerable depths. It is in the larval form that this group lays most of its claim to a right to be placed among the Chordata, for the young hatches as a larva which resembles the amphibian tadpole superficially. In this tadpole a dorsal nerve cord is present, and in the tail region a well-formed notochord as well. Gill slits also are found. Later in life the larva settles down to a sessile existence and the tail with its notochord is lost.

Examples: *Styela partita; Molgula manhattensis; Ciona intestinalis.*

Subphylum: Cephalochordata (Lancets)

To this group belong the familiar forms known as *Amphioxus.* Of all the lower chordates, the lancets possess characteristics closely resembling the higher chordate group. A dorsal tubular nerve cord is present, below which is an elongated notochord, and an extensive pharyngeal area is developed. The basic plan of the circulatory system resembles that of the vertebrate group, although many pulsating "hearts" are to be found, one in each of the numerous blood vessels coursing through the pharyngeal area.

Examples: *Branchiostoma virginiae; B. californiense; Asymmetron macricaudatum.*

Higher Chordata (Craniata)

Subphylum: Vertebrata

Group I: *Agnathostomata*

To this group belong the cyclostomes or the vertebrates without jaws. The cyclostomes include the lampreys (Hyperoartia) and the hagfishes (Hyperotreta). They are parasitic on other fishes in the adult. The notochord and its surrounding sheaths serve as the main skeletal axis. True vertebral elements do not reinforce the notochord, although certain vertebral elements are present in some species.

Examples: The California hagfish, *Polistotrema (Bdellostoma) stouti,* and the common sea lampreys, *Petromyzon marinus, Okkelbergia lamotteni, Lampetra ayresii.*

The California hagfish has 12 pairs of gill slits whereas the sea lamprey, *Petromyzon marinus,* has 7 pairs.

Group II: *Gnathostomata*

The Gnathostomata are vertebrates which possess jaws. In a sense, they are the only true vertebrates in the chordate phylum, for the notochordal axis always is supplemented or displaced by vertebral elements.

1. Class: *Pisces*

Division 1: *Chondrichthyes*

To this group belong the selachian or elasmobranch fishes. The word chondrichthyes means cartilaginous fishes, i.e. the fishes with endoskeletons of cartilage. The adjective *selachian* has a similar meaning, whereas the term *elasmobranch* means plate-like gill.

The *sharks, skates, rays,* and *chimaeras* comprise the numerous species of cartilaginous fishes. The skin is covered with small placoid scales; median and paired fins are present; the sexes are separate, and elaborate reproductive ducts are developed. The heart, exclusive of the sinus venosus, is two chambered.

Examples: *Squalus acanthias,* the dog fish; *Rhineodon typus,* the whale shark; *Manta birostus,* the "great devil ray."

Division 2: *Dipnoi*

The dipnoan or lungfishes effect external respiration by means of gills and well-formed lungs. The heart, in harmony with its respiratory mechanisms, is practically three-chambered. Paired fins have a segmented, cartilaginous, central axis.

Examples: The African lungfish, *Protopterus annectens;* the South American lungfish, *Lepidosiren paradoxa;* and the Australian lungfish, *Neoceratodus forsteri.*

Division 3: *Teleostomi*

In this group, the skeleton, in most species, is bony. A single opening for the gill-chamber is present on each side of the pharynx, the gills being covered by an operculum. An air bladder is found in most species. Paired fins are not supported by a median axis.

Series 1. The *Ganoidei*. The ganoid fishes, possessing ganoid or cycloid scales. An air bladder is to be found with an open duct united to the post-pharyngeal area. A spiral valve is developed in the intestine. There are two groups of ganoid fishes, viz. the *Chondrostei*, which possess a cartilaginous skeleton and dermal bony plates, and the *Holostei* which have a bony skeleton.

Examples of Chondrostei are *Acipenser fulvescens, Scaphirhynchus platorhynchus,* and *Parascaphirhynchus albus. Lepisosteus osseus* and *Amia calva* are representatives of the Holostei.

Series 2. *Teleostei.* In the bony fishes an air bladder is present but usually the pneumatic duct connecting the air bladder with the esophagus is rudimentary or absent. A spiral valve is absent in the intestine. The scales are cycloid or ctenoid, and in some instances are absent altogether.

Examples: *Oncorhynchus tschawytscha,* the chinook or king salmon, the most important source of food fish in the country; *Salmo salar,* the Atlantic salmon; *Trutta irideus,* the rainbow trout; *Salvelinus fontinalis,* the speckled brook trout, and a host of other genera and species.

2. Class: *Amphibia*

The amphibians are cold-blooded vertebrates adapted to an existence in a watery or moist medium. Some species such as *Necturus maculosus* and the axolotl, *Ambystoma mexicanum,* spend their entire life within water, while others such as the frogs and salamanders are in and out of the water. The toads, on the other hand, are able to get along under fairly dry conditions. The skin is soft, moist, and glandular, and, with the exception of the Gymnophiona, it is devoid of scales. External respiration is carried on by means of gills in the larva, but in the adult the lungs and skin are the principal areas concerned with respiration. However, in those adults which live exclusively in the water, gills may be retained. Some species do not possess lungs and in these the skin and lining surfaces of the pharynx accommodate respiratory functions. In forms such as *Necturus* and the *Axolotl,* external gills function as the principal mechanism of external respiration in the adult. Excluding the sinus venosus, a three-chambered heart is typical of the group.

Order 1: *Caudata (Urodela)*

The salamanders and newts form a large number of amphibian species. They have an elongate body with a conspicuous tail and the body muscles tend to retain a segmental condition. Many vertebrae are present.

Examples: *Cryptobranchus alleganiensis, Triturus viridescens, Ambystoma maculatum, Desmognathus fuscus, Plethodon cinereus, Amphiuma means, Necturus maculatus, Siren lacertina, Triton cristatus,* etc.

Order 2: *Anura (Salienta)*

The frogs and toads. Short compact body; tail absent in adult; only nine vertebrae present; ribs ankylosed to vertebrae as short processes; hind legs long and muscular.

Examples: *Ascaphus truei, Scaphiopus holbrookii, Bufo americanus, Rana pipiens, R. sylvatica, R. catesbiana, Hyla crucifer, Discoglossus pictus, Xenopus laevis, Pipa pipa, Nectophrynoides vivipara.*

Order 3: *Gymnophiona*

The caecilians are long-bodied, limbless amphibians resembling earthworms. They are inhabitants of the tropics with the exception of Madagascar. Scales are present in the dermal layer of the skin.

Examples: *Hypogeophis alternans, Scolecomorphus uluguruensis, Caecilia tentaculata.*

3. Class: *Reptilia*

Scale-covered, cold-blooded, claw-digited vertebrates with a three- or four-chambered heart, and generally inhabitants of dry land or streams. External respiration carried on exclusively by means of lungs.

Order 1: *Crocodila*

The crocodilians include the alligators and crocodiles. These are large greatly elongated reptiles covered with scales and bony plates. The eye has an upper and lower lid and a nictitating membrane. Teeth are thecodont. All species are oviparous. The anus is a longitudinal opening.

Examples: *Alligator mississippiensis* and *Crocodylus acutus.*

Order 2: *Lacertilia*

The lizards are elongated reptiles of diverse sizes. Teeth are pleurodont or acrodont. The eye has an upper and lower eyelid and a nictitating membrane. The tympanum is not at the surface, and the ear opening may be covered by scales. A vestigial pineal or median eye is often present, and the tongue is well developed and protusile. Most species are oviparous, a few are ovoviparous, and some may be classed as viviparous. The anus is a transverse slit.

Examples: *Anolis carolinensis,* the chameleon; *Sphaerodactylus notatus,* the reef gecko; *Phyrynosoma cornutum,* the horned toad; *Heloderma suspectum,* the Gila Monster; the Tuatera of New Zealand, and the dragon lizard of the Dutch East Indies.

Order 3: *Serpentes*

Snakes are crawling reptiles who have lost their legs. They form a large number of reptilian species. Acrodont teeth always are present. Functional eyelids are absent and they lack a tympanum or external ear opening. Some species are oviparous and others are ovoviviparous.

Examples: *Natrix sipedon,* the common water snake; *Thamnophis radix,* the common garter snake; *Crotalus horridus,* the common rattler.

Order 4: *Testudinata*

Turtles possess short, compact bodies encased more or less completely in a box constructed of bony plates integrated to form a dorsal covering, the *carapace,* and a ventral shield, the *plastron.* The jaws are toothless and covered by a horny cutting edge. The tympanum is at the surface of the body and eyelids and nictitating membrane are present. All species are oviparous.

Examples: *Sternotherus odoratus,* the musk turtle; *Chelydra serpentina,* the snapping turtle; *Clemmys guttata,* the spotted turtle; and *Terrapene carolina,* the common box turtle.

4. Class: *Aves*

Birds are warm-blooded, lung-breathing vertebrates with feathers, without teeth, and with a horny beak. The body is built for flight and most species fly. All species are oviparous. Other than the extinct birds or *Archaeornithes,* all modern birds may be grouped together under the heading *Neornithes.* The Neornithes may be divided into two main groups:

Series 1: *Ratitae* (running birds)

The flightless running birds such as the recently extinct moas, and present living forms such as the kiwi, *Apteryx;* the cassowary, *Casuarius* sp., and the ostrich, *Struthio* sp., belong in this group.

Series 2: *Carinatae (flying birds)*

This group contains many orders. The following orders are intimately associated with man:

Anseriformes: Geese, ducks, swans
Galliformes: The common fowl, turkey, pheasants, guinea hen, etc.
Columbiformes: Doves, pigeons
Passeriformes: Canary and other common song birds

5. Class: *Mammalia*

The mammals are warm-blooded, lung-breathing vertebrates with a coating of hair. They produce a nutritive substance for the young which is elaborated in glandular areas known as the *mammae* or *breasts.*

Division 1: *Prototheria*

These are highly specialized egg-laying mammals found only in Australia, Tasmania, and New Guinea. The spiny anteater, *Echidna aculeata,* is found in all of these localities and the Platypus or *Ornithorynchus paradoxus,* is an inhabitant of Australia. The urogenital ducts and intestine open posteriorly into a common chamber, the cloaca.

Division 2: *Theria* or true mammals

The Theria bring forth their young alive, possess true mammary glands with nipples, and all produce a small egg with little stored food material. They also possess separate openings to the exterior for the urogenital ducts and the intestine, a cloaca being absent in the adult condition.

Series 1: *Metatheria.* These are the marsupial or pouched mammals such as the Virginia opossum, *Didelphys virginiana.*

Series 2: *Eutheria.* The following orders are given:

Subseries 1. *Unguiculata* or mammals with claws

Order 1. *Insectivora* or insect-eating mammals
Examples: Moles and shrews

Order 2. *Chiroptera* or flying mammals
Example: The bats

Order 3. *Carnivora* or flesh-eating mammals
Examples: Wolves, dogs, foxes, raccoons, otters, skunks, weasels, mink, hyenas, cats, lions, tigers

Order 4: *Rodentia* or gnawing mammals
Examples: Rats, mice, rabbits, hares, guinea pigs, squirrels, beavers, gophers (ground squirrels), prairie dogs

Order 5. *Edentata* or mammals without teeth or with reduced condition of the teeth
Examples: Armadillos, three-toed sloths, anteaters

Order 6. *Pinnipedia* or mammals with bilateral appendages adapted for swimming
Examples: Seals, sea-lions, walruses

Subseries 2. *Ungulata* or mammals with hoofs

Order 7. *Artiodactyla* or even-toed mammals
Examples: Hippopotami, peccaries, swine, deer, moose, elk, pronghorn antelope, cows, sheep, goats, camels, giraffe, llamas, antelopes, gazelles

Order 8. *Perissodactyla* or odd-toed mammals
Examples: Horses, zebras, asses, tapirs, rhinoceroses

Order 9. *Sirenia* or mammals with hind limbs absent and adapted to living in the water
Example: The manatees or sea cows

Order 10. *Proboscidea*
Examples: The elephants

Subseries 3. Cetacea or marine mammals

    Order 11. *Odontoceti* or toothed whales

        Examples: Porpoises, sperm whales, killer whales, narwhals

    Order 12. *Mystacoceti* or whalebone whales

        Examples: Sulphur-bottom whales, right whales, finback whales

Subseries 4. Primates or mammals with flattened, distal modifications
of the digits known as nails

    Order 13. Primates

        Examples: Man, monkeys, lemurs, apes

PART I

The Period of Preparation

The events which precede the initiation of the new individual's development are:

(1) The preparation of the male and female parents and their reproductive structures for the act of reproduction (Chaps. 1 and 2).

(2) The preparation of the gametes (Chap. 3).

The anterior lobe of the pituitary gland, because of its secretion of the gonadotrophic (gonad-stimulating) hormones, is the pivotal structure in the reproductive mechanism. The gonadotrophic hormones are:

(1) Follicle-stimulating hormone, FSH;

(2) Luteinizing hormone, LH (ICSH), and

(3) Luteotrophin, LTH.

1

1

The Testis and Its Relation to Reproduction

A. Introduction
  1. General description of the male reproductive system
  2. Importance of the testis
B. Anatomical features of the male reproductive system
  1. Anatomical location of the testis
  2. Possible factors involved in testis descent
  3. General structure of the scrotum and the testis in mammals
     a. Structure of the scrotum
     b. General structure of the testis
  4. Specific structures of the mammalian testis which produce the reproductive cells and the male sex hormone
     a. Seminiferous tubules
     b. Interstitial tissue
  5. The testis of vertebrates in general
  6. Accessory reproductive structures of the male
     a. The reproductive duct in forms utilizing external fertilization
     b. The reproductive duct in species practicing internal fertilization
C. Specific activities of the various parts of the male reproductive system
  1. Introduction
     a. Three general functions of the male reproductive system
     b. Some definitions
  2. Activities of the testis
     a. Seasonal and non-seasonal types of testicular activity
     b. Testicular tissue concerned with male sex-hormone production
     c. Testicular control of body structure and function by the male sex hormone
        1) Sources of the male sex hormone
        2) Biological effects of the male sex hormone
           a) Effects upon the accessory reproductive structures
           b) Effects upon secondary sex characteristics and behavior of the individual
           c) Effects upon the seminiferous tubules
     d. Seminiferous-tubule activity and formation of sperm
     e. The seminiferous tubule as a sperm-storing structure
  3. Role of the reproductive duct in sperm formation
     a. Vertebrates without a highly tortuous epididymal portion of the reproductive duct
     b. The epididymis as a sperm-ripening structure
     c. The epididymis and vas deferens as sperm-storage organs
     d. Two types of vertebrate testes relative to sperm formation

3

  4. Function of the seminal vesicles (vesicular glands)
  5. Function of the prostate gland
  6. Bulbourethral (Cowper's) glands
  7. Functions of seminal fluid
   a. Amount of seminal fluid discharged and its general functions
   b. Coagulation of the semen
   c. Hyaluronidase
   d. Accessory sperm
   e. Fructose
   f. Enzyme-protecting substances
D. Internal and external factors influencing activities of the testis
  1. Internal factors
   a. Temperature and anatomical position of the testis
   b. Body nourishment in relation to testicular function
   c. The hypophysis and its relation to testicular function
  2. External environmental factors and testis function
   a. Light as a factor
   b. Temperature influences
E. Internal factors which may control seasonal and continuous types of testicular function
F. Characteristics of the male reproductive cycle and its relation to reproductive conditions in the female

A. Introduction

1. General Description of the Male Reproductive System

The male reproductive system of most vertebrate animals consists of two testis with a sperm-conveying duct and attendant auxiliary glands associated with each testis. In some species, such as the frog and many teleost fishes, the sperm-conveying duct is a simple structure, but in most vertebrate forms there is a tendency for the duct to be complicated. The cyclostomatous fishes do not possess sperm-conveying ducts from the testis to the outside.

In reptiles, some birds and all mammals, in gymnophionan amphibia and in the "tailed" frog, *Ascaphus,* in sharks and certain teleost fishes, an intromittent organ is added to the sperm-conveying structures for the purpose of internal fertilization. But an intromittent organ is not present in all species which practice internal fertilization. In many salamanders, internal fertilization is effected by the spawning of a spermatophore filled with sperm; the latter is picked up by the cloaca of the female. The sperm in these salamanders are stored in special pockets or tubules within the dorsal wall of the cloaca. These storage tubules form the **spermatheca** (fig. 10). Direct transfer of sperm to the female by cloacal contact may occur in some species.

2. Importance of the Testis

The word testis or testicle was formerly applied to the ovary of the female, as well as to the male sperm-producing organ, and the term "female testicle" was used in reference to the female organ. The use of the word "ovary" was introduced by Steno in 1667, and also by de Graaf (fig. 1) in 1672 in his work on the female generative organs. To quote from de Graaf: "Thus, the general function of the female testicles is to generate the ova, to nourish them, and to bring them to maturity, so that they serve the same purpose in women as the ovaries of birds. Hence, they should rather be called ovaries than testes because they show no similarity, either in form or contents, with the male testes properly so called." (See Corner, '43.) From the time of de Graaf the word "testis" has been restricted to designate the male organ essential to reproduction.

The phrase "essential to reproduction" does not describe fully the importance of testicular function. As we shall see later on, the testis not only assumes the major role in the male's activities during the period of reproduction, but also, in the interim between specific reproductive periods, it governs in many instances male behavior leading to protection and preservation of the species. Thus, the testis is the organ responsible for maleness in its broader, more vigorous sense.

B. Anatomical Features of the Male Reproductive System

Before endeavoring to understand the general functions of the testis in relation to reproduction, it is best to review some of the structural relationships of the testis in the vertebrate group.

FIG. 1. Reinier de Graaf. Born in Holland, 1641; died in Delft, Holland, 1673. Author of important works on the generative organs of the female. Described the Graafian follicle in the ovary of mammals but erroneously believed it to be the mammalian egg. (From Corner, '43.)

1. ANATOMICAL LOCATION OF THE TESTIS

In most vertebrates other than mammals, the testes are suspended well forward within the peritoneal cavity. In the *Mammalia,* however, the condition is variable. In the monotrematous mammals, *Echidna* and *Ornithorynchus,* the testes are located within the peritoneal cavity near the kidneys. In the elephant the testes also are located in this area. Schulte ('37) describes the position of the testes in an Indian elephant *(Elephas indicus),* 20 years old, as being "retroperitoneal lying on each side medial to the lower pole of the kidney." (The kidneys were found to lie retroperitoneally on either side of the lower thoracic and lumbar vertebrae, and each measured about 275 mm. in length.) However, in the majority of mammals the testes descend posteriad from the original embryonic site, the extent varying with the species. In some there is a slight posterior migration, and the testes of the adult are situated well forward in the pelvic region. Examples of this condition are found in conies, whales, sea cows, African jumping shrews, and in armadillos. In sloths and American anteaters, the testes may descend into the pelvic cavity and lie in the area between the urinary bladder and the posterior body wall. However, in most of the eutherian and marsupial mammals, a dual outpushing of the postero-ventral body wall occurs into which the testes come to lie either permanently, or, in some forms, temporarily during the breeding season. This outward extension of the body-wall tissues is known as the **scrotum;** it involves not only the skin, muscle and connective tissues of the body wall but the peritoneal lining as well (fig. 2). (The interested student may consult Weber ('28) and Wislocki ('33) for data concerning the extent of testis descent in mammals.)

The peritoneal evaginations into the scrotal sac are two in number, one for each testis; each evagination is known as a **processus vaginalis** (figs. 3E, F; 4A, B). In many mammals this evagination becomes separated entirely from the peritoneal cavity, and the testis, together with a portion of the sperm-conveying duct, lies suspended permanently in a small antechamber known as the **inguinal bursa** or **serous cavity** of the scrotum (fig. 4B). (See Mitchell, '39.) This condition is found in the horse, man, opossum, bull, ram, dog, cat, etc. In certain other mammals, such as the rat, guinea pig, and ground hog, the inguinal bursa does not become separated from the main peritoneal cavity, and a persistent inguinal canal remains to connect the inguinal bursa with the peritoneal cavity (fig. 4C). In some rodents the testes pass through this persisting inguinal canal into the scrotum as the breeding season approaches, to be withdrawn again after the breeding period is terminated. The ground squirrel, *Citellus tridecemlineatus* (Wells, '35) and the ground hog, *Marmota monax* (Rasmussen, '17) are examples of mammals which experience a seasonal descent of the testis.

In the majority of those mammals possessing a scrotum, it is a permanent structure. In a few, however, it is a temporary affair associated with the

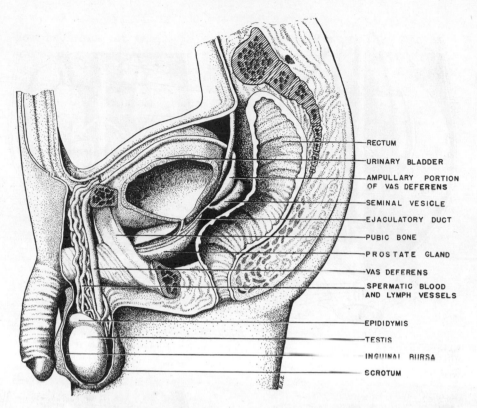

RECTUM

URINARY BLADDER

AMPULLARY PORTION
OF VAS DEFERENS

SEMINAL VESICLE

EJACULATORY DUCT

PUBIC BONE

PROSTATE GLAND

VAS DEFERENS

SPERMATIC BLOOD
AND LYMPH VESSELS

EPIDIDYMIS

TESTIS

INGUINAL BURSA

SCROTUM

FIG. 2. Sketch of male reproductive system in man.

breeding season, as in the bat, *Myotis,* where the testes pass into a temporary perineal pouch or outpushing of the posterior abdominal wall during the reproductive season, to be withdrawn again together with the scrotal wall when the breeding period is past (fig. 4D). A similar periodic behavior is true of many insectivores, such as the common shrews, the moles, and the European hedgehog (Marshall, '11).

The permanent scrotum is a pendent structure, in some species more so than others. In the bull and ram, it extends from the body for a considerable distance, whereas in the cat, hippopotamus, tapir, guinea pig, etc., it is closely applied to the integumentary wall. In primates, including man, in most carnivores, and many marsupials, the pendency of the scrotum is intermediate between the extremes mentioned above.

An exceptional anatomical position of the testes in the lower vertebrates is found in the flatfishes, such as the sole and flounder, where they lie in a caudal outpouching of the peritoneal cavity (fig. 5). The testis on either side may even lie within a special compartment in the tail. (The ovaries assume the latter position in the female.)

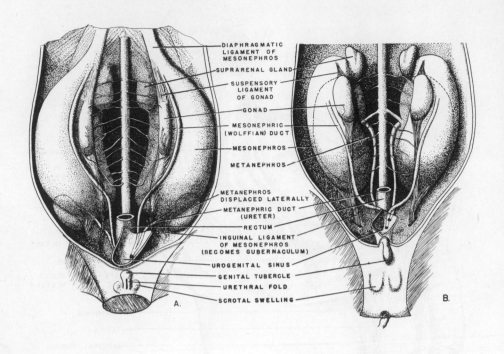

DIAPHRAGMATIC LIGAMENT OF MESONEPHROS

SUPRARENAL GLAND

SUSPENSORY LIGAMENT OF GONAD

GONAD

MESONEPHRIC (WOLFFIAN) DUCT

MESONEPHROS

METANEPHROS

METANEPHROS DISPLACED LATERALLY

METANEPHRIC DUCT (URETER)

RECTUM

INGUINAL LIGAMENT OF MESONEPHROS (BECOMES GUBERNACULUM)

UROGENITAL SINUS

GENITAL TUBERCLE

URETHRAL FOLD

SCROTAL SWELLING

A.

B.

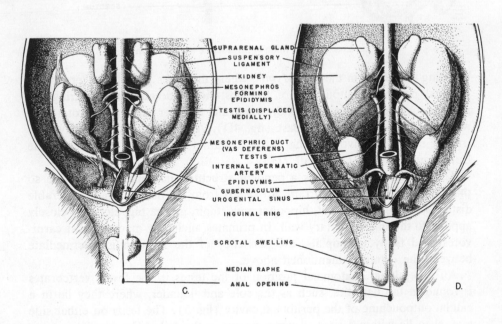

SUPRARENAL GLAND

SUSPENSORY LIGAMENT

KIDNEY

MESONEPHROS FORMING EPIDIDYMIS

TESTIS (DISPLACED MEDIALLY)

MESONEPHRIC DUCT (VAS DEFERENS)

TESTIS

INTERNAL SPERMATIC ARTERY

EPIDIDYMIS

GUBERNACULUM

UROGENITAL SINUS

INGUINAL RING

SCROTAL SWELLING

MEDIAN RAPHE

ANAL OPENING

C.

D.

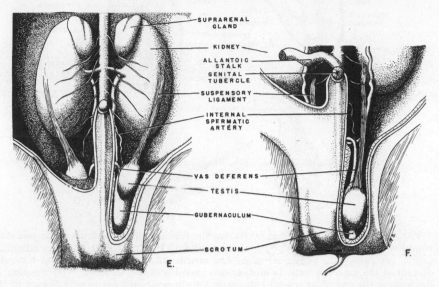

FIG. 3. Diagrammatic representations of the urogenital structures in the developing male pig, with special emphasis upon testicular descent. (A) Early relationship of the genital fold (genital ridge), mesonephric kidney and its duct, together with the metanephric kidney and the ureter in 20-mm. pig embryo. The relationship of the mesonephric and metanephric ducts to the urogenital sinus is shown. The Müllerian duct is omitted. (B) Male pig embryo about 45-mm., crown-rump length, showing relationship of gonad and metanephric kidney. The metanephric kidney is shown below (dorsal to) the mesonephric kidney. The gonad (testis) is now a well-defined unit. The portion of the genital fold tissue anterior to the testis becomes the anterior suspensory ligament of the testis, while the genital fold tissue caudal to the testis continues back to join the inguinal ligament of the mesonephros (the future gubernaculum). (C) About 80-mm., crown-rump, pig embryo. Observe that the metanephros is now the dominant urinary organ and has grown cephalad, displacing the mesonephric kidney which is regressing and moving caudally with the testis. The remains of the mesonephric kidney at this time are gradually being transformed into epididymal structures. (D) About 130-mm., crown-rump, pig embryo. Observe that the testis is approaching the internal opening of the inguinal canal. The anterior suspensory ligament is now an elongated structure extending over the latero-ventral aspect of the metanephric kidney; the gubernacular tissue is shown extending downward into the inguinal canal. (E) Later stage in testicular descent. The anterior suspensory ligament of the testis is a prominent structure, while the gubernaculum is compact and shortened. (F) The condition found in the full-term, fetal pig. The testis is situated in the scrotal swelling; the gubernaculum is much shortened, while the anterior suspensory ligament remains as a prominent structure, extending cephalad to the caudal portions of the metanephric kidney.

2. POSSIBLE FACTORS INVOLVED IN TESTIS DESCENT

The descent of the testis within the peritoneal cavity and into the scrotum poses an interesting problem. In embryonic development extensive migration of cell substance, or of cells, tissues, and organ structures is one of many processes by which the embryonic body is formed. That is to say, the dynamic movement or displacement of developing body structures from their original position is a part of the pattern of development itself. The casual factors in-

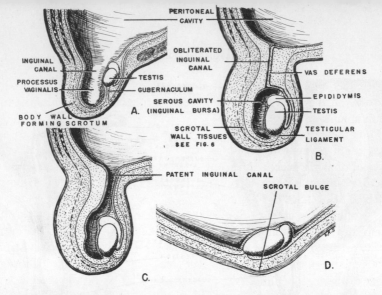

FIG. 4. Diagrammatic drawings portraying the relationship of the testis to the processus vaginalis (peritoneal evagination) and the scrotum. The testis is at all times retroperitoneal, i.e., outside the peritoneal cavity and membrane. (A) Earlier stage of testicular descent at the time the testis is moving downward into the scrotum. (B) Position of the testis at the end of its scrotal journey in a form possessing permanent descent of the testis, e.g., man, dog, etc. (C) Testis-peritoneal relationship in a form which does not have a permanent descent of the testis—the testis is withdrawn into the peritoneal cavity at the termination of each breeding season. Shortly before the onset of the breeding period or "rut," the testis once again descends into the scrotum, e.g., ground hog. (D) Position of testis in relation to body wall and peritoneum in the mole, shrew, and hedgehog in which there is no true scrotum. The testis bulges outward, pushing the body wall before it during the breeding season. As the testis shrinks following the season of rut, the bulge in the body wall recedes. True also of bat, *Myotis*.

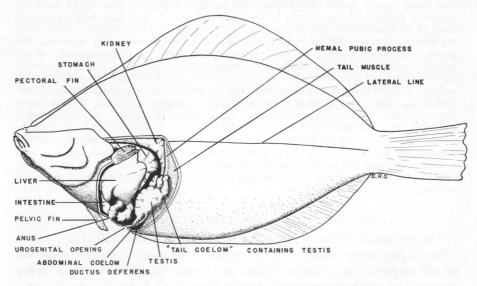

FIG. 5. Opened peritoneal cavity of a common flounder, *Limanda ferruginea*, showing the position occupied by the testes. Each testis is situated partly in a separate compartment on either side of the hemal processes of the tail vertebrae.

10

volved in such movements are still unknown, and the study of such behavior forms one of the many interesting aspects of embryological investigation awaiting solution.

Various theoretical explanations have been proposed, however, to explain the movement of the testis posteriad from its original embryonic site. Classical theory mentions the mechanical pull or tightening stress of the **gubernaculum,** a structure which develops in relation to the primitive genital fold or genital ridge (figs. 3B, C; 351C-7).

The genital ridge extends along the mesial aspect of the early developing mesonephric kidney from a point just caudal to the heart to the posterior extremity of the mesonephric kidney near the developing cloacal structures (Hill, '07). Anteriorly, the genital ridge (fold) merges with the diaphragmatic ligament of the mesonephros (fig. 3A). The gonad (testis or ovary) develops in a specialized region of the more cephalic portion of the genital ridge (Allen, '04). (See fig. 3A.) The caudal end of the mesonephric kidney eventually becomes attached to the posterior ventral body wall by means of a secondary formation of another cord of tissue, the **inguinal fold** (fig. 3A). The latter is attached to the posterior ventral body wall near the area where the scrotal outpushing (evagination) later occurs. This inguinal fold later becomes continuous with the genital fold (fig. 3B). The inguinal fold thus becomes converted into a ligament, the inguinal ligament of the mesonephros, uniting the caudal portion of the mesonephric kidney and adjacent genital fold tissue with the area of scrotal evagination (fig. 3B). The **gubernaculum** represents a later musculo connective tissue development of the inguinal ligament and the adjacent genital fold tissue. It contains smooth muscle fibers as well as connective tissue. As the scrotal evagination forms at the point where the gubernaculum attaches to the body wall, the gubernaculum from the beginning of its formation is connected with the developing scrotal sac.

As the testis migrates posteriad, the anterior suspensory ligament of the testis elongates and the gubernaculum shortens (fig. 3A–F). This decrease in length of the gubernaculum is both real and relative. It is real in that an actual shortening occurs; it is relative because the rapid enlargement of the developing pelvic cavity and its contained organs makes the length of the gubernaculum appear less extensive. This enlargement of the pelvic space and increase in size of its contained structures and a corresponding failure of the gubernaculum to elongate, certainly are factors in bringing about the *intra-abdominal descent of the testis;* that is, testis descent within the peritoneal cavity itself (Felix, '12).

Developmental preparations precede the extra-abdominal descent of the testes, for the scrotal chambers must be prepared in advance of the arrival of the testes. These developmental events are:

(1) two outpocketings of the abdominal wall which come to lie side by side below the skin to form the walls of the scrotal chamber, and

(2) an evagination of the peritoneum into each of the abdominal out-pocketings which act as peritoneal linings for each pocket.

It is worthy of mention that the above outpushings of the abdominal wall and of the peritoneum precede the movement of the testes into the scrotum. They serve to illustrate the theory that a shortening of the gubernaculum is not sufficient to explain testis descent. Rather, that in this descent a whole series of developmental transformations are involved; the shortening of the gubernaculum and scrotal development merely represent isolated phases of the general pattern of movement and growth associated with this descent.

More recent research emphasizes the importance of certain physiological factors relative to the descent problem. It has been determined, for example, that administration of the gonadotrophic hormone of pregnancy urine (chorionic gonadotrophin) or of the male sex hormone, testosterone, aid the process of extra-abdominal descent (i.e., descent from the inguinal ring area downward into the scrotum). Hormone therapy, using chorionic gonadotrophin together with surgery, is used most often in human cryptorchid conditions. The androgen, testosterone, aids testicular descent mainly by stimulating the growth of the scrotal tissues and the vas deferens; however, it is not too successful in effecting the actual descent of the testis (Robson, '40; Wells, '43; Pincus and Thimann, '50).

The phenomenon of testicular migration thus is an unsolved problem. Many activities and factors probably play a part in ushering the testis along the pathway to its scrotal residence.

3. General Structure of the Scrotum and the Testis in Mammals

a. Structure of the Scrotum

The scrotal modification of the body wall generally occurs in the postero-ventral area between the anus and the penial organ. However, in marsupials it is found some distance anterior to the latter.

Each scrotal evagination consists of three general parts: the skin with certain attendant muscles, the structures of the body wall below the skin, and the peritoneal evagination. The skin, with its underlying **tunica dartos** muscle tissue and **superficial perineal fascia,** forms the outer wall of the scrotum (fig. 6). Within this outer cutaneous covering lie the two body-wall and two peritoneal evaginations. The body-wall evaginations involve connective and muscle tissues·of the external oblique, internal oblique, and transversus muscles. The caudal part of each peritoneal outpocketing forms the serous cavity or inguinal bursa in which the testis is suspended after its descent, and its more anterior portion forms the inguinal canal (figs. 2, 4B, 6). The oblique and transversus layers of tissues thus are molded into a musculo-connective tissue compartment around each serous cavity. The **median septum of the scrotum** represents the area of partial fusion between the two musculo-connective tissue compartments, whereas the **median raphe of the scrotum** denotes the area of fusion of the two cutaneous coverings of the body-wall outpushings (fig. 6).

Consequently, passing inward from the superficial perineal fascia of the skin or outer wall, one finds the following tissue layers surrounding the testis:

(1) The **external spermatic fascia** represents the modified fascia of the external oblique muscle layer of the embryo.

(2) The **middle spermatic fascia** is a modification of the internal oblique muscular layer, whose tissue forms the **cremaster muscle loops** within the scrotum (fig. 6). (Some of the cremasteric musculature may be derived from the transversus layer.)

(3) The **internal spermatic fascia** or **tunica vaginalis communis** is derived from the transverse muscle layer of the embryo.

(4) Along the inner surface of the tunica vaginalis communis is the peritoneal membrane. The latter is reflected back over the surface of the suspended testis, and thus forms the visceral peritoneal covering of the testis. This lining tissue of the common vaginal tunic and the peritoneal membrane which covers the testis are derived from the original peritoneal evagination into the scrotal pocket; as such it forms the **tunica vaginalis propria.**

b. General Structure of the Testis

The testis is composed of the following structural parts:

(1) The inner layer of the tunica vaginalis propria, the **tunica vaginalis internus,** envelops the testis. The cavity between the outer and inner layers of the tunica vaginalis propria is the **inguinal bursa.** Obliteration by injury or infection of this inguinal bursa may cause degenerative changes in the testis. In other words, the testis normally must be free to move within its serous (peritoneal) cavity.

(2) Within the tunica vaginalis internus of the testis is a thick fibrous layer of connective tissue, the **tunica albuginea** (fig. 7). From this tunic, connective tissue partitions, the **septula of the testis,** extend inward and converge toward that testicular zone where supplying blood vessels enter and leave, including the lymphatics. The latter zone is known as the **mediastinum testis** and it represents a regional thickening of the tunica albuginea. Here the connective tissue fibers form a latticework which acts as a framework for the larger blood and lymph vessels and efferent ducts of the testis. The testis is attached to the scrotal wall in the mediastinal area.

(3) The spaces between the various septula partitions form the **septula compartments.** In the human testis there are about 250 septula compartments, each containing a lobule of the testis. The **lobuli testis**

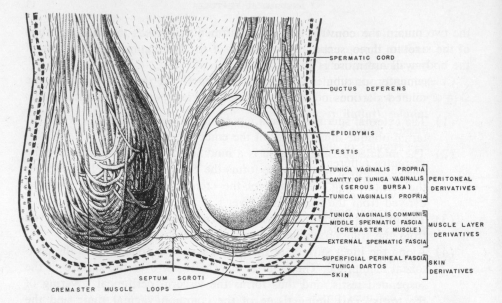

FIG. 6. Schematic drawing of the testis and its relationship within the scrotum. On the right side of the drawing the muscle and connective-tissue layers surrounding the inguinal bursa and testis are shown; on the left side may be seen the loops of the cremaster muscle surrounding the tunica vaginalis communis.

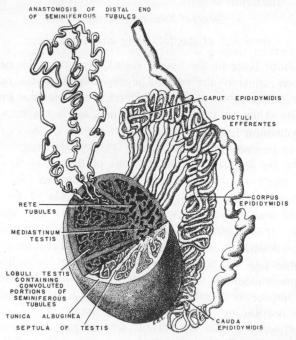

FIG. 7. Diagrammatic representation of the general structural relationship of the parts of the human testis. (Modified from Corner, 1943, after Spalteholz and Huber.)

14

contain the convoluted portions of the **seminiferous tubules.** From one to three seminiferous tubules are found in each lobule; they may anastomose at their distal ends. The combined length of all the seminiferous tubules approaches 250 meters in the human. The convoluted portions of the seminiferous tubules empty into the **straight tubules (tubuli recti)** and these in turn unite with the **rete tubules** located within the substance of the mediastinum. Connecting with the rete tubules of the testis, there are, in man, from 12 to 14 **ductuli efferentes** (efferent ductules of the epididymis) of about 4 to 6 cm. in length which emerge from the mediastinum and pass outward to unite with the duct of the epididymis. The epididymal duct represents the proximal portion of the reproductive duct which conveys the male gametes to the exterior.

4. Specific Structures of the Mammalian Testis Which Produce the Reproductive Cells and the Male Sex Hormone

Two very essential processes involved in reproduction are the formation of the sex cells or gametes and the elaboration of certain humoral substances, known as sex hormones. Therefore, consideration will be given next to those portions of the testis which produce the sperm cells and the male sex hormone, namely, the **seminiferous tubules** and the **interstitial tissue.**

a. Seminiferous Tubules

The **seminiferous tubules** lie in the septula compartments (fig. 7). The word seminiferous is derived from two Latin words: *semen,* denoting seed, and *ferre,* which means to bear or to carry. The seminiferous tubule, therefore, is a male "seed-bearing" structure. Within this tubule the male gametes or sperm are formed, at least morphologically. However, the word **semen** has a broader implication in that it is used generally to denote the entire reproductive fluid or seminal fluid. The seminal fluid is a composite of substances contributed by the seminiferous tubules and various parts of the accessory reproductive tract.

The exact form and relationship of the various seminiferous tubules (tubuli seminiferi) which occupy each testicular compartment have been the object of much study. It is a generally accepted belief at present that the tubules within each testicular lobule are attached at their distal ends; that is, that they anastomose (fig. 7). Some investigators also believe that there may be other anastomoses along the lengths of these very much contorted and twisted structures. Moreover, it appears that the septula or testicular compartmental partitions are not always complete; the seminiferous tubules of one lobule thus have the opportunity to communicate with those of adjacent lobules. The seminiferous tubules of any one lobule join at their proximal ends and empty into a single straight seminiferous tubule. The straight tubules or

tubuli recti pass into the mediastinum and join the anastomosing **rete tubules** of the **rete testis.**

The convoluted portions of the seminiferous tubules produce the sperm (spermia; spermatozoa). In the human testis, the length of one of these tubules is about 30 to 70 cm. and approximately 150 μ to 250 μ in diameter. Each tubule is circumscribed by a basement membrane of connective tissue and contains two cell types:

(1) supporting or **Sertoli cells,** and

(2) spermatogenic cells or **spermatogonia** (see fig. 8 and Chap. 3).

The cells of Sertoli are relatively long, slender elements placed perpendicularly to the basement membrane to which they firmly adhere. These cells may undergo considerable change in shape, and some observers believe that they may form a syncytium, known as the "Sertolian syncytium." Others believe them to be distinct elements. It is said that Sertoli cells may round up and form phagocytes which become free from the basement membrane and move, ameba-like, in the lumen of the seminiferous tubule, phagocytizing degenerating sperm cells. However, their main function appears to be associated with the development of sperm during the period when the latter undergo their transformation from the spermatid condition into the adult

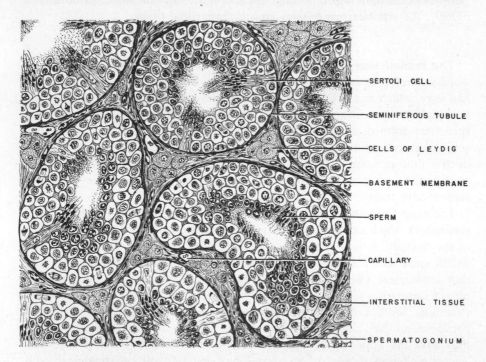

FIG. 8. Semidiagrammatic representation of section of cat testis, showing seminiferous tubules and interstitial tissue, particularly the cells of Leydig.

sperm form. The Sertolian cells thus may act as *nursing elements* during sperm metamorphosis.

The spermatogenic cells or spermatogonia (germinal epithelium of the tubule) lie toward the outer portion of the seminiferous tubule between the various Sertoli elements. As a rule spermatogonia lie apposed against the basement membrane of the tubule (see fig. 8 and Chap. 3).

b. Interstitial Tissue

The interstitial tissue of the testis is situated between the seminiferous tubules (fig. 8). It consists of a layer of connective tissue applied to the basement membrane of the seminiferous tubule and of many other structures, such as small blood and lymph vessels, connective tissue fibers, connective tissue cells, mast cells, fixed macrophages, etc. The conspicuous elements of this tissue are the so-called **interstitial cells** or **cells of Leydig** (fig. 8). In man, cat, dog, etc., the cells of Leydig are relatively large, polyhedral elements, possessing a granular cytoplasm and a large nucleus.

5. THE TESTIS OF VERTEBRATES IN GENERAL

In the vertebrate group, the testis shows marked variations in shape and size. In many fishes, the testes are irregular, lobular structures, but in other fishes, amphibia, reptiles, birds, and mammals, they assume an ovoid shape. The size of the testis is extremely variable, even in the same species. The testis of the human adult approximates 4 to 5 cm. in length by 3 cm. wide and weighs about 14 to 19 Gm. The testis of the horse averages 11 cm. long by 7 cm. wide with a weight of 30 to 35 Gm., while that of the cat is 1.6 cm. long and 1.1 cm. wide with a weight of 1.5 Gm. In the mud puppy, *Necturus,* the testis is approximately 3.5 cm. long and 0.8 cm. wide with a weight of 0.3 Gm. The testis of the large bullfrog is 1.2 cm. by 0.5 cm. with a weight of 0.8 Gm. In comparison to the foregoing, Schulte ('37) gives the weight of each testis of an Indian elephant as two kilograms!

Regardless of size or shape, the presence of seminiferous tubules and interstitial tissue may be observed in all vertebrate testes. In some species the seminiferous tubule is long; in others it is a short, blunt affair. The interstitial cells may be similar to those described above, or they may be small, inconspicuous oval elements.

6. ACCESSORY REPRODUCTIVE STRUCTURES OF THE MALE

a. The Reproductive Duct in Forms Utilizing External Fertilization

The accessory reproductive organs of the vertebrate male are extremely variable in the group as a whole. A relatively simple reproductive duct (or in some no duct at all) is the rule for those forms where fertilization is effected in the external medium. In cyclostome fishes, for example, the reproductive cells are shed into the peritoneal cavity and pass posteriad to emerge externally by means of two abdominal pores. Each pore empties into the urogenital sinus. In teleost fishes (perch, flounder, etc.) the conveying reproductive duct is a short, simple tube continuous with the testis at its caudal end and passing posteriorly to the urogenital sinus (fig. 9A). In frogs and toads, as well as in certain other fishes, such as *Amia* and *Polypterus,* the male reproductive duct is a simple, elongated tube associated with the testis by means of the efferent ductules of the latter, coursing posteriad to open into the cloaca (frogs and toads) or to the urogenital sinus *(Amia; Polypterus)* (fig. 9B, C). Simplicity of sperm duct development and external union of the gametes are associated reproductive phenomena in the vertebrate group.

b. The Reproductive Duct in Species Practicing Internal Fertilization

An entirely different, more complex male reproductive duct is found (with some exceptions) in those vertebrates where gametic union occurs within the protective structures of the maternal body. Under these circumstances there may be a tendency for one male to serve several females. Enlargement of the duct with the elaboration of glandular appendages, and structures or areas for sperm storage is the rule under these conditions (fig. 9D–F). This form of the male genital tract is found not only in those species where an intromittent organ deposits the sperm within the female tract, but also where the sperm are deposited externally in the form of spermatophores (fig. 10).

In many species, the reproductive duct is greatly lengthened and becomes a tortuous affair, especially at its anterior or testicular end. In fact, the cephalic end of the duct may be twisted and increased to a length many times longer than the male body itself. This coiled, cephalic portion is called the duct of the epididymis (epididymides, plural). (See figs. 7, 9E.) The word epididymis is derived from two Greek words: *epi =* upon, and *didymis =* testicle. The epididymis, therefore, is the body composed of the tortuous epididymal duct and the efferent ducts of the testis which lie upon or are closely associated with the testis. The complex type of reproductive duct is composed thus of two main portions, an anterior, contorted or twisted portion, the epididymal duct, and a less contorted posterior part, the vas deferens or sperm duct proper (fig. 9D, E).

In some vertebrates, in addition to the above complications, the caudal end of the reproductive duct has a pronounced swelling or diverticulum, the seminal vesicle (e.g., certain sharks and certain birds). The latter structures are **true seminal vesicles** in that they store sperm during the reproductive period.

The epididymal duct in man is a complex, coiled canal composed of a head (caput), a body (corpus), and a tail (cauda). (See fig. 7.) It is C-shaped with its concavity fitting around the dorsal border of the testis, the head portion being located at the anterior end of the latter. The total length of the epididymal duct in man is said to be about 4 to 7 m. In other mammals

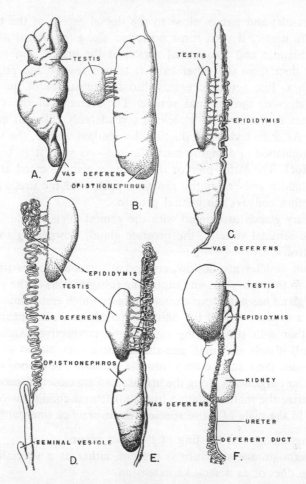

FIG. 9. Various vertebrate testes and reproductive ducts, emphasizing the relative simplicity of the duct where external fertilization is the rule while complexity of the duct is present when internal fertilization is utilized. There are exceptions to this rule, however. (A) Flounder *(Limanda ferruginea).* (B) Frog *(Rana catesbiana).* (C) Urodele *(Cryptobranchus ulleguniensis).* (D) Dog shark *(Squalus acanthias)* (E) Urodele *(Necturus maculosus).* (F) Rooster *(Gallus domesticus).*

the epididymal duct may be much longer. For example, in the ram, from 40 to 60 m.; in the boar, 62 to 64 m.; in the stallion, 72 to 86 m. (Asdell, '46). At its caudal end it becomes much less tortuous and gradually passes into the vas deferens (ductus deferens).

The ductus deferens has a length of about 30 to 35 cm. in man. Leaving the scrotum it passes anteriad together with accompanying nerves and blood vessels in the subcutaneous tissue over the front of the pelvic bone into the peritoneal cavity through the inguinal ring (fig. 2). Here it separates from the other constituents of the **spermatic cord** (i.e., it separates from the nerves and blood vessels) and passes close to the dorsal aspect of the bladder and dorsally to the ureter. It then turns posteriad along the dorsal aspect of the neck of the bladder and the medial region of the ureter, and accompanied by its fellow duct from the other side, it travels toward the prostate gland and the urethra. Just before it enters into the substance of the prostate, it receives the duct of the seminal vesicle. The segment of the vas deferens from the ureter to the seminal vesicle is considerably enlarged and is called the **ampulla.** After receiving the duct of the seminal vesicle, the vas deferens becomes straightened and highly muscularized—as such it is known as the **ejaculatory duct.** The latter pierces the prostate gland located at the caudal end of the bladder and enters the prostatic portion of the urethra; from this point the urethra conveys the genital products.

The auxiliary glands associated with the genital ducts of the human male consist of the seminal vesicles, the prostate gland, Cowper's glands, and the glands of Littré.

The **seminal vesicles** are hollow, somewhat tortuous bodies (fig. 2). Each vesicle arises in the embryo as an outpushing (evagination) of the vas deferens. The **prostate gland** has numerous excretory ducts which empty into the urethra. It represents a modification of the lining tissue of the urethra near the urinary bladder together with surrounding muscle and connective tissues. **Cowper's (bulbourethral) glands** are small pea-shaped structures placed at the base of the penial organ; their ducts empty into the urethra. The **glands of Littré** are small, glandular outgrowths along the urethra and are closely associated with it.

To summarize the matter relative to the structural conditions of the reproductive duct in the male of those species which practice internal fertilization:

(1) A lengthening and twisting of the duct occurs.
(2) A sperm-storage structure is present, either as a specialized portion of the duct or as a sac-like extension.
(3) Certain auxiliary glands may be present. These glands are sometimes large and vesicular structures, such as the seminal vesicles of the human duct, or they may be small glands distributed along the wall of the duct, such as the glands of Littré.

C. Specific Activities of the Various Parts of the Male Reproductive System

1. INTRODUCTION

a. Three General Functions of the Male Reproductive System

The activities of the testes and the accessory parts of the male reproductive system result in the performance of three general functions as follows:

(1) formation of the semen,
(2) delivery of the semen to the proper place where the sperm may be utilized in the process of fertilization, and
(3) elaboration of the male sex hormone.

b. Some Definitions

Semen or **seminal fluid** is the all-important substance which the male contributes during the reproductive event. It is the product of the entire reproductive system, including special glands of the accessory reproductive structures. The semen is composed of two parts:

(1) **The sperm** (spermatozoa, spermia) are the formed elements which take part in the actual process of fertilization.

(2) The **seminal plasma,** a fluid part, is a lymph-like substance containing various substances dissolved or mixed in it. These contained substances are important as a protection for the sperm and as an aid to the process of fertilization.

With regard to the second function of the male genital system, namely, *the delivery of sperm to the site of fertilization,* it should be observed that

Fig. 10. Spermatophores of common urodeles. (Redrawn from Noble: *Biology of the Amphibia,* New York, McGraw-Hill.) (A) *Triturus viridescens.* (After Smith.) (B) *Desmognathus fuscus.* (After Noble and Weber.) (C) *Eurycea bislineata.*

in some vertebrates this is a more simple problem than in others. In those forms which practice external fertilization, the male system simply discharges the seminal fluid into the surrounding external medium. However, in those vertebrates where internal fertilization is the rule, the female system assumes some of the burden in the transport of the semen to the region where fertilization is consummated, thus complicating the procedure. In these instances, the male genital tract is called upon to produce added substances to the seminal fluid which aid in protecting the sperm en route to the fertilization site.

The elaboration of the **androgenic or male sex hormone** is a most important function. Androgenic or male sex hormone substances are those organic compounds which induce maleness, for they aid the development of the male secondary sex characteristics, enhance the growth and functional development of the male accessory reproductive structures, and stimulate certain aspects of spermatogenesis. Like the estrogens, androgens are not confined to a particular sex; they have been extracted from the urine of women and other female animals. The androgens derived from urinary concentrates are **andros-**

terone and **dehydroisoandrosterone.** These two androgens are not as powerful as that prepared from testicular tissue. Testicular androgen was first isolated from testicular tissue in 1935 and was given the name **testosterone.** It also has been synthesized from cholesterol. It is the most powerful of the androgens and probably similar, if not identical, with the substance produced in the testis (Koch, '42).

2. ACTIVITIES OF THE TESTIS

a. Seasonal and Non-seasonal Types of Testicular Activity

The testis has two main functions: the *production of sperm* and *formation of the male sex hormone.* In many vertebrates these two activities represent a continuous procedure during the reproductive life of the male animal. This

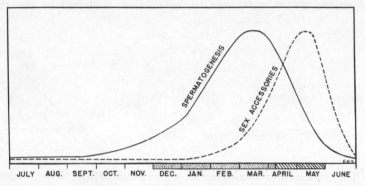

FIG. 11. Seasonal spermatogenesis and accessory gland development in the ground squirrel, *Citellus tridecemlineatus.* Stippling below base line shows period of hibernation, whereas crosshatching reveals the reproductive period. (From Turner: *General Endocrinology,* Philadelphia, Saunders, after L. J. Wells.)

condition is found in certain tropical fish, in the common fowl and various wild tropical birds, and in many mammals, such as man, the dog, bull, stallion, cat, etc. On the other hand, *in the majority of vertebrates these activities of the testis are a seasonal affair.* This condition is found in most fish, practically all amphibia, all temperate-zone-inhabiting reptiles, most birds, and many mammals. Among the latter, for example, are the ferret, deer, elk, fox, wolf, and many rodents, such as the midwestern ground squirrel. Seasonal periodicity is true also of the common goose and turkey.

Sperm-producing periodicity is not correlated with any particular season, *nor is spermatogenesis always synchronized with the mating urge, which in turn is dependent upon the male sex hormone.* In some forms, these two testicular functions may actually occur at different seasons of the year, as for example, in the three-spined stickleback, *Gasterosteus aculeatus* (fig. 15). (See Craig-Bennett, '31.) In general, it may be stated that sperm are produced during the weeks or months which precede the development of the mating instinct. Many species follow this rule. For example, in the bat of the genus *Myotis,* sperm are produced during the late spring and summer months, while mating or copulation takes place during the fall or possibly early the next spring (Guthrie, '33). In the common newt, *Triturus viridescens,* spermatogenesis comes to pass during the warm months of the summer, and sperm are discharged from the testis into the reproductive ducts during the late fall and early spring, while copulation is accomplished in the early spring. The testes in this species are quiescent during the cool winter months. In the midwestern ground squirrel, *Citellus tridecemlineatus,* spermatogenesis begins in November and is marked during February and March (fig. 11). The animal hibernates away the winter months and emerges the first part of April in a breeding condition. Mating occurs in the early spring (Wells, '35). In the garter snake, *Thamnophis radix,* sperm are produced in the testes in the summer months, stored in the epididymides during the hibernation period in the fall and winter, and used for copulation purposes in the spring (Cieslak, '45). Again, in the Virginia deer, *Odocoileus virginianus borealis,* studied by Wislocki ('43), active spermatogenesis is realized during the summer and early autumn months, while the mating season or "rut" which results from the driving power of the male sex hormone, is at its peak in October and November (fig. 12). In the fox, Bishop ('42) observed spermatogenesis to begin in the late fall months, while mating is an event of the late winter and early spring. In April and May the seminiferous tubules again assume an inactive state (fig. 13). In the common frog, *Rana pipiens,* spermatogenesis is present in the summer months and morphogenesis of spermatids into sperm happens in large numbers during September, October, and November. Sperm are stored in the testis over the winter, and the mating instinct is awakened in the early spring (Glass and Rugh, '44). Following the mating season in spring and early summer the testis of the teleost, *Fundulus heteroclitus,* is depleted of sperm until the next winter and spring (Matthews, '38).

As the seasonal type of testicular activity is present in a large number of vertebrate species, it seems probable that it represents the more primitive or fundamental type of testicular functioning.

b. Testicular Tissue Concerned with Male Sex-hormone Production

While one cannot rule out the indirect effects which activities of the seminiferous tubules may have upon the functioning of the testis as a whole, including the interstitial tissue, direct experimental evidence and other observations suggest that the interstitial tissue holds the main responsibility for the secretion of the male sex hormone, **testosterone,** or a substance very closely allied to it. For example, if a testis from an animal possessing a permanent scrotum is removed from the inguinal bursa and placed within the peritoneal cavity, the seminiferous tubules tend to degenerate, but the inter-

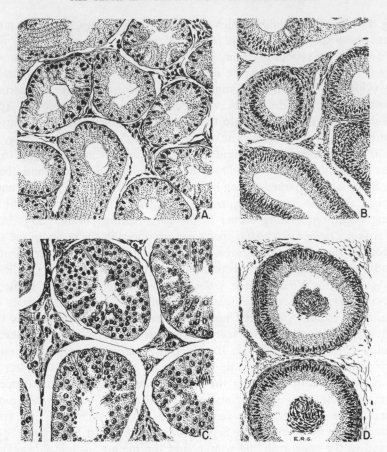

Fig. 12. Sections of the testis of the deer, *Odocoileus virginianus borealis*. (After Wislocki.)   (A) Seminiferous tubules of deer in June. Observe repressed state of tubules and absence of sperm.   (B) Epididymal duct of same deer. Observe absence of sperm and smaller diameter of duct compared with (D).   (C) Seminiferous tubules of October deer; spermatogenic activity is marked.   (D) Epididymal duct, showing well-developed epididymal tube and presence of many sperm.

stitial tissue remains. The sex hormone, under these circumstances, continues to be produced. Again, males having cryptorchid testis (i.e., testes which have failed in their passage to the scrotum) possess the secondary sex characteristics of normal males but fail to produce sperm cells. Also, it has been demonstrated that the mammalian fetal testis contains the male sex hormone. However, in this fetal condition, the seminiferous tubules are present only in an undeveloped state, whereas interstitial tissue is well differentiated. It is probable in this case that the interstitial tissue of the fetal testis responds to the luteinizing hormone in the maternal blood.

In hypophysectomized male rats injected with dosages of pure follicle-stimulating hormone (FSH) or with *small doses* of pure luteinizing hormone

(LH; ICSH), the seminiferous tubules of the testis respond and spermatogenesis occurs. However, the interstitial tissue remains relatively unstimulated and the accessory structures continue in the atrophic state. If larger doses of the luteinizing factor are given, the interstitial tissue responds and the secondary sexual characters are developed, showing a relationship between interstitial activity and sex-hormone production. (Consult Evans and Simpson in Pincus and Thimann, '50, pp. 355, 356.)

From certain species whose reproductive activities are confined to a particular season of the year, there also comes evidence that the interstitial tissue

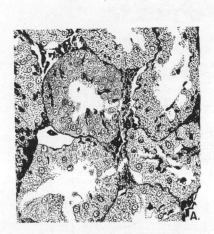
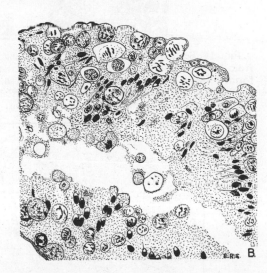

FIG. 13. Sections of seminiferous tubules of silver fox. (After Bishop.) (A) Regressed state of tubules following breeding season. (B) Tubule from fox during the breeding season, characterized by active spermatogenesis.

is the site of sex-hormone production. In the behavior of testicular tissue in the stickleback, *Gasterosteus,* as shown by van Oordt ('23) and Craig-Bennett ('31) sperm are produced actively in the seminiferous tubules during one period of the year when the interstitial tissue is in an undeveloped condition. The secondary sex characters also are in abeyance at this season of the year. However, during the months immediately following sperm production, sperm are stored within the seminiferous tubules and active spermatogenesis is absent. When the seminiferous tubules thus have completed their spermatogenic activity, the interstitial tissue begins to increase, followed by a development of secondary sex characteristics (figs. 14, 15). A similar difference in the rhythm of development of these two testicular tissues can be shown for many other vertebrates. All of these suggestive facts thus serve to place the responsibility for male sex-hormone production upon the interstitial tissue, probably the cells of Leydig.

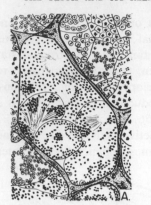
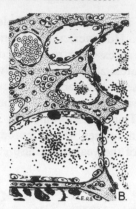

FIG. 14. Sections of the testis of the stickleback *(Gasterosteus pungitius).* (Modified from Moore, '39, after Van Oordt.) Cf. fig. 13. (A) Spermatogenic activity with many formed sperm in seminiferous tubules before the mating season, interstitial tissue in abeyance. (B) At mating period. Interstitial tissue well developed, spermatozoa stored in the tubules with spermatogenic activity absent.

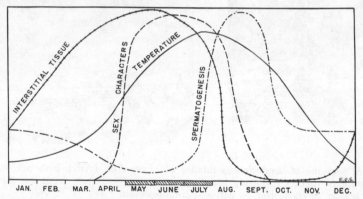

FIG. 15. Seasonal reproductive cycle in the stickleback *(Gasterosteus aculeatus).* Cf. fig. 14. Breeding season is indicated by crosshatching below base line. Observe that spermatogenic activity follows rise of temperature, whereas interstitial-tissue and sex-character development occur during ascending period of light. (Redrawn from Turner: *General Endocrinology,* Philadelphia, Saunders, modified from Craig-Bennett, 1931.)

c. Testicular Control of Body Structure and Function by the Male Sex Hormone

1) Sources of the Male Sex Hormone. Testosterone is prepared from testicular extracts. It is the most potent of the androgens. and is believed to be the hormone produced by the testis. The chemical formula of **testosterone** is:

The testis, however, is not the only site of androgen formation. As mentioned above, androgens are found in the urine of female animals, castrates, etc. It seems probable that the suprarenal (adrenal) cortex may secrete a certain androgenic substance, possibly **adrenosterone,** a weak androgen. Many androgens have been synthesized also in the laboratory (Schwenk, '44).

2) **Biological Effects of the Male Sex Hormone.** The presence of the male sex hormone in the male arouses the functional development of the accessory reproductive structures, the secondary sexual characters, and also stimulates the development of the seminiferous tubules.

a) EFFECTS UPON THE ACCESSORY REPRODUCTIVE STRUCTURES. Castration or removal of the testes from an animal possessing a continuous type of testicular activity produces shrinkage, and a general tendency toward atrophy, of the entire accessory reproductive structures. Injection of testosterone or other androgens under such conditions occasions a resurgence of functional development and enlargement of the accessory structures (fig. 16). Moreover, continued injections of the androgen will maintain the accessories in this functional state (Moore, '42; Dorfman in Pincus and Thimann, '50). Similarly, under normal conditions in those vertebrates which possess the seasonal type of testicular function, the accessory reproductive organs shrink in size with a loss of functional activity when the testis undergoes regression during the period immediately following the active season. An enlargement and acquisition of a normal functional condition of the accessories follows testicular development as the breeding season again approaches (Bishop, '42; Wislocki, '43; Matthews, '38; Turner, C. L., '19). (Compare figs. 12A–D.)

b) EFFECTS UPON SECONDARY SEX CHARACTERISTICS AND BEHAVIOR OF THE INDIVIDUAL. In addition to the primary effects upon the reproductive system itself, the androgens induce many other secondary structures and alterations of the physiology and behavior of the individual. The influence of the testicular hormone has been demonstrated in all of the vertebrate groups from fishes to mammals (Dorfman in Pincus and Thimann, '50). Examples of testosterone stimulation are: the singing and plumage of the male bird; hair development of certain mammals; the crowing and fighting, together with spur, comb, and wattle growth in the rooster. The disagreeable belligerency and positive energy drive of the bull, stallion, or human male may be attributed, largely, to the action of testicular hormone. However, lest we disparage this aggressive demeanor unduly, it should be recognized that upon such explosive force rests the preservation of species and races in some instances. As an example, witness that hairy dynamo of the barren northern tundras, the bull muskox, whose fiery pugnaciousness when the need arises undoubtedly has been a strong factor in the preservation of this species.

An excellent example of the effect of testosterone is shown in the development of antlers and change in behavior of the Virginia deer, *Odocoileus virginianus borealis* (Wislocki, '43). In the northern climate, the testes and male accessory organs reach a profound condition of regression in April and May. Growth of the new antlers starts at this time, and during the late summer the antlers grow rapidly and begin to calcify. During the summer, also, the testes develop rapidly, and spermatogenesis results. Loss of the "velvet" covering of the antlers is experienced during September, and mating is the rule in October and November. The antlers are shed in midwinter. If the testes are removed after the naked antler condition is reached, the antlers are shed rapidly. Testosterone administered to does or to young males which have been castrated induces the development of antlers. The general scheme of antler development suggests, possibly, that the testicular hormone acts upon an anterior pituitary factor, and this activated factor in turn initiates antler growth. Hardening of the antlers and loss of velvet results from testosterone stimulation. Loss of the antler is synchronized with a decrease in the amount of testosterone in the blood stream, accompanied by the acquisition of a docile, non-belligerent, more timid behavior.

c) EFFECTS UPON THE SEMINIFEROUS TUBULES. Testosterone has a stimulating effect upon the seminiferous tubule and sperm formation. This matter is discussed in Chap. 3.

d. Seminiferous-tubule Activity and Formation of Sperm
See Chap. 3.

e. The Seminiferous Tubule as a Sperm-storing Structure
See p. 31.

3. ROLE OF THE REPRODUCTIVE DUCT IN SPERM FORMATION

a. Vertebrates Without a Highly Tortuous Epididymal Portion of the Reproductive Duct

In a large number of vertebrates, morphologically developed sperm pass from the testis through the efferent ductules of the epididymis (vasa efferentia) to the epididymal duct where they remain for varying periods. However, in many vertebrates the anterior (proximal) portion of the sperm duct does not form a tortuous epididymal structure similar to that found in other vertebrates. This condition is present in the common frog, *Rana;* in the hellbender, *Cryptobranchus;* in the bowfin, *Amia;* etc. Because of this fact, the sperm pass directly into the vas deferens or sperm duct (Wolffian duct) without undergoing a sojourn through a convoluted epididymal portion of the duct.

Correlated with the type of testis and sperm-duct relationship in the frog, is the fact that one may obtain viable, fertilizing sperm directly from the testis. For example, if one removes the testis from a living frog and macerates it in pond water or in an appropriate saline solution, active sperm are obtained which are capable of fertilizing eggs in a normal manner. That is, *the frog testis matures sperm morphologically and physiologically*. This type of tes-

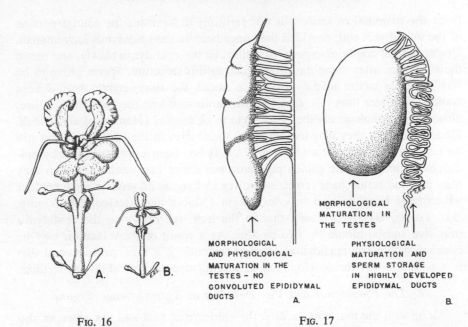

Fig. 16   Fig. 17

Fig. 16. Effects of the male sex hormone upon the functional development of the accessory reproductive structures of the male rat. (After Turner: *General Endocrinology*, Philadelphia, Saunders, p. 324.) (A) Normal male rat condition produced by injection of crystalline male sex hormone for 20 days into castrate before autopsy. (B) Castrated male litter mate of (A) receiving no replacement therapy.

Fig. 17. Diagrammatic drawings of the two types of testicular-reproductive relationships occurring in the vertebrate group. (A) Simplified type of reproductive duct connected with the testis by means of efferent ductules. The duct-testis relationship of many teleost fishes is similar to this but does not possess the efferent ductules, the sinus-like reproductive duct being attached directly to the testis. Sperm cells (spermatozoa) are matured and stored within the testis. This type of relationship generally is found where fertilization is external or where sperm are discharged all at once during a short reproductive period. (B) More complicated variety of reproductive duct, connected with the testis by means of efferent ducts, but possessing an anterior twisted portion, the epididymal duct in which the sperm are stored and physiologically matured. This type of duct generally is found in those vertebrates which utilize internal fertilization and where sperm are discharged over a short or extended reproductive period.

ticular maturation is characteristic of many of the lower vertebrates possessing simple reproductive ducts.

b. The Epididymis as a Sperm-ripening Structure

On the other hand, in those forms which possess an anterior convoluted epididymal portion of the reproductive duct, the journey of the sperm through this portion of the duct appears to be necessary in order that fertilizable sperm may be produced. In mammals it has been shown that the epididymal journey somehow conditions the physiological ripening of the sperm. Sperm taken from the mammalian testis will not fertilize; those from the caudal portion of the epididymis will, provided they have been in the epididymis long enough. Under normal conditions sperm pass through the epididymis slowly, and retain their viability after many days' residence in this structure. Sperm prove to be fertile in the rabbit epididymis up to about the thirty-eighth day; if kept somewhat longer than this, they become senile and lose the ability to fertilize, although morphologically they may seem to be normal (Hammond and Asdell, '26). In the rat, they may live up to 20 to 30 days in the epididymis and still be capable of fertilization (Moore, '28). It has been estimated that the epididymal journey in the guinea pig consumes about two weeks, although they may live and retain their fertilizing power as long as 30 days in epididymides which have been isolated by constriction (Moore and McGee, '28; Young, '31; Young, '31b). It is said that in the bull, sperm within the epididymis may live and be motile for two months. As a result of these facts, it may be concluded that the epididymal journey normally is a slow process, and that it is beneficial for the development of sperm "ripeness" or ability to fertilize.

c. The Epididymis and Vas Deferens as Sperm-storage Organs

Along with the maturing faculty, the epididymal duct and vas deferens also act as sperm-storage organs. As observed on p. 23, in the bat, *Myotis,* sperm are formed in great numbers in the seminiferous tubules and pass to the epididymal duct where they are stored during the fall, winter, and early spring months; the epididymal journey thus is greatly prolonged in this species. In the ovoviviparous garter snake, *Thamnophis radix,* sperm are produced during the summer months; they pass into the epididymides during early autumn and are stored there during the fall and winter. In the mammal, sperm are stored in the epididymal duct.

Aside from its main purpose of transporting sperm to the exterior (see sperm transport, p. 177), the caudal portion of the sperm duct or vas deferens also is capable of storing sperm for considerable periods of time. In the common perch, *Perca flavescens,* sperm are developed in the testes in the autumn, pass gradually into the accessory reproductive ducts, and are stored there for five or six months until the breeding season the following spring (Turner, C. L., '19). Again, in mammals, the ampullary region of the vas deferens appears to be a site for sperm storage. For example, the ampulla of the bull sometimes is massaged through the rectal wall to obtain sperm for artificial insemination. In this form sperm may be stored in the ampulla and still be viable, for as long as three days. Similarly, in lower vertebrates large numbers of sperm may be found in the posterior extremities of the vas deferens during the breeding season. Thus, the reproductive duct (and its epididymal portion when present) is instrumental in many vertebrate species as a temporary storage place for the sperm.

d. Two Types of Vertebrate Testes Relative to Sperm Formation

The importance of the epididymal duct in many vertebrates and its relative absence in others, focuses attention upon the fact that in many vertebrate species sperm are produced, stored, and physiologically matured entirely within the confines of the testis (frog, bowfin, stickleback, etc.). The reproductive duct under these circumstances is used mainly for sperm transport. In many other vertebrate species sperm are morphologically formed in the testis and then are passed on into the accessory structures for storage and physiological maturation. Functionally, therefore, two types of testes and two types of accessory reproductive ducts are found among the vertebrate group of animals (fig. 17). It naturally follows that the testis which produces, stores, and physiologically matures sperm is best adapted for seasonal activity, particularly where one female is served during the reproductive activities. That is, it functions as an "all at one time" spawning mechanism. On the other hand, that testis which produces sperm morphologically and passes them on to a tortuous epididymal duct for storage and physiological maturing is best adapted for the continuous type of sperm production or for the service of several females during a single seasonal period. The sperm, under these conditions, pass slowly through the epididymal duct, and, therefore, may be discharged intermittently.

4 FUNCTION OF THE SEMINAL VESICLES (VESICULAR GLANDS)

The seminal vesicles show much diversity in their distribution among various mammals. Forms like the cat, dog, opossum, rabbit, sloth, armadillo, whale, do not possess them, while in man, rat, elephant, mouse, they are well-developed structures. It was formerly thought that the seminal vesicles in mammals acted as a storehouse for the sperm, hence the name. In reality they are glandular structures which add their contents to the seminal fluid during the sexual act.

5. FUNCTION OF THE PROSTATE GLAND

The prostate gland also is a variable structure and is found entirely in the marsupial and eutherian mammals. In marsupials it is confined to the prostatic portion of the urethral wall; in man it is a rounded, bulbous structure which surrounds the urethra close to the urinary bladder. In many other mammals it is a much smaller and less conspicuous structure. It discharges its contents into the seminal fluid during the orgasm. It is probable that the prostatic and vesicular fluids form the so-called "vaginal plug" in the vagina of the rat, mouse, etc.

6. BULBOURETHRAL (COWPER'S) GLANDS

The bulbourethral glands are absent in the dog but present in most other mammals. In marsupials and monotremes these structures are exceptionally well formed. In the opossum there are three pairs of bulbourethral glands. The mucous contents of these and other small urethral glands are discharged at the beginning of the sexual climax and, as such, become part of the seminal fluid.

7. FUNCTIONS OF SEMINAL FLUID

a. Amount of Seminal Fluid Discharged and Its General Functions

As stated previously, the semen or seminal fluid is composed of two parts, the sperm cells (spermia; spermatozoa) and the **seminal plasma.** The presence of the sperm cells represents the most constant feature, although they may vary considerably from species to species in size, shape, structure, and number present. The seminal plasma varies greatly as to composition and amount discharged.

The quantity of seminal fluid discharged per ejaculate and the relative numbers of sperm present in man and a few other vertebrate species associated with him are as follows:*

Species	Volume of Single Ejaculate, Most Common Value, in CC.		Sperm Density in Semen, Average Value, per CC.
Boar	250	cc.	100,000,000 per cc.
Bull	4–5	cc.	1,000,000,000 per cc.
Cock	0.8	cc.	3,500,000,000 per cc.
Dog	6	cc.	200,000,000 per cc.
Man	3.5	cc.	100,000,000 per cc.
Rabbit	1	cc.	700,000,000 per cc.
Ram	1	cc.	3,000,000,000 per cc.
Stallion	70	cc.	120,000,000 per cc.
Turkey	0.3	cc.	7,000,000,000 per cc.

* Modified from Mann ('50).

Two important branches of study involving the semen pertain to:

(1) the chemical and physiological nature and numerical presence of the sperm, and

(2) the physiology and biochemistry of the seminal plasma.

(See Mann, '50, for discussion and bibliography.) As a result of the studies thus far, a considerable body of information has been accumulated.

The main function of the semen, including the plasma and accessory sperm, appears to be to assist the sperm cell whose chance fortune it is to make contact with the egg. Once this association is accomplished, the egg seemingly takes over the problem of fertilization. The seminal plasma *and* the accessory numbers of sperm appear to act as an important protective bodyguard and also as an aid for this event. Modern research emphasizes, therefore, that the work of the male reproductive system is not complete until this contact is made.

b. Coagulation of the Semen

In many mammalian species, the semen tends to coagulate after its discharge from the male system. In the mouse, rat, guinea pig, opossum, *rhesus* monkey, etc., the semen coagulates into a solid mass, the vaginal plug, once it reaches the vagina of the female. The probable function of the vaginal plug is to prevent the semen from seeping out of the vagina. The formation of this plug may be due to a protein present in the contents of the seminal vesicle which comes in contact with the enzyme, **vesiculase.** In the rat and guinea pig this catalyst probably is produced by the "coagulating gland," a specialized structure associated with the seminal vesicles in these forms. Some of it also may come from the prostate.

Coagulation of the seminal fluid also occurs in man, stallion, and boar but it is entirely absent in the dog, bull, and many other animals. Human semen coagulates immediately after discharge but liquefies a short time afterward. This liquefaction may be due to the presence of two enzymes, **fibrinogenase** and **fibrinolysin,** found in human semen and both derived from the prostate. These enzymes are found also in dog semen. In the latter their property of inhibiting blood coagulation may be of use where considerable amounts of blood may be present in the female genital tract at the onset of full estrous conditions. Another important contribution of the prostate gland is citric acid. Its role is not clear but it may enter into the above coagulation-liquefaction process (Mann, '50, p. 348).

c. Hyaluronidase

Various enzymes have been demonstrated to be present in the semen of certain invertebrates and vertebrates. One such enzyme is **hyaluronidase** which appears to be produced in the testes of the rat, rabbit, boar, bull, and man. It is not found in the testes of vertebrates below the mammals. Its specific function is associated with the dispersal of the follicle cells surrounding the egg; in so doing it may aid the process of fertilization in mammals.

d. Accessory Sperm

One sperm normally effects a union with the egg in fertilization. Accessory sperm may enter large-yolked eggs, but only one is intimately involved in the union with the egg pronucleus. However, what is meant by accessory sperm here is the large number of sperm which normally clusters around the egg during the fertilization process in many animal species. A suggestion of a function for these accessory sperm follows from the fact that hyaluronidase may be extracted from the semen, presumably from the sperm themselves. Rowlands ('44) and also Leonard and Kurzrok ('46) have shown that a seminal fluid deficient in sperm numbers may fertilize if hyaluronidase extracted from sperm (?) is added to such a weakened sperm suspension. The implication is that the accessory sperm thus may act as "cupbearers" for the one successful sperm in that they carry hyaluronidase which aids in liquefying the follicle cells and other gelatinous coating material around the egg.

e. Fructose

An older concept in embryology maintained that sperm were unable to obtain or utilize nourishment after they departed from the testis. More recent investigation has shown, however, that sperm do utilize certain sugar materials, and that their survival depends upon the presence of a simple sugar in the medium in which they are kept. (See Mann, '50.)

The sugar that is found normally in semen is **fructose.** It varies in quantity from species to species, being small in amount in the semen of the boar or stallion but considerably larger in quantity in the seminal fluid of the bull, man, and rabbit. The seat of origin of this sugar appears to be the seminal vesicle, at least in man, although the prostate may also be involved, particularly in the rabbit and also in the dog. The dog, however, has but a small amount of fructose in the seminal discharge. The real function of seminal fructose "might be as a readily utilizable store of energy for the survival of motile spermatozoa" (Mann, '50, p. 360).

f. Enzyme-protecting Substances

Runnström (personal communication) and his co-workers have demonstrated that the fertilizing life of sea-urchin sperm is increased by certain substances found in the jelly coat of the sea-urchin egg. Presumably these substances are protein in nature, and, according to Runnström, they may act to preserve the enzyme system of the sperm. Similarly, the seminal fluid may act to preserve the enzyme system of the sperm, while en route to the egg, especially within the female genital tract.

D. Internal and External Factors Influencing Activities of the Testis

Conditions which influence testicular activity are many. Many of the factors are unknown. Nevertheless, a few conditions which govern testis function have been determined, especially in certain mammalian species. The general results of experimental determination of some of the agents which affect testicular function are briefly outlined below.

1. INTERNAL FACTORS

a. Temperature and Anatomical Position of the Testis

It is well known that in those mammals which have a permanent scrotal residence of the testes failure of the testis or testes to descend properly into the scrotum results in a corresponding failure of the seminiferous tubules to produce sperm. In these instances the testis may appear shriveled and shrunken (fig. 18). However, such cryptorchid (ectopic) conditions in most cases retain the ability to produce the sex hormone at least to some degree. A question therefore arises relative to the factors which inhibit seminiferous tubule activity within the cryptorchid testis.

The failure of cryptorchid testes to produce viable sperm has been of interest for a long time. Observations have demonstrated that the more hidden

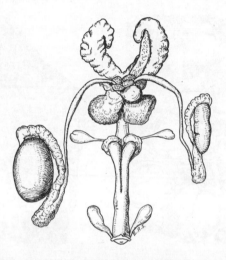

FIG. 18. Experimental unilateral cryptorchidism in adult rat. The animal's left testis was confined within the abdominal cavity for six months, whereas the right testis was permitted to reside in the normal scrotal position. Observe the shrunken condition of the cryptorchid member. (After Turner: *General Endocrinology,* Philadelphia, Saunders.)

the testis (i.e., the nearer the peritoneal cavity) the less likely are mature sperm to be formed. A testis, in the lower inguinal canal or upper scrotal area is more normal in sperm production than one located in the upper inguinal canal or inside the inguinal ring. Studies made upon peritoneal and scrotal temperatures of rats, rabbits, guinea pigs, etc., demonstrate a temperature in the scrotum several degrees lower than that which obtains in the abdomen. These observations suggest that the higher temperature of the non-scrotal areas is a definite factor in bringing about seminiferous tubule injury and failure to produce sperm.

With this temperature factor in mind, Dr. Carl R. Moore (in Allen, Danforth, and Doisy, '39) and others performed experiments designed to test its validity as a controlling influence. They found that confinement alone of an adult guinea pig testicle in the abdomen led to marked disorganization of all seminiferous tubules in seven days. After several months of such confinement the seminiferous tubules experience marked degenerative changes and only Sertoli cells remain (fig. 19A, B). The interstitial tissue, however, is not greatly impaired. If such a testis is kept not too long within the abnormal position and once again is returned to the scrotum, spermatogenesis is rejuvenated (fig. 20A, B). In a second experiment, the scrotum of a ram was encased loosely with insulating material; a rapid degeneration of the seminiferous tubules followed. Young ('27, '29) in a third type of experiment found that water 6 to 7°warmer than the body temperature applied to the external aspect of the guinea-pig testis for a 15-minute period evoked degenerative

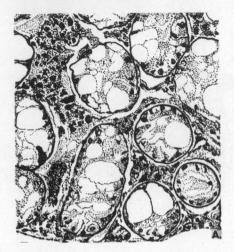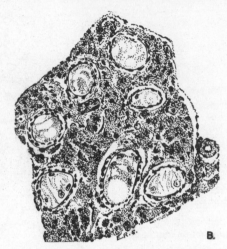

Fig. 19. Sections of experimental, cryptorchid, guinea-pig, seminiferous tubules and interstitial tissue. (Modified from C. R. Moore in Sex & Internal Secretions, Williams & Wilkins, Baltimore, 1939.)   (A) Testis confined to abdomen for three months.   (B) Testis confined to abdomen for six months. Observe degenerate state of seminiferous tubule after six months' confinement. Interstitial tissue not greatly affected by confinement.

changes with temporary sterility (fig. 21). Recovery, however, is the rule in the latter instance. Summarizing the effects of such experiments involving temperature, Moore (in Allen, Danforth, and Doisy, '39, p. 371) concludes: "The injury developing from applied heat, although more rapidly effective, is entirely similar to that induced by the normal body temperature when the testicle is removed from the scrotum to the abdomen."

The position of the scrotum and its anatomical structure is such as to enhance its purpose as a regulator of testicular temperature (figs. 2, 6). When the surrounding temperature is cold, the contraction of the dartos muscle tissue of the scrotal skin contracts the scrotum as a whole, while the contraction of the cremaster muscle loops pulls the testes and the scrotum closer to the body, thus conserving the contained heat. When the surrounding temperature is warm, these muscles relax, producing a more pendulous condition to permit heat loss from the scrotal wall.

In accordance with the foregoing description of the scrotum as a necessary thermoregulator for the testis, it has been further shown for those mammals which possess a scrotum that testis grafts fare much better when transplanted to the scrotal wall or into the anterior chamber of the eye (Turner, C. D.,

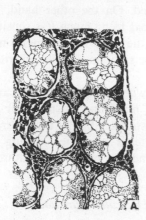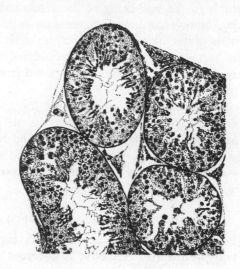

FIG. 20. Sections of testis during and after abdominal confinement. (Modified from C. R. Moore in Sex & Internal Secretions, Williams & Wilkins, Baltimore, 1939.)   (A) Section of left testis to show degenerate state of seminiferous tubules after 24 days of abdominal confinement.   (B) Section of right testis 74 days after replacement in scrotum. Observe spermatogenic activity in tubules.

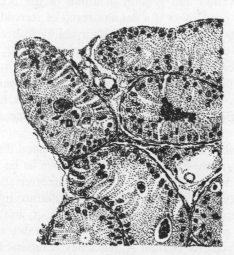

FIG. 21. Effect of higher temperature applied to external surface of guinea-pig testis. Water, 47°, was applied to surface of scrotum for period of 10 minutes. Testis was removed from animal 12 days after treatment. Seminiferous tubules are degenerate. (Modified from Moore, '39; see also Young, '27, J. Exp. Zool., 49.)

'48). The anterior chamber of the eyeball possesses a temperature much cooler than the internal parts of the body.

Two types of seminiferous tubules are thus found in mammals. In a few mammalian species (see p. 6) the temperature of the peritoneal cavity is favorable to the well-being of the seminiferous tubule; in most mammalian species, however, a lower temperature is required. On the other hand, the activities of the interstitial tissue of the testis appear to be much less sensitive to the surrounding temperature conditions, and the male sex hormone may be produced when the testes are removed from the scrotum and placed within the peritoneal cavity.

With regard to the functioning of the testis within the peritoneal cavity of birds it has been suggested that the air sacs may function to lower the temperature around the testis (Cowles and Nordstrom, '46). In the sparrow, Riley ('37) found that mitotic activity in the testis is greatest during the early morning hours when the bird is resting and the body temperature is lower, by 3 or 4° C.

b. Body Nourishment in Relation to Testicular Function

The testis is a part of, and therefore dependent upon, the well-being of the body as a whole. However, as observed in the preceding pages the interstitial cells and their activities in the production of the male sex hormone are less sensitive to the internal environment of the body than are the seminiferous tubules.

The separation of these two phases of testicular function is well demonstrated during starvation and general inanition of the body as a whole. A falling off of sperm production is a definite result of starvation diets, although the germinative cells do not readily lose their ability to proliferate even after prolonged periods of starvation. But the interstitial cells and the cells of Sertoli are not as readily affected by inadequate diets or moderate starvation periods. Sex drive may be maintained in a starving animal, while his ability to produce mature, healthy sperm is lost. On the other hand, long periods of inanition also affect sex hormone production and the sexual interests of the animal.

Aside from the abundance of food in a well-rounded dietary regime, adequate supplies of various vitamins have been shown to be essential. Vitamin B_1 is essential to the maintenance of the seminiferous tubules in pigeons. Pronounced degenerative changes in the seminiferous tubules of rats and other mammals occur in the absence of vitamins A and E (Mason, '39). Prolonged absence of vitamin E produces an irreparable injury to the testis of rats; injury produced by vitamin A deficiency is reparable. The B-complex of vitamins seems to be especially important for the maintenance of the accessory reproductive structures, such as the prostate, seminal vesicles, etc. The absence of vitamin C has a general body effect, but does not influence the testis directly. Some of these effects may be mediated through the pituitary gland. As vitamin D is intimately associated with the mineral metabolism of the body, it is not easy to demonstrate its direct importance.

c. The Hypophysis and Its Relation to Testicular Function

The word "hypophysis" literally means a process extending out below. The early anatomists regarded the **hypophysis cerebri** as a process of the brain more or less vestigial in character. It was long regarded 'as a structure through which waste materials from the brain filtered out through supposed openings into the nasal cavity. These wastes were in the form of mucus or phlegm, hence the name "pituitary," derived from a Latin word meaning "mucus." The word pituitary is often used synonymously with the word hypophysis.

The hypophysis is made up of the pars anterior or anterior lobe, pars intermedia or intermediate lobe, and a processus infundibuli or posterior lobe. The anterior lobe is a structure of great importance to the reproductive system; its removal (ablation) results in profound atrophic changes throughout the entire reproductive tract.

The importance of the pituitary gland in controlling reproductive phenomena was aroused by the work of Crowe, Cushing, and Homans ('10) and by Aschner ('12) who successfully removed the hypophysis of young dogs. One of the first fruits of this work was a demonstration of the lack of genital development when this organ was removed. Since that time many of the other cohabitants of man—rats, mice, cats, rabbits, etc.—have been hypophysectomized, and in all cases a rapid involution and atrophy of the genital structures results from pituitary removal. The testis undergoes profound shrinkage and regression following hypophysectomy, the degree of change varying with the species. In the rooster and monkey, for example, regressive changes are more marked than in the rat. (Consult Smith, '39, for data and references.)

A striking demonstration of the influence of the hypophysis upon the genital tract is the result of its removal from a seasonal-breeding species, such as the ferret. Ablation of the pituitary in this species during the nonbreeding season causes slight if any change in the testis and accessory reproductive organs. However, when it is removed during the breeding season, a marked regression to a condition similar to that present during the nonbreeding season occurs (Hill and Parkes, '33).

The experimental result of hypophysectomy on many animal species thus points directly to this structure as the site of hormonal secretion, particularly to the anterior lobe (Smith, '39). The initial work on the relation of pituitary hormones and the gonad was done upon the female animal. The results of these studies aroused the question whether one or two hormones were responsible. The latter alternative was suggested by the work of Aschheim and Zondek ('27) and Zondek ('30) who concluded that *two separate substances* appeared to be concerned with the control of ovarian changes.

Nevertheless, for a time the concept of only one gonad-controlling (gonadotrophic) hormone was produced by the pituitary, continued to gain attention, and some workers suggested that the two ovarian effects of follicular growth and luteinization of the follicle were due to the length of time of administration of one hormone and not to two separate substances. However, this position soon was made untenable by research upon the gonadotrophic substances derived from the pituitary gland. Studies along this line by Fevold, Hisaw, and Leonard ('31) and Fevold and Hisaw ('34) reported the fractionation, from pituitary gland sources, of two gonadotrophic substances, a **follicle-stimulating factor or FSH** and a **luteinization factor or LH.** This work has been extensively confirmed. It should be observed in passing that the male pituitary gland contains large amounts of FSH, although, as mentioned below, the function of the testis and the male reproductive system relies to a great extent upon the luteinizing factor. Some investigators refer to the LH factor as the interstitial-cell-stimulating hormone, ICSH. (See Evans, '47; and also Evans and Simpson in Pincus and Thimann, '50.)

The action of these two hormones upon testicular tissue, according to present information, is somewhat as follows: If pure follicle-stimulating hormone, FSH, which produces only FSH effects in the female, is injected in low doses into hypophysectomized male rats, the seminiferous tubules are stimulated and spermatogenesis occurs. Under these conditions, the interstitial tissue remains unstimulated and the accessories continue in an atrophic state. It has further been demonstrated that slight amounts of the luteinizing gonadotrophic hormone, LH (ICSH), added to the above injections of FSH, effects a much better stimulation of the spermatogonial tissue, and the interstitial tissue also develops well.

On the other hand, when pure LH (ICSH) is given alone in small doses, spermatogenesis is stimulated with slight or no effect upon the male accessory structures. However, when larger doses of the LH (ICSH) factor alone are injected, the interstitial tissue is greatly stimulated, and the testicular weight increases much more than when FSH alone is given. Furthermore, the accessory reproductive structures are stimulated and become well developed, suggesting the elaboration of the male sex hormone. In agreement with these results, the administration alone of testosterone, the male sex hormone, increases the weight and development of the accessory structures in hypophysectomized animals and it also maintains spermatogenesis. It appears, therefore, that the effects of the LH substance upon the seminiferous tubules and the accessory organs occur by means of its ability to arouse the formation of the male sex hormone.

A summary of the actions of the pituitary gonadotrophic hormones upon testicular tissue may be stated as follows:

(1) Pure FSH in small doses stimulates the seminiferous tubules and spermatogenesis with little or no effect upon the interstitial tissue or the accessory reproductive structures, such as the seminal vesicles or prostate gland;

(2) Small doses of pure LH also stimulate spermatogenesis with little or no stimulation of the accessory structures;

(3) Pure LH (ICSH) in larger doses stimulates the development of the interstitial tissue with the subsequent secretion of the male sex hormone and hypertrophy of the accessory reproductive organs;

(4) The male sex hormone in some way aids or stimulates the process of spermatogenesis, suggesting that the action of LH occurs through the medium of the sex hormone (fig. 22).

(Consult Evans and Simpson in Pincus and Thimann, '50, for data and references; also Turner, C. D., '48.)

The foregoing results of the action of the FSH and LH upon testicular function might suggest that the LH substance alone is essential in the male animal. However, it should be observed that without the presence of FSH, LH is not able to maintain the tubules in a strictly normal manner, the tubules showing a diminution of size. Also, in extreme atrophic conditions of the tubules, pure FSH stimulates spermatogenesis better than similar quantities of LH. It is probable that *FSH and LH (ICSH) work together to effect complete normality in the male.* This combined effect is known as a *synergistic effect.* It also is of interest that the injection of small doses of testosterone propionate into the normal male, with the pituitary gland intact, results in inhibition of the seminiferous tubules, *probably due to the suppression of pituitary secretion by the increased amount of the male sex hormone in the blood.* However, high doses, while they likewise inhibit the pituitary, result in a level of androgen which stimulates the seminiferous tubules directly (Ludwig, '50).

Aside from the above actions upon testicular tissue by the luteinizing hormone (LH;ICSH) certain other functions of this substance should be mentioned (see fig. 22). One of these is the apparent dependence of the Sertoli cells upon the presence of the interstitial cells (Williams, '50). Interstitial tissue behavior and development in turn relies mainly upon LH (ICSH) (Fevold, '39; Evans and Simpson in Pincus and Thimann, '50). As the sperm are intimately associated with the Sertoli elements during the latter phases of spermatogenesis in which they transform from the spermatid into the form of the adult sperm, a very close association and reliance upon the presence of the luteinizing hormone thus appears to be established in sperm development.

A further study of the LH factor is associated with the maintenance of

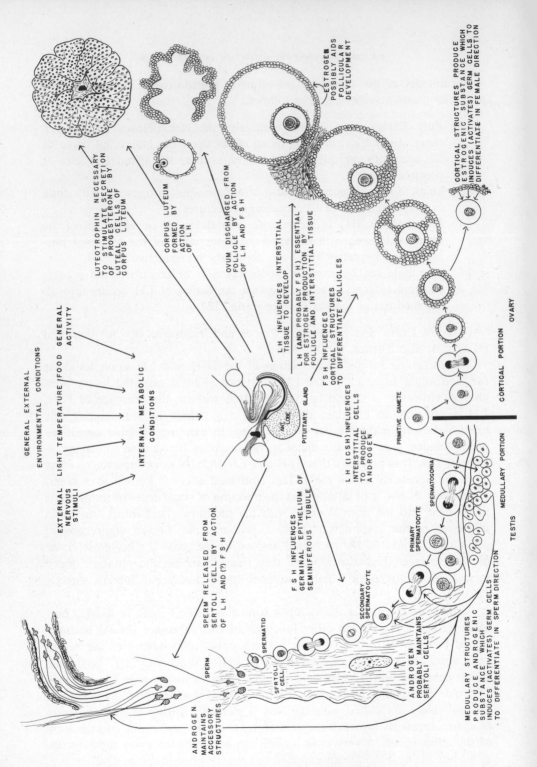

FIG. 22. (*See facing page for legend.*)

the seminiferous tubules themselves. In aged males, the interstitial tissue and the seminiferous tubules normally involute and regress with accumulation of large amounts of connective tissue material. In testicular grafts made into the rabbit's ear, Williams ('50) found, when interstitial tissue was present in the grafts, the seminiferous tubules were more nearly normal; when absent, the tubules underwent fibrosis.

Another function of the LH substance apparently is concerned with release of the sperm from the Sertoli cells. De Robertis, et al. ('46), showed that anterior pituitary hormones possibly cause release of sperm from the Sertoli cells in the toad by the production of vacuoles and apical destruction of the cytoplasm of the Sertoli elements. In testicular grafts Williams ('50) accumulated evidence which suggests that vacuoles and secretion droplets in the Sertoli cells occurred as a result of LH administration. The combined results of these investigators suggest that sperm release from the Sertoli cell is dependent, in some way, upon LH (ICSH) activity.

A final function is concerned with the physiological maturing of sperm in the reproductive duct, at least in many vertebrate species. The well-being of the epididymis and vas deferens is dependent upon the presence of the male sex hormone (Greep, Fevold, and Hisaw, '36). As the male sex hormone results from stimulation of the interstitial cells by the interstitial-cell-stimulating substance, LH (ICSH), the connection between this substance and the physiological maturation of the sperm cell is obvious.

2. External Environmental Factors and Testis Function

As we have seen above, the anterior lobe of the hypophysis acts as the main internal environmental factor controlling the testes and, through them, the reproductive ducts. It has been observed also that food, vitamins, and anatomical position of the testis are important influences in regulating testicular function. Furthermore, general physiological conditions such as health or disease have an important bearing upon the gonads (Mills, '19). All of

---

FIG. 22. Chart showing the effects of the hypophyseal anterior lobe upon the developing gametes. It also suggests the various factors influencing pituitary secretion of the gonadotrophic hormones, FSH and LH. Observe that the primitive gamete in the cortex of the ovary is subjected to the cortical environment and develops into an oocyte, whereas in the medullary or testicular environment it develops into a spermatocyte. Experiments upon sex reversal have demonstrated that the medullary and cortical portions of the gonad determine the fate of the germ cell. In the male area or medulla, the germ cell differentiates in the male direction, while in the cortex, the differentiation is in the direction of the female gamete or oocyte, regardless of the innate sex-chromosome constitution of the primitive germ cell. The fate of the germ cell thus is influenced by four main sets of factors: (1) Internal and external environmental factors, controlling the secretions of the pituitary body, (2) Environment of the testicular tissue (medulla) and possible humoral substances produced in this tissue, (3) Environment of the ovarian tissue (cortex) and possible humoral substances elaborated there, and (4) Secretions of the anterior lobe of the pituitary body.

the above conditions are contained within the body of the organism, and as such represent organismal conditions.

The following question naturally arises: Do factors or conditions external to the body impinge themselves in such a way as to control pituitary and gonadal function?

a. Light as a Factor

Aside from the supply of nutritive substances or the collision of the many nervous stimuli with the individual which may arouse or depress the sexual activities, two of the most important obvious external factors are temperature and light. Research on the reproductive behavior of many animal species, during the past twenty years, has shown that both of these factors have great significance on the reproductive activities of many vertebrate species. Bissonnette ('30, '32, '35, a and b) has accumulated evidence which demonstrates that light is a potent factor in controlling the reproductive behavior of the European starling *(Sturnus vulgaris)* and also of the ferret *(Putorius vulgaris)*. In the starling, for example, the evidence shows that green wave lengths of the spectrum inhibit testicular activity, while red rays and white light arouse the reproductive function (fig. 23). The addition of electric lighting to each day's duration produced a total testis size in midwinter which surpassed the normal condition in the spring. In the ferret artificially increased day length beginning at the first part of October brings the testis to maximum size and activity coupled with a normal mating impulse as early as November and December (fig. 24). Under normal conditions the male ferret is able to breed only during February and early March.

These findings relative to the influence of light on the reproductive periodicity of animals confirm a fact which has been known for a long time, namely, that seasonal breeders brought from the northern hemisphere to the southern hemisphere reverse their breeding season. For example, ferrets which normally breed from spring to summer in the northern hemisphere shift their breeding habits to the September-February period when moved to the southern hemisphere. Inasmuch as the hypophysis is instrumental in bringing about secretion of the gonadotrophic hormones responsible for the testicular activity, it is highly probable that light coming through the eyes (see Hill and Parkes, '33) influences the nervous system in some way arousing the hypophysis and stimulating it to secrete these substances in greater quantity. However, one must keep in mind the caution given by Bissonnette, that light is not the only factor conditioning the sexual cycles of ferrets and starlings.

While numerous animals, such as the migratory birds, ferret, mare, many fish, frogs, etc., normally are brought into a breeding condition during the period of light ascendency, a large number of animals experience a sexual resurgence only during the time of year when the light of day is regressing in span. This condition is found in some sheep, goats, buffalo in nature,

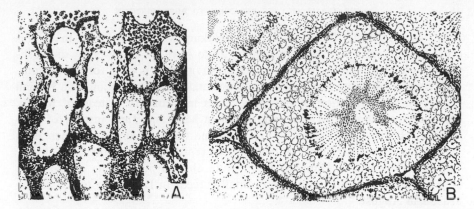

FIG. 23. Sections of testis of the starling *(Sturnus vulgaris)*, showing the effect of electric lighting added to the bird's normal daily duration of light during the autumn. (After Bissonnette, Physiol. Zool., 4.) (A) Inside young control bird—no light added —kept inside as control for (B) from November 9 to December 13. (B) Inside young experimental bird, receiving additional light from "25 watt" bulb from November 9 to December 13. Total treatment, 34 days.

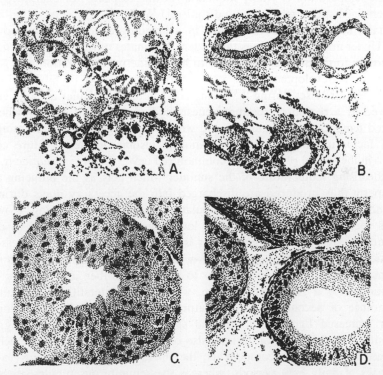

FIG. 24. Sections of testis and epididymis, showing modification of sexual cycle in the ferret, *Putorius vulgaris,* by exposure to increasing periods of light. (After Bissonnette, '35b.) (A) Seminiferous tubules from normal male over 1 year old, made on October 3, no lighting. (B) Epididymis of normal male on October 3, no lighting. (C) Seminiferous tubules of experimental male on November 7, 36 days of added lighting. (D) Epididymis of experimental males on Nov nber 7, 36 days of added lighting.

deer, some fish, etc. Bissonnette ('41) working with goats found that: "Increasing daily light periods from January 25 to April 5—followed by diminishing periods until July 5, while temperatures remained normal for the seasons, with four Toggenburg female goats and one male Toggenburg and one Nubian female—led to cessation of breeding cycles in February instead of March, followed by initiation of breeding cycles in May and June instead of September." In the ewe, Yeates ('47) also found that a change from increasing daylight to decreasing length of day induced reproductive activity. In a similar manner, Hoover and Hubbard ('37) were able to modify the sexual cycle in a variety of brook trout which normally breeds in December to a breeding season in August.

b. Temperature Influences

In the case of the animals mentioned above, temperature does not appear to be a major factor in inducing reproductive activity. However, in many animals temperature is vitally influential in this respect. For example, in the thirteen-lined spermophile (ground squirrel) Wells ('35) observed that breeding males kept at 40° F. continued in a breeding condition throughout the year. Under normal conditions this rodent hibernates during the winter months and comes forth in the spring ready to breed; sperm proliferation and general reproductive development take place during the period of hibernation. As the temperature rises during the spring and summer, testicular atrophy ensues, followed by a period of spermatogenesis and reproductive activity when the lowered temperatures of autumn and winter come again. Light, seemingly, is not a factor in this sexual cycle. Another instance of temperature control occurs in the sexual phase of the common red newt, *Triturus viridescens*. Here it is the rising temperature of the summer which acts as the inducing agent, and sperm thus produced are discharged into the accessory ducts during the fall and winter to be used when copulation occurs in early spring. However, if this species is kept at a relatively low temperature of 8 to 12° C. during the summer months, spermatogenesis is inhibited and the testis regresses. In the stickleback, *Gasterosteus aculeatus,* as reported by Craig-Bennett ('31), spermatogenesis occurs during July to early September and appears to be conditioned by a rising temperature, whereas the interstitial tissue and the appearance of secondary sexual features reach their greatest development under increased light conditions and slowly rising temperatures (fig. 15). Bissonnette, in his work on ferrets, also observed a difference in the behavior of these two testicular components; the interstitial tissue responds to large increases of daily light periods, whereas the seminiferous tubules are stimulated by small, gradually increasing periods of light.

The above examples emphasize the importance of a single environmental factor on the pituitary-gonadal relationship. However, in the hedgehog, Allanson and Deansley ('34) emphasize temperature, lighting, and hormone injections as factors modifying the sexual cycles, while Baker and Ransom ('32, '33, a and b) show that light, food, temperature, and locality affect the sexual cycles and breeding habits of the field mouse. In some vertebrates, therefore, a single factor may be the dominant one, whereas in others, numerous factors control the action of the pituitary and reproductive system.

E. Internal Factors Which May Control Seasonal and Continuous Types of Testicular Function

In endeavoring to explain the differences in response to external environmental factors on the part of seasonal and continuous breeders, one must keep in mind the following possibilities:

(1) The anterior lobe of the hypophysis in some forms (e.g., ferret) cannot be maintained in a secretory condition after it has reached its climax; that is, it apparently becomes insensitive to the light factor. As a result, regression of the pituitary and testis occurs (Bissonnette, '35b).

(2) In the starling, the anterior hypophysis may be maintained by the lighting, but the testis itself does not respond to the presence of the hypophyseal hormones in the blood (Bissonnette, '35b). The possibility in this instance may be that testicular function wanes because the body rapidly eliminates the hormone in some way (see Bachman, Collip, and Selye, '34).

(3) Consideration also must be given to the suggestion that the activities of the sex gland by the secretion of the sex hormone *may suppress anterior lobe activity* (Moore and Price, '32).

We may consider two further possibilities relative to continuous testicular function:

(4) If the "brake actions" mentioned above are not present or present only in a slight degree, a degree not sufficient to interrupt the activities of the anterior lobe or of the sex gland, a more or less continuous function of the testis may be maintained.

(5) When several or many environmental factors are concerned in producing testicular activity, a slight altering of one factor, such as light, may prove insufficient to interrupt the pituitary-germ-gland relationship, and a continuous breeding state is effected in spite of seasonal changes.

Underlying the above possibilities which may control testicular function is the inherent tendency or hereditary constitution of the animal. In the final analysis, it is this constitution which responds to environmental stimuli, and moreover, controls the entire metabolism of the body. In other words, the above-mentioned possibilities tend to oversimplify the problem. The organism as a whole must be considered; reproduction is not merely an environmental-pituitary-sex gland relationship.

F. Characteristics of the Male Reproductive Cycle and Its Relation to Reproductive Conditions in the Female

As indicated above, reproduction in the male vertebrate is either a continuous process throughout the reproductive life of the individual or it is a discontinuous, periodic affair. In the continuous form of reproduction the activities of the seminiferous tubules and the interstitial or hormone-producing tissues of the testis function side by side in a continuous fashion. In the discontinuous, periodic type of testicular function, the activities of the seminiferous tubules and of the interstitial tissue do not always coincide. The activities of the seminiferous tubules, resulting in the production of sperm for a particular reproductive cycle, tend to precede, in some species by many months, the activities of the sex-hormone-producing tissue. Evidently, the output of the FSH and LH substances from the pituitary gland are spread out over different periods of the year to harmonize with this activity of the testicular components.

It will be seen in the next chapter that a continuous breeding faculty is not present in the female comparable to that of the male. All females are discontinuous breeders. In some species, the cycles follow each other with little rest between each cycle unless the female becomes pregnant or "broody." Some have a series of cycles over one part of the year but experience sexual quiescence over the remaining portion of the year. However, in most female vertebrates there is but one reproductive cycle per year.

In harmony with the above conditions, the continuous variety of testicular function is always associated with the condition in the female where more than one reproductive cycle occurs per year. Continuous reproductive conditions in the male, therefore, are adapted to serve one female two or more times per year or several different females at intervals through the year. Furthermore, the complicated, highly glandular, greatly extended type of male-reproductive-duct system is adapted to conditions of (1) continuous breeding, or (2) service to more than one female during one breeding season of the year, whereas the simple type of reproductive duct is adapted to the type of service where all or most of the genital products are discharged during one brief period. In other words, the entire male reproductive system and reproductive habits are adapted to the behavior of female reproductive activities.

Bibliography

Allanson, M. and Deanesly, R. **1934.** The reaction of anoestrous hedgehogs to experimental conditions. Proc. Roy. Soc., London, s. B. **116**:170.

Allen, B. M. **1904.** The embryonic development of the ovary and testis of the mammal. Am. J. Anat. **3**:89.

Allen, E., Danforth, C. H., and Doisy, E. A. **1939.** Sex and Internal Secretions. Consult Chaps. 16, 17, 18, 19. The Williams & Wilkins Co., Baltimore.

Aschheim, S. and Zondek, B. **1927.** Hypophysenvorderlappenhormon und Ovarialhormon im Harn von Schwangeren. Klin. Wchnschr. **6**:1322.

Aschner, B. **1912.** Über die Funktion der Hypophyse. Pflüger's Arch. f. d. ges. Physiol. **146**:1.

Asdell, S. A. **1946.** Patterns of Mammalian Reproduction. Comstock Publishing Co., Inc., Ithaca, New York.

Bachman, C., Collip, J. B., and Selye, H. **1934.** Anti-gonadotropic substances. Proc. Soc. Exper. Biol. & Med. **32**:544.

Baker, J. R. and Ransom, R. M. **1932.** Factors affecting the breeding of the field mouse (*Microtus agrestis*). I. Light. Proc. Roy. Soc. London, s. B. **110**:313.

——— and ———. **1933a.** Factors affecting the breeding of the field mouse. (*Microtus agrestis*). II. Temperature and food. Proc. Roy. Soc., London, s. B. **112**:39.

——— and ———. **1933b.** Factors affecting the breeding of the field mouse (*Microtus agrestis*). III. Locality. Proc. Roy. Soc., London, s. B. **113**:486.

Bishop, D. W. **1942.** Germ cell studies in the male fox (*Vulpes fulva*). Anat. Rec. **84**:99.

Bissonnette, T. H. **1930.** Studies on the sexual cycle in birds. I. Sexual maturity, its modification and possible control in the European starling (*Sturnus vulgaris*). Am. J. Anat. **45**:289.

———. **1932.** Studies on the sexual cycle in birds. VI. Effects of white, green and red lights of equal luminous intensity on the testis activity of the European starling (*Sturnus vulgaris*). Physiol. Zoöl. **5**:92.

———. **1935a.** Modifications of mammalian sexual cycles. II. Effects upon young male ferrets (*Putorius vulgaris*) of constant eight and one-half hour days and of six hours of illumination after dark between November and June. Biol. Bull. **68**:300.

———. **1935b.** Modifications of mammalian sexual cycles. III. Reversal of the cycle in male ferrets (*Putorius vulgaris*) by increasing periods of exposure to light between October second and March thirtieth. J. Exper. Zool. **71**:341.

———. **1941.** Experimental modification of breeding cycles in goats. Physiol. Zoöl. **14**:379.

Cieslak, E. S. **1945.** Relations between the reproductive cycle and the pituitary gland in the snake, *Thamnophis radix*. Physiol. Zoöl. **18**:299.

Corner, G. W. **1943.** On the female testes or ovaries, by Reginer de Graaf, Chap. XII of De Mulierum Organis Generationi Inservientibus (Leyden:1672). Translated by G. W. Corner in Essays in Biology. The University of California Press, Berkeley and Los Angeles.

Cowles, R. B. and Nordstrom, A. **December 1946.** A possible avian analogue of the scrotum. Science. **104**:586.

Craig-Bennett, A. **1931.** The reproductive cycle of the three-spined stickleback, *Gasterosteus aculeatus*. Linn. Philos. Tr. Roy. Soc., London, s. B. **219**:197.

Cramer, A. J. **1937.** Evaluation of hormone therapy for undescended testes in man. Endocrinology. **21**:230.

Crouch, J. E. **1939.** Seasonal changes in the testes of the passerine bird, *Phainopepla nitens lepida*. Proc. Soc. Exper. Biol. & Med. **40**:218.

Crowe, S. J., Cushing, H., and Homans, J. **1910.** Experimental hypophysectomy. Bull. Johns Hopkins Hosp. **21**:127.

De Robertis, E., Burgos, M. H., and Breyter, E. **1946.** Action of anterior pituitary on Sertoli cells and on release of toad spermatozoa. Proc. Soc. Exper. Biol. & Med. **61**:20.

Dorfman, R. J. **1950**. Chap. II. Physiology of androgens in The Hormones. II, by Pincus and Thimann. Academic Press, Inc., New York.

Evans, H. M. **1947**. Recent advances in our knowledge of the anterior pituitary hormones. Am. Scientist. **35**:466.

—— and Simpson, M. E. **1950**. Chap. VI. Physiology of the gonadotrophins in The Hormones, II, by Pincus and Thimann. Academic Press, Inc., New York.

Felix, W. **1912**. The development of the urinogental organs in Manual of Human Embryology, by Keibal and Mall. J. B. Lippincott Co., Philadelphia and London.

Fevold, H. L. **1939**. Chap. XVII in Allen, et al., Sex and Internal Secretions. 2d ed., The Williams & Wilkins Co., Baltimore.

—— and Hisaw, F. L. **1934**. Interactions of gonad-stimulating hormones in ovarian development. Am. J. Physiol. **109**:655.

——, ——, and Leonard, S. L. **1931**. The gonad-stimulating and the luteinizing hormones of the anterior lobe of the hypophysis. Am. J. Physiol. **97**:291.

Glass, F. M. and Rugh, R. **1944**. Seasonal study of the normal and pituitary stimulated frog *(Rana pipiens)*. I. Testis and thumb pad. J. Morphol. **74**:409.

Greep, R. O., Fevold, H. L., and Hisaw, F. L. **1936**. Effects of two hypophyseal gonadotrophic hormones on the reproductive system of the male rat. Anat. Rec. **65**:261.

Guthrie, M. J. **1933**. The reproductive cycles of some cave bats. J. Mammalogy. **14**:199.

Hammond, J. and Asdell, S. A. **1926**. The vitality of the spermatozoa in the male and female reproductive tracts. Brit. J. Exper. Biol. **4**:155.

Henle, G. and Zittle, C. A. **1942**. Studies of the metabolism of bovine epididymal spermatozoa. Am. J. Physiol. **136**:70.

Hill, E. C. **1907**. On the gross development and vascularization of the testis. (Excellent figures showing migration of the testes in the pig.) Am. J. Anat. **6**:439.

Hill, M. and Parkes, A. S. **1933**. Studies on the hypophysectomized ferret. Proc. Roy. Soc., London, s. B. **116**:221.

Hoover, E. E. and Hubbard, H. F. **1937**. Modification of the sexual cycle of trout by control of light. Copeia. **4**:206.

Koch, F. C. **1942**. Biol. Symp., The excretion and metabolism of the male sex hormone in health and disease. Jaques Cattell Press. **9**:41.

Leonard, S. L. and Kurzrok, R. **1946**. Inhibitors of hyaluronidase in blood sera and their effect on follicle cell dispersal. Endocrinology. **39**:85.

Ludwig, D. J. **1950**. The effect of androgens on spermatogenesis. Endocrinology. **46**:453.

Mann, T. **1949**. Metabolism of semeñ. Adv. in Enzymology. **9**:329.

Marshall, F. H. A. **1911**. The male generative cycle in the hedgehogs, etc. J. Physiol. **43**:247.

Mason, K. E. **1939**. Chap. XXII in Allen, et al., Sex and Internal Secretions. 2d ed., The Williams & Wilkins Co., Baltimore.

Matthews, S. A. **1938**. The seasonal cycle in the gonads of *Fundulus*. Biol. Bull. **75**:66.

Mills, R. G. **1919**. The pathological changes in the testes in epidemic pneumonia. J. Exper. Med. **30**:505.

Mitchell, G. A. G. **1939**. The condition of the peritoneal vaginal processes at birth. J. Anat. **73**:658.

Moore, C. R. **1926**. The biology of the mammalian testis and scrotum. Quart. Rev. Biol. **1**:4.

——. **1928**. On the properties of the gonads as controllers of somatic and psychical characteristics. J. Exper. Zool. **50**:455.

——. **1939**. Chap. VII, Part V, in Allen, et al., Sex and Internal Secretions. 2d ed., The Williams & Wilkins Co., Baltimore.

——. **1942**. Physiology of the Testis in Glandular Physiology and Therapy. 2d ed., Am. M. A. Council on Pharmacy and Chemistry. Chicago.

—— and McGee, L. C. **1928**. On the effects of injecting lipoid extracts of bull testes into castrated guinea pigs. Am. J. Physiol. **87**:436.

—— and Price, D. **1932**. Gonad hormone functions and the reciprocal influence between gonads and hypophysis with its bearing on the problem of sex hormone antagonism. Am. J. Anat. **50**:13.

Pincus, G. and Thimann, K. V. **1950**. The Hormones, Vol. II. Academic Press, Inc., New York.

Rasmussen, A. T. **1917**. Seasonal changes in the interstitial cells of the testis in the woodchuck *(Marmota monax)*. Am. J. Anat. **22**:475.

Riley, G. M. **1937**. Experimental studies on spermatogenesis in the house sparrow, *Passer domesticus (Tinnaeus)*. Anat. Rec. **67**:327.

Robson, J. M. **1940**. Recent Advances in Sex and Reproductive Physiology. J. & A. Churchill, Ltd., London.

Rowlands, J. W. **1944**. Capacity of hyaluronidase to increase the fertilizing power of sperm. Nature, London. **154**:332.

Schulte, T. L. **1937**. The genito-urinary system of the *Elephas indicus* male. Am. J. Anat. **61**:131.

Schwenk, E. **1944**. Synthesis of the steroid hormones. Page 129 in The chemistry and physiology of hormones. Publication of Am. A. Adv. Sc.

Smith, P. E. **1939**. Chap. XVI in Allen, et al., Sex and Internal Secretions. 2d ed., The Williams & Wilkins Co., Baltimore.

Turner, C. D. **1948**. Chap. 12 in General Endocrinology. W. B. Saunders Co., Philadelphia.

Turner, C. L. **1919**. The seasonal cycle in the spermary of the perch. J. Morphol. **32**:681.

van Oordt, G. J. **1923**. Secondary sex characters and testis of the ten spined stickleback *(Gasterosteus pungitius)*. Proc. Kon. Akad. Wetensch., Amsterdam. **26**:309.

Weber, M. **1928**. Die Säugetiere. Gustav Fischer, Jena.

Wells, L. J. **1935**. Seasonal sexual rhythm and its modification in the experimental male of the thirteen-lined ground squirrel *(Citellus tridecemlineatus)*. Anat. Rec. **62**:409.

———. **1943**. Descent of the testis: anatomical and hormonal considerations. Surgery. **14**:436.

Williams, R. G. **1950**. Studies of living interstitial cells and pieces of seminiferous tubules in autogenous grafts of testis. Am. J. Anat. **86**:343.

Wislocki, G. B. **1933**. Location of the testes and body temperature in mammals. Quart. Rev. Biol. **8**:385.

———. **1943a**. Studies on the growth of deer antlers: I. On the structure and histogenesis of the antlers of the Virginia deer *(Odocoileus virginianus borealis)*. Am. J. Anat. **71**:371.

———. **1943b**. Studies on growth of deer antlers: II. Seasonal changes in the male reproductive tract of the Virginia deer *(Odocoileus virginianus borealis)*; with a discussion of the factors controlling antler-gonad periodicity. Essays in Biology In Honor of Herbert H. Evans. The University of California Press, Berkeley and Los Angeles.

———. et al. **1947**. The effects of gonadectomy and the administration of testosterone propionate on the growth of antlers in male and female deer. Endocrinology. **40**:202.

Yeates, N. T. M. **1947**. Influence of variation in length of day upon the breeding season in sheep. Nature, London. **160**:429.

Young, W. C. **1929**. The influence of high temperature on the reproductive capacity of guinea pig spermatozoa as determined by artificial insemination. Physiol. Zoöl. **2**:1.

———. **1931**. A study of the functions of the epididymis. III. Functional changes undergone by spermatozoa during their passage through the epididymis and vas deferens of the guinea pig. Brit. J. Exper. Biol. **8**:151.

Zondek, B. **1930**. Über die Hormone des Hypophysenvorderlappens. I. Wachstumshormon, Follikelreifungshormon (Prolan A). Luteinisierungshormon (Prolan B) Stoffwechselhormon? Klin. Wchnschr. **8**:245.

2

The Vertebrate Ovary and Its Relationship
to Reproduction

A. The ovary and its importance
B. Preformationism, past and present
C. General structure of the reproductive system of the vertebrate female
   1. General structure of the ovary
   2. General structure of the accessory reproductive organs
D. Dependency of the female reproductive system on general body conditions
   1. Inanition
   2. Vitamins
      a. Vitamin A
      b. Vitamin B
      c. Vitamin C
      d. Vitamin E
   3. The hypophysis (pituitary gland)
E. Activities of the ovary in producing the reproductive state
   1. The ovary as a "storehouse" of oogonia
   2. Position occupied by the primitive female germ cells in the ovarian cortex
   3. Primary, secondary, and tertiary follicles of de Graaf
   4. Hormonal factors concerned with the development of egg follicles
      a. Effects produced by the gonadotrophic hormones of the development of the mammalian egg follicle
      b. Stimulating effects of the gonadotrophins on the ovaries of other vertebrates
   5. Structure of the vertebrate, mature egg follicle
      a. Structure of the mature follicle in metatherian and eutherian mammals
      b. Structure of the prototherian egg follicle
      c. Egg follicles of other vertebrates
   6. Ovulatory process; possible factors controlling ovulation
      a. Process of ovulation in higher mammals
         1) Changing tissue conditions culminating in egg discharge from the ovary
         2) Hormonal control of the ovulatory process
      b. Ovulation in vertebrate groups other than the higher mammals
         1) Hen
         2) Frog
         3) Hormonal control of ovulation in lower vertebrates
      c. Comparison of the immediate factors affecting egg discharge in the vertebrate group
   7. Internal conditions of the ovary as an ovulatory factor

A. The Ovary and Its Importance

One of the editions of the treatise on development, "Exercitationes de Generatione Animalium," by William Harvey (1578–1657) contains a picture of Jupiter on a throne opening an egg from which various animals, including man, are emerging (fig. 25). Upon the egg (ovum) are engraved the words *"ex ovo omnia."* At the heading of chapter 62 of this work Harvey placed a caption which explains the phrase *ex ovo omnia* more explicitly. This heading reads: "Ovum esse primordium commune omnibus animalibus" —the egg is the primordium common to all animals. Published in 1651, this statement still maintains its descriptive force.

Many individual animals arise by asexual reproduction, that is, through a process of division or separation from a parent organism. In the phylum Chordata asexual reproduction is found among the Urochordata, where new

FIG. 25. Copy of the engraved title appearing in one edition of Harvey's dissertation on generation as shown on p. 139 of *Early Theories of Sexual Generation* by E. J. Cole. Observe the words "ex ovo omnia" upon the egg which Jupiter is opening. Various animals are emerging from the egg.

FIG. 26. Copy of Hartsoeker's figure of human spermatozoan, containing the homonculus or "little man," published in 1694. This figure represents a marked preformationist conception of development. However, it is to be noted that Hartsoeker later abandoned the preformationist concept as a result of his studies on regeneration.

54

individuals may arise by budding from a stolon-like base of the parent (fig. 27). This process often is called **gemmation,** the formation of a new individual by a protrusion of a mass of cells from the parental body followed by its partial or complete separation. It is a prominent method of reproduction among the lower Metazoa, particularly the coelenterates and sponges. Nevertheless, all animal species among the Metazoa ultimately utilize an egg as the primordium from which the new individual arises. **Sexual reproduction,** generally associated with the fertilization of an egg by a sperm element, appears to be a needful biological process.

True as the general statement made by Harvey may be, it is not clear what is meant by the word ovum or egg. We know certain of its characteristics, but, for the most part, it must be accepted as an accomplished fact enshrouded in mystery. To Harvey the egg was an indefinite, unorganized association of substance plus a "primordial generative principle" (see Cole, F. J., '30, p. 140). Other minds have conceived of other meanings. Nevertheless, descriptive and experimental embryology has forced the conclusion that the egg, during its development within the ovary, experiences a profound process of differentiation, resulting in the formation of an invisible organization. Although

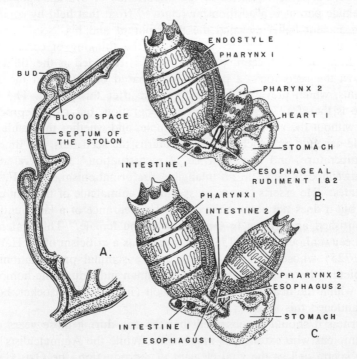

FIG. 27. Forms of asexual reproduction in the subphylum *Urochordata* of the phylum *Chordata.* (From MacBride: *Textbook of Embryology,* Vol. 1, London, Macmillan.) (A) Budding from stolon of *Perophora listeri,* from MacBride after Hjört. (B), (C) Two stages of budding in an *ascidian,* from MacBride after Pizon.

this organization is invisible, it is imbued with an invincibility which, when set in motion at the time of fertilization, drives the developmental processes onward until final fulfillment is achieved in the fully formed body of the adult organism.

Beyond the fundamental changes effected in the developing egg while in the ovary, the latter structure has still other roles to maintain. Through the mediation of the hormones produced within the confines of the ovarian substance, the female parent is prepared to assume the responsibilities of reproduction. In addition, in many vertebrates the further responsibility of taking care of the young during the embryonic period stems from the hormones produced in the ovary. In some vertebrates, the instinct of parental care of the young after hatching or after birth indirectly is linked to ovarian-pituitary relationships. Because of these profound and far-reaching influences which the ovary possesses in producing the new individual, it must be regarded as *the dynamic center of reproduction for most animal species.*

B. Preformationism, Past and Present

The above statement relative to the importance of ovarian influences and of the female parent is a position far removed from that held by some in the past. An ancient belief elevated the male parent and his "seed" or semen. As Cole, F. J., '30, p. 38, so aptly places the thinking of certain learned sources during the 16th century: "The uterus is regarded as the 'till'd ground for to sow the seeds on'—a popular idea, based obviously on the analogy with plants, which prevailed long before and after this period. The seed of the male is therefore the chief agent in generation, but cannot produce an embryo without the cooperation of the female, and whether the result is male or female depends on which side of the uterus the seed falls, the time of the year, temperature, and the incidence of menstruation." Or, in reference to the Leeuwenhoek's belief in an intangible preformationism, Cole, F. J., '30, p. 57, states: "He asserts that every spermatic animalcule of the ram contains a lamb, but it does not assume the external appearance of a lamb until it has been nourished and grown in the uterus of the female." This statement of A. van Leeuwenhoek (1632–1723) was made as a criticism of N. Hartsoeker (1656–1725) whose extreme adherence to a seminal preformationism led him to picture the preformed body of the human individual, the homonculus, encased within the head of the spermatozoon (fig. 26). Hartsoeker, however, later abandoned this idea.

In fairness it should be observed that the egg during these years did not lack champions who extolled its importance. While the Animalculists considered the sperm cell as the vital element in reproduction, the Ovists, such as Swammerdam (1637–80), Haller (1708–77), Bonnet (1720–93) and Spallanzani (1729–99) believed that the pre-existing parts of the new individual were contained or preformed within the egg.

An extreme form of preformationism was advocated by certain thinkers during this period. For example, Bonnet championed the idea of encasement or "emboitement." To quote from Bonnet:

The term "emboitement" suggests an idea which is not altogether correct. The germs are not enclosed like boxes or cases one within the other, but a germ forms part of another germ as a seed is a part of the plant on which it develops. This seed encloses a small plant which also has its seeds, in each of which is found a plantule of corresponding smallness. This plantule itself has its seeds and the latter bears plantules incomparably smaller, and so on, and the whole of this ever diminishing series of organized beings formed a part of the first plant, and thus arose its first growths. (Cole, '30, p. 99.)

On the other hand, there were those who maintained that for some animals, neither the sperm nor the egg were important as "many animals are bred without seed and arise from filth and corruption, such as mice, rats, snails, shell fish, caterpillars, moths, weevils, frogs, and eels" (Cole, '30, p. 38). This concept was a part of the theory of **spontaneous generation** of living organisms—a theory ably disproved by the experimental contributions of three men: Redi (1626–97); Spallanzani; and Louis Pasteur (1822–95).

Modern embryology embraces a kind of preformationism, a preformationism which does not see the formed parts of the new individual within the egg or sperm but which does see within the egg a vital, profound, and highly complex physiochemical organization capable of producing a new individual by a gradual process of development. This organization, this self-determining mechanism, is resident in the nucleus with its genes and the organized cytoplasm of the fully developed oocyte or egg. However, as shown later, this organization is dependent upon a series of activating agencies or substances for its ultimate realization. Some of these activating substances come from without, but many of them are produced within the developing organism itself.

C. General Structure of the Reproductive System of the Vertebrate Female

1. General Structure of the Ovary

Morphologically, the ovary presents a series of contrasts in the different vertebrate classes. In teleost fishes the size of the ovary is enormous compared to the body of the female (fig. 28), while in the human (fig. 29), cow, sow, etc., it is a small structure in comparison to the adult body. Again, it may contain millions of mature eggs in the ling, cod and conger, during each breeding season, whereas only a single egg commonly is matured at a time in the cow, elephant, or human. During the reproductive season the ovary may assume a condition of striking colored effects as in the bird, reptile, shark, and frog, only to recede into an appearance drab, shrunken, and disheveled in the non-breeding season.

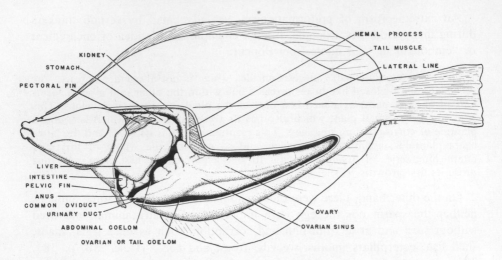

FIG. 28. Dissection of female specimen of the common flounder, *Limanda ferruginea*. It particularly shows the ovary with its laterally placed ovarian sinus. Observe that the ovary, during the breeding season, is an elongated structure which extends backward into the tail. There are two ovaries, one on either side of the hemal processes of the caudal vertebrae.

Its shape, also, is most variable in different species. In mammals it is a flattened ovoid structure in the resting condition, but during the reproductive phase it may assume a rounded appearance, containing mound-like protrusions. In birds and reptiles it has the general form of a bunch of grapes. In the amphibia it may be composed of a series of lobes, each of which is a mass of eggs during the breeding season, and in teleost and ganoid fishes it is an elongated structure extending over a considerable area of the body.

Regardless of their many shapes and sizes, the ovaries of vertebrates may be divided morphologically into two main types, namely, compact and saccular forms. The compact type of ovary is found in teleost, elasmobranch, cyclostome, ganoid, and dipnoan fishes, as well as in reptiles, birds and mammals. It has the following regions (figs. 30, 31):

(1) the **medulla,** an inner zone containing relatively large blood and lymph vessels;

(2) the **cortex,** an area outside of and surrounding the medulla (except at the hilus), containing many ova in various stages of development;

(3) a **tunica albuginea** or connective-tissue layer surrounding the cortex; and

(4) the **germinal epithelium** or the covering epithelium of the ovary.

The germinal epithelium is continuous with the mesovarium, the peritoneal support of the ovary, and the particular area where the mesovarium attaches to the ovary is known as the **hilus.** Within the mesovarium and passing through the hilus are to be found the blood and lymph vessels which supply the ovary (fig. 30).

The ovary of the teleost fish is a specialized, compact type of ovary adapted to the ovulation of many thousands, and in pelagic species, millions of eggs at one time. It has an elongate hilar aspect which permits blood vessels to enter the ovarian tissue along one surface of the ovary, whereas the opposite side is the ovulating area. In many teleosts the ovulating surface possesses a special sinus-like space or lumen (fig. 28) which continues posteriad to join the very short oviduct. At the time of ovulation the eggs are discharged into this space and move caudally as the ovarian tissue contracts. In other teleosts this ovulatory space is not a permanent structure but is formed only at the time of ovulation. In *Tilapia macrocephala*, for example, the ovulatory lumen is formed on the side of the ovary opposite the area where the blood vessels enter. The formation of this space at the time of ovulation is described by Aronson and Holz-Tucker ('49) as a rupture of the elastic follicles during ovulation whereupon the follicle walls shrink toward the ovarian midline,

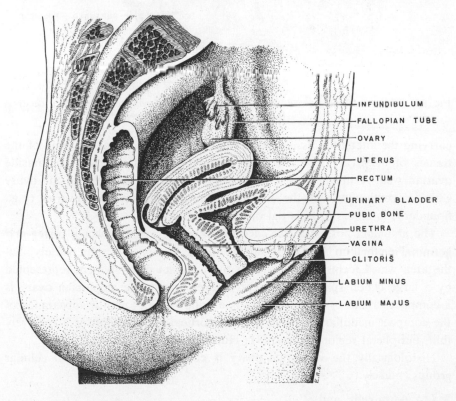

INFUNDIBULUM
FALLOPIAN TUBE
OVARY
UTERUS
RECTUM
URINARY BLADDER
PUBIC BONE
URETHRA
VAGINA
CLITORIS
LABIUM MINUS
LABIUM MAJUS

Fig. 29. Diagrammatic representation of a midsagittal section of the reproductive organs of the human female. (Slightly modified from Morris: *Human Anatomy*, Philadelphia, Blakiston.)

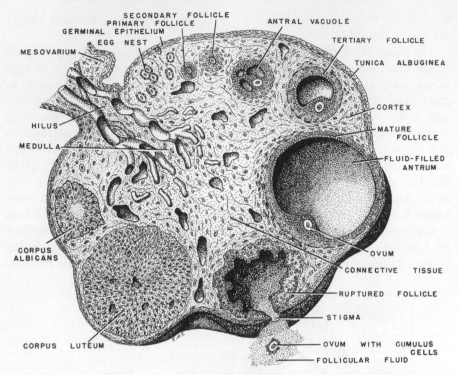

FIG. 30. Schematic three-dimensional representation of the cyclic changes which occur in the mammalian ovary.

carrying the interstitial tissue and immature ova. This shrinking away of the tissues of the ovary leaves a space between these tissues and the outside ovarian wall. A lumen thus is formed along the lateral aspect of the ovary which is continuous with the oviduct. Many teleosts have two ovaries (e.g., flounder); in others there is but one (e.g., perch).

The amphibia possess a true **saccular ovary** (fig. 32). It has a cortex and germinal epithelium somewhat similar to the compact ovarian variety, but the area which forms the medulla in the compact ovary is here represented by a large lymph space. During early development, the amphibian ovary is a compact structure, but later there is a hollowing out and disappearance of the compact medullary portion, and the cortical area remains as a relatively thin, peripheral region (Burns, '31; Humphrey, '29).

Histologically the vertebrate ovary is composed of two general cellular groups, namely:

(1) **germ cells,** and
(2) **general tissue cells** of various kinds, such as epithelium, connective tissue, smooth muscle fibers, and the complex of elements compris-

ing the vascular system of the ovary (figs. 30, 32). Some of the general cells form the so-called interstitial tissue of the ovary.

The **germ cells** differ from the general cells in that each of them has a latent potency for developing a new individual. This latent condition is converted into active potentiality during the differentiation of the primitive germ cell into the mature egg or ovum.

2. General Structure of the Accessory Reproductive Organs

The accessory reproductive structures of the female vertebrate may be separated into three general types, viz.:

(1) the total absence of or the presence of a pair of short funnel-like structures which convey the eggs from the peritoneal cavity through

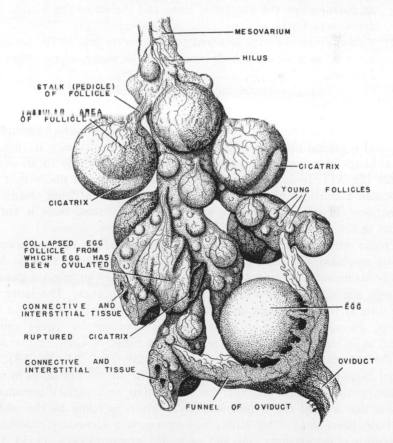

Fig. 31. Three-dimensional representation of the bird ovary together with the funnel portion (infundibulum) of the oviduct. Recently ovulated egg is shown in the process of engulfment by the infundibulum. Various stages of developing eggs are shown.

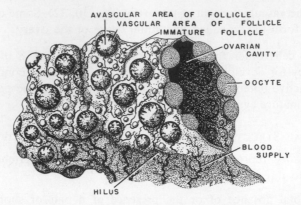

FIG. 32. Anterior half of the saccular ovary of *Necturus maculosus.*

an opening into the urogenital sinus and thence to the outside as in cyclostome fishes,

(2) a short sinus-like tube attached to each ovary and to the urogenital sinus or to a separate body opening as in many teleost fishes (fig. 28), and

(3) two elongated oviducal tubes variously modified (figs. 29, 33, 34, 35, 36, 37).

Except in the teleost fishes the cephalic end of each oviduct generally is open and is placed near the ovary but not united directly with it (figs. 29, 33) although in some species, such as the rat, it is united with an ovarian capsule (fig. 37). In some vertebrates the anterior orifice of the oviduct may be located a considerable distance from the ovary, as in frogs, toads, and salamanders. In many vertebrates, as in birds and snakes, there is but one oviduct in the adult.

In some vertebrates the oviduct is an elongated glandular tube, as in certain urodele amphibia (fig. 33) and in ganoid fishes; in others, such as frogs, birds or mammals, it is composed of two main parts: (1) an anterior glandular structure and (2) a more caudally placed uterine portion. The latter may unite directly with the cloaca, as in the frog (fig. 38) or by means of a third portion, the vaginal canal or vagina located between the uterus and the cloaca, as in elasmobranch fishes, reptiles, and birds, or between the uterus and the external urogenital sinus, as in mammals (figs. 35, 36, 37). The vaginal canal may be single, as in eutherian mammals, or double, as in metatherian mammals (figs. 35, 36). In metatherian (marsupial) mammals it appears that a third connection with the oviducts is made by the addition of a birth passageway. This birth canal represents a secondary modification of a portion of the vaginal canals and associated structures (figs. 34, 35, 114). (See Nelsen and Maxwell, '42.) One of the main functions of the vagina or vaginal canal is to receive the intromittent organ of the male during copulation.

The anterior opening of the oviduct is the **ostium tubae abdominale,** a funnel-shaped aperture generally referred to as the infundibulum. In the transport of the egg from the ovary to the oviduct the infundibulum, in many species, actually engulfs and swallows the egg.

The portion of the oviduct anterior to the uterus often is called the **convoluted glandular part;** it is highly twisted and convoluted in many species. In amphibians, reptiles, birds, and in some mammals the glandular portion

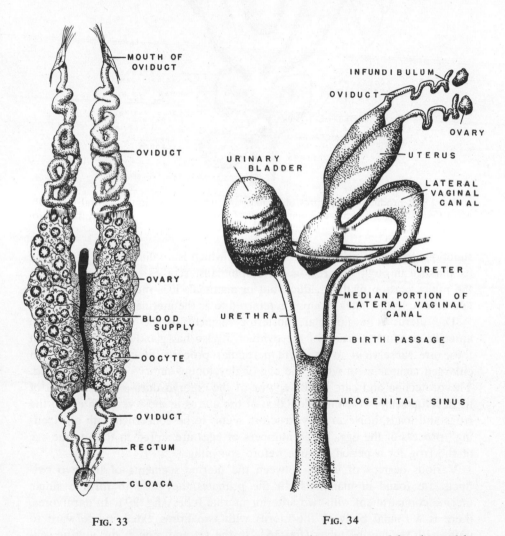

FIG. 33   FIG. 34

FIG. 33. Diagrammatic representation of the reproductive structures of female urodele, *Necturus maculosus.*

FIG. 34. Diagrammatic lateral view of female reproductive system of the opossum, showing pseudo-vaginal birth canal.

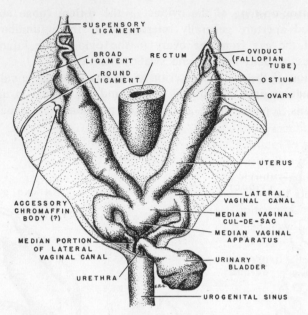

FIG. 35. Reproductive structures of female opossum shown from the ventral view. Observe that the ovary and infundibular portion of the Fallopian tube lie dorsal to the horn of the uterus.

functions to secrete an albuminous coating which is applied to the egg during its passage through this region. In amphibians, reptiles, and birds it forms the major portion of the oviduct, but in mammals it is much reduced in size and extent. In the latter group it is referred to as the uterine or Fallopian tube.

The uterus is a muscular, posterior segment of the oviduct. Like the anterior glandular portion of the oviduct, it also has glandular functions, but these are subservient to its more particular property of expanding into an enlarged compartment where the egg or developing embryo may be retained. The protection and care of the egg or of the embryo during a part or all of its development, is the main function of the uterus in most vertebrates. In the frogs and toads, however, this structure seems to be concerned with a "ripening" process of the egg. Large numbers of eggs are stored in the uterine sac of the frog for a period of time before spawning.

Various degrees of union between the uterine segments of the two oviducts are found in mammals. In the primates they fuse to form a single uterine compartment with two anterior uterine tubes (fig. 29). In carnivores, there is a caudal body of the uterus with two horns extending forward to unite with the uterine tubes (fig. 36). In the rat and mouse, the uterine segments may be entirely separate, coming together and joining the single vaginal chamber (fig. 37). In the opossum the uterine segments are entirely separated, joining a dual vaginal canal system posteriorly (figs. 34, 35, 114).

D. Dependency of the Female Reproductive System on General Body Conditions

1. Inanition

In the immature female mammal continued underfeeding results in general retardation of sexual development. The younger follicles may develop, but the later stages of follicular development are repressed. In the adult female, inanition produces marked follicular degeneration and atresia as shown by many records of retarded sexual development, reduced fertility, even cessation of the cyclic activities of menstruation and estrus occurring in man and domestic animals during war-produced or natural famine (Mason in Allen, Danforth, and Doisy, '39, p. 1153). The ovary thus seems to be especially susceptible to starvation conditions, even more so than the testis. As the condition and well-being of the secondary reproductive structures are dependent upon proper ovarian function, this part of the reproductive system suffers marked changes as a result of ovarian dysfunction during prolonged starvation.

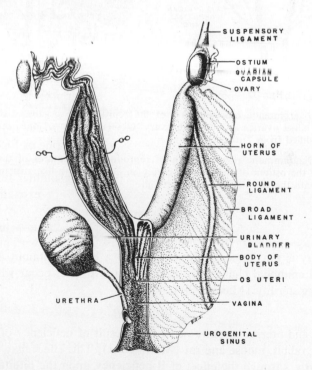

FIG. 36. Schematic representation of reproductive organs of the female cat. On the left side of the illustration, the body of the uterus and uterine horn have been cut open, and the Fallopian tube and ovary are highly schematized. Observe the partial ovarian capsule around the ovary shown on the right and the relatively fixed condition of the infundibular opening of the oviduct lateral to the ovary.

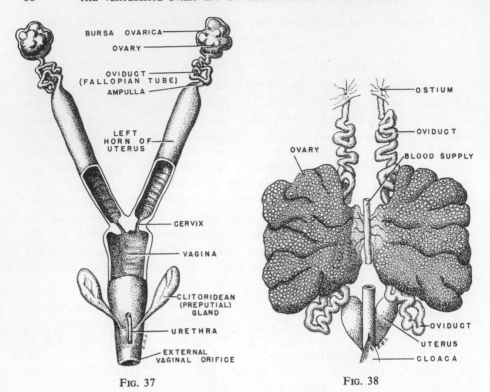

FIG. 37   FIG. 38

FIG. 37. Diagrammatic representation of the reproductive organs of the female rat, showing the bursa ovarica around each ovary. Observe that uteri open directly into the vagina. (Modified from Turner, '48.)

FIG. 38. Diagrammatic representation of reproductive structures of the female frog. Observe that the ostium of the oviduct is not an open, mouth-like structure. It remains constricted until the egg starts to pass through.

2. VITAMINS

a. Vitamin A

The ovary is not immediately sensitive to a lack in vitamin A in the diet but general epithelial changes in the reproductive tract occur which may aid in producing sterility (Mason, '39).

b. Vitamin B

Ovarian and uterine atrophy occur as a result of deficiency of this vitamin in monkey, rabbit, mouse and rat (Mason, '39). This effect may be mediated, at least partly, through the effect of B-deficiency upon the pituitary gland.

c. Vitamin C

During the earlier stages reproductive activity is maintained, but advanced stages of C-deficiency produce regressive effects (Mason, '39).

d. Vitamin E

E-deficiency in the female rat does not upset the ovarian and general reproductive behavior. However, established pregnancies are disturbed and are terminated by resorption of the embryo (Mason, '39). In the domestic fowl, unless sufficient amount of vitamin E is present in the egg, embryonic death occurs during early incubation periods of the egg.

3. THE HYPOPHYSIS (PITUITARY GLAND)

The ovaries experience pronounced atrophy as a result of hypophysectomy in mammals and non-mammalian species. The earlier stages of follicle formation in the higher mammalian ovary up to the stage of beginning antrum formation are not so much affected, but later follicular development and interstitial tissue growth are inhibited (Smith, P. E., '39). (See fig. 40.)

E. Activities of the Ovary in Producing the Reproductive State

1. THE OVARY AS A "STOREHOUSE" OF OOGONIA

The cortex of the ovary contains many young ova in various stages of development. In the human ovary shortly after birth, the number of oogonia in the cortex of each ovary has been estimated to reach a number as high as 300,000. This figure should not be taken too literally, as the amount of variability in the ovary from time to time is great and degeneration of ova is a common episode. Häggström ('21) estimated that each ovary of a 22-year-old woman contained 200,000 young ova. In the ovaries of young rats, Arai ('20, a and b) estimated that there were on the average around 5,000 ova under 20 μ in diameter.

Without entering into the controversy (Chap. 3) relative to the rhythmic origin of germ cells in the ovary, one must accept the conclusion that the normal ovary has within it at all times during its reproductive life large numbers of oogonia in various stages of development. Thus the ovary, aside from its other activities, functions as a storehouse and nursery for young oogonia. Relatively few of these oogonia develop into mature eggs in the mammals. For example, the reproductive life of the human female occurs from about the age of 10 or 14 years to about 48 years. If one egg per monthly cycle is discharged from the ovary which is functional during that cycle, only about 400 eggs would be matured in this way. The number would be less if pregnancies intervened. If one accepts the figures given by Häggström, an enormous number of eggs of the human ovary never reach their potential goal. Similarly, according to Corner ('43): "The most prolific egg producer among mammals, the sow, might possibly shed a total of 3,000 to 3,500 eggs, allowing ten years of ovarian activity not interrupted by pregnancy, and assuming the very high average of 20 eggs at each three weekly cycle, but she has vastly more than this in the ovaries at birth."

2. Position Occupied by the Primitive Female Germ Cells in the Ovarian Cortex

Within the cortex the definitive germ cells or oogonia are found in or near the germinal epithelium (figs. 39, 64). Some authors regard the oogonium as originating from the cells of the germinal epithelium. (See Chap. 3, section on "germ cell origin.") The definitive germ cell soon becomes associated with small epithelial cells (fig. 41). This complex of a germ cell with its associated epithelial cells is found somewhat deeper in the cortex, within or below the tunica albuginea. As the oogonium begins to experience the changes propelling it toward a state of maturity, it is regarded as an **oocyte** (Chap. 3). Characteristics of the primitive oocyte are:

(1) an enlargement of the nucleus,

(2) changes within the chromatin material of the nucleus pertaining to meiosis (Chap. 3), and

(3) a growth and increase in the cytoplasmic substances (fig. 41).

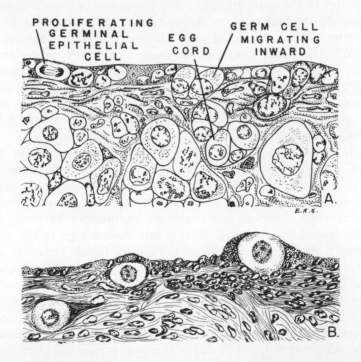

Fig. 39. (A) Diagrammatic representation of portion of the cortex of a young opossum ovary near the hilus, showing origin of germ cells from germinal epithelium or from cells lying in or near the germinal epithelium of the ovary. (After Nelsen and Swain, J. Morphol., 71.) (B) Young oocytes in rat ovary, lying in or near the germinal epithelium of the ovary. (After Jones, J. Morphol., 84.)

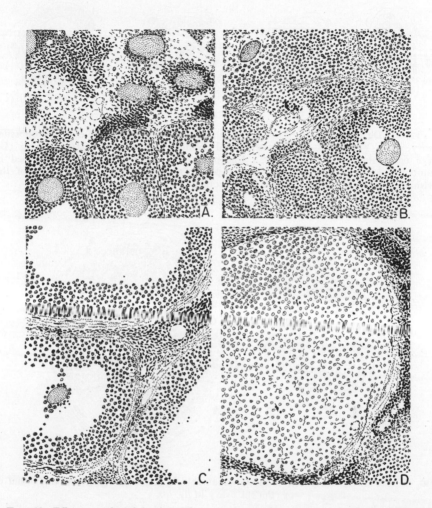

Fig. 40. Effects produced by hypophysectomy on the rat ovary and of replacement therapy utilizing injections of pituitary gonadotrophins. (After Evans, Simpson, and Penchaez: *Symposia of Quantitative Biology*, Vol. 5, 1937. The Biological Laboratory, Cold Spring Harbor, L. I., N. Y.)   (A) Ovary of hypophysectomized animal. Observe that Graafian follicles are small. They do not proceed further in their development than the beginning of antral vacuole formation unless replacement therapy is applied.   (B) Ovarian condition of hypophysectomized animal receiving replacement therapy in the form of injections of the LH (ICSH) gonadotrophic factor of the anterior lobe of the hypophysis. Interstitial tissue is well developed.   (C) Ovarian condition of hypophysectomized animal receiving the FSH gonadotrophic factor. Note follicular growth and antral vacuole formation; interstitial tissue between the follicles remains somewhat deficient. (D) Ovarian condition of hypophysectomized animal receiving injections of FSH plus LH. Corpora lutea are evident (as well as enlarged follicles not shown in the figure). Interstitial tissue remains deficient.

69

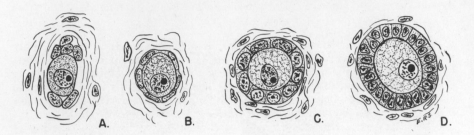

FIG. 41. Development of primary condition of the Graafian follicle in the opossum ovary. (A) Young oocyte with associated epithelial (granulosa) cells which in (B) have encapsulated the oocyte. (C) Encapsulating granulosa cells have increased in number and are assuming a cuboidal shape. (D) Fully developed condition of the **primary Graafian follicle.** Cf. secondary condition shown in fig. 42.

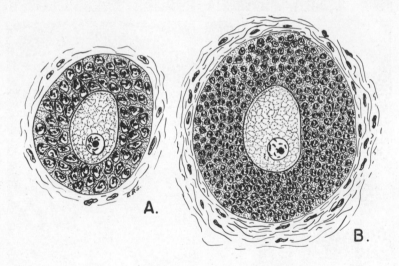

FIG. 42. Secondary conditions of the Graafian follicle in the opossum ovary. Cf. that of the rat ovary in fig. 40.

As these changes are initiated, the associated epithelial cells increase in number and eventually encapsulate the oocyte (fig. 41B). This complex of the oocyte with its surrounding layer of follicle cells is known as an **egg follicle.**

3. Primary, Secondary, and Tertiary Follicles of de Graaf

In the mammalian ovary the developing egg with its associated cells is called the **Graafian follicle,** so named after the Dutch scientist, Reinier de Graaf (fig. 1), who first described this structure in mammals in 1672–1673. De Graaf was in error, partly, for he believed that the whole follicular complex was the egg. The mammalian egg as such was first described in 1827 by Karl Ernst von Baer (1792–1876). The following statement is taken from de Graaf relative to egg follicles.

We may assert confidently that eggs are found in all kinds of animals, since they may be observed not only in birds, in fishes, both oviparous and viviparous, but very clearly also in quadrupeds and even in man himself. Since it is known to everyone that eggs are found in birds and fishes, this needs no investigation; but also in rabbits, hares, dogs, swine, sheep, cows, and other animals which we have dissected, those structures similar to vesicles exhibit themselves to the eyes of the dissectors like the germs of eggs in birds. Occurring in the superficial parts of the testicles, they push up the common tunic, and sometimes shine through it, as if their exit from the testis is impending. (See fig. 48; also Corner, '43, page 128.)

The mammalian egg with a single layer of epithelial cells surrounding it is known as a **primary Graafian follicle** (fig. 41B-D). As the egg and follicle grow, the number of epithelial cells increase and eventually there are several

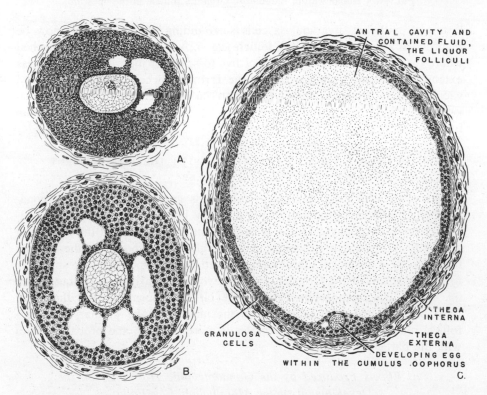

FIG. 43. Tertiary conditions of the Graafian follicle in the opossum ovary. Similar conditions are found in other mammalian ovaries. (A) Follicle in which the antral vacuoles are beginning to form. (B) This is a follicle in which the antral vacuoles are more numerous and are beginning to coalesce. (C) Condition of the Graafian follicle in the opossum ovary approaching maturity. Observe that the antral space is large and is filled with fluid, the liquor folliculi, while the egg and its surrounding cumulus cells are located at one end of the follicle. The thecal tissue around the follicle is well developed.

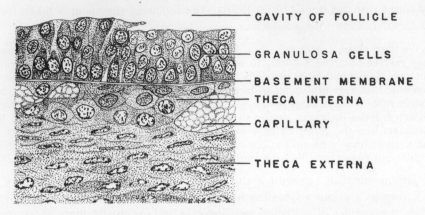

————— CAVITY OF FOLLICLE

————— GRANULOSA CELLS

————— BASEMENT MEMBRANE

————— THECA INTERNA

————— CAPILLARY

————— THECA EXTERNA

FIG. 44. Cellular wall of the mature Graafian follicle in the opossum.

layers of epithelial or granulosa cells surrounding the egg. It may now be regarded as a **secondary Graafian follicle** (fig. 42A, B). When a stage is reached where the granulosa cells form a layer five to seven or more cells in thickness extending outward from the egg to the forming thecal layers, small antral vacuoles begin to appear among the granulosa cells. The latter follicle, which is capable of forming antral vacuoles, may be regarded as a **tertiary Graafian follicle** (fig. 43A).

4. HORMONAL FACTORS CONCERNED WITH THE DEVELOPMENT OF EGG FOLLICLES

The ovary with its contained egg follicles is greatly affected by the gonadotrophic hormones produced in the pituitary body. The removal of the pituitary body (hypophysectomy) causes profound regression of the ovary and accessory reproductive structures. Accordingly, the response of the ovarian tissues to these hormonal substances produced by the hypophysis is responsible for development of the Graafian follicle beyond the early tertiary stage. (See fig. 40A.) The relationships between the pituitary hormones and the ovary have been studied most intimately in the mammals; the pituitary and egg-follicle relationship in lower vertebrates is more obscure, and probably varies with the particular group.

a. Effects Produced by the Gonadotrophic Hormones on the Development of the Mammalian Egg Follicle

The follicle-stimulating hormone, FSH, appears to increase the number of oogonia and to aid the growth and differentiation of the older follicles. It is possible that some of the effects of FSH upon follicular growth are mediated through its ability, together with small amounts of the luteinizing hormone, LH (ICSH), to cause the formation of estrogen or the female sex hormone, although some investigators believe that estrogen production depends mainly upon the action of LH (ICSH). (See Evans and Simpson in Pincus and Thimann, '50, p. 355.) In harmony with the idea that estrogen is involved in follicular growth there is some evidence which suggests that introduction of estrogens into the peritoneal cavities of fishes and mammals results in a stimulation of mitotic activity in the germinal epithelium of the ovary. It also has been shown that estrogenic substances retard ovarian atrophy in hypophysectomized immature rats.

When the Graafian follicles of the mammalian ovary reach the proper morphological and physiological conditions (i.e., when they reach the tertiary follicular stage) an increased sensitivity of the follicle cells to FSH occurs. As a result, antral vacuoles filled with fluid appear among the granulosa cells; these eventually coalesce and form the large antral cavity typical of the mature Graafian follicle of the metatherian and eutherian mammal (fig. 43). The presence of LH (ICSH) is necessary to augment the action of FSH during the latter part of follicle development. The beneficial action of FSH and LH together in later follicular development is shown by the fact that the injection of pure FSH alone is incapable of stimulating growth of the follicle to its full size or to initiate an increased secretion of estrogen. LH aids the maturing process of the follicle only when present in very minimal amounts during the early stages of follicle development and in larger amounts during the later stages of follicular growth. Large amounts of LH in the earlier phases of the follicle's development bring about a premature luteinization of the follicle with ultimate atresia. A proper quantitative balance of these hormones, therefore, is necessary, with FSH being in the ascendency during the earlier phases of follicle development, followed by increased amounts of LH with decreasing amounts of FSH as the follicle reaches maturity (figs. 22, 53, 59). (For references, consult Evans and Simpson, '50; Turner, '48.)

b. Stimulating Effects of the Pituitary Gonadotrophins on the Ovaries of Other Vertebrates

The hormonal control of the developing follicle of other vertebrate ovaries follows similar principles to those outlined above for the mammalian ovary, although data obtained from studies upon other vertebrates in no way compares with the large quantity of information obtained in mammalian studies. In the hen, FSH and LH injected together cause a rapid development of the follicles and premature discharge of the egg from the ovary (Fraps, Olsen, and Neher, '42). However, in the pigeon, Riddle ('38) reports that another pituitary hormone, **prolactin,** appears to decrease the production of these hormones and stops egg production with a subsequent atrophy of the ovary. This may be a special means which reduces the number of eggs laid at each nesting period. In regard to accessory reproductive structures, an estrogenic hormone is produced in the ovary of the hen which has profound stimulating effects upon the growth of the oviduct (Romanoff and Romanoff, '49, pp. 242–244). In the frog, *Rana pipiens,* mammalian pituitary gonadotrophins are able to effect ovulation (Wright and Hisaw, '46). Pituitary gonadotrophins have been shown also to have profound stimulative effects on the ovaries of fishes, salamanders, and reptiles.

5. Structure of the Vertebrate, Mature Egg Follicle

As a result of the differentiation and growth induced by the gonadotrophic hormones of the anterior lobe of the hypophysis described in the preceding paragraphs, the egg follicle reaches a state of maturity (fig. 43C). This state is achieved when the follicle is about to rupture with the resultant discharge of the egg. The size of the mature egg follicle varies greatly in different metatherian and eutherian mammals, although the size of the follicle is not related to the size of the egg. On the other hand the size of the mature egg follicle in prototherian mammals and in other vertebrate species shows great divergences, being dependent in this group upon the size of the egg at the time of ovulation (fig. 46).

a. Structure of the Mature Follicle in Metatherian and Eutherian Mammals*

The structural pattern of the mature Graafian follicle in the human is strikingly similar to the follicles in other members of this group. It is a vesicular structure with a diameter approximating five millimeters. Externally, the follicle is composed of two connective-tissue layers, an inner cellular layer containing blood capillaries, the **theca interna,** and an external, fibrous layer, the **theca externa** (figs. 43C, 44). These two layers are not clearly separable. Passing inward from the theca interna is the **basement membrane.** Resting upon this membrane are several layers of epithelial cells comprising the **membrana granulosa.** The latter membrane borders the cavity or **antrum** of the follicle, which is filled with the **liquor folliculi.** This liquid is under considerable pressure in the follicle at the time of egg discharge or ovulation.

Projecting inward into the antrum on one side is a small, mound-like mass of granulosa cells, the **cumulus oophorus** (fig. 43C). Within this hillock of epithelium, is the egg, which measures in the human about 130 μ to 140 μ in diameter. In the opossum, the fully developed Graafian follicle is about 1.25 by 2 mm. in diameter, while the slightly oval egg approximates 120 by 135 μ. The egg of the rat and mouse is small, having a diameter of 75 μ, while that of the dog is about 140 μ; sow, 120 to 140 μ; rabbit, 120 to 130 μ; monkey, 110 to 120 μ; deer, 115 μ; cat, 120 to 130 μ; mare, 135 μ; armadillo, 80 μ (Hartman, '29).

---

* According to Strauss, '39, the mature Graafian follicle of *Ericulus* is not a vesicular structure, as in other higher mammals, but is filled with a loose meshwork of granulosa cells.

While one Graafian follicle in only one ovary is generally developed in the human, monkey, cow, ewe, elephant, etc., at each reproductive period, a multiple condition is found in many other mammals. Each ovary in the opossum may ripen seven or more follicles, in the bitch (female dog) from 2 to 7 follicles, and in the sow from 4 to 10 follicles at each reproductive period.

b. Structure of the Prototherian Egg Follicle

The follicle of the prototherian mammals contains a relatively large egg, while the surrounding fluid and follicular tissue in comparison is small in quantity (fig. 46). In these mammals the egg fills most of the follicular cavity, with the exception of a small fluid-filled space intervening between it and the zona pellucida which lies contiguous to the granulosa cells. Internal and external thecal tissues surround the granulosa cells as in the Graafian follicle of the higher mammals.

c. Egg Follicles of Other Vertebrates

The fully-developed egg follicle in most vertebrates is similar to that found in the prototherian mammals in that the egg tends to fill the entire follicle. The general structural relationships also are similar (figs. 45, 47).

6. OVULATORY PROCESS; POSSIBLE FACTORS CONTROLLING OVULATION

The following description of the ovulatory process in the mammal and in other vertebrates should not be construed as a description of the mechanism, as the exact mechanism is unknown. However, a certain amount of general information has been obtained concerning ovulation and the factors involved. Much of this information has been obtained from studies of the ovulatory

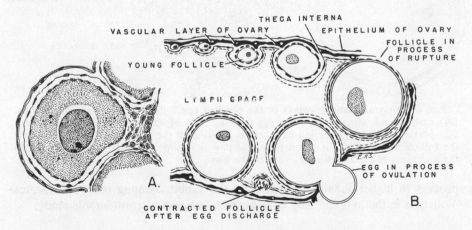

FIG. 45. (A) Young egg follicle of *Cryptobranchus alleganiensis,* a urodele. (From Noble: "Biology of the Amphibia," New York, McGraw-Hill, after Smith.) (B) Diagrammatic representation of ovarian events in the frog resulting in egg discharge. (From Turner: "General Endocrinology," Philadelphia, W. B. Saunders, slightly modified.)

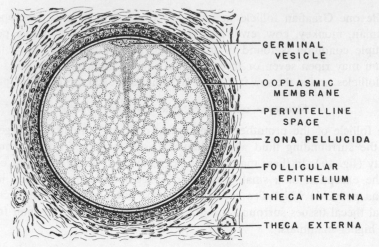

GERMINAL
VESICLE

OOPLASMIC
MEMBRANE

PERIVITELLINE
SPACE

ZONA PELLUCIDA

FOLLICULAR
EPITHELIUM

THECA INTERNA

THECA EXTERNA

FIG. 46. Diagrammatic representation of the egg of the prototherian mammal, *Echidna*.

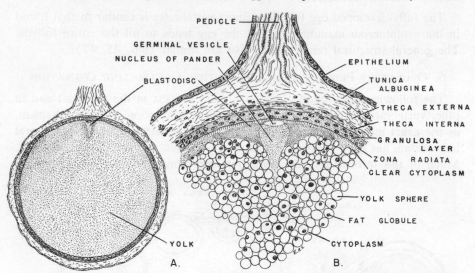

PEDICLE

GERMINAL VESICLE

NUCLEUS OF PANDER

BLASTODISC

EPITHELIUM

TUNICA
ALBUGINEA

THECA EXTERNA

THECA INTERNA

GRANULOSA
LAYER

ZONA RADIATA

CLEAR CYTOPLASM

YOLK SPHERE

FAT GLOBULE

CYTOPLASM

YOLK

A.   B.

FIG. 47. Diagrammatic drawings of the pendent egg follicle in the ovary of the hen. (A) Low magnification of the entire egg follicle. (B) More detailed view of the blastodisc portion of the egg, nearing maturity, in relation to the pedicle. The latter supports the follicle and permits the blood vessels to pass into and out of the follicle. Compiled from sections of the developing ovary of the hen.

process in higher mammals, especially the rabbit. Among other vertebrates ovulation in the hen and frog have been the objects of considerable study.

a. Process of Ovulation in Higher Mammals

1) Changing Tissue Conditions Culminating in Egg Discharge from the Ovary. As the Graafian follicle enlarges and matures under the influence of the follicle-stimulating and luteinizing hormones, it moves closer to the ovarian surface (fig. 30). The surface of the ovary over the ripening follicle bulges outward, forming a mound-like protuberance (fig. 30). In the rabbit as shown by Walton and Hammond ('28) and Hill, Allen, and Cramer ('35) the central part of the original protuberance pushes out still further and forms a papilla-like swelling (fig. 48A-D). As the papilla develops, it becomes avas-

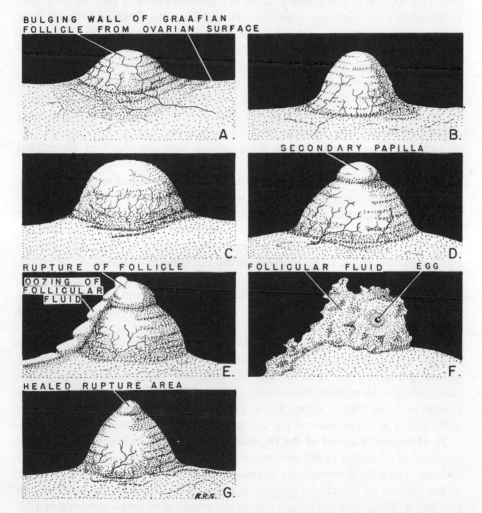

FIG. 48. Process of ovulation in the rabbit. (A–C) Early external changes of the surface of the ovary overlying the bulging Graafian follicle. (D) Formation of a secondary papilla. (E) Rupture of the secondary papilla with discharge of egg and follicular fluid, the latter oozing down over ovarian surface of the follicle. (F) Area of rupture with oozing follicular fluid and egg greatly magnified. (G) Follicle after egg discharge. (A–E and G, slightly modified from Walton and Hammond, Brit. J. Exp. Biol., 6; F, modified from Hill, Allen, and Kramer, Anat. Rec., 63.)

cular, and the underlying tissues become thin and greatly distended. The tunica albuginea of the ovary and the two thecal layers of the follicle also are involved in this thinning-out process. As the distended papillary area continues to grow thinner, a small amount of blood followed by some of the follicular fluid containing the egg emerges from the follicle and passes into the surrounding area in close proximity to the infundibulum of the Fallopian tube (fig. 48E, F). The entire process is a gradual one and may be described as gently but not violently explosive (Hill, Allen, and Cramer, '35). It is of interest and significance to observe that Burr, Hill, and Allen ('35) were able to detect a change in electromotive force preceding and during the known period of ovulation.

The process of papillary rupture in the rabbit occupies about five seconds; egg discharge with the surrounding liquor folliculi occurs in approximately 30 to 60 seconds. After the egg has emerged, the follicle as a whole may collapse. The slit-like opening through which the egg and follicular fluid passed during ovulation soon is filled with a clot composed of coagulated blood and follicular fluid (fig. 48G).

While the foregoing processes, visible on the ovarian surface, are consummated, certain internal changes occur which form a part of the ovulatory procedure. These changes are as follows: At about the time the egg is to be extruded, the follicular fluid reaches its maximum in quantity. This increase produces considerable follicular turgidity which may be associated with an endosmotic effect due to an increase in the salt content of the contained fluid. Shortly before the surface of the follicle ruptures, the cumulus begins to disintegrate, and the egg lies free in the antral fluid. At about this time the first maturation division of the oocyte occurs in the majority of mammals, and the first polar body is extruded.

Concerning the internal changes accompanying rupture of the mammalian follicle, passing mention should be made of the theory that bursting blood vessels discharge their contents into the follicular fluid and thus cause sufficient pressure to rupture the follicle (Heape, '05). Considerable blood discharge into the follicle seems to be present in some forms, e.g., the mare, quite absent in others such as the human, and present slightly in the opossum.

2) Hormonal Control of the Ovulatory Process. The hormonal mechanism involved in ovulation in the spontaneously-ovulating mammals probably is as follows: The follicle-stimulating hormone causes the growth and development of the follicle or follicles. Estrogen is released by the growing follicles and possibly by other ovarian tissues due to the presence of small amounts of LH, and, in consequence, the estrogenic hormone reaches a higher level in the blood stream (figs. 53; 59).

In the meantime, it is probable that the corpus luteum hormone, progesterone, is produced in small amounts. The exact source of this hormone is not clear. It may be produced by old corpora lutea or by the interstitial tissue of the ovary under the influence of **luteotrophin,** LTH. The presence of progesterone, in small quantities together with increasing amounts of estrogen, stimulates the anterior lobe to discharge increased amounts of the luteinizing hormone, LH (ICSH). (See figs. 22, 53, 59.) The elevated level of estrogen, according to this theory also causes a decreased output of FSH until it reaches a minimal level at the period shortly before egg discharge (figs. 53, 59). As a result, the increased quantity of LH together with FSH has an added effect upon the follicle which brings about the chain of events leading to egg discharge. Evans and Simpson in Pincus and Thimann ('50) give the proportion of 10 parts of FSH to 1 of LH (ICSH) as the proper hormonal balance in effecting ovulation in the hypophysectomized rat.

In those mammalian species where ovulation is dependent upon the act of copulation, a nervous stimulus is involved which increases the output from the pituitary gland of the gonadotrophic factors, particularly LH.

b. *Ovulation in Vertebrate Groups Other Than the Higher Mammals*

The physical mechanism involved in the ovulatory procedure in the lower vertebrate classes is different from that found in higher mammals. Two forms, the hen and the frog, have been studied in detail. These two animals represent somewhat different types of ovulatory behavior.

1) Hen. As the hen's egg develops in the ovary, it gradually pushes the ovarian surface outward; it ultimately becomes suspended from the general surface of the ovary by means of a narrowing stalk, the pedicle (figs. 31, 47). When the ovulatory changes are initiated, the musculature of the ovarian wall overlying the outer surface of the egg appears to contract, and an elongated narrow area along this outer surface becomes **avascular.** This avascular area represents the place where the ovarian surface eventually ruptures to permit the egg to leave the ovary; it is called variously, **the rupture area, stigma, or cicatrix.** Gradually, the cicatrix widens and finally a slit-like opening is formed by a tearing apart of tissues in the central region of the cicatrix. Contractions of the smooth muscle fibers appear to be responsible for this tearing procedure (Phillips and Warren, '37) The egg eventually is expelled through the opening and in many instances it rolls into the infundibular funnel of the oviduct which at this time is actively engaged in an endeavor to engulf or "swallow" the egg (fig. 31).

2) Frog. The egg of the frog projects into the ovarian cavity within the ovary and is attached to the ovarian wall by means of a broad area or stalk (fig. 45B). As the egg enlarges, it tends to push the ovarian surface outward, and the egg and its follicle thus forms a mound-like protuberance from the ovarian surface (figs. 45A, B; 72F). The egg and the surrounding ovarian tissue thus lies exposed on one aspect to the outer surface of the ovary. The outer surface of exposure is the stigma or area of rupture, and in the older follicles this area does not contain blood vessels (fig. 72F). As ovulation approaches, an opening suddenly appears in the area of rupture. The musculature within the theca interna around the follicle then contracts, and the egg rolls out through the opening in the rupture area like a big ameba (fig. 45B). As the egg passes through the aperture, it may assume an hourglass shape (Smith, B. G., '16). After the egg is discharged, the follicle contracts to a much smaller size (fig. 45B). It has been suggested that the rupture of the external surface of the follicle might be produced by a digestive enzyme (Rugh, '35, a and b).

3) Hormonal Control of Ovulation in Lower Vertebrates. The hormonal mechanism regulating ovarian rupture and egg discharge in the lower vertebrate groups has not been as thoroughly explored in all of the vertebrate groups as it has in the mammals. However, sufficient work has been done to demonstrate that pituitary hormones are responsible in all of the major vertebrate groups, including the fishes. Amphibian pituitary implants under the skin or macerated anterior-lobe pituitary tissue injected into the peritoneal cavity of various amphibia have been effective in producing ovulatory phenomena (Rugh, '35a). More recently, purified mammalian follicle-stimulating hormone, FSH, and luteinizing hormone, LH, have been used to stimulate egg discharge in frog ovarian fragments, as well as in normal and hypophysectomized females. However, the follicle-stimulating hormone alone will not elicit ovulation (Wright, '45; Wright and Hisaw, '46). Accordingly, both factors are necessary in the frog, as in mammals. In the hen, these two pituitary hormones have been shown to bring about ovulation when injected intravenously (Fraps, Olsen, and Neher, '42; Romanoff and Romanoff, '49, pp. 208–215). Also, Neher and Fraps ('50) present evidence which suggests that progesterone plays a part in the physiological chain which elicits ovulation in the hen. A close relationship between the physiological procedures effecting ovulation in the hen and the mammal thus appears to exist.

c. Comparison of the Immediate Factors Effecting Egg Discharge in the Vertebrate Group

In the vertebrates thus far studied contraction of muscle tissue of the follicle following the rupture of surface tissues presumably is the main factor which brings about egg expulsion. In higher mammals, associated with muscle contracture, there also may be an increase in follicular turgidity due to endosmotic phenomena associated with the contained follicular fluid (Walton and Hammond, '28). In the frog, hen, and mammal the changes involved in the surface tissues leading to their rupture are associated with the following sequence of events:

(1) avascularity of the surface tissues,

(2) a thinning of the surface tissues, and finally

(3) a rupture of these tissues.

7. Internal Conditions of the Ovary as an Ovulatory Factor

Internal conditions of the ovary undoubtedly are important in controlling follicular growth and ovulation. For example, in the Northern fur seal, *Callorhinus ursinus,* the female begins to breed at the age of two years. These seals travel north once a year to the Pribilof Islands in the Bering Sea where they go on land to give birth to the single young and also to breed. Most of the cows arrive between the middle of June and the middle of July. Heavy with young, the females give birth to their offspring within a few hours or days after their arrival. Breeding again takes place about six days after parturition. However, lactation continues, and the young are taken care of during the summer months.

Accordingly, these seals mate each year and it appears that for any particular year the mating behavior and ovulation of the egg are controlled by the ovary, which does not have a corpus luteum. As the corpus luteum, which forms after ovulation in the site of the Graafian follicle, from which the egg is discharged, remains intact for a considerable portion of the year, the ovary which does not have the corpus luteum develops the Graafian follicle for the next summer period. The following year the other ovary will function, and so on, alternating each year (Enders, et al., '46). Thus, the corpus luteum appears to function as a suppressor of follicular growth within the ovary in which it lies. In the human female, one ovary functions to produce an egg one month, while the following month the other ovary ovulates its single egg. It is possible that here also the large corpus luteum suppresses follicular growth within the particular ovary concerned.

During gestation, the presence of the corpus luteum and its hormone, progesterone, suppresses follicle growth and ovulation in most of the mammalian group. (The placenta may be the source of progesterone during the later phases of pregnancy in forms such as the human.) On the other hand, in the mare, according to Cole, Howell, and Hart ('31), ovulation may occur during pregnancy. Species differences, therefore, exist relative to the control of ovulation by the corpus luteum and its hormone, progesterone.

8. Number of Eggs Produced by Different Vertebrate Ovaries

The number of eggs produced during the lifetime of the female varies with the species and is correlated generally with the amount of care given to the young. In many fishes which experience little or no parental care, enormous numbers of eggs may be produced, as for example, in the cod where several millions of eggs are spawned in one season. However, in many of the elasmobranch fishes (i.e., the shark group) the eggs develop within the oviduct, and the young are born alive. Therefore, only six to a dozen eggs produced each reproductive period is sufficient to keep the shark species plentiful. In the hen, where careful breeding and selection have been carried out with a view to egg production, a good layer will lay from 250 to 300 eggs a year. The deer, moose, fur seal, etc., ovulate one egg per year over a life span of a few years. As stated previously, the human female might ovulate as many as 400 eggs in a lifetime. In some species the reproductive life is brief. For example, in the Pacific salmon *(Oncorhynchus)* females and males die after their single spawning season, and a similar demise occurs in the eel *(Anguilla)*.

9. Spontaneous and Dependent Ovulation in the Mammals and in Other Vertebrates

Spontaneous ovulation without apparent stimulation from external sources occurs commonly throughout the vertebrate series. However, dependent ovulation conditioned by psychic or other nervous stimuli also is found extensively. In certain mammals ovulation has been shown to be dependent upon the stimulus induced by copulation, as, for example, the ferret, mink, rabbit, cat, shrew, etc. The stimulus, carried through the nervous system, affects in some way the anterior lobe of the pituitary gland which then produces increased amounts of LH in addition to FSH. These females experience estrus spontaneously, but later follicle growth and egg discharge are dependent upon the added stimulation afforded by copulation.

The element of nervous stimulation has a fundamental relationship to the ovulatory phenomena in the vertebrates. Dependent ovulation occurs in certain birds, such as the pigeon, where mating provides a psychic or nervous stimulation which effects ovulation. The presence of two eggs in the nest tends to suppress ovulation. The removal of these eggs will arouse the ovulatory procedures. However, the pigeon may sometimes lay eggs without the presence of a male. In wild birds in general, the mating reaction is linked to the stimulus for egg laying. The hen, on the other hand, is not dependent upon copulation, but in many of the domestic varieties the presence of a number of eggs in the nest appears to suppress egg laying. In the lower vertebrates nervous stimuli also appear to have an influence upon ovulation. The mating antics of many fish and amphibia may be connected with ovulatory phenomena.

10. Egg Viability after Discharge from the Ovary

The length of time that the egg may survive and retain its capacity for fertilization after leaving the ovary depends upon the nature of the egg and its membrane and the surrounding environment. In the urochordate, *Styela,* the egg may remain for 3 to 4 hours after it is discharged into the sea water and still be capable of fertilization. In the elasmobranch fishes, reptiles, and birds the conditions of the oviduct are such that fertilization must take place in the upper part of the oviduct within a few seconds or minutes after the egg reaches the infundibular portion. In *Fundulus heteroclitus* and possibly many other teleost fishes, the egg must be fertilized within 15 to 20 minutes after spawning. In the frog, the egg passes to the uterus at the lower end of the oviduct shortly after it leaves the ovary. Under ordinary reproductive temperatures which obtain in the spring, the egg may remain there for 3 to 5 days without producing abnormalities. If kept at very cool temperatures, the period may be extended. Among the mammals the viability after ovulation varies considerably. In the mare, fertilization must occur within about 2 to 4 hours; rabbit, 2 to 4 hours (Hammond and Marshall, '25); rat, about 10 hours; mouse, 12 to 24 hours (Long, '12; Charlton, '17); opossum, probably within the first hour or so because of the deposition of the albuminous coating in the oviduct; fox, probably only a few hours; sow, about 24 hours or less; man, probably 24 hours or less. In the guinea pig, functional degeneration may begin within 4 to 8 hours after ovulation (Blandau and Young, '39).

11. HISTORY OF THE EGG FOLLICLE AFTER OVULATION

a. Follicles Which Do Not Develop a Post-ovulatory Body

The changes which occur within the egg follicle after the egg has departed are most variable in different vertebrate species. In most of the fish group the ovary as a whole shrinks to a fraction of its previous size, and many very small, immature eggs, interstitial tissue, and collapsed, contracted, empty follicles make up its composition. Similarly, in frogs, toads, and salamanders the collapsed follicle which follows ovulation does not develop an organized structure. The thecal tissue contracts into a small rounded form within which are a few follicle cells (fig. 45B). These bodies soon disappear.

In many snakes and in turtles, the follicle collapses after ovulation, and it is questionable whether organized bodies develop in the site of the ovulated follicle. A similar condition appears to be the case in birds. However, Pearl and Boring ('18) described an abbreviated form of a corpus luteum in the hen in both discharged and atretic follicles. Also, Rothschild and Fraps ('44) found that the removal of the recently ruptured follicle or of this follicle together with the oldest maturing follicle, at a time when the egg which originated from the ruptured follicle is in the oviduct, retarded the laying of the egg from 1 to 7 days. Removal of other portions of the ovary in control hens "practically never" resulted in egg-laying retardation. The ruptured follicle, therefore, is believed, by these investigators, to have some influence on the time of lay of the egg. Whether the hormone progesterone or something similar to it may be produced by the ruptured follicle of the hen is questionable, although present evidence appears to suggest that it does (Neher and Fraps, '50).

b. Follicles Which Develop a Post-ovulatory Body; Formation of the Corpus Luteum

Post-ovulatory bodies or corpora lutea (yellow bodies) develop in the ovaries of elasmobranch fishes which give birth to their young alive. Also in viviparous snakes of the genera *Natrix, Storeria,* and *Thamnophis,* it has been shown that the removal of the ovaries with their corpora lutea invariably results in resorption of the young during the first part of gestation and abortion of the young during the midgestational period, while their removal during the close of gestation permits normal birth to occur (Clausen, '40). The differentiation of the corpus luteum in the snake involves the granulosa cells of the follicle and possibly the theca interna. The differentiated organ appears similar to that of the mammal (Rahn, '39).

The function of the corpus luteum which develops in the site of the ruptured follicle in all mammals, including the *Prototheria* (fig. 49), has been the subject of a long series of studies. (See Brambell, '30, Chap. 9; Corner, '43, Chap. V.) Its function during the reproductive period of the female mammal is described below under the section of the ovarian hormones. The events leading to the formation of the corpus luteum in the mammalian ovary may be described as follows: After the discharge of the egg, the follicle collapses. The opening of the follicle at the ovarian surface through which the egg emerged begins to heal. A slight amount of blood may be deposited within the antrum of the follicle during the ovulation process in some mammals. If so, the follicle in this condition is known as the **corpus hemorrhagicum.**

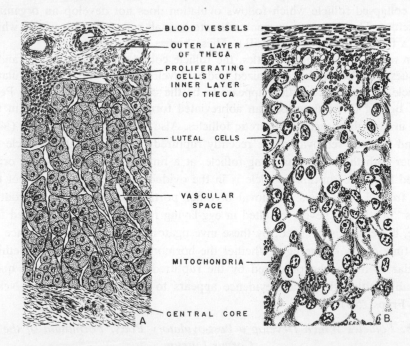

FIG. 49. (A) Luteal cells of the corpus luteum of the opossum. The cellular conditions in other higher mammals are similar. The central core has not yet been invaded and resorbed by the phagocytes accompanying the ingrowing luteal cells and blood vessels. This central core is composed of coagulated blood, blood cells, and connective tissue fibrils. (B) Corpus luteum of the platypus (*Ornithorhynchus*).

Then, under the influence of the luteinizing hormone, LH, the granulosa cells of the follicle and also cells from the theca interna, together with blood capillaries, proliferate and grow inward into the antral space (figs. 22, 30, 49). Phagocytes remove the blood clot within the antral space if present, during the inward growth of these structures. As the ingression of cells and capillaries into the follicle continues, the granulosa cells begin to form large, polyhedral lutein cells, while the epithelioid cells of the theca interna form a mass of smaller cells which resemble the true lutein cells; the latter are formed in the peripheral area of the corpus luteum and are called **paralutein cells.** The small spindle-shaped cells of the theca interna, together with blood capillaries, become dispersed between the lutein cells, forming a framework for the latter.

If the egg is fertilized, the corpus luteum persists and is known as the **corpus luteum of pregnancy;** if fertilization does not take place, it is called the **corpus luteum of ovulation.** The latter body soon degenerates. Histologically, both types of corpora are identical when first formed. Eventually the corpus luteum undergoes involution, and its site becomes infiltrated with connective tissue. The latter structure is sometimes referred to as the **corpus albicans.**

12. Hormones of the Ovary and Their Activities in Effecting the Reproductive Condition

The ovary produces two important hormones which have a profound effect upon the reproductive process. These two hormones are the female sex hormone, **estrogen,** and the gestational hormone, **progesterone.**

a. Estrogenic Hormone

1) Definition and Source of Production. The induction of estrus (see p. 93) or conditions simulating this state is a property of a relatively large number of organic compounds. Because of this estrus-inducing power, they are spoken of as estrogenic substances or estrogens. Estrogens are widely distributed in nature. Two of the most potent natural estrogens are **estradiol** and **estrone** (theelin). Both have been extracted from the mammalian ovary and are regarded as primary estrogenic hormones. The most powerful estrogen is estradiol, and it is regarded at present as the compound secreted by the ovary. During pregnancy it also is found in the placenta. These structures are not the only sources of estrogens, however, for it is possible to extract them from urine after ovariectomy, and they occur in the urine of males as well as that of females. The urine of the stallion is one of the richest sources of estrogens, and the testis contains a high estrogenic content (Pincus and Thimann, '48, p. 381). Estrogens are found also in various plants, such as the potato, pussy willow, etc.

The structural formulae of estradiol and of estrone are as follows:

Estradiol   **Estrone**

2) The Ovary as the Normal Source of Estrogen in the Non-pregnant Female. Aside from the fact that estradiol and estrone are readily extracted from the ovary, certain experiments tend to focus attention on the ovary as an important site of estrogen production. For example, the removal of the ovaries of a normal, adult female mammal causes the accessory reproductive organs to undergo profound atrophy. The administration of appropriate amounts of estrogen will restore the accessories of such a female to the condition normal for the resting state. (Consult Pincus, '50, in Pincus and Thimann, Chap. I.) The injection of follicle-stimulating hormone with small amounts of the luteinizing hormone into the diestrous (i.e., sexually-resting) female with intact ovaries results in follicular development within the ovaries, accompanied by hypertrophy of the accessory reproductive organs to the full estrous condition (Nelsen and White, '41; Pincus, '50, in Pincus and Thimann). These and similar experiments point to the ovary as the main site of estrogen formation in the body of the non-pregnant female.

The exact structures of the ovary responsible for estrogen elaboration are not easily determined. Estrogen is found in all parts of the ovary, but certain observations and experimental results suggest that it is formed in relation to the follicular tissues and also by the so-called interstitial tissue of the ovary. For example, when tumors occur within the thecal tissue of the egg follicle in women who have experienced the menopause, there is often an accompanying hypertrophy of the accessory organs. This relationship suggests that thecal gland tissue of the follicle may have the ability to elaborate estrogen (Geist and Spielman, '43). On the other hand, the normal hypertrophy of the granulosa cells of the egg follicle during the normal reproductive cycle, with the presence of follicular fluid containing estrogen in the antral space of the follicle, points to the granulosa cells as a possible source of estrogen. Also, it has been observed that tumorous growths of the granulosa cells of the follicle produce an excess of estrogenic substance (Geist and Spielman, '43). Thus, these observations point to the granulosa cells of the egg follicle of the ovary as being capable of estrogen formation. Another possible source of estrogen secretion in the ovary is the interstitial cells, derived in part from theca interna tissue and atretic follicles. These cells are large polyhedral epithelioid cells scattered between the follicles. Their growth appears to be directly stimulated by the injection of pure luteinizing hormone (LH; ICSH) in hypophysectomized rats (fig. 40). A rapid production of estrogen results from such injections and this may mean that these cells are involved in estrogen production within the ovary (Evans and Simpson in Pincus and Thimann, '50).

In the pregnant female mammal the placenta appears to be a source of estrogen production (Pincus and Thimann, '48, p. 380; Turner, '48, p. 422). This is suggested by the successful extraction of estrogen from the placenta of the human and the mare and also by the fact that in these females removal of the ovaries during the middle or latter phase of gestation does not result in estrogen diminution in urinary excretion.

3) Pituitary Control of Estrogen Formation. The removal of the anterior lobe of the pituitary gland of the female results in marked atrophy of ovarian structures (figs. 40, 50) and of the accessory reproductive organs. Replacement therapy (i.e., the injections of the pituitary gonadotrophins, FSH and LH) produces a normal reconstitution of the ovarian and reproductive duct tissues, effecting a normal appearance and functioning of these structures

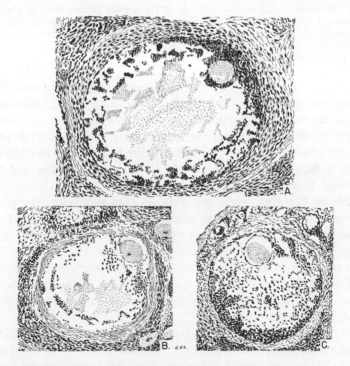

Fig. 50. Follicular atresia in guinea pig ovary. (Redrawn from Asdell, '46.) This atresia is a sporadic but not uncommon event in the normal ovary of the mammal. However, after removal of the pituitary gland, marked atresia and degeneration of the more mature follicles occur. (A) Fragmentation of granulosa cells is shown. (B) Beginning invasion of the antral space by theca interna tissue is depicted. (Cf. fig. 40A.) (C) Late stage of atresia with invasion of the antral space by internal thecal cells.

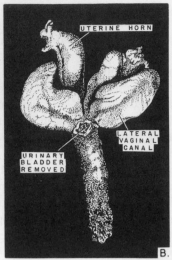
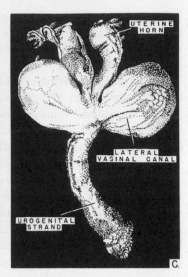

FIG. 51. Effects of estradiol (estrogen) upon the female genital tract of the opossum. (After Risman, J. Morphol., 81.)   (A) Reproductive tract of an ovariectomized female. (B) Hypertrophied condition of a female experiencing the normal estrous changes.   (C) Reproductive tract of an ovariectomized female injected with estradiol (0.9 mm.) 36 days after the ovaries were removed.

(fig. 40). This evidence suggests that the pituitary gonadotrophins, FSH and LH, control the development of the ovary and, through their influence upon the ovarian tissues, promote the secretion of estrogen with the subsequent hypertrophy of the female accessory reproductive structures. It is to be observed that it is not at all clear that FSH in pure form is able to elicit estrogen production without the presence of LH (ICSH). (See Evans and Simpson in Pincus and Thimann, '50, p. 355.)

4) Effect of Estrogen upon the Female Mammal. The changes in the mammalian accessory reproductive organs produced by estrogen are marked. An increase in vascularity and great hypertrophy of the accessory structures result from its injection into ovariectomized females. (See figs. 51, 52, 53.) Increased irritability and activity of the accessory structures also occur. This increased activity appears to be an important factor in the transportation of sperm upward within the female accessory organs to the region where the egg awaits the sperm's arrival.

The alterations in behavior of the female as a result of estrogen stimulation may be considerable. Females actually seek the presence of a male during the period of strong estrogenic influence. The long journey of the female fur seal to the mating grounds in the Bering Sea, the bellowing and tireless search of the cow moose, the almost uncontrollable demeanor of seeking the male on the part of the female dog or of the cow in "heat"—these are a few illustrations of the regnant power of this stimulant upon the female mammal.

The culmination of these changes in behavior, resulting in a receptive attitude toward the male, is reached at about the time when the egg is discharged from the ovary in many mammalian species. In certain other mammals the period of heat may precede the ovulatory phenomena.

5) Effects of Estrogen in Other Vertebrates. In the hen, estrogenic hormone causes enlargement and functional activity of the oviduct. Estrogenic substance, when injected into female chicks from the eighteenth to the fortieth day, causes an enlargement of the oviduct to about 48 times the natural size. Estrogen also has a profound effect upon the activities of the full-grown hen and aids in egg production (Romanoff and Romanoff, '49; Herrick, '44). Estrogen has a pronounced effect upon the oviducts of other vertebrate forms.

b. Progesterone—The Hormone of the Corpus Luteum

1) Production of Progesterone. The luteinizing hormone, LH, of the anterior lobe of the pituitary gland is concerned not only with the development

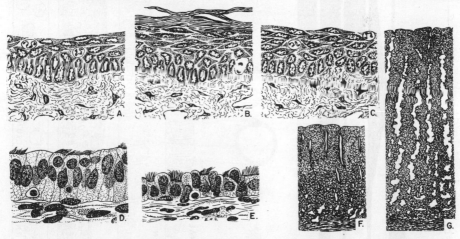

FIG. 52. Characteristic histological changes in the female reproductive tract under the influence of estrogen and progesterone. (A–C) Vaginal cyclic changes in the rat. In (A) is shown the condition of the vaginal wall in the diestrus (resting) condition; (B) shows changes in vaginal wall structure during estrus. Observe cornification of outer layer of cells; (C) shows vaginal wall tissue immediately following estrus, i.e., during metestrus. The presence of progesterone tends to suppress the action of estrogen. (After Turner: *General Endocrinology*, Philadelphia, Saunders.) (D, E) Cyclic changes of the Fallopian tube of the human female during the reproductive cycle. In (D) is shown the mid-interval of the cycle, i.e., at a time paralleling estrus in mammals in general; (E) shows the cellular condition of the lining tissue of the Fallopian tube just before menstruation. In (D) the tissue has responded to the presence of estrogen; (E) effect of progesterone is shown. (After Maximow and Bloom: *A Textbook of Histology*, Philadelphia, Saunders.) (F, G) Cyclic changes in the uterine-wall tissue during the reproductive cycle in the human female. In (F) is shown general character of the uterine wall during the follicular phase, i.e., responses to estrogen; (G) shows the general condition of the uterine wall following ovulation. The uterus is now responding to the presence of progesterone added to the follicular or estrogenic stimulation. (After Maximow and Bloom: *A Textbook of Histology*, Philadelphia, Saunders.)

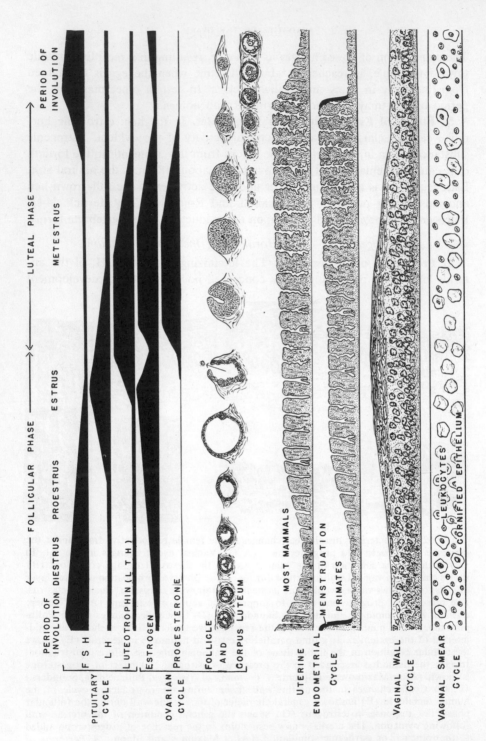

FIG. 53. (See facing page for legend.)

of the egg follicle, but also, after ovulation or the discharge of the egg from the egg follicle, the remaining granulosa cells, and also, some of the theca interna cells of the follicle are induced by the LH factor to form the corpus luteum (figs. 30, 49). Corpora lutea also may be induced by estrogens. This, however, appears to be an indirect stimulus aroused through estrogenic stimulation of the pituitary gland to secrete added amounts of the LH factor (Evans and Simpson in Pincus and Thimann, '50, p. 359).

A further pituitary principle, however, seems to be involved in the functional behavior of the corpus luteum. This principle, referred to as **luteotrophin** (LTH), is associated with the lactogenic-hormone complex produced by the anterior lobe of the pituitary body; it induces the morphologically developed corpus luteum to secrete progesterone. (Consult Evans and Simpson in Pincus and Thimann, '50, pp. 359, 360; Turner, '48, p. 379, for references.)

The structural formula of progesterone is as follows:

2) Effects of Progesterone. Progesterone reduces the irritability of the accessory structures and stimulates the mucosa of the uterus to undergo further development. This increased developmental and functional condition of the

---

FIG. 53. Relationship of the pituitary gonadotrophins and ovarian hormones to the developing Graafian follicle and reproductive-duct change in a polyestrous female mammal.

The Graafian follicle responds to the pituitary gonadotrophins, FSH and LH, with the subsequent growth and ultimate rupture of the follicle and ovulation. Ovulation terminates the **follicular phase of the cycle.** Under the influence of the LH factor the corpus luteum is established. The latter becomes functional as a result of stimulation by the luteotrophic (lactogenic) hormone. The progestational hormone (progesterone) then is elaborated by the luteal cells. The activity of the latter together with estrogen controls the **luteal phase of the cycle.**

The rising level of estrogen in the blood suppresses FSH secretion, and together possibly with small amounts of progesterone stimulates LH secretion. Estrogen and small amounts of progesterone also probably stimulate the secretion of large quantities of LTH, and the latter stimulates the secretion of progesterone from the recently formed corpus luteum. When the estrogen level falls, FSH again is secreted.

When the estrogen level rises, the endometrium of the uterus and vaginal mucosa are stimulated. The presence of progesterone suppresses vaginal development, but the uterine mucosa is stimulated to greater activity. Observe that the involution of the endometrial lining in most mammals is gradual but in primates it is precipitous and violent, resulting in menstruation (Cf. fig. 59). (The diestrous period on this chart is shown as a relatively brief period compared to the other aspects of the reproductive cycle. However, it may be very long in females which do not experience a polyestrous condition and in some species it may last a good portion of a year.) (Compiled from various sources in the literature. The portion of the chart showing pituitary and gonadal hormonal relationships is based on data obtained from The Schering Corporation, Bloomfield, N. J.)

accessory reproductive structures added normally to the estrogenic effects during the reproductive cycle constitutes the **luteal phase** of the cycle. In this phase of the cycle the uterine glands elongate and begin secretion, and the uterus as a whole is prepared for gestation as a result of the action of the progestational hormone, **progesterone,** associated with **estrogen.** (See figs. 53, 59.)

F. Reproductive State and Its Relation to the Reproductive Cycle in Female Vertebrates

The changes in the female reproductive organs resulting in structural growth and development referred to above (70-74, 85-88) are consummated in the ability of the female to fulfill the reproductive functions. The phase of the reproductive events characterized by the ability to reproduce is known as the reproductive climax. This period of culmination remains for a brief period, to be followed by recession and involution once again to a resting condition. This developmental progression to a state of reproductive climax followed by regression to a resting condition constitutes a cycle of changing events. When conditions again are right, the cycle is repeated. Each of these cyclic periods is known as a **reproductive or sexual cycle** (figs. 53–59). The reproductive life of all female vertebrates is characterized by this series of cyclic changes.

In most vertebrate species, the female experiences one sexual cycle per year, which corresponds to the seasonal cycle in the male. However, in various mammals and in certain birds, such as the domestic hen, several or many reproductive cycles may occur during the year. The male, under these conditions, is a continuous breeder; that is, he produces sperm continuously throughout the year.

1. SEXUAL CYCLE IN THE FEMALE MAMMAL

a. Characteristics and Phases of the Reproductive Cycle

The estrous cycle in mammals is a complex affair composed of a number of integrated subcycles. The changes occurring in the ovary are called the **ovarian cycle;** the cellular changes in the uterine (Fallopian tube) form a cycle; the responses in the mammary glands constitute the **mammary cycle;** the cyclic events in the uterus make up the **uterine cycle,** while those in the vagina form the **vaginal cycle** (figs. 53, 54, 57).

The entire estrous cycle may be divided by ovarian changes into two main phases: the **follicular phase** and the **luteal phase** (fig. 53). The former is under the immediate influence of the **enlarging Graafian follicle,** which in turn is stimulated by the follicle-stimulating and luteinizing hormones of the pituitary gland, with the subsequent production of estrogen. It is probable that the luteinizing hormone, LH, is mainly responsible for estrogen secretion. (See Evans and Simpson in Pincus and Thimann, '50, p. 355.) The luteal phase on the other hand is controlled by the activities of the **corpus luteum,** which has replaced the Graafian follicle under the influence of the luteinizing hormone. The production of progesterone by the corpus luteum is effected as stated previously by the pituitary hormone, luteotrophin (LTH). Ovulation is the pivotal point interposed between these two phases. The follicular phase may occur without ovulation, but the true luteal phase of a normal or fertile reproductive cycle is dependent upon the ovulatory phenomena. Certain luteal conditions may be elaborated in an anovulatory cycle, but we are here concerned with the normal events of the fertile reproductive cycle.

The **follicular phase** includes that portion of the reproductive cycle known as **proestrus** and a considerable part of estrus. Proestrus is the period of rapid follicular growth and elaboration of the estrogenic substance which precedes the period of estrus. Estrogen stimulates developmental changes in the cellular structure of the accessory reproductive organs, particularly the vagina and the uterus (figs. 52, 53). **Estrus** represents the climax of the follicular phase. As such, it is a period of sexual receptivity of the male, and, in spontaneously ovulating forms, of ovulation. During other periods of the cycle the female is indifferent or even antagonistic to the male. The period of estrus is often called period of heat, or period of rut. Estrus is followed by **pregnancy** if mating is allowed and is successful, or, in many species, by a period of pseudopregnancy if mating is not permitted or if the mating is sterile (figs. 53–57). In some animals, such as the dog, pseudopregnancy is a prolonged normal event even if mating does not occur, continuing over a period almost as long as that of normal pregnancy (fig. 54). In other animals, such as the opossum, pseudopregnancy forms but a brief episode.

Pseudopregnancy is, generally speaking, intermediate in duration between that of a normal luteal phase of the cycle and that of gestation. In those female mammals where it does not occur normally, it is aroused by such procedures as sucking of the nipples, stimulation of the vagina and cervix by the natural mating process, or by artificially stimulating these structures. In some forms, such as the rabbit, pseudopregnancy is aroused by mere handling or even by sight of a male. (For discussion, see Selye, '48, p. 813.)

The general changes of growth and development of the accessory organs which occur during pregnancy and pseudopregnancy are controlled largely by the secretions of the corpus luteum. The conditions thus imposed by the corpus luteum comprise the **luteal or progestational phase of the cycle** (fig. 57).

In most mammals, if pregnancy does not occur, the ovary and accessory organs again gradually return to the sexually-resting condition known as **diestrus** (fig. 53). In man and other primates the changes within the uterus are not gradual but are precipitous, and most of the endometrial lining, together with considerable amounts of blood, is discharged to the outside (figs. 53, 59). This phenomenon is called **menstruation.** The causes of menstruation are largely problematical; it is related to the fall of the level of either or both of the ovarian hormones, progesterone and estrogen. Why certain mammals should experience violent endometrial changes evident in menstruation and others a gradual involution and resorption is a question for the future. The general period of change following estrus in a non-fertile cycle is known as **metestrus** (fig. 53). In the rat and mouse, metestrus is short, about one or two days; in the human and opossum it occupies approximately ten days to two weeks of the cycle; in the dog, about 40 to 50 days, depending upon the pseudopregnant conditions experienced in different females. The word **anestrus** is applied to a prolonged diestrus or sexual quiescence between two sexual cycles. However, the involution experienced by the sexual organs in anestrus is somewhat more profound than that prevailing during a brief diestrus. The term **lactational diestrus** is used to refer to the prolonged diestrous condition in forms such as the rat, wherein estrus is suppressed in the mother while suckling the young.

The length of the sexual cycle varies with the species. When females of the rat or mouse are kept away from a male, the estrous or sexual cycle will repeat itself every 4 to 5 days. In the sow it occurs every 17 to 20 days. In the opossum there is a prolonged anestrous period during the summer and autumn months followed by a polyestrous period during the winter and spring when the estrous cycle reoccurs about every 28 days. In the human female, the sexual cycle occupies about 28 days, and there are probably about ten normal ovulatory cycles in a year. Some human females may have more, while others experience a slightly smaller number of true ovulatory cycles per year.

Many mammals have one estrous cycle per year. This condition, known as **monestrus,** is true of most wild mammals, such as the deer, wolf, fox, moose, and coyote. In the shrew, mink, and ferret the monestrous period may be prolonged if the female is kept away from the male.

Various types of **polyestrous** conditions exist. In the female dog, for example, there are two or three estrous periods per year about 4 to 6 months apart. In the cat there are several cycles about two weeks apart during the autumn, winter, and spring. In the domestic sheep there is a polyestrous period from September to February in which the cycles occur about every 17 days, followed by an anestrous period from early March to September. In the mare in North America, estrous cycles of about 19 to 23 days occur from March to August. In South America the breeding season is reversed, corresponding to the reversed seasonal conditions south of the equator. In England many mares breed in autumn and winter (Asdell, '46).

In some mammals estrus may follow immediately after parturition or birth of the young. This may occur occasionally in the rat. Under normal conditions in the fur seal, the female lactates and gestates simultaneously. It is not a common procedure.

It should be observed that there are two aspects of the female reproductive cycle of the mammal relative to fertilization or the bringing together of the male and female reproductive cell. One aspect is the sexual receptivity of the female; the other is the time of ovulation of the egg. In most female mammals sexual receptivity and ovulation are intimately associated and occur spontaneously in the cycle; in others the two events may be separated. In the former group, the development of "heat" and the maturing of the egg follicle are closely associated, while in the latter the conditions favoring sexual receptivity or heat are developed considerably in advance of the maturation of the follicle, as noted in the table below.

b. Relation of Estrus and Ovulation in Some Common Mammals

1) Spontaneously Ovulating Forms (Sexual Receptivity of Male Occurs at or near Time of Ovulation):

	Length of Estrus or Period of Heat	Time of Ovulation
Dog	True period of heat about 5–10 days in the middle of a 21-day estrous period	Variable: 1st day; 2nd day; 5th day; etc., of true period of heat
Guinea pig	6–11 hrs.	Views vary: 1–2 hrs. after heat or estrus begins; 10 hrs. after; at end of estrus
Man	Receptivity not always related to cyclic events	12–17 days after onset of preceding menstruation; average around 14th day
Mare	2–11 days; average length 5–6 days	About 1–2 days before end of estrus; best breeding about 3 days after heat begins
Sheep	About 36 hrs.	Late in estrus or just after estrus ends; presumably about 20–36 hrs. after estrus begins
Sow	1–5 days	About 1–3 days after onset of estrus
Silver fox	1–5 days; occurs once a year in February	1st or 2nd day of estrus
Rat	One determination estimates estrus to be 9–20 hrs.; most receptive to male about first 3 hrs. of heat. Another determination estimates estrus to be 12–18 hrs.	8–11 hrs. after beginning of heat

2) Dependent Ovulatory Forms (Sexual Receptivity [Heat] Occurs Previous to Time of Ovulation):

	Length of Estrus or Period of Heat	Time of Ovulation
Cat	2–3 days	Time of ovulation uncertain but is dependent upon copulation

	Length of Estrus or Period of Heat	Time of Ovulation
Rabbit (tame)	Estrus prolonged indefinitely during the breeding season from spring to summer; a series of different sets of egg follicles matured; each series lasts about a week, then becomes atretic	Ovulation 10–14 hrs. after mating
Shrew	Estrus prolonged	About 55–70 hrs. after mating
Ferret	Estrus prolonged	About 30 hrs. after mating

If ovulation and subsequent pregnancy are not permitted by mating, ovarian involution occurs, and an anestrous interlude is established. Anestrus in the common rabbit, *Oryctolagus cuniculus,* occurs from October to March, but is not absolute.

c. Non-ovulatory (Anovulatory) Sexual Cycles

Not all of the cyclic changes referred to above in those species which normally experience spontaneous ovulation are related to definite egg discharge. Some cycles occur, more or less abortively, without ovulation of the egg. This may happen in the human or in other mammals, such as the dog and monkey. Cycles without ovulations are called **non-ovulatory** cycles. Menstruation may follow non-ovulatory cycles in the human female.

d. Control of the Estrous Cycle in the Female Mammal

In the control of a reproductive cycle in the vertebrate animal, three main categories of factors appear to influence its appearance and course. These are:

(1) external environmental factors, such as light and temperature,
(2) external factors governing food supply, and
(3) internal factors resulting from an interplay of the activities of the pituitary gland, the ovary, general body health, and of the particular hereditary constitution of the animal.

These factors should be considered not alone in terms of the immediate production of fertile conditions in the parent, but rather, in view of the total end to be achieved, namely, the production of a new individual of the species. For example, the reproductive cycle in the deer reaches its climax or estrus in the autumn after a long period of lush feeding for the mother. The young are born the next spring amid favorable temperatures, followed by another period of bountiful food supply for the mother during lactation and for the fawn as it is weaned. A receding light factor in the late summer and early fall thus may be correlated with the period of heat, which in turn proves to be an optimum time of the year for conception with the resulting birth the following spring. Similarly, light ascendency is a factor in producing fertility in many birds. Here the incubation period for the young is short and a plentiful supply of food awaits the parents and young when it is needed. In other words, the factors which induce the onset of the reproductive state are correlated with the conditions which enhance the end to be achieved, namely, the production of a new individual.

Let us consider next the internal factors which induce the breeding state in the female mammal. The commonly held theory regarding the pituitary-ovarian relationship governing the control of the reproductive periods in the mammal which ovulates spontaneously is as follows (figs. 53 and 59):

(1) FSH of the pituitary gland stimulates later follicular growth. This factor probably is aided by small amounts of the luteinizing factor, LH, to effect an increased production by the ovarian tissues of the estrogenic hormone. Early follicle growth probably occurs without FSH.

(2) Estrogen output by the ovary rises steadily during the period previous to ovulation.

(3) Old corpora lutea or other ovarian tissue possibly secrete minimal amounts of progesterone under the influence of luteotrophin, LTH.

(4) As the quantity of estrogen rises in the blood stream, it inhibits the production of FSH and together with small quantities of progesterone, increases the output of LH from the pituitary gland. This combination also may cause an increased outflow of the luteotrophic factor.

(5) An increased amount of LH aids in effecting ovulation and the subsequent luteinization of the follicle. As the follicle becomes converted into the corpus luteum, the presence of the luteotrophic factor brings about the formation of increased quantities of progesterone and maintains for a time the corpus luteum and the functional luteal phase of the cycle.

(6) In those mammals possessing a series of repeating sexual cycles, it is assumed that the fall of estrogen in the blood stream after ovulation suppresses the LH outflow and permits a fresh liberation of FSH from the anterior lobe of the pituitary gland, thus starting a new cycle. The lowering of the estrogen level may be particularly and immediately effective in forms such as the rat and mouse, which have a short metestrus or luteal phase in the estrous cycle.

e. Reproductive Cycle in Lower Vertebrate Females

While the words estrus, heat, or rut are generally applied to the mammalian groups, the recurrent periods of sexual excitement in lower vertebrates are fundamentally the same sort of reaction, although the changes in the reproductive tract associated with ovarian events are not always the same as in mammals. However, similar cyclic changes in the ovary and reproductive tract are present in the lower vertebrates, and their correlation with the activities of the pituitary gland is an established fact. Consequently, the words estrus, rut, sex excitement, and heat basically designate the same thing throughout the vertebrate series—namely, a period during which the physiology and metabolism of the parental body is prepared to undertake the reproductive functions. In this sense, the words estrus, anestrus, heat, etc. also may be applied to the male as well as to the female when the male experiences periodic expressions of the sexual state.

Although the reproductive cycle in all vertebrates represents basically a periodic development of the reproductive functions, there is a marked difference between the estrous cycle in the female mammal and the reproductive cycle in most of the other female vertebrates with the exception of viviparous forms among the snakes, lizards, and certain fishes. This difference is due to the absence of a true **luteal phase** in the cycle. The follicular phase and elaboration of estrogen appears to be much the same in birds, amphibia, and fishes as in the mammals, but the phase of the cycle governed by progesterone secretion, associated with a gestational condition in the accessory reproductive organs, is found only among those vertebrates which give birth to their young alive.

The reproductive cycles in certain vertebrates may be changed by selective breeding and domestication. For example, the domestic hen is derived from the wild jungle fowl. The jungle fowl conform to the general stimuli of nature as do most wild birds, and the reproductive cycle is associated with a particular season of the year. However, domestication and selection by man of certain laying strains have altered the original hereditary pattern of seasonal laying. Consequently, good layers will lay eggs over an extended period of the year, although there is a strong tendency to follow the ancestral plan by laying most of the eggs during the spring and summer months; during the fall and winter months, a smaller number of eggs are laid. Some of the varieties of the domestic hen conform more closely to the ancestral condition than do other strains. Similar changes may be produced in the buffalo, which in nature breeds in middle to late summer but in captivity has estrous periods three weeks apart throughout the year (Asdell, '46).

G. Role of the Ovary in Gestation (Pregnancy)

1. Control of Implantation and the Maintenance of Pregnancy in Mammals

The ruling power of the ovary over the processes involved in pregnancy is absolute, particularly during its earlier phases. In the first place, the corpus-luteum hormone, progesterone, is necessary to change the uterus already conditioned by the estrogenic hormone into a functionally active state. The latter condition is necessary for the nutrition and care of the embryo. A second change which the gestational hormone imposes upon the genital tract of the female is to quiet the active, irritable condition aroused by the estrogenic factor. Progesterone thus serves to neutralize or antagonize the effects of the estrogenic hormone. A placid condition of the uterus must be maintained during the period immediately following copulation if the fertilized egg is to be cared for within the uterine structure. Large doses of estrogens injected into mammals shortly after copulation prevent implantation of the embryo in all species thus far studied. (See Selye, '48, p. 822.)

A third effect of the presence of progesterone is the inhibition of the copulatory responses. Immediately following estrus and ovulation, the female dog will fight off the aggressiveness of the male—an aggressiveness which she invited a day or two previously. This change in behavior is introduced by the development of the corpora lutea and the initiation of the luteal phase of the reproductive cycle. Similar anaphrodisiac changes are sometimes mentioned in the behavior of the human female during the luteal phase of the cycle. Progesterone injections also inhibit the copulatory responses in the ferret (Marshall and Hammond, '44). All of the above-mentioned activities of progesterone thus inhibit or antagonize the condition aroused by estrogenic stimulation.

However, aside from these immediate metestrous and post-ovulatory changes in behavior induced by progesterone, one of its most essential activities is concerned with the maintenance of gestation or pregnancy. Ovariectomy or the removal of the ovaries at any time during the gestational period in the rat, mouse, and goat results in death and abortion of the embryo. During the first part of pregnancy in the rabbit, the ovaries must be left intact but may be removed in the closing phase without endangering the gestational process. In the human female, and also in the mare, cat, dog, guinea pig, and monkey, the ovaries may be removed during the latter half of pregnancy without danger to the offspring. However, *ovariectomy performed in the early stages of pregnancy in these animals, as well as in all other mammals thus far studied, produces abortion* (Pincus, '36; Selye, '48, p. 820). The corpus luteum hormone, therefore, is essential in the early phases of gestation in all mammals, and it appears to be necessary during most of the pregnant period in many other mammals.

It is highly probable that the placenta takes over the elaboration of progesterone in those mammals where ovariectomy is possible after the first part of pregnancy has elapsed. In the human female the corpus luteum normally involutes at about the third month of pregnancy, but progesterone may be extracted from the placenta after this period.

Although certain effects of the estrogenic hormone appear to be neutralized (or antagonized) by progesterone during the early phases of reproduction, other effects of estrogen in relation to progesterone are important for the maintenance of the pregnant condition. In this connection the estrogenic hormone appears to suppress some of the growth-promoting effects of progesterone. The two hormones thus work together to promote a gradual development of the uterine tissue and maintain a regulated, balanced condition throughout pregnancy. The placenta, through its ability to elaborate progesterone and estrogen during the latter phases of pregnancy, is an important feature regulating pregnancy in some mammals.

It should be emphasized in connection with the above statements that the presence of the fertilized egg and its subsequent development in some manner affects the maintenance of the corpus luteum. The mechanism by which this influence is conveyed to the ovary is unknown.

2. Gestation Periods, in Days, of Some Common Mammals*

* Adapted from Asdell, '46; Cahalane, '47; Kenneth, '43.

Armadillo *(Dasypus novemcinctus)*	150
Bear, black *(Ursus americanus)*	210
Bear, polar *(Thalarctos maritimus)*	240
Beaver, Canadian *(Castor canadensis)*	94–100
Bison *(Bison bison)*	276
Cat, domestic *(Felis catus)*	60
Cattle *(Bos taurus)*	282
Chimpanzee *(Pan satyrus)*	250
Deer, Virginian *(Odocoileus virginianus)*	160–200
Dog, domestic *(Canis familiaris)*	58–65
Donkey, domestic *(Equus asinus)*	365–380
Elephant *(Elephas africanus)*	641
Elephant *(Elephas indicus)*	607–641
Elk *(Alces alces)*	250
Ferret *(Putorius furo)*	42
Fox, arctic *(Alopex lagopus)*	60
Fox, red *(Vulpes vulpes* and *V. fulva)*	52–63
Giraffe *(Giraffa camelopardalis)*	450
Goat, domestic *(Capra hircus)*	140–160
Guinea pig *(Cavia porcellus)*	68–71
Horse *(Equus caballus)*	330–380
Man *(Homo sapiens)*	270–295
Lion *(Felis leo)*	106
Lynx *(Lynx canadensis)*	63
Marten, American *(Martes americana)*	267–280
Mink *(Mustela vison)*	42–76
Mole *(Talpa europaea)*	30
Monkey, macaque *(Macaca mulato)*	160–179
Mouse, house *(Mus musculus)*	20–21
Opossum *(Didelphis virginiana)*	13
Pig *(Sus scrofa)*	115–120
Rabbit *(Lepus: Sylvilagus; Oryctolagus)*	30–43
Rats (Various species)	21–25
Seal, fur *(Callorhinus* sp.)	340–350
Sheep, domestic *(Ovis aries)*	144–160
Skunk, common *(Mephitis mephitis)*	63
Squirrel, red *(Tamiasciurus* sp.)	30–40

Tiger *(Felis tigris)*	106
Whale (Various species)	334–365
Wolf *(Canis lupus)*	63
Woodchuck *(Marmota monax)*	35–42
Zebra, mountain *(Equus zebra)*	300–345

3. Maintenance of Pregnancy in Reptiles and Other Vertebrates

In certain viviparous species of the genera *Storeria, Natrix* and *Thamnophis,* Clausen ('40) reports that ovariectomy during gestation results in resorption of the embryo when performed during the earlier phases of gestation and abortion during the middle of gestation, but during the terminal portion of pregnancy the process is unaffected and the young are born normally. These results are similar to those obtained from the rabbit as noted previously.

While experimental evidence is lacking in other vertebrate groups which give birth to the young alive, the evidence obtained from reptilian and mammalian studies suggests that hormones are responsible for the maintenance of pregnancy. In harmony with this statement, it may be pointed out that in the viviparous elasmobranch fishes (e.g., sharks) corpora lutea are developed in the ovaries.

H. Role of the Ovary in Parturition or Birth of the Young

The real factors bringing about parturition are not known, and any explanation of the matter largely is theoretical. However, certain aspects of the subject have been explored. For example, it was observed above that progesterone appears to antagonize the action of estrogen with the result that the uterus stimulated to irritability and contractility under the influence of estrogen is made placid by the action of progesterone. In harmony with this action studies have shown that estrogen tends to increase during the final stages of normal gestation, while progesterone appears to decrease, accompanied by an involution of the corpora lutea. Consequently, the foregoing facts have suggested the "estrogen theory," which postulates that activities of the uterine musculature are increased by the added amounts of estrogen in the presence of decreasing amounts of progesterone during the latter phases of pregnancy. In confirmation of this theory, it has been shown that progesterone injected into a pregnant rabbit near the end of the gestation period will tend to prolong gestation. A second theory of parturitional behavior assumes that the posterior lobe of the pituitary gland elaborates **oxytocin** which induces increased uterine activity, resulting in birth contractions (Waring and Landgrebe in Pincus and Thimann, '50). Again, a third concept emphasizes the possibility that the placenta may produce substances which bring about contractions necessary for the expulsion of the young (Turner, '48, p. 428). Oxytocic substances have been extracted from the placenta, which suggests the validity of this theory.

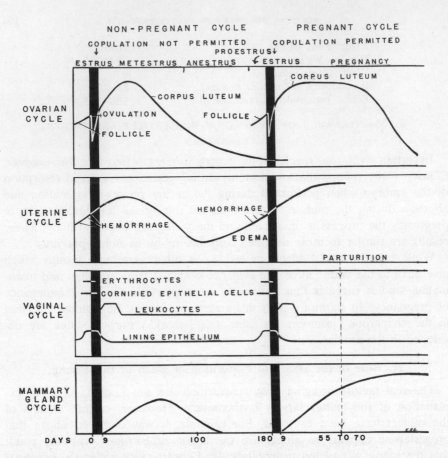

FIG. 54. Changes occurring in the reproductive organs and mammary glands of the bitch during the reproductive cycle. The student is referred to Asdell ('46), pp. 150–156 and Dukes ('43), pp. 678–682, for detailed description and references pertaining to the data supporting this chart. The gestation period is based upon data supplied by Kenneth ('43) and the author's personal experience with dogs.

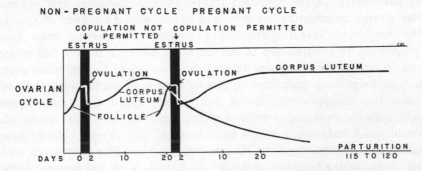

FIG. 55. Reproductive and pregnancy cycles in the sow. (Modified from data supplied by Corner, Carnegie Inst., Washington, pub. 276, Contrib. to Embryol., 13; the parturition data derived from Kenneth, '43.)

102

The specific functions of the ovary in parturition probably are more pronounced in those forms where it is essential throughout most of the gestational period, such as the viviparous snakes, and among the mammals, such forms as the opossum, rat, mouse, and rabbit. The waning of corpus-luteum activity in these species may serve to lower the level of progesterone in the body and thus permit some of the other factors, such as estrogen or the pituitary principle, to activate the uterus.

Another factor associated with the ovary and parturition is the hormone **relaxin.** This substance was first reported by Hisaw and further studied by this investigator and his associates (Hisaw, '25, '29; and Hisaw, et al., '44).

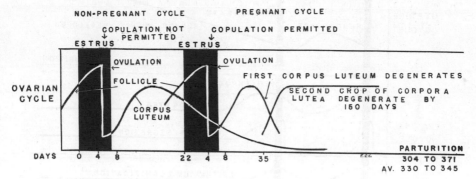

Fig. 56. Reproductive and pregnancy cycles in the mare. (Parturition period based upon data supplied by Kenneth ('43); other data supplied by Asdell ('46) and Dukes ('43).) It is to be noted that the first corpus luteum of pregnancy degenerates after about 35 days; the second "crop of corpora lutea" (Asdell) degenerate by 150 days. The ovaries may be removed after 200 days of pregnancy without causing abortion of young.

Relaxin aids in the production of a relaxed condition of the pelvic girdle, a necessity for the formation of a normal birth passageway for the young. Relaxin somehow is associated in its formation with the presence of progesterone in the blood stream and also with the *intact* reproductive system. Relaxin together with estrogen and progesterone establishes a relaxed condition of the tissues in the pubic area of the pelvic girdle.

I. Importance of the Ovary in Mammary-Gland Development and Lactation

Estrogen and progesterone together with the lactogenic hormone, luteotrophin, of the pituitary gland are necessary in mammary-gland development. The entire story of the relationship of these and of other factors in all mammals or in any particular mammal is not known. However, according to one theory of mammary-gland development and function, the suggestive roles played by these hormones presumably are as follows (fig. 58): Estradiol and other estrogens bring about the development of the mammary-gland ducts; as a result a tree-like branching of the ducts is effected from a simple im-

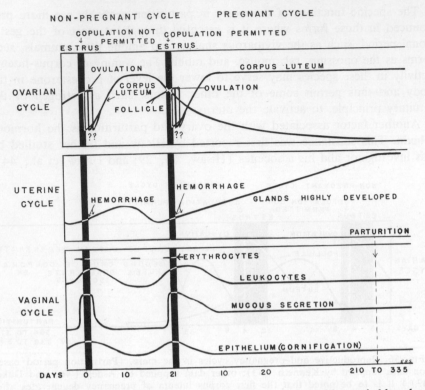

FIG. 57. Reproductive and pregnancy cycles in the cow. (Parturition period based upon data supplied by Kenneth ('43), also by Asdell ('46). Other data for chart derived from Asdell ('46).

Three main characteristics of heat or estrous period are evident: (1) A duration of heat of only about 10 to 18 hours; (2) abundant secretion during heat of a "stringy mucus," derived from mucoid epithelium of vagina and from sealing plug of cervix when cow not in estrus (Asdell); and (3) ovulation occurs from 13½ to 15½ hours after termination of estrus (Asdell). Variation in time of ovulation may be considerable, from 2 hours before end of estrus to 26 hours after (Asdell).

mature pattern established during earlier development (fig. 58A, A', B). The male mammary gland may remain similar to the condition shown in fig. 58A. The maturing of the egg follicles within the ovary and the concomitant formation of estrogen which accompanies sexual maturity is linked with the more complex state of the mammary-gland system shown in fig. 58B.

The next step of mammary-gland development is carried out under the influence of progesterone. Progesterone is necessary for the development of the terminal glandular tissue or alveoli associated with these ducts (fig. 58C, D). Finally, the pituitary lactogenic hormone (luteotrophin [LTH]; prolactin) stimulates the actual secretion of milk (fig. 58E). Recent research also has shown that the lactogenic hormone collaborates in some way with estrogen and progesterone in the development of the mammary-gland tissue.

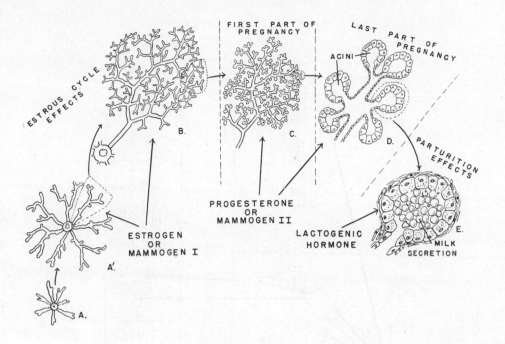

FIG. 58. Mammary gland changes in relation to reproduction. (Figures are a modification of a figure by Corner: *Hormones in Human Reproduction,* Princeton, Princeton
University Press. The figure in the latter work was based on a figure by C. D. Turner:
Chap. XI of *Sex and Internal Secretions,* by Allen, et al., Baltimore, Williams & Wilkins,
1939.) Factors involved in mammary gland development and secretion are somewhat as
follows: (A, A′) Condition of the young, infantile gland. (B) Development from a
simple, branched. tubular gland of the immature animal (A′) into a compound tubular
gland presumably under the direct stimulation of estrogen, according to one theory, or
by the action of estrogen upon the pituitary gland which then releases mammogen I,
producing these changes, according to Turner, et al.: Chap. XI, *Sex and Internal Secretions,* by Allen, et al., Baltimore, Williams & Wilkins. (C) Transformation of the compound tubular gland into a compound tubulo-alveolar gland under the influence of progesterone, during the first part of pregnancy, or, according to Turner, et al., by the influence
of estrogen plus progesterone which causes the pituitary to release a second mammogen
which produces the alveolar transformation. (D) Effect of the latter part of pregnancy
is to bring about a development of the cells of the acini of the acinous or alveolar system.
The unit shown in (D) represents a simple, branched, acinous gland, in which there are
six alveoli or acini associated with the duct. (E) Affect of parturition is to release the
lactogenic hormone (prolactin; luteotrophin) from the pituitary gland which brings about
milk secretion. During pregnancy the high levels of estrogen presumably inhibit milk
secretion. However, following pregnancy the level of estrogen is lowered permitting
lactogenic-hormone action upon the alveoli of the gland.

The removal of the placenta and embryo at any time during gestation permits milk
flow, provided the mammary glands are sufficiently developed. In the human, any remains
of the placenta after birth inhibit milk secretion, probably because the estrogenic hormone
is elaborated by the placental remnants. (See Selye, '48, p. 829.)

In the rabbit, estrogen and progesterone are necessary for the elaboration of the duct
and secretory acini; in the guinea pig and goat, and to some extent in the primates,
including the human female, estrogen alone is capable of producing the development of
the entire duct and acinous system. (See Turner, '48, p. 430.)

105

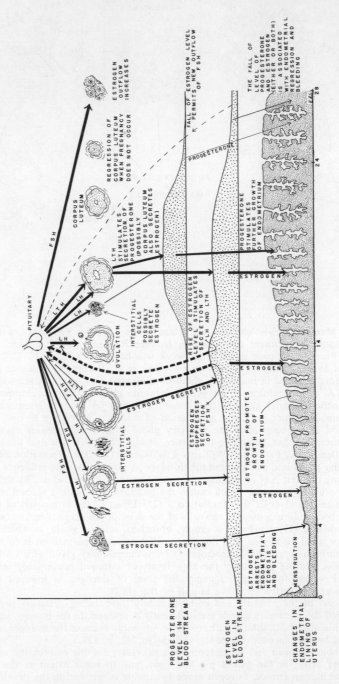

FIG. 59. *(See facing page for legend.)*

106

During pregnancy, the actual secretion of milk is inhibited by the estrogenic hormone produced by the ovary and the placenta. The role of estrogen as an inhibitor of lactation is suggested by the fact that, after lactation has started following normal parturition, it is possible in the cow and human to suppress milk flow by the administration of estrogens. After parturition, however, estrogen is no longer present in sufficient amounts to suppress the secretion of milk, and the mammary gland begins to function. (In the fur seal a post-partum estrus with ovulation follows a short time after parturition. However, the amount of estrogen produced by this reproductive cycle is not sufficient to curb lactation.) The neurohumoral reflex, or "suckling reflex," produced by the sucking young appears to maintain the flow of milk over a period of time. Probably this reflex causes a continuous discharge of the lactogenic hormone from the anterior lobe of the hypophysis.

Another theory of mammary-gland development maintains that estrogen stimulates the anterior pituitary gland to release **mammogen,** which causes development of the duct system, and estrogen plus progesterone induce a second mammogen which stimulates lobule-alveolar development. The lactogenic hormone produces the actual secretion of milk. The ovary thus assumes considerable importance in controlling the (morphological) development of the mammary glands in mammals, particularly in those forms in which the functional condition of the ovary is maintained throughout most

---

FIG. 59. Stages in the reproductive cycle of the human female and its pituitary-ovarian-endometrial relationships (Cf. fig. 53). (Compiled from various sources in the literature.) (a) As shown at the extreme right of the figure, *a fall in the level of estrogen and progesterone in the blood stream, either or both,* is associated with endometrial necrosis, bleeding, and discharge (menstruation). (b) The lowering of the estrogen level is associated with a new outflow of the follicle-stimulating hormone (FSH), as shown at the right of the figure. (c) In the left side of the figure, the influence of FSH induces egg follicles, probably several, to grow. Antral spaces appear and enlarge. The presence of a small amount of the luteinizing hormone (LH) together with FSH stimulates the secretion of estrogen by the ovarian tissues, possibly by the follicles and interstitial tissue between the follicles. (d) In consequence, the estrogen level rises in the blood stream, and menstruation subsides by the fourth day (e) The continued influence of estrogen produces endometrial growth, and probably increases the outflow of LH from the pituitary (fig. 53). It is probable, also, that the increased estrogen level stimulates a release of the luteotrophic hormone from the pituitary, which in turn stimulates the formation of a small quantity of progesterone by either the interstitial tissue of the ovary or in old corpora lutea. (f) Some of the developing egg follicles degenerate, while one continues to develop. (g) The elevation of estrogen suppresses the outflow of FSH as indicated by the heavy broken line to the left. (h) The elevated level of estrogen together possibly with small amounts of progesterone evokes an increased outflow of LH and LTH as indicated by the heavy broken line to the right. (i) LH and FSH bring about ovulation at about the fourteenth day. (j) LH causes development of corpus luteum. (k) LTH elicits secretion of progesterone by corpus luteum. Possibly some estrogen is secreted also by corpus luteum. (l) Progesterone and estrogen stimulate added development of endometrium. (m) In the absence of fertilization of the egg, the corpus luteum regresses, with a subsequent fall of progesterone and estrogen levels in the blood stream, terminating the cycle and permitting a new menstrual procedure.

of the gestational period, e.g., rat, rabbit, dog, etc. In other species, such as the human, mare, etc., the placenta through its ability to duplicate the production of the ovarian hormones, assumes a role during the latter phase of pregnancy. (For further details, consult Folley and Malpress in Pincus and Thimann, '48; Selye, '48, pp. 828–832; and Turner, '48, pp. 428–448.)

In the dog or opossum during each reproductive cycle, the mammary glands are stimulated to grow and may even secrete milk (dog). These changes closely parallel the ovarian activities, particularly the luteal phase of the cycle. In the human, functional growth changes occur in pregnancy, but, pending the events of the ordinary cycle, alterations in the duct system are slight although the breasts may be turgid due to increased blood flow and connective-tissue development.

J. Other Possible Developmental Functions Produced by the Ovary

As the eggs of the opossum and rabbit travel through the uterine (Fallopian) tube toward the uterus, they are coated with an albuminous, jelly-like coating. Similar jelly coatings are added to the eggs of the bird, reptile, frog, toad, and salamander. These coatings or membranes added to the egg as it travels through the oviduct are known as **tertiary egg membranes.**

In the toad, the secretion of the protective jelly by the oviduct can be elicited by the lactogenic hormone present in beef pituitary glands. The secretion of the albuminous jelly coatings around the eggs of frogs, salamanders, reptiles, and birds may be related to this hormone. The formation of the crop milk of pigeons has been shown by Riddle and Bates ('39) to be dependent upon the presence of the lactogenic hormone.

The function of the ovary in influencing the outflow of the lactogenic hormone from the pituitary, if present in the above cases of glandular secretion, must be an indirect one. Evans and Simpson in Pincus and Thimann ('50) ascribe the outflow of the "lactogenic hormone (luteotrophic hormone)" of the mammalian pituitary to estrin produced by the ovary. It is possible that in the salamanders, frogs, toads, and the birds an indirect ovarian influence may similarly induce secretion of the lactogenic hormone which in turn governs the elaboration of the albuminous jelly deposited around the egg in transit through the oviduct.

K. Determinative Tests for Pregnancy

Various tests have been used to determine the probability of pregnancy in the human female. These tests are discussed in Chapter 22.

Bibliography

Arai, H. 1920a. On the postnatal development of the ovary (albino rat) with especial reference to the number of ova. Am. J. Anat. 27:405.

————. 1920b. On the cause of hypertrophy of the surviving ovary after semispraying (albino rat) and the number of ova in it. Am. J. Anat. 28:59.

Aronson, L. R. and Holz-Tucker, M. 1949. Ovulation in the mouthbreeding cichlid fish, *Tilapiá macrocephala* (Bleeker). Anat. Rec. 105:568.

Asdell, S. A. 1946. Patterns of Mammalian Reproduction. Comstock Publishing Co., Inc., Ithaca, New York.

Blandau, R. J. and Young, W. C. 1939. The effects of delayed fertilization on the development of the guinea pig ovum. Am. J. Anat. 64:303.

Brambell, F. W. R. 1930. The Development of Sex in Vertebrates. The Macmillan Co., New York.

Burns, R. K., Jr. 1931. The process of sex transformation in parabiotic *Amblystoma*. II. Transformation from male to female. J. Exper. Zool. 60:339.

Burr, H. S., Hill, R. T., and Allen, E. 1935. Detection of ovulation in the intact rabbit. Proc. Soc. Exper. Biol. & Med. 33:109.

Cahalane, V. H. 1947. Mammals of North America. The Macmillan Co., New York.

Charlton, H. H. 1917. The fate of the unfertilized egg in the white mouse. Biol. Bull. 33:321.

Clausen, H. J. 1940. Studies on the effect of ovariotomy and hypophysectomy on gestation in snakes. Endocrinology. 27:700.

Cole, F. J. 1930. Early Theories of Sexual Generation. Oxford University Press, The Clarendon Press, New York.

Cole, H. H., Howell, C. E., and Hart, G. H. 1931. The changes occurring in the ovary of the mare during pregnancy. Anat. Rec. 49:199.

Corner, G. W. 1943. The Hormones in Human Reproduction. Princeton University Press, Princeton, New Jersey.

Dukes, H. H. 1943. The Physiology of Domestic Animals. Comstock Publishing Co., Inc., Ithaca, New York.

Enders, R. K., Pearson, O. P., and Pearson, A. K. 1946. Certain aspects of reproduction in the fur seal. Anat. Rec. 94:213.

Evans, H. M. and Simpson, M. E. 1950. Chap. VI. Physiology of the gonadotrophins in The Hormones, Vol. II., by Pincus and Thimann. Academic Press, Inc., New York.

Folley, S. J. and Malpress, F. H. 1948. Chaps. 15, 16. Hormonal control of mammary growth and lactation in The Hormones, Vol. I., by Pincus and Thimann. Academic Press, Inc., New York.

Fraps, R. M., Olsen, M. W., and Neher, B. H. 1942. Forced ovulation of normal ovarian follicles in the domestic fowl. Proc. Soc. Exper. Biol. & Med. 50:308.

Geist, S. H. and Spielman, F. 1943. Endocrine tumors of the ovary. J. Clin. Endocrinol. 3:281.

Häggström, P. 1921. Zahlenmässige Analyse der Ovarien eines 22-jährigen gesunden Weibes. Upsala Läkaref. Förh. 26:1.

Hammond, J. and Marshall, F. H. A. 1925. Reproduction in the Rabbit. Oliver & Boyd, Ltd., Edinburgh.

Hartman, C. G. 1929. How large is the mammalian egg? Quart. Rev. Biol. 4:373.

Heape, W. 1905. Ovulation and degeneration of ova in the rabbit. Proc. Roy. Soc. London, s.B. 76:260.

Herrick, E. H. 1944. Some influences of stilbestrol, estrone and testosterone propionate on the genital tract of young female fowls. Poul. Sc. 23:65.

Hill, R. T., Allen, E., and Kramer, T. C. 1935. Cinemicrographic studies of rabbit ovulation. Anat. Rec. 63:239.

Hisaw, F. L. 1925. The influence of the ovary on the resorption of the pubic bones of the pocket gopher, *Geomys bursarius* (Shaw). J. Exper. Zool. 42:411.

————. 1929. The corpus luteum hormone. I. Experimental relaxation of the pelvic ligaments of the guinea pig. Physiol. Zoöl. 2:59.

————, Zarrow, M. X., Money, W. L., Talmadge, R. V. N., and Abramowitz, A. A. 1944. Importance of the female reproductive tract in the formation of relaxin. Endocrinology. 34:122.

Humphrey, R. R. 1929. Studies on sex reversal in Amblystoma. I. Bisexuality and sex reversal in larval males uninfluenced by ovarian hormones. Anat. Rec. 42:119.

Kenneth, J. H. 1943. Gestation Periods. Oliver & Boyd, Ltd., Edinburgh.

Long, J. A. 1912. The living eggs of rats and mice with a description of apparatus for obtaining and observing them. Univ. California Publ., Zoöl. 9(3):105.

Marshall, F. H. A. and Hammond, J., Jr. 1944. Experimental control by hormone action of the oestrous cycle in the ferret. J. Endocrinol. 4:159.

Mason, K. E. 1939. Chapter 22 in Allen, et al., Sex and Internal Secretions. 2d ed., The Williams & Wilkins Co., Baltimore.

Neher, B. H. and Fraps, R. M. 1950. The addition of eggs to the hen's clutch by repeated injections of ovulation-inducing hormones. Endocrinology. 46:482.

Nelsen, O. E. and Maxwell, N. 1942. The structure and function of the urogenital region in the female opossum compared with the same region in other marsupials. J. Morphol. 71:463.

———— and White, E. L. 1941. A method for inducing ovulation in the anoestrous opossum (Didelphys virginiana). Anat. Rec. 81:529.

Pearl, R. and Boring, A. M. 1918. The corpus luteum in the ovary of the domestic fowl. Am. J. Anat. 23:1.

Phillips, R. E. and Warren, D. C. 1937. Observations concerning the mechanics of ovulation in the fowl. J. Exper. Zool. 76:117.

Pincus, G. 1936. The Eggs of Mammals. The Macmillan Co., New York.

————. 1950. The Physiology of Ovarian Hormones, Chap. I. The Hormones, Vol. II, in Pincus and Thimann, Academic Press, Inc., New York.

———— and Thimann, K. V. 1948. The Hormones. Vol. I. Academic Press, Inc., New York.

Rahn, H. 1939. Structure and function of placenta and corpus luteum in viviparous snakes. Proc. Soc. Exper. Biol. & Med. 40:381.

Riddle, O. 1938. Prolactin, a product of the anterior pituitary, and the part it plays in vital processes. Scient. Monthly. 47:97.

———— and Bates, R. W. 1939. Chap. 20. The preparation, assay and actions of the lactogenic hormone in Allen, et al., Sex and Internal Secretions. 2d ed., The Williams & Wilkins Co., Baltimore.

Romanoff, A. L. and Romanoff, A. J. 1949. The Avian Egg. John Wiley & Sons, Inc., New York.

Rothchild, I. and Fraps, R. M. 1944. On the function of the ruptured ovarian follicle of the domestic fowl. Proc. Soc. Exper. Biol. & Med. 56:79.

Rugh, R. 1935a. Ovulation in the frog. I. Pituitary relations in induced ovulation. J. Exper. Zool. 71:149.

————. 1935b. Ovulation in the frog. II. Follicular rupture to fertilization. J. Exper. Zool. 71:163.

Ryder, J. A. 1885. On the development of viviparous osseous fishes. Proc. U. S. Nat. Mus. 8: No. 9, 128.

Selye, H. 1948. Textbook of Endocrinology. Acta Endocrinologica. Université de Montréal, Montréal.

Smith, B. G. 1916. The process of ovulation in Amphibia. Michigan Acad. Sc., 18th Ann. Rep. p. 102.

Smith, P. E. 1939. Chap. XVI. The effect on the gonads of ablation and implantation of the hypophysis and the potency of the hypophysis under various conditions. Allen, et al., Sex and Internal Secretions. 2d ed., The Williams & Wilkins Co., Baltimore.

Strauss, F. 1939. Die Befruchtung und der Vorgang der Ovulation bei Ericulus aus der Familie der Centetiden. Biomorphosis. 1:281.

Turner, C. D. 1948. General Endocrinology. W. B. Saunders Co., Philadelphia.

Walton, A. and Hammond, J. **1928.** Observations on ovulation in the rabbit. British J. Exper. Biol. **6**:190.

Waring, H. and Landgrebe, F. W. **1950.** Chap. VIII. Hormones of the posterior pituitary in The Hormones, Vol. II, by Pincus and Thimann. Academic Press, Inc., New York.

Wright, P. A. **1945.** Factors affecting in vitro ovulation in the frog. J. Exper. Zool. **100**:565.

———— and Hisaw, F. L. **1946.** Effect of mammalian pituitary gonadotrophins on ovulation in the frog, *Rana pipiens*. Endocrinology. **39**:247.

3

The Development of the Gametes or Sex Cells

A. General considerations
B. Controversy regarding germ-cell origin
C. Maturation (differentiation) of the gametes
  1. General considerations
  2. Basic structure of the definitive sex cell as it starts to mature or differentiate into the male meiocyte (i.e., the spermatocyte) or the female meiocyte (i.e., the oocyte)
  3. Nuclear maturation of the gametes
    a. General description of chromatin behavior during somatic and meiotic mitoses
    b. Reductional and equational meiotic divisions and the phenomenon of crossing over
    c. Stages of chromatin behavior during the meiotic prophase in greater detail
      1) Leptotene (leptonema) stage
      2) Zygotene or synaptene (zygonema) stage
      3) Pachytene (pachynema) stage
      4) Diplotene (diplonema) stage
      5) Diakinesis
    d. Peculiarities of nuclear behavior in the oocyte during meiosis; the germinal vesicle
    e. Character of the meiotic (maturation) divisions in the spermatocyte compared with those of the oocyte
      1) Dependent nature of the maturation divisions in the female meiocyte
      2) Inequality of cytoplasmic division in the oocyte
    f. Resumé of the significance of the meiotic phenomena
  4. Cytosomal (Cytoplasmic) maturation of the gametes
    a. General aspects of the cytoplasmic maturation of the gametes
    b. Morphogenesis (spermiogenesis) (spermioteleosis) of the sperm
      1) Types of sperm
      2) Structure of a flagellate sperm
        a) Head
        b) Neck
        c) Connecting body or middle piece
        d) Flagellum
      3) Spermiogenesis or the differentiation of the spermatid into the morphologically differentiated sperm
        a) Golgi substance and acroblast; formation of the acrosome
        b) Formation of the post-nuclear cap
        c) Formation of the proximal and distal centrioles; axial filament

A. General Considerations

In the two preceding chapters the conditions which prepare the male and female parents for their reproductive responsibilities are considered. This chapter is devoted to changes which the male and female germ cells must experience to enable them to take part in the processes involved in the reproduction of a new individual.

The gamete is a highly specialized sex cell or protoplasmic entity so differentiated that it is capable of union (fertilization; syngamy) with a sex cell of the opposite sex to form the zygote from which the new individual arises. The process of differentiation whereby the primitive germ cell is converted into the mature gamete is called the maturation of the germ cell.

The main events which culminate in the fully-developed germ cell are possible only after the primitive or undifferentiated germ cell has reached a certain condition known as the **definitive state.** When this stage is reached, the germ cell has acquired the requisite qualities which make it possible for it to differentiate into a mature gamete. Before the definitive state is reached, germ cells pass through an eventful history which involves:

(1) their so-called "origin" or first detectable appearance among the other cells of the developing body, and

(2) their migration to the site of the future ovary or testis.

After entering the developing substance of the sex gland, the primitive germ cells experience a period of multiplication. If the sex gland is that of the male, these undifferentiated sex cells are called **spermatogonia;** if female, they are known as **oogonia.**

B. Controversy Regarding Germ-cell Origin

The problems of germ-cell origin in the individual organism and of the continuity of the germ plasm from one generation to the next have long been matters of controversy. Great interest in these problems was aroused by the ideas set forth by Waldeyer, Nussbaum, and Weismann during the latter part of the nineteenth century. Waldeyer, 1870, as a result of his studies on the chick, presented the "germinal epithelium" hypothesis, which maintains that the germ cells arise from the coelomic epithelium covering the gonad. Nussbaum, 1880, championed the concept of the extra-gonadal origin of the germ cells. According to this view, derived from his studies on frog and trout development, the germ cells arise at an early period of embryonic development outside the germ-gland area and migrate to the site and into the substance of the germ gland.

At about this time the speculative writings of August Weismann aroused great interest. In 1885 and 1892 Weismann rejected the popular Darwinian theory of pangenesis, which held that representative heredity particles or "gemmules" passed from the body cells (i.e., soma cells) to the germ cells and were there stored in the germ cells to develop in the next generation (Weismann, 1893). In contrast to this hypothesis he emphasized a complete independence of the germ plasm from the somatoplasm. He further suggested that the soma did not produce the germ plasm as implied in the pangenesis theory, but, on the contrary, the soma resulted from a differentiation of the germ plasm.

According to the Weismannian view, the germ plasm is localized in the chromosomal material of the nucleus. During development this germ plasm is segregated qualitatively during successive cell divisions with the result that the cells of different organs possess different determiners. However, the nuclear germ plasm (Keimplasma) is not so dispersed or segregated in those cells which are to become the primitive sex cells; they receive the full complement of the hereditary determiners for the various cells and organs characteristic of the species. Thus, it did not matter whether the germ cells were segregated early in development or later, so long as the nucleus containing all of the determinants for the species was kept intact. In this manner the germ plasm, an immortal substance, passed from one generation to the next via the nuclear germ plasm of the sex or germ cells. This continuity of the nuclear germ plasm from the egg to the adult individual and from thence through the germ cells to the fertilized egg of the next generation, constituted the Weismann "Keimbahn" or germ-track theory. The soma or body of any particular generation is thus the "trustee" for the germ plasm of future generations.

The Weismannian idea, relative to the qualitative segregation of the chromatin materials, is not tenable for experimental and cytological evidence suggests that all cells of the body contain the same chromosomal materials. However, it should be pointed out that Weismann was one of the first to suggest that the chromosome complex of the nucleus acts as a repository for all of the hereditary characteristics of the species. This suggestion relative to the role of the nucleus has proved to be one of the main contributions to biological theory in modern times.

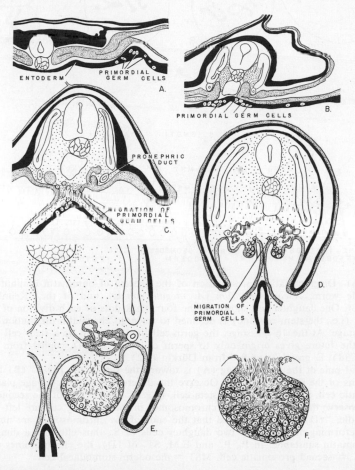

FIG. 60. Representation of the concept of the early embryonic origin of the primordial germ cells and their migration into the site of the developing germ gland. (A–C are adapted from the work of Allen, Anat. Anz. 29, on germ cell origin in *Chrysemys;* D–F are diagrams based on the works of Dustin, Swift, and Dantschakoff, etc., referred to in the table of germ-cell origins included in the text.) (A–C) Germ cells arising within the primitive entoderm and migrating through the dorsal mesentery to the site of the primitive gonad, shown in (D), where they become associated in or near the germinal epithelium overlying the internal mesenchyme of the gonad. (E, F) Increase of the primitive gonia within the developing germ gland, with a subsequent migration into the substance of the germ gland of many germ cells during the differentiation of sex.

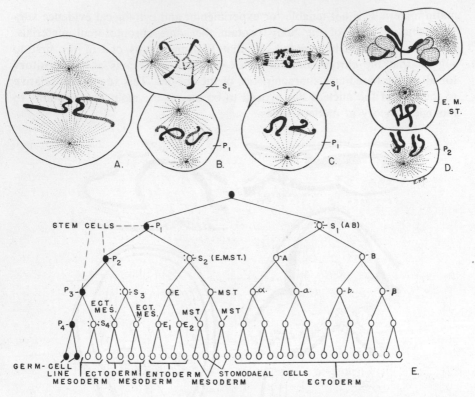

FIG. 61 Diagrammatic representation of the process of chromatin diminution in the nematode worm, *Ascaris equorum (A. megalocephala),* and of the "Keimbahn" (in black, E). One daughter cell shown by the four black dots of each division of the germ-cell line (i.e., the stem-cell line) is destined to undergo chromatin diminution up to the 16-cell stage. At the 16-cell stage, the germ-cell line ceases to be a stem cell (e.g., P_4), and in the future gives origin only to sperm cells (E). (A–D, copied from King and Beams ('38); E, greatly modified from Dürkin ('32).)

Animal pole of the cleaving egg (A) is toward the top of the page. (B) Metaphase conditions of the second cleavage. Observe the differences in the cleavage planes of the prosomatic cell, S_1, and that of the stem cell, P_1. (C) Anaphase of the second cleavage of S_1. Observe that the ends of the chromosomes in this cleaving cell are left behind on the spindle. (D) It is to be noted that the ends of the chromosomes are not included in the reforming nuclei of the two daughter cells of S_1, thus effecting a diminution of the chromatin substance. In P_1, P_2, and E.M. ST. of (D), the chromosomes are intact. E.M. ST. = second prosomatic cell. MST = mesoderm-stomodaeal cell.

A second contributory concept to the germ-cell (germ-plasm) theory was made by Nussbaum, 1880; Boveri, 1892, '10, a and b, and others. These investigators emphasized the possibility that a germinal cytoplasm also is important in establishing the germ plasm of the individual. A considerable body of observational and experimental evidence derived from embryological studies substantiates this suggestion. Consequently, the modern view of the germ cell (germ plasm) embodies the concept that the germ cell is composed of the nucleus as a carrier of the hereditary substances or genes and a peculiar, specialized, germinal cytoplasm. The character of the cytoplasm of the germ cell is the main factor distinguishing a germ cell from other soma cells.

The matter of a germinal cytoplasm suggests the necessity for a segregation of the germinal plasm in the form of specific germ cells during the early development of the new individual. As a result, great interest, as well as controversy, has accumulated concerning this aspect of the germ-cell problem: namely, is there a separate **germinal plasm** set apart in the early embryo which later gives origin to the **primordial germ cells,** and the latter, after migration (fig. 60), to the **definitive gonia;** or according to an alternative view, do some or all of the **definitive germ cells** arise from differentiated or relatively undifferentiated soma cells? The phrase **primary primordial germ cells** often is used to refer to those germ cells which possibly segregate early in the embryo, and the term **secondary primordial germ cells** is employed occasionally to designate those which may arise later in development.

The dispute regarding an early origin or segregation of the germinal plasm in the vertebrates also occurs relative to their origin in certain invertebrate groups, particularly in the *Coelenterata* and the *Annelida* (Berrill and Liu, '48). In other *Invertebrata,* such as the dipterous insects and in the ascarid worms, the case for an early segregation is beyond argument. An actual demonstration of the continuity of the Keimbahn from generation to generation is found in *Ascaris megalocephala* described by Boveri in 1887. (See Hegner, '14, Chap. 6.) In this form the chromatin of the somatic cells of the body undergoes a diminution and fragmentation, whereas the stem cells, from which the germ cells are ultimately segregated at the 16-cell to 32-cell stage, retain the full complement of chromatin material (fig. 61). Thus, one cell of the 16-cell stage retains the intact chromosomes and becomes the progenitor of the germ cells. The other 15 cells will develop the somatic tissues of the body. The diminution of the chromatin material in this particular species has been shown to be dependent upon a certain cytoplasmic substance (King and Beams, '38).

In some insects the Keimbahn also can be demonstrated from the earliest stages of embryonic development. In these forms a peculiar polar plasm within the egg containing the so-called "Keimbahn determinants" (Hegner, '14, Chap. 5) always passes into the primordial germ cells. That is, the ultimate formation and segregation of the primordial germ cells are the result of nuclear migration into this polar plasm and the later formation of definite cells from this plasm (fig. 62). The cells containing this polar plasm are destined thus to be germ cells, for they later migrate into the site of the developing germ glands and give origin to the definitive germ cells.

Many investigators of the problem of germ-cell origin in the vertebrate group of animals have, after careful histological observation, described the germ cells as taking their origin from among the early entodermal cells (see table, pp. 121–124). On the other hand, other students have described the origin of the germ cells from mesodermal tissue—some during the early period of embryonic development, while others suggest that the primordial germ cells arise from peritoneal (mesodermal) tissue at a much later time.

In more recent years much discussion has been aroused relative to the origin of the definitive germ cells in mammals, particularly in the female. According to one view the definitive germ cells which differentiate into the mature gametes of the ovary arise from the germinal epithelium (peritoneal covering) of the ovary during each estrous cycle (figs. 39A, 63, 64). For example, Evans and Swezy ('31) reached the conclusion that all germ cells in the ovaries of the cat and dog between the various reproductive periods degenerate excepting those which take part in the ovulatory phenomena. Accordingly, the new germ cells for each cycle arise from the germinal epithelium. A similar belief of a periodic proliferation of new germ cells by the

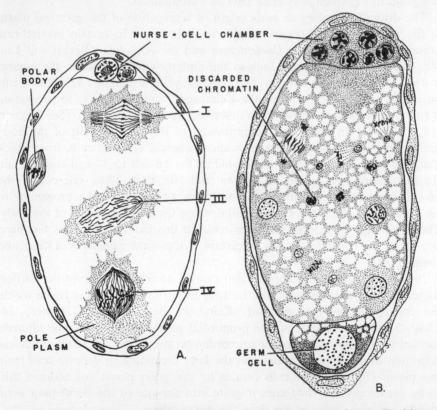

FIG. 62. Early development of the fly, *Miastor*. (A) *Miastor metraloas*. (B) *Miastor americana*. In (A) the division figures I and III (II not shown) are undergoing chromatin diminution, while nucleus IV divides as usual. In (B) one segregated germ is shown at the pole of the egg. This cell will give origin to the germ cells. Other division figures experiencing chromatin diminution.

PROLIFERATING
GERMINAL EPITHELIUM

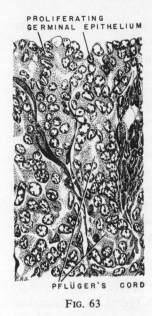

PFLÜGER'S CORD

FIG. 63

GERM CELLS WITH
FORMING FOLLICLES

FIG. 64

FIG. 63. Cells proliferating inward from germinal epithelium of the ovary of a one-day-old rat. Observe cords of cells (Pflüger's cords) projecting into the ovarian substance. Within these cords of cells are young oogonia. (After Vincent and Dornfeld, '48.)

FIG. 64. Cellular condition near the surface of the ovary of a young female opossum. This section of the ovary is near the hilar regions, i.e., near the mesovarium. Observe young oocytes and forming Graafian follicles. Primitive germ cells may be seen near the germinal epithelium.

germinal epithelium has been espoused by various authors. (See Moore and Wang, '47; and Pincus, '36, Chap. II.) More recent papers have presented views which are somewhat conflicting. Vincent and Dornfeld, '48 (fig. 63) concluded that there is a proliferation of germ cells from the germinal epithelium of the young rat ovary, while Jones ('49), using carbon granules as a vital-marking technic, found no evidence of the production of ova from the germinal epithelium in rat ovaries from 23 days until puberty. In the adult rat, she concedes that a segregation of a moderate number of oogonia from the germinal epithelium is possible.

Aside from the above studies of carefully-made, histological preparations relative to the time and place of origin of the primordial and definitive germ cells, many experimental attacks have been made upon the problem. Using an x-ray-sterilization approach, Parkes ('27); Brambell, Parkes and Fielding ('27, a and b), found that the oogonia and oocytes of x-rayed ovaries of the mouse were destroyed. In these cases new germ cells were not produced from the germinal epithelium. Brambell ('30) believed that the destruction of the primitive oogonia was responsible for the lack of oogenesis in these x-rayed ovaries. However, this evidence is not conclusive, for one does not know what injurious effects the x-rays may produce upon the ability of the various cells of the germinal epithelium to differentiate.

An experimental study of the early, developing, amphibian embryo relative to the origin of the primordial germ cells also has been made by various investigators. Bounoure ('39) applied a vital-staining technic to certain anuran embryos. The results indicate that the germinal plasm in these forms is associated with the early, entodermal, organ-forming area located at the vegetal pole of the cleaving egg. This germinal plasm later becomes segregated into definite cells which are associated with the primitive entoderm. At a later period these cells migrate into the developing germ gland or gonad. On the other hand, experimental studies of the urodele embryo indicate that the early germinal plasm is associated with the mesoderm (Humphrey, '25, '27; Nieuwkoop, '49). Existence of an early germinal plasm associated with the entoderm in the *Anura* and with the mesoderm in the *Urodela* thus appears to be well established for the amphibia.

The evidence derived from amphibian studies together with the observations upon the fish group presented in the table (see pp. 121–124) strongly suggests that an early segregation of a germinal plasm (germ cells) occurs in these two major vertebrate groups. Also, in birds, the experimental evidence presented by Benoit ('30), Goldsmith ('35), and Willier ('37) weighs the balance toward the conclusion that there is an early segregation of germ cells from the entoderm. Similar conditions presumably are present in reptiles. In many vertebrates, therefore, an early segregation of primordial germ cells and their ultimate migration by: (1) active ameboid movement, (2) by the shifting of tissues, or (3) through the blood stream (see table, pp. 121–124) to the site of the developing gonad appears to be well substantiated.

The question relative to the origin of the definitive ova in the mammalian ovary is still in a confused state as indicated by the evidence presented above and in the table on pp. 121–124. Much more evidence is needed before one can rule out the probability that the primordial germ cells are the progenitors of the definitive germ cells in the mammals. To admit the early origin of primordial germ cells on the one hand, and to maintain that they later disappear to be replaced by a secondary origin of primitive germ cells from the germinal epithelium has little merit unless one can disprove the following position, to wit: that, while some of the primordial germ cells undoubtedly do degenerate, others divide into smaller cells which become sequestered within or immediately below the germinal epithelium of the ovary and within the germinal epithelium of the seminiferous tubules of the testis, where they give origin by division to other gonial cells. Ultimately some of these primitive gonia pass on to become definitive germ cells.

However, aside from the controversy whether or not the primordial germ cells give origin to definitive germ cells, another aspect of the germ-cell problem emphasizing the importance of the primitive germ cells is posed by the following question: Will the gonad develop into a functional structure without the presence of the primordial germ cells? Experiments performed by Humphrey ('27) on *Ambystoma,* and the above-mentioned workers—Benoit ('30), Goldsmith ('35), and Willier ('37)—on the chick, suggest that only sterile gonads develop without the presence of the primordial germ cells.

Finally, another facet of the germ-cell problem is this: Are germ cells completely self differentiating? That is, do they have the capacity to develop by themselves; or, are the germ cells dependent upon surrounding gonadal tissues for the influences which bring about their differentiation? All of the data on sex reversal in animals, normal and experimental (Witschi, in Allen, Danforth, and Doisy, '39), and of other experiments on the development of the early embryonic sex glands (Nieuwkoop, '49) suggest that the germ cells are not self differentiating but are dependent upon the surrounding tissues for the specific influences which cause their development. Furthermore, the data on sex reversal shows plainly that the specific chromosome complex (i.e., male or female) within the germ cell does not determine the differentiation into the male gamete or the female gamete, but rather, that the influences of the cortex (in the female) and the medulla (in the male) determine the specific type of gametogenesis.

The table given on pp. 121-124 summarizes the conclusions which some authors have reached concerning germ-cell origin in many vertebrates. It is not complete; for more extensive reviews of the subject see Everett ('45), Heys ('31), and Nieuwkoop ('47, '49).

Species	Place of Origin, etc.	Author
Entosphenus wilderi (brook lamprey)	Germ cells segregate early in the embryo; definitive germ cells derived from "no other source"	Okkelberg. **1921.** J. Morphol. **35**
Petromyzon marinus unicolor (lake lamprey)	Definitive germ cells derive from: a) early segregated cells, primordial germ cells, and b) later from coelomic epithelium. Suggests that primordial germ cells may induce germ-cell formation in peritoneal epithelium	Butcher. **1929.** Biol. Bull. **56**
Squalus acanthias	Germ cells segregate from primitive entoderm; migrate via the mesoderm into site of the developing gonad	Woods. **1902.** Am. J. Anat. **1**
Amia and *Lepidosteus*	Germ cells segregate early from entoderm; continue distinct and migrate into the developing gonad via the mesoderm (see fig. 60)	Allen. **1911.** J. Morphol. **22**

Species	Place of Origin, etc.	Author
Lophius piscatorius	Germ cells segregate from primitive entoderm; migrate through mesoderm to site of gonad; migration part passive and part active	Dodds. 1910. J. Morphol. 21
Fundulus heteroclitus	Germ cells segregate from peripheral entoderm lateral to posterior half of body; migrate through entoderm and mesoderm to the site of the developing gonad	Richards and Thompson. 1921. Biol. Bull. 40
Cottus bairdii	Primordial germ cells derive from giant cells in the primitive entoderm; migrate through the lateral mesoderm into the site of the developing gonad	Hann. 1927. J. Morphol. 43
Lebistes reticulatus (guppy)	Germ cells segregate early in development; first seen in the entoderm-mesoderm area; migrate into the sites of the developing ovary and testis, giving origin to the definitive germ cells	Goodrich, Dee, Flynn, and Mercer. 1939. Biol. Bull. 67
Rana temporaria	Germ cells segregate from primitive entoderm; migrate into developing genital glands	Witschi. 1914. Arch. f. mikr. Anat. 85
Rana temporaria	Primordial germ cells from entoderm discharged at first spawning. Later, the definitive germs cells of adults originate from peritoneal cells	Gatenby. 1916. Quart. J. Micr. Sc. 61
Rana catesbiana	Primordial germ cells segregate from primitive entoderm; definitive germ cell derives from primordial cells according to author's view but admits possibility of germinal epithelium origin	Swingle. 1921. J. Exper. Zool. 32
Rana temporaria, Triton alpestris, Bufo vulgaris	Primordial germ cells segregate from entoderm	Bounoure. 1924. Compt. rend. Acad. d. Sc. 178, 179
Rana sylvatica	Primordial germ cells originate from entoderm and migrate into the developing gonads. They give origin to the definitive sex cells	Witschi. 1929. J. Exper. Zool. 52
Hemidactylium scutatum	Primordial germ cells arise in mesoderm between somite and lateral plate; move to site of gonad by shifting of tissues	Humphrey. 1925. J. Morphol. 41

Species	Place of Origin, etc.	Author
Ambystoma maculatum	Most germ cells somatic in origin from germinal epithelium, although a few may come from primordial germ cells of entodermal origin	McCosh. 1930. J. Morphol. 50
Triton, and *Ambystoma mexicanum*	Germ cells differentiate from lateral plate mesoderm	Nieuwkoop. 1946. Arch. Néerl. de zool. 7
Chrysemys marginata (turtle)	Primordial germ cells from entoderm; most of definitive germ cells arise from peritoneal cells	Dustin. 1910. Arch. biol., Paris. 25
Sternotherus odoratus (turtle)	Primordial cells segregate early from entoderm; later definitive cells derive from these and from peritoneal epithelium	Risley. 1934. J. Morphol. 56
Gallus (domesticus) gallus (chick)	Germ cells arise from primitive cells in entoderm of proamnion area and migrate by means of the blood vessels to the site of the developing gonad. Definitive germ cells of sex cords and later seminiferous tubules derive from primordial germ cells	Swift. 1914, 1916. Am. J. Anat. 15, 20
Gallus (domesticus) gallus (chick)	Primordial germ cells arise from entodermal cells	Dantschakoff. 1931. Zeit. f. Zellforsch., mikr. Anat. 15
Chick and albino rat	Early primordial cells degenerate; definitive cells from peritoneal epithelium	Firket. 1920. Anat. Rec. 18
Didelphys virginiana (opossum)	Germ cells arise from germinal epithelium	Nelsen and Swain. 1942. J. Morphol. 71
Mus musculus (mouse)	Oogonia derived from primordial germ cells; spermatogonia from epithelial cells of testis cords	Kirkham. 1916. Anat. Rec. 10
Mus musculus (mouse)	Primordial germ cells of ovary arise from germinal epithelium during development of the gonads. These presumably give origin to the definitive sex cells	Brambell. 1927. Proc. Roy. Soc. London, s.B. 101
Felis domestica (cat)	Primordial cells segregate early but do not give origin to definitive germ cells which derive from germinal epithelium	de Winiwarter and Sainmont. 1909. Arch. biol., Paris. 24

Species	Place of Origin, etc.	Author
Felis domestica (cat)	Definitive ova derived from germinal epithelium of the ovary at an early stage of gonad development	Kingsbury. **1938.** Am. J. Anat. **15**
Cavia porcellus (guinea pig)	Primordial germ cells from entodermal origin degenerate; the primordial germ cells derived from the germinal epithelium give rise to the definitive germ cells in the testis	Bookkout. **1937.** Zeit. f. Zellforsch, mikr. Anat. **25**
Homo sapiens (man)	Primordial germ cells found in entoderm of yolk sac; migrate by ameboid movement into developing gonad	Witschi. **1948.** Carnegie Inst., Washington Publ. 575. Contrib. to Embryol. **32**

C. Maturation (Differentiation) of the Gametes

1. GENERAL CONSIDERATIONS

Regardless of their exact origin definitive germ cells as primitive oogonia or very young oocytes are to be found in or near the germinal epithelium in the ovaries of all vertebrates in the functional condition (figs. 39B, 64). In the testis, the primitive spermatogonia are located within the seminiferous tubules as the germinal epithelium, in intimate association with the basement membrane of the tubule (figs. 65, 66).

The period of coming into maturity (maturation) of the gametes is a complicated affair. It involves profound transformations of the cytoplasm, as well as the nucleus. Moreover, a process of ripening or physiological maturing is necessary, as well as a morphological transformation. The phrase "maturation of the germ cells" has been used extensively to denote nuclear changes. However, as the entire gamete undergoes morphological and physiological change, the terms **nuclear maturation, cytosomal maturation,** and **physiological maturation** are used in the following pages to designate the various aspects of gametic development.

One of the most characteristic changes which the germ cell experiences during its maturation into a mature gamete is a reduction of chromatin material. Because of this, the germ cell which begins the maturing process is called a **meiocyte.** This word literally means a cell undergoing diminution and it is applied to the germ cell during **meiosis** or the period in which a reduction in the number of chromosomes occurs. The word **haplosis** is a technical name designating this reduction process.

The word meiocyte thus is a general term applicable to both the developing

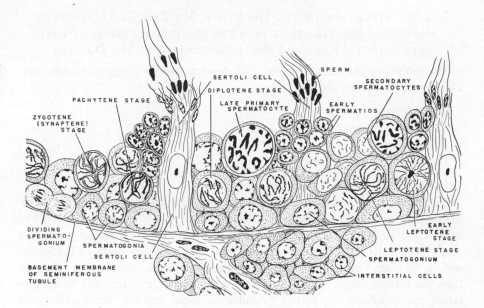

FIG. 65. Semidiagrammatic representation of a part of the seminiferous tubule of the cat testis.

male and female germ cells. On the other hand, the word **spermatocyte** is given to the developing male gamete during the period of chromosome diminution, whereas the word **oocyte** is applied to the female gamete in the same period. When, however, the period of chromosome diminution is completed and the chromosome number is reduced to the haploid condition, the developing male gamete is called a **spermatid** while the female gamete is referred to as an ootid or an **egg.** (*Note:* the word egg is applied often to the female gamete during the various stages of the oocyte condition as well as after the maturation divisions have been accomplished.)

The reduction of chromatin material is not the only effect which the meiotic process has upon the chromatin material, or possibly upon the developing cytosomal structures as well. This fact will become evident during the descriptions below concerning the meiotic procedures.

Another prominent feature of the gametes during the meiocyte period is their *growth* or *increase in size*. This growth occurs during the first part of the meiotic process when the nucleus is in the *prophase condition* and it involves both nucleus and cytoplasm. The growth phenomena are much more pronounced in the oocyte than in the spermatocyte. Due to this feature of growth, the oocyte and spermatocyte also are regarded as **auxocytes,** that is **growing cells,** a name introduced by Lee, 1897. The words **meiocyte** and **auxocyte** thus refer to two different aspects of the development of the oocyte and the spermatocyte.

2. BASIC STRUCTURE OF THE DEFINITIVE SEX CELL AS IT STARTS TO
MATURE OR DIFFERENTIATE INTO THE MALE MEIOCYTE (I.E., THE
SPERMATOCYTE) OR THE FEMALE MEIOCYTE (I.E., THE OOCYTE)

The definitive sex cells of both sexes have a similar cytological structure.
The component parts are (fig. 68):

(1) nucleus,
(2) investing cytoplasm,
(3) idiosome,
(4) Golgi substance, and
(5) chondriosomes.

The nucleus is vesicular and enlarged, and the nuclear network of chromatin may appear reticulated. A large nucleolus also may be visible. The
investing cytoplasm is clearer and less condensed in appearance than that
of ordinary cells. The **idiosome** (idiozome) is a rounded body of cytoplasm
which, in many animal species, takes the cytoplasmic stain more intensely
than the surrounding cytoplasm. Within the idiosome it is possible to demonstrate the centrioles as paired granules in some species. Surrounding the
idiosome are various elements of the Golgi substance, and near both the
idiosome and Golgi elements, is a mass of chondriosomes (mitochondria) of
various sizes and shapes. The idiosome and its relationship with the Golgi
material, the mitochondria, and the centrioles varies considerably in different
species of animals.

Much discussion has occurred concerning the exact nature of the idiosome.
Some investigators have been inclined to regard the surrounding Golgi substance as a part of the idiosome, although the central mass of cytoplasm containing the centrioles is the "idiosome proper" of many authors (Bowen, '22).
Again, when the maturation divisions of the spermatocyte occur, the idiosome
and surrounding Golgi elements are broken up into small fragments. However, in the spermatids the Golgi pieces (dictyosomes) are brought together
once more to form a new idiosome-like structure, with the difference that the
latter "seems never to contain the centrioles" (Bowen, '22). It is, therefore,
advisable to regard the idiosome as being separated into its various components during the maturation divisions of the spermatocyte and to view the
reassemblage of Golgi (dictyosomal) material in the spermatid as a different
structure entirely. This new structure of the spermatid is called the **acroblast**
(Bowen, '22; Leuchtenberger and Schrader, '50). (See fig. 68B.) A similar
breaking up of the idiosome occurs in oogenesis (fig. 68F, G). However, all
meiocytes do not possess a typical idiosome. This fact is demonstrated in
insect spermatocytes, where the idiosomal material is present as scattered
masses to each of which some Golgi substance is attached.

The various features which enter into the structure of the definitive germ cell do not behave in the same way in each sex during gametic differentiation. While the behaviors of the chromatin material in the male and female germ cells closely parallel each other (fig. 67), the other cytosomal features follow widely divergent pathways, resulting in two enormously different gametic entities (fig. 68A–H).

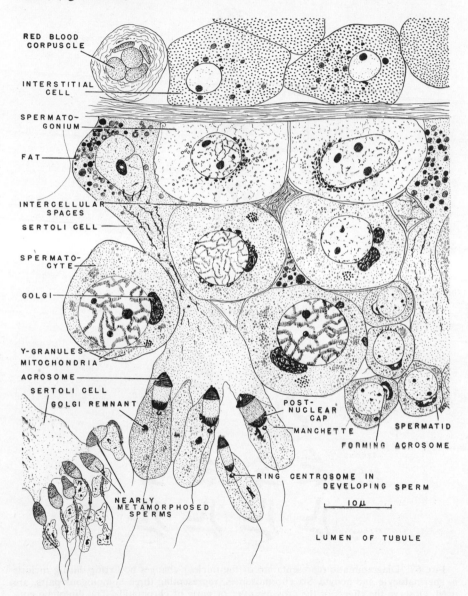

RED BLOOD CORPUSCLE

INTERSTITIAL CELL

SPERMATO-GONIUM

FAT

INTERCELLULAR SPACES

SERTOLI CELL

SPERMATO-CYTE

GOLGI

Y-GRANULES
MITOCHONDRIA
ACROSOME
SERTOLI CELL
GOLGI REMNANT

POST-NUCLEAR CAP
MANCHETTE
SPERMATID
FORMING ACROSOME

RING CENTROSOME IN DEVELOPING SPERM

10 μ

NEARLY METAMORPHOSED SPERMS

LUMEN OF TUBULE

FIG. 66. Section of part of a seminiferous tubule of human testis. (Redrawn from Gatenby and Beams, '35.)

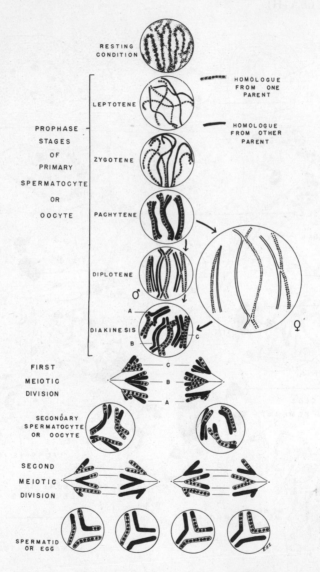

FIG. 67. Diagrammatic representation of the nuclear changes occurring during meiosis in spermatocyte and oocyte. Six chromosomes, representing three homologous pairs, are used. Observe the effects of the crossing over of parts of chromatids. The diplotene condition of oocyte depicted by arrows and the enlarged nucleus. The haploid condition is shown in each of the spermatids or in the egg and its three polocytes.

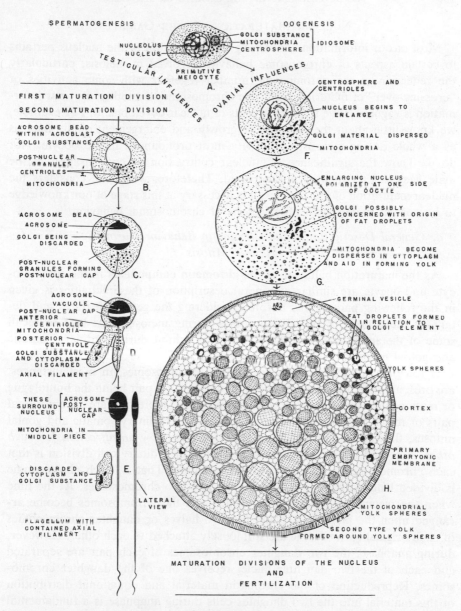

SPERMATOGENESIS   OOGENESIS

GOLGI SUBSTANCE
MITOCHONDRIA ⎤ IDIOSOME
CENTROSPHERE ⎦

NUCLEOLUS
NUCLEUS

TESTICULAR INFLUENCES

PRIMITIVE MEIOCYTE   A.

OVARIAN INFLUENCES

FIRST MATURATION DIVISION
SECOND MATURATION DIVISION

ACROSOME BEAD
WITHIN ACROBLAST
GOLGI SUBSTANCE

POST-NUCLEAR
GRANULES
CENTRIOLES
MITOCHONDRIA

B.

ACROSOME BEAD
ACROSOME

GOLGI BEING
DISCARDED

POST-NUCLEAR
GRANULES FORMING
POST-NUCLEAR CAP

C.

ACROSOME
VACUOLE
POST-NUCLEAR CAP
ANTERIOR
CENTRIOLES
MITOCHONDRIA
POSTERIOR
CENTRIOLE
GOLGI SUBSTANCE
AND CYTOPLASM
DISCARDED
AXIAL FILAMENT

D.

THESE
SURROUND
NUCLEUS ⎱ ACROSOME
POST-
NUCLEAR CAP

MITOCHONDRIA IN
MIDDLE PIECE

DISCARDED
CYTOPLASM AND
GOLGI SUBSTANCE

E.

LATERAL
VIEW

FLAGELLUM WITH
CONTAINED AXIAL
FILAMENT

CENTROSPHERE AND
CENTRIOLES

NUCLEUS BEGINS TO
ENLARGE

GOLGI MATERIAL DISPERSED

MITOCHONDRIA

F.

ENLARGING NUCLEUS
POLARIZED AT ONE SIDE
OF OOCYTE

GOLGI POSSIBLY
CONCERNED WITH ORIGIN
OF FAT DROPLETS

MITOCHONDRIA BECOME
DISPERSED IN CYTOPLASM
AND AID IN FORMING YOLK

G.

GERMINAL VESICLE

FAT DROPLETS FORMED
IN RELATION TO
GOLGI ELEMENT

YOLK SPHERES

CORTEX

PRIMARY
EMBRYONIC
MEMBRANE

H.

MITOCHONDRIAL
YOLK SPHERES

SECOND TYPE YOLK
FORMED AROUND YOLK SPHERES

MATURATION DIVISIONS OF THE NUCLEUS
AND
FERTILIZATION

FIG. 68. Possible fate of the primitive meiocyte and its cytoplasmic inclusions when exposed to testicular or ovarian influences. Particular attention is given to the idiosome. Under male-forming influences the idiosome components are dispersed during the maturation divisions and are reassembled into three separate component structures, namely, (1) Acroblast of Golgi substance, (2) centriolar bodies, and (3) mitochondrial bodies (see B). Each of these structures, together with the post-nuclear granules of uncertain origin, play roles in spermatogenesis as shown. Under ovarian influences the idiosome is dispersed before the maturation divisions. The Golgi substance and mitochondria play (according to theory, see text) their roles in the formation of the deutoplasm.

3. NUCLEAR MATURATION OF THE GAMETES

Most of our information concerning the maturation of the nucleus pertains to certain aspects of chromosome behavior involved in meiosis, particularly the reduction of the chromosome number together with some activities of "crossing over" of materials from one chromosome to another. But our information is vague relative to other aspects of nuclear development. For example, we know little about the meaning of growth and enlargement of the nucleus as a whole during meiosis, an activity most pronounced in the oocyte. Nor do we know the significance of nuclear contraction or condensation in the male gamete after meiosis is completed. Therefore, when one considers the nuclear maturation of the gametes, it is necessary at this stage of our knowledge to be content mainly with observations of chromosomal behavior.

a. General Description of the Chromatin Behavior During Somatic and Meiotic Mitosis

As the maturation behavior of the **chromatin components** in the spermatocyte and oocyte are similar, a general description of these activities is given in the following paragraphs. Before considering the general features and details of the actions of the chromosomes during meiosis, it is best to recall some of the activities which these structures exhibit during ordinary somatic and gonial mitoses.

Cytological studies have shown that the chromosomes, in most instances, are present in the nucleus in pairs, each member of a pair being the **homologue** or **mate** of the other. Homologous chromosomes, therefore, are chromosomal pairs or mates. During the prophase condition in ordinary somatic and gonial mitoses, the various chromosomal mates *do not show an attraction for each other*. A second feature of the prophase stage of ordinary cell division is that each chromosome appears as two chromosomes. That is, each chromosome is divided longitudinally and equationally into two chromosomes. At the time when the metaphase condition is reached and the chromosomes become arranged upon the metaphase plate, the two halves or daughter chromosomes of each original chromosome are still loosely attached to each other. However, during anaphase, the two daughter chromosomes of each pair are separated and each of the two daughter nuclei receives one of the daughter chromosomes. Reproduction of the chromatin material and equational distribution of this material into the two daughter cells during anaphase is a fundamental feature of the ordinary type of somatic and gonial mitoses. The two daughter nuclei are thus equivalent to each other and to the parent nucleus. In this way, chromosomal equivalence is passed on ad infinitum through successive cell generations.

On the other hand, a different kind of chromosomal behavior is found during meiosis, which essentially is a specialized type of mitosis, known as a **meiotic mitosis.** In one sense it is *two mitoses or mitotic divisions with only*

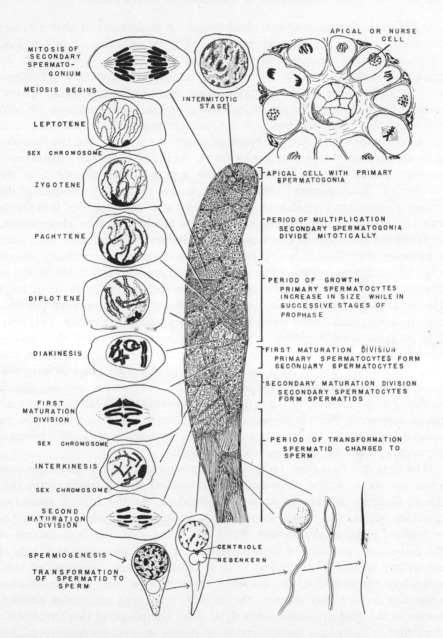

FIG. 69. Steps in spermatogenesis in the grasshopper. In the center of the chart is represented a longitudinal section of one of the follicles of a grasshoper testis with its various regions of spermatogenic activity. In the upper right of the chart the apical-cell complex is depicted with its central apical cell, spermatogonia, and surrounding epithelial cells. The primary spermatogonia lie enmeshed between the extensions of the apical cell and the associations of these extensions with the surrounding epithelial elements of the complex. (Also see Wenrich, 1916, Bull. Mus. Comp. Zool. Harvard College, 60.)

one prophase; that is, two metaphase–anaphase separations of chromosomes preceded by a single, peculiar prophase. The peculiarities of this meiotic prophase may be described as follows: As the prophase condition of the nucleus is initiated, an odd type of behavior of the chromosomes becomes evident—a behavior which is entirely absent from ordinary somatic mitosis: namely, *the homologous pairs or mates begin to show an attraction for each other* and they approach and form an intimate association. This association is called **synapsis** (figs. 67, 69, zygotene stage). As a result, the two homologous chromosomes appear as one structure. As the homologous chromosomes are now paired together and superficially appear as one chromosome, the number of "chromosomes" visible at this time is reduced to one-half of the ordinary somatic or diploid number. However, each "chromosome" is in reality two chromosomes and, therefore, is called a **bivalent or twin chromosome.**

While the homologous chromosomes are intimately associated, each mate reproduces itself longitudinally just as it would during an ordinary mitosis (fig. 67, pachytene stage). (The possibility remains that this reproduction of chromatin material may have occurred even before the synaptic union.) Hence, each bivalent chromosome becomes transformed into four potential chromosomes, each one of which is called a **chromatid.** This group of chromatids is, collectively speaking, a **tetrad chromosome.** (As described below, interchange of material or crossing over from one chromatid to another may take place at this time.) As a result of these changes, *the nucleus now contains the haploid number of chromosomes, (i.e., half of the normal, diploid number) in the form of tetrads* (fig. 67, pachytene stage). However, as each tetrad represents four chromosomes, actually there is at this time twice the normal number of chromosomes present in the nucleus (fig. 67; compare leptotene, pachytene, diplotene and diakinesis).

The next step in meiosis brings about *the separation of the tetrad chromosome into its respective chromatids* and it involves two divisions of the cell. These divisions are known as **meiotic divisions.** As the first of these two divisions begins, the tetrad chromosomes become arranged in the mid- or metaphase plane of the spindle. After this initial step, the first division of the cell occurs, and half of each tetrad (i.e., a dyad) passes to each pole of the mitotic spindle (fig. 67, first meiotic division). Each daughter cell (i.e., secondary spermatocyte or oocyte) resulting from the first maturation (meiotic) division thus contains the haploid or reduced number of chromosomes in the **dyad** condition, each dyad being composed of two chromatids. A resting or interphase nuclear condition occurs in most spermatocytes, following the first maturation division, but in the oocyte it usually does not occur (fig. 69, interkinesis).

As the second maturation division is initiated, the dyads become arranged on the metaphase plate of the mitotic spindle. As division of the cell proceeds, half of each dyad (i.e., a monad) passes to the respective poles of the spindle (fig. 67, second meiotic division; fig. 69). As a result of these two divisions, each daughter cell thus contains the haploid or reduced number of chromosomes in the **monad** (monoploid) condition (fig. 67, spermatid or egg). Meiosis or chromatin diminution is now an accomplished fact.

It is to be observed, therefore, that the meiotic phenomena differ from those of ordinary mitosis by two fundamental features:

(1) In meiosis there is a conjugation (synapsis) of homologous chromosomes during the prophase stage, and while synapsed together each of the homologues divides equationally; and

(2) following this single prophase of peculiar character, two divisions follow each other, separating the associated chromatin threads.

While the meiotic prophase is described above as a single prophase preceding two metaphase-anaphase chromosome separations, it is essentially a double prophase in which the process of synapsis acts to suppress one of the equational divisions normally present in a mitotic division; *a synapsed or double chromosome, therefore, is substituted for one of the longitudinal, equational divisions which normally appears during a somatic prophase.* It is this substitution which forms the basis for the reduction process, for two mitotic divisions follow one after the other, *preceded by but one equational splitting,* whereas in ordinary mitosis, *one equational splitting of the chromosomes always precedes each mitotic division.*

b. Reductional and Equational Meiotic Divisions and the Phenomenon of Crossing Over

In the first meiotic division (i.e., the first maturation division), if the two chromatids which are derived from one **homologous mate** of the tetrad are separated from the two chromatids derived from the other homologous mate the division is spoken of as **reductional** or **disjunctional.** In this case the two associated chromatids of each dyad represent the original chromosome which synapsed at the beginning of meiotic prophase (fig. 67, tetrads B and C, first meiotic division). If, however, the separation occurs not in the synaptic plane but in the equational plane, then the two associated chromatids of each dyad come, one from one synaptic mate and one from the other; such a division is spoken of as an **equational division** (fig. 67, tetrad A, first meiotic division). There appears to be no fixity of procedure relative to the separation of the tetrads, and great variability occurs. However this may be, one of the two meiotic divisions as far as any particular tetrad is concerned is disjunctional (reductional) and the other is equational, at least in the region of the kinetochore (see p. 135 and fig. 70). If the first division is reductional, the second is equational and vice versa. Disjunction in the first maturation division is often referred to as **pre-reduction,** while that in the second maturation division is called **post-reduction.**

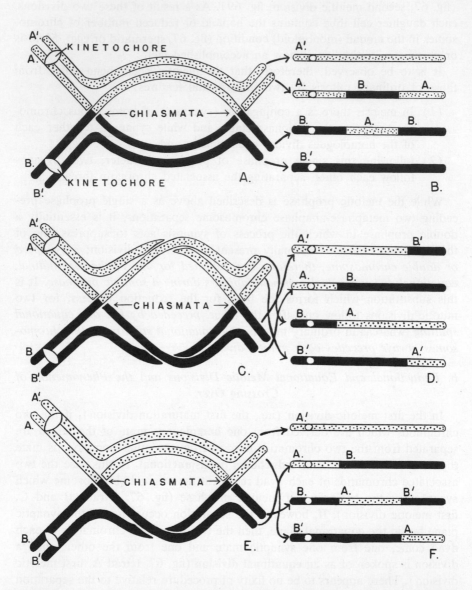

Fig. 70. **Some of the various possibilities which may occur as a result of the exchanges of parts of chromatids during the crossing-over phenomena associated with meiosis.** Two chiasmata (singular, chiasma) are shown in (A), (C), (E). Observe that homologous chromosome A has split equationally into chromatids A and A', while homologous chromosome B has divided equationally into B and B'. The resulting interchanges between respective chromatids of the original homologous chromosomes are shown in (B), (D), (F). The kinetochore (place of spindle-fiber attachment) is indicated by the oval or circular area to the left of the chromatids. (Modified from White: *Animal Cytology and Evolution,* London, Cambridge University Press, 1943.)

The foregoing statement regarding **disjunctional** and **equational** divisions should be considered in the light of the phenomenon of crossing over. In the latter process, a gene or groups of genes may pass from one chromatid to the other and vice versa during their association at the four strand stage (fig. 70). In the region of the **centromere** or **kinetochore** (i.e., the point) of the achromatic, spindle-fiber attachment) and nearby regions, cross overs are thought not to occur (fig. 70, kinetochore). Consequently, in the regions of the kinetochore, the statements above regarding **disjunctional** and **equational** divisions of the chromosomes appear to be correct. However, the terms disjunctional and equational may mean little in other regions of the chromosomes of a tetrad during the meiotic divisions. For example, let us assume as in fig. 70 (see also fig. 67), that we have chromatids A and A', B and B', A and B representing the original homologues or synaptic chromosomes which have divided into these chromatids respectively. Then during the tetrad stage of association or slightly before, let us assume that there has been a crossing over of genes from chromatid A to chromatid B and from chromatid B to chromatid A in a particular area (fig. 70A). (It is to be observed that chromatids A' and B' are not involved in this particular instance.) Further, let us assume that AA' and BB' as a whole are separated at the first maturation division, the kinetochore and immediate regions would represent a disjunctional division, but for the particular area where crossing over is accomplished, the division would be equational (fig. 70A, B; central portions of chromatids A and B in fig. 70B). Thus, it would be for other regions where cross overs may have occurred. Other cross-over possibilities are shown in fig. 70C–F.

c. Stages of Chromatin Behavior During the Meiotic Prophase in Greater Detail

The following five stages of chromatin behavior within the prophase nucleus during meiosis are now in common usage. They are based on the stages originally described by H. von Winiwarter, '00. The substantive form is presented in parentheses.

1) Leptotene (Leptonema) Stage. The leptotene stage (figs. 69, 71) represents the initial stage of the meiotic process and is seen especially well in the spermatocyte. At this time the nucleus of the differentiating germ cell begins to enlarge, and the diploid number of very long, slender chromatin threads make their appearance. (Compare "resting" and leptotene nuclei in figs. 69, 71.) The chromatin threads may lie at random in the nucleus or they may be directed toward one side, forming the so-called "bouquet" condition (fig. 69, leptotene stage). The nucleolus is evident at this time (fig. 71B).

2) Zygotene or Synaptene (Zygonema) Stage. The zygotene stage (figs. 69, 71, 85) is characterized by a synapsis of the chromatin threads. This synapsis or conjugation occurs between the homologous chromosomes, that is, the chromosomes which have a similar genic constitution. Synapsis appears to

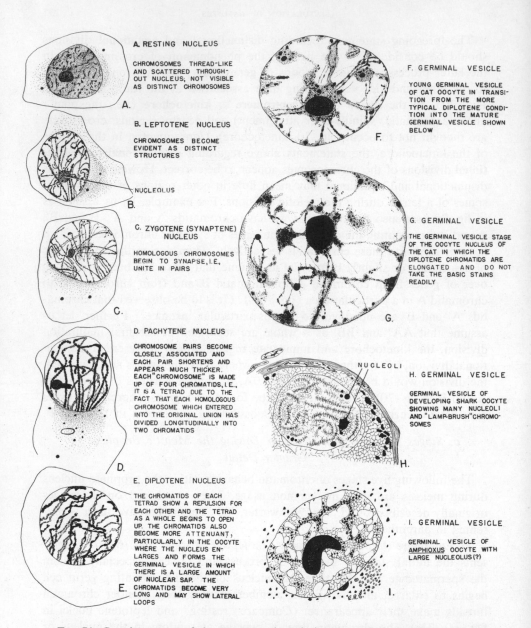

A. RESTING NUCLEUS

CHROMOSOMES THREAD-LIKE AND SCATTERED THROUGH-OUT NUCLEUS; NOT VISIBLE AS DISTINCT CHROMOSOMES

B. LEPTOTENE NUCLEUS

CHROMOSOMES BECOME EVIDENT AS DISTINCT STRUCTURES

NUCLEOLUS

C. ZYGOTENE (SYNAPTENE) NUCLEUS

HOMOLOGOUS CHROMOSOMES BEGIN TO SYNAPSE, I.E., UNITE IN PAIRS

D. PACHYTENE NUCLEUS

CHROMOSOME PAIRS BECOME CLOSELY ASSOCIATED AND EACH PAIR SHORTENS AND APPEARS MUCH THICKER. EACH "CHROMOSOME" IS MADE UP OF FOUR CHROMATIDS, I.E., IT IS A TETRAD DUE TO THE FACT THAT EACH HOMOLOGOUS CHROMOSOME WHICH ENTERED INTO THE ORIGINAL UNION HAS DIVIDED LONGITUDINALLY INTO TWO CHROMATIDS

E. DIPLOTENE NUCLEUS

THE CHROMATIDS OF EACH TETRAD SHOW A REPULSION FOR EACH OTHER AND THE TETRAD AS A WHOLE BEGINS TO OPEN UP. THE CHROMATIDS ALSO BECOME MORE ATTENUANT, PARTICULARLY IN THE OOCYTE WHERE THE NUCLEUS EN-LARGES AND FORMS THE GERMINAL VESICLE IN WHICH THERE IS A LARGE AMOUNT OF NUCLEAR SAP. THE CHROMATIDS BECOME VERY LONG AND MAY SHOW LATERAL LOOPS

F. GERMINAL VESICLE

YOUNG GERMINAL VESICLE OF CAT OOCYTE IN TRANSI-TION FROM THE MORE TYPICAL DIPLOTENE CONDI-TION INTO THE MATURE GERMINAL VESICLE SHOWN BELOW

G. GERMINAL VESICLE

THE GERMINAL VESICLE STAGE OF THE OOCYTE NUCLEUS OF THE CAT IN WHICH THE DIPLOTENE CHROMATIDS ARE ELONGATED AND DO NOT TAKE THE BASIC STAINS READILY

NUCLEOLI

H. GERMINAL VESICLE

GERMINAL VESICLE OF DEVELOPING SHARK OOCYTE SHOWING MANY NUCLEOLI AND "LAMP-BRUSH" CHROMO-SOMES

I. GERMINAL VESICLE

GERMINAL VESICLE OF AMPHIOXUS OOCYTE WITH LARGE NUCLEOLUS (?)

E.R.G.

FIG. 71. Certain aspects of the oocyte nucleus during the meiotic prophase. (A–G) Chromatin and nuclear changes in the oocyte of the cat up to the diplotene condition when the germinal vesicle is fully developed. (After de Winiwarter and Sainmont, Arch. biol., Paris, 24.) (H, I) Germinal vesicle in the dogfish, *Scyllium canicula,* and in *Amphioxus.* (After Marechal, La Cellule, 24.) Observe the typical "lamp-brush" chromosome conditions in the germinal vesicle of the shark oocyte. These lamp-brush chromosomes are developed during the diplotene stage of meiosis by great attenuation of the chromosomes and the formation of lateral extensions or loops from the sides of the chromosomes.

136

begin most often at the ends of the threads and progresses toward the middle (fig. 67, zygotene). At this stage the chromatin threads may show a strong tendency to collapse and shrink into a mass toward one end of the nucleus (fig. 85C, D). This collapsed condition, when present, is called **synizesis.** The zygotene stage gradually passes into the pachytene condition.

3) **Pachytene (Pachynema) Stage.** Gradually, the synapsis of the homologous chromosomes becomes more complete, and the threads appear shorter and thicker. The contracted threads in this condition are referred to as **pachynema** (figs. 69, 71, 85E). The nucleus in this manner comes to contain a number of bivalent chromosomes, each of which is made up of two homologous mates arranged side by side in synaptic union, known technically as **parasynapsis. (Telosynapsis** probably is not a normal condition.) Consequently, the number of chromosomes now appears to be haploid. Each pachytene chromosome (i.e., each of the pair of homologous chromosomes) gradually divides equationally into two daughter thread-like structures, generally referred to as chromatids. The exact time at which division occurs during meiosis is questionable. The entire group of four chromatids which arise from the splitting of the synapsed homologues is called a **tetrad.**

4) **Diplotene (Diplonema) Stage.** In the diplotene stage (figs. 67, 69, 71, 85F, G), two of the chromatids tend to separate from the other two. (See fig. 70A, C, E.) The four chromatids in each tetrad may now be observed more readily, at least in some species, because the various chromatids of each tetrad show a repulsion for one another, and the chromatids move apart in certain areas along their length. This condition is shown in both the male and female meiocyte, but in the latter, the repulsion or moving apart is carried to a considerable degree and is associated with a great lengthening and attenuation of the chromatids. (See fig. 67.) In the female meiocyte at this stage, the chromosomes become very diffuse and are scattered throughout the nucleus, somewhat resembling the non-mitotic condition (figs. 71F–I; 72B–E). The peculiar behavior of the chromosomes and nucleus of the oocyte in the diplotene stage of meiosis is described more in detail on p. 141.

Although there is a tendency for the chromatids to widen out or separate from each other at this time, they do remain associated in one or more regions. In these regions of contact, the paired chromatids appear to exchange partners. This point of contact is called a **chiasma** (plural, chiasmata). Hence, a **chiasma** is the general region where the chromatids appear to have exchanged partners when the tetrad threads move apart in the diplotene state. (See fig. 70, chiasmata.)

5) **Diakinesis.** The diplotene stage gradually transforms into the diakinesis state (figs. 67, 69, 72F, 85H) by a process of marked chromosomal contraction. There also may be an opening up of the tetrads due to a separation of the homologous mates in the more central portions of the tetrad, with the result that only the terminal parts of the chromatids remain in contact. This

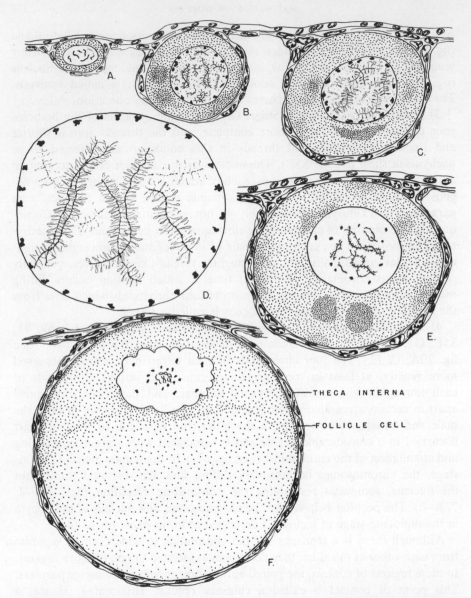

THECA INTERNA

FOLLICLE CELL

FIG. 72. Growth of the nucleus during meiosis in the amphibian egg, showing the enlarged germinal vesicle and diplotene lamp-brush chromosomes with lateral loops. (A) Early diplotene nucleus of the frog. (B, C, E) Different phases of the diplotene nucleus in this form. These figures are based upon data provided by Duryee ('50) and sections of the frog ovary. (D) Drawing of the unfixed germinal vesicle of *Triturus*. Some aspects of the attenuate chromatin threads with lateral loops are shown. The nucleoli are numerous and occupy the peripheral region of the germinal vesicle. (F) Semidiagrammatic drawing of the later phases of the developing frog egg. It shows the germinal vesicle assuming a polar condition, with the initial appearance of germinal vesicle shrinkage before the final dissolution of the nuclear membrane. Observe that the chromosomes are contracting and now occupy the center of the germinal vesicle.

latter process is called "terminalization." Coincident with this partial separation, a further contraction of the tetrads may occur. As a result, at the end of diakinesis the tetrads may assume such curious shapes as loops, crosses, rings, etc., scattered within the nucleus of the female and male meiocyte (fig. 69, diakinesis). The nuclear membrane eventually undergoes dissolution, and

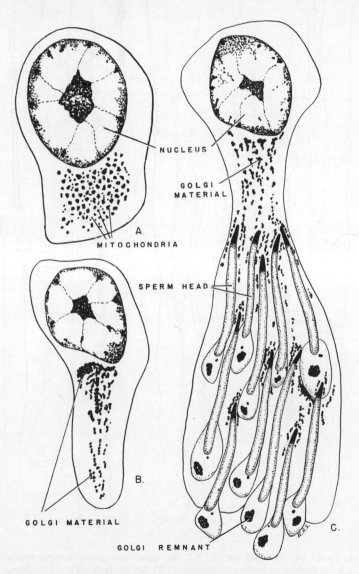

Fig. 73. Various aspects of Sertoli-cell conditions in the fowl. (Redrawn from Zlotnick, Quart. J. Micr. Sc., 88.) (A) Resting Sertoli cell, showing mitochondria. (B) Sertoli element at the beginning of cytoplasmic elongation. (C) Sertoli cell with associated late spermatids.

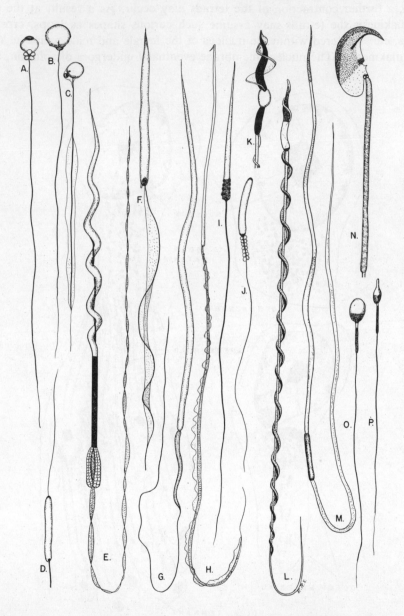

Fig. 74. Types of chordate sperm. All the chordate sperm belong to the flagellate variety. (A) *Amphioxus* (protochordate). (B) *Salmo* (teleost). (C) *Perca* (teleost). (D) *Petromyzon* (cyclostome). (E) *Raja* (elasmobranch). (F) *Bufo* (anuran). (G) *Rana* (anuran). (H) *Salamandra* (urodele). (I) *Anguis* (lizard). (J) *Crex* (bird). (K) *Fringilla* (bird). (L) *Turdus* (bird). (M) *Echidna* (monotrematous mammal). (N) *Mus* (eutherian mammal). (O, P) Man (full view and side view, respectively).

the tetrads become arranged on the metaphase plate of the first maturation division. (See figs. 69, first maturation division; 72F, 119A, B.) This division is described on pp. 132 and 133.

d. Peculiarities of Nuclear Behavior in the Oocyte During Meiosis; the Germinal Vesicle

Although the movements of the chromosomes during meiosis in the developing male and female gamete appear to follow the same general behavior

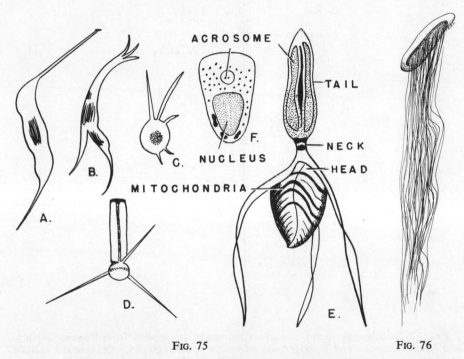

FIG. 75

FIG. 76

FIG. 75. Non-flagellate sperm. (A–C) Ameboid sperm of *Polyphemus*. (After Zacharias.) (D) Lobster, *Homarus* (After Herrick.) (E) Decapod crustacea, *Galathea* (Anomura). (After Koltzoff.) (F) Nematode worm, *Ascaris*.

FIG. 76. Conjugate sperm of grasshopper associated temporarily to form the "sperm boat."

pattern (fig. 67), some differences do occur. For example, in the female when the diplotene stage is reached, the repulsion of the tetrad threads is greater (figs. 67, ♂ and ♀; 72). Furthermore, the chromatids elongate and become very attenuate although they appear to retain their contacts or chiasmata (fig. 72). Side loops and extensions from the chromatids also may occur, especially in those vertebrates with large-yolked eggs (e.g., amphibia, fishes, etc.). (See figs. 71H, 72B–D.) When these lateral extensions are present, the chromosomes appear diffuse and fuzzy, taking on the characteristics which

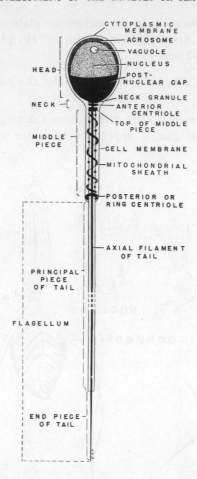

FIG. 77. Spatula-type sperm of various mammals. (Compiled from Bowen; Gatenby and Beams; Gatenby and Woodger; see references in bibliography.) Observe the vacuole inside the head of the sperm. Gatenby and Beams found that this vacuole, in some instances, stains similar to a nucleolus, but suggest it may be a hydrostatic organ, or respiratory structure. (P. 20, Quart. J. Micr. Sc., 78.)

suggest their description as "lamp-brush" chromosomes. Another difference of chromatic behavior is manifested by the fact that the chromosomes in the developing female gamete during the diplotene stage are not easily stained by the ordinary nuclear stains, whereas the chromosomes in the spermatocyte stain readily.

Aside from the differences in chromosomal behavior, great discrepancies in the amount of growth of the nucleus occur in the two gametes during meiosis. The nucleus of the oocyte greatly increases in size and a large quantity of nuclear fluid or sap comes to surround the chromosomes (figs. 71F, G; 72C, F, E). Correlated with this increase in nuclear size, the egg grows rapidly, and deutoplasmic substance is deposited in the cytoplasm (fig. 68F–H). As differentiation of the oocyte advances, the enlarged nucleus or **germinal vesicle** assumes a polar position in the egg (figs. 68H, 70F). When the oocyte has finished its growth and approaches the end of its differentiation, the

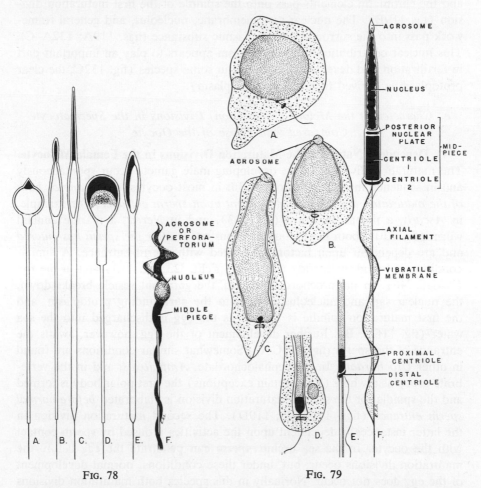

FIG. 78   FIG. 79

FIG. 78. Different shapes and positions of the acrosome. (A) Type of acrosome found in *Mollusca, Echinodermata,* and *Annelida.* (B) *Reptilia, Aves,* and *Amphibia.* (C) *Lepidoptera.* (D) *Mammalia.* (E) Many *Hemiptera* and *Coleoptera.* (After Bowen, Anat. Rec., 28.) (F) Sperm of certain birds, i.e., finches. (After Retzius, Biol. Untersuchungen, New Series 17, Stockholm, Jena.) Observe the well-developed acrosome in the form of a perforatorium. The spiral twist of the acrosome shown in this drawing is characteristic of passerine birds.

FIG. 79. Sperm of urodele amphibia. (After Meves, 1897, Arch. f. mikr. Anat. u. Entwichlingsgesch., 50; McGregor, 1899, J. Morphol., 15. (A–E) Stages in the morphogenesis of the sperm of *Salamandra.* (F) Diagram of head, middle piece, etc. of the sperm of the urodele.

chromosomes within the germinal vesicle condense once again, decrease in length (fig. 72F), and assume conditions more typical of the diakinesis stage (figs. 67; 119A). The tetrad chromosomes now become visible. Following the latter chromosomal changes, the nuclear membrane breaks down (fig. 119A), and the chromatin elements pass onto the spindle of the first maturation division (fig. 119B). The nuclear sap, membrane, nucleolus, and general framework pass into the surrounding cytoplasmic substance (figs. 119A; 132A–C). This nuclear contribution to the cytoplasm appears to play an important part in fertilization and development, at least in some species (fig. 132C; the clear protoplasm is derived from the nuclear plasm).

e. Character of the Meiotic (Maturation) Divisions in the Spermatocyte Compared with Those of the Oocyte

1) Dependent Nature of the Maturation Divisions in the Female Meiocyte. The maturation divisions in the developing male gamete occur spontaneously and in sequence in all known forms. But in most oocytes, *either one or both of the maturation divisions are dependent upon sperm entrance*. For example, in *Ascaris,* a nematode worm (fig. 133), and in *Nereis,* a marine annelid worm (fig. 130), both maturation divisions occur *after the sperm has entered* and are dependent upon factors associated with sperm entrance. A similar condition is found in the dog (van der Stricht, '23; fig. 115) and in the fox (Asdell, '46). In the urochordate, *Styela,* the germinal vesicle breaks down, the nuclear sap and nucleolus move into the surrounding protoplasm, and the first maturation spindle is formed as the egg is discharged into the sea water (fig. 116A, B). Further development of the egg, however, awaits the entrance of the sperm (fig. 116C–F). Somewhat similar conditions are found in other *Urochordata.* In the cephalochordate, *Amphioxus,* and in the vertebrate group as a whole (with certain exceptions) the first polar body is formed and the spindle for the second maturation division is elaborated *before normal sperm entrance* (figs. 117C, D; 119D). The second maturation division in the latter instances is dependent upon the activities aroused by sperm contact with the oocyte. In the sea urchin, sperm can penetrate the egg before the maturation divisions occur; but, under these conditions, normal development of the egg does not occur. Normally in this species both maturation divisions are effected before sperm entrance, while the egg is still in the ovary. When the egg is discharged into the sea water, the sperm enters the egg, and this event affords the necessary stimulus for further development (fig. 131).

2) Inequality of Cytoplasmic Division in the Oocyte. When the first maturation division occurs, the two resulting cells are called secondary spermatocytes in the male and secondary oocytes in the female (figs. 67, 69). The secondary spermatocytes are smaller both in nuclear and cytoplasmic volume. They also form a definite nuclear membrane. Each secondary spermatocyte then divides and forms two equal spermatids. In contrast to this condition of equality in the daughter cells of the developing male gamete during and following the maturation divisions, an entirely different condition is found in the developing female gamete. In the latter, one of the secondary oocytes is practically as large as the primary oocyte, while the other or first polar body (polocyte) is extremely small in cytoplasmic content although the nuclear material is the same (fig. 117D). During the next division the secondary oocyte behaves in a manner similar to that of the primary oocyte, and a small second polocyte is given off, while the egg remains large (fig. 117E, F). Unlike the secondary spermatocyte, the secondary oocyte does not form a nuclear membrane. The polar body first formed may undergo a division, resulting in a total of three polar bodies (polocytes) and one egg (ootid).

f. Résumé of the Significance of the Meiotic Phenomena

In view of the foregoing data with regard to the behavior of the male and female gametes during meiosis, the significant results of this process may be summarized as follows:

(1) There is a mixing or scrambling of the chromatin material brought about by the crossing over of genic materials from one chromatid to another.

(2) Much chromatin material with various genic combinations is discarded during the maturation divisions in the oocyte. In the latter, two polar bodies are ejected with their chromatin material as described above. The egg thus retains one set of the four genic combinations which were present at the end of the primary oocyte stage; the others are lost. (A process of discarding of chromatin material occurs in the male line also. For although four spermatids and sperm normally develop from one primary spermatocyte, great quantities of sperm never reach an egg to fertilize it, and much of the chromatin material is lost by the wayside.)

(3) A reduction of the number of chromosomes from the diploid to the haploid number is a significant procedure of all true meiotic behavior.

(For more detailed discussions and descriptions of meiosis, see De Robertis, et al., '48; Sharp, '34, '43; Snyder, '45; White, '45.)

4. CYTOSOMAL (CYTOPLASMIC) MATURATION OF THE GAMETES

a. General Aspects of Cytoplasmic Maturation of the Gametes

During the period when the meiotic prophase changes occur in the nucleus of the oocyte, the cytoplasm increases greatly and various aspects of cytoplasmic differentiation are effected. That is, differentiation of both nuclear and cytoplasmic materials tend to occur synchronously in the developing

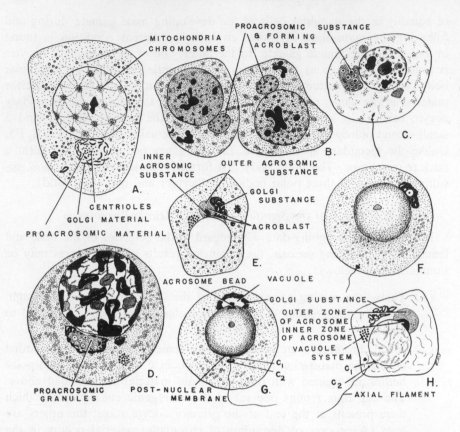

FIG. 80. Morphogenesis of guinea-pig and human sperm. (A) Spermatocyte of guinea pig before first maturation division. The Golgi complex with included proacrosomic granules and centrioles is shown. (After Gatenby and Woodger, '21.) (B) Young sister spermatids of guinea pig. (C) Later spermatid of guinea pig showing acroblast with proacrosomic granules. (D) Young human spermatocyte, showing Golgi apparatus with proacrosomic granules similar to that shown in (A). (After Gatenby and Beams, '35.) (E) Spermatid of guinea pig later than that shown in (C), showing acroblast with Golgi substance being discarded from around the acroblast. (F) Later human spermatid, showing Golgi substance surrounding acroblast with acrosome bead. (After Gatenby and Beams, '35.) (G) Later human spermatid, showing acroblast, with acrosome bead within, surrounded by a vacuole. (After Gatenby and Beams, '35.) (H) Later spermatid of guinea pig, showing outer and inner zones of the acrosome. The inner zone corresponds somewhat to the acrosome bead shown in (G) of the human spermatid. (After Gatenby and Wigoder, Proc. Roy. Soc., London, s.B., 104.)

female gamete. In the male gamete, on the other hand, the meiotic processes are completed before morphological differentiation of the cytoplasm is initiated.

Another distinguishing feature in the morphogenesis of the sperm relative to that of the egg is that the cytoplasmic differentiation of the sperm entails a discarding of cytoplasm and contained cytoplasmic structures, whereas the oocyte conserves and increases its cytoplasmic substance (fig. 68). In regard to the behavior of the cytoplasms of the two developing gametes, it is interesting to observe that the idiosome-Golgi-mitochondrial complex behaves very differently in the two gametes (fig. 68).

A third condition of egg and sperm differentiation involves the possible function of the "nurse cells." In the vertebrate ovary the follicle cells which surround the egg have much to do with the conditions necessary for the differentiation of the oocyte. The latter cannot carry the processes of differentiation to completion without contact with the surrounding follicle cells. Spermiogenesis also depends upon the presence of a nurse cell. In the vertebrate seminiferous tubule, the Sertoli cell is intimately concerned with the transformation of the spermatid into the morphologically adult sperm, and a close contact exists between the developing sperm element and the Sertoli cell during this period (figs. 65, 66, 73). In the discharge of the formed sperm elements into the lumen of the tubule, the Sertoli cell also is concerned (Chap. 1).

b. Morphogenesis (Spermiogenesis; Spermioteleosis) of the Sperm

1) Types of Sperm. There are two main types of sperm to be found in animals, namely, **flagellate** and **non-flagellate** sperm (figs. 74, 75). Flagellate sperm possess a flagellum or tail-like organelle; non-flagellate sperm lack this structure. The flagellate type of sperm is found quite universally among animals; non-flagellate sperm occur in certain invertebrate groups, particularly in the nematode worms, such as *Ascaris,* and in various crustacea, notably the lobster, crab, etc. (fig. 75). Flagellate sperm may be either uniflagellate or biflagellate. Single flagellate sperm occur in the majority of animals, while a biflagellate form is found in the platode, *Procerodes.* However, biflagellate sperm may be found as abnormal specimens among animals normally producing uniflagellate sperm.

Conjugate sperm are produced in certain animal species. For example, two sperm heads adhere closely together in the opossum (fig. 125), also in the beetle, *Dytiscus,* and in the gastropod, *Turritella.* Many sperm heads become intimately associated in the grasshopper to form the so-called "sperm boat" (fig. 76). However, all conjugate sperm normally separate from each other in the female genital tract.

2) Structure of a Flagellate Sperm. The flagellate sperm from different species of animals vary considerably in size, shape, and morphological details. Some possess long, spear-shaped heads, some have heads resembling a hatchet, in others the head appears more or less cigar-shaped, while still others possess a head which resembles a spatula (fig. 74). The spatula-shaped head is found in the sperm of the bull, opossum, man, etc. The description given below refers particularly to the spatula-shaped variety. Although all flagellate sperm resemble one another, diversity in various details is the rule,

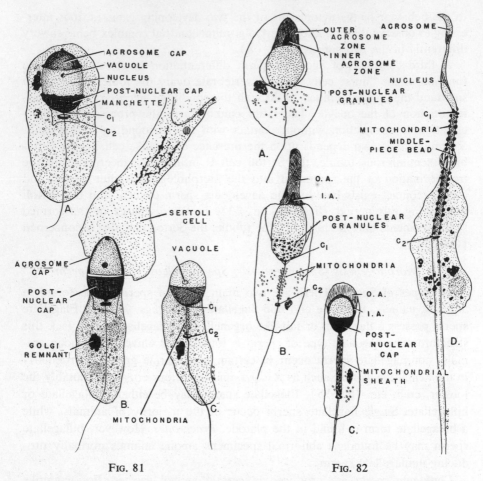

FIG. 81

FIG. 82

FIG. 81. Later stages of human spermatogenesis. (Redrawn from Gatenby and Beams, 1935.)

FIG. 82. Stages of guinea-pig spermatogenesis. Observe dual nature of the acrosome; also, middle-piece bead (kinoplasmic droplet). (A–C redrawn from Gatenby and Beams, 1935; D redrawn from Gatenby and Woodger, '21.)

and the description given below should be regarded as being true of one type of sperm only and should not be applied to all flagellate sperm.

A fully differentiated spatulate sperm of the mammals possesses the following structural parts (fig. 77).

a) HEAD. Around the head of the sperm there is a thin, enveloping layer of cytoplasm. This cytoplasmic layer continues posteriad into the neck, middle piece, and tail. Within the cytoplasm of the head is the oval-shaped **nucleus.** Over the anterior half of the nucleus the **apical body or acrosome** is to be found, forming, apparently, a cephalic covering and skeletal shield for the nucleus. The caudal half of the nucleus is covered by the **post-nuclear cap.** This also appears to be a skeletal structure supporting this area of the nucleus; moreover, it affords a place of attachment for the anterior centrosome and the anterior end of the axial filament.

In human and bull sperm the acrosome is a thin cap, but in some mammalian sperm it is developed more elaborately. In the guinea pig it assumes the shape of an elongated, shovel-shaped affair (fig. 82), while in the mouse and rat it is hatchet or lance shaped (fig. 74N). In passerine birds the acrosome is a pointed, spiral structure often called the **perforatorium** (fig. 78). On the other hand, in other birds, reptiles, and amphibia it may be a simple, pointed perforatorial structure (figs. 74, 78, 79). In certain invertebrate species, it is located at the caudal or lateral aspect of the nucleus (figs. 75, 78).

b) NECK. The neck is a constricted area immediately caudal to the posterior nuclear cap and between it and the middle piece. Within it are found the **anterior centriole** and the anterior end of the **axial filament.** In this particular region may also be found the so-called **neck granule.**

c) CONNECTING BODY OR MIDDLE PIECE. This region is an important portion of the sperm. One of its conspicuous structures is the **central core** composed of the **axial filament** and its surrounding cytoplasmic sheath. At the distal end of the middle piece, the central core is circumscribed by the **distal,** or **ring centriole.** Investing the central core of the middle piece is the mitochondrial sheath. The enveloping cytoplasm is thicker to some degree in this area of the sperm than that surrounding the head.

d) FLAGELLUM. The flagellum forms the **tail** or **swimming organ** of the sperm. It is composed of two general regions, an anterior **principal or chief piece** and a posterior **end piece.** The greater part of the *axial filament and its sheath* is found in the flagellum. A relatively thick layer of cytoplasm surrounds the filament and its sheath in the **chief-piece** region of the flagellum, but, in the caudal tip or **end piece,** the axial filament seems to be almost devoid of enveloping cytoplasm. The end piece often is referred to as the naked portion of the flagellum.

In figure 79 is shown a diagrammatic representation of a urodele amphibian sperm. Two important differences from the mammalian sperm described above are to be observed, namely, the middle piece is devoid of mitochondria and is composed largely of centrioles 1 and 2, and the tail has an elaborate undulating or vibratile filament associated with the chief piece.

3) Spermiogenesis or the Differentiation of the Spermatid into the Morphologically Differentiated Sperm. The differentiation of the spermatid into the fully metamorphosed sperm is an ingenious and striking process. It involves changes in the nucleus, during which the latter as a whole contracts and in some forms becomes greatly elongated into an attenuant structure. (See figs. 79B–F; 85L–P.) It also is concerned with profound modifications of the cytoplasm and its constituents; the latter changes transform the inconspicuous spermatid into a most complicated structure. Some of these changes are outlined below.

a) GOLGI SUBSTANCE AND ACROBLAST; FORMATION OF THE ACROSOME. The **Golgi substance** or parts thereof previously associated with the idiosome of the spermatocyte (fig. 80A) proceeds to form the acrosome of the developing spermatid as follows: In the differentiating human sperm, the Golgi substance of the spermatocyte (fig. 80D) becomes aggregated at the future anterior end of the nucleus, as shown in fig. 80F, where it forms an acroblast within a capsule of Golgi substance. This acroblast later forms a large vacuole within which is the acrosomal "bead" (figs. 68B; 80G). The acrosomal bead proceeds to form the acrosomal cap, shown in figure 81A, and the latter grows downward over the anterior pole of the nucleus (fig. 81A, B). Most of the Golgi substance in the meantime is discarded (fig. 81A, B). (See Gatenby and Beams, '35.)

In the guinea pig the acroblast together with other Golgi substance, migrates around the nucleus toward the future anterior pole of the latter where the acroblast takes up its new position (fig. 80B, C, E). (See Gatenby and Woodger, '21.) As shown in figure 80E, the acroblast is composed of inner and outer acrosomal substances. These inner and outer areas of the acroblast give origin respectively to the inner and outer zones of the acrosome (fig. 82). The peripheral or surrounding Golgi material of the acroblast detaches itself meanwhile from the developing acrosome (fig. 80E, H) and drifts downward toward the posterior end of the sperm. Eventually it is discarded with the excess cytoplasm and some mitochondrial material. In some animal species (e.g., grasshopper) the acrosomal substance arises from a multiple type of acroblast (Bowen, '22). (See fig. 83.) Nevertheless, the general process of acrosome formation is similar to that outlined above.

b) FORMATION OF THE POST-NUCLEAR CAP. All spatulate sperm of mam-

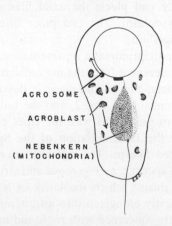

ACROSOME

ACROBLAST

NEBENKERN
(MITOCHONDRIA)

FIG. 83. Formation of the acrosome from a multiple acroblast in the grasshopper. (After Bowen, Anat. Rec., 24.)

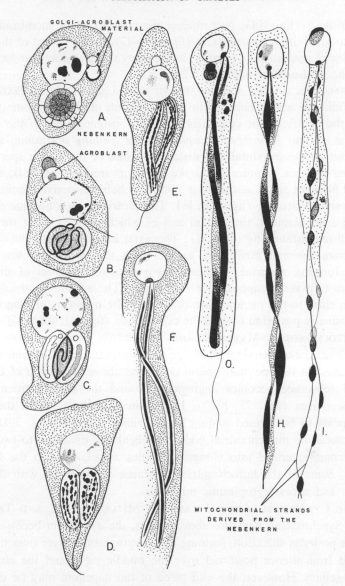

GOLGI- ACROBLAST
MATERIAL

NEBENKERN

ACROBLAST

A.

B.

C.

D.

E.

F.

O.

H.

I.

MITOCHONDRIAL STRANDS
DERIVED FROM THE
NEBENKERN

FIG. 84. The mitochondrial nebenkern and its elaborate development in *Brachynema*. (After Bowen, J. Morphol., 37 and Biol. Bull., 42.) (B–I) Division of the nebenkern (A) and its elaboration into two attenuant strands extending posteriad into the flagellum.

mals possess a nucleus which has an acrosomal cap over its anterior aspect and a post-nuclear cap covering its posterior area. Both of these caps tend to meet near the equator of the nucleus (fig. 77).

The exact origin of the post-nuclear cap is difficult to ascertain. In the human sperm it appears to arise from a thickened membrane in association with centriole 1 (fig. 80G, post-nuclear membrane). This membrane grows anteriad to meet the acrosomal cap (fig. 81A–C). In the sperm of the guinea pig, a series of post-nuclear granules in the early spermatid appear to coalesce to form the post-nuclear cap (fig. 82A–C).

c) FORMATION OF THE PROXIMAL AND DISTAL CENTRIOLES; AXIAL FILA- MENT. While the above changes in the formation of the acrosome are pro- gressing, the centriole (or centrioles) of the idiosome move to the *opposite side of the nucleus from that occupied by the forming acrosome,* and here in this position the **proximal** and **distal centrioles** of the future sperm arise. In this area the neck granules also make their appearance (figs. 68B; 80F–H). The **axial filament** arises at this time and it probably is derived from the two centrioles simultaneously (fig. 80F, H). The centrioles soon become displaced along the axial filament, the caudal end of which projects from the surface of the cell membrane (fig. 80F–H). The axial filament grows outward pos- teriorly from the cell membrane in line with the two centrioles and the acrosome-forming material. The anterior-posterior elongation of the sperm thus begins to make its appearance (fig. 80H). The anterior centriole retains a position close to the nuclear membrane, but the posterior or **ring centriole** moves gradually posteriad toward the cell surface (figs. 81, 82A–C).

d) MITOCHONDRIAL MATERIAL AND FORMATION OF THE MIDDLE PIECE OF THE SPERM. The behavior of the mitochondria in the formation of sperm varies greatly. In the spatulate sperm described above, a portion of the mito- chondrial substance becomes aggregated around the axial filament in the middle-piece area (figs. 77, 82D). In certain amphibian sperm the middle piece appears to be formed mainly by centrioles 1 and 2 (fig. 79D–F). In certain insects the mitochondrial body or nebenkern, divides into two masses which become extended into elongated bodies associated with the flagellum (fig. 84). Some of the mitochondrial substance is discarded with the Golgi substance and excess cytoplasmic materials.

e) THE CYTOPLASM, AXIAL FILAMENT, MITOCHONDRIA, AND TAIL FOR- MATION. Synchronized with the above events, the cytoplasm becomes drawn out in the posterior direction, forming a thin cytoplasmic layer over the sperm head, and from thence posteriad over the middle piece and the chief piece of the flagellum. However, the end piece of the flagellum may be devoid of investing cytoplasm (fig. 77). As the cytoplasm is elongating posteriorly over the contained essential structures of the forming sperm, much of the cytoplasm and Golgi substance and some mitochondria are discarded and lost from the sperm body. It may be that these discarded bodies form a part of the essential substances of the spermatic (seminal) fluid. (See Chap. 1.) (See figs. 66; 68B–E; 81; 82; 85M–O.)

The centralized core of the tail is the axial filament which arises in relation to centrioles 1 and 2 and grows posteriad through the middle piece and tail (figs. 80F–H; 81A–C; 82A–C; 85M–P). A considerable amount of mitochondrial material may also enter into the formation of tail (fig. 84).

A peculiar, highly specialized characteristic of many sperm tails is the development of a vibratile membrane associated with the axial filament (fig. 79E, F). Its origin is not clear, but it probably involves certain relationships with the mitochondrial material as well as the cytoplasm and axial filament.

In the formation of the human and guinea-pig sperm, the nucleus experiences only slight changes in shape from that of the spermatid. However, in many animal species, spermiogenesis involves considerable nuclear metamorphosis as well as cytoplasmic change (figs. 69, 79, 85).

In summary it may be stated that while the various shapes and sizes of mature flagellate sperm in many animal species, vertebrate and invertebrate,

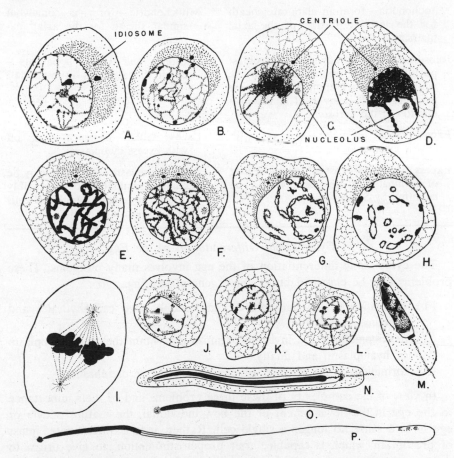

FIG. 85. Spermatogenesis in the common fowl. Observe extreme nuclear metamorphosis. (After Miller, Anat. Rec., 70.)   (A) Resting spermatocyte.   (B) Early leptotene stage.   (C, D) Synaptene stage.   (E) Pachytene stage.   (F, G) Diplotene stage.   (H) Diakinesis.   (I) First division, primary sperm.   (J–P) Metamorphosing sperm.

are numerous, there is a strong tendency for spermiogenesis to follow similar lines of development. Deviations occur, but the following comparisons between mammalian and insect spermiogenesis, somewhat modified from Bowen ('22), illustrate the uniformity of transformation of the basic structures of the primitive meiocyte:

Mammalian Sperm	Insect Sperm
Nucleus—head	Nucleus—head
Centrioles—originally double and arranged in a proximal-distal formation. The axial filament arises from both centrioles	Centrioles—same as in mammals
Mitochondria—form an elaborate sheath for the anterior portion of the axial filament	Mitochondria—form a somewhat similar sheath for the axial filament
Idiosome and Golgi apparatus (acroblast portion)—gives origin to a vesicle which contains a granule, the acrosome granule, which is involved in the production of the acrosome	Idiosome and Golgi apparatus—much the same as in mammals
Excess Golgi substance—cast off with excess cytoplasm	Excess Golgi substance—cast off with excess cytoplasm
Excess cytoplasm—cast off—may be part of seminal fluid or possibly may be engulfed by Sertoli cells	Excess cytoplasm—cast off—may be part of seminal fluid or possibly may be engulfed by epithelial cells of the sperm cyst wall

c. Cytoplasmic Differentiation of the Egg

The cytoplasmic differentiation of the egg involves many problems. These problems may be classified under three general headings, viz.:

(1) Formation of the deutoplasm composed of fats, carbohydrates and proteins,

(2) development of the invisible organization within the true protoplasm or hyaloplasm, and finally,

(3) formation of the vitelline or egg membrane or membranes.

In view of the complexity of these three problems and of their importance to the egg in the development of the new individual, the mature oocyte or egg is in a sense no longer a single cell. Rather, it is a differentiated mass of protoplasm which is capable, after proper stimulation, to give origin to a new individual composed of many billions of cells. As such, the differentiation of the oocyte within the ovary represents a relatively unknown period of embryological development.

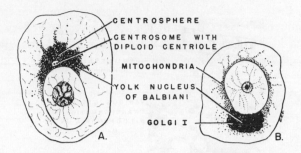

FIG. 86. Young oogonia of the fowl entering the growth (oocyte) stage. (A) Idiosome from which the Golgi substance has been removed and stained to show the centrosphere (archoplasm). The centrosome has two centrioles. (B) Idiosome with surrounding Golgi substance. The mitochondria surround the Golgi substance and the nucleus. (After Brambell, '25.)

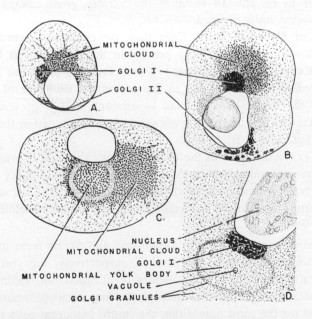

FIG. 87. The so-called mitochondrial yolk body in the developing egg of the fowl. (A) Oocyte from 11-week-old chick, showing mitochondrial cloud and Golgi substances I and II. (B) Oocyte from ovary of adult fowl, showing both types of Golgi substance and mitochondrial cloud. (C) Oocyte from ovary of adult fowl, showing the appearance of the mitochondrial yolk body within the mitochondrial cloud. (D) Oocyte from ovary of adult fowl, showing fragmentation of Golgi substance I and the association of the resulting Golgi granules around the mitochondrial yolk body. (After Brambell, '25.)

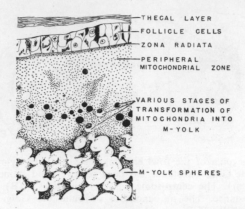

FIG. 88. Portion of follicle and periphery of oocyte from ovary of the adult bird, showing the mitochondria and their transformation into the M-yolk spheres of Brambell. (After Brambell, '25.)

Before considering the various aspects of cytoplasmic differentiation of the oocyte, it is best for us to review the types of vertebrate and other chordate eggs in order to be able to visualize the various goals toward which the developing oocyte must proceed.

1) Types of Chordate Eggs. Eggs may be classified according to the amount of deutoplasm (yolk, etc.) present in the cytoplasm as follows:

a) HOMOLECITHAL (ISOLECITHAL) EGGS. True homolecithal eggs in the phylum *Chordata* are found only in the mammals, exclusive of the *Prototheria*. Here the deutoplasm is small in amount, and is present chiefly in the form of fat droplets and small yolk spherules, distributed in the cytoplasm of the egg (figs. 118A, B; 147A).

b) TELOLECITHAL EGGS. In the telolecithal egg the yolk is present in considerable amounts and concentrated at one pole. Telolecithality of the egg in the phylum *Chordata* exists in various degrees. We shall arrange them in sequence starting with slight and ending with very marked telolecithality as follows:

(1) *Amphioxus* and *Styela*. In *Amphioxus* and *Styela* from the subphyla *Cephalochordata* and *Urochordata,* respectively, the yolk present is centrally located in the egg before fertilization but becomes concentrated at one pole at the time of the first cleavage where it is contained for the most part within the future entoderm cells (figs. 132D, 167A).

(2) In many *Amphibia,* such as the frogs and toads, and also in the *Petromyzontidae* or fresh-water lampreys among the cyclostome fishes, the yolk present is greater in amount than in the preceding eggs. As such, it is concentrated at one pole, the future entodermal or vegetal

pole, and a greater degree of telolecithality is attained than in the eggs of *Amphioxus* or *Styela* (fig. 141A).

(3) In many *Amphibia,* such as *Necturus,* also in *Neoceratodus* and *Lepidosiren* among the lung fishes, and in the cartilaginous ganoid fish, *Acipenser,* yolk is present in considerable amounts, and the cytoplasm of the animal pole is smaller in comparison to the yolk or vegetal pole (figs. 150, 151, 152).

(4) In the bony ganoid fishes, *Amia* and *Lepisosteus,* as well as in the *Gymnophiona* (legless *Amphibia*) the yolk is situated at one pole and is large in quantity (figs. 153B–F; 154).

(5) Lastly, in a large portion of the vertebrate group, namely, in reptiles, birds, prototherian mammals, teleost and elasmobranch fishes, and in the marine lampreys, the deutoplasm is massive and the protoplasm which takes part in the early cleavages is small in comparison. In these eggs the yolk is never cleaved by the cleavage processes, and development of the embryo is confined to the animal pole cytoplasm (figs. 46, 47).

2) Formation of the Deutoplasm. The cytoplasm of the young oocyte is small in quantity, with a clear homogeneous texture (figs. 68A; 86A, B). As the oocyte develops, the cytoplasmic and nuclear volumes increase (fig. 68F), and the homogeneity of the cytoplasm is soon lost by the appearance of deutoplasmic substances (fig. 68G, H). In the oocyte of the frog, for example, lipid droplets begin to appear when the oocyte is about 50 μ in diameter (fig. 72A). (See Brachet, '50, p. 53.) A little later glycogen makes its appearance, and finally yolk protein arises.

The origin of fat droplets and yolk spherules has been ascribed variously to the activities of chondriosomes (mitochondria and other similar bodies), Golgi substance, and of certain vacuoles. Most observers place emphasis upon the presence of a so-called "yolk nucleus" or "yolk-attraction sphere" situated near the nucleus of many oocytes as a structure associated with fat and yolk formation. In general, two types of yolk bodies have been described. One is the yolk nucleus of Balbiani and the other the mitochondrial yolk body of Brambell. The yolk nucleus of Balbiani (fig. 86A, B) consists of the following:

(1) a central body, the centrosphere or archoplasmic sphere within which one or more centriole-like bodies are found, and

(2) surrounding this central body, a layer of Golgi substances and chondriosomes (i.e., mitochondria, etc.).

This cytoplasmic structure probably is related to the idiosome of the oogonia (fig. 68A).

The formation of the deutoplasm, according to the theory associated with the Balbiani type of yolk nucleus is as follows: The surrounding pallial layer of Golgi substance and mitochondria moves away from the central portion (i.e., away from the centrosphere) of the yolk nucleus and becomes scattered and dispersed as small fragments within the cytosome (fig. 68F, G). The yolk nucleus as an entity thus disappears, and its fragments become immersed within the substance of the cytoplasm. Coincident with this dispersion of yolk nuclear material, rapid formation of small yolk spherules and fat droplets occur (fig. 68H). It appears thus that the formation of the deutoplasm composed of fat droplets and yolk spherules is directly related to the activities of the Golgi substance and chondriosomes.

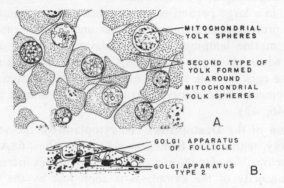

FIG. 89. (A) Cytoplasm of oocyte, showing formation of a second kind of yolk (the M-C-yolk) in a vacuole surrounding the M-yolk sphere. (After Brambell, '25.)   (B) Passing of Golgi substance from the follicle cells into the ooplasm of developing oocyte of the fowl. (After Brambell, '25.)

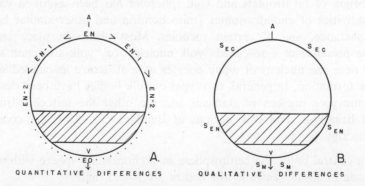

FIG. 90. Diagrams showing contrasting theories explaining the organization of polarity of the cytoplasm of the fully developing egg or oocyte. Diagram at left shows polarity explained according to quantitative differences, while the diagram to the right shows qualitative differences. A = animal pole; V = vegetal pole. E represents a substance or a factor, while EN-1, EN-2, etc., represent different quantities of substance E distributed from pole to pole. SEC, SEN and SM are different chemical substances assumed to be responsible for the determination of the ectoderm, entoderm, and mesoderm of the developing embryo. (After Barth: *Embryology,* New York, Dryden Press.)

On the other hand, the interpretation and description of the yolk body and its subsequent activities given by Brambell ('25) present a different view. According to the latter author, the yolk body is composed entirely of mitochondria; the Golgi substance and centrosphere are absent. Yolk formation proceeds as follows: As the young oocyte grows, the mitochondria increase in number and form the **mitochondrial cloud** (fig. 87A, B). The transitory **mitochondrial yolk body** differentiates within this cloud (fig. 87C). The mitochondrial yolk body ultimately breaks up into a mass of mitochondria, and the latter becomes dispersed in the cytoplasm of the oocyte (figs. 68F, G; 87D). Some of these dispersed mitochondria transform directly into yolk spheres (figs. 68H, 88, 89). Following this, another kind of yolk is formed in vacuoles surrounding these original yolk spheres (figs. 68H, 89A, yolk spheres plus vacuoles). The fat droplets (C-yolk) within the ooplasm are formed according to Brambell "possibly under the influence of Golgi elements" (fig. 68H, fat droplets). Relative to the function of the yolk nucleus and its mitochondria, Brachet ('50), p. 57, considers it significant at the beginning, but its real importance is still to be understood.

The relationship, if any, of the oocyte nucleus to the deposition of yolk materials is not apparent. One must not overlook the real probability that the germinal vesicle (i.e., the enlarged nucleus of the oocyte) may be related to the increase and growth of the cytoplasm and to yolk formation, for it is at this time that the chromatin threads surrender their normal diplotene appearance and become diffusely placed in the germinal vesicle. They also lose much of their basic chromatin-staining affinities while the Feulgen reaction is diminished (Brachet, '50, p. 63). With regard to the possible function of the germinal vesicle in yolk synthesis, the following quotation is taken from a publication by Brachet ('47):

It is well worth pointing out that Duspiva (1942), using a very delicate and precise technique, found no correlation between the dipeptidase content of the nucleus and the onset of vitellus synthesis: such a correlation exists, however, in the case of the cytoplasm where dipeptidase increases markedly when the first yolk granules make their appearance. These results suggest that there is not evidence that the nucleus is the site of an especially active metabolism; cytoplasmic dipeptidase probably plays a part in yolk protein synthesis; if the nucleus controls such a synthesis, it works in a very delicate and still unknown way.

However, the means by which protein synthesis is effected still is a problem which awaits explanation (Northrop, '50). (The interested student should consult Brachet, '50, Chap. III, for a detailed discussion of the cytochemistry of yolk formation.)

Another aspect of the problem of cytoplasmic growth and differentiation of the oocyte presents itself for further study. Brambell ('25) concluded from his observations that Golgi substance passes from the follicle cells into the ooplasm of the growing bird oocyte and contributes to the substance of the peripheral layer (fig. 89B). Palade and Claude ('49) suggest that at least some of the Golgi substance be identified as myelin figures which develop "at the expense of lipid inclusions." Thus it may be that the Golgi substance which Brambell observed (fig. 89B) passing from the follicle cells to the oocyte represents lipid substance. In the growing oocyte of the rat, Leblond ('50) demonstrated the presence of small amounts of polysaccharides in the cytoplasm of the oocyte, while the surrounding zona pellucida and follicle cells contained considerable quantities. These considerations suggest that the blood stream using the surrounding follicle cells as an intermediary may contribute food materials of a complex nature to the growing cytoplasm of the oocyte.

The localization of the yolk toward one pole of the egg is one of the movements which occurs during fertilization in many teleost fishes. In these forms, the deutoplasmic materials are laid down centrally in the egg during oogenesis, but move poleward at fertilization (fig. 122). A similar phenomenon occurs also during fertilization in *Amphioxus* and *Styela* among the protochordates. In many other fishes and in the amphibia, reptiles, birds, and monotrematous mammals, the yolk becomes deposited or polarized toward one pole of the oocyte during the later stages of oocyte formation, as the cytoplasm and the germinal vesicle move toward the other pole (figs. 68H, 72F). The polarization of the deutoplasmic substances thus is a general feature of the organization of the chordate egg.

3) Invisible Morphogenetic Organization Within the Cytoplasm of the Egg.
Two general categories of substances are developed within the cytoplasm of the oocyte during its development within the ovary, viz.:

(1) the visible or formed cytoplasmic inclusions, and
(2) an invisible morphogenetic ground substance.

The former group comprises the yolk spherules, fats, and other visible, often pigmented bodies which can be seen with the naked eye or by means of the microscope. The morphogenetic ground substance probably is composed of enzymes, hormones, and various nucleocytoplasmic derivatives enmeshed within the living cytoplasm. However, although we may assume that the basic, morphogenetic ground substance is composed of enzymes, hormones, etc., the exact nature of the basic substance or its precise relationship to the various formed inclusions of the cytoplasm is quite unknown (see Fankhauser, '48, for discussion). More recent experiments demonstrate that the yolk or deutoplasmic material not only serves as a reservoir of energy for embryonic development but also is in some way connected with the essential, basic organization of the egg.

Although we know little concerning the exact nature of the morphogenetic organization of the egg or how it forms, studies of embryological development force upon us but one conclusion, to wit, that, during the period when the oocyte develops in the ovary, basic conditions are elaborated from which the future individual arises (Fankhauser, '48). Within the cytoplasm of the mature egg of many chordates, this inherent organization is revealed at the time of fertilization by the appearance of definite areas of presumptive organ-forming substances. For example, in the egg of the frog and other amphibia, the yolk pole is the stuff from which the future entodermal structures take their origin; the darkly pigmented animal or nuclear pole will eventually give origin to epidermal and neural tissues; and from the zone between these two areas mesodermal and notochordal tissues will arise (fig. 119K). Similar major organ-forming areas in the recently fertilized egg have been demonstrated in other chordates, as in the ascidian, *Styela,* and in the cephalochordate, *Amphioxus.* In the eggs of reptiles, birds, and teleost and elasmobranch fishes, while the relationship to the yolk is somewhat different, major organ-forming areas of a similar character have been demonstrated at a later period of development (Chaps. 6–9). This suggests that these eggs also possess a fundamental organization similar, although not identical, to that in the amphibian egg.

4) Polarity of the Egg and Its Relation to Body Organization and Bilateral Symmetry of the Mature Egg. One of the characteristic features of the terminal phase of egg differentiation in the chordate group is the migration of the germinal vesicle toward the animal pole of the egg (figs. 72F, 119A). As stated above, in many vertebrate eggs the deutoplasmic material becomes situated at the opposite pole, known as the vegetal (vegetative) or yolk pole, either before fertilization or shortly after. The relatively yolk-free protoplasm aggregates at the animal pole. Consequently the maturation divisions of the egg occur at this pole (fig. 119A, B, D). The formation of a definite polarity of the egg, therefore, is one of the main results of the differentiation of the oocyte.

Various theories have been suggested in an endeavor to explain polarity in the fully developed egg or oocyte. All these theories emphasize qualitative and quantitative differences in the cytoplasmic substances extending from one pole of the egg to the other (fig. 90).

The animal and vegetal poles of the egg have a definite relationship to the organization of the chordate embryo. In *Amphioxus,* the animal pole becomes the ventro-anterior part of the embryo, while in the frog the animal pole area becomes the cephalic end of the future tadpole, and the yolk pole comes to occupy the posterior aspect. In teleost and elasmobranch fishes the yolk-laden pole lies in the future ventral aspect of the embryo, and it occupies a similar position in the reptile, bird, and prototherian mammal (see fig. 215). Studies have shown that the early auxiliary or trophoblastic cells in eutherian mammals lie on the ventral aspect of the future embryo. Consequently, it is to be observed that the various substances in mature vertebrate and protochordate eggs tend to assume a polarized relationship to the future embryonic axis and body organization.

Many vertebrate and protochordate eggs possess a bilateral symmetry which becomes evident when the fertilization processes are under way or shortly after their conclusion. The appearance of the gray crescent in the frog's egg (fig. 119K) and in other amphibian eggs during fertilization and the similar appearance of the yellow crescent in the fertilized egg of the ascidian, *Styela* (fig. 132D) serve to orient the future right and left halves of the embryo. Conditions similar to that of *Styela,* but lacking the yellow pigment, are present in *Amphioxus*. Similarly, in the chick, if one holds the blunt end of the egg to the left, and the pointed end to the right, the early embryo appears most often at right angles, or nearly so, to the axis extending from the broader to the smaller end of the egg, and in the majority of cases the cephalic end of the embryo will appear toward the side away from the body of the observer. There is some evidence that the "yolk" or egg proper is slightly elongated in this axis. It appears, therefore, that the general plane of bilateral symmetry is well established in the early chick blastoderm, although the early cleavages do not occur in a manner to indicate or coincide with this plane. In prototherian mammals, a bilateral symmetry and an antero-posterior orientation is established in the germinal disc at the time of fertilization, soon after the second polar body is discharged (fig. 136).

5) Membranes Developed in Relation to the Oocyte; Their Possible Sources of Origin. A series of membranes associated with the surface of the oocyte are formed during its development within the ovary. Three general types of such membranes are elaborated which separate from the oocyte's surface at or before fertilization, leaving a perivitelline space between the egg's surface and the membrane. They are:

(1) A true vitelline membrane which probably represents a specialization or product of the ooplasmic surface. For a time this membrane adheres closely to the outer boundary of the ooplasm, but at fertilization it separates from the surface as a distinct membrane.

(2) A second membrane in certain *chordates* is elaborated by the follicle cells. It is known as a **chorion** in lower *Chordata* but is called the **zona pellucida** in mammals.

(3) A **zona radiata** or a thickened, rather complex, membrane is formed in many vertebrates; it may be considered to be a product of the ooplasm or of the ooplasm and the surrounding follicle cells.

All of the above membranes serve to enclose the egg *during the early phases of embryonic development* and therefore may be considered as **primary embryonic membranes.** As such, they should be regarded as a definite part of the egg and of the egg's differentiation in the ovary. A description of these membranes in relation to the egg and possible source of their origin in the various chordate groups is given below.

a) CHORION IN *Styela*. A previously held view maintained that the chorion

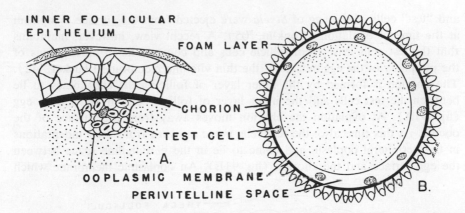

FIG. 91. Formation of the chorion in the egg of *Styela*. (A) Chorion is shown along the inner aspect of the follicular epithelium. The test cells lie in indentations of the peripheral ooplasm. (B) Optical section of an ovulated egg. (Redrawn and modified from Tucker, '42.)

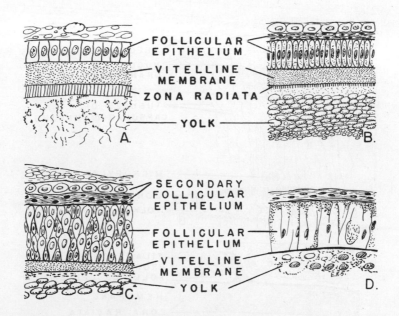

FIG. 92. Developing vitelline membranes of *Scyllium canicula*. Observe that two membranes are present in the young egg; later these membranes fuse into one membrane. (A) Surface area of young oocyte with a vitelline membrane and zona radiata. (B) Slightly older oocyte with the radiate zone not as prominent. (C) Older oocyte with a single, relatively thick, vitelline membrane. (D) Nearly mature oocyte with a thin vitelline membrane. (After Balfour, Plate 25, *The Works of Francis Maitland Balfour*, ed. by Foster and Sedgwick, London, Macmillan, 1885.)

and "test" cells of the egg of *Styela* were ejected from the surface cytoplasm at the time of ovulation (Conklin, '05). A recent view, however, maintains that the test cells arise from follicle cells and come to lie in indentations of the periphery of the egg outside of the thin vitelline membrane (Tucker, '42). The chorion is formed by the inner layer of follicle cells and comes to lie between the test cells and the inner layer of follicle cells in the mature egg (fig. 91A). At ovulation the chorion moves away from the surface of the oocyte. At this time also, the test cells move outward from their indentations in the peripheral ooplasm and come to lie in the perivitelline space between the egg surface and the chorion (fig. 91B). An ooplasmic membrane which

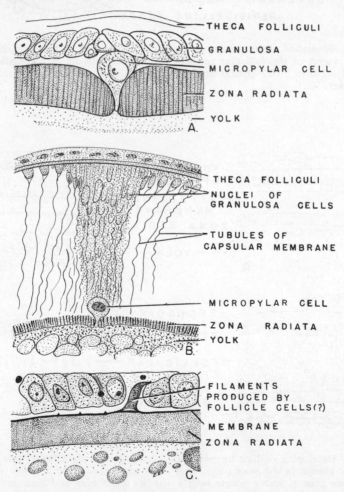

FIG. 93. Vitelline membranes of certain teleost fishes. (After Eigenmann, 1890.)   (A) *Pygosteus pungtius.* Radial section through micropyle of egg about 0.4 mm. in diameter. (B) Radial section through micropyle of egg of *Perca,* the perch.   (C) Vitelline membranes of *Fundulus heteroclitus* about 0.8 mm. in diameter.

represents the thin surface layer of ooplasm is present. However, it does not separate from the periphery of the egg at fertilization. During its early development, the embryo remains within this chorionic shell. The chorion thus represents the **primary embryonic membrane** of this species.

b) EGG MEMBRANES OF *Amphioxus*. Two surface membranes are formed and eventually separate from the egg of *Amphioxus*. The outer vitelline membrane is elaborated on the surface of the egg and remains in contact with this surface until about the time of the first maturation division. It then begins to separate from the egg's surface. (See Chap. 5.) After the sperm enters and the second maturation division occurs, a second, rather thick, vitelline membrane also separates from the egg. The first and second vitelline membranes then fuse together and become greatly expanded to form the **primary embryonic membrane.** (See Chap. 5.) A thin ooplasmic membrane remains at the egg's surface.

c) VITELLINE MEMBRANE AND ZONA RADIATA OF ELASMOBRANCH FISHES. In the egg of the shark, *Scyllium canicula,* two egg membranes are formed, an outer and an inner membrane. The outer membrane is a **homogeneous vitelline membrane,** while the membrane which comes to lie beneath this outer membrane has a radiate appearance and hence may be called a **zona radiata.** This latter membrane soon loses its radiate appearance and becomes a thin membrane along the inner aspect of the vitelline membrane (fig. 92A, B). In the mature egg both of these membranes form a thin, composite, vitelline membrane (fig. 92C, D). At about the time of fertilization the latter membrane separates from the egg's surface; a perivitelline space then lies between these structures and the surface ooplasm of the egg.

d) ZONA RADIATA OF TELEOST FISHES. The surface ooplasm in teleost fishes gives origin to a membrane which in many cases has a radiate appearance. In some species this membrane appears to be composed of two layers. This radiate membrane which forms at the surface of the egg of teleost fishes appears to be the product of the ooplasm, and, therefore, should be regarded as a true vitelline membrane. In the perch a **true chorion** also is formed as a gelatinous or filamentous layer produced external to the radiate membrane by the follicle cells (fig. 93B). In *Fundulus heteroclitus* there are apparently three distinct parts to the membrane which surrounds the ooplasm of the egg:

(1) a zona radiata,
(2) a thin structureless membrane external to the zona, and,
(3) the filamentous layer whose filaments are joined to the thin membrane around the zona (fig. 93C).

These three layers are probably derived from the ooplasm of the egg (Eigenmann, '90). Consequently, the filamentous chorion or gelatinous layer, if derived from the egg itself, is not a **true chorion** in this particular egg.

VITELLINE MEMBRANE
FOLLICLE LAYER

FIG. 94. Vitelline membrane of an almost mature egg of the frog.

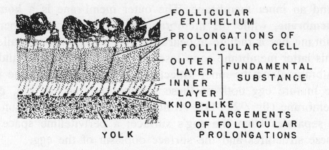

FOLLICULAR EPITHELIUM
PROLONGATIONS OF FOLLICULAR CELL
OUTER LAYER } FUNDAMENTAL
INNER LAYER } SUBSTANCE
KNOB-LIKE ENLARGEMENTS OF FOLLICULAR PROLONGATIONS
YOLK

FIG. 95. Zona radiata (zona pellucida) or vitelline membrane of *Chrysemys picta*. (After Thing, '18.)

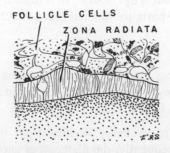

FOLLICLE CELLS
ZONA RADIATA

FIG. 96. Zona radiata of the egg of the fowl. (After Brambell, '25.)

At one end of the forming egg, a follicle cell sends an enlarged pseudopodium-like process inward to the surface of the egg. As a result of this enlarged extension of the follicle cell to the ooplasmic surface, an enlarged pore-like opening in the zona radiata is formed. This opening persists as the micropyle after the egg leaves the ovary (fig. 93A).

As the teleost egg is spawned, the chorionic layer hardens when it comes in contact with the water. If fertilization occurs, the surface of the egg emits a fluid and shrinks inward from the zona radiata. In this manner, a **perivitelline space** is formed between the egg, and the zona is filled with a fluid. The egg is thus free to revolve inside of the zona (Chap. 5).

e) VITELLINE MEMBRANE (ZONA RADIATA) IN Amphibia. In the amphibia, a vitelline membrane is formed probably by the surface ooplasm, although there may be contributions by the follicle cells of the ovary (Noble, '31, p. 281). This membrane separates from the egg at the time of fertilization, forming a perivitelline space (fig. 94). The latter space is filled with fluid. Later the vitelline membrane expands greatly to accommodate the developing embryo. A delicate surface layer or membrane forms the outer portion of the ooplasm below the vitelline membrane. In some amphibia the vitelline membrane may have a radiate appearance.

f) ZONA RADIATA (ZONA PELLUCIDA) OF THE REPTILE OOCYTE. In the turtle group, the development of the zona radiata (pellucida) appears to be the product of the follicle cells (Thing, '18). Filamentous prolongations of the follicle cells extend to the surface ooplasm of the developing egg (fig. 95). A homogeneous substance produced by the follicle cells then fills the spaces between these prolongations. The filamentous extensions of the follicle cells in this way produce a radiating system of canals passing through the homogeneous substance; hence the name, zona radiata. Bhattacharya describes Golgi substance as passing from the follicle cells through the canals of the zona radiata into the egg's ooplasm in the developing eggs of *Testudo graeca* and *Uromastix hardwicki*. (See Brambell, '25, p. 147.)

In contradistinction to the above interpretation, Retzius ('12) describes the homogeneous substance which forms the **zona radiata** of the lizard, *Lacerta viridis,* as originating from the ooplasm of the egg.

g) VITELLINE MEMBRANE (ZONA RADIATA) OF THE HEN'S EGG. The vitelline membrane, as in the turtle groups, appears to form about the young oocyte as a result of contributions from the surrounding follicle cells although the superficial ooplasm of the oocyte may contribute some substance. This occurs before the rapid deposition of yolk within the developing oocyte. It is probable that the follicle cells send small pseudopodium-like strands of cytoplasm through the numerous perforations of the very thin vitelline membrane around the oocyte's surface into the superficial ooplasm in a similar manner to that which occurs in reptiles. The vitelline membrane (zona radiata) thus assumes a radiate appearance as it increases in thickness (figs. 47, 96).

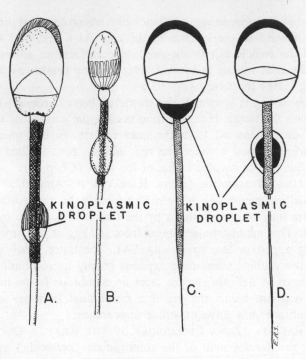

FIG. 97. Kinoplasmic bead or droplet upon the middle piece of mammalian sperm. (A) Pig sperm. (After Retzius, Biol. Untersuchungen, New Series, 10; Stockholm: Jena.) (B) Cat sperm. (After Retzius, Biol. Untersuchungen, New Series, 10; Stockholm: Jena.) (C–D) Dog sperm. (C) Upper part of epididymis. (D) Lower or caudal part of epididymis.

When the vitelline membrane thickens, the loci where the cytoplasmic strands from the follicle cells pass through the membrane become little canals or canaliculi. As the oocyte increases in size, a thin space forms between the vitelline membrane or zona radiata and the follicle cells; it is filled with fluid and forms the follicular space. The egg now is free to rotate within the follicle. In consequence, the pole of the egg containing the blastodisc always appears uppermost. Due to the increasing pendency of the egg follicle as the egg matures, the blastodisc comes to rest, a short while previous to ovulation, at the base of the pedicle where the blood vessels are most abundant (fig. 47B). During the latter phases of oocyte development, the vitelline membrane constitutes an osmotic membrane through which all nourishment must pass to the oocyte, particularly in its later stages of growth. The surface ooplasm forms a delicate surface membrane beneath the zona radiata.

h) MEMBRANES OF THE MAMMALIAN OOCYTE. All mammalian oocytes possess a membrane known as the **zona pellucida.** It is a homogeneous layer interposed between the ooplasm and the follicle cells. By some investigators it is regarded as a product of the oocyte, while others regard it as a contribution of the ooplasm and follicle cells. The majority opinion, however, derives the zona pellucida from the follicle cells. In addition to the **zona pellucida,** the oocyte of the prototherian mammals has a striate layer lying close to the surface of the oocyte. This striated layer probably is derived from the surface ooplasm. This membrane later disappears, and a perivitelline space occupies the general area between the surface of the oocyte and the zona pellucida (fig. 46; Chap. 5). The zona pellucida separates from the egg surface after sperm contact.

5. Physiological Maturation of the Gametes

a. Physiological Differentiation of the Sperm

Added to the nuclear and cytoplasmic transformations of the sperm described above, a further process of sperm ripening or **maturing** appears to be necessary. In the mammal, for example, the sperm cell must pass through the epididymis to achieve the ability to fertilize the egg. This is shown by the fact that sperm taken from the seminiferous tubules will not fertilize, although, morphologically, two sperm, one from the testis and one from the epididymis cannot be distinguished other than by the presence in some mammals of the so-called "kinoplasmic droplet" (figs. 82D, 97). These droplets do not appear in great numbers upon ejaculated sperm but are found on sperm, particularly in epididymides. It is possible that these droplets may arise from a secretion from the epididymal cells (Collery, '44). In the dog, these droplets are attached to the neck of the sperm in the caput epididymidis but are found at the posterior end of the middle piece of the sperm in the cauda epididymidis and vas deferens and are probably lost at the time of ejaculation (Collery, '44). Investigators differ greatly in interpreting the significance of this body. However, these droplets do seem in some way to be directly or indirectly concerned with the physiological maturing of the sperm. In this connection Collery ('44) notes that sperm are probably motile on leaving the seminiferous tubules, but active forward movement is not seen until the bead has reached the junction of middle piece and tail.

In the fowl, Domm ('30, p. 318) suggests the probability that the sperm may undergo an aging or ripening process essential for reproduction somewhere in the reproductive system other than the seminiferous tubules. The work of Lipsett quoted in Humphrey ('45) suggests that the accessory reproductive system also is necessary for a ripening process of the sperm in urodele amphibia.

On the other hand, in the frog, sperm taken from the testis have the ability to fertilize eggs. In this case, the sperm probably undergo a physiological ripening in the testis along with morphological differentiation.

The foregoing considerations suggest that a physiological maturation of the sperm is necessary to enable the sperm to take part in the fertilization process.

b. Physiological Ripening of the Female Gamete

The physiological maturing of the oocyte is linked to factors which influence the developing egg at about the time the maturation divisions occur. Sea-urchin sperm may penetrate the egg before the maturation divisions occur (Chap. 5). However, development does not take place in such instances. On the other hand, sperm entrance after both maturation divisions are completed initiates normal development. In the protochordate, *Styela,* marked cortical changes transpire at about the time the egg leaves the ovary, and as it reaches the sea water, the germinal vesicle begins to break down. The oocyte becomes fertilizable at about this time. In *Amphioxus,* although the first polar body is given off within the adult body, the egg apparently is not fertilizable until it reaches the external salt-water environment. The secondary oocyte of the frog presumably must remain within the uterus for a time to ripen in order that ensuing development may be normal. These and other instances suggest that physiological changes—changes which are imperative for the normal development of the egg—are effected at about the time that the maturation divisions occur.

D. Summary of Egg and Sperm Development

From the foregoing it may be seen that the development of the gametes in either sex involves a process of maturation. This maturation entails changes in the structure and constitution of the nucleus and cytoplasm, and, further, a functional or physiological ripening must occur. The comparative maturation events in the egg and sperm may be summarized as follows:

Egg (in Oogenesis)	Sperm (in Spermatogenesis)
1. Nuclear maturation	1. Nuclear maturation
a. Homologous chromosomes synapse and undergo profound changes during which parts of homologous chromosomes may be interchanged; ultimately, the chromosome number is reduced to the haploid number	a. (Similar to the female)
b. Nucleus enlarges, and contained nuclear fluid increases greatly; ultimately the nuclear fluid is contributed to cytoplasm upon germinal vesicle break down	b. Nucleus remains relatively small and enlargement is slight; nuclear fluid small in amount; during spermiogenesis the nucleus may contract into a compact mass; considerable elongation of nucleus occurs in many species
c. Nuclear maturation occurs simultaneously with cytoplasmic differentiation	c. Nuclear maturation occurs before spermiogenesis or cytoplasmic differentiation

Egg (in Oogenesis)	*Sperm (in Spermatogenesis)*
2. Cytoplasmic maturation This involves:	2. Cytoplasmic maturation This involves:
a. Polarization of cytoplasmic materials and the nucleus in relation to the future maturation phenomena; the nucleus becomes displaced toward one pole, the animal pole, and the yolk, and other cytoplasmic materials; in many eggs becomes displaced toward the opposite or vegetal pole	a. Polarization of nucleus and cytoplasmic materials along an elongated antero-posterior axis, with the head, neck, middle piece, and tail occupying specific regions along this axis. The nucleus occupies a considerable portion of the anterior region or head
b. Formation of deutoplasm or stored food material, varying greatly in amount in different animal species. The deutoplasm is composed of fats, carbohydrates, and protein substances	b. Little food substances stored within cytoplasm; food reserve in seminal fluid
c. Cytoplasm increased in amount; formation of basic organ-forming areas or cytoplasmic stuffs from which the future embryo arises	c. Discarding of a considerable amount of cytoplasm, some Golgi elements and mitochondria. Retention of some Golgi elements, centrioles, mitochondria, etc.
d. Formation of primary embryonic membranes	d. No specific membranes formed around sperm, although elaborate membranes for motile purposes are formed in some sperm
3. Physiological maturation or the development of a fertilizable stage This involves:	3. Physiological maturation or the development of the ability to contact and fertilize the egg This involves:
a. Formation of an organization which when stimulated by external influences initiates and carries on the processes necessary for normal embryonic development	a. Development of an organization which, when stimulated by proper external substances, responds by a directed movement resulting in locomotion; also capable of being attracted by egg substances
b. Acquisition of ability to enter into a developmental union with a sperm	b. Acquisition of ability to fertilize, i.e., to enter into a developmental union with an egg or oocyte
c. Development of ability to form and secrete gynogamic substances which aid in the fertilization process. (See Chap. 5)	c. Acquisition of ability to produce and secrete androgamic substances which aid in the fertilization process
d. Assumption of an inhibited or dormant condition during which metabolic processes proceed slowly in anticipation of the fertilization event	d. Assumption of an active metabolic state

Bibliography

Asdell, S. A. **1946.** Patterns of Mammalian Reproduction. Comstock Publishing Co., Inc., Ithaca, New York.

Benoit, J. **1930.** Destruction des gonocytes primaires dans le blastoderme du poulet par les rayons ultra-violets, aux premiers stades du developpement embryonnaire. Proc. 2nd Internat. Cong. for Sex Research. p. 162.

Berrill, N. J. and Liu, C. K. **1948.** Germplasm, Weismann, and *Hydrozoa*. Quart. Rev. Biol. **23**:124.

Bolles, Lee A. **1897.** Les cinèses spermatogénétiques chez *l'Helix pomatia*. La Cellule. **13**:199.

Bounoure, L. **1939.** L'origine des Cellules Reproductrices et le Problème de la Lignée Germinale Gauthier Villars, Paris.

Boveri, T. **1887.** Über differenzierung der Zellkerne während der Furchung des Eies von *Ascaris megalocephala*. Anat. Anz. **2**:688.

――. **1892.** Über die Entstehung des Gegensatzes zwischen den Geschlechtszellen und den somatischen Zellen bei *Ascaris megalocephala*. Sitz. d. Gesellsch. f. Morph. u. Physiol. München. **8**:114.

――. **1910a.** Über die Teilung centrifugierter Eier von *Ascaris megalocephala*. Arch. f. Entwicklungsmech der Organ. **30**(2):101.

――. **1910b.** Die Potenzen der *Ascaris*-Blastomeren bei abgeänderter Furchung. Festschrift für R. Hertwig. **3**:131.

Bowen, R. H. **1922.** On the idiosome, Golgi apparatus, and acrosome in the male germ cells. Anat. Rec. **24**:159.

――. **1922.** Studies on insect spermatogenesis. J. Morphol. **37**:79.

Brachet, J. **1947.** Nucleic acids in the cell and the embryo, in Symposia of the Society for Experimental Biology, No. 1, Nucleic Acid. p. 207.

――. **1950.** Chemical Embryology. Interscience Publishers, Inc., New York.

Brambell, F. W. R. **1925.** The oogenesis of the fowl *(Gallus bankiva)*. Philos. Tr. Roy. Soc., London, s.B. **214**:113.

――. **1930.** The Development of Sex in Vertebrates. The Macmillan Co., New York.

――, Parkes, A. S., and Fielding, V. **1927a.** Changes in the ovary of the mouse following exposures to x-rays. I. Irradiation at three weeks old. Proc. Roy. Soc., London, s.B. **101**:29.

――, ――, and ――. **1927b.** Changes in the ovary of the mouse following exposures to x-rays. II. Irradiation at or before birth. Proc. Roy. Soc., London, s.B. **101**:95.

Brown, G. L., Callan, H. G., and Leaf, G. **1950.** Chemical nature of the nuclear sap. Nature, London. **165**:600.

Collery, L. **1944.** Note on the physiology of the mammalian epididymis and spermatozoon. Proc. Roy. Irish Acad. **49**: Section B, 213.

Conklin, E. G. **1905.** The organization and cell-lineage of the ascidian egg. J. Acad. Nat. Sc. Philadelphia. **13**:5.

――. **1932.** The embryology of *Amphioxus*. J. Morphol. **54**:69.

De Robertis, E. D. P., Nowinski, W. W., and Saez, F. A. **1948.** General Cytology. W. B. Saunders Co., Philadelphia.

Domm, L. V. **1930.** Artificial insemination with motile sperm from ovariectomized fowl. Proc. Soc. Exper. Biol. & Med. **28**:316.

Dürkin, B. **1932.** Experimental Analysis of Development. W. W. Norton & Co., Inc., New York.

Duryee, W. R. **1950.** Chromosomal physiology in relation to nuclear structure. Ann. New York Acad. Sc. **50**:920.

Eigenmann, C. H. **1890.** On the egg membranes and micropyle of some osseous fishes. Bull. Mus. Comp. Zool. at Harvard College. **19**:129.

Evans, H. M. and Swezy, O. **1931.** Ovogenesis and the normal follicular cycle in adult mammalia. Memoirs. The University of California Press. **9**: No. 3.

Everett, N. B. **1945.** The present status of the germ-cell problem in vertebrates. Biol. Rev. **20**:45.

Fankhauser, G. **1948.** The organization of the amphibian egg during fertilization and cleavage. Ann. New York Acad. Sc. **49**:684.

Flynn, T. T. and Hill, J. P. **1939.** The development of the *Monotremata,* Part IV. Growth of the ovarian ovum, maturation, fertilization and early cleavage. Tr. Zool. Soc. London. **24**: Part 6, 445.

Gatenby, J. B. and Beams, H. W. **1935.** The cytoplasmic inclusions in the spermatogenesis of man. Quart. J. Micr. Sc. **78**:1.

———— and Woodger, J. H. **1921.** The cytoplasmic inclusions of the germ cells. Part IX. On the origin of the Golgi apparatus on the middle-piece of the ripe sperm of Cavia, and the development of the acrosome. Quart. J. Micr. Sc. **65**:265.

Goldsmith, J. B. **1935.** The primordial germ cells of the chick. I. The effect on the gonad of complete and partial removal of the "germinal" crescent and of removal of other parts of the blastodisc. J. Morphol. **58**:537.

Hegner, R. W. **1914.** The germ cell cycle in animals. The Macmillan Co., New York.

Heys, F. **1931.** The problem of the origin of germ cells. Quart. Rev. Biol. **6**:1.

Humphrey, R. R. **1925.** The primordial germ cells of *Hemidactylium* and other *Amphibia.* J. Morphol. & Physiol. **41**:1.

————. **1927.** Extirpation of the primordial germ cells of *Amblystoma;* its effect upon the development of the gonad. J. Exper. Zool. **49**:363.

————. **1945.** Sex determination in *Ambystomid* salamanders. Am. J. Anat. **76**:33.

Jones, R. M. **1949.** The use of vital staining in the study of the origin of germ cells in the female rat, *Mus norwegicus.* J. Morphol. **84**:293.

King, R. N. and Beams, H. W. **1938.** An experimental study of chromatin diminution in *Ascaris.* J. Exper. Zool. **77**:425.

Leblond, C. P. **1950.** Distribution of periodic acid-reactive carbohydrates in the adult rat. Am. J. Anat. **86**:1.

Leuchtenberger, C. and Schrader, F. **1950.** The chemical nature of the acrosome in the male germ cells. Proc. Nat. Acad. Sc. **36**:677.

Maréchal, J. **1907.** Sur l'ovogénèse des sélaciens et de quelques autres chordates. La Cellule. **24**:15.

Moore, C. R. and Wang, H. **1947.** Ovarian activity in mammals subsequent to chemical injury of the cortex. Physiol. Zoöl. **20**:300.

Nieuwkoop, P. D. **1947.** Experimental investigations on the origin and determination of the germ cells, and on the development of the lateral plates and germ ridges in urodeles. Arch. néerl. de zool. **8**:1.

————. **1949.** The present state of the problem of the "Keimbahn" in the vertebrates. Experientia. **5**:308.

Noble, G. K. **1931.** Biology of the Amphibia. McGraw-Hill Book Co., Inc., New York.

Northrop, J. H. **1949.** Chap. I. Enzymes and the synthesis of proteins in The Chemistry and Physiology of Growth. Edited by Parpart, A. K. Princeton University Press, Princeton, New Jersey.

Nussbaum, M. **1880.** Zur Differenzirung des Geschlechts im Thierreich. Arch. f. mikr. anat. **18**:1.

Palade, G. E. and Claude, A. **1949.** The nature of the Golgi apparatus. I. Parallelism between intercellular myelin figures and Golgi apparatus in somatic cells. II. Identification of the Golgi apparatus with a complex of myelin figures. J. Morphol. **85**:35, 71.

Parkes, A. S. **1927.** On the occurrence of the oestrous cycle after x-ray sterilization. Part III. The periodicity of oestrus after sterilization of the adult. Proc. Roy. Soc. London, s.B. **101**:421.

Pincus, G. **1936.** The Eggs of Mammals. The Macmillan Co., New York.

Retzius, G. **1912.** Zur Kenntnis der Hüllen und besonders des Follikelepithelels an den Eiern der Wirbeltiere. Biol. Untersuch. N.F. **17**:1.

Sharp, L. W. **1934.** Introduction to Cytology. 3d ed., 441–445. McGraw-Hill Book Co., Inc., New York.

————. **1943.** Fundamentals of Cytology. 1st ed. McGraw-Hill Book Co., Inc., New York.

Snyder, L. H. **1945.** The Principles of Heredity. 3d ed. D. C. Heath and Co., New York, Boston, London.

Thing, A. 1918. The formation and structure of the zona pellucida in the ovarian eggs of turtles. Am. J. Anat. 23:237.

Tucker, G. H. 1942. The histology of the gonads and development of the egg envelopes in an ascidian (Styela plicata Lesueur). J. Morphol. 70:81.

van der Stricht, O. 1923. Etude comparée des ovules des mammifères aux differentes périodes de l'ovogénèse. Arch. biol., Paris. 33:229.

Vincent, W. S. and Dornfeld, E. J. 1948. Localization and role of nucleic acids in the developing rat ovary. Am. J. Anat. 83:437.

Waldeyer, W. 1870. Eierstock und Ei. Wilhelm Engelmann, Leipzig.

Weismann, A. 1893. The Germ-plasm—A Theory of Heredity. English translation by W. N. Parker and H. Rönnfeldt. Walter Scott, Ltd., London.

White, M. J. D. 1945. Animal Cytology and Evolution. Cambridge University Press, London.

Willier, B. H. 1937. Experimentally produced sterile gonads and the problem of the origin of germ cells in the chick embryo. Anat. Rec. 70:89.

Wilson, E. B. 1925. The Cell in Development and Heredity. 3d ed., p. 310. The Macmillan Co., New York.

Winiwarter, H. von. 1900. Recherches sur l'ovogénèse et l'organogénèse de l'ovaire des mammifères (lapin et homme). Arch. biol., Paris. 17:3.

Witschi, E. 1939. Chap. IV in Allen, et al., Sex and Internal Secretions. 2d ed., The Williams and Wilkins Co., Baltimore.

———. 1948. Migration of the germ cells of human embryos from the yolk sac to the primitive gonadal folds. Carnegie Inst., Washington Publ. 575. Contrib. Embryol. 32:67.

PART II

The Period of Fertilization

The period of fertilization involves:

(1) The **transportation of the gametes** to the site normal for the species where environmental conditions are suitable for gametic union (Chap. 4), and

(2) **Fertilization** or the union of the gametes (Chap. 5).

The union of the gametes may be divided into two phases, viz.:

(1) The **primary phase** which is terminated when the sperm has made intimate contact with the egg's surface, and

(2) The **secondary phase** or the fusion of the two gametes resulting in the initiation of development.

4

Transportation of the Gametes (Sperm and Egg) from the Germ Glands to the Site Where Fertilization Normally Occurs

A. Introduction
  1. Activities of the male and female gametes in their migration to the site of fertilization
B. Transportation of the sperm within the male accessory reproductive structures
  1. Transportation of sperm from the testis to the external orifice of the genital duct in the mammal
    a. Possible factors involved in the passage of the seminal fluid from the testis to the main reproductive duct
      1) Accumulated pressure within the seminiferous tubules
      2) Activities within the efferent ductules of the testis
    b. Movement of the semen along the epididymal duct
      1) Probable immotility of the sperm
      2) Importance of muscle contraction, particularly in the vas deferens
      3) Summary of factors which propel the seminal fluid from the testis to the external orifice of the reproductive duct in the mammal
  2. Transportation of sperm in other vertebrates with a convoluted reproductive duct
  3. Transportation of sperm from the testis in vertebrates possessing a relatively simple reproductive duct
C. Transportation of sperm outside of the genital tract of the male
  1. Transportation of sperm in the external watery medium
  2. Transportation of sperm in forms where fertilization of the egg is internal
    a. General features relative to internal fertilization
      1) Comparative numbers of vertebrates practicing internal fertilization
      2) Sites or areas where fertilization is effected
      3) Means of sperm transfer from the male genital tract to that of the female
    b. Methods of sperm transport within the female reproductive tract
      1) When fertilization is in the lower or posterior portion of the genital tract
      2) When fertilization occurs in the upper extremity of the oviduct
      3) When fertilization occurs in the ovary
D. Sperm survival in the female genital tract
E. Sperm survival outside the male and female tracts
  1. In watery solutions under spawning conditions
  2. Sperm survival under various artificial conditions; practical application in animal breeding

F. Transportation of the egg from the ovary to the site of fertilization
   1. Definitions
   2. Transportation of the egg in those forms where fertilization occurs in the anterior portion of the oviduct
      a. Birds
      b. Mammals
   3. Transportation of the egg in those species where fertilization is effected in the caudal portion of the oviduct or in the external medium
      a. Frog
      b. Other amphibia
      c. Fishes
G. Summary of the characteristics of various mature chordate eggs together with the site of fertilization and place of sperm entrance into the egg

A. Introduction

1. Activities of the Male and Female Gametes in Their Migration to the Site of Fertilization

The first step in the actual process of fertilization and the reproduction of a new individual is the transportation of the mature gametes from the place of their development in the reproductive structures to the area or site where conditions are optimum for their union (fig. 98). This transport is dependent upon the development of the proper reproductive conditions in the male and the female parent—a state governed by sex hormones. That is to say, the sex hormones regulate the behavior of the parents and the reproductive ducts in such a way that the reproductive act is possible.

The transport of the female gamete to the site of fertilization is a passive one, effected by the behavior of the reproductive structures. Also, the transportation of the sperm within the confines of the male tract largely is a passive affair. However, outside of the male reproductive tract, sperm motility is a factor in effecting the contact of the sperm with the egg. Not only is sperm motility a factor in the external watery medium of those species accustomed to external fertilization, but also to some degree within the female genital tract in those species utilizing internal fertilization. However, in the latter case, sperm transport is aided greatly by the activities of the female genital tract.

B. Transportation of the Sperm Within the Male Accessory Reproductive Structures

1. Transportation of Sperm from the Testis to the External Orifice of the Genital Duct in the Mammal

Sperm transport within the male genital tract of the mammal is a slow process. It might be defined better by saying that it is efficiently slow, for the ripening process of the sperm described in the previous chapter is dependent

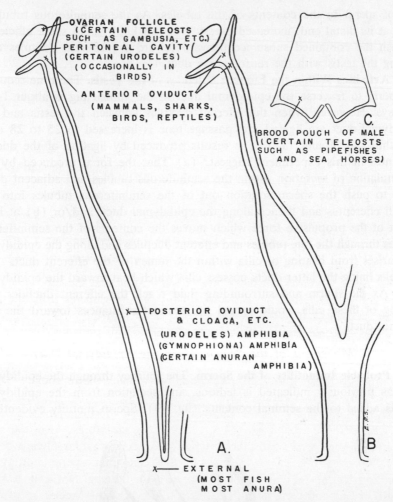

FIG. 98. Sites of normal fertilization (x) in the vertebrate group. (A, C) Vertebrates below mammals. (B) Mammalia.

upon a lingering passage of the sperm through the epididymal portion of the male genital tract.

a. Possible Factors Involved in the Passage of the Seminal Fluid from the Testis to the Main Reproductive Duct

1) Accumulated Pressure Within the Seminiferous Tubules. The oozing of sperm and seminal fluid from the seminiferous tubules through the rete tubules into the efferent ductules of the epididymis possibly may be the result of accumulated pressure within the seminiferous tubules themselves. This pressure may arise from secretions of the Sertoli cells, the infiltration of fluids from the interstitial areas between the seminiferous tubules, and by the addition of sperm to the contents of the tubules. As the seminiferous tubule is blind at its distal end, increased pressure of this kind would serve efficiently to push the contained substance forward toward the efferent ductules connecting the testis with the reproductive duct.

2) Activities Within the Efferent Ductules of the Testis. The time required for sperm to traverse the epididymal duct in the guinea pig is about 14 to 16 days. However, when the efferent ductules between the testis and the epididymal duct are ligated, the passage time is increased to 25 to 28 days (Toothill and Young, '31). The results produced by ligation of the ductuli efferentes in this experiment suggest: (a) That the force produced by the accumulation of secretion within the seminiferous tubules and adjacent ducts tends to push the sperm solution out of the seminiferous tubules into the ductuli efferentes and thence along the epididymal duct, and/or (b) at least a part of the propulsive force which moves the contents of the seminiferous tubules through the rete tubules and efferent ductules and along the epididymal duct arises from beating of cilia within the lumen of the efferent ducts. The tall cells lining the latter ducts possess cilia which beat toward the epididymal duct. As the sperm and surrounding fluid reach the efferent ductules, the beating of these cilia would propel the seminal substances toward the epididymal duct.

b. Movement of the Semen Along the Epididymal Duct

1) Probable Immotility of the Sperm. The journey through the epididymal duct as previously indicated is tedious, and secretion from the epididymal cells is added to the seminal contents (fig. 99). Sperm motility evidently is

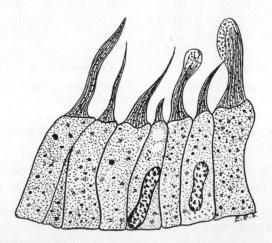

FIG. 99. Human epididymal cells. (Slightly modified from Maximow and Bloom: *A Textbook of Histology,* Philadelphia, W. B. Saunders Co.) These cells discharge secretion into the lumen of the epididymal duct. Observe large, non-motile stereocilia at distal end of the cells.

not a major factor in sperm passage along the epididymal portion of the reproductive duct, as conditions within the duct appear to suppress this motility. It has been shown, for example (Hartman, '39, p. 681), that sperm motility increases for trout sperm at a pH of 7.0 to 8.0, in the mammals a pH of a little over 7.0 seems optimum for motility for most species, while in the rooster a pH of 7.6 to 8.0 stimulates sperm movements. On the other hand, an increase of the CO_2 concentration of the medium raises the hydrogen ion concentration of the suspension. The latter condition suppresses sperm motility and increases the life of sea-urchin sperm (Cohn, '17, '18). These facts relative to the influence of pH on the motility of sperm suggest that motility during the slow and relatively long epididymal journey—a journey which may take weeks—apparently is inhibited by the production of carbon dioxide by the large aggregate of sperm within the lumen of the epididymal duct, a condition which serves to keep the spermatic fluid on the acid side. This suppressed activity of the sperm in turn increases their longevity. The matter of sperm motility within the epididymal duct, however, needs more study before definite conclusions can be reached relative to the actual presence or absence of motility.

2) Importance of Muscle Contraction, Particularly of the Vas Deferens. If sperm are relatively immobilized during their passage through the epididymal duct by the accumulation of carbon dioxide, we must assume that their transport through this area is due mainly to the activities of the accessory structures together with some pressure from testicular secretion and efferent-ductule activity as mentioned above. Aside from the forward propulsion resulting from the accumulation of glandular secretion within the epididymal duct, muscle contraction appears to be the main factor involved in effecting this transport. The epididymal musculature is not well developed, and muscle contraction in this area may be effective but not pronounced. However, added to the contracture of the epididymal musculature is the *contraction of the well-developed musculature of the vas deferens* (fig. 100). During sexual stimulation this organ contracts vigorously, producing strong peristaltic waves which move caudally along the duct. The activity of the vas deferens may be regarded as a kind of "pump action" which produces suction sufficient to move the seminal fluid from the caudal portions of the epididymis, i.e., from the cauda epididymidis into the vas deferens where it is propelled toward the external orifice. Furthermore, the removal of materials from the cauda epididymidis would tend to aid the movement of the entire contents of the epididymal duct forward toward the cauda epididymidis. From this point of view, the vas deferens is an efficient organ for sperm transport, while the epididymal duct functions as a nursery and a "storage organ" for the sperm (see Chap. 1). Some sperm also are stored in the ampullary portion of the vas deferens (fig. 101), but this storage is of secondary importance inasmuch as sperm do not retain their viability in this area over extended periods of time.

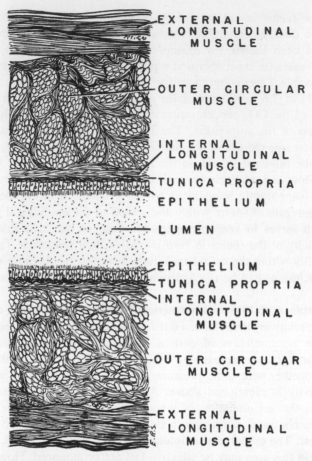

EXTERNAL
LONGITUDINAL
MUSCLE

OUTER CIRCULAR
MUSCLE

INTERNAL
LONGITUDINAL
MUSCLE
TUNICA PROPRIA
EPITHELIUM

LUMEN

EPITHELIUM
TUNICA PROPRIA
INTERNAL
LONGITUDINAL
MUSCLE

OUTER CIRCULAR
MUSCLE

EXTERNAL
LONGITUDINAL
MUSCLE

FIG. 100. Highly muscular character of the ductus deferens. This particular drawing was made from a longitudinal section of the ductus deferens of a young rat. Observe cilia (stereocilia?) on inner surface of epithelium, lining the lumen.

3) Summary of Factors Which Propel the Seminal Fluid from the Testis to the External Orifice of the Reproductive Duct in the Mammal.

The following probable influences are at work, propelling sperm from the testis through the accessory ducts in the mammal:

(1) The pressure of accumulated secretions within the seminiferous tubules may push the sperm outward toward the accessory ducts;

(2) the beating of cilia and accumulation of secretion within the ductuli efferentes is another probable force which ushers the sperm and seminal fluid forward;

(3) the secretion from the cells of the anterior epididymis and the body of the epididymis may serve, together with weak muscle contraction, to advance the sperm mass toward the posterior epididymis;

(4) the possibility of a weak sperm motility aiding the advance of the sperm through the body of the epididymis must not be denied;

(5) the vigorous pumping action of the vas deferens, especially during the stimulation attending ejaculation, serves to transport the sperm from the "epididymal well" (the cauda epididymidis) through the vas deferens to the external areas.

2. TRANSPORTATION OF SPERM IN OTHER VERTEBRATES WITH A CONVOLUTED REPRODUCTIVE DUCT

The transportation of sperm in other vertebrates which possess an extended and complicated reproductive duct similar to that of the mammal presumably involves the same general principles observed above (fig. 105A, B). However, certain variations of sperm passage exist which are correlated with structural modifications of the accessory reproductive organs. For example, the reproductive duct may be somewhat more tortuous and complicated in some instances, such as in the pigeon, turkey, and domestic cock (figs. 102, 105B). That is, the entire deferent duct extending from the epididymis caudally to the cloaca may be regarded as a sperm-storage organ, as sperm may be collected in large numbers all along the reproductive duct. As the cock is capable of effecting repeated ejaculations over an extended period of time,

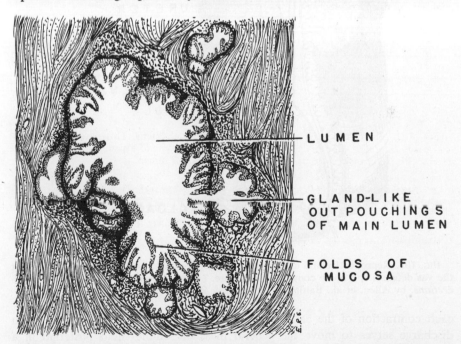

LUMEN

GLAND-LIKE OUTPOUCHINGS OF MAIN LUMEN

FOLDS OF MUCOSA

FIG. 101. Portion of a cross section of the ampullary region of the ductus deferens in man. Observe gland-like outpouchings of the main lumen and character of mucosal folds. Surrounding the lumen may be seen the highly muscularized walls of the ampullary area.

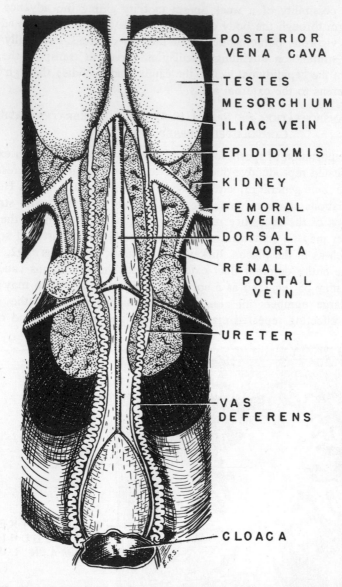

POSTERIOR
VENA CAVA

TESTES

MESORCHIUM

ILIAC VEIN

EPIDIDYMIS

KIDNEY

FEMORAL
VEIN

DORSAL
AORTA

RENAL
PORTAL
VEIN

URETER

VAS
DEFERENS

CLOACA

FIG. 102. Reproductive and urinary structures of the adult Leghorn cock. Observe that the vas deferens is a much convoluted structure. (After Domm: In *Sex and Internal Secretions,* by Allen, et al., Baltimore, Williams & Wilkins, 1939.)

each contraction of the caudal portion of the deferential duct during sperm discharge serves to move the general mass of seminal fluid posteriad in a gradual manner. The reproductive conditions present in the cock fulfill the requirements of a continuous breeder capable of serving many individual

FIG. 103. Amplexus in the toad, *Bufo fowleri*. (Modified from Rugh: *The Frog, Its Reproduction and Development*, Philadelphia, Blakiston, 1951.)

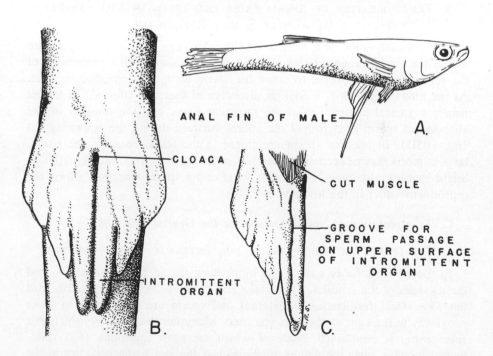

ANAL FIN OF MALE

A.

CLOACA

CUT MUSCLE

GROOVE FOR
SPERM PASSAGE
ON UPPER SURFACE
OF INTROMITTENT
ORGAN

INTROMITTENT
ORGAN

B.

C.

FIG. 104. Modifications of the fins of male fishes with the resulting elaboration of an intromittent organ. (A) *Gambusia affinis*. (B) Ventral view of pelvic fins of *Squalus acanthias*. (C) Dorsal view of left fin to show genital groove in intromittent structure.

185

females. It is to be observed in this connection that Mann ('49) gives the amount of ejaculate in the cock as 0.8 cc., highly concentrated with sperm.

Another variation found in certain birds is the presence of a seminal vesicle located at the caudal end of the reproductive duct. This outgrowth is a sperm-storage organ and is not comparable to the secretory seminal vesicle found in mammals. Such seminal vesicles are found in the robin, ovenbird, wood thrush, catbird, towhee, etc. These structures enlarge enormously during the breeding season, but in the fall and winter months they shrink into insignificant organs (Riddle, '27). It is apparent that the seminal fluid is moved along and stored at the distal (posterior) end of the reproductive duct in these species. Other birds, such as the pigeon and mourning dove, lack extensively developed seminal vesicles, but possess instead pouch-like enlargements of the caudal end of the reproductive duct when the breeding season is at its maximum.

In many lower vertebrates which practice internal fertilization, large seminal vesicles or enlargements of the caudal end of the reproductive duct are present. Such conditions are found in the elasmobranch fishes. These structures act as sperm-storage organs during the breeding season.

3. TRANSPORTATION OF SPERM FROM THE TESTIS IN VERTEBRATES POSSESSING A RELATIVELY SIMPLE REPRODUCTIVE DUCT

In forms such as the frog, toad, and hellbender (figs. 9, 105C), the pressure within the seminiferous tubules of the testis associated with contractions of the reproductive duct serve to move the sperm along the reproductive duct. At the time of spawning, a copious discharge of sperm is effected. In teleost fishes, a general contraction of the testicular tissue and the muscles of the abbreviated sperm duct propel the sperm outward during the spawning act (fig. 105D). In teleosts, sperm are stored in the testis, or as in the perch, large numbers may be accommodated within the reproductive duct (fig. 105D). Slight motility also may be a factor in effecting sperm transport down the reproductive duct in the lower vertebrates.

C. Transportation of Sperm Outside of the Genital Tract of the Male

1. TRANSPORTATION OF SPERM IN THE EXTERNAL WATERY MEDIUM

In most teleost fishes and in amphibia, such as the frogs and toads, and the urodeles of the families *Hynobiidae* and *Cryptobranchidae* (possibly also the *Sirenidae*), fertilization is external and sperm are discharged in close proximity to the eggs as they are spawned. Many are the ways by which this relationship is established, some of which are most ingenious (fig. 103). Sperm motility, once the watery medium near the egg is reached, brings the sperm into contact with the egg in most instances. However, exceptional cases are present where the sperm are "almost completely immobile," such as in

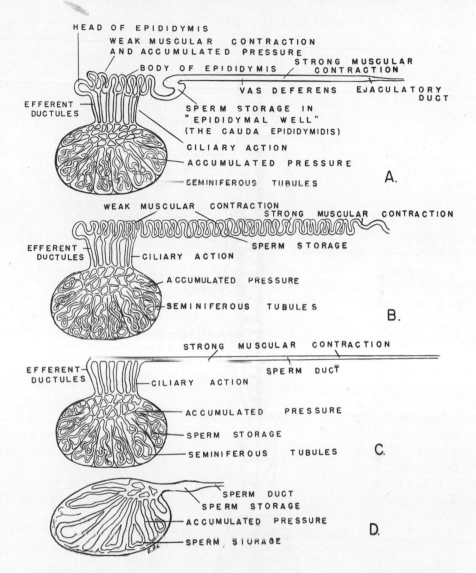

HEAD OF EPIDIDYMIS
WEAK MUSCULAR CONTRACTION
AND ACCUMULATED PRESSURE
BODY OF EPIDIDYMIS
STRONG MUSCULAR CONTRACTION
VAS DEFERENS   EJACULATORY DUCT
EFFERENT DUCTULES
SPERM STORAGE IN "EPIDIDYMAL WELL" (THE CAUDA EPIDIDYMIDIS)
CILIARY ACTION
ACCUMULATED PRESSURE
SEMINIFEROUS TUBULES   A.

WEAK MUSCULAR CONTRACTION
STRONG MUSCULAR CONTRACTION
EFFERENT DUCTULES
CILIARY ACTION
SPERM STORAGE
ACCUMULATED PRESSURE
SEMINIFEROUS TUBULES   B.

STRONG MUSCULAR CONTRACTION
EFFERENT DUCTULES
SPERM DUCT
CILIARY ACTION
ACCUMULATED PRESSURE
SPERM STORAGE
SEMINIFEROUS TUBULES   C.

SPERM DUCT
SPERM STORAGE
ACCUMULATED PRESSURE
SPERM STORAGE   D.

FIG. 105. Various types of reproductive ducts in male vertebrates. The possible activities which transport the sperm along the ducts are indicated. (A) Mammalian type. (B) Bird, urodele, elasmobranch fish type. (C) Frog type. (D) Teleost fish type.

the primitive frog, *Discoglossus* (see Hibbard, '28). Here the sperm must be deposited in close contact with the egg at the time of spawning. In fishes which lay pelagic eggs (i.e., eggs that float in the water and do not sink to the bottom), the male may swim about the female in an agitated manner during the spawning act. This behavior serves to broadcast the sperm in relation to the eggs.

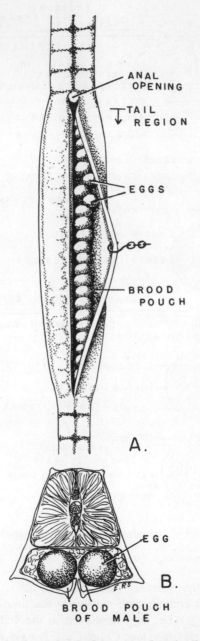

ANAL
OPENING

TAIL
REGION

EGGS

BROOD
POUCH

A.

EGG

B.

BROOD POUCH
OF MALE

E.R.S

FIG. 106. Brood pouch in the male pipefish. (A) Longitudinal view with left flap
pulled aside to show the developing eggs within the pouch. (B) Transverse section to
show relation of eggs to the pouch and dorsal region of the tail.

2. TRANSPORTATION OF SPERM IN FORMS WHERE FERTILIZATION OF THE EGG IS INTERNAL

a. General Features Relative to Internal Fertilization

1) Comparative Numbers of Vertebrates Practicing Internal Fertilization. Of the 60,000 or more species of vertebrates which have been described, a majority practice some form of internal fertilization of the egg. Internal fertilization, therefore, is a conspicuous characteristic of the reproductive phenomena of the vertebrate animal group.

2) Sites or Areas where Fertilization is Effected. The fertilization areas (fig. 98) for those vertebrates which utilize internal fertilization are:

(1) the lower portions of the oviduct near or at the external orifice,

(2) the oviduct, especially its upper extremity,

(3) possibly the peritoneal cavity,

(4) the follicles of the ovary, and

(5) the brood pouch of the male (figs. 98, 106).

Though the exact place where internal fertilization occurs may vary considerably throughout the vertebrate group as a whole, the specific site for each species is fairly constant.

3) Means of Sperm Transfer from the Male Genital Tract to That of the Female. In those fishes adapted to internal fertilization, sperm transport from the male to the female is brought about by the use of the anal or pelvic fins which are modified into intromittent organs (fig. 104). In the amphibia two genera of *Anura* are known to impregnate the eggs within the oviduct of the female. In the primitive frog, *Ascaphus truei,* the male possesses a cloacal appendage or "tail," used to transport the sperm from the male to the female, and the oviducts become supplied with sperm which come to lie between the mucous folds (Noble, '31). (See fig. 107.) In East Africa, in the viviparous toad, *Nectophrynoides vivipara,* fertilization is internal, and the young, a hundred or more, develop in each uterus. (See Noble, '31, p. 74.) Just how the sperm are transmitted to the oviduct and whether fertilization is in the lower or upper parts of the oviduct in this species is not known.

In contrast to the conditions found in most *Anura,* the majority of urodele amphibia employ internal fertilization. In many species the male deposits a spermatophore or sperm mass (fig. 10). The jelly-like substance of the spermatophore of the salamanders is produced by certain cloacal or auxiliary reproductive glands. The spermatophore may in some species be picked up by the cloaca of the female or in other species it appears to be transmitted directly to the cloaca of the female from the cloaca of the male. As the spermatophore is held between the lips of the cloaca of the female, it disintegrates and the sperm migrate to and are retained within special dorsal diverticula of the cloacal wall known as the **spermatheca** (Noble and Weber, '29) (fig. 108).

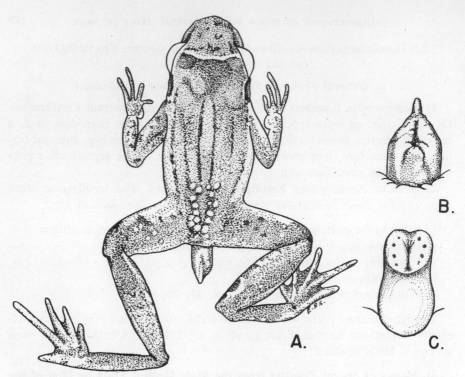

FIG. 107. Intromittent organ of the tailed frog of America, *Ascaphus truei*. (After Noble, '31.) (A) Cloacal appendage. (B) Ventral view of same. (C) Fully distended appendage, showing spines on distal end. Opening of cloaca shown in the center.

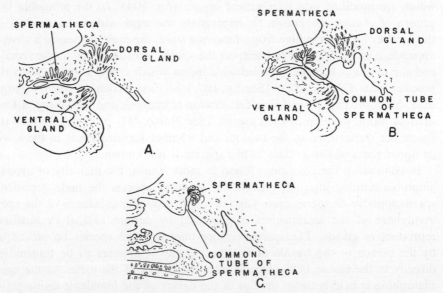

FIG. 108. Diagrammatic sagittal sections of the cloacas of three salamanders, showing types of spermatheca. (A) *Necturus*. (B) *Ambystoma*. (C) *Desmognathus*. (Redrawn from Noble, '31.)

190

In the male of the gymnophionan amphibia, a definite protrusible copulatory organ is present as a cloacal modification, and fertilization occurs within the oviducts (fig. 109). Extensible copulatory organs are found generally in reptiles and mammals, and are present also in some birds, such as the duck, ostrich, cassowary, emu, etc. In most birds the eversion of the cloaca with a slight protrusion of the dorsal cloacal wall functions very effectively as a copulatory organ.

b. Methods of Sperm Transport Within the Female Reproductive Tract

1) When Fertilization Is in the Lower or Posterior Portion of the Genital Tract. In many of the urodele amphibia, fertilization is effected apparently in the caudal areas of the female genital tract or as the egg passes through the cloacal region. It is probable in these cases that sperm motility is the means of transporting the sperm to the egg from the ducts of the spermatheca or from the recesses of the folds of the oviduct.

2) When Fertilization Occurs in the Upper Extremity of the Oviduct. In several species of salamanders, fertilization of the egg and development of the embryo occur within the oviduct. Examples are: *Salamandra salamandra, S. atra, Hydromantes genei* and *H. italicus,* all in Europe, and the widely spread neotropical urodele, *Oedipus.* The latter contains many species. The exact region of the oviduct where fertilization occurs is not known, but presumably, in some cases, it is near the anterior end. Weber ('22) suggests that fertilization may occur normally in the peritoneal cavity of *Salamandra atra.* In these instances, the method by which the sperm reach the fertilization area is not clear. It is probable that motility of the sperm themselves has much to do with their transport, although muscular contraction and ciliary action may contribute some aid.

On the other hand, studies of sperm transport in the female genital tract in higher vertebrates have supplied some interesting data relative to the methods and rate of transport. In the painted turtle, *Chrysemys picta,* sperm are deposited within the cloacal area of the female during copulation; from the cloaca they pass into the vaginal portion of the oviduct and thence into the uterus. It is possible that muscular contractions, antiperistaltic in nature, propel the sperm from the cloaca through the vagina and into the uterus. It may be that similar muscle contractions propel them through the uterus up into the albumen-secreting portions of the oviduct, or it is possible that sperm motility is the method of transport through these areas. However, once within the albumen-secreting section of the oviduct, a band of pro-ovarian cilia (i.e., cilia which beat toward the ovary) (fig. 110A, B) appears to transport the sperm upward to the infundibulum of the oviduct (Parker, '31). Somewhat similar mechanisms of muscular contraction, antiperistaltic in nature, and beating of pro-ovarian cilia are probably the means of sperm transport in the pigeon and hen (Parker, '31). Antiperistaltic muscular contractions are

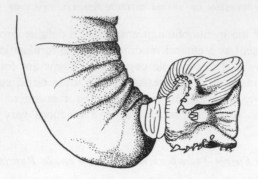

FIG. 109. Intromittent organ of male gymnophionan amphibia (*Scolecomorphus uluguruensis*). (After Noble, '31.)

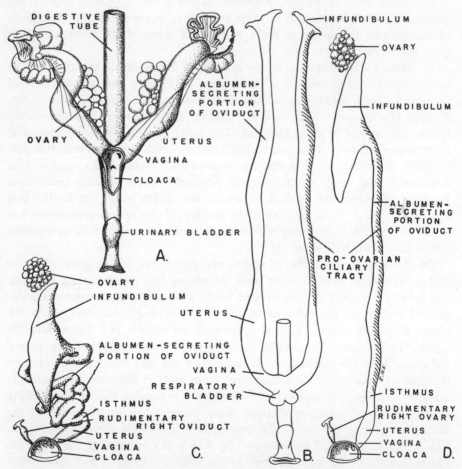

FIG. 110. Female reproduction systems of turtle and bird. (Slightly modified from Parker, '31.) (A) Reproductive organs of the female tortoise, *Chrysemys picta*. (B) The same, spread out, showing region of ciliary tract. (C) Reproductive organs of the female pigeon. (D) The same, spread out, ciliary tract region indicated.

known to be possible in the hen (Payne, '14). Active muscular contractions are suggested, as sperm travel upward to the infundibulum of the oviduct in about one and one-half hours in the hen.

In the rabbit, antiperistaltic contractions of the cervix and body of the uterus at the time of copulation pump or suck the sperm through the os uteri from the vagina and transport them into the uterus at its cervical end (Parker, '31). This transportation occupies about one to three minutes. Passage through the body of the uterus to the Fallopian tube occurs in one and one-half to two hours after copulation. It is not clear whether sperm motility alone or sperm motility plus uterine antiperistalsis effects this transportation. The transport of the sperm upward through the Fallopian tube to the infundibular region takes about two hours more. The behavior of the uterine (Fallopian) tube is somewhat peculiar at this time. Churning movements similar to that of the normal activity of the intestine are produced. Also, temporary longitudinal constrictions of the wall of the tube produce longitudinal compartments along the length of the tube. Within these compartments cilia beat vigorously in an abovarian direction (i.e., away from the ovary). The general result of these activities is a thorough mixing and churning of the contents of the tubes. At the same time these movements succeed in transporting the sperm up the tube to the infundibular area. The entire journey through the uterus and Fallopian tube consumes about four hours (Hartman, '39, pp. 698–702; Parker, '31).

Sperm transport through the female genital tract in the rabbit occupies a relatively long period of time compared to that which obtains in certain other mammalian species. The journey to the infundibular area of the Fallopian tube takes only 20 minutes in the majority of cases in the ewe, following normal service by the ram. The rate of sperm travel toward the ovaries is approximately four cm. per minute (Schott and Phillips, '41). The passage time through the entire female duct may be considerably less than this in the guinea pig, dog, mouse, etc. (Hartman, '39, p. 698). It is probable that the latter forms experience antiperistaltic muscular contractions of the uterine cervix, uteri, and Fallopian tubes, which propel the sperm upward to the infundibular region, the normal site of fertilization.

In the marsupial group the lateral vaginal canals complicate the sperm transport problem. In the opossum, the bifid terminal portion of the penial organ (fig. 114A) probably transmits the sperm to both lateral vaginal canals simultaneously, where they are churned and mixed with the vaginal contents. From the lateral vaginal canals the sperm are passed on to the median vaginal cul-de-sac. From this compartment they travel by their own motive power or are propelled upward through the uterus and Fallopian tubes to the infundibular area of the latter (figs. 34, 35, 114).

The foregoing instances regarding sperm transport in the female mammal involve active muscle contractions presumably mediated through nerve im-

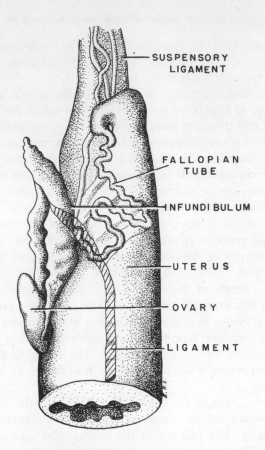

SUSPENSORY
LIGAMENT

FALLOPIAN
TUBE

INFUNDIBULUM

UTERUS

OVARY

LIGAMENT

Fig. 111. Dorsal view of anterior end of uterine horn of the common opossum, *Didelphys virginiana,* showing relation of ovary to infundibulum.

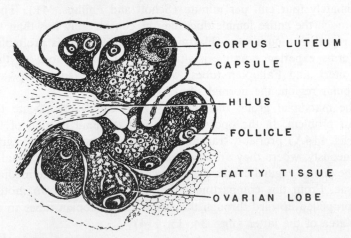

CORPUS LUTEUM

CAPSULE

HILUS

FOLLICLE

FATTY TISSUE

OVARIAN LOBE

Fig. 112. Section through ovary of mature rat, showing lobed condition and ovarian capsule. (Adapted from Heys, Quart. Rev. Biol., VI.)

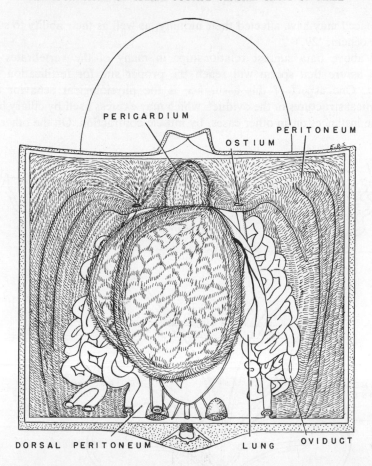

FIG. 113. Open body cavity of adult female of *Rana pipiens,* showing distribution of cilia and ostium of oviduct. (Slightly modified from Rugh, '35.)

pulses aroused during the reproductive act or orgasm together with the actual presence within the reproductive tract of seminal fluid. However, this nerve-muscular activity is assuredly not the only means of sperm transport although it may be the more normal and common method. A slower means of transport, that of sperm motility, plays an important role in many instances. This is suggested by such facts as fertility being equal in women who experience no orgasm during coitus compared to those who do; proven fertility in rabbits and dogs whose genital tracts are completely de-afferented by spinal section; and conception by females artificially inseminated *intra vaginum.* (See Hartman, '39, p. 699.) Moreover, Phillips and Andrews ('37) have shown that rat sperm injected into the vagina of the ewe along with ram sperm lag behind the ram sperm in their migration upward in the genital tract. That is, the abnormal environment of the genital tract of the ewe in which the rat sperm were placed may have affected their motility, as well as their ability to survive. (See Yochem, '29.)

The above data suggest relationships in many of the vertebrates which doubly assure that sperm will reach the proper site for fertilization in the oviduct. One aspect of this assurance is the physiological behavior of the anatomical structures of the oviduct, which may express itself by ciliary beating in some instances or, in other cases, by muscle contraction. On the other hand,

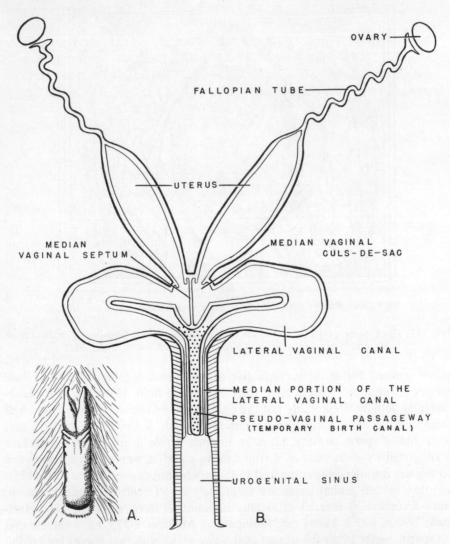

FIG. 114. Bifid penis of the male opossum; diagram of female reproductive tract. (A) Extended penis. (After McCrady, Am. Anat. Memoirs, 16, The Wistar Institute of Anatomy and Biology, Philadelphia.) (B) Female reproductive tract.

if this method fails or is weakened, sperm motility itself comes to the rescue, and sperm are transported under their own power.

In view of the above-mentioned behavior of the oviduct in transporting sperm, it is important to observe that the estrogenic hormone is in a large way responsible for the activities of the oviduct during the early phases of the reproductive period and, consequently, influences the conditions necessary for sperm transport. It enhances this process by arousing a state of irritability and reactivity within the musculature of the uterus and the Fallopian tubes. It also induces environmental conditions which are favorable for sperm survival within the female genital tract.

3) **When Fertilization Occurs in the Ovary.** In certain viviparous fishes the egg is fertilized in the ovary (e.g., *Gambusia affinis; Heterandria formosa*). (See Turner, '37, '40; Scrimshaw, '44.) As the sperm survive for months in the female tract, sperm transport is due probably to the movements of the sperm themselves. Motility evidently is a factor in the case of the eutherian mammal, *Ericulus,* where ovarian fertilization presumably occurs according to Strauss, '39.

D. Sperm Survival in the Female Genital Tract

The length of life of sperm in the female genital tract varies considerably in different vertebrates. In the common dogfish, *Squalus acanthias,* and also in other elasmobranch fishes, sperm evidently live within the female genital tract for several months, and retain, meanwhile, their ability to fertilize. In the ordinary aquarium fish, the guppy *(Lebistes),* sperm may live for about one year in the female tract (Purser, '37). A long sperm survival is true also of the "mosquito fish," *Gambusia.* Within the cloacal spermatheca of certain urodele amphibia, sperm survive for several months. Within the uterus of the garter snake they may live for three or more months (Rahn, '40), while in the turtle, *Malaclemys centrata,* a small percentage of fertile eggs (3.7 per cent) were obtained from females after four years of isolation from the male (Hildebrand, '29). Sperm, within the female tract of the hen, are known to live and retain their fertility for two or three weeks or even longer (Dunn, '27). In the duck the duration of sperm survival is much shorter (Hammond and Asdell, '26).

Among mammals, the female bat probably has the honor of retaining viable sperm in the genital tract for the longest period of time, for, while the female is in hibernation, sperm continue to live and retain their fertilizing power from the middle of autumn to early spring (Hartman, '33; Wimsatt, '44). According to Hill and O'Donoghue ('13) sperm can remain alive within the Fallopian tubes of the Australian native cat, *Dasyurus viverrinus,* for "at least two weeks." However, it is problematical whether such sperm are capable of fertilizing the egg, for motility is not the only faculty necessary in the fertilization process. In most mammals, including the human female, sperm survival is probably not longer than 1 to 3 days. In the rabbit, sperm are in the female genital tract about 10 to 14 hours before fertilization normally occurs; they lose their ability to fertilize during the early part of the second day (Hammond and Asdell, '26). In the genital tract of the female rat, sperm retain their motility during the first 17 hours but, when injected into the guinea pig uterus, they remain motile for only four and one-half hours. However, guinea-pig sperm will remain alive for at least 41 hours in the guinea-pig uterine horns and Fallopian tubes (Yochem, '29).

E. Sperm Survival Outside the Male and Female Tracts

1. In Watery Solutions Under Spawning Conditions

In watery solutions in which the natural spawning phenomena occur, the life of the sperm is of short duration. The sperm of the frog, *Rana pipiens,* may live for an hour or two, while the sperm of *Fundulus heteroclitus* probably live 10 minutes or a little longer. In some other teleost fishes, the fertilizing ability is retained only for a few seconds.

2. Sperm Survival Under Various Artificial Conditions; Practical Application in Animal Breeding

One of the main requisites for the survival of mammalian and bird sperm outside the male or female tract is a lowered temperature. The relatively high temperature of 45 to 50° C. injures and kills mammalian sperm while body temperatures are most favorable for motility of mammalian and bird sperm; lower temperatures reduce motility and prolong their life. Several workers have used temperatures of 0 to 2° C. to preserve the life of mammalian and fowl sperm, but a temperature of about 8 to 12° C. is now commonly used in keeping mammalian and fowl sperm for purposes of artificial insemination. Slow freezing is detrimental to sperm, but quick freezing in liquid nitrogen permits sperm survival even at a temperature of −195° C. (See Shettles, '40; Hoaglund and Pincus, '42.)

Another requirement for sperm survival outside the genital tract of the male is an appropriate nutritive medium. Sperm ejaculates used in artificial insemination generally are diluted in a nutritive diluent. The following diluent (Perry and Bartlett, '39) has been used extensively in inseminating dairy cattle:

Na_2SO_4	1.36 gr.	⎫
Dextrose	1.20 gr.	⎬ per 100 ml. H_2O.
Peptone	0.50 gr.	⎭

Also, a glucose-saline diluent has been used with success (Hartman, '39, p. 685). Its composition is as follows:

Glucose	30.9 gr.	⎫
$Na_2HPO_2 12H_2O$	6.0 gr.	⎬ per 1000 ml. H_2O.
NaCl	2.0 gr.	⎪
KH_2PO_4	0.1 gr.	⎭

Some workers in artificial insemination use one type of diluent for ram sperm, another for stallion sperm, and still another for bull sperm, etc.

Artificial insemination of domestic animals and of the human female is extensively used at present. It is both an art and a science. In the hands of adequately prepared and understanding practitioners, it is highly successful. The best results have been obtained from semen used within the first 24 hours after collection, although cows in the Argentine have been inseminated with sperm sent from the United States seven days previously (Hartman, '39, p. 685).

F. Transportation of the Egg from the Ovary to the Site of Fertilization

1. DEFINITIONS

The transportation of the egg from the ovary to the oviduct is described as **external (peritoneal) migration** of the egg, whereas transportation within the confines of the female reproductive tract constitutes **internal (oviducal) migration.** It follows from the information given above that the site of fertilization determines the extent of egg migration. In those species where external fertilization of the egg is the habit, the egg must travel relatively long distances from the ovary to the watery medium outside the female body. On the other hand, in most species accustomed to internal fertilization, the latter occurs generally in the upper region of the oviduct. Of course, in special cases as in certain viviparous fishes, such as *Gambusia affinis* and *Heterandria formosa,* fertilization occurs within the follicle of the ovary and migration of the egg is not necessary. The other extreme of the latter condition is present in such forms as the pipefishes. In the latter instance the female transfers the eggs into the brood pouch of the male; here they are fertilized and the embryos undergo development (fig. 106).

2. TRANSPORTATION OF THE EGG IN THOSE FORMS WHERE FERTILIZATION OCCURS IN THE ANTERIOR PORTION OF THE OVIDUCT

a. Birds

A classical example of the activities involved in transportation of the egg from the ovary to the anterior part of the oviduct is to be found in the birds. In the hen the enlarged funnel-shaped mouth of the oviduct or infundibulum actually wraps itself around the discharged egg and engulfs it (fig. 31). Peristalsis of the oviduct definitely aids this engulfing process. Two quotations relative to the activities of the mouth of the oviduct during egg engulfment are presented below. The first is from Patterson, '10, p. 107:

> Coste describes the infundibulum as actually embracing the ovum in its follicle at the time of ovulation, and the writer [i.e., Patterson] has been able to confirm his statement by several observations. If we examine the oviduct of a hen that is laying daily, some time before the deposition of the egg, it will be found to be

inactive; but an examination shortly after laying reveals the fact that the oviduct is in a state of high excitability, with the infundibulum usually clasping an ovum in the follicle. In one case it was embracing a follicle containing a half-developed ovum, and with such tenacity that a considerable pull was necessary to disengage it. It seems certain, therefore, that the stimulus which sets off the mechanism for ovulation is not received until the time of laying, or shortly after.

If the egg falls into the ovarian pocket (i.e., the space formed around the ovary by the contiguous body organs), the infundibulum still is able to engulf the egg. Relative to the engulfment of an egg lying within the ovarian pocket, Romanoff and Romanoff, '49, p. 215, states:

The infundibulum continues to advance, swallow, and retreat, partially engulfing the ovum, then releasing it. This activity may continue for half an hour before the ovum is entirely within the oviduct.

b. Mammals

In those mammals in which the ovary lies free and separated from the mouth of the oviduct (figs. 29, 111) it is probable that the infundibulum moves over and around the ovary intermittently during the ovulatory period. Also, the ovary itself changes position at the time when ovulation occurs, with the result that the ovary moves in and out of the infundibular opening of the uterine tube (Hartman, '39, p. 664). In the *Monotremata* (prototherian mammals) during the breeding season, the enlarged membranous funnel (infundibulum) of the oviduct engulfs the ovary, and a thick mucous-like fluid lies in the area between the ovary and the funnel (Flynn and Hill, '39). At ovulation the relatively large egg passes into this fluid and then into the Fallopian tube. In the rat and the mouse which have a relatively closed ovarian sac, the **bursa ovarica,** around the ovary (figs. 37, 112) contractions of the Fallopian tube similar to those of other mammals tend to move the fluid and contained eggs away from the ovary and into the tube. Thus it appears that the activities of the mouth and upper portions of the oviduct serve to move the egg from the ovarian surface into the reproductive duct at the time of ovulation in the mammal and bird. This method of transport probably is present also in reptiles and elasmobranch fishes. In the mammal this activity has been shown to be the greatest at the time of estrus. The estrogenic hormone, therefore, is directly involved in those processes which transport the egg from the ovary into the uterine tube.

In women, and as shown experimentally in other mammals, the removal of the ovary of one side and the ligation or removal of the Fallopian tube on the other side does not exclude pregnancy. In these cases, there is a transmigration of the egg from the ovary on one side across the peritoneal cavity to the opening of the Fallopian tube on the other where fertilization occurs. This transmigration is effected, presumably, by the activities of the intact infundibulum and Fallopian tube of the contralateral side.

Another aspect of egg transport in the mammal is the activity of the cilia lining the fimbriae, mouth, and to a great extent, the ampullary portions of the uterine (Fallopian) tube itself. The beating of these cilia tend to sweep small objects downward into the Fallopian tube. However, these activities are relatively uninfluential in comparison to the muscular activities of the infundibulum and other portions of the Fallopian tube.

Egg transport between the ovary and the oviduct is not always as efficient as the above descriptions may imply. For, under abnormal conditions the egg "may lose its way" and if fertilized, may begin its development within the spacious area of the peritoneal cavity. This sort of occurrence is called an **ectopic pregnancy.** In the hen, also, some eggs never reach the oviduct and are resorbed in the peritoneal cavity.

3. TRANSPORTATION OF THE EGG IN THOSE SPECIES WHERE FERTILIZATION IS EFFECTED IN THE CAUDAL PORTION OF THE OVIDUCT OR IN THE EXTERNAL MEDIUM

a. Frog

In the adult female of the frog (but not in the immature female or in the male) cilia are found upon the peritoneal lining cells of the body wall, the lateral aspect of the ovarian ligaments, the peritoneal wall of the pericardial cavity and upon the visceral peritoneum of the liver. Cilia are not found on the coelomic epithelium supporting and surrounding the digestive tract, nor are they found upon the epithelial covering of the ovary, kidney, lung, bladder, etc. (fig. 113). (See Rugh, '35.) This ciliated area has been shown to be capable of transporting the eggs from the ovary anteriad to the opening of the oviduct on either side of the heart (fig. 113) (Rugh, '35). In this form, therefore, ciliary action is the main propagating force which transports the egg (external migration) from the ovary to the oviduct. Internal migration of the egg (transportation of the egg within the oviduct) also is effected mainly by cilia in the common frog, although the lower third of the oviduct "is abundantly supplied with smooth muscle fibers," and "shows some signs of peristalsis" (Rugh, '35). The passage downward through the oviduct to the uterus consumes about two hours at 22° C. and, during this transit, the jelly coats are deposited around the vitelline membrane. The jelly forming "the innermost layer" is deposited "in the upper third of the oviduct, and the outermost layer just above the region of the uterus." The ciliated epithelium, due to the spiral arrangement of the glandular cells along the oviduct, rotates the egg in a spiral manner as it is propelled posteriad (Rugh, '35). Once within the uterus, the eggs are stored for various periods of time, depending upon the temperature. During amplexus, contractions of the uterine wall together, possibly, with contractions of the musculature of the abdominal wall, expel the eggs to the outside. At the same time, the male frog, as in the toad, discharges sperm into the water over the eggs (fig. 103). In the toad, the eggs pass continuously through the oviduct and are not retained in the uterus as in the frog (Noble, '31, p. 282).

b. Other Amphibia

The transport of the eggs to the site of fertilization in other anuran amphibia presumably is much the same as in the frog, although variations in detail may occur. In the urodeles, however, conditions appear to diverge from the frog pattern considerably. As mentioned previously, fertilization of the eggs of *Salamandra atra* may occur within the peritoneal cavity before the egg reaches the oviduct, while fertilization in most urodeles occurs internally in the oviduct, either posteriorly or in some cases more anteriorly. In this amphibian group, the ostium of the oviduct is funnel-shaped and is open, whereas in the frog it is maintained in a constricted condition and opens momentarily as the egg passes through it into the oviduct. (Compare figs. 34, 113.) The open condition of the oviducal ostium in the urodeles suggests that the ostium and anterior part of the oviduct may function as a muscular organ in a manner similar to that of birds and mammals.

c. Fishes

Egg transport in the fishes presents a heterogeneous group of procedures. In the cyclostomes the eggs are shed into the peritoneal cavity and are transported caudally on either side of the cloaca to lateral openings of the urogenital sinus. The eggs pass through these openings into the sinus and through the urogenital papilla to the outside. Contractions of the musculature of the abdominal wall may aid egg transport.

In most teleost fishes, the contraction of ovarian tissue together with probable contractions of the short oviduct is sufficient to expel the eggs to the outside (fig. 28). A somewhat similar condition is found in the bony ganoid fish, *Lepisosteus,* where the ovary and oviduct are continuous. However, in the closely related bony ganoid, *Amia,* the eggs are shed into the peritoneal cavity and make their way into an elongated oviduct with a wide funnel-shaped anterior opening and from thence to the outside. A similar condition is found in the cartilaginous ganoid, *Acipenser.* In the latter two forms, the anatomy of the reproductive ducts in relation to the ovaries suggests that the egg-transport method from the ovary to the ostium of the duct is similar to that found in birds and mammals. Muscular contractions of the oviduct probably propel the egg to the outside where fertilization occurs. This may be true also of the salmon group of fishes, including the trout, where a short, open-mouthed oviduct is present. In the lungfishes (Dipnoi) the anatomy of the female reproductive organs closely simulates that of urodele amphibia. It is probable that egg transport in this group is similar to that of the urodeles, although fertilization in the Dipnoi is external.

G. Summary of the Characteristics of Various Mature Chordate Eggs Together with the Site of Fertilization and Place of Sperm Entrance into the Egg

Animal	Size of Egg	Egg Envelopes	Yolk Present	Site of Fertilization	Place of Sperm Entrance
Styela partita	150 μ in diameter in living cordition	Clear homogeneous layer together with yolk (test) cells separate from egg at time of ovulation from ovary. Clear layer forms the chorion. Chorion and test cells are products of the follicle cells	Small in amount and distributed in center of the egg until after fertilization when the egg becomes telolecithal with the yolk centered at the caudal pole	Sea water outside of body	At future vegetal pole sperm enters immediately after germinal vesicle breaks down
Branchiostoma lanceolatum (*Amphioxus*)	Fixed and stained egg 100–150 μ in diameter	A chorionic (?) or primary vitelline membrane is present around egg as it leaves ovary. Later, a fertilization membrane is formed after sperm enters; the latter eventually fuses with the primary vitelline membrane	Yolk spherules distributed in center of the egg and toward vegetal pole. Egg becomes telolecithal after fertilization, with yolk centered at vegetal pole	Sea water outside of body	At vegetal pole
Squalus acanthias (dog fish)	Oval-shaped egg about 40 mm. × 50–70 mm.	Vitelline membrane; later enclosed by horny egg membrane secreted by oviduct	Very strongly telolecithal; free protoplasm restricted to small disc at one pole	Upper part of the oviduct	At animal pole; polyspermy
Amia calva (bowfin)	2 × 2.8 mm.	Chorion with micropyle present around zona radiata	Large amount of yolk present and egg is strongly telolecithal	External in fresh water	Micropyle of chorion and vitelline membrane at animal pole; enters egg at animal pole

Animal	Size of Egg	Egg Envelopes	Yolk Present	Site of Fertilization	Place of Sperm Entrance
Fundulus heteroclitus (killifish)	2–2.5 mm.	Three egg membranes, viz., a filamentous chorion-like layer surrounds a thin vitelline membrane which lies external to the zona radiata	Centrolecithal before fertilization; strongly telolecithal after	External in sea water	Micropyle at animal pole; enters egg at animal pole
Heterandria formosa	Egg minute	Thin vitelline membrane	Oil globules coalesce at fertilization to form large, centrally-located oil globule	Internal in ovisac of ovary	Blastodisc area at animal pole
Salvelinus (trout)	4.5–5 mm.	Chorion with micropyle	Strongly telolecithal	External in fresh water	Micropyle at animal pole
Rana pipiens (leopard frog)	1.7 mm.	Primary vitelline membrane separates from egg after fertilization. Three jelly-like membranes deposited in the oviduct. Eggs laid in masses	Telolecithal—moderately so	External in fresh water	About 20° down from mid-animal pole
Necturus maculosus (mud puppy)	5–5.2 mm.	Vitelline membrane formed as in *Rana*; jelly-like membranes formed in oviduct around the egg; eggs laid singly, attached to stones, etc.	Strongly telolecithal	Cloaca or lower oviduct	Animal pole; polyspermy at other areas of the egg
Alligator mississippiensis (alligator)	Almost 25–30 mm. in diameter	Zona radiata or vitelline membrane; albuminous and membranous envelopes in oviduct; size of egg with membranes about 42 mm. × 74 mm.	Strongly telolecithal	Infundibular region of the oviduct	Disc of cytoplasm at animal pole

Animal	Size of Egg	Egg Envelopes	Yolk Present	Site of Fertilization	Place of Sperm Entrance
Gallus (domesticus) gallus (hen)	31 mm. vertical, 32 mm. transverse, 34 mm. long = average diameter of white Leghorn egg (after Romanoff and Romanoff)	Zona radiata or vitelline membrane before egg leaves ovary. Envelopes of albuminous, membranous and calcareous nature formed in oviduct. Size of egg with membranes about 42 mm. × 57 mm. (Size of hen's egg varies considerably)	Strongly telolecithal	Infundibular region of oviduct; possibly also in peritoneal cavity	Disc of protoplasm at animal pole
Platypus (Ornithorhynchus)	2.5 mm.	Zona pellucida formed around egg while in ovary. Albuminous and membranous egg envelopes deposited in oviduct	Strongly telolecithal	Infundibular region of oviduct	Disc of protoplasm at animal pole
Echidna	3.0 mm.	Same as Platypus	Strongly telolecithal	Infundibular area of oviduct	Disc of protoplasm at animal pole
Dasyurus viverrinus (marsupial cat)	40 μ	Zona pellucida. Note: regarding the origin of the zona of this and the eggs that follow, three theories have been propounded: (a) It originates from the egg as a secretion product; (b) as a product of the egg and follicle cells; and (c) as a secretion product of the follicle cells. The last theory probably is the true one	Isolecithal with relatively large yolk spherules in cytoplasm	Infundibular region of Fallopian tube	Probably at nuclear pole of egg

Animal	Size of Egg	Egg Envelopes	Yolk Present	Site of Fertilization	Place of Sperm Entrance
Didelphys virginiana (opossum)	120–140 μ	Zona pellucida; albuminous and outer chitinous layer laid down in Fallopian tube	Isolecithal with large yolk spherules	Infundibular region of Fallopian tube	Probably at nuclear pole of egg
Dasyurus novemcinctus (armadillo)	80 μ	Zona and surrounding corona radiata cells at time of discharge from ovarian follicle	Isolecithal	Infundibular region of Fallopian tube	Probably at nuclear pole of egg
Whale	140 μ	Provided with a zona pellucida when discharged from ovary; also surrounding corona cells	Isolecithal	Infundibular region of Fallopian tube	Probably at nuclear pole of egg
Scalopus aquaticus (mole)	125 μ	Zona plus corona radiata	Isolecithal	Infundibular region of Fallopian tube	Probably at nuclear pole of egg
Mus musculus (mouse)	70–75 μ	Zona plus corona radiata	Isolecithal	Infundibular region of Fallopian tube	Probably at nuclear pole of egg
Rattus rattus (rat)	70–75 μ	Zona plus corona radiata	Isolecithal	Infundibular region of Fallopian tube	Probably at nuclear pole of egg
Cavia porcellus (guinea pig)	75–85 μ	Zona plus corona radiata	Isolecithal with large yolk spherules in cytoplasm	Infundibular region of Fallopian tube	Probably at nuclear pole of egg
Oryctolagus cuniculus (rabbit)	120–130 μ	Zona plus corona radiata; albuminous layers deposited in Fallopian tube after corona radiata has been dissipated	Isolecithal	Infundibular area of Fallopian tube	Probably nuclear pole of egg

Animal	Size of Egg	Egg Envelopes	Yolk Present	Site of Fertilization	Place of Sperm Entrance
Canis familiaris (dog)	135–145 μ	Zona plus corona radiata	Isolecithal	Infundibular area of Fallopian tube	Probably nuclear pole of egg
Felis domestica (cat)	120–130 μ	Zona plus corona radiata	Isolecithal	Infundibular area of Fallopian tube	Probably nuclear pole of egg
Equus caballus (horse)	135 μ	Zona plus corona radiata	Isolecithal	Infundibular area of Fallopian tube	Probably nuclear pole of egg
Ovis aries (sheep)	120 μ	Zona plus corona radiata	Isolecithal	Infundibular area of Fallopian tube	Probably nuclear pole of egg
Sus scrofa (pig)	120–140 μ	Zona plus corona radiata	Isolecithal	Infundibular area of Fallopian tube	Probably nuclear pole of egg
Macaca mulatta (rhesus monkey)	110–120 μ	Zona plus corona radiata	Isolecithal	Infundibular area of Fallopian tube	Probably nuclear pole of egg
Gorilla sp.	130–140 μ	Zona plus corona radiata	Isolecithal	Infundibular area of Fallopian tube	Probably nuclear pole of egg
Homo sapiens (man)	130–140 μ	Zona plus corona radiata	Isolecithal	Infundibular area of Fallopian tube	Probably nuclear pole of egg

Bibliography

Cohn, E. J. **1917.** The relation between the hydrogen ion concentration of sperm suspensions and their fertilizing power. Anat. Rec. **11**:530.

————. **1918.** Studies in the physiology of spermatozoa. Biol. Bull. **34**:167.

Dunn, L. C. **1927.** Selective fertilization in fowls. Poul. Sc. **6**:201.

Flynn, T. T. and Hill, J. P. **1939.** The development of the monotremata: Part IV. Growth of the ovarian ovum. Maturation, fertilisation and early cleavage. Trans. Zool. Soc. London **24**: Part 6:445.

Hammond, J. and Asdell, S. A. **1926.** The vitality of spermatozoa in the male and female reproductive tracts. Brit. J. Exper. Biol. **4**:155.

Hartman, C. G. **1933.** On the survival of spermatozoa in the female genital tract of the bat. Quart. Rev. Biol. **8**:185.

————. **1939.** Chap. 9. Physiology of eggs and spermatozoa in Allen, et al., Sex and Internal Secretions. 2d ed., The Williams & Wilkins Co., Baltimore.

Hibbard, H. **1928.** Contribution à l'étude de l'ovogenèse de la fécondation et de l'histogenèse chez, *Discoglossus Pictus Otth.* Arch. biol., Paris. **38**:251.

Hildebrand, S. F. **1929.** Review of experiments on artificial culture of diamondback terrapin. Bull. U. S. Bur. Fisheries. **45**:25.

Hill, J. P. and O'Donoghue, C. H. **1913.** The reproductive cycle in the marsupial *Dasyurus viverrinus.* Quart. J. Micr. Sc. **59**:133.

Hoaglund, H. and Pincus, G. **1942.** Revival of mammalian sperm after immersion in liquid nitrogen. J. Gen. Physiol. **25**:337.

Mann, T. **1949.** Metabolism of semen. Adv. in Enzymology. **9**:329.

Noble, G. K. **1931.** Biology of the Amphibia. McGraw-Hill Book Co., Inc., New York.

———— and Weber, J. A. **1929.** The spermatophores of *Desmognathus* and other plethodontid salamanders. Am. Mus. Novit. No. 351.

Parker, G. H. **1931.** The passage of sperms and of eggs through the oviducts in terrestrial vertebrates. Philos. Tr. Roy. Soc., London, s.B. **219**:381.

Patterson, J. T. **1910.** Studies on the early development of the hen's egg. 1. History of the early cleavage and of the accessory cleavage. J. Morphol. **21**:101.

Payne, L. F. **1914.** Vitality and activity of sperm cells and artificial insemination of the chicken. Circular No. 30, Oklahoma Agricultural Experimental Station, Stillwater, Oklahoma.

Perry, E. J. and Bartlett, J. W. **1939.** Artificial insemination of dairy cows. Extension Bulletin 200 from New Jersey State College of Agriculture and Agriculture Experimental Station, New Brunswick, New Jersey.

Phillips, R. W. and Andrews, F. N. **1937.** The speed of travel of ram spermatozoa. Anat. Rec. **68**:127.

Purser, G. L. **1937.** Succession of broods of *Lebistes.* Nature, London. **140**:155.

Rahn, H. **1940.** Sperm viability in the uterus of the garter snake *Thamnophis.* Copeia. **2**:109-115.

Riddle, O. **1927.** The cyclical growth of the vesicula seminalis in birds is hormone controlled. Anat. Rec. **37**:1.

Romanoff, A. L. and Romanoff, A. J. **1949.** The Avian Egg. John Wiley & Sons, Inc., New York.

Rugh, R. **1935.** Ovulation in the frog. II. Follicular rupture to fertilization. J. Exper. Zool. **71**:163.

Schott, R. G. and Phillips, R. W. **1941.** Rate of sperm travel and time of ovulation in sheep. Anat. Rec. **79**:531.

Scrimshaw, N. S. **1944.** Embryonic growth in the viviparous poeciliid, *Heterandria formosa.* Biol. Bull. **87**:37.

Shettles, L. B. **1940.** The respiration of human spermatozoa and their response to various gases and low temperatures. Am. J. Physiol. **128**:408.

Toothill, M. C. and Young, W. C. **1931.** The time consumed by spermatozoa in passing through the epididymis in the guinea pig. Anat. Rec. **50**:95.

Turner, C. L. **1937.** Reproductive cycles and superfetation in poeciliid fishes. Biol. Bull. **72**:145.

————. **1940.** Adaptations for viviparity in jenynsiid fishes. J. Morphol. **67**:291.

Weber, A. **1922.** Le fécondation chez la *salamandre alpestre.* Compt. rend. de l'Assoc. d. anat. **17**:322.

Wimsatt, W. A. **1944.** Further studies on the survival of spermatozoa in the female reproductive tract of the bat. Anat. Rec. **88**:193.

Yochem, D. E. **1929.** Spermatozoön life in the female reproductive tract of the guinea pig and rat. Biol. Bull. **56**:274.

5

Fertilization

A. Definition of fertilization
B. Historical considerations concerning gametic fusion and its significance.
C. Types of egg activation
   1. Natural activation of the egg
   2. Artificial activation of the egg
      a. Object of studies in artificial parthenogenesis
      b. Some of the procedures used in artificial activation of the egg
      c. Results obtained by the work on artificial parthenogenesis
D. Behavior of the gametes during the fertilization process
   1. General condition of the gametes when deposited within the area where fertilization is to occur
      a. Characteristics of the female gamete
         1) Oocyte stage of development
         2) Inhibited or blocked condition
         3) Low level of respiration
         4) Loss of permeability
      b. Characteristics of the male gamete
   2. Specific activities of the gametes in effecting physical contact of the egg with the sperm
      a. Activities of the female gamete in aiding sperm and egg contact
         1) Formation of egg secretions which influence the sperm
            a) Fertilizin complex
            b) Spawning-inducing substances
      b. Activities of the male gamete in aiding the actual contact of the two gametes
         1) Sperm secretions
            a) Secretions producing lysis
            b) Secretions related specifically to the fertilization reactions
            c) Secretions which induce the spawning reaction in the female
         2) Relation and function of sperm number in effecting the contact of the sperm with the egg
         3) Influences of the seminal plasma in effecting sperm contact with the egg
         4) Roles played by specific structural parts of the sperm in effecting contact with the egg
            a) Role of the flagellum
            b) Role of the acrosome in the egg-sperm contact
         5) Summary of the activities of the egg and sperm in bringing about the primary or initial stage of the fertilization process, namely, that of egg and sperm contact

3. Fusion of the gametes or the second stage of the process of fertilization
4. Detailed description of the processes involved in gametic union as outlined above
   a. Separation and importance of a protective egg membrane, exudates, etc.
   b. Fertilization cone or attraction cone
   c. Some changes in the physiological activities of the egg at fertilization
   d. Completion of maturation divisions, ooplasmic movements, and copulatory paths of the male and female pronuclei in eggs of various chordate species
      1) Fertilization in *Styela* (Cynthia) *partita*
         a) Characteristics of the egg before fertilization
         b) Entrance of the sperm
         c) Cytoplasmic segregation
         d) Copulatory paths and fusion of the gametic pronuclei
      2) Fertilization of *Amphioxus*
      3) Fertilization of the frog's egg
      4) Fertilization of the teleost fish egg
      5) Fertilization in the egg of the hen and the pigeon
      6) Fertilization in the rabbit
      7) Fertilization in the *Echidna,* a prototherian mammal
E. Significance of the maturation divisions of the oocyte in relation to sperm entrance and egg activation
F. Micropyles and other physiologically determined areas for sperm entrance
G. Monospermic and polyspermic eggs
H. Importance of the sperm aster and the origin of the first cleavage amphiaster
I. Some related conditions of development associated with the fertilization process
   1. Gynogenesis
   2. Androgenesis
   3. Merogony
J. Theories of fertilization and egg activation

A. Definition of Fertilization

The union or fusion (syngamy) of the oocyte or egg (female gamete) with the sperm (male gamete) to form a zygote is known as fertilization. From this zygotic fusion the new individual arises. Strictly speaking, the word fertilization denotes the process of making the egg fruitful (i.e., develop) by means of the sperm's contact with the egg, and as such may not always imply a fusion of the sperm with the egg. In certain types of hybrid crosses, such as in the toad egg *(Bufo)* inseminated with urodele sperm *(Triton),* egg activation may occur without fusion of the sperm nucleus with the egg nucleus. Ordinarily, however, the word fertilization denotes a fusion of the two gametes (see Wilson, '25, pp. 460–461).

The word zygote is derived from a basic Greek word which means *to join or yoke together*. The word is particularly appropriate in reference to the behavior of the nuclei of the two gametes during fertilization. For, during gametic union, the haploid group of chromosomes from one gamete is added to the haploid group from the other, restoring the diploid or normal number of chromosomes. In most instances, each chromosome from one gamete has a mate or homologue composed of similar genes in the other gamete. Therefore, the union of the two haploid groups of chromosomes forms an integrated association in which pairs of similar genes are yoked together to perform their functions in the development of the new individual.

In most animal species aside from the union of the chromosome groups, there is a coalescence of most of the cytoplasm of the male gamete with that of the female gamete as the entire sperm generally enters the egg (figs. 115, 118). However, in some species the tail of the sperm may be left out, e.g., rabbit, starfish, and sea urchin, while in the marine annelid, *Nereis,* the head of the sperm alone enters, the middle piece and tail being left behind.

The morphological fusion of the two sets of nucleoplasms and cytoplasms of the gametes during fertilization is made possible by certain physiological changes which accompany the fusion process. These changes begin the instant that a sperm makes intimate contact with the surface of the oocyte (or egg). As a result, important ooplasmic activities are aroused within the egg which not only draw the sperm into the ooplasm but also set in motion the physico-chemical machinery which starts normal development. The initiation of normal development results from the **complete activation** of the egg. **Partial activation** of the egg is possible, and in these instances, various degrees of development occur which are more or less abnormal. Partial activation of the egg happens in most instances when the various methods of artificial activation (see p. 217) are employed.

While the main processes of activation leading to development are concerned with the organization and substances of the egg, one should not overlook the fact that *the sperm also is activated (and in a sense, is fertilized) during the fusion process.* Sperm activation is composed of two distinct phases:

(1) Before the sperm makes contact with the oocyte or egg, it is aroused by environmental factors to swim and move in a directed manner and is attracted to the oocyte or egg by certain chemical substances secreted by the latter; and

(2) after its entrance into the egg's substance, the sperm nucleus begins to enlarge and its chromosomes undergo changes which make it possible for them to associate with the egg chromosomes in the first cleavage spindle. Also, the first cleavage amphiaster in the majority of animal species appears to arise within the substance of the middle piece of the sperm *as a result of ooplasmic stimulation.*

In the process of normal fertilization it is clear, therefore, that two main conditions are satisfied:

(1) There is a union of two haploid chromosome groups, one male and the other female, bringing about the restoration of a proper diploid genic balance; and

(2) an activation of the substances of the fused gametes, both cyto-

plasmic and nuclear, is effected, resulting in the initiation of normal development.

The biochemical and physiological factors which accomplish the union of the haploid chromosome groups and the activation of the gametes are the objectives of one of the main facets of embryological investigation today.

B. Historical Considerations Concerning Gametic Fusion and Its Significance

The use of the word "fertilization" in the sense of initiating development and the idea of making fertile or fruitful, which the word arouses in one's mind, reaches back to the dawn of recorded history. The concept of this fruitfulness as being dependent upon the union of one sex cell with another sex cell and of the fusion of the two to initiate the development of a new individual originated in the nineteenth century. However, Leeuwenhoek, in 1683, appears to have been the first to advance the thesis that the egg must be impregnated by a seminal animalcule (i.e., the sperm) in order to become fruitful, but the real significance of this statement certainly was not appreciated by him.

Moreover, to Leeuwenhoek, the idea behind the penetration of the egg by the seminal animalcula was to supply nourishment for the latter, which he believed was the essential element in that it contained the preformed embryo in an intangible way. That is, the sperm animalcule of the ram contains a lamb, which does not assume the external appearance of one until it has been nourished and grown in the uterus of the female (Cole, '30, pp. 57, 165). It should be added parenthetically that actual presence of the little animalcules as living entities had previously been called to Leeuwenhoek's attention in 1677 by a Mr. Ham (Cole, '30, p. 10).

In the years that followed Leeuwenhoek the exact interpretation to be applied to the seminal animalcules (sperm) was a matter of much debate. Many maintained that they were parasites in the seminal fluid, the latter being regarded as the essential fertilizing substance in the male semen. In 1827, von Baer, who regarded the sperm as parasites, named them **spermatozoa,** that is, parasitic animals in the spermatic fluid (Cole, '30, p. 28). Finally, in the years from 1835–1841, Peltier, Wagner, Lallemand, and Kölliker, established the non-parasitic nature of the sperm. Kölliker in 1841 traced their origin from testicular tissue, and thus settled the argument once and for all as to the true nature of the seminal animals or sperm.

Various individuals have laid claim to the honor of being the first to describe the sperm's entry into the egg at fertilization, but the studies of Newport and Bischoff (1853, 1854) resulted in the first exact descriptions of the process. (See Cole, '30, pp. 191–195.) Thus the general proposition set forth by Leeuwenhoek 170 years earlier became an accepted fact, although the illumination of the details of sperm and egg behavior during fertilization really began with the studies of O. Hertwig in 1875. The more important studies which have shed light upon the problems involved in gametic fusion are presented below:

(1) O. Hertwig, 1875, 1877, in the former paper, described the fusion of the egg and sperm pronuclei in the Mediterranean sea urchin, *Toxopneustes lividus.* One aspect of the work published in 1877 was concerned with the formation of the polar bodies in *Haemopis* and *Nephelis.* In a part of the latter publication O. Hertwig presented descriptions of sperm migration from the periphery of the egg and the ultimate association of the sperm and egg pronuclei during the fertilization in the frog, *Rana temporaria* (fig. 119I, J).

(2) Fol, 1879, contributed detailed information relative to the actual entrance of the sperm into the sea-urchin egg and showed that in the eggs of various animal species only one sperm normally enters. He also described the formation of the fertilization membrane in the egg of the sea urchin, *Toxopneustes lividus.*

(3) Mark, 1881, made important contributions relative to the formation of the polar bodies in the slug, *Deroceras laeve (Limax campestris).* He also presented information which showed that the egg and sperm pronuclei, although associated near the center of the egg during fertilization, do not actually form a fusion nucleus in this species as described for the sea urchin by O. Hertwig. This is an important contribution to the fertilization problem, as fusion nuclei are not formed in all animal species.

(4) Van Beneden, 1883, in his studies on maturation of the egg and fertilization in *Ascaris megalocephala,* demonstrated that half of the chromatin material of the egg nucleus was discharged in the maturation divisions. (He erroneously thought, however, that the female ejected the male chromosomes at this time, and in the male, the reverse process occurred.) (See fig. 133C, D.) He demonstrated also that the two pronuclei in *Ascaris* do not join to form a fusion nucleus at fertilization. His work revealed further that the male and female pronuclei each contributes the *haploid or half the normal number of chromosomes at fertilization* and that each haploid group of chromosomes enters the equatorial plate of the first cleavage spindle as an independent unit (fig. 133F-I). Upon the equatorial plate each chromosome divides and contributes one chromosome to each of the two daughter nuclei resulting from the first cleavage division. This contribution of the haploid number (half the typical, somatic number) of chromosomes from each parent Van Beneden assumed to be a fundamental principle of the fertilization process. This principle was defi-

nitely established by later workers and it has become known as Van Beneden's Law.

(5) Boveri, 1887 and the following years, further established the fact of Van Beneden's Law and also demonstrated that half of the chromosomes of the cells derived from the zygote are maternal and half are paternal in origin. (Fig. 133 is derived from Boveri's study of *Ascaris*.) In '00 and '05 he emphasized the importance of the centrosome and centrioles and presented the theory that the centrosome contributed by the sperm to the egg at the time of fertilization constituted the dynamic center of division which the egg lacked; hence, it was a causal factor in development. This latter concept added new thinking to the fertilization problem, for O. Hertwig, 1875, had suggested that the activation of the egg was due to the fusion of the egg and sperm nuclei. The centrosome theory of Boveri eventually became one of the foremost theories of egg activation (see end of chapter).

(6) During the last five years of the nineteenth century, intensive studies on artificial activation of the egg (artificial parthenogenesis) were initiated. This matter is discussed on page 217 in the section dealing with artificial activation.

(7) Another attack on the problem of fertilization and its meaning had its origin in the "idioplasm theory" of Nägeli. This theory (1884) postulated an "idioplasm" carried by the germ cells which formed the essential physical basis of heredity. A little later O. Hertwig, Kölliker, and especially Weismann, identified the idioplasm of Nägeli with the chromatin of the nucleus. In the meantime, Roux emphasized the importance of the chromatin threads of the nucleus and stated that the division of these threads by longitudinal splitting (separation) during mitosis implied that different longitudinal areas of these threads *embodied different qualities.* (See Wilson, '25, p. 500.) In harmony with the foregoing ideology and as a result of his own intensive work on maturation and fertilization in *Ascaris* and also upon other forms, Boveri came to the conclusion in 1902 and 1907 (Wilson, '25, p. 916) *that development was dependent upon the chromosomes and further that the individual chromosomes possessed different qualities.*

(8) As a result, the field of biological ideas was at this time well plowed and ready for another important suggestion. This came in '01 and '02 when McClung offered the view that the *accessory chromosome* described by Henking (1891) as the x-chromatin-element or nucleolus was, in the germ cell of the male grasshopper, a sex chromosome which carried factors involved in the determination of sex. McClung first made this suggestion and stated a definite hypothesis, immediately stimulating work by others; in a few years McClung's original suggestion was well rounded out and the complete cycle of sex chromo-

somes in the life history was formulated. E. B. Wilson led this work, and the theory that he formulated became the assured basis of cytological and genetical sex studies constituting one of the greatest present day advances in zoology. "McClung's anticipation of this theory is a striking example of scientific imagination applied to painstaking observation" (Lillie, F. R., '40).

Not only were the sex chromosomes studied, but other chromosomes as well, and an intense series of genetical investigations were initiated by Morgan and his students and others which succeeded in tying a large number of hereditary traits to individual chromosomes and also to definite areas or parts of the chromosomes. Thus the assumptions of Roux and Boveri were amply demonstrated. Moreover, these observations established experimental proof for the concept that in the gametic fusion which occurs during fertilization, the chromosomes pass from one generation to the next as individual entities, carrying the hereditary substances from the parents to the offspring. The heredity of the individual was in this way demonstrated to be intimately associated with the reunion of the haploid groups of chromosomes in the fertilization process.

C. Types of Egg Activation

1. NATURAL ACTIVATION OF THE EGG

Natural parthenogenesis, i.e., the development of the egg spontaneously without fertilization was suggested by Goedart, in 1667, for the moth, *Orgyia gnastigma,* and by Bonnet, in 1745, in his study of reproduction in the aphid. (See Morgan, '27, p. 538.) Since this discovery by Goedart and Bonnet, many observations and cytological studies have shown that there are two kinds of eggs which are capable of natural parthenogenesis:

(1) That which occurs in the so-called, non-sexual egg, i.e., the egg which has not undergone the maturation divisions and, hence, has the diploid number of chromosomes; and

(2) that which results in the sexual egg, i.e., the egg which has experienced meiosis (Chap. 3) and thus has the reduced or haploid number of chromosomes (Sharp, '34, pp. 409, 410).

Parthenogenesis from a non-sexual egg is found in daphnids, aphids, flatworms, and certain orthopterans. In the case of the sexual egg, parthenogenesis normally occurs in bees, wasps, ants, some true bugs, grasshoppers, and arachnids. In this type of egg, development may result with or without fertilization. For example, in the honeybee, *Apis mellifica,* haploid males arise from eggs which are not fertilized, workers and queens from fertilized eggs.

Extensive studies of the animal kingdom as a whole have demonstrated, however, that the majority of oocytes or eggs depend upon the *fertilization process for activation.* Consequently, eggs may be regarded in the following light: Some eggs are self-activating and develop spontaneously, while others require sperm activation before development is initiated. However, *the differences between these two types of eggs may not be as real as it appears,* for it is probable that subtle changes in the environment of the so-called self-activating or parthenogenetic eggs are sufficient to activate them, whereas in those eggs which require fertilization a strong, abrupt, stimulus is requisite to extricate them from their blocked condition and to start development. This idea is enhanced by the information obtained from the methods employed in the studies on artificial activation of the egg of different animal species.

2. ARTIFICIAL ACTIVATION OF THE EGG

a. Object of Studies in Artificial Parthenogenesis

"The ultimate goal in the study of artificial parthenogenesis is the discovery of the chemical and physical forces which are assumed to cause the initiation of development" (Heilbrunn, '13). A brief resumé of some of the results obtained in the studies on artificial activation of the egg is considered in the following paragraphs.

b. Some of the Procedures Used in Artificial Activation of the Egg

Tichomiroff, 1885 (Morgan, '27, p. 538), stated that eggs from virgin silkworm moths could be activated by rubbing or by treatment with sulfuric acid. Somewhat later Mead, 1896–1897, published results of studies on artificial parthenogenesis in the annelid worm, *Chaetopterus.* The egg of this worm has the germinal vesicle intact when it is deposited in sea water. Almost immediately after entrance into sea water, the germinal vesicle breaks down, and the chromatin proceeds to form the spindle for the first maturation division. At this point, however, it stops and awaits the entrance of the sperm for further activation. Thus, the immersion of the *Chaetopterus* egg in sea water under normal spawning conditions *partially activates the egg* (Mead, 1897). Mead attempted by artificial means to complete this activation initiated by the sea water. In doing so, he took eggs from normal sea water, which thus had the first polar spindle, and placed them in sea water to which ¼ to ½ per cent of potassium chloride had been added. Eggs thus treated proceeded to form normal polar bodies and the beginnings of the first cleavage occurred. Development ceased, however, at this point. These eggs were further *activated,* but not *completely activated.* Two steps in partial activation are here demonstrated:

(1) When the egg is spawned into sea water, the nuclear membrane breaks down and the first polar spindle is formed; and

(2) by the immersion in hypertonic sea water the first and second maturation divisions occur, and the first cleavage begins.

This experiment by Mead was one of a number of pioneering studies made during this period in an endeavor to activate artificially the egg. Another such experiment was reported by R. Hertwig (1896), using eggs of the sea urchin. In a strychnine solution the nucleus underwent changes preparatory to the first division. Also, Morgan (1896) found it possible to produce cleavage, normal and abnormal, if unfertilized eggs of the sea urchin, *Arbacia,* were placed in sea water to which certain amounts of sodium chloride had been added and then were returned to normal sea water. Morgan ('00) later found that magnesium chloride added to sea water induced cleavage in eggs treated for various intervals. Loeb, in 1899 (see Loeb, '06), initiated a series of experiments on activation of the sea-urchin egg. As a result of many similar experiments, Loeb reached the conclusion that *membrane formation was the essential part of the activation process* in that it stimulates the formation of the membrane by initiating cytolysis of the egg (see Loeb's theory at end of chapter). Consequently, he sought substances which would elicit *membrane formation* and found that monobasic fatty acids, such as butyric, acetic, formic, or valerianic, would produce membrane formation, and, also, that ether, bile salts, saponin, etc., would do the same. However, although these substances aroused certain initial activities of the egg, Loeb found it necessary to apply a so-called *corrective treatment* of hypertonic sea water to arrest the cytolytic effect of the first treatment, which, according to his belief, restored respiration to its normal level. As a result, Loeb perfected a treatment as follows which produced development in a considerable number of sea-urchin eggs so exposed (Loeb, '06):

(1) Unfertilized eggs were placed for ½ to 1½ min. in 50 cc. of sea water to which 3 cc. of N/10 solution of butyric or other monobasic fatty acid had been added. This treatment effected membrane formation when the eggs were returned to normal sea water, provided the eggs had been exposed long enough to the acid.

(2) The eggs were allowed to remain in normal sea water for 5 to 10 min. and then were subjected to the corrective treatment in hypertonic sea water, made by adding 15 cc. of 2½ N. NaCl solution to 100 cc. normal sea water, and allowed to remain for 20 to 50 min. Lesser times of exposures also were used successfully.

(3) Following this treatment, the eggs were returned to normal sea water.

An example of an entirely different method from the solution technics employed above on the sea-urchin egg is that of Guyer ('07) and especially Bataillon ('10, '11, '13) on the egg of the frog. The method employed by the latter with success was as follows: Eggs were punctured with a fine glass or platinum needle and then covered for a time with frog blood. Puncturing alone is not sufficient; a second factor present in the blood is necessary for successful parthenogenetic development. The number of actual developments procured by this method is small, however. In many cases an early cleavage or larval stage is reached, but the advanced tadpole state or that of the fully developed frog is quite rare.

The method introduced by Bataillon is still used extensively in studies on artificial parthenogenesis in the frog. Recently, Shaver ('49) finds that the "second factor" is present on certain cytoplasmic granules obtained by centrifugal fractionation. Heat at 60° C. and the enzyme, ribonuclease, destroy the second-factor activity. Successful second-factor granules were obtained from blood, early frog embryos, and "extracts of testis, brain, lung, muscle and liver." This author also reports that heparin suppresses parthenogenetic cleavage.

In some of these parthenogenetically stimulated eggs of the frog, the diploid chromosome relationships appear to be restored during early cleavage; in others both diploid and triploid cells may be present. Some of these tadpoles may be completely triploid (Parmenter, '33, '40). However, a large percentage remain in the haploid condition (Parmenter, '33).

A third method of approach in stimulating parthenogenetic development was used by Pincus ('39) and Pincus and Shapiro ('40) on the rabbit. In the former work, Pincus reports the successful birth of young from tubal eggs activated by exposure to a temperature of 47° C. for three minutes. The treated eggs were transplanted into the oviducts of pseudopregnant females. In the latter work, eggs were exposed to a cooling temperature in vivo, that is, the eggs were allowed to remain in the Fallopian tube during exposure to cold. The birth of one living female was reported from such parthenogenetic stimulation.

The foregoing experiments illustrate three different procedures used on three widely separated animal species, namely, changing the external chemical environment of the egg, a tearing or injuring of the egg's surface followed by the application of substances obtained from living tissues, and, finally, changing the physical environment of the egg. To these three general approaches may be added that of mechanical shaking. For example, Mathews ('01) states that mechanical shaking of the eggs of the starfish, *Asterias forbesi,* results in the development of a small percentage of eggs to the free-swimming blastula stage.

Some of the recent work on the initiation of development and in stimulating cells to divide has emphasized the importance of cellular injury as a factor. Little is known concerning the mode of action of the injuring substances. Harding ('51) concludes that an acid substance is released as the result of "injury" and that this acid substance causes "an increase in protoplasmic viscosity and initiates cell division" in the sea-urchin egg. (Cf. theory of R. S. Lillie at end of chapter.)

That no single method has been found which activates eggs in general is not surprising. The eggs of different species are not only in different states of maturation (i.e., development) when normally fertilized (fig. 137), but they behave differently during the normal fertilization process. In some eggs, such as the egg of *Chaetopterus,* there is only a slight change within the egg cortex during fertilization, whereas in the egg of the teleost fish, the egg of the frog, or in the egg of the urochordate, *Styela,* marked cortical changes involving mass movements of protoplasmic materials can be demonstrated.

c. Results Obtained by the Work on Artificial Parthenogenesis

The question naturally arises: What has the work on artificial activation of the egg contributed to the solution of the problems involved in egg activation? It has not, of course, solved the problem, but it has contributed much toward a better understanding of the processes concerned with egg activation and of the general problem of growth stimulation including cell division. We may summarize the contributions of this work as follows:

(1) It has demonstrated that the egg in its normal development reaches a condition when a factor (or factors) inhibits further development. That is, it becomes blocked in a developmental sense.

(2) It has shown that this inhibited state may be overcome and development initiated by appropriate types of treatment.

(3) It has revealed that activation of the egg is possible only at the time when normal fertilization occurs in the particular species. In other words, activation is possible only when favorable conditions are developed in the egg—conditions which enable it to respond to the activating stimulus.

(4) It has demonstrated that one of the primary conditions necessary for the initiation of division or cleavage of the egg is an initial increase in the viscosity of the egg's cytoplasm.

(5) Certain experiments suggest that chemical compounds, such as heparin or heparin-like substances, may suppress cleavage and cell division, presumably due to their ability to decrease the viscosity of the egg.

(6) It therefore follows that substances and conditions which tend to increase the egg's viscosity tend to overcome the inhibited state referred to in (1) above and thus initiate development.

(7) Recent evidence suggests that substances which produce cell injury tend to initiate cell division in the egg. As states of injury have been shown to produce growths of various kinds during embryonic development and also during the post-embryonic period, it is probable that the principles involved in egg activation are similar to those which cause differentiation and growth in general.

(8) A common factor, therefore, involved in egg stimulation and other types of growths, including tumor-like growths, is the liberation of some substance in the egg or in a cell which overcomes an inhibiting

factor (or factors) *and thus frees certain morphogenetic or developmental conditions within the egg or within a cell.* Once the inhibiting or blocking condition is overcome, differentiation and growth begin.

(9) Finally, the work on artificial parthenogenesis has demonstrated that the egg is an organized system which, when properly stimulated, is able to produce a new individual without the aid of the sperm cell. This does not mean that the sperm is not an important factor in normal fertilization, but rather, that the egg has the power to regulate its internal conditions in such a way as to compensate for the absence of the sperm.

D. Behavior of the Gametes During the Fertilization Process

The activities of the gametes during the fertilization process may be divided for convenience into two major steps:

(1) *activities of the gametes which bring about their physical contact with each other,* and
(2) *activities which result in the actual fusion of the gametes after this contact is made.*

Before considering these two major steps, we shall first observe certain of the characteristics of the two gametes when they are about to take part in the fertilization process.

1. GENERAL CONDITION OF THE GAMETES WHEN DEPOSITED WITHIN THE AREA WHERE FERTILIZATION IS TO OCCUR

a. Characteristics of the Female Gamete

1) Oocyte Stage of Development. In the case of most animal species, the female gamete is in the oocyte stage when it enters into the fertilization process. (See Chap. 3; also fig. 137.) In the dog and fox the female gamete is in the primary oocyte stage, and both maturation processes happen after sperm entrance (fig. 115). In the protochordate, *Styela,* the first maturation spindle already is formed when the sperm enters (fig. 116A–D), and in *Amphioxus* the first polar body has been given off, and the second maturation spindle is developed when the sperm enters (fig. 117A–D). The last condition probably holds true for most vertebrate species (figs. 118B; 119D). However, in the invertebrates, the sea-urchin egg experiences both maturation divisions normally before sperm entry.

2) Inhibited or Blocked Condition. When the female gamete thus reaches a state of development determined for the species, its further development is blocked or inhibited, and its future development depends on the circumvention of this state of inhibition. If not fertilized or artificially aroused when this inhibited state is reached, the oocyte or egg begins cytolysis. Eggs fertilized, when these degenerative (cytolytic) conditions are initiated, fail to develop normally. If allowed to continue, cytolysis soon produces a condition in which development is impossible, and dissolution of the egg results.

3) Low Level of Respiration. While the egg is in this inhibited or arrested state awaiting the event of fertilization, respiration is carried on at a steady but low level. This respiratory level varies in different animal species (fig. 120). That this respiration rate may not be the direct cause of egg inhibition, is shown by the fact that the rate of respiration does not always increase imme-

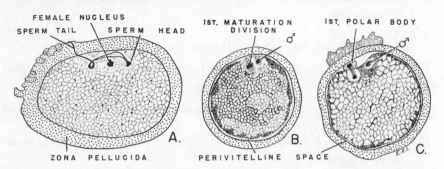

FIG. 115. (A) Early fertilized egg in upper Fallopian tube of the bitch (dog). Observe the female nucleus before the first maturation division together with the sperm head and tail. Note that the sperm, as in other mammals, enters the nuclear pole of the egg. Observe further that the zona pellucida and the ooplasm are contiguous.   (B) Section of the egg of the dog, taken from the upper part of the Fallopian tube. Observe the following features: (1) The sperm pronucleus is forming; (2) the egg nucleus has now entered the metaphase of the first maturation division; (3) the ooplasm of the egg has shrunk away from the zona pellucida and a space is present between the egg and the zona. This space is the perivitelline space, containing an ooplasmic exudate.   (C) Section of the egg in the Fallopian tube of the bitch, showing the formation of the first polar body.

diately following fertilization in all species (fig. 120). (Consult Brachet, J., '50, p. 105.) Among the vertebrates, the low rate of oxygen consumption of the unfertilized egg has been shown to continue for some time after fertilization in the toad and frog egg and also in the egg of the teleost fish, *Fundulus heteroclitus*. However, in the case of the egg of the lamprey the respiration rate rises after fertilization (Brachet, J., '50, p. 108).

4) Loss of Permeability. A final characteristic of the female gamete immediately before fertilization is the loss of permeability of the egg surface to various substances. Correlated with this fact is the presence of definite ooplasmic or other egg membranes associated with the egg surface. The relationship between the ooplasmic surface of the egg and these membranes is altered greatly after fertilization when the egg and the membranes tend to separate. To what extent the loss of permeability of the egg surface is caused by the intimate association of these membranes with the egg surface is problematical. The evidence to date suggests that under normal circumstances they are integrated with the conditions which restrict permeability and egg activation.

b. Characteristics of the Male Gamete

In contrast to the inertia and metabolic quietude experienced by the female gamete, the gamete of the male experiences quite opposite conditions. When the sperm, for instance, is brought into an environment which favors motility, such as the posterior region of the vas deferens of the mammal, it becomes highly motile and continues this motility in the female genital tract. Similarly, the normal sperm of other vertebrate species is a very active cell when placed in the normal fertilization area (fig. 121, primary phase of fertilization). To quote from J. Brachet ('50), page 91: "This very active cell has an intense metabolism and the maintenance of this latter (condition) is indispensable to the continuance of motility." As mentioned previously (Chap. 1), this high respiratory metabolism at least in some species is supported partially by the utilization of a simple sugar in the seminal fluid as the sperm "is rich in oxidative enzymes and in hydrogen transporters" (J. Brachet, '50).

2. SPECIFIC ACTIVITIES OF THE GAMETES IN EFFECTING PHYSICAL CONTACT OF THE EGG WITH THE SPERM

(Consult fig. 121, primary phase of fertilization.)

While the gametes are in the condition mentioned, they are physiologically adapted to fulfill certain definite activities which enhance their contact with each other and bring about actual union in the fertilization process.

a. Activities of the Female Gamete in Aiding Sperm and Egg Contact

1) **Formation of Egg Secretions Which Influence the Sperm.** The activities of the female gamete at this time are concerned mainly with the effusion of certain egg secretions. These secretions are known as **gynogamic substances,** or **gynogamones.** They are elaborated by the egg when the latter becomes physiologically mature, i.e., when it becomes fertilizable (fig. 137).

A study of the natural secretions of the egg in relation to the fertilization process has occupied the attention of numerous investigators. These studies began during the early part of the twentieth century. In reference to the egg, two main groups of substances have been recognized:

(1) *the fertilizin complex,* and
(2) *substances which induce the spawning reactions in the male.*

a) FERTILIZIN COMPLEX. Some of the earliest studies upon **fertilizin substances** were made by von Dungern in '02, Schücking in '03, and De Meyer in '11. In these experiments an egg-water solution was obtained by allowing ripe eggs of the sea urchin to stand in sea water for a period of time or by disintegrating the eggs. All of these observers found that some substance from

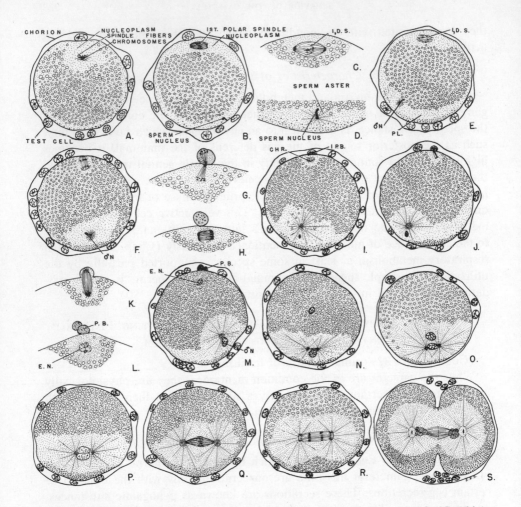

FIG. 116. Fertilization and maturation of the egg in the urochordate, *Styela* (Cynthia) *partita.* (After Conklin, '05.)　(A) Egg shortly after spawning but before sperm entrance. The spindle fibers of the first maturation division are forming, and the nucleoplasm is located toward the animal pole.　(B) Egg showing the spindle for first maturation division. Observe the sperm nucleus just inside the ooplasmic membrane near the midvegetal pole of the egg. The nucleoplasm (karyoplasm) of the female nucleus has spread into a thin cap at the animal pole.　(C) Metaphase of first division spindle (1, D.S.) nearly parallel to the surface of the egg; no centrosomes are present.　(D) Higher powered representation of sperm a little later than that shown in (B). The aster for the first cleavage spindle is forming in the middle piece of the sperm.　(E) Slightly more advanced stage than that shown in (B). Collection of yellow-pigmented, peripheral protoplasm (PL.) is shown at bottom of the egg.　(F) Anaphase of second polar spindle. Sperm aster enlarging. (See (G) and (H).)　(G) Separation of first polar body.　(H) Metaphase of second polar spindle, paratangential in position.　(I) First polar body (1 P.B.) formed; chromatin of second spindle (CHR.). Sperm has revolved 180°; sperm aster enlarging.　(J) Telophase of second polar spindle. Sperm aster enlarges, and sperm nucleus assumes vesicular condition.　(K) Separation of second polar body.　(L) Two

(Continued on facing page.)

224

the egg, when present in dilute solution, caused the sperm of the sea urchin to loose their motility and to become clumped together or agglutinated. A little later, F. R. Lillie, '13, '14, '15, studied the activity of the egg water of the sea urchin, *Arbacia,* extensively. Lillie associated the egg secretion found in the egg water with a definite theory concerning the mechanism of fertilization. He called the substance given off when the sea-urchin egg is allowed to stand in sea water, "fertilizin"; for, according to his results, washed eggs deprived of this egg secretion fail to fertilize. Only ripe eggs give off fertilizin according to his observations. Lillie found further that the activities of the sperm, introduced by means of a pipette into the egg-water solution are changed greatly. At first they are activated, to be followed by an agglutination. Moreover, a drop of egg water introduced into a sperm suspension activates the sperm and appears to influence them chemically, causing them to be attracted to the drop. Lillie therefore concluded that fertilizin has a threefold action upon the sperm:

(1) that it activates the sperm (that is, stimulates their movement),

(2) attracts the sperm by a positive chemotaxis, and

(3) agglutinates the sperm, that is, causes the sperm to associate in clumps.

The agglutination effect F. R. Lillie found is reversible in most sea-urchin sperm, providing the egg water containing fertilizin is not allowed to act too long. On the other hand, in the annelid, *Nereis,* agglutination of the sperm is "essentially permanent" (Lillie, F. R., '13). Lillie placed most emphasis upon the "agglutinin" factor in the egg water. He further postulated that fertilizin not only affected the sperm, *but also activates the egg to cause its development* (see theory at end of chapter). Lillie also obtained another substance from crushed or laked eggs which combines "with the agglutinating group of fertilizin, but which is separate from it as long as the egg is inactive." This substance present within the egg he called "antifertilizin."

Since the time of F. R. Lillie's original contribution, the subject of fertilizin and antifertilizin has been actively investigated by various students of the problem. Some investigators criticized the conclusions drawn by Lillie, but more recent work substantiates them. For example, M. Hartmann, et al. ('40), working on the sea urchin, *Arbacia pustulosa,* and Tyler and Fox ('40) and Tyler ('41), using eggs from *Strongylocentrotus purpuratus,* find that fertilizin

---

FIG. 116—*(Continued)*

polar bodies (P.B.); fusion of chromosomal vesicles to form egg pronucleus (E.N.). (M) Movement of sperm nucleus, aster, and of surrounding yellow-pigmented and clear protoplasm to the posterior pole of the egg. The copulation path of egg pronucleus (E.N.) to meet the sperm nucleus is in progress. (N) Sperm aster has divided; egg pronucleus progresses along its copulation path toward posterior pole of egg to meet the male pronucleus. (O) Egg and sperm pronuclei are making contact with each other. (P) Pronuclei associate and begin to form early prophase conditions of the first cleavage. (Q) Metaphase of first cleavage. (R) Anaphase of first cleavage. (S) Late anaphase of first cleavage.

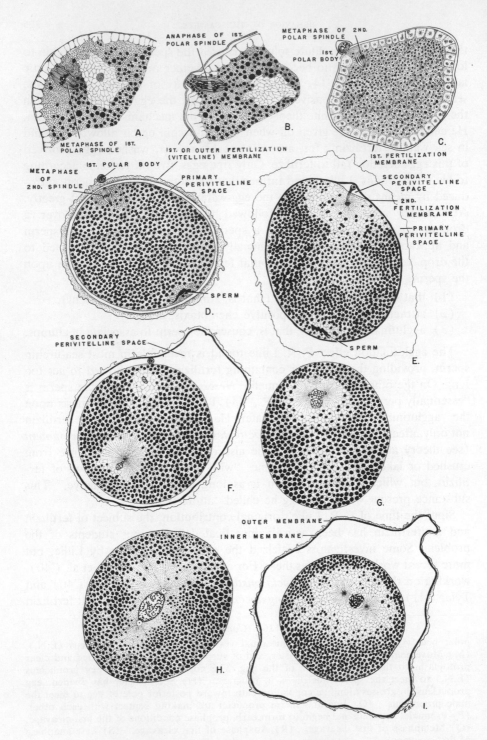

A.

METAPHASE OF 1ST.
POLAR SPINDLE

METAPHASE OF 1ST.
POLAR SPINDLE

ANAPHASE OF 1ST.
POLAR SPINDLE

B.

1ST. OR OUTER FERTILIZATION
(VITELLINE) MEMBRANE

1ST. POLAR BODY

METAPHASE OF 2ND.
POLAR SPINDLE

1ST.
POLAR BODY

C.

1ST. FERTILIZATION
MEMBRANE

METAPHASE
OF
2ND. SPINDLE

1ST. POLAR BODY

PRIMARY PERIVITELLINE
SPACE

D.

SPERM

SECONDARY
PERIVITELLINE
SPACE

2ND.
FERTILIZATION
MEMBRANE

PRIMARY
PERIVITELLINE
SPACE

E.

SPERM

SECONDARY
PERIVITELLINE SPACE

F.

G.

OUTER MEMBRANE

INNER MEMBRANE

H.

I.

FIG. 117. (See facing page for legend.)

226

is present and that it is associated with the jelly layer around the egg. Tyler ('41) concludes:

(1) When fertilizin is present in the form of a gelatinous coat around the egg, it enhances fertilization;

(2) when present only in solution around the egg after the gelatinous coat is removed, it hinders fertilization by agglutinating the sperm; and

(3) that fertilizin is not entirely essential since eggs can be fertilized when the jelly coat is removed, but a greater number of sperm are needed under these circumstances.

Tyler also has detected antifertilizin below the surface of the egg and by crushing the eggs was able to show that antifertilizin from the interior of the egg is able to neutralize the fertilizin of the jelly coat surrounding the egg (Tyler, '40, '42). In Germany, Hartmann and his associates (see Hartmann, M., et al., '39, a and b, '40) have demonstrated that by exposing fertilizin to heat or light one may separate the "agglutinating factor" from the "activating factor." Heat at 95° C. destroys the "agglutinating factor," while exposure to bright light causes the "chemotactic" and "activating" factors to disappear. The factual presence of the egg products, fertilizin and antifertilizin, postulated by Lillie thus is well established.

Fertilizin appears to be widely distributed as an egg secretion among animals, invertebrate and vertebrate. Among the latter it has been identified in cyclostomes, certain teleost fishes, and in the frog, *Rana pipiens* (Tyler, '48). Moreover, it is becoming increasingly clear that the term, fertilizin, as employed originally by F. R. Lillie, includes more than one secretion. How many separate enzymes or other substances may be included under the general terms of fertilizin and antifertilizin remains for the future to determine. Moreover, the exact presence of particular gynogamic substances in the egg secretions of different animal species may vary considerably. For example, the sperm-activating principle may not be present in all animal species. In fact, there is good evidence to show that it is not present, for example, in all species of sea urchins.

FIG. 117. Fertilization and maturation of the egg in *Amphioxus*. (A, B, H after Cerfontaine, '06; C–I after Sobotta, 1897.) (A) Metaphase of first maturation division before sperm entrance. (B) Anaphase of first maturation division before sperm entrance. (C) First polar body and metaphase of second maturation division before sperm entrance. Observe the first or primary fertilization membrane. (D) Sperm has entered near vegetal pole of egg. (E) Outer egg membrane has enlarged and is now much thinner; the second egg membrane is separating from the egg, and the second polar body is forming. (F) Outer and inner egg membranes have fused and expanded; pronuclei of sperm and egg are evident; the sperm aster is to be observed in connection with the sperm nucleus. (G) Meeting of the two pronuclei between the developing amphiaster. (H) Fusion nucleus complete. (I) Diploid chromosomes now evident preparatory to the first cleavage of the egg.

The general term "gamones" (Hartmann, M., '40) has been applied to the substances produced by the gametes at the time of fertilization. The Hartmann school further has identified the factor responsible for chemotaxis and activation as "echinochrome A," that is, the bluish-red pigment of the egg, and have called it "Gynogamone I." This factor will attract sperm and stimulate their movements "at the enormous dilution of 1 part in 2,500,000,000 parts of water" (Brachet, J., '50, p. 96). However, Tyler has not been able to detect echinochrome in the egg of the Pacific coast sea urchin, *Strongylocentrotus*. But the egg water of this species does activate the sperm of this species, which suggests that the activating factor may be something else than echinochrome. To the agglutinating factor, M. Hartmann and his associates have given the name "Gynogamone II."

The exact identity of these gamones with particular chemical substances present in the egg water at the present time is impossible. To quote from J. Brachet, '50, p. 99:

It is clear that research in this field is complicated by the fact that a number of agents activate the movements of sperm (alkalinity, glutathione, echinochrome (?), etc.) . . .'. There is strong evidence in favor of the protein nature of agglutinin, while the sperm-activating principle is probably a substance with a small molecule, its identity with echinochrome being doubtful at the present time.

b) SPAWNING-INDUCING SUBSTANCES. In addition to the fertilizin substances which act in effecting the actual contact of the sperm with the egg, a **spawning-inducing agent** is present in the egg water of certain species. In the annelid, *Nereis,* for example, there is something present in the egg water which induces spawning in the males. Townsend ('39) suggested that this substance may be glutathione, but Tyler ('48) does not readily concur with this conclusion. A spawning-inducing agent is found also in the egg water of oysters (Galtsoff, '40). Among the vertebrates, the spawning behavior of the female appears to be the important factor in inducing the male reaction.

b. *Activities of the Male Gamete in Aiding the Actual Contact of the Two Gametes*

The activities of the male gamete, including those of seminal fluid, are much more complicated and devious than those of the female gamete. These activities entail:

(1) production of certain sperm secretions,
(2) activities of large sperm numbers,
(3) presence of a healthy seminal plasma or protective substance for the sperm, and
(4) physical movements and functioning of specific parts of the sperm cell itself.

(1) **Sperm Secretions.** The sperm secretions are known as **androgamic substances or androgamones.** These substances have been the object of much

study since the initial endeavors of Pieri in 1899. In recent years, three general types of substances have come to be recognized in relation to the sperm of different species. These three groups of substances are:

(1) secretions which cause lysis,
(2) a substance or substances related specifically to the fertilization reaction (i.e., egg and sperm contact), and
(3) substances which bring about the spawning reaction in the female.

a) SECRETIONS PRODUCING LYSIS. To cite the importance of lytic substances produced by the sperm, reference is made first to the situation in the amphibian, *Discoglossus pictus*. In this primitive anuran, the sperm, although about 2 mm. long, are almost incapable of motility. However, they do accumulate in the region of a thickened portion of the egg capsule which overlies a depressed area of the egg. They are capable of passing through this thickened area of jelly by the aid of a digestive enzyme probably associated with the acrosome (Hibbard, '28). Hibbard also suggests that "nuclear fluids" accumulate in the bottom of the egg depression and these fluids attract the sperm to the thickened area of the capsule. If so, here is an example of two chemical substances, one elaborated by the egg and the other by the sperm, both working together to bring about fertilization. In substantiation of Hibbard's views of the presence of a lytic enzyme associated with the sperm of this species, Wintrebert ('29) found that extracts from the sperm contained an enzyme which is capable of digesting the inner jelly coat of the egg.

More recently, Tyler ('39) has found that sea-water extracts of frozen and thawed sperm of two mollusks *(Megathura crenulata* and *Haliotis cracherodii)* were able to dissolve the egg membranes of the respective species. Cross-species reactions were not obtained, however. Strong extracts of concentrated sperm suspensions bring about egg-membrane disappearance in less than one-half minute, but with the jelly coat present around the egg it takes about three minutes. Also, Runnström and his collaborators ('44, '45, a and b, '46) made methanol extracts of sea-urchin sperm which were able to liquefy the superficial cortical area of the egg.

A most interesting enzyme, known as **hyaluronidase,** has been extracted from mammalian testes and from mammalian sperm. This substance is capable of dispersing the follicle cells of the corona radiata present around most mammalian eggs when discharged from the ovary. (Sheep and opossum eggs as well as those of the monotremes do not possess a layer of follicle cells around the newly ovulated egg.) This dispersing effect aids fertilization, for it enables sperm to reach the egg surface before degeneration processes occur in the egg. Rowlands ('44) effected artificial insemination in the rabbit with dilute sperm solutions by adding the enzyme hyaluronidase from other sperm to the dilute suspensions. Without the addition of hyaluronidase, fertilization did not result. In certain cases in women where artificial insemination was tried but failed when semen alone was used, the addition of hyaluronidase from bull testis to the semen produced successful fertilization (Leonard and Kurzrok, '46).

b) SECRETIONS RELATED SPECIFICALLY TO THE FERTILIZATION REACTIONS. The substances mentioned in the preceding paragraphs are related to the general fertilization process, but they may not be related specifically to the reactions which bring the sperm in direct contact with the egg. In the egg we have observed the presence of fertilizin which stimulates a series of sperm activities directed to this end. Similarly, in the male gamete, sperm of various species seem capable of producing "androgamic substances which neutralize, in part, the action of the gynogamic substances and thus assure the precise mechanism necessary for precise fusion of the gametes" (J. Brachet, '50).

An introductory study by Frank ('39) suggests the presence of a sperm substance which reacts directly with the fertilizin complex of the egg. It was shown by this investigator that an extract from the sperm of the sea urchin, *Arbacia,* is:

(1) able to destroy the sperm agglutinating factor when added to a solution of fertilizin derived from the sea-urchin egg, and

(2) possesses the power to agglutinate eggs of the same species.

Other students of the problem have found a similar substance associated with the sperm. (See Hartmann, Schartau, and Wallenfels, '40; Southwick, '39; Tyler, '40.) The general term **"sperm antifertilizin"** has been given to this substance (or substances) by Tyler and O'Melveney ('41). Sperm antifertilizin unites with fertilizin produced by the egg, with the result that the sperm is entrapped at the egg's surface. Tyler and O'Melveney ('41) regard the reaction between antifertilizin of the sperm and fertilizin of the egg to be the "initial (perhaps essential) step in the union of the gametes whereby the spermatozoon is entrapped by the . . . fertilizin, on the egg."

c) SECRETIONS WHICH INDUCE THE SPAWNING REACTION IN THE FEMALE. Galtsoff ('38) has shown that the presence of sperm of the oyster, *Ostrea virginica,* "easily induces spawning in oysters." He also found that the spawning reaction is specific in that sperm of different species cannot provoke it. The active principle of the sperm suspension is thermolabile and insoluble in water. However, it may be readily extracted in 95 per cent ethyl alcohol and benzene.

To what extent spawning-inducing substances may be present in other animal species is questionable, but it may not be an uncommon phenomenon, especially in sedentary species, such as the oyster and other mollusks. In the vertebrate group, surface contact of the male and female bodies is an important factor in many cases.

2) Relation and Function of Sperm Number in Effecting the Contact of the Sperm with the Egg. In the preceding chapter, sperm transport is considered. This transportation journey is an efficient one with regard to the end achieved, namely, contact of a single sperm with an egg, but from the viewpoint of sperm survival it may appear as waste and caprice. This fact is especially true in those forms utilizing fertilization where only one or a very few eggs are fertilized. It has been shown by Walton ('27) in experiments dealing with artificial insemination in the rabbit, when dilution of the sperm is such that the number falls below 3,000 to 4,000 per cc., fertilization does not take place. Recent observations by Farris ('49) on the human suggest that numbers of sperm below 80,000,000 per cc. are precarious when conception is the end to be achieved. (For the total number of sperm ejaculated by certain males during a single copulation, see Chap. 1.) Although exceedingly large numbers of sperm are deposited in the posterior area of the female reproductive tract, the number becomes less and less as the ovarian end of the duct is reached. The ability of effective sperm transport within the female tract probably varies considerably in different species and with different females in the same species. The rat and the dog appear to be more efficient in this respect than the rabbit.

The relation of sperm numbers to the efficiency of the fertilization process is not to be considered merely as a mechanical hit and miss device, whereby the presence of a greater number of sperm may assure an accurate "hit" or sperm-egg collision (Rothschild, Lord, and Swann, '51). Hammond ('34) has shown in the rabbit that fertilization is not effected by the few sperm which reach the region of the egg first, but by the later aggregations of numbers of sperm. The work on hyaluronidase mentioned on page 229 suggests strongly that one object of the excess sperm is to transport hyaluronidase to the vicinity of the egg. The presence of this enzyme close to the egg possibly facilitates the passage through the cells of the corona radiata and also through the zona pellucida of the single sperm which makes contact with the egg in the process of fertilization (Tyler, '48). The general result should be regarded as the working of a cooperative enterprise, where many sperm aid in the dissolution of the interference in order that one sperm may reach the egg's surface.

3) Influences of the Seminal Plasma in Effecting Sperm Contact with the Egg. The importance of the seminal plasma (i.e., the fluid part of the semen; see Chap. 1) cannot be overestimated (Mann, '49). It is, to a great extent, the *natural environment* and at the same time the *nutritive medium* for the sperm during the transport from the male ducts through the external medium or within the lower region of the female genital tract. Its functions may be stated as follows:

(1) It increases the motility of the sperm;

(2) it has a high buffering capacity, which protects the sperm from injurious acids or other injurious substances; and

(3) it is a vehicle for nutritive substances, such as fructose, vitamin C, and the B complex which provide nourishment for the sperm.

The B group of vitamins may be directly related to sperm motility. Other substances, such as iron, copper, etc., are present. One should consider the seminal plasma, therefore, as a most important association of substances which aids in producing a protective environment for the sperm while the latter is in migration to the egg.

The importance of the environment of the sperm and also that of the egg cannot be overemphasized. If normal fertilization is to be effected, optimum conditions for both sperm and egg must be present. An example of this fact is shown by the observations of Reighard on fertilization of the walleyed pike. (See Morgan, '27, p. 18.) The best results with the eggs of this teleost fish were obtained when the eggs were fertilized as soon as they entered the water from the female genital tract. After two minutes only 40 per cent of the eggs segment, and after ten minutes no eggs segment. For many fish, "dry fertilization" gives the best results. Dry fertilization consists in stripping the female to force out the eggs into a dry container and then stripping the milt (seminal fluid) from the male directly over the eggs. The eggs are then placed in water after a few minutes. This work suggests strongly that a deleterious environment for either the egg or the sperm is disturbing to the fertilization process.

4) Roles Played by Specific Structural Parts of the Sperm in Effecting Contact with the Egg: a) ROLE OF THE FLAGELLUM. As indicated in the foregoing paragraphs, when the sperm cells have reached the normal fertilization site, the activities which bring about actual contact of the sperm with the egg largely is a sperm problem. Aside from enzymes elaborated by the sperm, sperm motility is extremely important in achieving this end. Although sperm may appear to swim rather aimlessly, vigorous, healthy sperm do lash forward more or less in a straight line for some distance; ill-developed or otherwise impaired sperm may simply swim round and round or move forward feebly. In the case of flagellate sperm, the structure which makes the forward swimming movement possible is the flagellum or tail (figs. 74, 77, 78, 79). A two-tailed sperm or one in which the flagellate mechanism is not well developed would be at a disadvantage in this race to reach the confines of the egg. Brachet ('50) considers the rate of metabolism necessary to support the activities of the tail or flagellum in sperm movement as directly comparable to that of muscle.

An interesting peculiarity of a different type of sperm mechanism useful in achieving contact with the egg's surface is that of the so-called "rocket sperm" of certain decapod *Crustacea* described by Koltzoff (fig. 75). After attachment of the sperm to the egg by its tripod-like tips, the caudal compartment, containing a centriole and the acrosome, explodes. "Koltzoff considers that the force of the explosion drives the sperm upon, or even into, the egg" (Wilson, '25, p. 299).

b) ROLE OF THE ACROSOME IN THE EGG-SPERM CONTACT. The acrosome of the sperm (fig. 78) has long been regarded as a structure which has a function in the reactions involved in fertilization. The older conception of Waldeyer that the acrosome was a perforating device which enabled the sperm to pass through the egg membranes and thus to enter the egg is untenable in the light of later observation. Many years ago Bowen ('24) though admitting a minor mechanical role for the acrosome, emphasized that the acrosome essentially is a secretory product whose principal function is to initiate the physicochemical reactions of fertilization. It should be recalled in this connection that Hibbard ('28) and also Parat ('33, a and b) have attributed to the acrosome of the anuran, *Discoglossus,* the ability of carrying or producing an enzyme which enables it to reach the egg's surface through the jelly surrounding the egg. Parat further suggested that the acrosome in this species contains a "proteolytic enzyme" which, when introduced into the egg, results in development.

The concept of a proteolytic enzyme associated with the acrosome of *Discoglossus* is interesting in the light of the suggestion by Leuchtenberger and Schrader ('50) that the mucolytic enzyme, hyaluronidase, in the bull sperm may be associated with the acrosome. Both of the above suggestions need more work before it can be stated with certainty that the acrosome is connected with either of these enzymes in the above species. However, these suggestions do serve to emphasize the possibility that the acrosome may be an enzyme-producing or enzyme-carrying device which enables the sperm to make its way through the egg's surroundings to the egg surface, and also, that it may play a part in egg activation.

5) Summary of the Activities of the Egg and Sperm in Bringing About the Primary or Initial Stage of the Fertilization Process, Namely, that of Egg and Sperm Contact.

a) The secretion of fertilizin by the egg:

(1) activates the sperm to increased motility, and

(2) through chemotaxis, entices the sperm to move in the direction of the egg.

b) In moving toward the egg the lytic substances elaborated by the sperm enable it to "plow" through the gelatinous envelopes and cellular barriers to the surface of the egg. This movement undoubtedly is aided by movement of the flagellum in some species, but not in all (see *Discoglossus*). The acrosome of the sperm may function at this time either as an instrument carrying lytic substances or as one which actually manufactures these substances. The presence of large numbers of sperm near the egg may aid sperm penetration to the egg's surface by contributing lytic substances to the environment around the egg which aid in the removal of membranes and other barriers surrounding the egg.

c) The antifertilizin of the sperm may then unite with the fertilizin of the egg (probably with the agglutinin factor); this reaction presumably agglutinates the sperm to the egg's surface.

d) An egg-surface, liquefying factor, androgamone III, has been isolated by Runnström, et al. ('44), from sea-urchin sperm (Runnström, '49, p. 270). A similar "sperm lysin" has been isolated also from mackerel testes. This work suggests that a specific sperm lysin may be involved in the activation processes within the egg cortex. (See theory of fertilization according to J. Loeb at end of chapter.)

e) Lastly, in certain animal species, substances may be present in the seminal fluid which induce the spawning reaction in the female, while in the egg secretion of certain species, a factor may be present which induces spawning in the male.

3. Fusion of the Gametes or the Second Stage of the Process of Fertilization

The actual fusion or union phase of fertilization begins once the sperm has made contact with the egg (fig. 121B). From this instant the rest of the fertilization story becomes essentially an egg problem. The egg up to the time of sperm contact literally has been waiting, discharging fertilizin substances into the surrounding medium. However, when a sperm has made successful contact with the surface of the egg, the waiting period of the egg is over, its work begins, the fusion of the two gametes ensues, and the drama of a new life is initiated!

The following events of the fusion process may be listed—events which occur quite synchronously, once the mechanisms involved in egg activation and gametic fusion are set in motion:

(a) The separation of an egg membrane (fertilization membrane, vitelline membrane, chorion, zona pellucida, etc.) from the egg's surface and the exudation of fluid-like substances from the egg's surface.

(b) A fertilization cone may be elaborated in some species.

(c) Changes in the physicochemical activities of the egg.

(d) The maturation division (or divisions) is completed in most eggs.

(e) Profound cytoplasmic movements occur in many eggs which bring about various degrees of localization of cytoplasmic substances; these substances orient themselves into a pattern definite for the species. In some species a cytoplasmic pattern composed of future, organ-forming substances is rigidly established and definitely correlated with the first cleavage of the egg *(Styela);* in others it is less rigid (frog); and in still others it appears gradually during cleavage of the egg (teleost fishes).

(f) The sperm nucleus enlarges, and the middle-piece area in most animal species develops a cleavage aster.

(g) The copulation movements of the egg and sperm pronuclei take place. These movements bring about the association of the two pronuclei near the center of the protoplasm of the egg which is actively concerned with the cleavage phenomena.

(h) The pronuclei may fuse to form a fusion nucleus or they may associate less intimately. Regardless of the exact procedure of nuclear behavior, the female and male haploid chromosome groups eventually become associated in the first cleavage spindle to form one harmonious diploid complex of chromosomes, composed (in most cases) of paired chromosomal mates or homologues.

(i) The first cleavage plane is established.

4. Detailed Description of the Processes Involved in Gametic Union as Outlined Above

a. Separation and Importance of a Protective Egg Membrane, Exudates, etc.

The term "fertilization membrane" is applied to the egg (vitelline) membrane which, in many species, becomes apparent only at the time of fertilization. In many other eggs a definite and obvious vitelline membrane is present before the egg is fertilized and in many respects functions similarly to the more dramatically formed fertilization membrane. Both types of membrane fulfill definite functions during fertilization and early development. The fertilization membrane which forms only as a distinct membrane during fertilization was observed first by Fol, in the autumn of 1876, in the starfish egg (Fol, '79). In the cephalochordate, *Amphioxus,* two definite membranes separate from the egg's surface. One membrane forms just before the sperm enters the egg, while the second membrane separates from the egg after the sperm enters. Both membranes soon fuse and expand to a considerable size, leaving a **perivitelline space** between them and the egg; the latter space is filled with fluid, the **perivitelline fluid** (fig. 117B–F, I). In the urochordate, *Styela,* no such membrane arises from the egg's surface, but the chorion previously formed by the follicle cells serves to fulfill the general functions of a fertilization membrane (figs. 91B, 116). In teleost fishes, the egg emits a considerable quantity of perivitelline fluid at the time of fertilization, effecting a slight shrinkage in egg size with the production of a space filled with this fluid between the egg's surface and the zona radiata (fig. 122A–C). The zona radiata thus functions as a fertilization membrane. In the gobiid fish, *Bathygobius soporator,* the chorion and/or vitelline membrane expands greatly after the egg is discharged into sea water, and an enlarged capsule is soon formed which assumes the size and shape of the future embryo at the time of hatching (fig. 123). (See Tavolga, '50.) In the brook lamprey, according to Okkelberg ('14), shrinkage of the egg at fertilization is considerable, amounting to about 14 per cent of its original volume. A slight egg shrinkage with

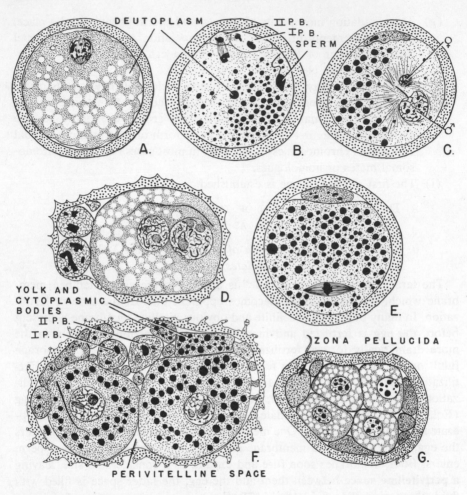

Fig. 118. Fertilization in the guinea pig. (After Lams, Arch. Biol., Paris, 28, figures slightly modified.) (A) Spindle of first maturation division. (B) Second maturation division completed; head of sperm in cytoplasm beginning to swell. (C) Sperm pronucleus, with tail still attached, greatly enlarged; female pronucleus small. (D) Pronuclei ready to fuse; chromatin material (chromosomes) evident within. (E) First cleavage spindle. (F) First cleavage completed. Observe deutoplasmic and cytoplasmic globules which have been exuded into the space between the blastomeres and the zona pellucida. (G) Four-cell cleavage stage. Observe that the zona pellucida encloses the four blastomeres and the cytoplasmic globules which have been exuded. The zona functions to keep the entire mass intact.

the emission of fluid is present in the amphibia and the egg thus is enabled to revolve within a relatively thick vitelline membrane. The latter membrane expands gradually during development, and is associated intimately with the surrounding jelly membranes secreted by the oviduct. In the reptiles and birds, the separation of the egg from the vitelline membrane or zona radiata and the formation of the perivitelline space is less precipitous. In the egg of the bird (e.g., pigeon or hen) (fig. 126), a vitelline space filled with fluid appears during the latter phase of oocyte growth in the ovary which separates the surface ooplasm of the egg from the vitelline membrane. The egg is free to revolve in this vitelline space. In the prototherian mammals, the zona pellucida evidently functions in a manner similar to that of the bird or reptile (figs. 46, 127). However, in the metatherian and eutherian mammalia, the zona pellucida becomes separated from the ooplasm of the egg's surface with the subsequent development of a perivitelline space at fertilization or during early cleavage (figs. 115, 118, 124, 125).

It is to be observed, therefore, that there are two general groups of egg or vitelline membranes in the phylum *Chordata* which assume an important role at fertilization and during the earlier part of embryonic development:

(1) those membranes which become separated from the egg surface in a somewhat dramatic manner at fertilization, and

(2) membranes which separate gradually during the late phases of ovarian development and during early embryonic development.

In the former group are to be found the egg membranes of the eggs of *Amphioxus,* telcost and many other fishes, and the amphibia; in the latter group are the membranes of eggs of *Styela,* elasmobranch fishes, reptiles, birds, and prototherian mammals. The higher mammalian eggs appear to occupy an intermediate position.

The separation of the so-called fertilization membrane has been most intensively studied in certain invertebrate forms. As a matter of interest, some of the processes involved in membrane elevation in various invertebrate eggs are herewith described briefly.

In the nematode, *Ascaris,* the egg exudes a jelly-like substance after the sperm has entered. This substance hardens to form a thin, tough membrane which later thickens and expands. The egg also appears to shrink, leaving an enlarged perivitelline space between the egg surface and the outer hardened membrane (figs. 128, 133C–E).

The formation of the fertilization membrane in *Echinarachnlus,* a genus of sea urchins, was the subject of intensive study by Just ('19). In this species the egg is larger than that of the sea urchin, *Arbacia.* According to Just's account, the fertilization membrane starts as a "blister" at the point of sperm contact; from this area it spreads and rapidly becomes lifted off from the general surface of the egg. Heilbrunn ('13) studied the fertilization membrane of the sea urchin's egg before fertilization and describes it as a vitelline membrane, "probably a gel or semi-gel" which is present at the surface of the egg. It becomes visible as a distinct membrane when lifted off from the egg's surface after fertilization. As this elevation occurs, according to Runnström, cortical granules are exuded from the surface of the egg, accompanied by a

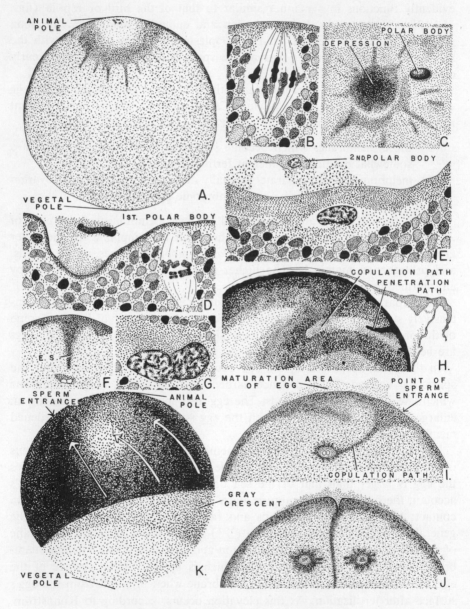

FIG. 119. *(See facing page for legend.)*

general contraction of the egg surface. These cortical granules later become merged with the vitelline membrane to form a relatively thick structure (fig. 129). (See Runnström, '49.) Fluid collects between the egg surface and the fertilization membrane.

On the other hand, in the annelid worm, *Nereis,* there is a complicated reaction at the egg's surface at the time of fertilization (Lillie, F. R., '12). In this egg a definite membrane is present around the newly laid egg. When a sperm has made an intimate contact with the egg's surface, the cortical layer of the egg exudes a substance which passes through the membrane to the outside; this substance turns into jelly on coming in contact with sea water (fig. 130B). The jelly layer carries away the excess sperm from the egg's surface. A striated area then appears between the vitelline membrane and the surface of the egg. This area, shown in fig. 130B as the cortical layer, represents the collapsed walls of small spaces of the superficial layer of the cortex of the egg which exude their contents through the vitelline membrane to form the surrounding jelly. The egg then forms a new ooplasmic surface beneath the collapsed walls of the small spaces of the original cortex (fig. 130B, ooplasmic membrane).

All of these changes and reactions, namely, the formation of the fertilization membrane, the exudation of cortical granules, and the emission of a fluid or jelly together with the shrinkage of the egg result from changes which occur in the outer layer of the egg's protoplasm or cortex, and consequently may be classified as **cortical changes.** The activation of the egg at the time of fertilization or during artificial stimulation thus appears to be closely integrated with cortical phenomena. It is debatable whether these changes are the result of activation or are a part of the "cause" of activation.

The particular activity of egg behavior at the time of fertilization which

---

Fɪɢ. 119. Fertilization phenomena in the egg of *Rana pipiens.* (Drawings B, D–G made from prepared slides by the courtesy of Dr. C. L. Parmenter.) (A) Semidiagrammatic representation of the egg shortly before ovulation. The germinal vesicle has broken down, and the chromosomes in diakinesis have migrated toward the apex of the animal pole preparatory to the first maturation spindle formation shown in (B). (D) First polar spindle. Tetrad condition of chromosomes in process of separation into the respective dyads. (C) Polar view of egg after first maturation division. Compare with (D), which represents a section of a comparable condition. (D) Lateral view of spindle of second maturation division. First polar body present in a slight depression at animal pole. The egg is spawned in this condition. (E) Second polar body shown in a depression of the animal pole. Within the superficial ooplasm of the egg, the reorganized female pronucleus is shown. (F) Meeting of the two pronuclei is shown in this section of the egg at the bottom of the female copulation path or "egg streak," E.S. (G) Two pronuclei in contact (shown in F) under higher magnification. (H) Entrance and copulation paths of sperm nucleus. (Modified from Rugh: *The Frog,* Philadelphia, The Blakiston Co., 1951.) (I) Sperm-entrance path, copulation path, and meeting of pronuclei. (From O. Hertwig, 1877.) (J) First cleavage path, showing daughter nuclei. (From O. Hertwig, 1877.) (K) External, lateral view of the egg just before first cleavage. Arrows show direction of pigment migration with resulting formation of gray crescent.

appears to be common to the eggs of many species (sea urchin, cyclostomatous and teleost fishes, frog, and mammal) is the *contraction of the egg's surface, together with the exudation of various substances from the egg.* (See, in this connection, the fertilization theory of Bataillon at the end of this chapter.) It is this behavior of the egg's surface which makes the fertilization membranes and other egg membranes more apparent; it represents one of the essential and immediate activities associated with egg activation. Separation of the various egg membranes at the time of fertilization appears to be secondary to this primary activity.

Aside from the immediate functions at the time of fertilization, the activities of the various types of vitelline membranes are concerned mainly with nutritional, environmental, and protective conditions of the early embryo. The presence of a fluid in the perivitelline space between the membrane and the developing egg affords a favorable environment for early developmental processes. Moreover, it permits the egg to rotate when its position is disturbed, a proper developmental orientation being maintained. A further accommodation is evident in that it permits the developing egg to exude substances, including yolk, into the surrounding area, which may be retained in the immediate environment of the egg and later utilized in a nutritional way. If the surrounding vitelline membrane were not present, this material, solid or fluid, would be dissipated. For example, in the early cleavage stage of the opossum or guinea-pig egg, yolk material is discharged into the area surrounding the early blastomeres (figs. 118, 125). The exuded yolk and dissolved substances later come to lie in the cavity within the blastomeres and, thereby, may be used for nutritional purposes. Also, in some forms, such as the opossum, the early blastomeres utilize the zona pellucida as a framework upon which they arrange themselves along its inner aspect during the development of the early

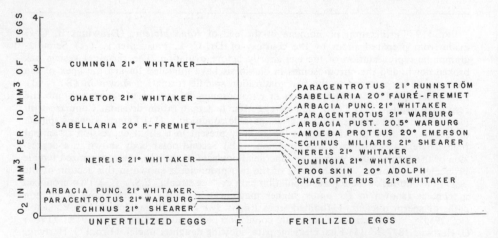

FIG. 120. Effects of fertilization on oxygen consumption in various marine eggs. (After J. Brachet, '50; data supplied by Whitaker.)

blastula. This apparent independence of the early cleavage blastomeres in the opossum and their lack of cohesiveness is evident in other mammals, also. The tendency of the blastomeres in mammals in general to separate from each other emphasizes the importance of the zona as a capsule which functions to hold the blastomeres together.

The surrounding egg membrane, in many cases, may act osmotically to permit a nice balance between the developing egg and the substances outside of the membrane. For example, in birds, the egg and its contained embryo together with its immediate environment are largely maintained as a physicochemical system due to the osmotic properties of the zona radiata or vitelline membrane. This membrane separates the watery albumen from the nutritive yolk material. These two substances have different osmotic conditions. Consequently, the vitelline membrane must maintain the proper conditions between these two general areas, and it performs this function in an admirable fashion. It should be emphasized further that the vitelline membrane in the chick's egg is a living membrane, and consequently its osmotic properties are different from that of a non-living membrane, such as a collodion membrane. If the egg and albumen of the hen's egg are separated by a thin collodion membrane, for example, they will reach an osmotic equilibrium more rapidly than when separated by the thin vitelline membrane. If, however, the vitelline membrane is isolated from its normal relationships in the egg, it behaves similarly to a collodion membrane. It is best to regard the vitelline membrane, the yolk, and the albumen of the bird's egg as forming an harmonious system, in which all parts are responsible for the maintenance of the necessary conditions for development. (Consult Romanoff and Romanoff, '49, pp. 388–391.)

Undoubtedly in other eggs, such as that of the frog, the delicate relationship existing between the egg, the perivitelline fluid, the vitelline membrane, and the surrounding external medium forms a complete unit for the proper maintenance of developmental conditions. In most eggs the vitelline or similar membranes maintain the protective function until a relatively late period in development.

b. Fertilization Cone or Attraction Cone

The fertilization cone results from specialized activity of the surface of the egg (egg cortex) at the point of sperm contact (fig. 130). This structure has been described in various invertebrate eggs, such as those of the sea urchins, annelid worms, mollusks, and in some of the ascidians among the protochordata. In the annelid worm, *Nereis virens,* as the sperm makes its way through the egg membrane, a cone of cortical ooplasm flows out to meet the sperm, making an intimate contact with the perforatorium (acrosome) of the sperm (fig. 130B, C). When this contact is made, the extended cone withdraws again gradually, and appears to pull the sperm head into the egg's substance (fig. 130D–G). In the egg of the sea urchin, *Toxopneustes varie-*

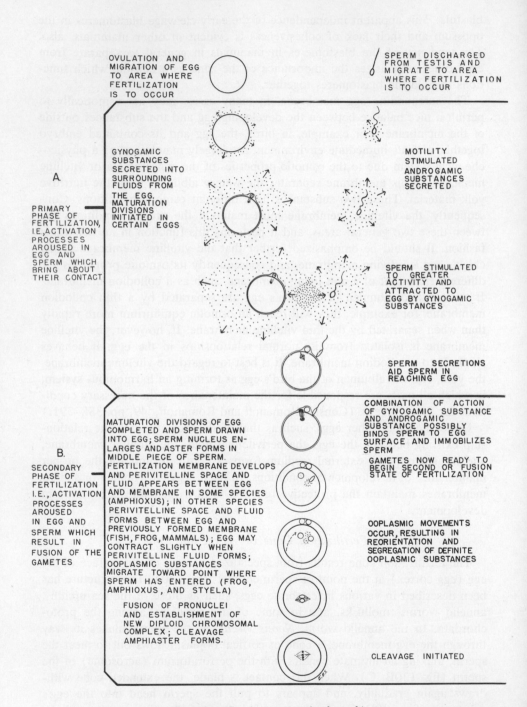

OVULATION AND MIGRATION OF EGG TO AREA WHERE FERTILIZATION IS TO OCCUR

SPERM DISCHARGED FROM TESTIS AND MIGRATE TO AREA WHERE FERTILIZATION IS TO OCCUR

A.

PRIMARY PHASE OF FERTILIZATION, I.E., ACTIVATION PROCESSES AROUSED IN EGG AND SPERM WHICH BRING ABOUT THEIR CONTACT

GYNOGAMIC SUBSTANCES SECRETED INTO SURROUNDING FLUIDS FROM THE EGG. MATURATION DIVISIONS INITIATED IN CERTAIN EGGS

MOTILITY STIMULATED ANDROGAMIC SUBSTANCES SECRETED

SPERM STIMULATED TO GREATER ACTIVITY AND ATTRACTED TO EGG BY GYNOGAMIC SUBSTANCES

SPERM SECRETIONS AID SPERM IN REACHING EGG

B.

SECONDARY PHASE OF FERTILIZATION I.E., ACTIVATION PROCESSES AROUSED IN EGG AND SPERM WHICH RESULT IN FUSION OF THE GAMETES

MATURATION DIVISIONS OF EGG COMPLETED AND SPERM DRAWN INTO EGG; SPERM NUCLEUS EN-LARGES AND ASTER FORMS IN MIDDLE PIECE OF SPERM. FERTILIZATION MEMBRANE DEVELOPS AND PERIVITELLINE SPACE AND FLUID APPEARS BETWEEN EGG AND MEMBRANE IN SOME SPECIES (AMPHIOXUS); IN OTHER SPECIES PERIVITELLINE SPACE AND FLUID FORMS BETWEEN EGG AND PREVIOUSLY FORMED MEMBRANE (FISH, FROG, MAMMALS); EGG MAY CONTRACT SLIGHTLY WHEN PERIVITELLINE FLUID FORMS; OOPLASMIC SUBSTANCES MIGRATE TOWARD POINT WHERE SPERM HAS ENTERED (FROG, AMPHIOXUS, AND STYELA)

FUSION OF PRONUCLEI AND ESTABLISHMENT OF NEW DIPLOID CHROMOSOMAL COMPLEX; CLEAVAGE AMPHIASTER FORMS.

COMBINATION OF ACTION OF GYNOGAMIC SUBSTANCE AND ANDROGAMIC SUBSTANCE POSSIBLY BINDS SPERM TO EGG SURFACE AND IMMOBILIZES SPERM

GAMETES NOW READY TO BEGIN SECOND OR FUSION STATE OF FERTILIZATION

OOPLASMIC MOVEMENTS OCCUR, RESULTING IN REORIENTATION AND SEGREGATION OF DEFINITE OOPLASMIC SUBSTANCES

CLEAVAGE INITIATED

FIG. 121. *(See facing page for legend.)*

242

gatus, a protoplasmic prominence appears only after a sperm begins to pass into the egg. It persists until about the time that the pronuclei unite (Wilson and Mathews, 1895). (See fig. 131B–F.) A prominent fertilization cone is found also in the starfish, *Asterias forbesi* (Wilson and Mathews, 1895). In the vertebrate group, fertilization cones are not generally observed, but the protoplasmic bridge from the egg membrane to the ooplasmic surface in *Petromyzon* evidently fulfills the functions of a cone (fig. 134C).

The formation of the fertilization cone and its withdrawal again, suggests that ooplasmic movements are concerned mainly with the sperm's entry into the interior of the egg. These movements appear to be aroused by some stimulus emanating from the sperm as it contacts the egg's surface. That is to say, although the sperm becomes immobile once it has touched the egg's surface, various stimuli, chemical and/or physical, issue from the sperm into the egg substance. Here these stimuli inaugurate movements in the ooplasm which draw the sperm into the egg. This modern view thus emphasizes motility of the cortical area of the egg as the factor which conveys the sperm into the interior of the egg. It suggests further that the older view of sperm entry which was presumed to result from sperm motility alone does not agree with the actual facts demonstrated by observation.

c. Some Changes in the Physiological Activities of the Egg at Fertilization

The separation of the egg membrane from the egg surface, the emission of fluid substances from the egg's surface into the perivitelline space, and contraction of the egg's surface have been noted above. Associated with these immediate results of sperm contact with the egg, a pronounced movement of cytoplasmic substances within the egg can be demonstrated in many species. Examples of cytoplasmic movements within the ooplasm of the egg are given below in the descriptions of the fertilization processes which occur in various chordate species.

Accompanying the above-mentioned activities, pronounced changes of a metabolic nature occur. In the egg of the frog and toad, for example, there is little change in the oxygen consumption during fertilization, although there

---

FIG. 121. Two stages of fertilization in animals. (A) In the primary phase of fertilization ("external fertilization" of F. R. Lillie), the sperm is activated to greater motility by the environmental factors encountered at the fertilization site, including the gynogamic substances secreted by the egg. It is also drawn to the egg by a positive chemotaxis. The lytic substances (androgamic substances) enable the stimulated sperm to make its way more easily through the jelly membranes and ooplasmic membranes surrounding the egg to the egg's surface. At the egg's surface the interaction of gynogamic and androgamic substances brings about the agglutination of the sperm to the egg's surface. This initiates stage B, on the secondary phase of the fertilization process ("internal fertilization" of F. R. Lillie). (B) Secondary phase of fertilization or fusion of the gametes. (See text for further description.) This stage begins when the sperm has made contact with the egg and terminates when the first cleavage spindle has formed.

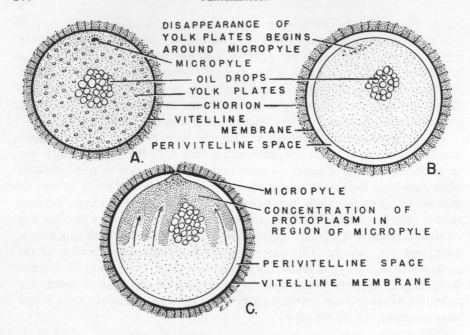

FIG. 122. Changes during fertilization in the egg of *Fundulus heteroclitus*. (A) Egg
before fertilization. (B, C) Changes in the egg shortly after sperm entrance into the
egg. In (B) is shown the contraction of the egg from the vitelline membrane, the disappearance of the yolk plates, and the formation of the perivitelline space. In (C) is shown
the migration of the peripheral cytoplasm toward the point where the sperm has entered
the egg, forming a cytoplasmic or polar cap.

is a pronounced drop in the **respiratory quotient,** presumably indicating a
change in the character of oxygen consumption (Brachet, J., '50, p. 106).
Fertilization does not change the rate of oxygen consumption in the teleost
fish, *Fundulus heteroclitus,* but, in the lamprey, oxygen consumption is increased (Brachet, J., '50, p. 108). Also, in the egg of the sea urchin, following artificial activation or normal fertilization, there is a considerable
increase in oxygen consumption (fig. 120). In the unfertilized and fertilized
egg of the starfish *(Asterias)* apparently there is no change in the rate of oxygen
metabolism. In the eggs of certain sea urchins it has been shown by Runnström
and co-workers (Runnström, '49, p. 306) that acid formation occurs following fertilization. It is of brief duration. (Consult also Brachet, J., '50, p. 120,
for references.) Other changes have been described, such as an increase in
viscosity of the egg (Heilbrunn, '15), and an increase in permeability of the
egg membrane (Heilbrunn, '15). Fertilization may produce a higher dispersity
of the egg colloidal material, at least in some species. Changes of a metabolic
nature, therefore, are a part of the fertilization picture. (The reader should
consult Brachet, J., '50, Chap. 4, for a thorough discussion of physiological
changes at fertilization.)

d. Completion of Maturation Divisions, Ooplasmic Movements, and Copulatory Paths of the Male and Female Pronuclei in Eggs of Various Chordate Species

A description of the maturation processes, ooplasmic movements, and the behavior of the male and female pronuclei in the fertilization processes of various chordate species is given below. It should be observed that all of these events occur rather synchronously in the urochordate, *Styela,* and in the egg of the frog, while in others, such as the prototherian mammal, *Echidna,* they may come to pass in sequence.

1) Fertilization in *Styela* (Cynthia) *partita:* a) CHARACTERISTICS OF THE EGG BEFORE FERTILIZATION. The living, fully formed, primary oocyte of the urochordate, *Styela* (Cynthia) *partita,* is about 150 μ in diameter. It possesses at this time three areas which can be distinguished with clearness, namely, a peripheral transparent layer which contains a sparsely distributed yellow pigment, a central mass of gray-appearing yolk, and the area of the germinal vesicle, located near the future animal pole of the egg (fig. 132A).

The first steps leading to the maturation divisions of the chromatin material take place before sperm entrance, at the time the egg is spawned or shortly before. At this time the wall of the germinal vesicle (i.e., the nuclear membrane) breaks down, and the contained clear cytoplasm moves up to the animal pole of the egg where it spreads out to form a disc. The chromosomes then line up on the metaphase plate of the first maturation spindle; *they remain thus in the metaphase of the first maturation until the sperm enters* (fig. 116A, B).

b) ENTRANCE OF THE SPERM. The sperm enters the egg (i.e., the primary oocyte) at the future vegetal (vegetative) pole, either exactly at the pole or a little to one side (fig. 116B). Sperm entrance at this pole probably is due to a fundamental structural and physiological condition which in turn reflects a definite polarity of the egg. Only one sperm normally enters the egg, but several sperm may penetrate through the chorion into the perivitelline space.

c) CYTOPLASMIC SEGREGATION. A striking series of changes appear within the cytoplasm of the egg immediately following sperm entrance. The yellow-pigmented, peripheral layer of protoplasm flows toward the point of sperm entrance (i.e., the vegetal pole) and collects into a "deep, orange-yellow spot" which surrounds the sperm (fig. 132B, C, peripheral protoplasm). It later spreads again and then covers most of the lower or vegetal pole of the egg. Accompanying the flow of yellow peripheral protoplasm toward the vegetal egg pole, most of the clear protoplasm of the germinal vesicle (i.e., the nuclear plasm mentioned above) flows with the yellow protoplasm toward the vegetal pole. The clear protoplasm, to some extent, tends to mingle with the yellow-pigmented, peripheral protoplasm. In figure 132C, the clear protoplasm may be observed as a clear area above the yellow-pigmented protoplasm.

The sperm pronucleus next moves upward away from the vegetal pole and toward one side of the egg to a point which marks the posterior pole of the egg and future embryo (fig. 116M). The clear protoplasm and the yellow-pigmented protoplasm move upward with the sperm (fig. 132D). The yellow-pigmented protoplasm at this time forms a yellow crescent just below the egg's equator, and the middle point of this crescent marks the posterior end of the future embryo (fig. 132D, E). A distinct crescent of clear protoplasm appears just above the yellow crescent at this time (fig. 132D–F). The crescent substance is therefore plainly differentiated at once into clear and yellow protoplasm, which remain distinct throughout the entire development (Conklin, '05, p. 21).

The yolk material, which at first is centrally located in the egg, moves toward the animal pole when the clear and yellow-pigmented protoplasms migrate to the vegetal pole. As the yellow and clear protoplasmic crescents are formed, the yolk material moves to occupy its ultimate position at the vegetal pole of the egg (fig. 132D). Later when the first cleavage division occurs, another crescentic area, the gray crescent, appears on the side of the egg opposite the yellow crescent.

As a result of the segregation of ooplasmic materials, four definite areas are localized:

(1) a vegetal, yolk-laden area,
(2) a gray crescent,
(3) the yellow and clear protoplasmic crescents opposite the latter, and finally
(4) the more or less homogeneous cytoplasm at the animal pole of the egg.

The movements of cytoplasmic materials in the cephalochordate, *Amphioxus,* are similar to those in *Styela* (Conklin, '32).

d) COPULATORY PATHS AND FUSION OF THE GAMETIC PRONUCLEI. The entrance of the sperm into the egg substance, its migratory movements in the ooplasm, its meeting with the egg pronucleus, and final fusion or association of the pronuclei afford an interesting problem. The factors governing the movements of the female and male pronuclei are unknown, although the movements in many eggs are spectacular. The movements of the pronuclei in *Styela partita* offer an excellent illustration of the copulatory migrations of the pronuclei within the cytoplasm of the egg.

The sperm enters the egg of *Styela partita,* as stated previously, at the vegetal pole near the midpolar area or a little to one side (fig. 116B). The sperm moves inward through the yellow-pigmented protoplasm and eventually becomes surrounded with the yellow and clear protoplasms (figs. 132C; 116B–F). This initial pathway through the superficial protoplasm of the egg constitutes the **penetration path of the sperm** (Wilhelm Roux). The sperm head in the meantime begins to swell and becomes vesicular (figs. 116F, J; 133B–G, *Ascaris*). The nucleus and the middle piece of the sperm with its forming aster now rotate 180 degrees, so that the aster lies anterior to the nucleus as it migrates within the egg (fig. 116F, I, J). The sperm aster thus precedes the pronucleus as the latter moves through the cytoplasm (fig. 116M).

With the movement of the clear and pigmented protoplasmic substances upward toward the equator and to the point marking the future posterior end of the embryo, the sperm pronucleus and aster move upward. This latter movement of the sperm constitutes the **copulation path,** and it is formed at a sharp angle to the penetration path (figs. 116M, 139B). The egg chromatin in the meantime undergoes its first and second maturation divisions (fig. 116F–L). After the second polar body has been formed, the haploid number of chromosomes reform the egg nucleus, now called the female pronucleus (fig. 116L, M). The latter then moves downward through the yolk along its copulation path to meet the sperm pronucleus near the posterior pole of the egg (figs. 116M–P; 139B). The actual meeting place in the clear cytoplasm is about halfway between the posterior pole and the center of the egg (fig. 139B).

Shortly before the pronuclei meet, the sperm aster divides, each aster moving to opposite poles of the sperm pronucleus (fig. 116N). The two pronuclei now meet *between the amphiaster of the first cleavage* (fig. 116O, P) and thus become enclosed by the amphiaster spindle (fig. 116P). Following this association, the entire complex migrates toward the center of the egg together with a mass of clear cytoplasm. Some of the yellow protoplasm also migrates slightly centerward. The latter movement of the pronuclei toward the center of the egg is called the **cleavage path.** In the new position, slightly posterior to the egg's center, the pronuclei form an intimate association (figs. 116P, 139). The chromosomes then make their appearance, the nuclear membranes disappear, and the chromosomes line up in the metaphase plate of the first cleavage spindle preparatory to the first cleavage (fig. 116Q). The first cleavage plane always bisects the midplane of the future embryo and hence bisects the yellow and clear protoplasmic crescents (figs. 116R, S; 132F, G).

2) Fertilization of *Amphioxus*. The fertilization stages of *Amphioxus* are shown in figures 117A–I; 139C. The general process of fertilization in this species appears much the same as in *Styela*. However, in *Amphioxus* the fertilization phenomena cannot be studied as readily for a pigmented material is not formed in the peripheral cytoplasm. According to Conklin ('32), the general movements of the cytoplasmic substances resemble those of *Styela*. It is to be observed, however, that the copulation paths of the sperm and egg pronuclei, and also the cleavage path of the two pronuclei, are different slightly in *Amphioxus* from those present in *Styela* (fig. 139B, C).

3) Fertilization of the Frog's Egg. The egg of *Rana pipiens* is spherical and approximately 1.75 mm. in diameter as it lies in the uterine portion of the oviduct just before spawning. The size, however, may vary considerably. It has a darkly pigmented animal pole and a lightly colored vegetal pole. The first maturation division occurs when the egg is ovulated or shortly after ovulation during its passage through the peritoneal cavity en route to the oviduct (fig. 119B, C). The secondary oocyte then enters the oviduct, and during its passage posteriad in the latter, the maturation spindle of the second maturation division is formed (fig. 119D). The egg is in this condition when it is spawned. Immediately upon its entrance into the water, it is fertilized by the sperm from the amplectant male.

The sperm enters the egg at a point about 20 to 30 degrees down from the midregion of the animal pole. As it penetrates through the cortex of the egg, a trail of dark pigment from the egg's periphery flows in after the sperm (fig. 119H, I). This **initial entrance path** of the sperm constitutes the **penetration path.** After making its initial entrance, the sperm begins to travel toward its meeting place with the female pronucleus. This secondary path is the **copulation path of the sperm** (fig. 119I). If the sperm should continue more or less in a straight line toward the egg pronucleus, the **penetration path** and **copulation path** would be continuous. However, if the sperm should veer away at an angle from the original penetration path in its journey to meet the female pronucleus, the copulation path would be at an angle to the penetration path.

The second maturation division of the oocyte occurs in about 20 to 30 minutes after sperm entrance with a surrounding temperature approximating 22° C. After the female pronucleus is organized, it migrates along its copulation path toward the meeting place with the sperm pronucleus, located near the center of the animal pole cytoplasm of the egg (fig. 119F, G).

Shortly after the sperm penetrates the egg, it revolves 180 degrees, and the middle-piece area travels foremost. This revolving movement, whereby the middle-piece area assumes a foremost position, is similar to that which occurs in the protochordates, *Styela* and *Amphioxus*. This revolving movement appears to be characteristic of all sperm after entering the egg. (See figs. 116, 117, 131.) The sperm pronucleus gradually enlarges as it continues along the copulation path, and the first cleavage amphiaster arises in relation to the middle-piece region.

Fusion of the two pronuclei occurs at about one and one-half to two hours after fertilization at a normal room temperature of about 22° C. (fig. 119G). At about two and three-quarter hours after fertilization the first cleavage furrow begins (figs. 119J; 142A).

As stated above, the peripheral egg cytoplasm with its pigment tends to flow into the interior of the egg, following the trail of the sperm and thus forms a **pigmented trail.** The migration of the superficial cytoplasm with its pigmented granules is general over the upper pole of the egg and its direction of flow is toward the point of sperm penetration (see arrows, fig. 119K). Consequently, at a point on the egg's surface opposite the point of sperm entrance, the peripheral area of the egg becomes lighter in color and assumes a gray appearance. This area is crescentic in shape and is known as the **gray crescent** (fig. 110K).

The formation of the gray crescent occurs in the cytoplasmic area just above the margin where the yellow-white vegetal pole material merges with the darkly pigmented animal pole. The gray crescent is continuous with the lighter vegetal pole material and is seen most clearly during the first cleavage of the egg. The plane which bisects the gray crescent into two equal halves represents the future median plane of the embryo.

In the frog, *Rana fusca,* Ancel and Vintemberger ('33) have shown that extensive movements of egg-surface materials accompanies the formation of the gray crescent. Sperm contact with the egg's surface thus appears to set in motion ooplasmic substances which fix the final symmetry of the egg and the future embryo.

4) Fertilization of the Teleost Fish Egg. When the egg of the teleost fish is spawned, the yolk lies near the center of the egg, and its yolk-free cytoplasm forms a peripheral layer. Around the egg the yolk-free cytoplasm is somewhat more abundant in the region where the egg nuclear material is situated. This concentration of the peripheral cytoplasm at the nuclear pole is more evident in the eggs of some species than in others. The area of nuclear residence is situated near the micropyle in many teleost eggs, but not in all. For example, the concentration of cytoplasm with the contained nuclear material is located in *Bathygobius soporator* at the opposite end to the micropyle (Tavolga, '50). (See fig. 123A.)

The sperm enters the egg through the micropyle (figs. 122, 123, 134A), and the actual processes of fertilization are initiated when the sperm makes contact with the peripheral ooplasm near the point where the egg nuclear material is located. This normally occurs in about a minute or less after the egg reaches the water. Within a few minutes the second polar body is given off. Meanwhile, the peripheral cytoplasm flows toward the area where the sperm has made contact, and a protoplasmic cap forms at this pole (figs. 122C; 123D–D). The remainder of the egg, with the exception of a thin layer of surface protoplasm, contains the deutoplasmic or yolk material. The egg is converted in this manner from a more or less centrolecithal egg into a strongly telolecithal egg. (Compare with *Styela* and *Amphioxus.*)

While these events are progressing, the egg as a whole contracts slightly, and a fluid is given off into the forming perivitelline space between the egg's surface and the vitelline membrane (fig. 122B, C). (However, a space between the egg membrane and the egg is evident to some extent in certain teleost eggs before the sperm enters the egg (fig. 123A).) The egg is now free to rotate within the perivitelline space, being cushioned and bathed by the perivitelline fluid.

The expansion of the vitelline membrane of the egg in certain teleosts is both dramatic and prophetic of the future shape of the embryo (fig. 123B–H).

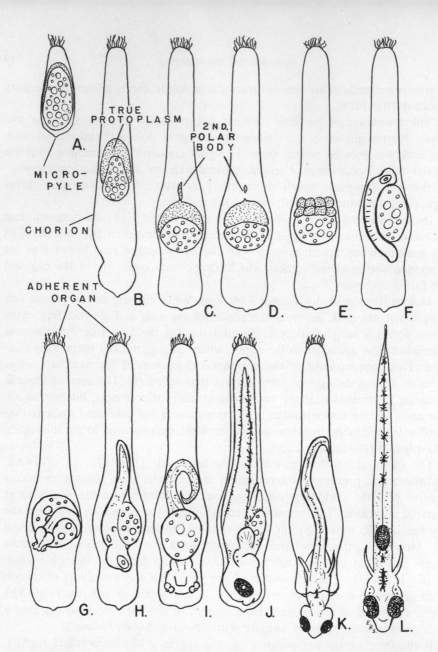

FIG. 123. Development of the gobiid fish, *Bathygobius soporator*. (After Tavolga, '50, slightly modified.) (A) Freshly stripped egg. Adherent filaments at proximal end of chorion; micropyle at distal end. Peripheral cytoplasm partly concentrated at the pole of the egg containing the female nucleus. (B) Fifteen minutes after fertilization; cytoplasm concentrating at nuclear pole of the egg; chorion expanding into shape of future embryo. (C) Twenty minutes after fertilization; second polar body given off. (D) Twenty-five minutes after fertilization. (E) Ninety minutes after fertilization. (F) Seventeen hours after fertilization. (G) Twenty-four hours after fertilization. (H) Thirty hours after fertilization. (I) Thirty-six hours after fertilization. (J) Ninety-six hours after fertilization. (K) Ninety-six hours after fertilization. Hatching. (L) Three days after hatching, temperature 27 to 29°.

In demersal eggs, that is, eggs which sink to the bottom, the protoplasmic cap tends to assume an uppermost position. In pelagic eggs, i.e., eggs which float in the water, the protoplasmic disc turns downward since it is the heaviest part of the egg.

After the polar bodies are given off, the egg-chromatin material reforms the female pronucleus. The latter and the sperm pronucleus migrate to a position near the center of the protoplasmic disc. The first cleavage plane is established within thirty minutes to an hour following sperm entrance.

5) Fertilization in the Egg of the Hen and the Pigeon. Fertilization in the hen's egg occurs without any demonstrable movement of cytoplasmic materials, as manifested in the eggs of *Styela, Amphioxus,* frog, and teleost fish. The egg is strongly telolecithal, and the true protoplasm or blastodisc, which takes part in active development, is a flattened mass about 3 mm. in width. The germinal vesicle in the mature egg is approximately 350 μ in diameter and about 90 μ in thickness (fig. 126A). Approximately 24 hours *before* ovulation occurs, the wall of the germinal vesicle begins to break down, and the contained nuclear sap spreads in the form of a thin sheet below the ooplasmic membrane overlying the blastodisc (fig. 126B). (See Olsen, '42.)

Changes in the chromatin material of the germinal vesicle are synchronized with the breakdown of the membranous wall of the vesicle. The chromatin material, extremely diffuse during the period when the yolk material was formed and the egg as a whole was growing rapidly, contracts and assumes the character of thickened chromosomes in the tetrad condition. The diffuse

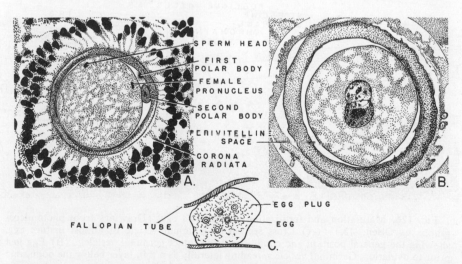

Fig. 124. Fertilization stages in the rabbit egg. (A, B after Pincus, '39.) (A) Second polar body exuded; male and female pronuclei. (B) Twenty-two hours after copulation, showing two pronuclei close together. (C) Coagulated plug in infundibular portion of Fallopian tube, containing eggs. This plug is dissolved by sperm during fertilization process.

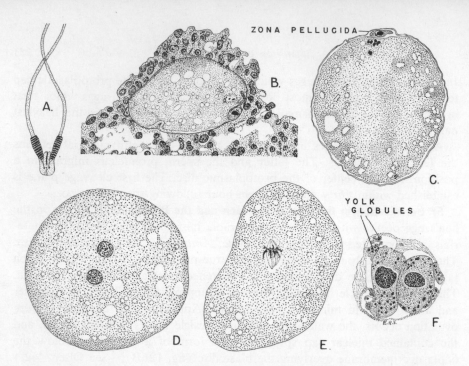

FIG. 125. Fertilization in the opossum. (A after McCrady, '38, from Duesberg; B–F after Hartman, '16.) (A) Conjugate sperm of opossum. (B) Ovarian egg showing discus proligerus around the egg; first polar body extruded; chromosomes of egg nucleus evident. (C) Tubal ovum. (D) Uterine ovum with pronuclei near center of the egg. (E) First cleavage spindle of uterine egg. (F) Two-cell stage, showing zona pellucida and exuded yolk material lying in perivitelline space.

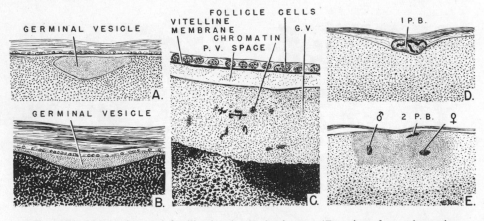

FIG. 126. Maturation and fertilization in the hen's egg. (Drawings from photomicrographs by Olsen, '42.) (A) Cross section of germinal vesicle of almost mature egg, showing the general position and condition of the intact germinal vesicle. (B) Egg just prior to ovulation. Germinal vesicle spreading laterally as a thin layer below the ooplasmic membrane. (C) Chromatin material near center of disintegrating germinal vesicle (G.V.) of an egg estimated to be one hour prior to ovulation. (D) First polar body (1 P.B.) of recently ovulated egg. (E) Cross section of blastodisc of recently ovulated egg showing male pronucleus (♂), female pronucleus (♀), and second polar body (2 P.B.).

diplotene state thus passes into the diakinesis stage (figs. 126C; 135A, show the breakdown of the nuclear wall and appearance of chromosomes in the pigeon).

The first maturation division occurs and the first polar body is extruded shortly before ovulation (fig. 126D). The second maturation spindle is then formed. In this state the egg is ovulated. From four to six sperm penetrate into the egg shortly after it enters the infundibulum of the oviduct. The latter events are consummated within fifteen minutes after ovulation. The second maturation division then occurs, followed by the discharge of the second polocyte, which becomes manifest about the time of, or shortly before, the fusion of a single male pronucleus with the female pronucleus (fig. 126E). Thus, although **polyspermy** is the rule, only one sperm pronucleus takes part in the syngamic process.

After the two pronuclei become closely associated, the chromosomes become evident, the nuclear membranes disintegrate, and the first cleavage spindle is formed in about five and one-quarter hours after the sperm enters the egg (Olsen, '42).

In the egg of the pigeon, according to Harper ('04), the germinal vesicle breaks down, and the first polar spindle forms in the egg just before ovulation (fig. 135A, B). Fertilization then occurs just as the egg (in reality the primary oocyte) enters the oviduct. Normally from 15 to 20 sperm enter the blastodisc of the pigeon's egg. However, only one sperm pronucleus associates with the female pronucleus. Consequently, unlike the condition in the hen's egg, both maturation divisions occur and the first and second polar bodies are given off after sperm entrance (fig. 135C, D). Following the maturation divisions, the two pronuclei proceed to associate (fig. 135E, F). The first cleavage nucleus is shown in fig. 135G with two accessory sperm nuclei shown to the extreme left of the figure.

6) Fertilization in the Rabbit. In the rabbit, ovulation occurs around 10 to 11 hours after copulation. It takes about four hours for the sperm to travel to the upper parts of the Fallopian tube. (See Chap. 4.) The sperm thus lie waiting for about six to seven hours before the eggs are ovulated. When the eggs are discharged from the ovary, each egg is surrounded by its cumulus cells. The latter form the **corona radiata,** surrounding the zona pellucida (fig. 124A). As the eggs are discharged from their follicles, an albuminous substance from the follicles forms a clot, and several eggs are included within this clot (fig. 124C). A sperm, therefore, must make its way through the substance of the clot, as well as between the cells of the corona radiata, and then through the zona pellucida to reach the egg. This feat is accomplished partly by its own swimming efforts and partly also by means of an enzyme (or enzymes) which dissolves a pathway for the sperm. (See hyaluronidase, etc., mentioned on pp. 229.) The ferment hyaluronidase, associated with the sperm, frees the eggs from the albuminous clot and aids in the dissolution of the

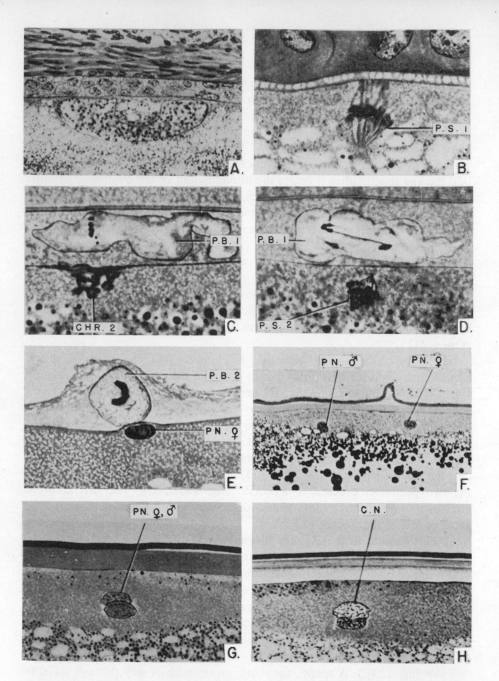

FIG. 127. Maturation and fertilization in *Echidna*. (Courtesy, Flynn and Hill, '39.)
(A) Oocyte, diameter 3.9 by 3.6 mm. Section of upper pole of egg showing saucer-shaped germinal vesicle lying in the germinal disc. (B) First polar spindle of egg just previous to ovulation. (C) First polar body and chromatin of female nucleus just previous to formation of second polar spindle shown in (D). (D) Second polar spindle of newly ovulated egg. Sperm presumably enters germinal disc at this time but possibly may wait until condition shown in (E) in some instances. (E) Second polar body and female pronucleus. (F) Male and female pronuclei. (G, H) Fusion stages of pronuclei.

corona radiata cells, so that each egg lies free in the Fallopian tube, surrounded by the zona pellucida. It may be that some other lytic substance associated with the sperm also is active in aiding the sperm to reach the egg's surface.

The first maturation division of the egg occurs as the egg is being ovulated. The egg remains in this condition until the sperm enters, which normally occurs within two hours after ovulation. Thus, sperm entrance into the rabbit's egg presumably is much slower than in the case of the hen's egg, possibly due to the albuminous and cellular barriers mentioned above. Several sperm may penetrate through the zona pellucida into the perivitelline space, but only one succeeds in becoming attached to the egg's surface (Pincus, '39). The sperm tail is left behind in the perivitelline fluid, and the sperm head and middle piece "appear to be drawn into the egg cytoplasm rather rapidly" (Pincus and Enzmann, '32). The second polar body is then extruded, a process which ordinarily is completed about the thirteenth hour following copulation (fig. 124A). About three or four hours later (that is, about 17 hours after copulation) the two pronuclei are formed and begin to approach one another, and at 20 to 23 hours after copulation the pronuclei have expanded to full size and come to lie side by side (fig. 124B). The migration of the pronuclei to the center of the egg thus consumes about four to six hours. The spindle for the first cleavage division generally is found from 21 to 24 hours after copulation (Pincus, '39). (Consult also Gregory, '30; Lewis and Gregory, '29.)

7) **Fertilization in the *Echidna*, a Prototherian Mammal.** The egg of the Tasmanian anteater, *Echidna,* when it reaches the pouch is about 15 by 13 mm. in diameter. This measurement, of course, is only approximate, and it includes the egg proper plus its external envelopes of albumen and the leathery shell. (The egg of *Ornithorhynchus* is slightly larger, approximating 17 by 14 mm.) At the time of fertilization in the upper portion of the Fallopian tube, the fresh ovum of *Echidna* without its external envelopes measures about four to 4.5 mm. in diameter.

The fully developed eggs of the monotreme (prototherian) mammals are strongly telolecithal, with a small disc of true protoplasm situated at one pole as in the bird or reptile egg. In *Echidna aculeata* this disc measures about 0.7 mm. in diameter during the maturation stages. Just before the onset of the maturation divisions of the nucleus, the germinal vesicle is saucer-shaped and lies in the midportion of the upper part of the disc (fig. 127A). The first maturation division (fig. 127B, C) occurs before ovulation, while the second maturation division (fig. 127D, E) occurs after ovulation. There is some evidence that the second maturation division, in some cases, may precede the actual entrance of the sperm into the germinal disc (Flynn and Hill, '39). In figure 127F–H, the stages in the association of the male and female pronuclei are shown.

As fertilization is accomplished, a rearrangement and movement of the ooplasmic substances of the germinal disc occur. As a result, the blastodisc, circular during the maturation period, becomes transformed into an oval-shaped affair with the polar bodies situated on one end (fig. 136). The first plane of cleavage is indicated by numerals I–I, and the second plane of cleavage by numerals II–II. A distinct bilateral symmetry thus is established by the rearrangement of ooplasmic materials during the fertilization process. (Compare with *Styela, Amphioxus,* and frog.)

E. Significance of the Maturation Divisions of the Oocyte in Relation to Sperm Entrance and Egg Activation

As indicated in the foregoing pages, the maturation divisions of the oocyte vary greatly in different animal species. Figure 137 shows that the time of sperm entrance in the majority of eggs occurs either before or during the maturation divisions, that is, when the female gamete is in the primary or secondary oocyte condition. In some animals, however, the sperm enters normally after the two maturation divisions are completed.

The correlation between the maturation period of the egg and sperm entrance indicates that the breakdown of the germinal vesicle and the accompanying maturation divisions has a profound effect upon the egg. This conclusion is substantiated by experimental data. For example, A. Brachet ('22) and Runnström and Monné ('45, a and b), working on the sea-urchin egg, found

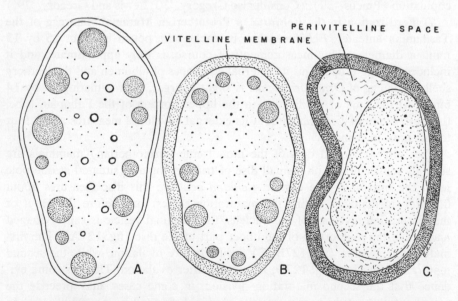

Fig. 128. Formation of the vitelline membrane in the egg of *Ascaris* after fertilization. (After Collier, '36.) (A) Heavy cell wall (vitelline membrane) is beginning to thicken. (B) Cell wall is reaching condition of maximum thickness. (C) Egg contracts away from vitelline membrane, leaving perivitelline space filled with fluid-like substance, forming the typical fertilized egg of *Ascaris* as ordinarily observed.

that several sperm enter the egg in the sea urchin if insemination is permitted before the maturation divisions occur. The immature egg, therefore, lacks the mechanism for the control of sperm entrance. Moreover, A. Brachet ('22) and Bataillon ('29) demonstrated that the sperm nuclei and asters behave abnormally under these conditions, and normal development is impossible. Runnström and Monné have further shown for the sea-urchin egg that the normal fertilization process, permitting the entrance of but one sperm, requires a mechanism which is built up gradually by degrees during the time when the maturation divisions of the egg occur, even extending to a necessary short period after the divisions are completed. Not only is the mechanism which permits but one sperm to enter the egg established at this time in the sea-urchin egg, but Runnström and Monné further conclude, p. 25, *"that the cytoplasmic maturation"* which occurs at the period of the maturation divisions, *"involves the accumulation at the egg surface of substances which participate in the activating reactions."* It appears, therefore, that the break-down of the germinal vesicle together with the phenomena associated with the maturation divisions is an all-important period of oocyte development, controlling sperm entrance on the one hand and, on the other, presumably being concerned with formation of substances which permit egg activation.

F. Micropyles and Other Physiologically Determined Areas for Sperm Entrance

A micropyle is a specialized structural opening in the membrane or membranes surrounding many eggs which permits the sperm to enter the egg. For example, in the eggs of teleostean fishes or in the eggs of cyclostomatous fishes, a small opening through the vitelline membrane (or chorion) at one pole of the egg permits the sperm to enter (figs. 93A; 134A–F). On the other hand, many chordate eggs do not possess a specialized micropyle through the egg membrane. The latter condition is found in the protochordates, *Styela* and *Amphioxus,* and in vertebrates in general other than the fish group. In *Styela* and *Amphioxus* the sperm enters the vegetal pole of the egg, i.e., the pole opposite the animal or nuclear pole. In most of the vertebrate species the sperm enters the animal or nuclear pole of the egg usually to one side of the area where the maturation divisions occur (figs. 115, 118, 119I). In urodele amphibians, the passage of several sperm into the egg at the time of fertilization complicates the picture. However, the sperm which finally conjugates with the egg pronucleus is the one nearest the area where the egg pronucleus is located. The several sperm entering other parts of the egg ultimately degenerate (fig. 138). Presumably this condition is present in reptiles and birds where many sperm normally enter the egg at fertilization.

In conclusion, therefore, it may be stated that the point of sperm entrance in chordate eggs in general appears to be definitely related to one area of the egg, either by the presence of a morphologically developed micropyle or

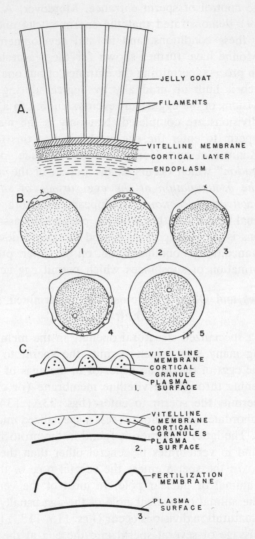

FIG. 129. Formation of the fertilization membrane in the mature egg of the sea urchin. (A) Surface of the egg and surrounding jelly coat before fertilization. (After Runnström, '49, p. 245.)   (B1, 2, 3, 4, 5) Point x marks the point of sperm contact. The fertilization membrane separates from the egg at the point of sperm contact and spreads rapidly around the egg from this point. (After Just, '39, p. 106.)   (C) Membrane formation in greater detail. (After Runnström, '49, p. 276.)   (1) As the vitelline membrane is lifted off from the plasma surface of the egg, cortical granular material is exuded from the egg cortex and passes out across the perivitelline space toward the fertilization membrane.   (2) Cortical granules begin to consolidate with the vitelline membrane.   (3) Fully developed fertilization membrane is formed by a union of the vitelline membrane with the cortical granules derived from the egg cortex.

by some physiological condition inherent in the organization of the egg. In the majority of chordate eggs, the place of sperm penetration is at that pole of the egg which contains the egg nuclear material, although in some, such as in the gobiid fish (fig. 123), the micropyle, permitting the sperm to get through the egg membrane, may be situated at a point opposite the nuclear pole of the egg.

G. Monospermic and Polyspermic Eggs

In the eggs of most animal species only one sperm normally enters the egg. Such eggs are known as **monospermic eggs.** Among the chordates, the eggs of *Styela, Amphioxus,* frog, toad, and mammals are monospermic. Abnormal cleavage and early death of the embryo is the general result of dispermy and polyspermy in frogs (Brachet, A., '12; Herlant, '11). In those chordates whose eggs possess much yolk, the eggs are normally **polyspermic,** and several sperm enter the egg at fertilization, although only one male pronucleus enters into syngamic relationship with the egg pronucleus; the other sperm soon degenerate and die in most cases (fig. 138). (See Fankhauser, '48.) In some urodele amphibia, it appears that syngamic conjugation of more than one sperm pronucleus with the egg pronucleus may occur in certain instances and may give origin to heteroploidy, and development may be quite normal (Fankhauser, '45). Examples of normal polyspermic eggs are: birds, reptiles, tailed amphibia, elasmobranch fishes, and possibly some teleost fishes. Among the invertebrates, polyspermy is found in some insects and in the *Bryozoa.* In the sea urchin, polyspermy may occur, but abnormal embryos are the rule in such cases as indicated above. Similar conditions are found in certain other invertebrates (Morgan, '27, pp. 84–86).

Two explanations of normal polyspermy are suggested:

(1) The presence of a superabundance of yolk hinders the operation of the mechanism whereby the egg inhibits the entrance of extra sperm; the egg, therefore, falls back upon a second line of defense within its own substance which excludes the sperm from taking part in or hindering the normal functioning of the syngamic nucleus in its relation to development; and

(2) a large amount of yolk makes it advantageous to the egg for extra sperm to enter, as they may contribute enzymes or other substances which enable the egg better to carry on the metabolism necessary in utilizing yolk material.

H. Importance of the Sperm Aster and the Origin of the First Cleavage Amphiaster

One of the older views of fertilization maintained that the egg possessed the cytoplasm but lacked a potent centrosome or "cell center" capable of

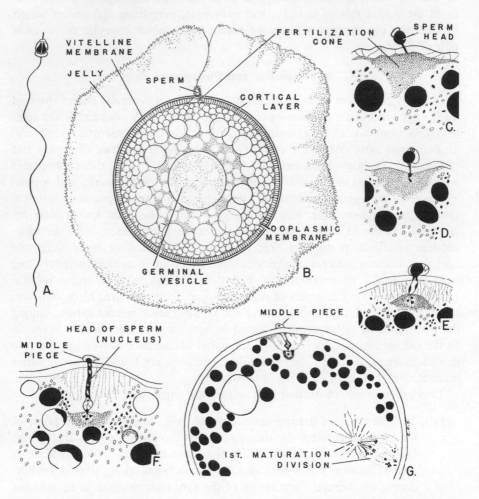

FIG. 130. Fertilization in *Nereis*. (After F. R. Lillie, '12.) (A) Sperm of *Nereis*, entire. (B) Egg of *Nereis*, 15 minutes after insemination. The fertilization cone is evident below point of sperm contact. Observe that the **intact germinal vesicle** is present in the center of the egg. It will break down as the sperm enters the egg (G). The cortical substance from the empty cortical compartments in the cortical layer shown around the periphery of the egg has passed out through the vitelline membrane to form the jelly layer around the egg. (C–G) Entrance of the sperm head into the ooplasm of the egg as the fertilization cone substance is withdrawn inward from the vitelline membrane. (C) Fifteen minutes after insemination. (D) Thirty-seven minutes after insemination. (E) Forty-eight and one-half minutes after insemination. (F) Fifty-four minutes after insemination. (G) Sperm head has completed penetration. Observe that the middle piece of the sperm remains outside, attached to the vitelline membrane. Anaphase of first maturation division.

giving origin to the first cleavage amphiaster, whereas the sperm possessed a dynamic centrosome with its included centriole but lacked sufficient cytoplasm for division or cleavage. Consequently, fertilization brought together a relationship necessary for cleavage and development. This idea was first set forth by Boveri (see fertilization theories at the end of this chapter).

In the majority of animals, the central body (i.e., the centrosome) with its surrounding aster, which ultimately divides and gives origin to the first cleavage amphiaster, does not arise until after the sperm has entered the egg. In these cases the aster complex arises in the middle piece of the sperm in close proximity to the nucleus. These facts are well illustrated in figures 116, 117, and 131. Many studies of the fertilization process and early cleavage bolster this general conclusion. There are some exceptions, however, to this rule. For example, Wheeler (1895) in his studies of fertilization in *Myzostoma glabrum* demonstrated that the centrioles of the egg near the germinal vesicle give origin to the amphiaster concerned with polar body formation. Following the maturation divisions, the female pronucleus with its centrioles and forming amphiaster, migrates along the copulation path to meet the sperm pronucleus. The amphiaster and centrioles are closely adherent to the egg pronucleus during the migration of the latter. In the honeybee, Nachtsheim ('13) found a similar situation, while in the mollusk, *Crepidula plana,* Conklin ('04) found evidence which suggests that one aster of the cleavage amphiaster arises from the egg, whereas the other aster arises from the sperm, "although there is not positive evidence that they are directly derived from egg and sperm centrosomes."

Where the egg develops as a result of artificial stimulation the first cleavage spindle arises without the aid of the sperm middle piece. In these instances the amphiaster probably is derived from the central body of the last maturation division, or, it may be, from certain asters or cytasters artificially induced in the egg cytoplasm by the activation process. The production of numerous asters in the cytoplasm of the egg by artificial stimulation has long been known (Mead, 1897; Morgan, 1899, '00).

The general conclusion to be extracted from the evidence at hand, therefore, suggests that the central body from the last maturation spindle or other artificially induced asters in the egg cytoplasm may form the amphiaster of the first cleavage spindle *in the case of an emergency.* Such an emergency arises in normal parthenogenesis or in cases of artificial activation (artificial parthenogenesis) of the egg. However, under the conditions of normal fertilization the sperm aster fulfills the role of developing the first cleavage amphiaster.

Regardless of the fact that the first cleavage amphiaster appears to be derived from the middle piece of the sperm, the influence of the egg protoplasm is undoubtedly an important factor in its formation. In the normal polyspermy of the newt, *Triton* (fig. 138; Fankhauser, '48), the sperm aster nearest the

egg pronucleus enlarges and develops the amphiaster, whereas the more dis-
tantly located sperm asters fade and disintegrate. This fact suggests that some
influence from the egg pronucleus stimulates the further development of the
amphiaster in the sperm nearest the egg pronucleus. In experiments on insemination of egg fragments in the urodele, *Triton,* Fankhauser ('34) found
that the sperm aster in that fragment which did not contain the egg nucleus
failed to reach the size of the aster in the fragment containing the egg nucleus.
He concludes, p. 204, "The interactions between the sperm complex and the
cytoplasm of the egg seem, therefore, to be stimulated in the presence of the
egg nucleus."

On the other hand, the experiments on androgenesis by Whiting ('49) in
Habrobracon, and the insemination of the "red halves" of the sea-urchin egg
by Harvey ('40) demonstrate that the sperm aster can, without the egg
pronucleus, produce the first cleavage amphiaster. However, *the presence of
a nucleoplasmic substance in both of these cases cannot be ruled out.* For
example, A. Brachet ('22) and Bataillon ('29), the former working on the
sea-urchin egg and the latter on the eggs of two amphibian species, demonstrated that large, normal sperm asters and large vesicular sperm nuclei do
not form until after the germinal vesicle breaks down and the egg becomes
mature. Premature fertilization results in polyspermy, small sperm nuclei, and
small sperm asters. In normal fertilization, therefore, it is very probable that
the development of the sperm aster into a normal cleavage amphiaster is
dependent:

(1) upon the egg cytoplasm, and
(2) upon some factor contributed to the egg cytoplasm by the nuclear sap
    or from the chromosomes of the female nucleus at the time of the break-
    down of the germinal vesicle or during the maturation divisions.

I. Some Related Conditions of Development Associated with the Fertilization Process

1. GYNOGENESIS

The word **gynogenesis** means "female genesis." Therefore, gynogenesis is
the development of the egg governed by the female pronucleus alone. The
male gamete may enter the egg but plays no further role (Sharp, '34, p. 406;
Wilson, '25, p. 460). In the nematode, *Rhabdites aberrans,* the egg produces
but one polar body, and diploidy is retained. The egg is penetrated by the
sperm which takes no part in later development, as it degenerates upon entering
the egg.

In the above instance, it is doubtful whether or not sperm is necessary to
activate the egg. However, in the nematode, *Rhabdites pellio,* the egg is penetrated by the sperm which plays no further role in development. Nevertheless,
in the latter instance, sperm entrance appears to be necessary for egg acti-

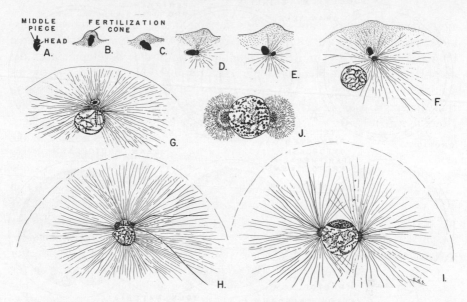

FIG. 131. Fertilization in the sea urchin, *Toxopneustes variegatus*. (After Wilson and Mathews, 1895.)   (A) Sperm head and middle piece.   (B) Fertilization cone (attraction cone; "cone of exudation" of Fol). The fertilization cone forms after the sperm head and middle piece have entered the egg, and persists through (F) when the pronuclei begin to come together.   (C–J) Different stages in the fusion of the pronuclei. Observe that the sperm rotates at about 180° and that the sperm aster appears near base of nucleus (D, E). The aster grows rapidly (F, G) as the sperm pronucleus advances toward the female pronucleus, and appears between the two pronuclei in (G). In (H) the aster has divided, and the daughter asters are found at either end of the two fusing pronuclei. In (I, J) the two asters are at either end of the fusion nucleus.   (J) Fusion nucleus between the amphiaster of the first cleavage.

vation. A somewhat similar phenomenon may also occur in other animal species taking part in hybrid crosses, where some or all of the paternal chromosomes may be eliminated; activation normally occurs in these instances, and development results. Gynogenesis is experimentally produced in amphibia by radiating the sperm before fertilization. Development is carried on by the female pronucleus in the latter instance, although it may produce larvae which ultimately die. Parthenogenesis, natural and artificial, in all its essential features in a sense may be regarded as gynogenesis.

2. ANDROGENESIS

This form of development is experimentally produced by removal of egg pronucleus with a small pipette before nuclear syngamy occurs (Porter, '39) or by treating the egg with x-rays before fertilization (Whiting, '49). The male pronucleus seems incapable of bringing about normal and full development in amphibia, but in wasps, where the egg pronucleus has been destroyed by radiation, it has been successful (Whiting, '49).

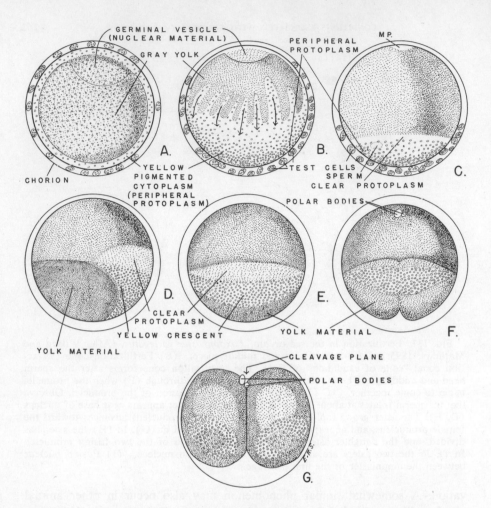

FIG. 132. Movement of ooplasmic substances in the egg of *Styela* (Cynthia) *partita*
at the time of fertilization. (All figures after Conklin, '05.)   (A) Unfertilized egg after
the disappearance of the nuclear membrane of the germinal vesicle. The gray yolk is
shown in the center of the egg, surrounded by the yellow-pigmented cytoplasm. The test
cells and chorion surround the egg.   (B) Egg five minutes after fertilization, showing
the streaming of the peripheral protoplasm indicated by arrows toward the vegetal pole,
where the sperm has entered. The gray yolk is shown in the upper part of the egg below
the nuclear material. The clear protoplasm, derived from the nuclear sap of the germinal
vesicle, also flows down with the peripheral protoplasm.   (C) Side view of an egg after
peripheral protoplasm has migrated to the vegetal pole of the egg. The clear protoplasm
is shown at the upper edge of the yellow cap. The polar bodies are forming in the
midpolar area (MP.) at the animal pole.   (D) Side view of the egg showing the yellow
crescent and the area of clear protoplasm above the yellow crescent. The yolk material
is shown at the vegetal pole below and to one side of the yellow crescent.   (E) Yellow
crescent and clear protoplasm viewed from the posterior pole of the egg. Animal pole
is above the crescent; yolk material is below.   (F) Same view as (E) a little later,
showing the external beginnings of the first cleavage. The polar bodies are shown above
the crescent material.   (G) View similar to that of (E, F) a little later. The first cleavage
is complete. Observe that the clear protoplasm and the yellow crescent have been bisected
equally. The cleavage plane corresponds to the median axis of the embryo.

264

3. MEROGONY

Merogony is the development of part of the egg, that is, an egg fragment. Egg fragments are obtained by shaking the egg to pieces, by cutting with a sharp instrument, or by the use of centrifugal force. **Andromerogony** is the development of a non-nucleate egg fragment after it has been fertilized by

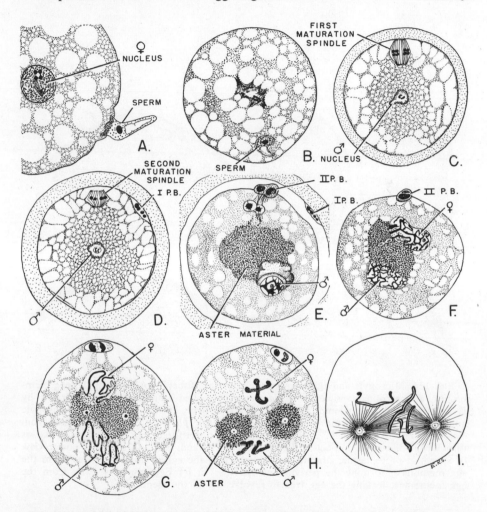

FIG. 133. Stages in the fertilization of *Ascaris*. (After Boveri, 1887.) (A) Ameboid sperm on the periphery of the egg; germinal vesicle in center of primary oocyte. (B) Sperm entered egg substance; germinal vesicle broken down and tetrads becoming evident. (C) Sperm in center of the egg; first maturation division, showing tetrads on spindle. (D) Second maturation division; first polar body at egg's surface. (E) First and second polar bodies shown; sperm aster forming in relation to sperm. (F) Second polar body; male and female pronuclei. (G) Male and female haploid chromosomes evident; amphiaster forming. (H) Chromosomes distinct, showing haploid condition. Observe amphiaster. (I) Amphiaster complete; metaphase of first cleavage.

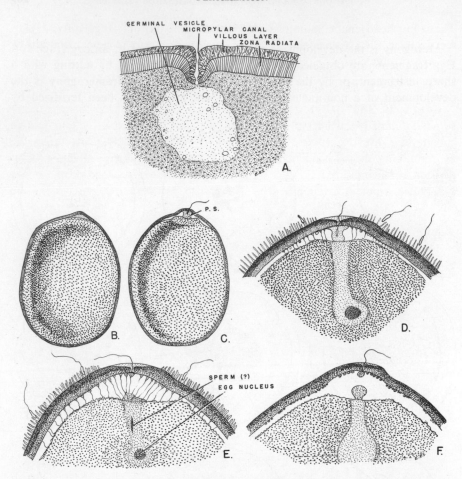

FIG. 134. Micropyle and egg membranes of certain fishes. (A) Micropyle, egg membranes, and germinal vesicle in *Lepidosteus*. (Modified from three figures drawn by E. L. Mark, Bull. Mus. Comp. Zool. at Harvard College, 19: No. 1.) (B–F) Micropyle and egg membranes of the cyclostome, *Petromyzon planeri*. (Slightly modified from Calberla, Zeit. Wiss. Zool., 30.) (B) Mature, unfertilized egg. (C) Sperm passes through the micropyle and enters the protoplasmic strand, P.S. (D) Higher power view of sperm in protoplasmic strand; also observe that the egg is shrinking away from the egg membrane, forming the perivitelline space. (E, F) Egg contracts away from the egg membrane, leaving the egg free to revolve within the membrane.

sperm. Development is not normal and does not go beyond the larval condition. **Parthenogenetic merogony** is the development of non-nucleate parts of the egg which have been artificially activated. Artificial activation of non-nucleate parts of the egg of the sea urchin, *Arbacia,* is possible by immersion of these parts of the egg for 10 to 20 minutes in sea water, concentrated to about one half of the original volume, or by the addition of sodium chloride to sea water to bring it to a similar hypertonicity (Harvey, '36, '38, '51).

These parthenogenetic merogons develop to the blastula stage only. **Gyno-merogony** is the **parthenogenetic development** of an egg fragment containing the egg pronucleus.

J. Theories of Fertilization and Egg Activation

Boveri, T., 1887, 1895. In somatic mitoses, the division center or centrosome is handed down from cell to cell. In the development of the female gamete, the division center degenerates or becomes physiologically incapable of continuing the division of the egg either before or after the maturation divisions. The mature egg thus contains all the essentials for development other than a potent division center. The sperm, on the other hand, lacks the

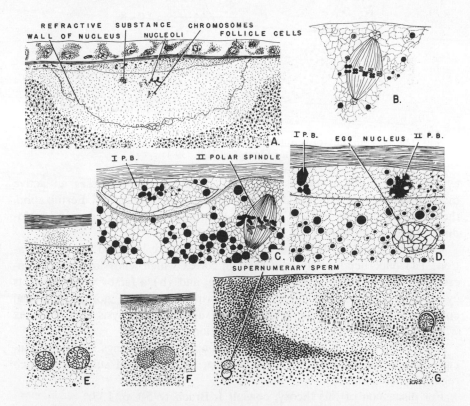

Fig. 135. Fertilization phenomena in the pigeon. (After Harper, '04.) (A) Germinal vesicle of late ovarian egg. The chromatin material is shown in the center of the vesicle; the nuclear wall is beginning to break down. (B) Spindle of first maturation division. Egg just ovulated and entering the oviduct. Sperm enters the egg at this time. (C) Second polar spindle and first polar body. (D) First and second polar bodies; egg pronucleus reorganizing. (E) Two pronuclei approaching, preparatory to fusion. Sperm nucleus to the left. (F) Two pronuclei fusing. (G) Accessory sperm nuclei to the left of this figure; fusion nucleus to the right.

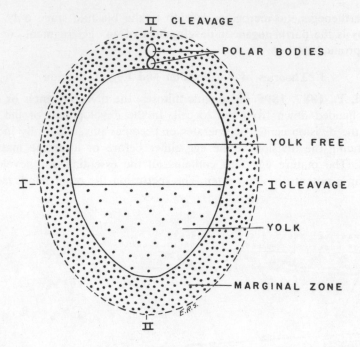

II CLEAVAGE

POLAR BODIES

YOLK FREE

I—

I CLEAVAGE

YOLK

MARGINAL ZONE

II

FIG. 136. Organization of germinal disc of the *Echidna* egg following fertilization. (After Flynn and Hill, '39.)

cytoplasmic conditions necessary for development, but possesses an active division center which it introduces into the egg at fertilization. Fertilization, therefore, restores the diploid number of chromosomes to the egg and introduces an active division center.

Loeb, J., '13. Loeb believed that two factors were involved in egg activation: (a) Superficial cytolysis of the egg cortex which leads to a sudden increase in the oxidation processes of the egg, and (b) a factor which corrects cytolysis and excess oxidation, thus restoring the egg to normal chemical conditions. He placed great emphasis on superficial cytolysis of the cortex with the resultant elevation of the fertilization membrane.

Loeb suggested that in normal fertilization the sperm brings in a **lytic principle** which brings about cortical cytolysis, and a second substance which regulates oxidation.

For discussion of this theory, consult J. Brachet, '50, p. 138.

Bataillon, E., '10, '11, '13, '16. Like Loeb, Bataillon emphasized two steps in the activation process of the egg: (a) **First treatment,** whether it is the puncture of the frog's egg by a fine needle or the butyric acid treatment of the egg of the sea urchin, according to the method of Loeb, causes; (1) elevation of fertilization membrane and the excretion of toxic substances from the egg, and (2) the formation of a monaster. (b) **Second treatment,** whether it is blood, in the case of the frog, or hypertonic sea water, as used by Loeb in the sea-urchin egg, introduces a catalyzer which converts the monaster into an amphiaster, and in this way renders the egg capable of cleavage.

Bataillon placed great emphasis upon the exudation (excretion) of substances into the perivitelline space and the elevation of the fertilization membrane. He believed that the unfertilized egg was *inhibited because of an accumulation of metabolic products* and that activation or fertilization led to a release of these substances to the egg's exterior.

For discussion, consult Wilson, '25, p. 484; J. Brachet, '50, p. 144.

Lillie, F. R., '14, '19. This author postulated that a substance, **fertilizin,** carried in the cortex of the egg, exerts two kinds of actions in the activation process: (1) An activating, attracting, and agglutinating action on the sperm, and (2) an activating effect on the egg itself. In essence, the egg is self-fertilizing, for the fertilizing substance is present in the egg. The procedure is somewhat as follows: At the period optimum for fertilization, **inactive fertilizin** (i.e., inactive from the viewpoint of possessing the ability to activate the egg) is produced by the egg. Released into the surrounding water, it activates, attracts, and agglutinates the sperm at the egg's surface. As the sperm touches the egg, it unites with a part of the fertilizin molecule. The

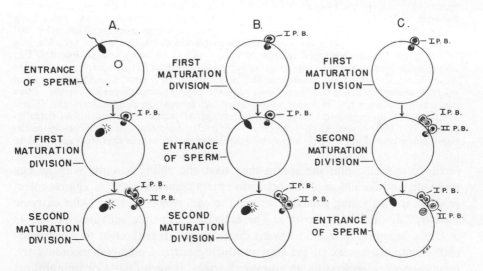

Fig. 137. Maturation divisions of the oocyte relative to time of sperm entrance. (A) Sperm enters the primary oocyte before maturation divisions. In some, e.g., *Nereis, Thalassema, Ascaris, Platynereis, Myzostoma,* etc., the sperm enters before the germinal vesicle breaks down; in *Styela, Chaetopterus,* pigeon, etc., the first maturation spindle is formed or forming; in the dog, the condition is somewhat similar to *Nereis, Ascaris,* etc. (B) Sperm enters the egg after first maturation division, i.e., in secondary oocyte stage (*Asterias* (starfish), *Amphioxus,* hen, rabbit, man, frog, salamander, newt, most vertebrates). (C) Sperm enters the egg after maturation divisions are completed, i.e., in the mature egg (*Arbacia* and other sea urchins; possibly in monotreme, *Echidna,* on occasion).

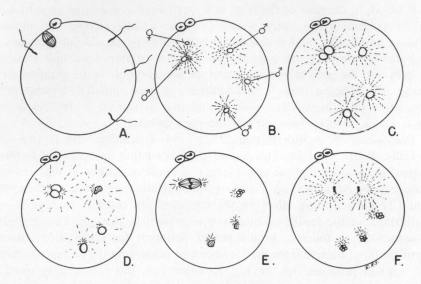

FIG. 138. Polyspermy in the European newt, *Triton*. (After Fankhauser, '48.)   (A) Ten minutes after insemination at 23° C. Metaphase of second maturation division; four sperm have entered the egg, one of which is at the vegetal pole of the egg, and another between the two poles of the egg.   (B) One hour and 30 minutes; second polar body given off; small egg pronucleus moves toward nearest sperm nucleus. The latter will become the principal sperm nucleus. Observe that accessory sperm nuclei are enlarging and a sperm aster is developed relative to each.   (C) Two hours and 30 minutes. Egg and principal sperm pronuclei in contact; maximum development of sperm asters.   (D) Three hours. Fusion of egg pronucleus and principal sperm pronucleus. Accessory sperm nucleus nearest to fusion nucleus shows signs of degeneration. Accessory sperm asters remain undivided, while principal sperm aster has formed an amphiaster.   (E) Three hours and 30 minutes. Metaphase of first cleavage; all accessory sperm nuclei degenerating.   (F) Four hours. Early telophase of first cleavage; remnant of accessory nuclei being pushed out of animal pole region by amphiaster and spindle of first cleavage division.

fertilizin molecule plus the sperm then have the ability to unite with an egg receptor, and the union of the fertilizin-sperm complex with the egg receptor, releases the activating principle within the egg, which spreads "with extreme rapidity" around the egg cortex. The activating principle activates the egg as a whole, setting it in motion toward development. It is thought to work especially upon the cortex of the egg, producing cortical changes, including the formation of a **fertilization membrane.** Further, it agglutinates or immobilizes all other sperm around the egg. Consequently, polyspermy may be hindered by this **agglutination effect** and by the **fertilization membrane.** In regard to polyspermy, Lillie also postulated another substance, antifertilizin, within the egg which unites with the remaining fertilizin molecules in the egg the instant that one sperm has made successful union with a molecule of fertilizin, thus preventing other sperm from entering the egg.

For discussion, see J. Brachet, '50, p. 143; Dalcq, '28.

Lillie, R. S., '41. Like Loeb, R. S. Lillie conceived of cortical changes as being the main aspect of activation, particularly changes such as a decrease in viscosity which permits interaction of various substances which normally are kept separated in the unactivated egg. Lillie's hypothesis may be stated as follows: An activating substance, comparable to a growth hormone or auxin, is formed in the egg. This substance may be called (A). The formation of (A) results from the interaction of two substances, (S) and (B), present in low concentrations in the egg. One of these substances, (S), is synthesized in the egg by treating the egg in various ways, such as immersion in sea water in the presence of oxygen. The other substance, (B), is freed from pre-existing combination by a simple splitting (hydrolytic) process initiated or catalyzed by acid. This reaction is independent of oxygen. The union of the two substances, (S) and (B), forms the activating substance, (A). Lillie thus believes in a single factor as the initiator of development. Complete activation of the egg results when (A) is produced in adequate concentration; partial activation occurs when it is present in quantity below the optimum concentration.

For discussion, see Brachet, J., '50, p. 141.

Heilbrunn, L. V., '15, '28, '43. This author believes that an increase in viscosity with resultant coagulation or gelation of egg cytoplasm is involved directly with the initiation of development. Heilbrunn regards this gelation process to be similar to the clotting of blood. He also regards calcium as the main agent in bringing about this effect, and therefore believes calcium to be concerned directly with egg activation. According to this view, calcium is bound to the proteins localized in the egg cortex. At the time of activation, artificially or by sperm contact, part of this calcium is liberated which in turn produces a coagulation of the cytoplasm, initiating development. Dalcq and his associates also have emphasized the importance of calcium in the activation process.

For discussion, see Brachet, J., '50, p. 146; Dalcq, '28; Runnström, '49.

Runnström, J., '49. Runnström more recently has contended that an inhibitor of proteolytic enzymes may be present in the vitelline membrane and cortex of the egg. He assumes that the inhibitor, possibly fertilizin, may be identical with a heparin-like substance. He further assumes that the inhibitor is bound to a kinase and is released when protein substances associated with the sperm unite with the inhibitor. "A kinase acting on a proenzyme may then be released"; the latter, i.e., the kinase, acts upon the proenzyme in the cortex of the egg, giving origin to an enzyme or enzymes which initiate development. Runnström's position in essence is a modern statement of the inhibition theory of F. R. Lillie (see J. Morphol., vol. 22).

Bibliography

Allyn, H. M. **1912.** The initiation of development in *Chaetopterus.* Biol. Bull. **24**:21.

Ancel, P. and Vintemberger, P. **1933.** Sur la soi-disant rotation de fécondation dans l'oeuf des amphibiens. Compt. rend. Soc. de biol. **114**:1035.

Bataillon, E. **1910.** L'embryogénèse complète provoquée chez les amphibiens par piqûre de l'oeuf vierge, larves parthénogénétiques de *Rana fusca.* Compt. rend. Acad. d. sc. **150**:996.

————. **1911.** Les deux facteurs de la parthénogénèse traumatique chez les amphibiens. Compt. rend. Acad. d. sc. **152**:920.

————. **1913.** Démonstration définitive de l'inoculation superposée à la piqûre en parthénogénèse traumatique. Compt. rend. Acad. d. sc. **156**:812.

————. **1916.** Nouvelle contribution à l'analyse expérimentale de la fécondation par la parthénogénèse. Ann. Inst. Pasteur. **30**:276.

————. **1929.** Etudes cytologiques et expérimentales sur les oeufs immatures de batraciens. Arch. Entw.-mech. **117**:146.

Boveri, Theodor. **1887.** Zellen-Studien. Jena. Zeit. f. Nature.; Jena. **21**:423.

————. **1887.** Über die Befruchtung der Eier von *Ascaris megalocephala.* Sitzungsb. d. Gesellsch. f. Morph. u. Physiol., München III.

————. **1895.** Über das Verhalten der Centrosomen bei der Befruchtung des Seeigel-Eies nebst allgemeinen Bemerkungen über Centrosomen und Verwandtes. Verh. phys.-med. Ges. Würzburg. **29**:1.

————. **1900.** Über die Natur der Centrosomen. Gustav Fischer, Jena.

Bowen, R. H. **1924.** On the acrosome of the animal sperm. Anat. Rec. **28**:1.

Brachet, A. **1912.** La polyspermie expérimentale dans l'oeuf de *Rana fusca.* Arch. f. mikr. Anat. **79**, Abt. 2:96.

————. **1922.** Recherches sur la fécondation prématurée de l'oeuf d'oursin *(Paracentrotus lividus).* Arch. biol., Paris. **32**:205.

Brachet, J. **1950.** Chemical Embryology. Interscience Publishers, Inc., New York, London.

Cerfontaine, P. **1906.** Recherches sur le développement de *l'Amphioxus.* Arch. biol., Paris. **22**:229.

Cole, F. J. **1930.** Early Theories of Sexual Generation. Oxford University Press, Inc., Clarendon Press, New York.

Collier, V. **1936.** Studies on the cytoplasmic components in fertilization. I. *Ascaris suilla.* Quart. J. Micr. Sc. **78**:397.

Conklin, E. G. **1904.** Experiments on the origin of the cleavage centrosomes. Biol. Bull. **7**:221.

————. **1905.** The organization and cell-lineage of the ascidian egg. J. Acad. Nat. Sc., Philadelphia. XIII. page 1.

————. **1932.** The embryology of *Amphioxus.* J. Morphol. **54**:69.

Dalcq, A. M. **1928.** Les bases physiologiques de la fécondation et de la parthénogénèse. Presses Uni. de France, Paris.

De Meyer, J. **1911.** Observations et expériences relatives à l'action exercée par des extraits d'oeufs et d'autres substances sur les spermatozoïdes. Arch. biol., Paris. **26**:65.

Fankhauser, G. **1934.** Cytological studies on egg fragments of the salamander *Triton.* III. The early development of the sperm nuclei in egg fragments without the egg nucleus. J. Exper. Zool. **67**:159.

————. **1945.** The effects of changes in chromosome number on amphibian development. Quart. Rev. Biol. **20**:20.

————. **1948.** The organization of the amphibian egg during fertilization and cleavage. Ann. New York Acad. Sc. **49**:684.

Farris, E. J. **1949**. The number of motile spermatozoa as an index of fertility in man: a study of 406 semen specimens. J. Urol. **61**: No. 6, 1099.

Flynn, T. T. and Hill, J. P. **1939**. The development of the *Monotremata*. Part IV. Growth of the ovarian ovum, maturation, fertilization and early cleavage. Trans. Zool. Soc. London, s.A. **24**: Part 6, 445.

Fol, H. **1879**. Recherches sur la fécondation et le commencement de l'hénogénie chez divers animaux. Mém. Soc. de physique et hist. nat. Genève. **26**:89.

Frank, J. A. **1939**. Some properties of sperm extracts and their relationship to the fertilization reaction in *Arbacia punctulata*. Biol. Bull. **76**:190.

Galtsoff, P. S. **1938**. Physiology of reproduction of *Ostrea virginica*. II. Stimulation of spawning in the female oyster. Biol. Bull. **75**:286.

———. **1940**. The physiology of reproduction of *Ostrea virginica*. III. Stimulation of spawning in the male oyster. Biol. Bull. **78**:117.

Gregory, P. W. **1930**. The early embryology of the rabbit. Contrib. Embryol. **21**: No. 125, p. 141. Carnegie Inst. Publications.

Guyer, M. F. **1907**. The development of unfertilized frog eggs injected with blood. Science. **25**:910.

Hammond, J. **1934**. The fertilisation of rabbit ova in relation to time. A method of controlling the litter size, the duration of pregnancy and the weight of the young at birth. J. Exper. Biol. **11**:140.

Harding, D. **1951**. Initiation of cell division in the *Arbacia* egg by injury substances. Physiol. Zoöl. **24**:54.

Harper, E. H. **1904**. Fertilization and early development of the pigeon's egg. Am. J. Anat. **3**:349.

Hartman, C. G. **1916**. Studies in the development of the opossum *Didelphys virginiana* L. I. History of the early cleavage. II. Formation of the blastocyst. J. Morphol. **27**:1.

Hartmann, M. **1940**. Die stofflichen Grundlagen der Befruchtung und Sexualität im Pflanzen- und Tierreich. I. Die Befruchtungsstoffe (Gamone) der Seeigel. Naturwissensch. **28**:807.

———, Kuhn, R., Schartau, O., and Wallenfels, K. **1939b**. Über die Sexualstoffe der Seeigel. Naturwissensch. **27**:433.

———, ———, ———, and ———. **1940**. Über die Wechselwirkung von Gyno- und Androgamonen bei der Befruchtung der Eier des Seeigels. Die Naturwissensch. **28**:144.

——— and Schartau, O. **1939a**. Untersuchungen über die Befruchtungsstoffe der Seeigel. I. Biol. Zentralbl. **59**:571.

———, ———, and Wallenfels, K. **1940**. Untersuchungen über die Befruchtungsstoffe der Seeigel. II. Biol. Zentralbl. **60**:398.

Harvey, E. B. **1936**. Parthenogenetic merogony or cleavage without nuclei in *Arbacia punctulata*. Biol. Bull. **71**:101.

———. **1938**. Parthenogenetic merogony or development without nuclei of the eggs of sea urchins from Naples. Biol. Bull. **75**:170.

———. **1940**. A new method of producing twins, triplets and quadruplets in *Arbacia punctulata*, and their development. Biol. Bull. **78**:202.

———. **1951**. Cleavage in centrifuged eggs, and in parthenogenetic merogones. Ann. New York Acad. Sc. **51**:1336.

Heilbrunn, L. V. **1913**. Studies in artificial parthenogenesis. I. Membrane elevation in the sea-urchin egg. Biol. Bull. **24**:343.

———. **1915**. Studies in artificial parthenogenesis. II. Physical changes in the egg of *Arbacia*. Biol. Bull. **29**:149.

———. **1928**. Colloid Chemistry of Protoplasm. Protoplasma Monographien, 1, Gebrüder Borntraeger, Berlin.

———. **1943**. Chap. 42 in An Outline of General Physiology. 2d ed., W. B. Saunders Co., Philadelphia.

Henking, H. **1891**. Untersuchungen über die ersten Entwicklungsvorgänge in den Eiern der Insekten. II. Über spermatogenese und deren Beziehung zur Ei Entwicklung bei Pyrrhocoris apterus L. Zeit. Wiss. Zool. **51**:685.

Herlant, M. **1911**. Recherches sur les oeufs di- et trispermiques de grenouille. Arch. biol., Paris. **26**:173.

Hertwig, O. **1875**. Beiträge zur Kenntniss der Bildung, Befruchtung und Theilung des thierischen Eies. Morph. Jahrb. (Gegenbauer) **1**:347.

————. 1877. Berträge zur Kenntniss der Bildung, Befruchtung und Theilung des thierischen Eies. Morph. Jahrb. (Gegenbauer) III:1.

Hertwig, R. 1896. Über die Entwickelung des unbefruchteten Seeigeleies. Festschr. f. Carl Gengenbauer, II. p. 21.

Hibbard, H. 1928. Contribution à l'étude de l'ovogenèse, de la fécondation, et de l'histogenèse chez Discoglossus pictus Otth. Arch. biol., Paris. 38:251.

Just, E. E. 1919. The fertilization reaction in Echinarachnius parma. I. Cortical response of the egg to insemination. Biol. Bull. 36:1.

————. 1939. The Biology of the Cell Surface. P. Blakiston's Son & Co., Inc., Philadelphia.

Leonard, S. L. and Kurzrok, R. 1946. Inhibitors of hyaluronidase in blood sera and their effect on follicle cell dispersal. Endocrinology. 39:85.

Leuchtenberger, C. and Schrader, F. 1950. The chemical nature of the acrosome in the male germ cells. Proc. Nat. Acad. Sc. 36: No. 11, P677.

Lewis, W. H. and Gregory, P. W. 1929. Cinematographs of living developing rabbit-eggs. Science. 69:226.

Lillie, F. R. 1912. Studies of fertilization in Nereis. III. The morphology of the normal fertilization of Nereis. IV. The fertilizing power of portions of the spermatozoon. J. Exper. Zool. 12:413.

————. 1913. Studies of fertilization. V. The behavior of the spermatozoa of Nereis and Arbacia with special reference to egg-extractives. J. Exper. Zool. 14:515.

————. 1914. Studies of fertilization. VI. The mechanism of fertilization in Arbacia. J. Exper. Zool. 16:523.

————. 1915. Studies of fertilization. VII. Analysis of variations in the fertilizing power of sperm suspensions of Arbacia. Biol. Bull. 28:229.

————. 1919. Problems of Fertilization. University of Chicago Press (University of Chicago Science Series), Chicago.

————. 1940. To Dr. C. E. McClung on reaching the age of seventy. J. Morphol. 66:5.

Lillie, R. S. 1941. Further experiments on artificial parthenogenesis in starfish eggs: with a review. Physiol. Zoöl. 14:239.

Loeb, J. 1899. On the nature of the process of fertilization and the artificial production of normal larvae, etc. Am. J. Physiol. 3:135.

————. 1905. On an improved method of artificial parthenogenesis. University of California Publ., Physiol. 2:83.

————. 1906. Untersuchungen über künstliche Parthenogenese. J. A. Barth, Leipzig.

————. 1921. The Mechanistic Conception of Life. University of Chicago Press, Chicago.

McClung, C. E. 1902. The accessory chromosome-sex determinant (?). Biol. Bull. 3:43.

McCrady, E., Jr. 1938. The embryology of the opossum. Am. Anat. Memoirs, 16, The Wistar Institute of Anatomy and Biology, Philadelphia.

Mann, T. 1949. Metabolism of semen. Adv. in Enzymology. 9:329.

Mark, E. L. 1881. Maturation, fecundation, and segmentation of Limax campestris Binney. Bull. Mus. Comp. Zool. at Harvard College, VI Part II: No. 12.

Mathews, A. P. 1901. Artificial parthenogenesis produced by mechanical agitation. Am. J. Physiol. 6:142.

Mead, A. D. 1896–1897. The rate of cell division and the function of the centrosome. Lecture 9, Biological Lectures, Woods Hole, Mass. Ginn & Co., Boston.

————. 1897. The origin of the egg centrosomes. J. Morphol. 12:391.

Morgan, T. H. 1896. The production of artificial astrospheres. Arch. f. Entwicklungsmech. d. Organ. 3:339.

————. 1899. The action of salt-solutions on the unfertilized and fertilized eggs of Arbacia and of other animals. Arch. f. Entwicklungsmech. d. Organ. 8:448.

————. 1900. Further studies on the action of salt-solutions and of other agents on the eggs of Arbacia. Arch. f. Entwicklungsmech. d. Organ. 10:489.

————. 1927. Experimental Embryology. Columbia University Press, New York.

Nachtsheim, H. **1913.** Cytologische Studien über die Geschlechtsbestimmung bei der Honigbiene *(Apis mellifica* L.). Arch. f. Zellforsch. **11**:169.

Okkelberg, P. **1914.** Volumetric changes in the egg of the brook lamprey, *Entosphenus (Lampetra) wilderi* (Gage) after fertilization. Biol. Bull. **26**:92.

Olsen, M. W. **1942.** Maturation, fertilization, and early cleavage in the hen's egg. J. Morphol. **70**:513.

Parat, M. **1933a.** Nomenclature, genèse, structure et fonction de quelques éléments cytoplasmiques des cellules sexuelles males. Compt. rend. Soc. de biol. **112**:1131.

————. **1933b.** L'acrosome du spermatozöide dans la fécondation et la parthénogénèse expérimentale. Compt. rend. Soc. de biol. **112**:1134.

Parmenter, C. L. **1933.** Haploid, diploid, triploid and tetraploid chromosome numbers, and their origin in parthenogenetically developed larvae and frogs of *Rana pipiens* and *R. palustris.* J. Exper Zool. **66**:409.

————. **1940.** Chromosome numbers in *Rana fusca* parthenogenetically developed from eggs with known polar body and cleavage histories. J. Morphol. **66**:241.

Pasteels, J. **1937.** Sur l'origine de la symétrie bilatérale des amphibiens anoures. Arch. Anat. Micr. **33**:279.

————. **1938.** A propos du déterminisme de la symétrie bilatérale chez les amphibiens anoures. Conditions qui provoquent l'apparition du croissant gris. Compt. rend. Soc. de biol. **129**:59.

Pincus, G. **1939.** The comparative behavior of mammalian eggs in vivo and in vitro. IV. The development of fertilized and artificially activated rabbit eggs. J. Exper. Zool. **82**:85.

———— and Enzmann, E. V. **1932.** Fertilization in the rabbit. J. Exper. Biol. **9**:403.

———— and Shapiro, H. **1940.** The comparative behavior of mammalian eggs in vivo and in vitro. VII. Further studies on the activation of rabbit eggs. Proc. Am. Philos. Soc. **83**:631.

Porter, K. R. **1939.** Androgenetic development of the egg of *Rana pipiens*. Biol. Bull. **77**:233.

Romanoff, A. L. and Romanoff, A. J. **1949.** The Avian Egg. John Wiley & Sons, Inc., New York.

Rothschild, Lord, and Swann, M. M. **1951.** The fertilization reaction in the sea-urchin. The probability of a successful sperm-egg collision. J. Exper. Biol. **28**:403.

Rowlands, I. W. **1944.** Capacity of hyaluronidase to increase the fertilizing power of sperm. Nature, London. **154**:332.

Runnström, J. **1949.** The mechanism of fertilization in Metazoa. Adv. in Enzymology. **IX**:241.

———— and Lindvall, S. **1946.** The effect of some agents upon the reaction of *Echinocardium* spermatozoa towards egg-water. Arkiv. Zool. **38A**: No. 10.

————, ————, and Tiselius, A. **1944.** Gamones from the sperm of the sea urchin and salmon. Nature, London. **153**:285.

———— and Monné, L. **1945a.** On some properties of the surface layers of immature and mature sea-urchin eggs, especially the changes accompanying nuclear and cytoplasmic maturation. Arkiv Zool. **36A**: No. 18, 1.

———— and ————. **1945b.** On changes in the properties of the surface layers of the sea-urchin egg due to external conditions. Arkiv. Zool. **36A**: No. 20, 1.

Schücking, A. **1903.** Zur Physiologie der Befruchtung, Parthenogenese und Entwicklung. Arch. f. d. ges. Physiol. **97**:58.

Sharp, L. W. **1934.** Introduction to Cytology. 3d ed., McGraw-Hill Book Co., Inc., New York.

Shaver, J. R. **1949.** Experimental study of artificial parthenogenesis in the frog. Anat. Rec. **105**:571.

Sobotta, J. **1897.** Die Reifung und Befruchtung des Eies von *Amphioxus lanceolatus.* Arch. f. mikr. Anat. u. Entwicklungsgesch. **50**:15.

Southwick, W. E. **1939.** Activity-preventing and egg-sea-water neutralizing substances from the spermatozoa of *Echinometra subangularis*. Biol. Bull. **77**:147.

Tavolga, W. N. **1950.** Development of the gobiid fish, *Bathygobius soporator*. J. Morphol. **87**:467.

Tung Ti-chow. **1933.** Recherches sur la détermination du plan médian dans l'oeuf de *Rana fusca.* Arch. biol., Paris. 44:809.

Townsend, G. **1939.** The spawning reaction and spawning integration of *Nereis limbata* with emphasis upon chemical stimulation. Distributed by University of Chicago Libraries, Chicago.

Tyler, A. **1939.** Extraction of an egg membrane-lysin from sperm of the giant key-hole limpet *(Megathura crenulata).* Proc. Nat. Acad. Sc. **25**:317.

———. **1940.** Agglutination of sea-urchin eggs by means of a substance extracted from the egg. Proc. Nat. Acad. Sc. **26**:249.

———. **1941.** The role of fertilizin in the fertilization of the eggs of the sea urchin and other animals. Biol. Bull. **81**:190.

———. **1942.** A complement-release reaction; the neutralization of the anticomplementary action of sea-urchin fertilizin by antifertilizin. Proc. Nat. Acad. Sc. **28**:391.

———. **1948.** Fertilization and immunity. Physiol. Rev. **28**:180.

——— and Fox, S. W. **1940.** Evidence for the protein nature of the sperm agglutinins of the keyhole limpet and the sea urchin. Biol. Bull. **79**:153.

——— and O'Melveney, K. **1941.** The role of antifertilizin in the fertilization of sea-urchin eggs. Biol. Bull. **81**:364.

Van Beneden, E. **1883.** Recherches sur la maturation de l'oeuf, la fécondation et la division cellulaire. Masson & Cie., Paris.

Van der Stricht, O. **1923.** Etude comparée des ovules des mammifères aux différentes périodes de l'ovogenèse. Arch. d. Biol. **33**:223.

von Dungern, E. **1902.** Neue Versuche sur Physiologie der Befruchtung. Zeit. Allgemeine Physiol. **1**:34.

Walton, A. **1927.** The relation between "density" of sperm-suspension and fertility as determined by artificial insemination of rabbits. Proc. Roy. Soc., London, s.B. **101**:303.

Wheeler, W. M. **1895.** The behavior of the centrosomes in the fertilized egg of *Myzostoma glabrum,* Leuckart. J. Morphol. **10**:305.

Whiting, A. R. **1949.** Motherless males from irradiated eggs. Science. **103**:219.

Wilson, E. B. **1925.** The cell in Development and Heredity. 3d ed., The Macmillan Co., New York.

——— and Mathews, A. P. **1895.** Maturation, fertilization, and polarity in the echinoderm egg. New Light on the "quadrille of the centers." J. Morphol. **10**:319.

Wintrebert, P. **1929.** La digestion de l'enveloppe tubulaire interne de l'oeuf par des ferments issus des spermatozoides et l'ovule chez le *Discoglossus pictus* Otth. Compt. rend. Acad. d. Sc. **188**:97.

PART III

The Development of Primitive
Embryonic Body Form

The general procedures leading to the development of primitive embryonic body form in the chordate group of animals are:

(1) **Cleavage.** Cleavage is the division of the egg into progressively smaller cellular units, the **blastomeres** (Chap. 6).

(2) **Blastulation.** Blastulation results in the formation of the **blastula.** The blastula is composed of a **cellular blastoderm** in relation to a fluid-filled cavity, the **blastocoel.** The blastoderm of the late blastula is composed of **neural, epidermal, notochordal, mesodermal, and entodermal** major presumptive organ-forming areas. In the phylum Chordata, the notochordal area is the central region around which the other areas are oriented (Chap. 7). The major presumptive organ-forming areas of the late blastula exist in various degrees of **differentiation** (Chap. 8).

(3) **Gastrulation.** This is the process which effects a reorientation of the presumptive organ-forming areas and brings about their axiation antero-posteriorly in relation to the notochordal axis and the future embryonic body (Chap. 9). During gastrulation the **major organ-forming areas** are subdivided into **minor areas** or **fields,** each field being restricted to the development of a particular organ or part. (Pp. 378, 446, 447.

(4) Following gastrulation, the next step in the development of embryonic body form is **tubulation and extension of the major organ-forming areas** (Chap. 10).

(5) As tubulation and extension of the organ-forming areas is effected, the basic or fundamental conditions of the future organ systems are established, resulting in the **development of primitive body form.** As the development of various vertebrate embryos is strikingly similar up to this point, the primitive embryonic body forms of all vertebrates resemble each other (Chap. 11).

In the drawings presented in Part III, the following scheme for designating the major organ-forming areas existing within the three germ layers is adhered to:

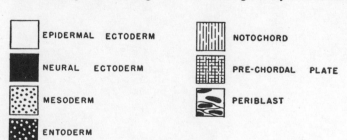

EPIDERMAL ECTODERM	NOTOCHORD
NEURAL ECTODERM	PRE-CHORDAL PLATE
MESODERM	PERIBLAST
ENTODERM	

277

6

Cleavage (Segmentation) and Blastulation

A. General considerations
  1. Definitions
  2. Early history of the cleavage (cell-division) concept
  3. Importance of the cleavage-blastular period of development
    a. Morphological relationships of the blastula
    b. Physiological relationships of the blastula
      1) Hybrid crosses
      2) Artificial parthenogenesis
      3) Oxygen block studies
  4. Geometrical relations of early cleavage
    a. Meridional plane
    b. Vertical plane
    c. Equatorial plane
    d. Latitudinal plane
  5. Some fundamental factors involved in the early cleavage of the egg
    a. Mechanisms associated with mitosis or cell division
    b. Influence of cytoplasmic substance and egg organization upon cleavage
      1) Yolk
      2) Organization of the egg
    c. Influence of first cleavage amphiaster on polyspermy
    d. Viscosity changes during cleavage
    e. Cleavage laws
      1) Sach's rules
      2) Hertwig's laws
  6. Relation of early cleavage planes to the antero-posterior axis of the embryo
B. Types of cleavage in the phylum *Chordata*
  1. Typical holoblastic cleavage
    a. *Amphioxus*
    b. Frog *(Rana pipiens* and *R. sylvatica)*
    c. *Cyclostomata*
  2. Atypical types of holoblastic cleavage
    a. Holoblastic cleavage in the egg of the metatherian and eutherian mammals
      1) General considerations
      2) Early development of the rabbit egg
        a) Two-cell stage
        b) Four-cell stage
        c) Eight-cell stage
        d) Sixteen-cell stage

279

A. General Considerations

1. DEFINITIONS

The period of cleavage (segmentation) immediately follows normal fertilization or any other means which activates the egg to develop. It consists of a division of the entire egg or a part of the egg into smaller and smaller cellular entities. In some species, however, both chordate and non-chordate, the early cleavage stages consist of nuclear divisions alone, to be followed later by the formation of actual cell boundaries (fig. 62). The cells which are formed during cleavage are called **blastomeres.**

As cleavage of the egg continues, the blastular stage ultimately is reached. The blastula contains a cavity or **blastocoel** together with an associated layer or mass of cells, the **blastoderm.** The blastula represents the culmination and end result of the processes at work during the cleavage period. Certain aspects and problems concerned with blastulation are considered separately in the following chapter. However, the general features of blastular formation are described here along with the cleavage phenomena.

2. Early History of the Cleavage (Cell-division) Concept

An initial appreciation of the role and importance of the cell in embryonic development was awakened during the middle period of the nineteenth century. It really began with the observations of Prevost and Dumas in 1824 on the cleavage (segmentation) of the frog's egg. The latter observations represented a revival and extension of those of Swammerdam, 1738, on the first cleavage of the frog's egg and of Spallanzani's description in 1780 of the first two cleavage planes, "which intersect each other at right angles," in the egg of the toad. Other studies on cleavage of the eggs of frogs, newts, and various invertebrates, such as the hydroids, the starfish, and nematodes, followed the work of Prevost and Dumas. The first reported cleavage of the eggs of a rabbit was made in 1838–1839, a fish in 1842, and a bird in 1847. (See Cole, '30, p. 196.) Newport, in 1854, finally founded the new preformation by showing that the first cleavage plane in the frog's egg coincided with the median plane of the adult body (Cole, '30, p. 196).

In the meantime, the minute structures of the bodies of plants and animals were intensively studied, and in 1838–1839, the basic cellular structure of living organisms was enunciated by Schleiden and Schwann. Following this generalization, many studies were made upon the phenomenon of cell division in plant and animal tissues. These observations, together with those made upon the cleaving egg, established proof that cells arise only by the division of pre-existing cells; and that through cell division the new generation is formed and maintained. Thus it is that protoplasm, in the form of cells, assimilates, increases its substance, and reproduces new cells. Life, in this manner, flows out of the past and into the present, and into the future as a never-ending stream of cellular substance. This idea of a continuous flow of living substance is embodied well in the famed dictum of R. Virchow, "Omnis Cellula e Cellula," published in 1858 (Wilson, E. B., '25, p. 114).

The consciousness of life at the cellular level acquired during the middle period of the nineteenth century thus laid the groundwork for future studies in cytology and cellular embryology. Much progress in the study of the cell had been made since R. Hooke, in 1664, described the cells in cork. In passing, it should be observed, that two types of cell division, direct and indirect, were ultimately defined. For the latter, Flemming in 1882, proposed the name **mitosis,** while the direct method was called **amitosis.**

3. Importance of the Cleavage-Blastular Period of Development

The period of cleavage and blastular formation is a time of profound differentiation as well as one of cell division. For, at this time, fundamental conditions are established which serve the purposes of the next stage in development, namely, **gastrulation.** Experimental embryology has demonstrated that optimum morphological conditions must be elaborated during the cleavage phase of development along with the developing physiology of the blastula.

a. Morphological Relationships of the Blastula

There are two aspects to the developing morphology of the blastula, namely, the formation of the **blastoderm** and the **blastocoel.**

During cleavage and blastulation, the structure of the blastoderm is elaborated in such a manner that the **major, presumptive, organ-forming areas** of the future embryonic body are segregated into definite parts or districts of the blastoderm. The exact pattern of arrangement of these presumptive, organ-forming areas varies from species to species. Nevertheless, for a particular species, they are arranged always according to the pattern prescribed for that species. This pattern and arrangement of the major, presumptive, organ-forming areas permit the ordered and symmetrical migration and rearrangement of these areas during gastrulation.

Similarly, the blastocoel is formed in relation to the blastoderm according to a plan dictated by the developing mechanisms for the species. One of the main functions of the blastocoel is to permit the migration and rearrangement of the major, presumptive, organ-forming areas during gastrulation. Consequently, at the end of the blastular period, the blastoderm and the blastocoel are arranged and poised in relation to each other in such a balanced fashion that the dramatic cell movements of gastrulation or the next period of development may take place in an organized manner.

b. Physiological Relationships of the Blastula

The development of a normal-appearing, late blastula or beginning gastrula in a morphological sense is no proof that proper, underlying, physiological states have been established. A few examples will be given to illustrate this fact:

1) Hybrid Crosses. When the sperm of the wood frog, *Rana sylvatica,* are used to fertilize the eggs of the ordinary grass frog, *Rana pipiens,* cleavage and blastulation appear normal. However, gastrulation is abortive, and the embryo soon dies (Moore, '41, '46, '47).

2) Artificial Parthenogenesis. In the case of many embryos, chordate and non-chordate, in which the egg is stimulated to develop by means of artificial activation, the end of the blastular stage may be reached, but gastrulative processes do not function properly. A cessation of development often results.

3) Oxygen-block Studies. In oxygen-block studies, where the fertilized eggs of *Rana pipiens* are exposed to increased partial pressures of oxygen from the time of fertilization to the four- or eight-cell stage, the following cleavages and the morphology of the blastula may appear normal, but gastrulation does not occur. Similar oxygen–pressure exposures during the late blastular and early gastrular stages have no effect upon gastrulation. This fact suggests that important physiological events accompany the earlier cleavage stages of development (Nelsen, '48, '49).

Aside from the foregoing examples which demonstrate that invisible changes in the developing blastula are associated with morphological transformations is the fact that experimental research has demonstrated conclusively that an **organization center** is present in the very late blastula and beginning gastrula. The organization center will be discussed later. However, at this point it is advisable to state that the organization center is the instigator and the controller of the gastrulative processes, and gastrulation does not proceed unless it is developed.

The above considerations suggest that the period of cleavage and blastulation is a period of preparation for the all-important period of gastrulation. Other characteristics of this phase of development will be mentioned in the chapter which follows.

4. GEOMETRICAL RELATIONS OF EARLY CLEAVAGE

a. Meridional Plane

The **meridional plane of cleavage** is a furrow which tends to pass in a direction which, if carried to completion, would bisect both poles of the egg passing through the egg's center or median axis. The latter axis theoretically passes from the midpolar region of the animal pole to the midpolar region of the vegetal pole. The beginning of the cleavage furrow which follows the meridional plane may not always begin at the animal pole (fig. 140D) although in most cases it does (figs. 142A–C; 154A–C; 155A).

b. Vertical Plane

A **vertical plane of cleavage** is a furrow which tends to pass in a direction from the animal pole toward the vegetal pole. It is somewhat similar to a meridional furrow. However, it does not pass through the median axis of the egg, but courses to one side of this axis. For example, the third cleavage planes in the chick are furrows which course downward in a vertical plane; paralleling one of the first two meridional furrows (fig. 155C). (See also figs. 153D; 154E relative to the third cleavage furrows of the bony ganoid fishes, *Amia calva* and *Lepisosteus (Lepidosteus) osseus.*)

c. Equatorial Plane

The equatorial plane of cleavage bisects the egg at right angles to the median axis and halfway between the animal and vegetal poles. It is never ideally realized in the phylum *Chordata,* and the nearest approach to it is found, possibly, in one of the fifth cleavage planes of the egg of *Ambystoma maculatum* (fig. 149F) and the first cleavage plane of the egg of the higher mammals (fig. 145A).

d. Latitudinal Plane

The latitudinal plane of cleavage is similar to the equatorial, but it courses through the cytoplasm on either side of the equatorial plane. For example, the third cleavage planes of the egg of *Amphioxus* (fig. 140I) and of the frog (figs. 141E; 142F) are latitudinal planes of cleavage.

5. SOME FUNDAMENTAL FACTORS INVOLVED IN THE EARLY CLEAVAGE OF THE EGG

a. Mechanisms Associated with Mitosis or Cell Division

There are two mechanisms associated with cleavage or cell division:

(1) that associated with the chromosomes and the achromatic (amphiastral) spindle, which results in the equal division of the chromosomes and their discribution to the daughter nuclei, and

(2) the mechanism which enables the cytoplasm to divide.

In ordinary cell division or mitosis these two mechanisms are integrated into one process. However, in embryonic development they are not always so integrated. The following examples illustrate this fact: (1) In the early development of insects, the chromatin materials divide without a corresponding division of the cytoplasm (fig. 62). (2) During the early cleavage phenomena of the elasmobranch fishes, the chromatin material divides before corresponding cleavages of the cytoplasm appear (fig. 158A). (3) In the later cleavage stages of teleost fishes, the peripheral cells of the blastoderm fuse and form a continuous cytoplasm; within this cytoplasm the separate nuclei continue to divide without corresponding cytoplasmic divisions and in this way form the marginal syncytial periblast (fig. 159J, L, M).

On the other hand, cytoplasmic division may occur without a corresponding nuclear division. This behavior has been illustrated in various ways but most emphatically by the work of Harvey ('36, '38, '40, '51) which demonstrates that non-nucleate parts of the egg may divide for a period without the presence of a nucleus. (See, particularly, Harvey, '51, p. 1349.) Similarly, in the early development of the hen's egg, a cytoplasmic furrow or division occurs in the formation of the early segmentation cavity without involving a nuclear division (fig. 156C, E). This type of activity on the part of the cytoplasm illustrates the fact that the cytoplasm has a mechanism for cell division independent of the nuclear mechanism. Lewis ('39) emphasizes the importance of the production of a superficial plasmagel "constriction ring" which constricts the cytoplasm into two parts during cell division.

b. Influence of Cytoplasmic Substance and Egg Organization upon Cleavage

1) Yolk. Since the time of Balfour, much consideration has been given to the presence or absence of yolk as a factor controlling the rate and pattern of cleavage. Undoubtedly, in many instances, the accumulation of yolk materials does impede or alter the cleavage furrows, although it does not suppress mitotic divisions of the nucleus as shown in the early cleavages in many insects, ganoid fishes, etc. On the other hand, the study of cleavage phenomena as a whole brings out the fact that other intrinsic factors in the cytoplasm and organization of the egg largely determine the rate and planes of the cleavage furrows.

2) Organization of the Egg. An illustration of the dependence of the pronuclei and of the position of the first cleavage amphiaster upon the general organization of the cytoplasm of the egg is shown in the first cleavage spindle in *Amphioxus* and *Styela*. In the eggs of these species, the amphiaster of the first cleavage always orients itself in such a way that the first cleavage plane coincides with the median plane of the future embryonic body. The first cleavage plane, consequently, divides the egg's substances into two equal parts, *qualitatively* and *quantitatively*. The movements of the pronuclei and the first cleavage amphiaster are correlated and directed to this end.

Various theories have been offered in the past to account for the migrations of the pronuclei at fertilization and for the position of the first cleavage amphiaster. All of them, however, are concerned with the cytoplasm of the egg or its movements, which in turn are correlated with the organization of the egg. (See Wilson, E. B., '25, p. 426.)

A second illustration of the dependence of the chromatin-amphiaster complex on conditions in the cytoplasm is afforded by experiments of Hans Driesch in 1891 on the isolation of the blastomeres of cleaving eggs of the sea urchin. He found that the first cleavage of the egg occurred from the animal to the vegetal pole, resulting in two blastomeres. Now, if these blastomeres are shaken apart, the following cleavages in the isolated blastomeres behave exactly as if the two blastomeres were still intact, indicating a definite progression of the cleavage planes. That is, there is a mosaic of cleavage planes determined in the cytoplasm of the early egg.

A third example of the influence of egg organization upon cleavage is afforded by the egg of higher mammals. In this group, the first cleavage plane divides the egg in many cases into a larger and a smaller blastomere. The larger blastomere then begins to divide at a faster rate than the smaller blastomere. This accelerated division is maintained in the daughter cells resulting from the larger blastomere. Here, then, is an egg whose yolk material is at a minimum. Nevertheless, the blastomeres which result from the first cleavage are unequal in size, and the cellular descendants of one of these blastomeres divide faster than the descendants of the other blastomere. Some conditioning effect must be present in the egg's cytoplasm which determines the size of the blastomeres and the rate of the later cleavages. Many other illustrations might be given from the studies on cell lineage. However, the conclusion is inevitable that under normal conditions the cause of the cleavage pattern and the rate of blastomere formation is an internal one resident in the organization of the egg and the peculiar protoplasmic substances of the various blastomeres. This apparent fact suggests strongly that the egg in its development "is a builder which lays one stone here, another there, each of which is placed with reference to future development" (F. R. Lillie, 1895, p. 46).

c. Influence of First Cleavage Amphiaster on Polyspermy

In figure 138 is shown the behavior of the sperm nuclei during fertilization in the urodele, *Triton*. This figure demonstrates that the developing first cleavage amphiaster suppresses the development of the accessory sperm nuclei. Similar conditions appear to be present in the elasmobranch fishes, chick, pigeon, etc.

d. Viscosity Changes During Cleavage

"The viscosity changes that occur in the sea-urchin egg are probably typical of mitosis in general. There is marked viscosity increase in early prophase, then a decrease, and finally an increase just before the cell divides" (Heilbrunn, '21). Similarly, Heilbrunn and W. L. Wilson ('48) in reference to the cleaving egg of the annelid worm, *Chaetopterus,* found that during the metaphase of the first cleavage the protoplasmic viscosity is low, but immediately preceding cell division protoplasmic viscosity increases markedly.

e. Cleavage Laws

Aside from the factors involved in cleavage described above, other rules governing the behavior of cells during division have been formulated. These statements represent tendencies only, and many exceptions exist. "The rules of Sachs and Hertwig must not be pushed too far" (Wilson, E. B., '25, p. 985).

1) Sachs' Rules:
(a) Cells tend to divide into equal daughter cells.
(b) Each new cleavage furrow tends to bisect the previous one at right angles.

2) Hertwig's Laws:
(a) The typical position of the nucleus tends to lie in the center of the protoplasmic mass in which it exerts its influence.
(b) The long axis of the mitotic spindle typically coincides with the long axis of the protoplasmic mass. In division, therefore, the long axis of the protoplasmic mass tends to be cut transversely.

6. RELATION OF EARLY CLEAVAGE PLANES TO THE ANTERO-POSTERIOR AXIS OF THE EMBRYO

In the protochordate, *Styela,* the first cleavage plane always divides the yellow and gray crescent material and other cytosomal substances into equal right and left halves; it therefore achieves a sundering of the egg substances along the future median plane of the embryo. The second cleavage plane occurs at right angles to the first (Conklin, '05, a and b). This condition appears to be true of other ascidians, such as *Ciona, Clavelina,* etc. (Wilson, E. B., '25, p. 1012). The behavior of the early cleavage planes is similar in *Amphioxus* (Conklin, '32). Cleavage planes such as the foregoing, which always divide the egg in a definite way have been described as **"determinate cleavage"** (Conklin, 1897). Study figures 116, 132 and 167.

The first cleavage plane in the eggs of some frogs (e.g., *Rana fusca* and *Rana pipiens*) shows a great tendency to bisect the gray crescent and thus divide the embryo into right and left halves. However, unlike *Styela,* and *Amphioxus,* the first plane is not definitely fixed; considerable deviation may occur in a certain percentage of cases in any particular batch of eggs. In the newt, *Triturus viridescens,* the first cleavage plane generally is at right angles to the median plane of the future embryo (Jordan, 1893). In *Necturus maculosus* the first cleavage plane may in some eggs coincide with the median plane of the embryo, while the second cleavage plane may agree with this plane in other eggs. In some eggs there is no correspondence between the first two cleavage planes and the median plane of the embryo; however, the planes always cut from the animal to the vegetal pole of the egg (Eycleshymer, '04).

In the teleost fish, *Fundulus heteroclitus,* in the greater percentage of cases, the long axis of the embryo tends to coincide with either the first or second cleavage planes (Oppenheimer, '36). Other teleost fishes appear to be similar. In the hen's egg the first cleavage plane may or may not lie in the future median plane of the embryo (Olsen, '42).

In some species it appears that the unfertilized egg may possess bilateral symmetry. For example, in the frog, *Rana fusca,* the point of sperm entrance evidently has an influence in orienting the plan of bilateral symmetry, and, as a result, the gray crescent appears opposite the point of sperm contact with the egg. However, in *Rana esculenta* and in *Discoglossus pictus,* two other anuran species, there is no constant relationship between the point of sperm entry and the plan of bilateral symmetry of the egg (Pasteels, '37, '38). In the latter cases, unlike that of *Rana fusca,* the stimulus of sperm entry presumably does not influence the plan of bilateral symmetry which is determined previous to sperm entrance.

It is to be noted that there is a strong tendency in many of the above species for the first cleavage amphiaster to orient itself in such a manner as to *coincide with the median plane of the embryo or to be at right angles to this plane.* This fact suggests that the first cleavage amphiaster is oriented in terms of the egg's organization. It further suggests that the **copulation paths** of the respective pronuclei, as they move toward each other, together with the resulting **cleavage path** of the pronuclei (fig. 139), are conditioned by the inherent organization of the egg's cytoplasm.

B. Types of Cleavage in the Phylum *Chordata*

Cleavage in the phylum *Chordata* often is classified as either **holoblastic** or **meroblastic**. These terms serve a general approach to the subject but fail to portray the varieties and problems of cleavage which one finds within the phylum. Under more careful scrutiny, three main categories of cleavage types appear with **typical holoblastic cleavage** occupying one extreme and **typical meroblastic cleavage** the other, while between these two are many examples of atypical or **transitional cleavage** types. Moreover, the phenomena of cleavage are variable, and while we may list the typical cleavage of any one species as holoblastic, transitional or meroblastic, under certain modifying circumstances the cleavage pattern may be caused to vary.

Holoblastic cleavage is characterized by the fact that the cleavage furrows bisect the entire egg. In **meroblastic cleavage,** on the other hand, the disc of protoplasm at the animal pole only is affected, and the cleavage furrows cut through this disc superficially or almost entirely. **Superficial cleavage** occurs typically in certain invertebrate forms, particularly among the *Insecta*. However, in a sense, the very early cleavages in elasmobranch fishes, certain teleost fishes, and in birds may be regarded as a kind of superficial cleavage.

1. TYPICAL HOLOBLASTIC CLEAVAGE

In typical holoblastic cleavage, the first cleavage plane bisects both poles of the egg along the median egg axis, that is, the first plane of cleavage is **meridional.** The second cleavage plane is similar but at right angles to the first, thereby dividing the "germ" into four approximately equal **blastomeres.** (See Sachs' rule (a), p. 286.) The third cleavage plane in typical holoblastic cleavage occurs at right angles to the median axis of the egg and the foregoing two meridional planes. (See Sachs' rule (b), p. 286.) As it does not cut along the equatorial plane, but nearer the animal pole, it is described as a **latitudinal cleavage.** Two meridional cleavage planes (see definition, p. 283) followed by a latitudinal plane (see definition, p. 284) is the cleavage sequence characteristic *of the first three cleavage planes* of typical holoblastic cleavage. The following chordate species exemplify typical holoblastic cleavage:

a. Amphioxus

In this cephalochordate there exists as typical a form of holoblastic cleavage as is found anywhere in the phylum *Chordata*. The process of cleavage or segmentation in *Amphioxus* has been described in the studies of four different men; as such, these descriptions form four of the classics of embryonic study. These studies were made by Kowalewski in 1867; Hatschek in 1881, English translation, 1893; Cerfontaine, '06; and Conklin, '32. With the exception of certain slight errors of observation and interpretation, Hatschek's work is a masterpiece.

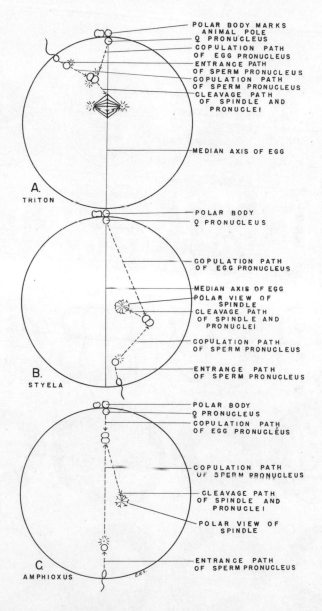

FIG. 139. Penetration path of the sperm, copulation paths of the pronuclei, the cleavage path of the pronuclei, and first cleavage spindle. (A) Conditions such as found in the urodele, *Triton*. (B) Conditions such as found in the protochordate, *Styela*. (C) Conditions such as found in the protochordate, *Amphioxus*.

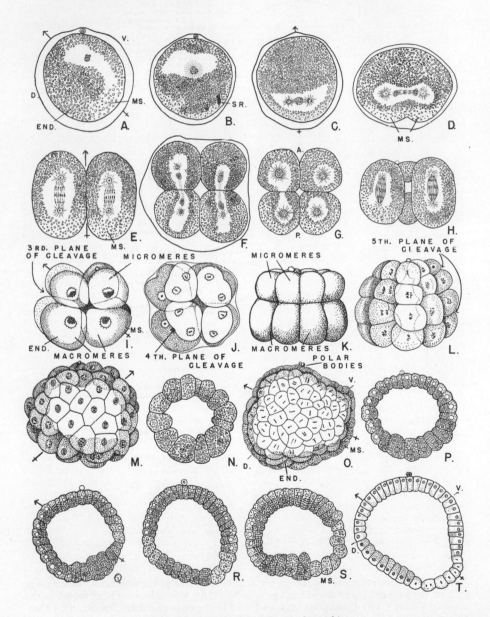

FIG. 140. *(See facing page for legend.)*

The **first cleavage furrow** cuts through the egg along the median axis of the egg, starting at the postero-ventral side of the egg (fig. 140D, E). It, therefore, is a meridional plane of cleavage. The **second cleavage plane** cuts at right angles to the first plane, producing four equal cells (fig. 140E, F). The **third cleavage** involves four blastomeres. Its plane of cleavage is almost equatorial but slightly displaced toward the animal pole, and therefore, more truly described as latitudinal plane of cleavage. This cleavage plane divides each of the four blastomeres into a smaller **micromere** at the animal pole and a larger **macromere** at the vegetal pole. Eight blastomeres are thereby produced (fig. 140G I). In certain cases and at least in some varieties of *Amphioxus,* the four micromeres may not be placed exactly above the macromeres, but may be rotated variously up to 45 degrees, forming a type of spiral cleavage (fig. 140J). (See Wilson, E. B., 1893.) The **fourth cleavage planes** are meridional, and all of the eight cells divide synchronously. The result is sixteen cells, eight micromeres and eight macromeres (fig. 140J, K). The **fifth planes of cleavage** are latitudinal and simultaneous (fig. 140L). The

FIG. 140. Early cleavage and blastulation in *Amphioxus.* (K after Hatschek, 1893; all others after Conklin, '32.)   (A) Median section through egg in the plane of bilateral symmetry, one hour after fertilization. Second polar body at animal pole; egg and sperm pronuclei in contact in cytoplasm containing little yolk. Approximate antero-posterior axis shown by arrow. D. and V. signify dorsal and ventral aspects of future embryo. MS. = mesodermal crescent.   (B) Sperm and egg nuclei in contact surrounded by astral rays. Sperm remnant, SR., shown at right.   (C) First cleavage spindle in postero-ventral half of the egg (see fig. 139C). Arrow shows median plane of future embryo and also the median plane of the egg. Observe that the spindle is at right angles to this plane of the egg.   (D) Egg in late anaphase of first cleavage. Cleavage furrow deeper at postero-ventral side of the egg. MS. = mesodermal crescent.   (E) Two-cell stage. Arrow shows median plane of embryo. MS. = mesodermal crescent now bisected into two parts.   (F) Four-cell stage at conclusion of second cleavage, 1½ hours after fertilization.   (G) Four-cell stage at beginning of third cleavage. Posterior cells, P., slightly smaller than anterior cells.   (H) Animal pole above, vegetal pole below. Cell at left is posterior, the one at right anterior. Spindles show third or horizontal cleavage plane. (I) Eight-cell stage, 2½ hours after fertilization. Posterior cells, below at right, contain most of mesodermal crescent. Arrow denotes antero-posterior axis of embryo.   (J) Late anaphase of fourth cleavage.   (K) Sixteen-cell stage viewed laterally. There are eight micromeres and eight macromeres.   (L) Side view of 32-cell stage, 3¼ hours after fertilization. Every nucleus in anaphase or metaphase of sixth cleavage.   (M) Left side of 64-cell stage. Arrow denotes antero-posterior axis of embryo.   (N) Blastula, 3⅓ hours after fertilization. Animal pole above, vegetal below. Entoderm cells at vegetative pole are larger, are full of yolk, and are dividing. Blastocoel is large.   (O) Eighth cleavage period with more than 128 cells, 4 hours after fertilization. Antero-posterior axis of future embryo shown by arrows. Polar body indicates animal pole of original egg. Dorsal and ventral aspects indicated by D. and V., respectively. MS. = mesodermal crescent.   (P) Section of blastula, 4½ hours after fertilization. Entoderm cells have nuclei shaded with lines.   (Q) Section of blastula, 5½ hours after fertilization.   (R) Section of blastula, 6 hours after fertilization. Mesoderm cells lighter and on each side of entoderm cells. Section nearly transverse to embryonic axis.   (S) Section of blastula at stage of preceding but in a plane as in (Q). MS. = mesodermal crescent.   (T) Pear-shaped, late blastula. Pointed end is mesodermal; entoderm cells have cross-lined nuclei. D. and V. indicate dorsal and ventral aspects of embryo. See also fig. 167.

plane nearest the animal pole divides each of the eight micromeres into an upper and a lower micromere, while the plane which furrows the eight macromeres divides each into upper and lower macromeres. Thirty-two cells are, thus, the result of the fifth cleavage planes. The lowest of the macromeres are larger and laden with yolk material (fig. 140L). The **sixth cleavage planes** are synchronous and approximately meridional in direction in all of the 32 cells, resulting in 64 cells (fig. 140M). The blastocoelic cavity is a conspicuous area in the center of this cell mass and is filled with a jelly-like substance (fig. 140N). Study also figure 167.

When the **eighth cleavage furrows** occur, the blastocoel contained within the developing blastula is large (fig. 140P). As the blastula continues to enlarge, the blastocoel increases in size, and the contained jelly-like substance assumes a more fluid condition (fig. 140Q–S). The fully formed blastula is piriform or "pear-shaped" (fig. 140T). (See Conklin, '32.)

The cleavage pattern of the urochordate, *Styela partita,* is somewhat similar to that of *Amphioxus,* but considerable irregularity may exist after the first three or four cleavages. In *Styela* the ooplasm of the egg contains differently pigmented materials, and yellow and gray crescentic areas are visible at the time of the first cleavage. (See fig. 132.) These different cytoplasmic areas give origin to cells which have a definite and particular history in the embryo. Observations devoted to the tracing of such cell histories are grouped under the heading of "cell lineage." Cell-lineage observations are more easily made in the eggs of certain species because of definitely appearing cytoplasmic areas, where colored pigments or other peculiarities associated with various areas of the egg make possible a ready determination of subsequent cell histories. The general organization of the egg of *Amphioxus,* regardless of the fact that its cytoplasmic stuffs do not have the pigmentation possessed by the egg of *Styela,* appears similar to that of the latter (cf. figs. 140A; 167A). (See Conklin, '32.)

b. Frog (Rana pipiens and R. sylvatica)

The egg of the frog is telolecithal with a much larger quantity of yolk than is found in the egg of *Amphioxus*. The pattern of cleavage in the frog, therefore, is somewhat less ideally holoblastic than that of *Amphioxus.*

The **first cleavage plane** of the frog's egg is meridional (figs. 141C; 142A–C). It occurs at about three to three and one-half hours after fertilization at ordinary room temperature in *Rana pipiens*. It begins at the animal pole and travels downward through the nutritive or vegetal pole substance, bisecting both poles of the egg. In the majority of eggs, it bisects the gray crescent. (See p. 287.) The **second cleavage plane** divides each of the first two blastomeres into two equal blastomeres; its plane of cleavage is similar to the first cleavage plane but is oriented at right angles to the first plane (figs. 141D; 142D–E). The upper, animal pole end of each of the four blastomeres contains most of the dark pigment, while in the lower portion of each blastomere the yellow-white yolk is concentrated. As a rule, *the substance of the gray crescent is found in two of the blastomeres;* the four blastomeres under the circumstances are not qualitatively equal.

The **third or latitudinal cleavage plane** is at right angles to both of the foregoing and somewhat above the equator, dividing each of the four blastomeres into an animal pole micromere and a larger vegetal pole macromere

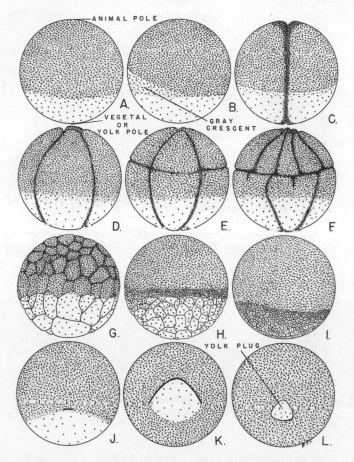

Fɪɢ. 141. Normal development of *Rana sylvatica*. (A) Egg at fertilization. (B) Formation of gray crescent, sharply defined at one hour after sperm entrance. (C) First cleavage furrow meridional. (D) Second cleavage furrow meridional. (E) Third cleavage furrows, latitudinal in position. Four micromeres above and four macromeres below. (F) Fourth set of cleavage furrows, meridional in position, although some variation may exist and vertical furrows may occur. (G–I) Later cleavage stages. Pigmented pole cells become very small, and pigmented cells creep downward over vegetative pole area. (J) Appearance of dorsal blastoporal lip. (K) Blastoporal lips spread laterally, forming a broad, V-shaped structure. Pigmented cells proceed toward blastoporal lips. (L) Yolk-plug stage of gastrulation. (After Pollister and Moore, '37.)

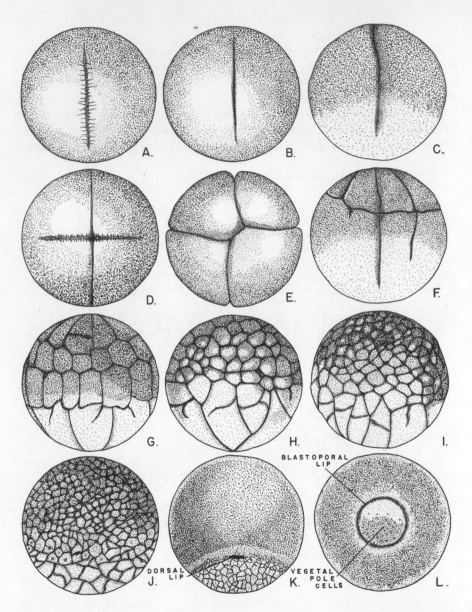

FIG. 142. Early development of *Rana pipiens*. (A) Polar view of first cleavage. The animal pole is considerably flattened at this time and tension lines are visible extending outward along either side of the furrow. (About 3½ hours after fertilization in the laboratory, room temperature 20 to 22° C.) (B) First cleavage furrow a little later. (C) First furrow proceeds slowly though the yolk of vegetative (vegetal) pole. (D) Second cleavage furow meridional and at right angles to the first furrow. (E) Four-cell stage, view from animal pole. Observe short "cross furrow" connecting first and second cleavage planes. (F) Fourth cleavages meridional or nearly so. Taken from egg spawned in nature. Considerable variation may exist. Some cleavages may be vertical and not meridional. (G–I) Later blastula stage. (J) Stage just before appearance of dorsal lip of blastopore. (K) Dorsal lip of blastopore. (L) Yolk-plug stage of gastrulation.

294

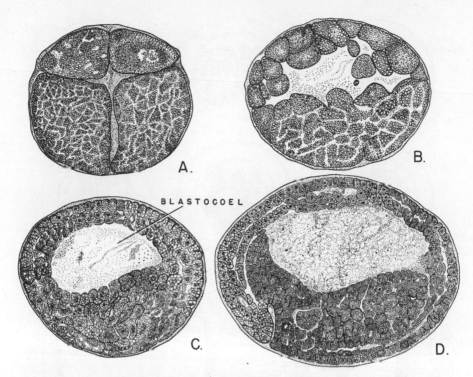

FIG. 143. Stages in formation of the blastocoel in the cleaving egg of *Rana pipiens* taken from stained sections. (A) Eight-cell stage; blastocoel appearing particularly between micromeres. The macromeres form the floor of the developing blastocoel. (B, C) Later stages of formation of the blastocoel. Blastocoel situated at animal pole. Yolk-laden, vegetal pole cells form floor of the blastocoel while smaller, animal pole cells form its sides and roof. (D) Blastocoel at beginning of gastrulation.

(figs. 141E; 142F). The fourth set of cleavages, both in *Rana sylvatica* and *Rana pipiens,* in eggs that are spawned naturally, are oriented in a meridional direction (figs. 141F; 142F). These furrows first involve only the animal pole micromeres, but later meridionally directed furrows begin to develop in the yolk-laden macromeres (figs. 141F; 142F).

The cleavage of the various blastomeres of the egg to this point tends to be synchronous, and is comparable to that of *Amphioxus.* However, from this time on **asynchronism** is the rule and different eggs in a given lot manifest various degrees of irregularity. Exceptional eggs may occur in which the next two cleavage planes resemble the fourth and fifth series of planes in *Amphioxus.* But, on the whole, the micromeres divide faster than do the macromeres and thus give origin to many small, heavily pigmented, animal pole cells, while the macromeres or vegetal pole cells are larger and fewer in number. The smaller pigmented cells creep downward gradually in the direction of the larger vegetal pole cells (figs. 141G–I; 142G–K). The latter migration of the

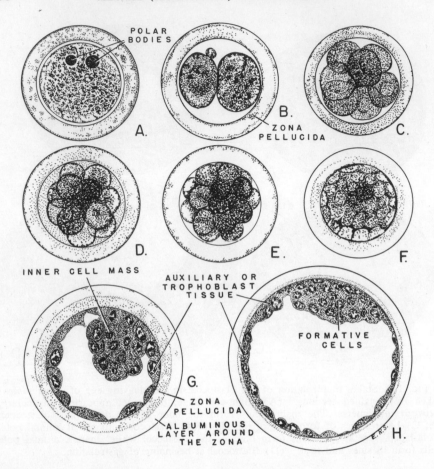

FIG. 144. Cleavage in the rabbit egg. (After Gregory, '30.)   (A) One-cell stage.   (B) Two primary blastomeres, one larger than the other.   (C) Eight-cell stage.   (D) Sixteen-cell stage.   (E) Morula stage of 32 cells.   (F) External view of stage approximating that in (G).   (G) Inner cell mass and blastocoelic cleft showing in embryo, about 7½ hours after copulation.   (H) Inner cell mass and blastocoelic space in embryo, approximately 90 hours after copulation. Entoderm cells have not yet appeared.

pigment cells is marked toward the end of the blastular period and during gastrulation. Cf. figs. 141H–L; 142H–L.

The blastocoel within the mass of blastomeres of the cleaving egg of the frog forms somewhat differently from that in *Amphioxus* in that the cavity arises nearer the animal pole. The smaller micromeres of the animal pole, therefore, are more directly involved than the macromeres of the vegetal pole. Beginning at the eight-cell stage, a spatial separation is present between the four micromeres at the animal pole. The floor of this space or beginning blastocoel is occupied by the yolk-laden macromeres (fig. 143A, B). As development proceeds, this eccentricity of position is maintained, and the

blastocoel or **segmentation cavity** becomes an enlarged space filled with fluid, displaced toward the animal pole (fig. 143B–D). The contained fluid of the blastocoel of amphibia is alkaline, according to the work of Buytendijk and Woerdeman ('27), having a pH of 8.4 to 8.6.

For general references regarding cleavage in the frog, see Morgan (1897); Pollister and Moore ('37); Rugh ('51); and Shumway ('40).

c. Cyclostomata

Cleavage in the eggs of the genera of the family, *Petromyzonidae,* resembles very closely that of the frog. Further description will not be included. However, in the marine cyclostomes or hagfishes, the cleavage phenomena are strongly meroblastic. (See description of the marine cyclostomatous fish at the end of this chapter.)

2. ATYPICAL TYPES OF HOLOBLASTIC CLEAVAGE

A variety of cleavage types is found in the eggs of many vertebrate species which do not follow the symmetrical, ideally holoblastic pattern exhibited in the egg of *Amphioxus* or even in the egg of the frog. In all of these atypical forms the entire egg ultimately is divided by the cleavage furrows with the possible exception of the eggs of the bony ganoid fishes, *Amia calva* and *Lepisosteus osseus* (and also in certain of the gymnophionan amphibia). In the latter species the yolk material at the yolk-laden pole of the egg is invaded by isolated nuclei which form a syncytium in the yolk material. Eventually this yolk material is formed into definite cells and incorporated into the gut area of the embryo.

a. Holoblastic Cleavage in the Egg of the Metatherian and Eutherian Mammals

1) General Considerations. The eggs of metatherian and eutherian mammals are the most truly isolecithal of any in the phylum *Chordata*. They have also a cleavage pattern distinct from other chordate eggs. The first cleavage plane in the higher mammalian egg very often divides the egg into a larger and a slightly smaller blastomere (figs. 144B; 145A, F; 147B, J). As shown by the work of Heuser and Streeter ('41) in the pig, the smaller blastomere is destined to give origin to the **formative tissue** of the embryo's body, while the larger blastomere gives rise to **auxiliary tissue,** otherwise known as the **nourishment-obtaining** or **trophoblast tissue** (fig. 145A–E). The smaller blastomere also contributes some cells to the trophoblast tissue. A similar condition of progressive specialization of the smaller and the larger blastomeres of the two-cell stage, producing two classes of cells, the one mainly formative and the other auxiliary or trophoblast, is present in the monkey (Heuser and Streeter, '41) and probably in other higher mammals as well.

If one compares the early history of these two blastomeres with the early

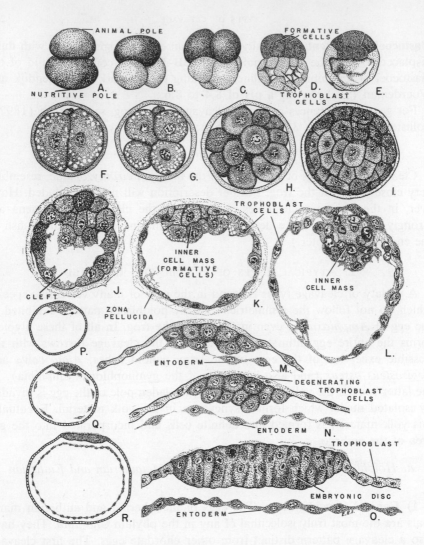

FIG. 145. Early development of the pig. (A–E) Fate of the first two blastomeres. The larger blastomere of the two-cell stage gives rise to trophoblast tissue, whereas from the smaller blastomere, formative cells and trophoblast cells arise. (After Heuser and Streeter, Carnegie Inst., Washington, Contrib. Embryol., 20:3.) (F) Section of two-cell stage. Specimen secured from oviduct of sow, killed two days, 3½ hours after ovulation. (G) Section of four-cell stage. Age is approximately 2½ days. (H) Sixteen-cell stage, drawn from unsectioned specimen, probably 3½ days old. (I) Blastular stage. Specimen secured from sow, 4¾ days after copulation. (J–L) Stages showing the formation of the blastocoel. (J) About 4¾ days after copulation. (K) Six days, 1¾ hours after copulation. (L) Six days, 20 hours after copulation. (M) Beginning disintegration of trophoblast cells over the inner cell mass and separation of entoderm cells from the inner cell mass. (N) Trophoblast cells over inner cell mass almost absent, entoderm forms a definite layer below inner cell mass. (O) Trophoblast cells almost absent over the embryonic disc; entoderm layer continuous. (P–R) Stages shown in (M), (N), (O) respectively, showing the whole blastocyst. In (Q) the entoderm cells are shown migrating outward to line the cavity of the blastocyst.

development of other vertebrate eggs, it is apparent that the nutritive (tropho-blast) cells are located at one pole, while the formative cells of the embryo are found toward the opposite pole. The latter condition resembles the ar-rangement of formative cells and nutritive substances in teleost and elasmo-branch fishes, in reptiles, birds, and prototherian mammals. This comparison suggests, therefore, that the first cleavage plane in the higher mammals cuts at right angles to the true median axis of the egg (cf. fig. 145A–E). If this is so, the first cleavage furrow should be regarded as latitudinal and almost equatorial, and the two blastomeres should theoretically be arranged as shown in figure 145A.

The determination of the animal and vegetal poles of the egg in this group of vertebrates is difficult by any other means than that suggested above. In many lower chordate species the polar bodies act as indicators of the animal pole, for they remain relatively fixed at this pole of the egg (e.g., *Styela, Amphioxus,* etc.). But in higher mammals the polar bodies "are never sta-tionary, and there is evidently much shifting" (Gregory, '30, relative to the rabbit), although in the two-cell stage, the polar bodies often appear between the two blastomeres at one end. It appears in consequence that the fates of the two blastomeres of the two-cell stage serves as a better criterion of egg symmetry at this time than is afforded by the polocytes. According to this view, the smaller blastomere should be regarded as indicating the animal pole, while the larger blastomere signifies the vegetative pole (fig. 145A).

With respect to the statements in the previous paragraph, it is well to mention that Nicholas and Hall ('42) reported that two early embryos may be produced by isolating the blastomeres of the two-cell stage in the rat, and one embryo is produced as a result of experimental fusion of two fertilized eggs. These experimental results suggest that the potencies of the two blas-tomeres are not so rigidly determined that two different kinds of development result when the blastomeres are isolated. In normal development, however, it may be that the innate potencies of the two blastomeres are not precisely the same. The ability to **regulate** and thus compensate for lost substances shown by many different types of early embryonic blastomeres, may explain the production of two early embryos from the separated blastomeres of the two-cell stage.

The second cleavage divides the larger blastomere into two cells, giving origin to three cells. Then the smaller blastomere divides, forming four cells. Cleavage from this time on becomes irregular, and five-, six-, seven-, eight-, etc., cell stages are formed.

Segmentation of the higher mammalian egg, therefore, is unique in its cleavage pattern. The synchrony so apparent in the egg of *Amphioxus* is lacking. Irregularity and individuality is the rule, with the auxiliary or nutritive pole cells dividing faster than those of the formative or animal pole cells.

Moreover, the blastomeres not only show their apparent independence of each other through their irregularity in division but also by their tendency to shift their position with respect to one another. One function of the zona pellucida during the early cleavage period appears to be to hold "the blastomeres together" (Heuser and Streeter, '29). From the 16-cell stage on, the trophoblast or auxiliary cells begin to form the blastocoelic space, first by a flattening process and later by the formation of a cleft among the cells (fig. 145D). The growing presence of the blastocoel consigns the formative or **inner cell-mass cells** to one pole of the blastula (fig. 145J–L). A blastocoelic space thus is formed which is surrounded largely by trophoblast or nutritive cells (fig. 145K, L). The blastular stage of development of the mammalian embryo is called the **blastocyst.**

2) Early Development of the Rabbit Egg. The following brief description pertains to the early development of the rabbit egg up to the early blastocyst condition.

a) TWO-CELL STAGE. The two-cell stage is reached about 22 to 24 hours after mating or 10 to 12 hours after fertilization. One cell has a tendency to be slightly larger than the other (fig. 144B). (Cf. also figs. 145A, F; 146A; 147B, J.)

b) FOUR-CELL STAGE. This stage is present about 24 to 32 hours after mating or 13 to 18 hours after fertilization. The larger cell divides first, giving origin to three cells; the smaller cell then divides. (Cf. figs. 145B, C; 146B, C; 147K, L.) The mitotic spindles tend to assume positions at right angles to each other during these cleavages.

c) EIGHT-CELL STAGE. Eight cells are found 32 to 41 hours after mating. One member of the larger blastomeres of the four-cell stage divides, forming a five-cell condition, followed by the division of the second larger cell, producing six cells. (Cf. figs. 145C; 147M.) After a short period, one of the smaller cells segments, and thus, a total of seven blastomeres is formed. The last cleavage is followed by the division of the other smaller cell, producing eight blastomeres (fig. 144C; compare with fig. 147N). The mitotic spindles of each of these cleavages form at right angles to one another, thus demonstrating an independence and asynchrony. The latter conditions are demonstrated further by the fact that the blastomeres shift their position continually in relation to each other during these divisions.

d) SIXTEEN-CELL STAGE. The mitotic divisions increase in rate, and at about 45 to 47 hours after mating the 16-cell stage is reached (fig. 144D). The cells at the future trophoblast pole *begin to flatten,* and gradually certain blastomeres are enclosed within. In the macaque monkey, 16 cells are present at about 96 hours after fertilization.

e) MORULA STAGE. At about 65 to 70 hours after mating a solid mass of cells is present. This condition is known as the morula (mulberry-like) stage (fig. 144E, F). The trophoblast portion of the cell mass is more active in cell division.

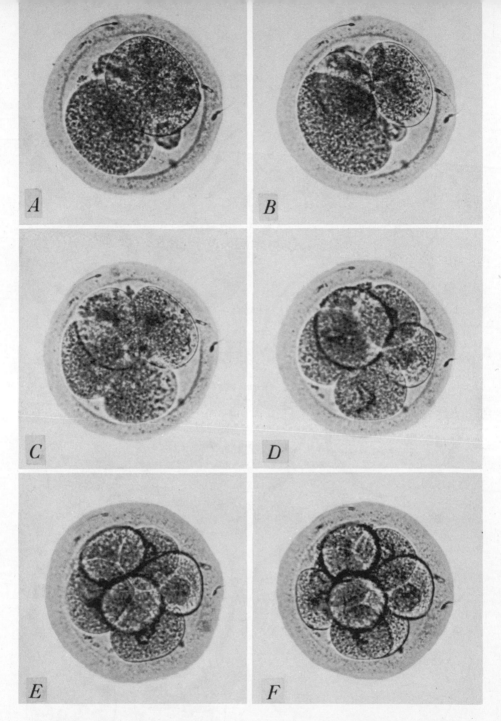

Fig. 146. Photomicrographs of cleavage in living monkey eggs. (After Lewis and Hartman, Carnegie Inst., Washington, Contrib. Embryol., 24.) (Figures borrowed from fig. 33, Patten, '48.) (A) Late two-cell stage. (B) Early three-cell stage. (C) Late four-cell stage. (D) Five-cell stage. (E) Six-cell stage. (F) Eight-cell stage; next cleavage beginning.

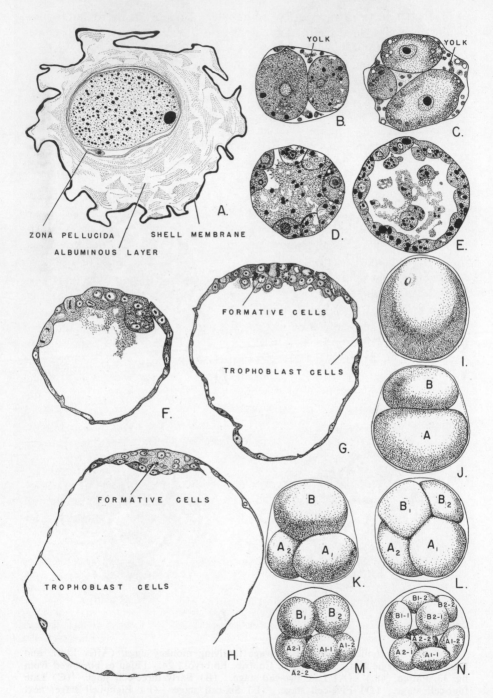

Labels within the figure:

YOLK

YOLK

ZONA PELLUCIDA   SHELL MEMBRANE

ALBUMINOUS LAYER

A.

B.

C.

D.

E.

FORMATIVE CELLS

TROPHOBLAST CELLS

F.

G.

I.

B

A

J.

FORMATIVE CELLS

TROPHOBLAST CELLS

B

A₂   A₁

B₁   B₂

A₂   A₁

K.

L.

H.

B₁   B₂

A2-1   A1-1   A1-2

A2-2

M.

B1-2   B2-2

B1-1   B2-1

A2-2   A1-2

A2-1   A1-1

N.

FIG. 147. *(See facing page for legend.)*

f) EARLY BLASTOCYST. A few hours later or about 70 to 75 hours after mating, a well-defined cleft within the cells of the trophoblast pole becomes evident (fig. 144G). (Cf. fig. 145D, J.) This cleft or cavity enlarges, and the surrounding trophoblast cells lose their rounded shape and become considerably flattened. As the blastocoel gradually increases in size, *the formative tissue or inner cell mass* becomes displaced toward one end of the early blastocyst, as indicated in fig. 144G, H. The blastocoelic space at this time is filled with fluid, and the blastocyst as a whole completely fills the area within the zona pellucida (fig. 144G, H). The pig embryo reaches a similar condition in about 100 hours after fertilization, and that of the guinea pig in 140 hours.

During its passage down the Fallopian tube, the developing mass of cells continues to be encased by the zona pellucida. The general increase in size is slight. In the rabbit and in the opossum, as the cleaving egg passes down the Fallopian tube, an albuminous coating is deposited around the outside of the zona pellucida (figs. 144G, H; 147A). This albuminous layer forms an **accessory egg membrane or covering** similar to the albuminous layers deposited around the egg by the oviducal cells in prototherian mammals, birds, and reptiles. At about 80 to 96 hours after mating, the rabbit blastocyst enters the uterus and gradually increases in size. Implantation of the mammalian blastocyst upon the uterine wall will be considered later. (See Chap. 22.)

3) Types of Mammalian Blastocysts (Blastulae). The early blastocyst of the rabbit described above is representative of the early condition of the developing blastula of the eutherian (placental) mammal. However, in the metatherian or marsupial mammals the early blastocyst does not possess a prominent inner cell mass similar to that found in the eutherian mammals. Comparing the early blastocysts of the higher mammals, we find, in general, that there are three main types as follows:

(1) In most of the *Eutheria* or placental mammals the **inner cell mass (embryonic knob)** is a prominent mass of cells located at one pole of the blastocyst during the earlier stages of blastocyst formation. (See

---

FIG. 147. Early development of the opossum egg. (A–H after Hartman, '16; I–N after McCrady, '38.) (A) Unfertilized uterine egg, showing the first polar body; yolk spherules (in black) within the cytoplasm; zona pellucida; albuminous layer; and the outer shell membrane. (B) Two-cell stage. Observe yolk spherules discharged into the cavity of the zona pellucida. (C) Section through three blastomeres of four-cell stage. Observe yolk within and without the blastomeres. (D) Section through 16-cell cleavage stage. Observe yolk within blastomeres and also in cavity of the zona between the blastomeres. (E) Section through early blastocyst showing yolk and cytoplasmic fragments and an included nucleated cell within the blastocoel. (F–H) Early and later blastocyst of the opossum, showing the formative tissue at one pole of the blastocyst. (I) Surface view, fertilized egg. (J) Two-blastomere stage. (K) Cell A has divided meridionally into A_1 and A_2. (L) Cell B has divided into B_1 and B_2. (M) A_1 and A_2 have divided as indicated. (N) B_1 and B_2 divide next as indicated.

figs. 144G, H; 145J–L.) This condition is found in the monkey, human, pig, rabbit, etc.

(2) On the other hand, in certain marsupials, such as the American opossum, *Didelphys virginiana,* and the Brazilian opossum, *Didelphys aurita,* the inner cell mass is much less prominent during earlier stages of the blastocyst. In these species it is indicated merely by a thickened aggregation of cells at one pole of the blastocyst (fig. 147E–G).

(3) In the marsupial or native cat of Australia, *Dasyurus viverrinus,* cleavage results in an early blastocyst in the form of a hollow sphere of rounded cells. As the blastocyst expands, the cells increase in number and become flattened to form a thin layer of cells apposed against the shell membrane *without an apparent inner cell mass or embryonic knob* (fig. 148A–C).

A conspicuous feature of cleavage and early blastocyst formation in the marsupials should be emphasized. For in this group, the early blastomeres apparently use the framework of the zona pellucida as a support upon which they arrange themselves. As a result, the blastocoelic space of the blastocyst

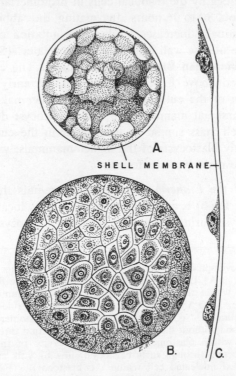

FIG. 148. Early blastular conditions of the marsupial cat of Australia, *Dasyurus viverrinus.* (After Hill, '10.) (A) Early blastula. (B) External view of blastocyst, 0.6 mm. in diameter. The cells are becoming flattened and finally reach the condition shown in (C). (C) Section of wall of blastocyst, 2.4 mm. in diameter.

forms directly by cell arrangement and not by the development of a cleft within the trophoblast cells, as in the eutherian mammals. (See fig. 147C–E; compare with figs. 144G; 145J.)

The descriptions of the mammalian blastocysts presented above pertain only to the **primary condition of the blastocyst.** The changes involved in later development, resulting in the formation of the **secondary blastocyst,** will be described in the next chapter which deals specifically with blastulation.

(For more detailed descriptions of early cleavage in the metatherian and eutherian mammals see: Hartman ('16) on the American opossum; Hill ('18) on the opossum from Brazil; Hill ('10) on the Australian native cat, *Dasyurus viverrinus;* Heuser and Streeter ('29), and Patten ('48) on the pig; Lewis and Gregory ('29), Gregory ('30), and Pincus ('39) on the rabbit; Huber ('15) on the rat; Lewis and Wright ('35) and Snell ('41) on the mouse; Lewis and Hartman ('41) and Heuser and Streeter ('41) on the *Rhesus* monkey.)

b. *Holoblastic Cleavage of the Transitional or Intermediate Type*

Contrary to the conditions where small amounts of yolk or deutoplasm are present in the egg of the higher mammal or in *Amphioxus,* the eggs of the vertebrate species described below are heavily laden with yolk. As the quantity of yolk present increases, the cleavage phenomena become less and less typically holoblastic and begin to assume meroblastic characteristics. Hence the designation transitional or intermediate cleavage.

1) *Ambystoma maculatum (punctatum).* The newly spawned egg of *Ambystoma maculatum* is nearly spherical and measures about 2 mm. in diameter, although the egg size is somewhat variable. The animal pole contains within its median area a small depression, the "light spot" or "fovea." Within the fovea is a small pit harboring the first polar body. (A comparable pit is shown in the frog's egg, fig. 119C.) After the second polar body is formed, this pit may appear somewhat elongated, and the light spot disappears. Just before the first cleavage, the animal pole appears flattened similar to the condition in the frog's egg. The flattened area soon changes to an elongated furrow which progresses gradually downward toward the opposite pole (fig. 149A, B). This cleavage furrow is meridional, dividing the egg into two, nearly equal blastomeres. The second cleavage furrow is similar to the first but at right angles to the first furrow (fig. 149C). However, considerable variation may exist, and the second furrow may arise at various angles to the first, dividing each of the first two blastomeres into two, slightly unequal, daughter blastomeres. The third set of cleavages is latitudinal, and each blastomere is divided into a smaller animal pole micromere, and a larger vegetal pole macromere (fig. 149D). Later cleavages may not be synchronous.

The first three cleavages described above conform generally to the rules of typical holoblastic cleavage. However, from this time on cleavage digresses from the holoblastic pattern *and begins to assume certain characteristics of*

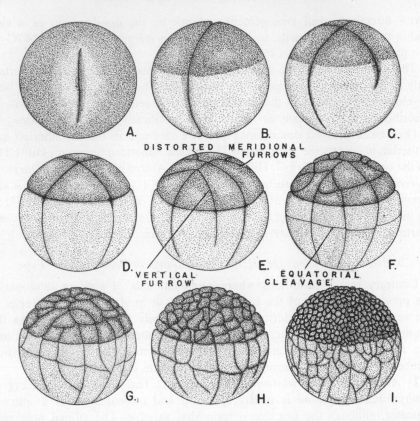

A.   B.   C.

DISTORTED MERIDIONAL FURROWS

D.   VERTICAL FURROW   E.   EQUATORIAL CLEAVAGE   F.

G.   H.   I.

FIG. 149. Early cleavage in *Ambystoma maculatum (punctatum)*. (After Eycleshymer, J. Morphol., 10, and eggs in the laboratory.) (A, B) First cleavage furrow, meridional plane. (C) Second cleavage furrow at right angles to first furrow, meridional plane. (D) Third cleavage furrow, latitudinal, forming four micromeres and four macromeres. (E) Fourth cleavage furrow; mixture of meridional and vertical planes of cleavage. (F) Fifth cleavage furrows; mixture of latitudinal and vertical planes of cleavage. Observe equatorial plane cutting the large macromeres. (G–I) Later cleavage stages.

meroblastic cleavage. For example, the fourth set of cleavages may be a mixture of vertical and meridional furrows, as shown in figure 149E. The fifth cleavages are a mixture of horizontal (i.e., latitudinal and equatorial, fig. 149F), vertical and meridional furrows. The sixth set of cleavages is made up of vertical and horizontal cleavage planes of considerable variableness (fig. 149G). From this time on cleavage becomes most variable, with the animal pole micromeres dividing much more rapidly than the yolk-laden macromeres at the vegetal pole (figs. 149H, I).

The blastocoel makes its appearance at the eight-cell stage and appears as a small space between the micromeres and the macromeres, the latter forming the floor of the blastocoelic space. At the late blastula stage, the blastocoel is roofed over by the smaller micromeres, and floored by the yolk-

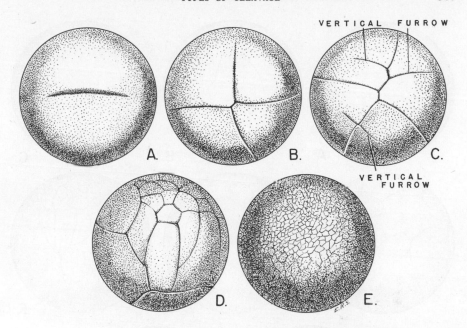

FIG. 150. Cleavage in the egg of *Lepidosiren paradoxa*. (After Kerr, '09.) (A) Beginning of first cleavage, meridional in position. (B) Second cleavage planes, approximately meridional in position. (C) Third cleavage planes vertical in position, demonstrating a typical meroblastic pattern. (D) Early blastula. (E) Late blastula.

laden macromeres. The blastocoel is small in relation to the size of the egg (Eycleshymer, 1895).

2) *Lepidosiren paradoxa*. The egg of the South American lungfish, *Lepidosiren paradoxa,* measures about 6.5 to 7 mm. in diameter. Cleavage of the egg is complete (i.e., holoblastic), and a relatively large blastocoel is formed. As in *Ambystoma,* the blastocoel is displaced toward the animal pole. The floor of the blastocoel is formed by the large, yolk-laden macromeres.

The first two cleavage furrows are approximately meridional (fig. 150A, B). These two furrows are followed by four vertical furrows, which, when completed, form eight blastomeres (fig. 150C). The latter cleavages are subject to much variation. Although cleavage of the egg is complete, a distinct meroblastic pattern of cleavage is found, composed of two meridional furrows followed by vertical furrowing (see Kerr, '09).

3) *Necturus maculosus*. In this species of amphibia the egg is large and its contained yolk is greater than that of *Ambystoma*. It measures about 5 to 6 mm. in diameter. The egg and its envelopes are attached individually by the female beneath the flattened surface of a stone (Bishop, '26).

Cleavage in this egg proceeds slowly. The first two cleavage furrows tend to be meridional, but variations may occur in different eggs. Sometimes they are more vertical than meridional (fig. 151A). (See Eycleshymer, '04). The

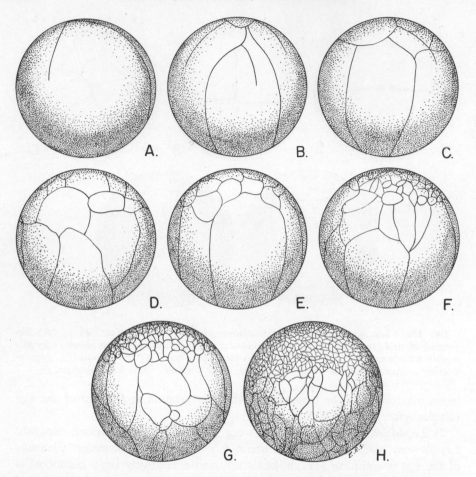

FIG. 151. Cleavage in the egg of *Necturus maculosus*. (After Eycleshymer and Wilson, '10.)   (A) First two cleavage planes are meridional.   (B) Third cleavage planes tend to be vertical and meridional.   (C) Fourth cleavage planes are vertical, meridional, and irregular.   (D–H) Following cleavage planes become irregular, offering a mixture of modified latitudinal, vertical, and meridional varieties.

third cleavage furrows are irregularly vertical (fig. 151B), while the fourth are latitudinal, cutting off four very irregular micromeres at the animal pole. Segmentation then becomes exceedingly irregular. (See Eycleshymer and Wilson, '10). One characteristic of cleavage in *Necturus* is a torsion and twisting of the cleavage grooves due to a shifting in the position of the blastomeres.

As shown in the figures, the first three cleavage planes assume a distinct meroblastic pattern of two meridional furrows followed by vertical furrows. The yolk material evidently impedes the progress of the furrows considerably.

4) *Acipenser sturio*. In the genus *Acipenser* are placed the cartilaginous ganoid fishes. Cleavage in *Acipenser sturio,* the sturgeon, resembles that of

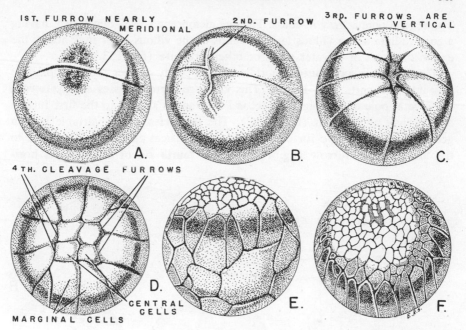

FIG. 152. Cleavage in the egg of the sturgeon, *Acipenser sturio*. (After Dean, 1895.) (A, B) First and second cleavage planes are approximately meridional. (C) Third cleavage planes are vertical, usually parallel to first cleavage plane. (D) Fourth cleavage planes are vertical, cutting off four central cells from the 12 marginal cells. (E, F) Later cleavage stages.

Necturus, although the furrows in the yolk pole area are retarded more and are definitely superficial. The third and fourth sets of cleavage furrows are vertical and succeed in cutting off four central cells from twelve larger marginal cells (fig. 152). Cleavage in this form is more holoblastic in its essential behavior than that in the egg of *Amia* and *Lepisosteus* described below (Dean, 1895).

   5) *Amia calva.* *Amia calva* is a species of bony ganoid fishes, and it represents one of the oldest living species among the fishes. Its early embryology follows the ganoid habit, namely, its cleavages adhere to the microblastic pattern of the teleost fishes, with the added feature that the furrows eventually pass distally toward the vegetal pole of the egg. A few yolk nuclei appear to be formed during cleavage. These nuclei aid in dividing the yolk-filled cytoplasm into distinct cells. The latter gradually are added to the early blastomeres and to the later entoderm cells of the developing embryo. In other words, *cleavage in this species is holoblastic, but it represents a transitional condition between meroblastic and holoblastic types of cleavage.*

   The egg of *Amia* assumes an elongated form, averaging 2.2 by 2.8 mm. The germinal disc is a whitish cap in the freshly laid egg, reaching down over the animal pole to about one third of the distance along the egg's longer axis.

The vegetal pole is gray in color. The egg membrane is well developed, having a zona radiata and a villous layer. Strands of the villous layer may attach the egg to the stem of a water weed or other structure (fig. 153A).

The **first cleavage plane** is meridional and partly cleaves the protoplasmic disc into two parts (fig. 153B). This cleavage furrow passes slowly toward the vegetal pole of the egg. The **second cleavage** is similar to the first furrow and at right angles to it (fig. 153C). The **third cleavage** is variable but, in general, consists of two furrows passing in a vertical plane at right angles to the first cleavage furrow (fig. 153D). The **fourth set of cleavages** is hori-

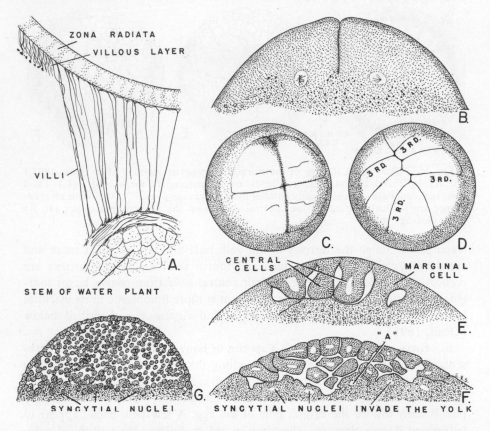

FIG. 153. Cleavage in the egg of *Amia calva*. (After Dean, 1896.) (A) Egg membranes of *Amia*, showing the filamentous (villous) layer attaching the egg to the stem of a water weed. (B) Second cleavage plane shown cutting through the protoplasmic disc at one pole of the egg. Section made parallel to the first cleavage plane. (C) First and second cleavage planes seen from above. (D) Third cleavage planes are vertical in position as indicated. (E) Fourth cleavage, sectioned in a plane approximately parallel to first (or second) cleavage. (F) Section through protoplasmic disc at eighth cleavage. (G) Blastular stage. Blastocoel is indistinct and scattered between (?) blastomeres of blastoderm. The description given by Whitman and Eycleshymer (1897) does not agree in certain features with the above.

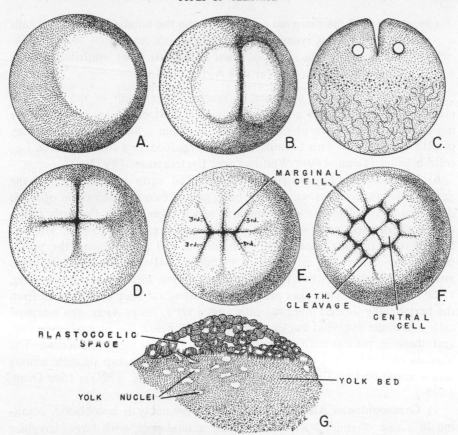

FIG. 154. Early development of *Lepisosteus osseus*. (After Dean, 1895.) (A) Uncleaved egg, showing germinal disc. (B) First cleavage is trench-like, extending beyond (i.e., laterally) to the margin of the germinal disc. (C) Transverse section of cleavage furrows shown in (B). (D) Four-cell stage. (E) Third cleavage planes are vertical as indicated. (F) Fourth cleavage planes also are vertical. (G) Germinal disc, sectioned 25 hours after fertilization. Blastocoelic spaces dispersed.

zontal. While the latter is in progress the **fifth cleavages,** which are vertical, begin. As a result of the fourth and fifth sets of cleavages, a mass of eight central cells and twenty or more marginal cells arises. Horizontal (i.e., latitudinal) cleavages begin among the central cells at this time, and other cells (see cell A, fig. 153F) appear to be budded off from the yolk floor from this period on. The latter are contributed to the growing disc of cells above.

Four types of cleavage furrows now appear in the growing blastoderm as follows:

(1) cleavage among the central cells, increasing their number,

(2) cleavage among the marginal cells, contributing cells to the central cells,

(3) cleavage of the marginal cells, increasing the number of marginal cells and contributing syncytial nuclei to the yolk floor,

(4) cleavage within the syncytial mass of the yolk floor, contributing cells to the central cells, such as cell A, figure 153F.

Eventually a blastular condition is reached as a result of the foregoing cleavages which does not possess an enlarged blastocoelic space; rather the blastocoel is in the form of scattered spaces within a loosely aggregated cap of cells (fig. 153G). This blastula might be regarded as a **stereoblastula,** i.e., solid blastula (Dean, 1896; Whitman and Eycleshymer, 1897).

6) Lepisosteus (Lepidosteus) osseus. The early development of the gar pike, *Lepisosteus osseus,* another bony ganoid fish, resembles that of *Amia* described above. The disc of protoplasm which takes part in the early cleavages is a prominent mass located at one pole of the egg (fig. 154A). The first two cleavage furrows appear to be meridional and partly cleave the protoplasmic cap of the egg, as indicated in figure 154B–D. The next cleavages are vertical and somewhat parallel to one of the meridional furrows (fig. 152E). The fourth cleavages are vertical, cutting off four central cells from the peripherally located marginal cells (fig. 152F). As in *Amia,* the marginal cells contribute syncytial nuclei to the yolk bed below the protoplasmic cap, and these in turn contribute definite cells to the growing blastodisc. The blastula of *Lepisosteus* consists of a loosely aggregated cap of cells among which are to be found indefinite blastocoelic spaces (fig. 152G). (See Dean, 1895.)

7) Gymnophionan Amphibia. Cleavage presumably is holoblastic, resulting in a disc of small micromeres at the animal pole, with large, irregular macromeres, heavily yolk laden, located toward the vegetal pole (fig. 182A). (See Svensson, '38.) The latter cells become surrounded during gastrulation by the smaller micromeres (Brauer, 1897). The blastula of the gymnophionan amphibia essentially is solid and may be regarded as a stereoblastula.

3. MEROBLASTIC CLEAVAGE

The word meroblastic is an adjective which refers to a part of the germ; that is, a part of the egg. In meroblastic cleavage only a small portion of the egg becomes segmented and thus gives origin to the blastoderm. Most of the yolk material remains in an uncleaved state and is encompassed eventually by the growing tissues of the embryo. A large number of vertebrate eggs utilize the meroblastic type of cleavage. Some examples of meroblastic cleavage are listed below.

a. Egg of the Common Fowl

(*Note:* As cleavage in reptiles resembles that of birds, a description of reptilian cleavage will not be given. The reader is referred to figure 231, concerning the cleavage phenomena in the turtle. The information given below is to be correlated also with the developing pigeon's egg.)

The **germinal disc** (blastodisc) of the hen's egg at the time that cleavage begins measures about 3 mm. in diameter. Its general relationship to the egg as a whole is shown in figure 157A.

1) Early Cleavages. The first cleavage furrow makes its appearance at about four and one-half to five hours after fertilization at the time when the egg reaches the isthmus of the oviduct (figs. 155A; 157C, D). The first

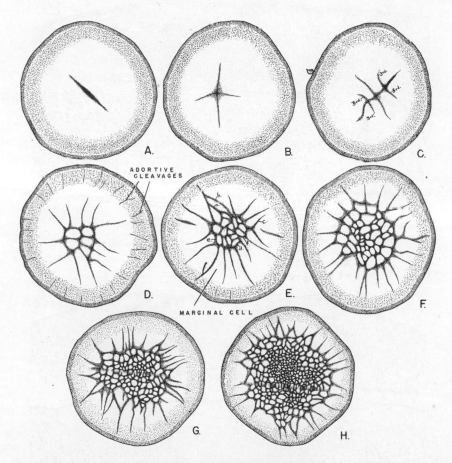

FIG. 155. Cleavage in the chick blastoderm, surface views. (C after Olsen, '42; the rest after Patterson, '10.) (A) First cleavage is approximately meridional. (B) Second cleavage is at right angles to first. (C) Third cleavage planes are vertical as indicated and approximately parallel to one of the other cleavage planes. Considerable inequality may exist at this time. (This figure slightly modified from original.) (D) Seventeen-cell stage. Observe central and marginal cells. (E) Stage approximating 32-cell condition. (F) Surface view of 64-cell stage; 41 central and 23 marginal cells. (G) Surface view of blastoderm in lower portions of oviduct; 31 marginal and 123 central cells. (H) Later blastoderm, showing 34 marginal and 312 central cells.

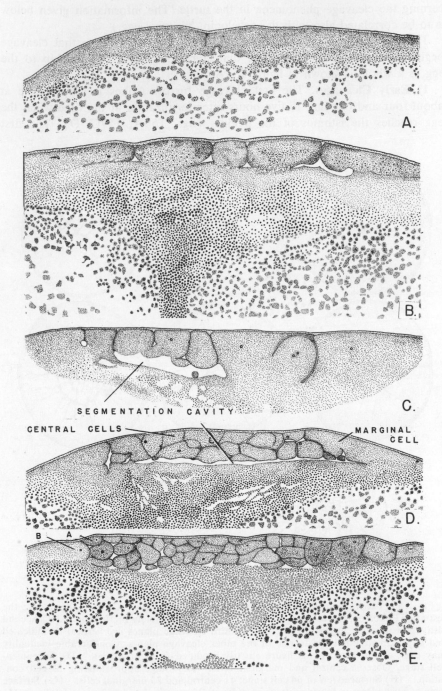

SEGMENTATION CAVITY

CENTRAL CELLS

MARGINAL CELL

B A

FIG. 156. (*See facing page for legend.*)

314

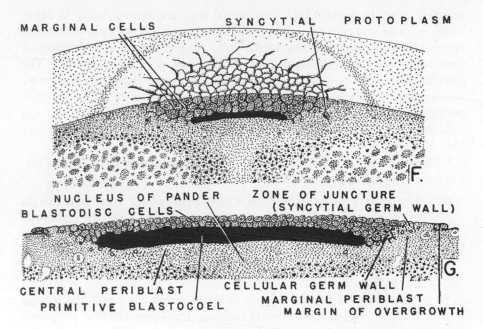

MARGINAL CELLS   SYNCYTIAL   PROTOPLASM

F.

NUCLEUS OF PANDER   ZONE OF JUNCTURE
BLASTODISC CELLS   (SYNCYTIAL GERM WALL)

G.

CENTRAL PERIBLAST   CELLULAR GERM WALL
PRIMITIVE BLASTOCOEL   MARGINAL PERIBLAST
    MARGIN OF OVERGROWTH

FIG. 156. Cleavage in chick blastoderm, sectional views. (After Patterson, '10.) (A) Median section through blastoderm approximately at right angles to furrow shown in fig. 155A. (B) Section through blastoderm of about eight-cell stage. (C) Section through blastoderm, showing 32 cells, also showing horizontal cytoplasmic cleft (segmentation cavity). (D) Median section through blastoderm similar to that shown in fig. 155E. (E) Median section through blastoderm similar to that of fig. 155G. (F, G) Diagrammatic views of developing avian blastoderms. (F) Diagrammatic section and surface view of chick blastoderm shown in fig. 155G and fig. 156E. (G) Section of chick blastoderm about time that egg is laid, depicting the primary blastocoel below the blastoderm and syncytial tissue at the margins. Observe that the syncytial tissue serves to implant the blastoderm upon the yolk substance.

furrow consists of a slight **meridional** incision near the center of the blastodisc, cutting across the disc to an extent of about one half of the diameter of the latter (fig. 155A). This furrow passes yolkward but does not reach the lower portion of the disc where the cytoplasm is filled with coarse yolk granules (fig. 156A). The second cleavage occurs about 20 minutes later and consists of two furrows, one on either side of the first furrow and approximately at right angles to the first furrow. These furrows may be regarded as **meridional** (fig. 155B). Though both of the second furrows tend to meet the first furrow at its midpoint, one of the second furrows may be displaced and, hence, may not contact the corresponding furrow of the other side. The third set of furrows is vertical, cutting across the second set of meridional furrows, and, consequently, tends to parallel the first cleavage furrow (fig. 155C). The fourth set of furrows is also vertical and, although not synchronous, it proceeds gradually to form eight central cells which are surrounded by twelve marginal cells. In figure 155D, five central cells are shown, while in figure 157E, eight central cells are present. The central cells do not have boundaries below and, thus, are open toward the yolk. As a result, their protoplasm is continuous with the protoplasm in the deeper-lying portions of the disc. The marginal cells have boundaries only on two sides, and the cleavage furrows which form the sides of the marginal cells continue slowly to extend in a peripheral direction toward the margins of the disc (fig. 155D). The egg is in this stage of development when it leaves the isthmus and enters the uterus (fig. 157A, F).

Cleavage from this point on becomes very irregular, but three sets of furrows are evident:

(a) There are vertical furrows which extend peripherad toward the margin of the blastodisc. These furrows meet at various angles the previously established furrows which radiate toward the periphery of the blastodisc (in fig. 155E, see a., b., c.). A branching effect of the radiating furrows, previously established, in this manner may be produced (in fig. 155E, see c.).

(b) Another set of vertical furrows is found which cut across the median (inner) ends of the radiating furrows. The latter produce *peripheral boundaries* for the centrally located cells (see fig. 155E, d., e., f.). The central cells thus increase in number as the blastodisc extends peripherally. As a result of this set of cleavage furrows, a condition of the blastodisc is established in which there is a mass of **central cells,** having peripheral boundaries, and an area of **marginal cells** which lies more distally between the radiating furrows. It is to be observed that the marginal cells lack peripheral boundaries (fig. 155E, F).

(c) A third and new kind of cleavage, cytoplasmic but not mitotic, now occurs below the centrally placed cells, namely, a **latitudinal or horizontal cleft** which establishes a lower boundary for the centrally located cells with the subsequent appearance of a blastocoelic space filled with fluid (fig. 156B, C).

Thus, at the 16- to 32-cell stages (fig. 155D, E) some of the more centrally located central cells have complete cellular boundaries (fig. 156C), but central cells, located more peripherally, may not have the lower boundary. The marginal cells also lack a lower boundary.

A little later, at the 60- to 100-cell stages (fig. 155F), the chick blastoderm presents the following characteristics:

(a) There is a mass of **centrally located cells.** These cells lie immediately above the horizontal cleft mentioned above (fig. 156C, D). They are completely bounded by a surface membrane and represent distinct cells. These cells continue to increase by mitotic division and, as early as the 64-cell stage (fig. 155F), the centrally located cells are in the

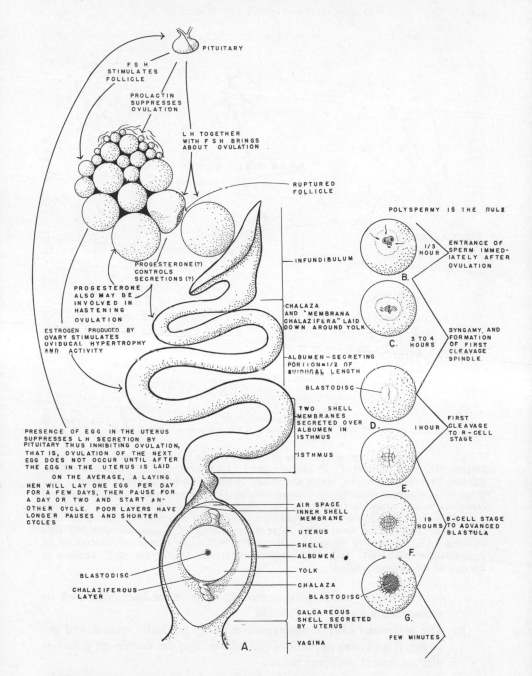

PITUITARY

FSH STIMULATES FOLLICLE

PROLACTIN SUPPRESSES OVULATION

LH TOGETHER WITH FSH BRINGS ABOUT OVULATION

RUPTURED FOLLICLE

POLYSPERMY IS THE RULE

INFUNDIBULUM

PROGESTERONE(?) CONTROLS SECRETIONS (?)

PROGESTERONE ALSO MAY BE INVOLVED IN HASTENING OVULATION

ESTROGEN PRODUCED BY OVARY STIMULATES OVIDUCAL HYPERTROPHY AND ACTIVITY

1/3 HOUR — ENTRANCE OF SPERM IMMEDIATELY AFTER OVULATION

B.

CHALAZA AND "MEMBRANA CHALAZIFERA" LAID DOWN AROUND YOLK

3 TO 4 HOURS — SYNGAMY, AND FORMATION OF FIRST CLEAVAGE SPINDLE

C.

ALBUMEN—SECRETING PORTION≈1/2 OF OVIDUCAL LENGTH

BLASTODISC

D.

TWO SHELL MEMBRANES SECRETED OVER ALBUMEN IN ISTHMUS

1 HOUR — FIRST CLEAVAGE TO 8-CELL STAGE

ISTHMUS

PRESENCE OF EGG IN THE UTERUS SUPPRESSES LH SECRETION BY PITUITARY THUS INHIBITING OVULATION, THAT IS, OVULATION OF THE NEXT EGG DOES NOT OCCUR UNTIL AFTER THE EGG IN THE UTERUS IS LAID

E.

ON THE AVERAGE, A LAYING HEN WILL LAY ONE EGG PER DAY FOR A FEW DAYS, THEN PAUSE FOR A DAY OR TWO AND START ANOTHER CYCLE. POOR LAYERS HAVE LONGER PAUSES AND SHORTER CYCLES

AIR SPACE
INNER SHELL MEMBRANE
UTERUS
SHELL
ALBUMEN
YOLK
CHALAZA
BLASTODISC

19 HOURS — 8-CELL STAGE TO ADVANCED BLASTULA

F.

BLASTODISC

CHALAZIFEROUS LAYER

CALCAREOUS SHELL SECRETED BY UTERUS

G.

FEW MINUTES

A.

VAGINA

Fig. 157. Chart showing ovary, oviducal, and pituitary relationships in passage of egg from the ovary down the oviduct. Developing blastodisc shown in (B–G) in relation to the oviducal journey. This chart shows an egg which has just been ovulated. Ordinarily, however, this egg would not be ovulated until sometime after the egg shown in the uterus has been laid.

317

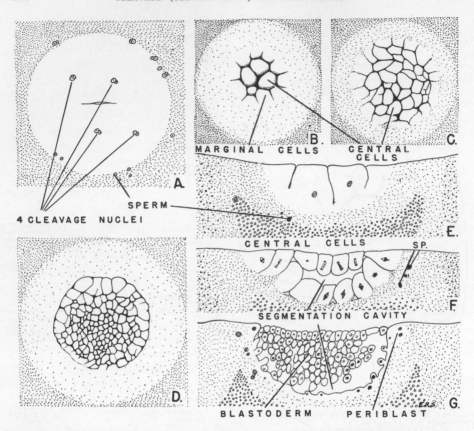

FIG. 158. Early cleavage phenomena in elasmobranch fishes. (A, B, E, F, G after Ziegler, '02, from Rüchert; C, D after Ziegler.)   (A) Germ disc of *Torpedo ocellata,* showing four cleavage nuclei, sperm nuclei, and beginning of first cleavage furrow.   (B) Stage of cleavage, possessing 16 cleavage nuclei. Four central cells and ten marginal cells are evident from surface view.   (C) Surface view of blastoderm of *Scyllium canicula* with 64 cleavage nuclei. Twenty-nine central cells and seventeen marginal cells are evident from surface view.   (D) Later cleavage stage of *S. canicula* with 145 cells showing.   (E) Transverse section of (B).   (F) Transverse section of blastoderm of *T. ocellata* with 64 cells.   (G) Median section through blastoderm of *T. ocellata* at the end of the cleavage period.

form of two layers situated immediately above the **horizontal cleft** or **segmentation cavity** (fig. 156D).

(b) The **horizontal cleft** or **segmentation cavity** gradually widens and enlarges. It separates the central cells above from the uncleaved germinal disc or central periblast below.

(c) At the **margins of the central cells,** these cleavages may be found: (1) **Vertical cleavages** occur which cut off more central cells from inner ends of the marginal cells. As a result, there is an increase in the number of central cells around the periphery of the already-established central mass of cells. (2) **Vertical cleavages** arise whose furrows extend peripherad toward the margin of the disc. These furrows and previously formed, similar furrows now approach the outer edge of the blasto-disc (germinal disc). (See figs. 155H; 156D). (3) **True latitudinal or horizontal cleavages** occur which serve to provide lower cell bound-aries for the more peripherally located, central cells (see cell A, fig. 156E), *and which also contribute nuclei without cell boundaries to the disc substance in this immediate area* (see cell B, fig. 156E). As a result, the marginal or peripheral areas of the blastodisc around the mass of completely formed, central cells are composed of: (*a*) **mar-ginal cells** which appear near the surface of the blastodisc, having partial boundaries at the blastodisc surface, and (*b*) a deeper-lying *protoplasm, possessing nuclei without cell boundaries.* This deeper-lying, multinucleated, marginal protoplasm constitutes a **syncytium** (fig. 156F).

2) **Formation of the Periblast Tissue.** As indicated above, the activities of the blastoderm extend its margins peripherad. In so doing, some of the mitotic divisions in the peripheral areas contribute nuclei which come to lie in the deeper portions of the blastodisc. Some of these nuclei wander distally and yolkward into the more peripherally located, uncleaved portions of the protoplasm below the enlarging primary segmentation cavity or **blastocoel.** A syncytial protoplasm containing isolated nuclei thus arises around the pe-ripheral margin of the blastoderm in its deeper areas. This entire syncytial protoplasm, composed of a continuous cytoplasm with many nuclei, is known as **periblast tissue.** It is made up of two general areas: (1) the **peripheral periblast** around the margin of the blastodisc and (2) a **central periblast** below the **primitive blastocoel** (fig. 156G). This periblast tissue is a **liaison tissue** which brings the yolk and the growing mass of cells of the blastodisc into nutritive contact.

When this condition is reached, two kinds of embryonic tissues exist:

(a) the **formative or embryonic tissue** proper, composed of an aggrega-tion of distinct cells. These cells constitute the cellular portion of the **blastoderm** (see blastodisc cells, fig. 156G), and

(b) the **peripheral and central periblast tissue** (see fig. 156G). The latter functions as a trophoblast tissue, and it is continuous with the **seg-mented portion of the blastoderm** around the peripheral areas of the blastodisc. Centrally, however, it is separated from the segmented area of the blastoderm by the **primary blastocoelic cavity.** The devel-opmental condition at this time may be regarded as having reached the **primary blastular** stage.

3) **Morphological Characteristics of the Primary Blastula.** This condition of development is reached while the egg continues in the uterus (fig. 157G).

A transverse section through one of the diameters of the primary blastula presents the following features (fig. 156G):

(a) **A central mass of cells** of two or several cells in depth overlies the blastocoelic space. This is the central or cellular portion of the **blastoderm.**

(b) Underneath this central blastoderm is the **primary segmentation cavity** or **primary blastocoel.**

(c) Below the primary blastocoel is the **central syncytial periblast,** which continues downward to the yolk material; many yolk granules are present in the layer of the central periblast near the yolk. Nuclei *are not present* in the central area of the central periblast, but may be present in its more peripheral portions.

(d) Around the peripheral areas of the central periblast and the cellular portion of the blastoderm is the **marginal periblast tissue** which now is called the **germ wall.** The germ-wall tissue contains much yolk material in the process of digestion and assimilation.

The **central mass of cells** or **cellular blastoderm** increases in cell number and in size by the multiplication of its own cells and by the contribution of marginal periblast tissue which gradually forms cells with boundaries from its substance. The germ wall thus may be divided into two main zones: (1) an **inner zone of distinct cells,** which are dividing rapidly and, in consequence, contribute cells to the peripheral portions of the growing cellular blastoderm and (2) an outer peripheral zone, the **syncytial germ wall** (zone of junction). The latter is in intimate contact with the yolk (fig. 156G). The **central periblast tissue** gradually disappears. At the outer boundary of the **peripheral periblast,** there is an edge of blastodermic cells overlying the yolk. These cells have complete boundaries and are known as the **margin of overgrowth** (fig. 156G). A resumé of the early development of the hen's egg in relation to the parts of the oviduct, pituitary control, laying, etc., is shown in figure 157.

4) Polyspermy and Fate of the Accessory Sperm Nuclei. The bird's egg is polyspermic and several sperm make their entrance at the time of fertilization (see fig. 157B). The supernumerary sperm stimulate abortive cleavage phenomena in the peripheral area of the early blastodisc (fig. 155D). However, these cleavage furrows together with the extra sperm nuclei soon disappear.

(References: Blount ('09); Lillie ('30); Olsen ('42); and Patterson ('10).) For later stages in the development of the hen's egg, see chapter 7.

b. Elasmobranch Fishes

1) Cleavage and Formation of the Early Blastula. Like the egg of the bird, the egg of the elasmobranch fishes is strongly telolecithal, and a small disc of protoplasm at one pole of the egg alone takes part in the cleavage phenomena. Cleavage in the majority of these fishes simulates that of the bird, but certain exceptional features are present. In some, as in *Torpedo ocellata,* meroblastic cleavage is present in an extreme form. The zygotic nucleus divides and the two daughter nuclei divide again forming a **syncytial state** before the appearance of the first cleavage furrow. The tendency of retardation or suppression of the cytoplasmic mechanism of cleavage which occurs in the bird blastoderm thus is carried to an extreme form in the early development of some elasmobranch fishes.

The first cleavage furrow is **meridional** or nearly so (fig. 158A), and the second furrow is similar and at right angles to the first furrow. The third set of furrows is vertical and meets the previous furrows at various angles The fourth set of cleavages is vertical and synchronous, as is the preceding, and gives origin to three or four central cells, which, on surface viewing, have complete cell boundaries but below their cytoplasms are confluent with the cytoplasm of the blastodisc (fig. 158B and E). Around the periphery of these central cells, are on the average ten **marginal cells** which have their cytoplasms confluent below and peripherally with the general cytoplasm of the disc. The fifth cleavage furrows are mixed. That is, in the central part of the disc the cleavage furrows are latitudinal, as the mitotic spindles in this area form *perpendicular to the surface.* As a result, distinct daughter cells are cut off above, while the daughter cells below *have cytoplasms confluent with the general cytoplasm of the disc.* A blastocoelic cavity appears between these two sets of central cells. In the marginal areas the fifth set of cleavages is vertical, cutting off more central cells and giving origin to more marginal cells. The sixth set of cleavages is a mixture of vertical cleavages at the periphery and latitudinal cleavages centrally; it produces a condition shown in figure 158F. In surface view, the blastoderm appears as in figure 158C, D.

From this time on cleavage becomes very irregular and a developmental condition soon is produced which possesses a central blastoderm of many cells with an enlarged blastocoelic cavity below (fig. 158G). A syncytial periblast tissue is present at the margins of the blastoderm which also extends centrally below the blastocoelic space where it forms a central periblast (fig. 158G). In this manner, two kinds of cells are produced:

(a) **a blastoderm of distinct cells** which ultimately produces the embryo and

(b) **a surrounding trophoblast or periblast tissue** which borders the yolk substance peripherally and centrally. As in the chick, the periblast tissue has nutritive (i.e., trophoblast) functions.

2) Problem of the Periblast Tissue in Elasmobranch Fishes. Two views have been maintained, regarding the origin of the periblast nuclei in the elasmobranch fishes. One view maintains that they arise from the accessory sperm nuclei derived from polyspermy, for polyspermy is the rule here as it is in reptiles and birds. In the latter groups, these accessory nuclei may divide for a time but ultimately degenerate, playing no real part in ontogeny. In the case of the elasmobranch fishes, the accessory nuclei tend to persist somewhat longer, and accordingly, it is upon this evidence that some have maintained that the periblast nuclei arise from them. Others hold that the sperm nuclei degenerate as they do in reptiles and birds, and the periblast nuclei arise as a result of the regular embryonic process. A third view concedes that both these sources contribute nuclei.

In view of the origin of the periblast nuclei in teleost fishes, in the ganoid fishes, *Amia* and *Lepisosteus,* and in reptiles and birds, and of the syncytial tissue of the later mammalian trophoblast, it is probable that embryonic cells and tissues and not accessory sperm nuclei are the progenitors of the periblast tissue. This probability is suggested by figure 158F, G. Furthermore, later on in the development of the elasmobranch fishes, the entoderm appears to contribute nuclei which wander into the periblast tissue which lies between the entoderm and the yolk material (fig. 213K, L). In later stages the periblast tissue is referred to as the **yolk syncytium.** In the yolk syncytium the periblast nuclei gradually assume a much larger size.

For further details of the early development of the elasmobranch fishes, consult Ziegler ('02) and Kerr ('19) and Chapter 7.

c. Teleost Fishes

1) Cleavage and Early Blastula Formation. During the fertilization process of the egg in teleost fishes, the superficial cytoplasm of the egg migrates toward the point of sperm entrance and hence a mound-like disc of protoplasm forms at the pole of the egg where the sperm enters (figs. 122C; 123B, C). It is this protoplasmic mass which takes part in cleavage (fig. 123E). The cleavage planes in the teleost fishes manifest great regularity. The early cleavage furrows almost cut through the entire protoplasmic disc in most teleost eggs, and a mere strand of cytoplasm is left near the yolk which is not cleaved (fig. 159E).

In the sea bass, *Serranus atrarius,* the first two cleavage planes are meridional and at right angles to each other (fig. 159A); the third planes are vertical and parallel to the first plane. The result is a group of eight cells in two rows (fig. 159B). The fourth cleavage furrows are vertical and parallel to the long axis of the eight cells previously established. These furrows divide each of the eight blastomeres into inner and outer daughter cells. The result is 16 cells, arranged in parallel rows of four cells each (fig. 159C, D).

As the 16-cell condition is converted into 32 cells, the four inner cells divide latitudinally, that is, the cleavage spindle forms perpendicular to the surface, while the twelve surrounding cells divide vertically (fig. 159D, F, G). From this time on latitudinal and vertical cleavages become mixed, and the

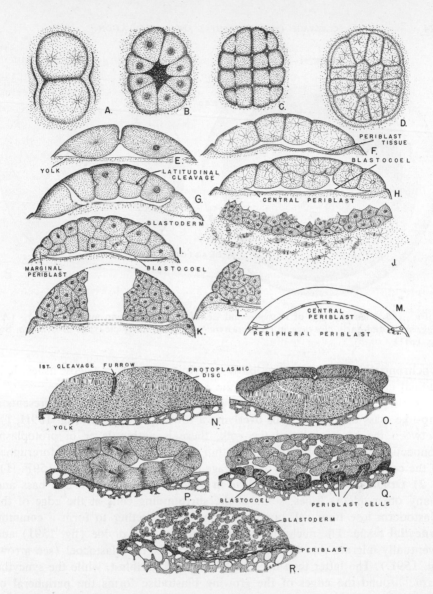

FIG. 159. Early development of the sea bass, *Serranus atrarius,* and the trout, *Salmo fario.* (A–M after Wilson, 1889 and 1891; N–R after Kopsch, '11.) (A) Two-blastomere stage, showing anaphase of next division. (B) Eight-blastomere stage (slightly modified). (C) Sixteen-cell blastoderm. (D) Sixteen-cell stage, showing anaphase nuclei of next division. In the four centrally placed cells, the spindles are at right angles to the surface, thus forming a latitudinal cleavage furrow in these cells. (E) Section through center of four-blastomore stage. (F) Section through center of (D). Observe periblast tissue. (G) Section showing change from 16-cell stage into 32 cells; see (D). (H) Thirty-two to 64 cells. (I) Late cleavage blastoderm. Observe marginal and central periblast. (J) Multiplication of periblast nuclei around the margin of the blastoderm. (K–M) Late blastoderm, showing marginal and central periblast tissue. (N–R) Cleavage of the blastodisc of the trout. Observe that periblast tissue is derived from the blastodisc cytoplasm directly.

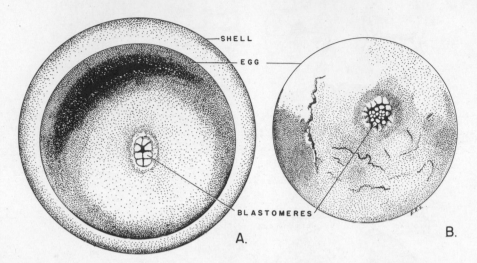

FIG. 160. Cleaving eggs of *Platypus* and *Echidna*. (After **Flynn** and **Hill**, '39.)   (A) Egg, shell, and early cleavage in *Ornithorhynchus*.   (B) Early cleavage in *Echidna*. See fig. 161D.

synchronization of mitotic division is lost. In certain other teleost fishes, latitudinal cleavages begin as early as the 8-cell stage.

At the 32- to 64-cell stages in *Serranus atrarius,* the blastoderm presents a cap-like mass of dividing cells overlying a forming blastocoel (fig. 159H, I). Between the blastocoel and the yolk, there is a thin layer of protoplasm connecting the edges of the cap. This thin protoplasmic layer is the forerunner of the **central periblast tissue;** at this stage it contains no nuclei (fig. 159F, H).

2) Origin of the Periblast Tissue in Teleost Fishes. In the sea bass and many other teleost fishes, some of the surrounding cells at the edge of the blastoderm lose their cell boundaries and fuse together to form a **common syncytial tissue.** The nuclei in this tissue continue to divide (fig. 159J) and eventually migrate into the periblast tissue below the blastocoel (see arrow, fig. 159L). The latter then becomes the **central periblast,** while the syncytial tissue around the edges of the growing blastodisc forms the **peripheral or marginal periblast** (fig. 159K–M).

In the trout, the early cleavage furrows of the blastodisc are incomplete, and the periblast arises from the syncytial tissue established directly below and at the sides of the protoplasmic cap (fig. 159N–R). This condition resembles the cleavage process in the elasmobranch fishes.

See Kerr ('19); Kopsch ('11); and H. V. Wilson (1889).

d. *Prototherian* Mammalia

The *Prototheria* normally are placed in the class *Mammalia* along with the *Metatheria* (marsupials) and *Eutheria* (true placental mammals). How-

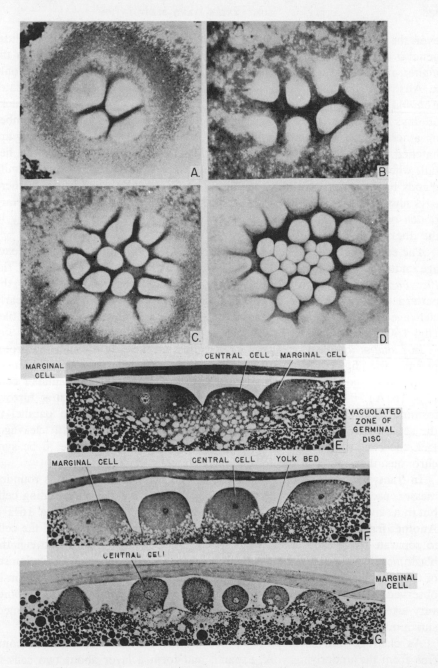

FIG. 161. Early cleavage in *Echidna*. (Courtesy, Flynn and Hill, '39.)   (A) Four-cell
stage.   (B) Eight-cell stage.   (C) About 16-cell stage. Two meridional and four vertical
cleavages have occurred.   (D) About 32-cell stage. Observe marginal and central cells.
(E) Section through blastodisc of 4 to 8-cell stage.   (F) Section through blastoderm
of 16-cell stage. See (C).   (G) Section through blastoderm of 32-cell stage, showing
central and marginal cells.

ever, the prototherian mammals are aberrant, highly specialized animals, whose general anatomy and embryology delineates a group quite distinct from the higher mammals. The duckbill or *Platypus (Ornithorhynchus)* is found only in Australia. The other species belonging to this group is the spiny anteater *Echidna aculeata* found in New Guinea, Tasmania, and Australia. The duckbill lays from one to three heavily yolk-laden eggs in an underground chamber on a nest of weeds and grasses. The eggs have a leathery shell. The young are hatched naked, and the mother holds them against her abdomen with her tail, where they feed upon a milk-like substance which exudes from the milk glands by means of pore-like openings. The *Echidna* lays two white, leathery eggs about the size of the eggs of a sparrow which she places in a temporary pouch or fold of skin on the ventral abdominal wall. They feed similarly to the duckbill young.

The early cleavages of *Echidna* and *Ornithorhynchus* follow different cleavage patterns. (See Flynn and Hill, '39, '42.) The cleavage planes of the *Platypus* are more regular and symmetrical and resemble to a degree the pattern of early cleavage in teleost fishes (fig. 160A), whereas the early cleavage planes in *Echidna* simulate to some degree those found in reptiles (fig. 160B). In both species cleavage is meroblastic.

In *Echidna* the cleavage furrows cut almost all the way through the protoplasmic disc (fig. 161E). The second cleavage in this species is at right angles to the first, and divides the blastodisc into two larger and two smaller cells (fig. 161A). The third cleavage furrows tend to parallel the first furrow, forming eight cells (fig. 161B), while the fourth cleavages run parallel to the second furrow, and 16 cells are formed (fig. 161C). The fifth cleavages lack the constancy of the first four sets although they continue to be synchronous; they result in the formation of 32 cells (fig. 161D).

In transverse section, the cells of the 32-cell blastoderm appear as rounded masses, each cell in its upper portion being free from the surrounding cells but in its lower extremity intimately attached to the yolk substance (fig. 161F). Another feature of the early cleavages in *Echidna* is the tendency of the cells to separate from each other; wide spaces consequently appear between the blastomeres (fig. 161G). This tendency toward independence and isolationism of the early blastomeres is characteristic of the higher mammals, as previously observed. After the 32-cell stage, synchronization is lost and cleavage becomes very irregular. A central mass of blastodermic cells eventually is formed, surrounded by marginal cells, known as **vitellocytes** (fig. 175A).

As cleavage and development proceeds, the central blastomeres become free from the underlying yolk, expand, and form a layer about two cells in thickness (fig. 175B). The vitellocytes around the periphery of the blastoderm eventually fuse to form a **syncytium** or multinucleated cytoplasmic mass intimately associated with the yolk (fig. 175B, C). This marginal mass of syncytial tissue forms the **marginal periblast.** Within the central portion of the blastoderm itself two types of cells may be observed, namely, a **superficial ecto-dermal cell** and **a more deeply situated, somewhat vacuolated, smaller ento-dermal cell** (fig. 175B). (For later stages of blastulation, see chapter 7.)

e. Cleavage in the California Hagfish, Polistotrema (Bdellostoma) stouti

The California hagfish spawns an egg which is strongly telolecithal. The germinal disc (blastodisc) is situated immediately below the egg membrane at one end of the egg, adjacent to the micropyle and the anchor filaments (fig. 162A). Cleavage begins in this disc, and the enlarging blastoderm slowly creeps downward to envelop the massive yolk material. The freshly laid egg measures about 29 mm. by 14 mm., including the shell. Without the shell, the egg is about 22 mm. by 10 mm. and is rounded at each end (Dean, 1899).

The first two cleavage planes may be regarded as meridional (or vertical) (fig. 162B). The third cleavage appears to be a mixture of vertical and horizontal (latitudinal) cleavages, with the former predominating (fig. 162D, E). Cleavage from this time on becomes irregular, and a typical meroblastic blastoderm soon is attained with central and marginal cells (fig. 162F).

C. What is the Force Which Causes the Blastomeres to Adhere Together During Early Cleavage?

A question naturally arises concerning the force which makes the blasto-meres of most chordates adhere to one another during the early cleavage

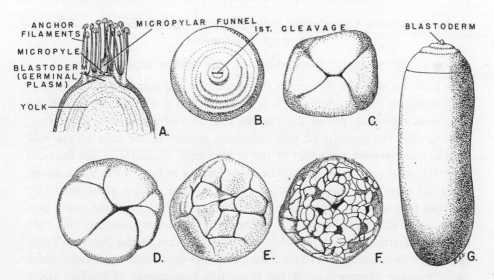

FIG. 162. Egg and cleavage in the marine lamprey, *Polistotrema (Bdellostoma) stouti.* After Dean, 1899.) (A) Animal pole end of the egg. (B) Surface view of blasto-dermic hillock, showing first cleavage furrow. (C) Same, second cleavage. (D) Third cleavages. (E, F) Later cleavages, strongly irregular. (G) Egg with shell removed.

period. This subject was investigated in the amphibian blastula by Holtfreter, '39. According to this investigator, blastomeres, when isolated by mechanical means, appear to wander aimlessly about. When contact is made with other blastomeres during this wandering process the cells stick or adhere together. As a result, the mass of adhering cells gradually is formed which becomes rounded into a ball-shaped structure. The results of this work suggest that the force which draws the cells together is one of **thigmotaxis** or contact affinity, aided by a surface stickiness of the cells. This force only becomes influential when an isolated cell has made contact with another cell or cells.

On the other hand, the early blastomeres of the cleaving mammalian egg are evidently held together also by the binding influence of the egg membrane or zona pellucida. An adhering influence is not prominent until later cleavage stages.

However, one must not be too ready to espouse a single, mechanical factor as the main binding force which causes the blastomeres to adhere together, to move in relation to each other, and *to form a definite configuration.* Factors tending toward organization are at work during early and late cleavage as well as in subsequent development. Relative to these matters, it is well to cogitate upon the statement of Whitman (1893). "Comparative embryology reminds us at every turn that the organism dominates cell-formation, using for the same purpose one, several, or many cells, massing its material and directing its movements, and shaping its organs, as if cells did not exist, or as if they existed only in complete subordination to its will" (p. 653).

D. Progressive Cytoplasmic Inequality and Nuclear Equality of the Cleavage Blastomeres

1. CYTOPLASMIC INEQUALITY OF THE EARLY BLASTOMERES

In harmony with the differences in the location and activities of the various blastomeres of the cleaving egg, it is apparent that a difference exists in the ooplasmic substance within the various cells in many species. In the frog, for example, the quantity of yolk substance present in the cells of the yolk pole is much greater than that of the animal pole. Similarly in the four-cell stage the substance of the gray crescent is located in two of the blastomeres, while the other two blastomeres have little or none of this substance. Two of these four cells, therefore, are qualitatively different from the other two. In the ascidian, *Styela partita,* the presence of the yellow crescent, yolk substance, and gray crescent materials demonstrates that in the four- or eight-cell stages there are qualitative differences in the ooplasmic substances which enter into the composition of the respective blastomeres (Conklin, '05, a and b). Similar conditions may be demonstrated for *Amphioxus* although pigmented materials are not present in the egg (fig. 167). (See Conklin, '32, '33.) As cleavage continues in the eggs of *Styela* and *Amphioxus,* a progres-

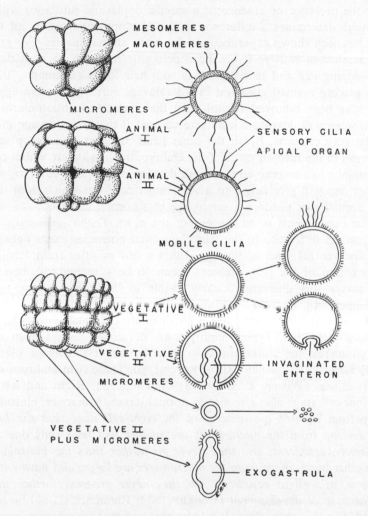

MESOMERES

MACROMERES

MICROMERES

ANIMAL I

ANIMAL II

SENSORY CILIA OF APICAL ORGAN

MOBILE CILIA

VEGETATIVE I

VEGETATIVE II

MICROMERES

INVAGINATED ENTERON

VEGETATIVE II PLUS MICROMERES

EXOGASTRULA

FIG. 163. Developmental potencies (cell lineage) of isolated blastomeres of the cleaving sea-urchin egg, representing different levels along the egg axis (from Huxley and DeBeer, '34, after Horstadius). Observe the following: (1) Progressing from the animal pole to the vegetative pole, the potency for developing the sensory cilia decreases from animal pole cells I to animal pole cells II. (2) The potency for developing motile cilia increases from animal pole cell II to vegetative pole cell I. (3) The potency for gastrulation becomes greater from vegetative pole cell I to vegetative pole cell II. (4) In the development of vegetative pole cell I, shown at the right of vegetative I, if the third (equatorial) cleavage plane happens to be displaced near the animal pole, an isolated vegetative cell I has more animal pole potencies and will develop apical cilia; if the cleavage plane is displaced toward the vegetative pole, the vegetative pole cell I will attempt to gastrulate. (5) The disc of vegetative cells II plus the micromeres produce a gut so large it will not invaginate and hence forms an exogastrula.

329

sive difference in the cytoplasmic substances which enter into the various blastomeres becomes evident.

That the presence or absence of a specific ooplasmic substance within the blastomeres determines a difference in the developmental history of the cell or cells has been shown experimentally for many animal species. For example, in the amphibian embryo it has been demonstrated both by constriction of the developing egg and its membranes with hair loops (Spemann, '02, '03) and by placing a small glass rod in the cleavage furrow after the egg membranes have been removed (Ruud, '25) that each of the blastomeres of the two-cell stage will develop a complete embryo *if the first cleavage plane* bisects the gray crescent. If, on the other hand, the first cleavage plane *is at right angles* to the median plane of the embryo, the blastomere which contains the substance of the gray crescent will develop a complete embryo, whereas the other one will give origin to a very imperfect form which does not gastrulate normally or produce a semblance of a normal embryo.

Similar experiments upon the egg of the newt, *Triton palmatus,* indicate that a marked difference in the "developmental potencies exists between the dorsal and ventral sides of the egg within a few minutes from fertilization. The formation of the gray crescent seems to be a secondary phenomenon which makes this difference clearly visible in the eggs of some species" (Fankhauser, '48, p. 694).

In *Amphioxus,* similar evidence is obtained after the blastomeres have been mechanically isolated. Typical embryos are developed always from the first two blastomeres, for unlike the frog or newt, the first cleavage plane *consistently* furrows the median axis of the embryo. These twin embryos are half the normal size (Wilson, E. B., 1893; Conklin, '33). Right and left halves of the four-cell stage also give rise to normal larvae. Moreover, blastulae also develop from isolated blastomeres of the *eight-cell stage, but the blastulae which develop from the micromeres are smaller and have only one type of cell, namely, ectoderm, and they never go further than the blastular stage.* On the other hand, *those from the macromeres are larger and have entoderm, mesoderm, as well as ectoderm, but they never progress further than the gastrular stage of development* (Conklin, '33). Reference should be made to figure 167B in this connection. It is to be observed that the macromeres contain potential mesodermal, entodermal, and ectodermal ooplasm, whereas the micromeres lack the mesodermal and entodermal substances and contain only ectodermal material.

In the protochordate, *Styela,* a somewhat different condition is found. If the cleaving egg of this species is separated at the two-cell stage into two separate blastomeres, each blastomere develops only one half of an embryo (Conklin, '05b, '06). That is, the right blastomere develops an embryo minus the left half, while the left blastomere produces the opposite condition. There is some tendency to develop or regulate into a complete embryo in that the

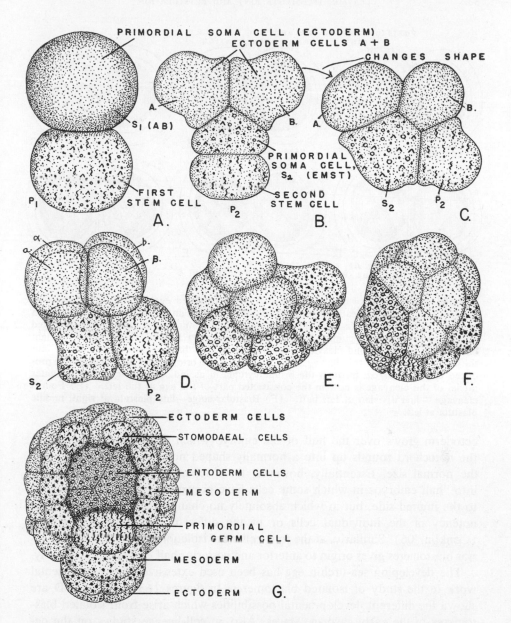

PRIMORDIAL SOMA CELL (ECTODERM)
ECTODERM CELLS A + B
CHANGES SHAPE

S_1 (AB)
A.
B.
A.
B.

PRIMORDIAL
SOMA CELL
S_2 (EMST)
SECOND
STEM CELL

P_1
FIRST
STEM CELL

P_2
S_2
P_2

A.
B.
C.

α
b.
a
β

S_2
P_2

D.
E.
F.

ECTODERM CELLS
STOMODAEAL CELLS
ENTODERM CELLS
MESODERM
PRIMORDIAL GERM CELL
MESODERM
ECTODERM

G.

FIG. 164. Distribution of presumptive organ regions (cell lineage) during cleavage in *Ascaris*. (After Durken: *Experimental Analysis of Development*, New York, W. W. Norton, based upon figures by Boveri and zur Strassen.) (A) Two-cell stage, showing primordial soma cell and first stem cell. (B) Two ectodermal cells, A and B. Soma cell, S_2, is a mixture of mesoderm, stomodaeum, and entoderm; second stem cell, P_2, is a mixture of mesoderm and germ-cell material. The symbolism used to designate the various organ-forming substances is shown in (G). The progressive segregation into separate cells of the substances shown in cells S_2 and P_2 is given in (C–G). Cf. also fig. 61E.

331

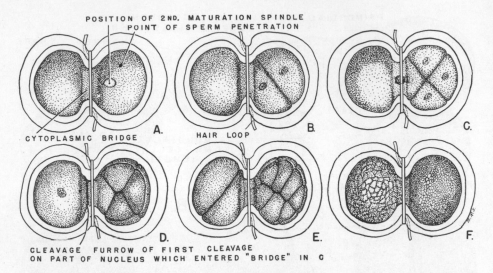

FIG. 165. Drawings of cleavage of a partially constricted egg of *Triturus viridescens,* illustrating delayed nucleation. (Slightly modified from Fankhauser, '48.)   (A) Shows constricting loop, point of sperm entrance, and second maturation spindle. The constricted portion to the right will contain the fusion nucleus.   (B) First cleavage furrow in right half of egg.   (C) Second cleavage. The nucleus in the "bridge" area has migrated into the "bridge."   (D) Third cleavage. The nucleus in the bridge area has divided and produced cleavage furrow through the bridge cytoplasm as indicated. One of the daughter nuclei of this cleavage is now in the constricted part of the egg at the left.   (E) Fourth cleavage = first division of left half.   (F) Blastular stage—late blastula at right, middle blastula at left.

ectoderm grows over the half of the embryo which failed to develop. Also, the notochord rounds up into a normally shaped notochord but is only half the normal size. Essentially, however, these separated blastomeres develop into "half embryos in which some cells have grown over from the uninjured to the injured side, but in which absolutely no change has taken place in the potency of the individual cells or of the different ooplasmic substances" (Conklin, '06). Similarly, at the four-cell stage isolation of anterior and posterior blastomeres gives origin to anterior and posterior half embryos respectively.

The developing sea-urchin egg has been used extensively for experimental work in the study of isolated blastomeres. In figures 163 and 166A–D are shown the different developmental possibilities which arise from isolated blastomeres of the early cleavage stages. Also, in cell-lineage studies on the developing egg of *Ascaris,* a difference in the developmental potencies of the blastomeres is evident (fig. 164). (See also fig. 145A–D in respect to the early development of the pig.)

The foregoing experiments and observations and others of a similar nature suggest that, during the early cleavage stages of many different animal species, a sorting-out process is at work which segregates into different blastomeres distinct ooplasmic substances which possess different developmental potencies. *This segregation of different substances into separate blastomeric channels is one of the functions of cleavage.*

2. Nuclear Equality of the Early Blastomeres

Another question next arises: Is there a similar sorting out of nuclear substances during the cleavage period and do the nuclei in certain cells become different from those of other cells? Or, do all of the nuclei retain an equality during cleavage and development? Experimental evidence indicates a negative answer to the former question and a positive one to the latter.

A precise and illuminating experiment demonstrating nuclear equality of the early blastomeres may be performed by the hair-loop constriction method (Spemann, '28; Fankhauser, '48). For example, the fertilized egg of the newt, *Triturus viridescens,* may be constricted partially by a hair loop so that the zygotic nucleus is confined to one side (fig. 165A, B). The side possessing the nucleus divides, but the other side does not divide (fig. 165B, C). By releasing the ligature between the two sides at various stages of development of the cleaving side, i.e., 2-, 4-, 8-, 16-, and 32-cell stages, a nucleus is permitted to "escape" into the cytoplasm of the uncleaved side (fig. 165C, E; in D the escaped nucleus is seen in the blastomere to the left). By tightening the loop again after the escaping nucleus has entered the uncleaved cytoplasm, further nuclear "invasion" of the uncleaved part is blocked. If the original constriction was made so that the plane of constriction coincides with the plane of bilateral symmetry, i.e., if it constricts the gray crescent into two halves, the result is two normal embryos. This occurs after the 2-, 4-, 8- and 16-cell stages of the cleaving half of the egg. Nuclei permitted to escape when the cleaving side has reached the 32-cell stage do not produce normal embryos in the uncleaved side, probably because of the changes which have occurred in the meantime in the cytoplasm of the uncleaved side and not to the qualitative differences in the nuclei at this stage.

Another type of experiment upon the early cleaving blastomeres which demonstrates nuclear equality may be performed. It has been shown by Pflüger, Roux, and Driesch (Wilson, E. B., '25, p. 1059) that a cleaving egg pressed between two glass surfaces will divide parallel to the pressure surfaces. That is, the mitotic spindle is moved into a position parallel to the pressure surfaces. Under these circumstances, the spindle obeys the second law of Hertwig, namely, that the mitotic spindle tends to coincide with the long axis of the protoplasmic mass. Cleavage under pressure so applied, therefore, will result in a series of **vertical cleavage planes.** In the sea urchin (fig. 166) if pressure is applied in the four-cell stage, the mitotic spindles will form in a horizontal position, as shown in figure 166E, instead of in the vertical position, as indicated in figure 166B, C, where no pressure is applied. In other words, all of the nuclei shown in white in the upper blastomeres of figure 166C will be displaced horizontally by the applied pressure, as shown in figure 165F. If pressure is released at this stage, the mitotic spindle again obeys Hertwig's rule and forms in the long axis of the cytoplasm which is now vertical in position. As a result, upper and lower cells are formed, as in figure 166G. The original destiny of the nuclei in the cells producing ecto-derm is shown in white circles; that for the cells destined to produce mesen-chyme, entoderm, and ectoderm is shown in black (figs. 163, mesomeres; 166C, D). As shown in figure 166G, there is a mixture of these nuclei after the pressure is released. Regardless of this redistribution of nuclei, develop-ment proceeds almost normally. Development thus appears to be governed by the presence of special ooplasmic substances contained within the respective blastomeres (figs. 163; 166A–D).

The evidence from the foregoing experiments suggests the conclusion that the nuclei in the early blastomeres are qualitatively equal. Consequently, this body of experimental evidence is antagonistic to the older view of Weismann, who held that differences in the various parts of the developing organism are to be attributed to "differential nuclear divisions" whereby different he-reditary qualities (i.e., biophors) are dispersed to different cells. To quote from Weismann (1893, p. 76):

> Ontogeny depends on a gradual process of disintegration of the id of germ-plasm, which splits into smaller and smaller groups of determinants in the devel-opment of each individual, so that in place of a million different determinants, of which we may suppose the id of the germ-plasm to be composed, each daughter-cell in the next ontogenetic stage would only possess half a million, and each cell of the following stage only a quarter of a million and so on. Finally, if we neglect possible complications, only *one* kind of determinant remains in each cell, viz., that which has to control that particular cell or group of cells.

E. Quantitative and Qualitative Cleavages and Their Influence upon Later Development

One of the earliest students of the problem of the developmental possi-bilities of isolated blastomeres was Hans Driesch (1891 and 1892). In these publications, Driesch offered the results of experiments in which he shook apart the early blastomeres of the sea urchin and studied their development. Driesch found that the two blastomeres resulting from the first division con-tinued to divide, and as though the other blastomeres were present. The first division of the isolated blastomere was meridional, as if it had retained contact with its mate of the two-cell stage. The next division was latitudinal, also, as if it had retained contact with its original mate. Ultimately each iso-lated blastomere developed into swimming blastulae of half the normal size. The four blastomeres of the four-cell stage were similarly isolated. Here, also, each divides as if it were part of the whole, and free-swimming blastulae develop. However, later development is imperfect or definitely abnormal.

Isolation of blastomeres in the eight-cell stage of development, in most cases, results in abnormal development.

In *Amphioxus,* as mentioned previously, isolation of the first two blastomeres results in the production of twin embryos of half the normal size. In the eight-cell stage in *Amphioxus,* the isolated smaller micromeres will develop blastulae of ectoderm only, whereas the macromeres will develop blastulae with developed entoderm, mesoderm, and ectoderm. In the four-cell stage, if the two posterior blastomeres are separated from the two anterior blastomeres, the former develop early embryos which have entoderm and mesoderm together with ectoderm; the latter have notochord and neural plate together with ectoderm and possibly a little of the mesoderm (Conklin, '33). Similarly, in the frog or in the newt, when the first cleavage plane bisects the gray crescent, the isolation of the first two blastomeres results in the

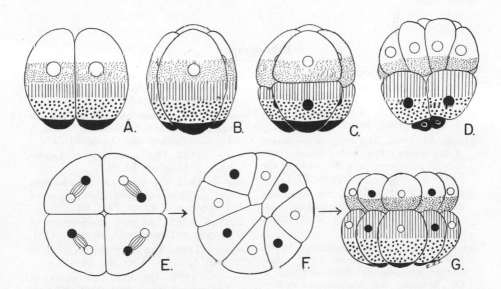

FIG. 166. Nuclear equality in the sea-urchin egg. (A–D) Normal cleavage. White nuclei and black nuclei theoretically so designed to show nuclei in animal and vegetal pole cells respectively. (E) Four-cell stage flattened by pressure, showing position of spindles for the third cleavage parallel to pressure surface. (F) Eight-cell stage under pressure. Compare with (C), normal. (G) Horizontal cleavage resulting from release of pressure after eight-cell stage. Note mixed distribution of nuclei. Later development normal, with cytoplasmic, organ-forming substances determining development as in fig. 163. Thus it appears that the nuclei are equal within the blastomeres, whereas the cytoplasm is unequally (i.e., qualitatively) distributed to the respective blastomeres, the particular type of development of the blastomeres being dependent upon the cytoplasmic substance present.

Black cytoplasm = micromeres which form primary mesenchyme. Coarse dotting = entoderm, secondary mesenchyme and coelomic material. White, light stipple, and vertical lines = ectodermal cells.

formation of two normal embryos. However, if the first cleavage is at right angles to the plane of bilateral symmetry of the egg, the blastomere containing the **gray crescent material** will develop a normal embryo, but the other blastomere will not do so.

The above results from isolated blastomeres suggest the following: When the division of the early egg is purely **quantitative,** so that the resulting blastomeres contain all of the cytoplasmic substances equally, as in the first one or two cleavage planes in the sea urchin (fig. 166A, B) or the first cleavage in the frog when it bisects the gray crescent, the isolation of the resulting blastomeres tends to produce complete embryos. Such blastomeres are known as **totipotent blastomeres.** (See Chap. 8.) However, when cleavage is **qualitative,** such as the second cleavage of *Amphioxus,* the third cleavage of the sea urchin (fig. 166C), or the first cleavage of the frog when it occurs at right angles to the median axis of the embryo, the resulting development depends upon the qualities (that is, ooplasmic substances) resident in the isolated blastomeres.

Bibliography

Bishop, S. C. **1926.** Notes on the habits and development of the mud puppy, *Necturus maculosus* (Rafinesque). New York State Mus. Bull., Albany, New York, May 1926, No. 268.

Blount, M. **1909.** The early development of the pigeon's egg, with especial reference to polyspermy and the origin of the periblast nuclei. J. Morphol. **20**:1.

Brauer, A. **1897.** Beiträge zur Kenntniss der Entwicklungsgeschichte und der Anatomie der *Gymnophionen.* Zool. Jahrb. **10**:389.

Buytendijk, F. J. J. and Woerdeman, M. W. **1927.** Die physico-chemischen Erscheinungen während der Eientwicklung. I. Die Messung der Wasserstoffionenkonzentration. Roux' Arch. f. Entwick. d. Organ. **112**:387.

Cerfontaine, P. **1906.** Recherches sur le développement de *l'Amphioxus.* Arch. biol., Paris. **22**:229.

Cole, F. J. **1930.** Early Theories of Sexual Generation. Oxford University Press, Inc., Clarendon Press, New York.

Conklin, E. G. **1897.** The embryology of *Crepidula.* J. Morphol. **13**:1.

———. **1905a.** Mosaic development in ascidian eggs. J. Exper. Zool. **2**:145.

———. **1905b.** The organization and cell-lineage of the ascidian egg. J. Acad. Nat. Sc:̣, Philadelphia. **13**:5.

———. **1906.** Does half of an ascidian egg give rise to a whole larva? Arch. f. Entwicklngsmech. der Organ. **21**:727.

———. **1932.** The embryology of *Amphioxus.* J. Morphol. **54**:69.

———. **1933.** The development of isolated and partially separated blastomeres of *Amphioxus.* J. Exper. Zool. **64**:303.

Dean, B. **1895.** The early development of gar-pike and sturgeon. J. Morphol. **11**:1.

———. **1896.** The early development of *Amia.* Quart. J. Micr. Sc. **38**:413.

———. **1899.** On the embryology of *Bdellostoma stouti.* Festschrift von Carl von Kupffer. Gustav Fischer, Jena.

Driesch, H. **1891.** Entwicklungsmechanische Studien I–II. Zeit. Wiss. Zool. **53**:160.

———. **1892.** Entwicklungsmechanische Studien III–VI. Zeit. Wiss. Zool. **55**:1.

Eycleshymer, A. C. **1895.** The early development of *Amblystoma* with observations on some other vertebrates. J. Morphol. **10**:343.

———. **1904.** Bilateral symmetry in the egg of *Necturus.* Anat. Anz. **25**:230.

———— and Wilson, J. M. **1910.** Normal plates of the development of *Necturus maculosus.* Entwicklungsgeschichte der Wirbeltiere, Part 11. F. Keibel. Gustav Fischer, Jena.

Fankhauser, G. **1948.** The organization of the amphibian egg during fertilization and cleavage. Ann. New York Acad. Sc. **49**:684.

Flynn, T. T. and Hill, J. P. **1939.** The development of the *Monotremata.* Part IV. Growth of the ovarian ovum, maturation, fertilisation, and early cleavage. Trans. Zool. Soc., London, s.A. **24,** Part 6:445.

———— and ————. **1942.** The later stages of cleavage and the formation of the primary germ-layers in the *Monotremata* (preliminary communication). Proc. Zool. Soc., London, s.A. **111**:233.

Gregory, P. W. **1930.** The early embryology of the rabbit. Carnegie Inst., Wash. Publ. 407. Contrib. Embryol. **21**:141.

Harding, D. **1951.** Initiation of cell division in the *Arbacia* egg by injury substances. Physiol. Zoöl. **24**:54.

Hartman, C. G. **1916.** Studies in the development of the opossum, *Didelphys virginiana L.* I. History of the early cleavage. II. Formation of the blastocyst. J. Morphol. **27**:1.

Harvey, E. B. **1936.** Parthenogenetic merogony or cleavage without nuclei in *Arbacia punctulata.* Biol. Bull. **71**:101.

————. **1938.** Parthenogenetic merogony or the development without nuclei of the eggs of sea urchins from Naples. Biol. Bull. **75**:170.

————. **1940.** A comparison of the development of nucleate and non-nucleate eggs of *Arbacia punctulata.* Biol. Bull. **79**:166.

————. **1951.** Cleavage in centrifuged eggs and in parthenogenetic merogones. Ann. New York Acad. Sc. **51**: Art. 8, 1336.

Hatschek, B. **1893.** *Amphioxus* and Its Development. The Macmillan Co., New York.

Heilbrunn, L. V. **1921.** Protoplasmic viscosity changes during mitosis. J. Exper. Zool. **34**:417.

———— and Wilson, W. L. **1948.** Protoplasmic viscosity changes during mitosis in the egg of *Chaetopterus.* Biol. Bull. **95**:57.

Heuser, C. H. and Streeter, G. L. **1929.** Early stages in the development of pig embryos from the period of initial cleavage to the time of the appearance of limb-buds. Contrib. to Embryol. Carnegie Inst., Washington. Publ. No. 394. **20**(109):1.

———— and ————. **1941.** Development of the macaque embryo. Contrib. to Embryol. Carnegie Inst., Washington. Publ. **538**:17.

Hill, J. P. **1910.** The early development of the *Marsupialia,* with special reference to the native cat *(Dasyurus viverrinus).* Quart. J. Micr. Sc. **56**:1.

————. **1918.** Some observations on the early development of *Didelphys aurita* (Contributions to the embryology of the *Marsupialia*—V). Quart. J. Micr. Sc. **63**:91.

Holtfreter, J. **1939.** Studien zur Ermittlung der Gestaltungsfaktoren in der Organentwicklung der Amphibien. I. Dynamisches Verhalten isolierter Furchungszellen und Entwicklungsmechanik der Entodermorgane. Roux' Arch. f. Entwick. d. Organ. **139**:110.

Hooke, R. **1664.** Micrographia. See page 114. Martyn and Allestry, London.

Huber, G. C. **1915.** The development of the albino rat, *Mus norvegicus albinus.* I. From the pronuclear stage to the stage of mesoderm anlage: end of the first to the end of the ninth day. J. Morphol. **26**:247.

Huxley, J. S. and De Beer, G. R. **1934.** The Elements of Experimental Embryology. Cambridge University Press, London.

Jordan, E. O. **1893.** The habits and development of the newt *(Diemyctylus viridescens).* J. Morphol. **8**:269.

Kerr, J. G. **1909.** Normal plates of the development of *Lepidosiren paradoxa* and *Protopterus annectens.* Entwicklungsgeschichte der Wirbeltiere, Part 10. F. Keibel. Gustav Fischer, Jena.

————. **1919.** Textbook of Embryology. Vol. **2.** The Macmillan Co., New York.

Kopsch, F. **1911.** Die Entstehung des Dottersackentoblast und die Furchung bei der Forelle *(Salmo fario).* Arch. f. mikr. Anat. **78**:618.

Kowalewski, A. **1867.** Entwicklungsgeschichte des *Amphioxus lanceolatus.* Mém. Acad. imp. d. sc. de St. Petersburg, VIIᵉ Série. **11**: No. 4.

Lewis, W. H. 1939. The role of a superficial plasmagel layer in changes of form, locomotion and division of cells in tissue cultures. Arch. f. exper. Zellforsch. 23:1.

—— and Gregory, P. W. 1929. Cinematographs of living developing rabbit eggs. Science. 69:226.

—— and Hartman, C. G. 1941. Tubal ova of the Rhesus monkey. Contrib. to Embryol. Carnegie Inst., Washington. Publ. 538:9.

—— and Wright, E. S. 1935. On the early development of the mouse egg. Contrib. to Embryol. Carnegie Inst., Washington. Publ. No. 459. 25:113.

Lillie, F. R. 1895. The embryology of the Unionidae. A study in cell lineage. J. Morphol. 10:1.

——. 1930. The Development of the Chick. 2d ed., Henry Holt & Co., New York.

McCrady, E. 1938. The embryology of the opossum. Am. Anat. Memoirs, 16, The Wistar Institute of Anatomy and Biology, Philadelphia.

Moore, J. A. 1941. Developmental rate of hybrid frogs. J. Exper. Zool. 86:405.

——. 1946. Studies in the development of frog hybrids. I. Embryonic development in the cross Rana pipiens ♀ x Rana sylvatica ♂. J. Exper. Zool. 101:173.

——. 1947. Studies in the development of frog hybrids. II. Competence of the gastrula ectoderm of Rana pipiens ♀ x Rana sylvatica ♂ hybrids. J. Exper. Zool. 105:349.

Morgan, T. H. 1897. Development of the Frog's Egg. An Introduction to Experimental Embryology. The Macmillan Co., New York.

Nelsen, O. E. 1948. Changes in the form of the blastophore in blocked gastrulae of Rana pipiens. Anat. Rec. 101:60.

——. 1949. The cumulative effect of oxygen-pressure in the blocking of gastrulation in the embryo of Rana pipiens. Anat. Rec. 105:599.

Nicholas, J. S. and Hall, B. V. 1942. Experiments on developing rats. II. The development of isolated blastomeres and fused eggs. J. Exper. Zool. 90:441.

Olsen, M. W. 1942. Maturation, fertilization and early cleavage in the hen's egg. J. Morphol. 70:513.

Oppenheimer, J. M. 1936. Processes of localization in developing Fundulus. J. Exper. Zool. 73:405.

Pasteels, J. 1937. Sur l'origine de la symétrie bilatérale des amphibiens anoures. Arch. Anat. Micr. 33:279.

——. 1938. A propos du déterminisme de la symétrie bilatérale chez les amphibiens anoures. Conditions qui provoquent l'apparition du croissant gris. Compt. rend. Soc. de biol. 129:59.

Patten, B. M. 1948. Embryology of the Pig. 3d ed., The Blakiston Co., Philadelphia.

Patterson, J. T. 1910. Studies on the early development of the hen's egg. I. History of the early cleavage and of the accessory cleavage. J. Morphol. 21:101.

Pincus, G. 1939. The comparative behavior of mammalian eggs in vivo and in vitro. IV. The development of fertilized and artificially activated rabbit eggs. J. Exper. Zool. 82:85.

Pollister, A. W. and Moore, J. A. 1937. Tables for the normal development of Rana sylvatica. Anat. Rec. 68:489.

Rugh, R. 1951. The Frog, Its Reproduction and Development. The Blakiston Co., Philadelphia.

Ruud, G. 1925. Die Entwicklung isolierter Keimfragmente frühester Stadien von Triton taeniatus. Arch. f. Entwicklngsmech. d. Organ. 105:209.

Shumway, W. 1940. Cleavage and gastrulation in the frog. Anat. Rec. 78:143.

Snell, G. D. 1941. Chap. 1. The early embryology of the mouse in Biology of the Laboratory Mouse, by staff of Roscoe B. Jackson Memorial Laboratory. The Blakiston Co., Philadelphia.

Spemann, H. 1902. Entwickelungsphysiologische Studien am Triton—Ei. II. Arch. f. Entwicklngsmech. d. Organ. 15:448.

——. 1903. Entwicklungsphysiologische Studien am Triton—Ei. III. Arch. f. Entwicklngsmech. d. Organ. 16:551.

——. 1928. Die Entwicklung seitlicher und dorso-ventraler Keimhälften bei verzögerter Kernversorgung. Zeit. Wiss. Zool. 132:105.

Svensson, G. S. O. 1938. Zur Kenntniss der Furchung bei den Gymnophionen. Acta zool. 19:191.

Weismann, A. 1893. The Germ-plasm: A Theory of Heredity. English translation by W. N. Parker and H. Rönnfeldt. Walter Scott, Ltd., London.

Whitman, C. O. **1893.** The inadequacy of the cell-theory of development. J. Morphol. **8**:639.

—— and Eycleshymer, A. C. **1897.** The egg of *Amia* and its cleavage. J. Morphol. **12**:309.

Wilson, E. B. **1893.** *Amphioxus,* and the mosaic theory of development. J. Morphol. **8**:579.

——. **1925.** The Cell in Development and Heredity. 3d ed., The Macmillan Co., New York.

Wilson, H. V. **1889.** The embryology of the sea bass *(Serranus atrarius).* Bull. U. S. Fish Comm. **9**:209.

Wilson, J. T. and Hill, J. P. 1908. Observations on the development of *Ornithorhynchus.* Philos. Tr. Roy. Soc., London, s.B. **199**:31.

Ziegler, H. E. **1902.** Lehrbuch der vergleichenden Entwicklungsgeschichte der niederen Wirbeltiere in systematischer Reihenfolge und mit Berücksichtigung der experimentellen Embryologie bearbeitet. Gustav Fischer, Jena.

7

The Chordate Blastula and Its Significance

A. Introduction

In the previous chapter it was observed that two main types of blastulae are formed in the chordate group:

(1) those blastulae without accessory or trophoblast tissue, e.g., *Amphioxus,* frog, etc. and

(2) those possessing such auxiliary tissue, e.g., elasmobranch and teleost fishes, reptiles, birds, and mammals.

1. BLASTULAE WITHOUT AUXILIARY TISSUE

The blastulae which do not have the auxiliary tissues are rounded affairs composed of a layer of blastomeres surrounding a blastocoelic cavity (figs.

340

140T; 143C). The layer of blastomeres forms the **blastoderm.** The latter may be one cell in thickness, as in *Amphioxus* (fig. 140T), or several cells in thickness, as in the frog (fig. 143C). This hollow type of blastula often is referred to as a **coeloblastula** or **blastosphere.** However, in the gymnophionan amphibia, the blastula departs from this vesicular condition and appears quite solid. The latter condition may be regarded as a **stereoblastula,** i.e., a solid blastula. A somewhat comparable condition is present in the bony ganoid fishes, *Amia* and *Lepisosteus.*

The main characteristic of the blastula which does not possess auxiliary tissue is that the entire blastula is composed of formative cells, i.e., all the cells enter directly into the formation of the embryo's body.

2. Blastulae with Auxiliary or Trophoblast Tissue

An examination of those blastulae which possess auxiliary or trophoblast tissues shows a less simple condition than the round blastulae mentioned above. In the first place, two types of cells are present, namely, **formative cells** which enter into the composition of the embryonic body and **auxiliary cells** concerned mainly with trophoblast, or nutritional, functions. In the second place, in the blastula which possesses auxiliary tissue, the latter often develops precociously, that is, in advance of the formative cells of the blastula. As a result, the arrangement of the formative cells into a configuration comparable to that of those blastulae without trophoblast cells may be much retarded in certain instances. This condition is true particularly of the mammalian blastula (blastocyst).

Generally speaking, the blastulae which possess auxiliary tissue consist in their earlier stages of a disc or a **mass of formative cells** at the peripheral margins of which are attached the **non-formative, auxiliary cells** (fig. 159, blastoderm-formative cells, periblast-non-formative; also figs. 145K, L; 147G, H). The blastocoelic space lies below this disc of cells. However, in mammals the auxiliary or nourishment-getting tissue tends to circumscribe the blastocoel, whereas the formative cells occupy a polar area (fig. 145G, H). Blastulae, composed of a disc-shaped mass of cells overlying a blastocoelic space, have been described in classical terms as **discoblastulae.**

3. Comparison of the Two Main Blastular Types

If we compare these two types of blastulae in terms of structure, it is evident that a comparison is not logical *unless the essential or formative cells and their arrangement are made the sole basis for the comparison,* for only the formative cells are common to both types of blastulae. To make the foregoing statement more obvious, let us examine the essential structure of a typical coeloblastula, such as found in *Amphioxus,* as it is defined by the present-day embryologist.

The studies by Conklin, '32 and '33, demonstrated that the fertilized egg of *Amphioxus* possesses *five major, presumptive, organ-forming areas* (fig. 167A). These areas ultimately give origin to the ectodermal, mesodermal, entodermal, notochordal, and neural tissues. In the eight-cell stage of cleavage, the cytoplasmic substances concerned with these areas are distributed in such a way that the blastomeres have different substances and, consequently, differ *qualitatively* (fig. 167B). Specifically, the entoderm forms the ventral part of the four ventral blastomeres; the ectoderm forms the upper or dorsal portion of the four micromeres, while the mesodermal, notochordal, and neural substances lie in an intermediate zone between these two organ-forming areas, particularly so in the blastomeres shown at the left in figure 167B. In figure 167C and D is shown a later arrangement of the presumptive, organ-forming areas in the middle and late stages of blastular development. These figures represent sections of the blastulae. Consequently, the organ-forming areas are contained within cells which *occupy definite regions of the blastula*. In figure 167E–G are presented lateral, vegetal pole, and dorso-posterior pole views of the mature blastula (fig. 167D), representing the organ-forming areas as viewed from the outside of the blastula.

It is evident from this study by Conklin *that the organization of the fertilized egg of Amphioxus passes gradually but directly through the cleavage stages into the organization of the mature blastula;* also, that the latter, like the egg, is composed of *five, major, presumptive, organ-forming areas*. It is evident further that one of the important tasks of cleavage and blastulation is to develop and arrange these major, organ-forming areas into a particular pattern. (*Note:* Later the mesodermal area divides in two, forming a total of six, presumptive, organ-forming areas.)

If we analyze the arrangement of these presumptive, organ-forming areas, we see that the mature blastula is composed of a floor or **hypoblast,** made up of **potential, entoderm-forming substance,** and a roof of **potential ectoderm** with a zone of **mesoderm and chordoneural cells** which lie in the area between these two general regions. In fact, the mesodermal and chordoneural materials form the lower margins of the roof of the mature blastula (fig. 167D). Consequently, the mature blastula of *Amphioxus* may be pictured as a bilaminar affair composed essentially of a *hypoblast or lower layer of presumptive entoderm,* and *an upper concave roof or epiblast containing presumptive ectoderm, neural plate, notochord, and mesodermal cells*. It is to be observed further that the blastocoel is interposed between these two layers. This is the basic structure of a typical coeloblastula. Furthermore, this blastula *is composed entirely of formative tissue* made up of certain definite, potential, organ-forming areas which later enter into the formation of the body of the embryo; auxiliary or non-formative tissue has no part in its composition. All **coeloblastulae** conform to this general structure.

If we pass to the blastula of the early chick embryo, a striking similarity may be observed in reference to the presumptive, organ-forming areas (fig.

173). An upper, **epiblast layer** is present, composed of presumptive ecto-dermal, neural, notochordal, and mesodermal cells, while a **hypoblast layer** of entodermal potency lies below. Between these two layers the blastocoelic space is located. However, in the chick blastoderm, *in addition to the formative cells, a peripheral area of auxiliary or trophoblast (periblast) tissue is present.*

B. History of the Concept of Specific, Organ-forming Areas

The idea that the mature egg or the early developing embryo possesses certain definite areas having different qualities, each of which contributes to the formation of a particular organic structure or of several structures, finds its roots in the writings of Karl Ernst von Baer, 1828–1837. Von Baer's comparative thinking and comprehensive insight into embryology and its proc-esses established the foundation for many of the results and conclusions that have been achieved in this field during the past one hundred years.

Some forty years later, in 1874, Wilhelm His in his book, *Unsere Körperform,* definitely put forth the organ-forming concept relative to the germ layers of the chick, stating that "the germ-disc contains the organ-germs spread out in a flat plate," and he called this the principle of the organ-forming germ-regions (Wilson, '25, p, 1041). Ray Lankester, in 1877, advanced views supporting an early segregation from the fertilized egg of "already formed and individualized" substances, as did C. O. Whitman (1878) in his classical work on the leech, *Clepsine.* In this work, Whitman concludes that there is definite evidence in favor of the preformation of organ-forming stuffs within the egg. Other workers in embryology, such as Rabl, Van Beneden, etc., began to formulate similar views (Wilson, '25, pp. 1041–1042).

The ideology embodied within the statement of Ray Lankester referred to above was the incentive for considerable research in that branch of em-bryological investigation known as "cell lineage." To quote more fully from Lankester's statement in this connection, p. 410:

Though the substance of a cell may appear homogeneous under the most powerful microscope, excepting for the fine granular matter suspended in it, it is quite pos-sible, indeed certain, that it may contain, already formed and individualized, various kinds of physiological molecules. The visible process of segregation is only the sequel of a differentiation already established, and not visible.

The studies on cell lineage in many invertebrate forms, such as that of Whitman (1878) on *Clepsine,* of Wilson (1892) on *Nereis,* of Boveri (1892) and zur Strassen (1896; fig. 163B) on *Ascaris,* or the work of Horstadius ('28, '37; fig. 163A) on the sea urchin, serve to emphasize more forcefully the implications of this statement. In these studies the developmental pro-spective fates of the various early cleavage blastomeres were carefully observed and followed.

Much of the earlier work on cell lineage was devoted to invertebrate forms. One of the first students to study the matter in the phylum *Chordata* was

E. G. Conklin who published in 1905 a classical contribution to chordate embryology relative to cell lineage in the ascidian, *Styela* (Cynthia) *partita*. This monumental work extended the principle of organ-forming, germinal areas to the chordate embryo. However, the significance of the latter observations, relative to the chordate phylum as a whole, was not fully appreciated until many years later when it was brought into prominence by the German investigator, W. Vogt ('25, '29).

Vogt began a series of studies which involved the staining of different parts of the amphibian blastula with vital dyes and published his results in 1925 and 1929. The method employed by Vogt is as follows:

Various parts of the late amphibian blastula are stained with such vital dyes as Nile-blue sulfate, Bismarck brown, or neutral red (fig. 168A). These stains color the cells but do not kill them. When a certain area of the blastula is stained in this manner, its behavior during later stages of development can be observed by the following procedure: After staining a particular area, the embryo is observed at various later periods, and the history of the stained area is noted. When the embryo reaches a condition in which body form is fully established, it is killed, fixed in suitable fluids, embedded in paraffin, and sectioned. Or, the embryo may be dissected after fixation in a suitable fluid. The cellular area of the embryo containing the stain thus may be detected and correlated with its original position in the blastula (cf. fig. 168A, B). This procedure then is repeated for other areas of the blastula (fig. 168C–E). Vogt thus was able to mark definite areas of the late blastula, to follow their migration during gastrulation, and observe their later contribution to the formation of the embryonic body. Definite maps of the amphibian blastula in relation to the future history of the respective blastular areas were in this way established (fig. 169C).

This method has been used by other investigators in the study of similar phenomena in other amphibian blastulae and in the blastulae and gastrulae of other chordate embryos. Consequently, the *principle of presumptive, organ-forming areas of the blastula* has been established for all of the major chordate groups other than the mammals. The latter group presents special technical difficulties. However, due to the similarity of early mammalian development with the development of other *Chordata,* it is quite safe to conclude that they also possess similar, organ-forming areas in the late blastular and early gastrular stages.

The major, presumptive, organ-forming areas of the late chordate blastula are as follows (figs. 167, 169, 173, 174, 179, 180, 181):

(1) There is an ectodermal area which forms normally the epidermal layer of the skin;

(2) also, there is an ectodermal region which contributes to the formation of the neural tube and nervous system;

(3) a notochordal area is present which later gives origin to the primitive axis;

(4) the future mesodermal tissue is represented by two areas, one on either side of the notochordal area. In *Amphioxus,* however, this mesodermal area is present as a single area, the ventral crescent, which divides during gastrulation into two areas;

(5) the entodermal area, which gives origin to the future lining tissue of the gut, occupies a position in the blastula either at or toward the vegetative pole;

(6) there is a possibility that another potential area, containing germinal plasm, may be present and integrated with the presumptive entoderm or mesoderm. This eventually may give origin to the **primitive germ cells;**

(7) the pre-chordal plate region is associated with the notochordal area in all chordates in which it has been identified and lies at the caudal margin of the latter. In gastrulation it maintains this association. The pre-chordal plate material is an area which gives origin to some of the head mesoderm and possibly also to a portion of the roof of the foregut. It acts potently in the organization of the head region. Accordingly, it may be regarded as a complex of entomesodermal cells, at least in lower vertebrates.

C. Theory of Epigenesis and the Germ-layer Concept of Development

As the three classical germ layers take their origin from the blastular state (see Chap. 9), it is well to pause momentarily to survey briefly the germ-layer concept.

That the embryonic body is derived from definite tissue layers is an old concept in embryology. Casper Friedrich Wolff (1733–94) recognized that the early embryonic condition of the chick blastoderm possessed certain layers of tissue. This fact was set forth in his *Theoria Generationis,* published in 1759, and in *De formatione intestinorum praecipue,* published in 1769, devoted to the description of the intestinal tract and other parts of the chick embryo. In these works Wolff presented the thesis that embryonic development of both plants and animals occurred by "a host of minute and always visible elements that assimilated food, grew and multiplied, and thus gradually in associated masses" produced the various structures which eventually become recognizable as "the heart, blood vessels, limbs, alimentary canal, kidneys, etc." (The foregoing quotations are from Wheeler, 1898.) These statements contain the essence of Wolff's theory of *epigenesis.* That is, that development is not a process of unfolding and growth in size of preformed structures; rather, it is an indirect one, in which certain elements increase in number and gradually become molded into the form of layers which later give rise to the organ structures of the organism.

Two other men contributed much to the layer theory of development, namely, Heinrich Christian Pander (1794–1865) and Karl Ernst von Baer (1792–1876). In 1817, Pander described the trilaminar or triploblast condition of the chick blastoderm, and von Baer, in his first volume (1828) and second volume (1837) on comparative embryology of animals, delineated four body layers. The four layers of von Baer's scheme are derived from Pander's three layers by dividing the middle layer into two separate layers of tissue. Von Baer is often referred to as the *founder of comparative embryology* for various reasons, one of which was that he recognized that the layer concept described by Pander held true for many types of embryos, vertebrate and invertebrate. The layer concept of development thus became an accepted embryological principle.

While Pander and von Baer, especially the latter, formulated the germ-layer concept as a structural fact for vertebrate embryology, to Kowalewski (1846–1901) probably belongs the credit for setting forth the idea, in his paper devoted to the early development of *Amphioxus* (1867), that a primary, single-layered condition changes gradually into a double-layered condition. The concept of a single-layered condition transforming into a double-layered condition by an invaginative procedure soon became regarded as a fundamental embryological sequence of development.

Gradually a series of developmental steps eventually became crystallized from the fact and speculation present during the latter half of the nineteenth century as follows:

(1) The blastula, **typically a single-layered, hollow structure,** becomes converted into

(2) the **two-layered gastrula** by a process of invagination of one wall or delamination of cells from one wall of the blastula; then,

(3) by an outpouching of a part of the inner layer of the gastrula, or by an ingression of cells from this layer, or from the outside ectoderm, a **third layer of cells,** the mesoderm, comes to lie between the entoderm and ectoderm; and finally,

(4) the inner layer of mesoderm eventually develops into a two-layered structure with a coelomic cavity between the layers.

This developmental progression became accepted as the basic procedure in the development of most *Metazoa.*

The original concept of the germ layers maintained that the layers were specific. That is, entodermal tissue came only from entoderm, ectodermal tissue from ectoderm, etc. However, experimental work on the early embryo in which cells are transplanted from one potential layer to another has overthrown this concept (Oppenheimer, '40). The work on cell lineage and the demonstration of the early presence of the presumptive, organ-forming areas also have done much to overthrow the concept concerning the rigid specificity of the three primary germ layers of entoderm, mesoderm, and ectoderm.

D. Introduction of the Words *Ectoderm, Mesoderm, Endoderm*

Various students of the *Coelenterata*, such as Huxley (1849), Haeckel (1866) and Kleinenberg (1872), early recognized that the coelenterate body was constructed of two layers, an outer and an inner layer. Soon the terms **ectoderm** (outside skin) and **endoderm** (inside skin) were applied to the outer and inner layers or membranes of the coelenterate body, and the word **mesoderm** (middle skin) was used to refer to the middle layer which appeared in those embryos having three body layers. The more dynamic embryological words **epiblast, mesoblast,** and **hypoblast (entoblast)** soon came to be used in England by Balfour, Lankester, and others for the words *ectoderm, mesoderm,* and *endoderm,* respectively. The word entoderm is used in this text in preference to endoderm.

E. Importance of the Blastular Stage in Haeckel's Theory of "The Biogenetic Law of Embryonic Recapitulation"

In 1859, Charles Darwin (1809-82) published his work *On the Origin of Species by Means of Natural Selection.* This theory set the scientific world aflame with discussions for or against it.

In 1872 and 1874, E. Haeckel (1834–1919), an enthusiast of Darwin's evolutionary concept, associated the findings of Kowalewski regarding the early, two-layered condition of invertebrate and vertebrate embryos together with the adult, two-layered structure of the *Coelenterata* and published the **blastaea-gastraea theory** and **biogenetic principle of recapitulation.** In these publications he applied the term **gastrula** to the two-layered condition of the embryo which Kowalewski has described as the next developmental step succeeding the blastula and put forward the idea that the gastrula was an embryonic form common to all metazoan animals.

In his reasoning (1874, translation, '10, Chap. 8, Vol. I), Haeckel applied the word **blastaea** to a "long-extinct common stem form of substantially the same structure as the blastula." This form, he concluded, resembled the "permanent blastospheres" of primitive multicellular animals, such as the colonial *Protozoa.* The body of the **blastaea** was a "simple hollow ball, filled with fluid or structureless jelly with a wall composed of a single stratum of homogeneous ciliated cells."

The next phylogenetic stage, according to Haeckel, was the **gastraea,** a permanent, free-swimming form which resembled the embryonic, two-layered, gastrular stage described by Kowalewski. This was the simple stock form for all of the *Metazoa* above the *Protozoa* and other *Protista.* Moreover, he postulated that the gastrula represented an embryonic recapitulation of the adult stage of the gastraea or the progenitor of all *Metazoa.*

The assumed importance of the blastula and gastrula thus became the foundation for Haeckel's biogenetic principle of recapitulation. Starting with the postulation that the hypothetical **blastaea** and **gastraea** represented the adult phylogenetic stages comparable to the embryonic blastula and gastrula, respectively, Haeckel proceeded, step by step, to compress into the embryological stages of all higher forms the adult stages of the lower forms through which the higher forms supposedly passed in reaching their present state through evolutionary change. The two-chambered condition of the developing mammalian heart thus became a representation of the two-chambered, adult heart of the fish, while the three-chambered condition recapitulated the adult amphibian heart, etc. Again, the visceral arches of the embryonic pharyngeal regions of the mammal represented the gill-slit condition of the fish. *Ontogeny thus recapitulates phylogeny, and phylogeny of a higher species is the result of the modification of the adult stages of lower species in the phylogenetic scale.* The various steps in the embryological development of any particular species, according to this reasoning, were caused by the evolutionary history of the species; the conditions present in the adult stage of an earlier phylogenetic ancestor became at once the cause for its existence in the embryological development of all higher forms. Embryology in this way became chained to a repetition of phylogenetic links!

Many have been the supporters of the biogenetic law, and for a long time it was one of the most popular theories of biology. A surprising supporter of the recapitulation doctrine was Thomas Henry Huxley (1825–95). To quote from Oppenheimer ('40): "One wonders how the promulgator of such a distorted doctrine of cause and effect could have been championed by the same Huxley who wrote: 'Fact I know and Law I know; but what is this Necessity save an empty Shadow of my own mind's throwing?'."

The Haeckelian dogma that ontogeny recapitulates phylogeny fell into error because it was formulated upon three false premises due to the fragmentary knowledge of the period. These premises were:

(1) That in evolution or phylogeny, recently acquired, hereditary characters were added to the hereditary characters already present in the species;

(2) that the hereditary traits revealed themselves during embryonic development in the same sequence in which they were acquired in phylogeny; and

(3) that Darwin's concept of heredity, namely, **pangenesis,** essentially was correct.

The theory of pangenesis assumed that the germ cells with their hereditary factors were produced by the parental body or soma and that the contained hereditary factors within the germ cells were produced by gemmules which migrated from the various soma cells into the germ cells. This theory further postulated the inheritance of acquired characters.

If these three assumptions are granted, then it is easy to understand Haeckel's contention that embryological development consists in the repetition of previous stages in phylogeny. For example, if we assume that the **blastaea** changed into the **gastraea** by the addition of the features pertaining to the primitive gut with its enteric lining, then the gastraea possessed the hereditary factors of the blastaea plus the new enteric factors. These enteric features could easily be added to the deric (outer-skin) factors of the blastaea, according to Darwin's theory of pangenesis. Furthermore, according to assumption (2) above, in the embryonic development of the gastraea, the hereditary factors of the blastaea would reveal themselves during development first and would produce the blastaea form, to be followed by the appearance of the specific enteric features of the gastraea. And so it proceeded in the phylogeny and embryology of later forms. In this way the preceding stage in phylogeny became at once the cause of its appearance in the development of the next phylogenetic stage.

These assumptions, relative to heredity and its mechanism of transference, were shown to be untenable by the birth of the Nägeli-Roux-Weismann concept of the germ plasm (see Chaps. 3 and 5) and by the rebirth or rediscovery of Mendelism during the latter part of the nineteenth century. Studies in embryology since the days of Weismann have demonstrated in many animal species the essential correctness of Weismann's assumption that the germ plasm produces the soma during development, as well as the future germ plasm, and thus have overthrown the pangenesis theory of Darwin. The assiduous study of Mendelian principles during the first twenty-five years of the twentieth century have demonstrated that a fixed relation does not exist between the original character and the appearance of a new character as implied in the Haeckelian law (Morgan, '34, p. 148). Furthermore, that "in many cases, perhaps in most, a new end character simply replaces the original one. The embryo does not pass through the last stage of the original character and then develop the new one—although this may happen at times—but the new character takes the place of the original one" (Morgan, '34, p. 148).

How then does one explain the resemblances of structure to be found among the embryos at various stages of development in a large group of animals such as the *Chordata?* Let us endeavor to seek an explanation.

In development, nature always proceeds from the general to the specific, both in embryological development and in the development of phylogeny or a variety of forms. The hereditary factors which determine these generalized states or structural conditions apparently are retained, and specialized factors come into play after the generalized pattern is established. Generalized or basic conditions, therefore, appear before the specialized ones. An example of this generalized type of development is shown in the formation of the blastula in chordate animals. Although many different specific types and shapes of blastulae are present in the group as a whole, all of them can be resolved into two basic groups. These groups, as mentioned in the beginning of this chapter, are:

(1) blastulae without auxiliary, nutritive tissue and
(2) blastulae with auxiliary tissue.

Moreover, if the auxiliary tissue of those blastulae which possess this tissue is not considered, all mature chordate blastulae can be reduced to a fundamental condition which contains two basic layers, namely, *hypoblast* and *epiblast layers.* The epiblast possesses presumptive epidermal, neural, notochordal, and mesodermal, organ-forming areas, while the hypoblast cells form the presumptive entodermal area. The shapes and sizes of these blastulae will, of course, vary greatly. Moreover, the hypoblast cells may be present in various positions, such as a mass of cells at the caudal end of a disc-shaped epiblast (teleost and elasmobranch fishes), an enlarged, thickened area or pole of a hollow sphere (many *Amphibia*), a single, relatively thin layer of cells, forming part of the wall of a hollow sphere *(Amphioxus),* a rounded, disc-shaped mass of cells overlain by the thin, cup-shaped epiblast *(Clavelina),* a thickened mass attached to the underside of the caudal end of the disc-shaped epiblast (chick; certain reptiles), a thin layer of cells situated below the epiblast layer (mammals), or a solid mass of cells, lying below a covering of epiblast cells (gymnophionan *Amphibia*). Although many different morphological shapes are to be found in the blastulae of the chordate group, the essential, presumptive, organ-forming areas always are present, *and all are organized around the presumptive notochordal area.*

But the question arises: Why is a generalized blastular pattern developed instead of a series of separate, distinct patterns? For instance, why should the notochordal area appear to occupy the center of the presumptive, organ-forming areas of all the chordate blastulae when this area persists as a prominent morphological entity only in the adult condition of lower chordates? The answer appears to be this: The notochordal area at this particular stage of development is not alone a morphological area, *but it is also a physiological instrument,* an instrument which plays a part in *a method or procedure of development.* The point of importance, therefore, in the late blastular stage of development is not that the notochordal area is going to contribute to the skeletal axis in the adult of the shark, but rather that *it forms an integral part of the biolgical mechanism which organizes the chordate embryo during the period immediately following the blastular stage.* Thus, if the notochordal material can play an important role in the organization of the embryo and in the induction of the neural tube in the fish or in the frog, it also can fulfill a similar function in the developing chick or human embryo. Whatever it does later in development depends upon the requirements of the species. To use a naïve analogy, nature does not build ten tracks to send ten trains with different destinies out of a station when she can use one track for all for at least part of the way. So it is in development. A simple tubular heart appears in all vertebrate embryos, followed by a simple, two-chambered* condition, not because the two-chambered heart represents the recapitulated, two-chambered, fish heart but rather because it, like the notochord, is a stage in a dynamic developmental procedure of heart development in all vertebrates. As far as the fish is concerned, when the common, two-chambered, rudimentary stage of the heart is reached, nature shunts it off on a special track which develops this simple, two-chambered condition into 'the highly muscular and efficient two-chambered, adult heart adapted to the fish level of existence in its watery environment. The three-chambered,* amphibian heart follows a similar pattern, and it specializes at the three-chambered level because it fits into the amphibian way of life. So it is with the embryonic pharyngeal area with its visceral and aortal arches which resemble one another throughout the vertebrate group during early embryonic development. The elaboration of a common, pharyngeal area with striking resemblances throughout the vertebrate group can be explained more easily and rationally on the assumption that it represents a common, physiologically important step in a developmental procedure.

This general view suggests the conclusion that ontogeny tends to use common developmental methods wherever and whenever these methods can be utilized in the development of a large group of animals. Development or ontogeny, therefore, *recapitulates phylogenetic procedures and not adult morphological stages.* One explanation for this conservation of effort may be that, physiologically speaking, the number of essential methods, whereby a specific end may be produced, probably is limited. Another explanation suggests that *an efficient method never is discarded.*

F. Importance of the Blastular Stage in Embryonic Development

Superficially in many forms, chordate and non-chordate, the blastula is a hollow, rounded structure containing the blastocoelic space within. It is tempting to visualize this form as the basic, essential form of the blastula. However, the so-called blastular stage in reality presents *many forms* throughout the animal kingdom, some solid, some round and hollow, and others in the form of a flattened disc or even an elongated band. Regardless of their shape, all blastulae have this in common: they represent an association of presumptive organ-forming areas, areas which later move to new positions in *the forming body, increase in cellular mass, and eventually become molded into definite structures.* One of the main purposes of blastulation, therefore, may be stated as the elaboration (or establishment) of the *major, presumptive organ-forming areas* of the particular species and *their arrangement in a particular pattern which permits their ready manipulation during the next*

---

* Exclusive of the sinus venosus.

step of development or gastrulation. The particular shape of the blastula has its importance. However, this importance does not lie in the supposition that it conforms to a primitive spherical type but rather that the various, presumptive, organ-forming areas are so arranged and so poised that the cell movements so necessary to the next phase of development or **gastrulation** may be properly executed for the particular species. In most species, the formation of a blastocoelic space also is a necessary function of blastulation. In some species, however, this space actually is not formed until the next stage of development or gastrulation is in progress.

In summary, therefore, it may be stated that the importance of the blastula does not reside in the supposed fact that it is a one-layered structure or blastoderm having a particular shape. Rather, its importance emerges from the fact that the blastoderm has certain, well-defined areas segregated within it—areas which will give origin to future organ structures. Moreover, these areas foreshadow the future germ layers of the body. In *diploblastic Metazoa, two germ layers are foreshadowed,* while in *triploblastic forms, three germ layers are outlined.* As far as the *Chordata* are concerned, the **hypoblast** is the forerunner of the entoderm or the **internal germ layer;** whereas the **epiblast** is composed potentially of two germ layers, namely, the **epidermal, neural plate areas** which form the **ectodermal layer** and the **chordamesodermal or marginal zone cells** which give origin to the **middle germ layer.**

In the following pages, the chordate blastula is described as a two-layered structure composed of various, potential, organ-forming areas. This two-layered configuration, composed of a lower **hypoblast** and an upper **epiblast,** is used to describe the chordate blastula for the dual purpose of comparison and analysis of the essential structure of the various blastulae. The bilaminar picture, it is believed, will enable the student to understand better the changes which the embryo experiences during the gastrulative period.

G. Description of the Various Types of Chordate Blastulae with an Outline of Their Organ-forming Areas

1. PROTOCHORDATE BLASTULA

The following description pertains particularly to *Amphioxus.* With slight modification it may be applied to other protochordates, such as *Clavelina, Ascidiella, Styela,* etc.

As noted in the introduction to this chapter, the potential entodermal cells of *Amphioxus* lie at the vegetal pole and form most of the floor or **hypoblast** of the blastula (fig. 167D). The upper or animal pole cells form a roof of presumptive epidermal, notochordal, mesodermal, and neural cells arched above and around the entoderm. The latter complex of organ-forming cells forms the **epiblast.** The blastocoelic cavity is large and insinuated between the hypoblast and epiblast. The presumptive notochordal and mesodermal

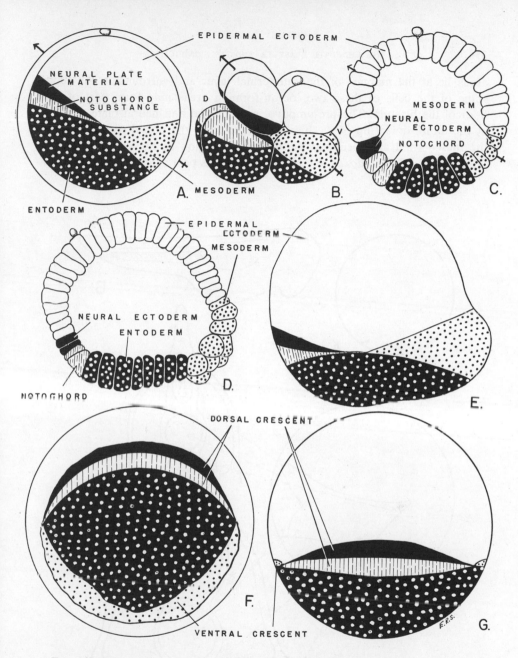

FIG. 167. Presumptive organ-forming areas in the uncleaved egg and during cleavage and blastulation in *Amphioxus*. (Original diagram based upon data obtained from Conklin, '32, '33.) (A) Uncleaved egg. (B) Eight-cell stage. (C) Early blastula in section. (D) Late blastula in section. (E) Late blastula, external view from side. (F) Late blastula, external, vegetal pole view. (G) Late blastula, external, dorsoposterior view. The localization of cytoplasmic materials in *Styela partita* is similar to that of Amphioxus. Observe that the pointed end of the arrow defines the future cephalic end of the embryo. The position of the polar body denotes the antero-ventral area, while the position of the notochordal and neural plate material represents the antero-dorsal region. The "tail end" of the arrow is the postero-ventral area of the embryo.

areas lie at the margins of the entodermal layer and surround it. As such, some of the cells of these two, organ-forming areas may form part of the floor of the blastula. The presumptive, notochordal and neural plate cells lie at the future dorsal lip of the blastopore and form the **dorsal crescent,** while the mesodermal area occupies the ventral-lip region as the **ventral crescent** (fig. 167F). In *Amphioxus,* the mature blastula is pear shaped, with the body

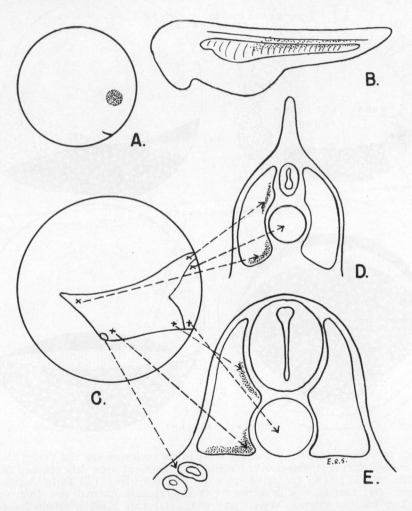

FIG. 168. Ultimate destiny within the developing body of presumptive organ-forming areas of the late amphibian blastula, stained by means of vital dyes. (After Pasteels: J. Exper. Zool., 89.) (A) Area of blastula, stained. (B) Destiny of cellular area, stained in (A). (D, E) Ultimate destiny shown by broken lines of cellular areas, stained in late blastula shown in (C). (E) Anterior trunk segment. (D) Posterior trunk segment.

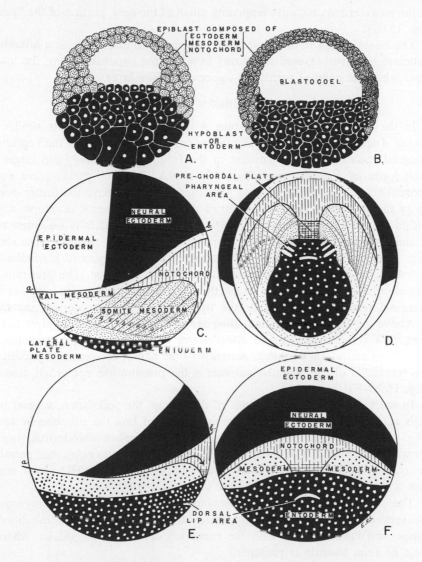

Fig. 169. Presumptive organ-forming areas in the amphibian late blastula and beginning gastrula. (A, B) General epiblast and hypoblast areas of the early and late blastular conditions, respectively. The hypoblast is composed mainly of entodermal or gut-lining structures, whereas the epiblast is a composite of ectodermal (i.e., epidermal and neural), mesodermal, and notochordal presumptive areas. Observe that the epiblast gradually grows downward over the hypoblast as the late blastula is formed. (C) Beginning gastrula of the urodele, *Triton*. (Presumptive areas shown according to Vogt, '29.) (D) Same as above, from vegetative pole. (Slightly modified from Vogt, '29.) (E) Lateral view of beginning gastrula of anuran amphibia. (F) Dorsal view of the same. (E, F derived from description by Vogt, '29, relative to *Rana fusca* and *Bombinator*; also Pasteels: J. Exper. Zool., 89, relative to *Discoglossus*.) Observe that an antero-posterior progression of somites is indicated in C and D.

355

of the mesodermal crescent comprising much of the neck portion of the "pear" (fig. 167E).

The blastula of *Amphioxus* thus may be regarded essentially as a **bilaminar structure** (i.e., two-layered structure) in which the hypoblast forms the lower layer while the epiblast forms the upper composite layer.

2. AMPHIBIAN BLASTULA

In the amphibian type of blastula, a spherical condition exists similar to that in *Amphioxus* (fig. 169). The future entoderm is located at the vegetative (vegetal) pole, smaller in amount in the frog, *Rana pipiens,* and larger in such forms as *Necturus maculosus* (fig. 169A, B). The presumptive notochordal material occupies an area just anterior to and above the future dorsal lip of the blastopore. The dorsal lip of the gastrula, when it develops, arises within the entodermal area (fig. 169C–F). Extending laterally on either side of the presumptive notochordal region is an area of presumptive mesoderm (fig. 169C–F). Each of these two mesodermal areas tapers to a smaller dimension as it extends outward from the notochordal region. The presumptive notochordal and mesodermal areas thus form a composite area or circular marginal zone which surrounds the upper rim of the entodermal material.

Above the chordamesodermal zone are two areas. The presumptive neural area is a crescent-like region lying above or anterior to the presumptive notochord-mesoderm complex. Anterior to the neural crescent and occupying the remainder of the blastular surface, is the presumptive epidermal crescent (fig. 169C–F).

In the various kinds of blastulae of this group, the yolk-laden, vegetal pole cells actually form a mass which projects upward into the blastocoelic space (fig. 169A, B). The irregularly rounded, presumptive entodermal, organ-forming area, therefore, is encapsulated partially by the other potential germinal areas, particularly by the chordamesodermal zone (fig. 169B). In a sense, this is true also of the protochordate group (fig. 167D).

The amphibian type of blastula includes those of the petromyzontoid Cyclostomes, the ganoid fishes with the exception of bony ganoids, the dipnoan fishes, and the *Amphibia* with the exception of the *Gymnophiona,* where a kind of solid blastula is present.

It is to be observed that the amphibian and protochordate blastulae differ in several details. In the first place, there is a greater quantity of yolk material in the blastula of the *Amphibia;* hence the presumptive **entodermal area or hypoblast** projects considerably into and encroaches upon the blastocoel. Also, in *Amphioxus,* the presumptive notochordal area forms a distinct **dorsal crescent** apart from the presumptive mesodermal or **ventral crescent** (fig. 167F), whereas, in the *Amphibia,* the notochordal material is sandwiched in between the two wings of mesoderm, so that these two areas form one composite **marginal zone crescent** (fig. 169D, E).

As in *Amphioxus,* the amphibian blastula may be resolved into a two-layered structure composed of a presumptive entodermal or **hypoblast layer** and an upper, **epiblast layer** of presumptive epidermal, notochordal, mesodermal, and neural tissues. Each of these layers, unlike that of *Amphioxus,* is several cells in thickness.

3. Mature Blastula in Birds

Development of the hen's egg proceeds rapidly in the oviduct (fig. 157B–G), and at the time that the egg is laid, the blastodisc (blastula) presents the following cellular conditions:

(1) a central, cellular blastoderm above the primary blastocoel and
(2) a more peripheral portion, associated with the yolk material forming the germ-wall tissue (fig. 156G).

The central blastoderm is free from the yolk substance and is known as the **area pellucida,** whereas the germ-wall area with its adhering yolk material forms the **area opaca** (fig. 170). Around its peripheral margin the area pellucida is somewhat thicker, particularly so in that region which will form the posterior end of the future embryo. In the latter area, the pellucid margin may consist of a layer of three or even four cells in thickness (fig. 172A). This thickened posterior portion of the early pellucid area forms the **embryonic shield** (fig. 170). Anterior to the embryonic shield, the pellucid area is one or two cells in thickness (figs. 171A; 172B).

Eventually the pellucid area becomes converted into a two-layered structure with an upper or overlying layer, the **primitive ectoderm or epiblast** and a lower underlying sheet of cells, the **primitive entoderm or hypoblast** (figs. 171A; 172A). The space between these two layers forms the **true or secondary blastocoel.** The cavity below the hypoblast is the primitive **archenteric space.** At the caudal and lateral edges of the pellucid area, cells from the inner zone of the germ wall appear to contribute to both hypoblast and epiblast.

The two-layered condition of the avian blastula shown in figure 171A may be regarded as a **secondary or late blastula.** At about the time that the secondary blastula is formed (or almost completely formed), the hen's egg is laid, and further development depends upon proper incubational conditions outside the body of the hen. Shortly after the latter incubation period is initiated, the primitive streak begins to make its appearance in the midcaudal region of the blastoderm, as described in Chapter 9.

Much controversy has prevailed concerning the method of formation of the entoderm and the two-layered condition in the avian blastoderm. Greatest attention has been given to the origin of the entoderm in the eggs of the pigeon, hen, and duck. The second layer is formed in the pigeon's egg as it passes down the oviduct, in the hen's egg at about the time of laying, and in the duck's egg during the first hours of the external incubation period. The

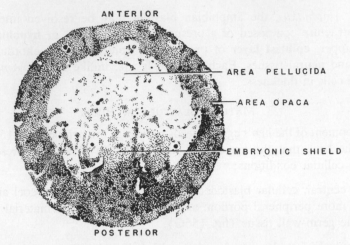

FIG. 170. Early pre-primitive streak blastoderm of the chick. Blastoderm about 3.2 mm. in diameter at this time. (After Spratt, '42.)

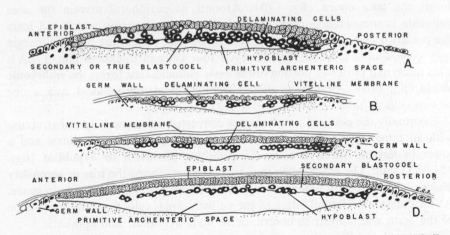

FIG. 171. Origin of the hypoblast (entoderm) in the avian blastoderm. (A) Median, antero-posterior section of chick blastoderm. Entoderm arises by delamination from upper or epiblast layer; possibly also by cells that grow anteriad from thickened posterior area. (Based upon data supplied by Peter, '34, '38, and Jacobson, '38.) (B–D) Formation of the hypoblast (entoderm) from epiblast by a process of delamination in the duck embryo. (Based upon data supplied by Pasteels, '45.)

unincubated chick blastoderm is about 3 mm. in diameter, that of the duck, about 2 to 3 mm.

The most recent observations, relative to the formation of the second or hypoblast layer, have been made upon the duck's egg (Pasteels, '45). In this egg, Pasteels found that, at about nine hours after incubation is initiated, a two-layered condition is definitely formed and that "the primary entoblast of the duck is the result of a progressive delamination of the segmenting blastodisc separating the superficial cells from the deeper ones" (fig. 171B–D). He further suggests that "the bilaminar embryo of birds is to be homologized with the blastula of the *Amphibia,* the cleft separating the two layers being equivalent to the blastocoele" (p. 13). The formation of the hypoblast (primary entoderm) by a process of delamination from the upper layer or epiblast agrees with the observations by Peter ('38) on the developing chick and pigeon blastoderm (fig. 172) and of Spratt ('46) on the chick. It also agrees with some of the oldest observations, concerning the matter of entoderm formation, going back to Öllacher in 1869, Kionka, 1894, and Assheton, 1896. Others, such as Duval (1884, 1888) in the chick, and Patterson ('09) in the pigeon, have ascribed the formation of the primary entoderm to a process of invagination and involution at the caudal margin of the blastoderm, while Jacobson ('38) came to the conclusion that the entoderm of the pellucid area arose in chick and sparrow embryos through a process of outgrowth of cells from the **primitive plate** and from an archenteric canal produced by an inward bending of the epiblast and primitive plate tissue. The latter author believed that the entoderm of the area opaca arose by delamination.

The **hypoblast** of the chick gives origin to most of the tissue which lines the future gut, and, therefore, may be regarded as the potential entodermal area. As in the amphibia and *Amphioxus,* the **epiblast** is composed of several, presumptive organ forming areas (fig. 173A). (See Pasteels, '36c; Spratt, '42, '46.) At the caudal part of the epiblast is an extensive region of presumptive mesoderm bisected by the midplane of the future embryonic axis. Just anterior to this region and in the midplane is the relatively small, presumptive notochordal area. Between the latter and the mesodermal area is located the presumptive prechordal plate of **mesodermal cells.** Immediately in front of the notochordal region lies the presumptive neural area in the form of a crescent with its crescentic arms extending in a lateral direc-

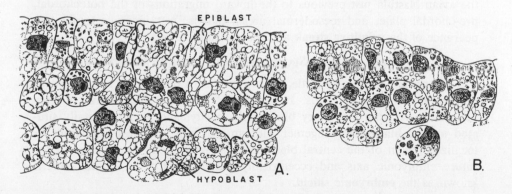

EPIBLAST

HYPOBLAST

A.

B.

FIG. 172. Delamination of hypoblast (entoderm) cells from upper or epiblast layer in the chick blastoderm. (A) Posterior end of blastoderm (cf. fig. 171A). (B) Anterior end of blastoderm.

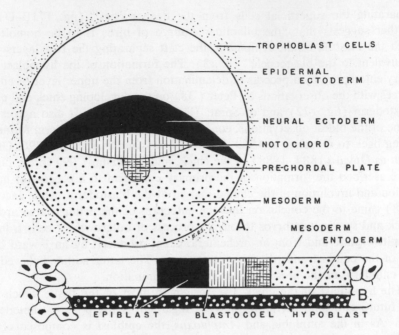

FIG. 173. Presumptive organ-forming areas in the chick blastoderm. (A) Slightly modified from Spratt, '46. (B) Schematic section of early chick blastoderm passing through antero-posterior median axis.

tion from the midline of the future embryonic axis. Anterior to the neural crescent is the presumptive epidermal crescent. Within the area opaca is found potential blood-vessel and blood-cell-forming tissue, as well as the extensive extra-embryonic-tissue materials.

The above description of the presumptive organ-forming areas pertains to the avian blastula just previous to the inward migrations of the notochordal, pre-chordal plate, and mesodermal areas; that is, just previous to the appearance of the **primitive streak** and the gastrulative process.

4. PRIMARY AND SECONDARY REPTILIAN BLASTULAE

The primary blastula of turtle, snake, and lizard embryos is akin in essential features to that of birds. It consists of a **central blastoderm** or area pellucida, overlying a primary blastocoelic cavity, and a more distally situated **opaque blastoderm,** together with an indefinite **periblast syncytium.** A localized region of the central blastoderm, situated along the midline of the future embryonic axis and eccentrically placed toward the caudal end, is known as the **embryonic shield.**

A specialized, posterior portion of the embryonic shield, in which the upper layer (epiblast) is not separated from the underlying cells (hypoblast), is known as the **primitive plate** (fig. 174A–D). (Consult also Will, 1892, for

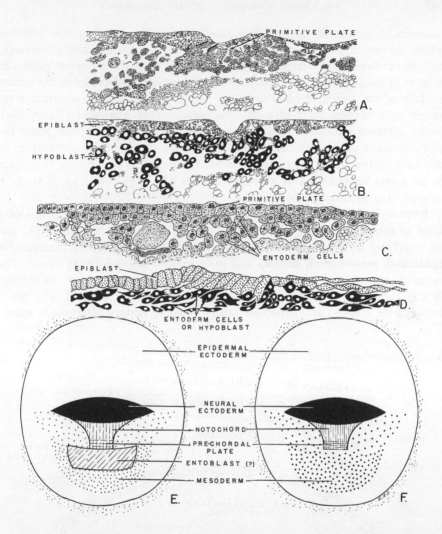

FIG. 174. Formation of hypoblast (entoderm) layer in certain reptiles; major presumptive organ-forming areas of reptilian blastoderm. (A) Section through blastoderm of the turtle, *Clemmys leprosa*. This section passes through the primitive plate in the region where the entoderm cells are rapidly budded off (invaginated?) from the surface layer. It presumably passes through (E) in the area marked entoblast. It is difficult to determine whether the entoderm cells are actually invaginated, according to the view of Pasteels, or whether this area represents a region where cells are delaminated or budded off in a rapid fashion from the overlying cells. (B) Similar to (A), diagrammatized to show hypoblast cells in black. (C) Section through early blastoderm of the gecko, *Platydactylus*. Epiblast cells are shown above, primitive entoderm cells below. (D) A later stage showing primitive plate area with the appearance of a delamination or proliferation of entoderm (hypoblast) cells from the upper layer of cells. (E) Presumptive, organ-forming areas of the turtle, *Clemmys leprosa*, before gastrulation. (F) Presumptive, organ-forming areas of the epiblast of turtle and other reptiles if the hypoblast is budded off or separated from the underside of the epiblast without invagination. It is to be observed that B and D represent modifications by the author.

361

accurate diagrams of the reptilian blastoderm.) Surrounding the primitive plate, the central blastoderm is thinner and is but one (occasionally two cells) cell in thickness (see margins of figs. 174A, C). As development proceeds, a layer of cells appears to be delaminated or proliferated off from the under-surface of the primitive plate area (fig. 174C, D). This delamination gives origin to a second layer of cells, the **entoderm or hypoblast** (Peter, '34). Some of these entodermal cells may arise by delamination from more pe-ripheral areas of the central blastoderm outside the primitive plate area. In the case of the turtle, *Clemmys leprosa,* Pasteels ('37a) believes that there is an actual invagination of entodermal cells (fig. 174A–B). More study is needed to substantiate this view.

Eventually, therefore, a **secondary blastula** arises which is composed of a floor of entodermal cells, the hypoblast, closely associated with the yolk, and an overlying layer or epiblast. The epiblast layer is formed of presumptive **epidermal, mesodermal, neural,** and **notochordal, organ-forming areas.** The essential arrangement of the presumptive organ-forming areas in the reptiles is very similar to that described for the secondary avian blastula. The space between the epiblast and hypoblast layers is the **secondary blastocoelic space.**

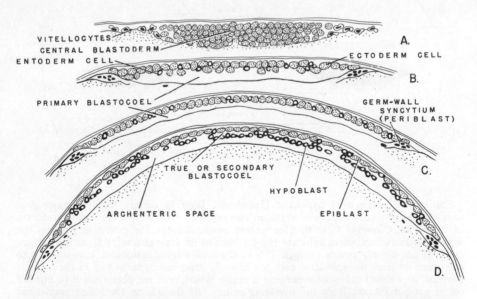

FIG. 175. Early blastoderms of the prototherian mammal, *Echidna.* (A) Early blasto-derm showing central mass of cells with peripherally placed vitellocytes. (B) Later blastoderm. Central cells are expanding and the blastoderm is thinning out. Smaller cells (in black) are migrating into surface layer. Vitellocytes have fused to form a peripheral syncytial tissue. (C) Later blastoderm composed of a single layer of cells of two kinds. The smaller cells in black represent potential entoderm cells. (D) Increase of hypoblast cells and their migration into the archenteric space below to form a second or hypoblast layer.

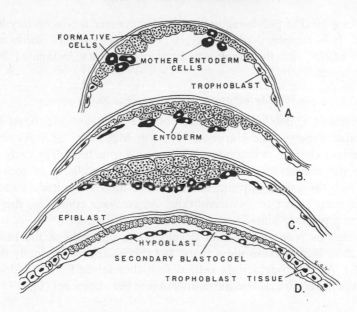

FORMATIVE CELLS

MOTHER ENTODERM CELLS

TROPHOBLAST

A.

ENTODERM

B.

C.

EPIBLAST

HYPOBLAST

SECONDARY BLASTOCOEL

TROPHOBLAST TISSUE

D.

FIG. 176. Early development of blastoderm of the opossum. (Modified from Hartman, '16.) (A) Blastocyst wall composed of one layer of cells from which entoderm cells are migrating inward. (B–D) Later development of the formative portion of the blastoderm. Two layers of cells are present in the formative area, viz., an upper epiblast layer and a lower hypoblast. Trophoblast cells are shown at the margins of the epiblast and hypoblast layers.

Both hypoblast and epiblast are connected peripherally with the periblast tissue.

5. Formation of the Late Mammalian Blastocyst (Blastula)

a. Prototherian Mammal, Echidna

In *Echidna,* according to Flynn and Hill ('39, '42), a blastoderm somewhat comparable to that of reptiles and birds is produced. An early primary blastular condition is first established, consisting of a mass of central cells with specialized vitellocytes at its margin (fig. 175A). A little later, an extension of this blastoderm occurs, and a definite **primary blastocoelic space** is formed below the blastoderm (fig. 175B). During this transformation, small, deeper lying cells (shown in black, fig. 175B) move up to the surface and become associated with the thinning blastoderm which essentially becomes a single layer of cells (fig. 175C). The marginal vitellocytes in the meantime fuse to form a **germ-wall syncytium.** This state of development may be regarded as the fully developed **primary blastula.** A little later, this primary condition becomes converted into a two-layered, **secondary blastula,** as shown in figure 175D by the secondary multiplication and migration inward of the small cells to form a lower layer or **hypoblast.** The latter process may be regarded as a kind of **polyinvagination.** In this manner the secondary blastula is formed. It is composed of two layers of cells, the epiblast above and the hypoblast below with the secondary blastocoelic space insinuated between these two layers.

b. Metatherian Mammal, Didelphys

The opossum, *Didelphys virginiana,* possesses a hollow blastocyst akin to the eutherian variety. (See Hartman, '16, '19; McCrady, '38.) As observed in the previous chapter, it is produced by a peculiar method. The early blasto-meres do not adhere together to form a typical morula as in most other forms; rather, they move outward and adhere to the zona pellucida and come to line the inner aspect of this membrane. As cleavage continues, they even-tually form a primary blastula with an enlarged blastocoel.

Following this primary phase of development, one pole of the blastocyst begins to show increased mitotic activity, and this polar area gradually thickens (fig. 176A). At this time certain cells detach themselves from the thickened polar area of the blastocyst and move inward into the blastocoel (fig. 176A, B).

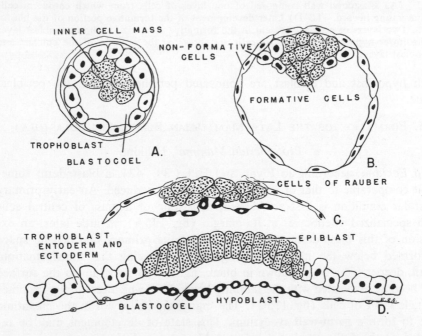

FIG. 177. Schematic drawings of early pig development. (A) Early developing blasto-cyst. (B) Later blastocyst, showing two kinds of cells in the inner cell mass. (C) Later blastocyst, showing disappearance of trophoblast cells overlying the inner cell mass. (D) Later blastocyst. Two layers of formative cells are present as indicated with tropho-blast tissue attached at the margins.

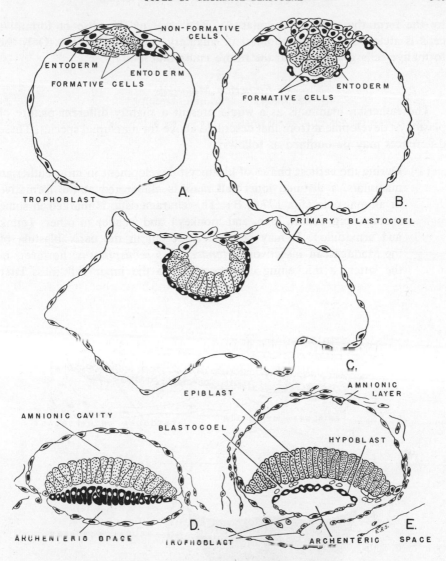

FIG. 178. Schematic drawings of the developing blastocyst of the monkey. (After Heuser and Streeter: Carnegie Inst., Washington, Publ. 538. Contrib. to Embryol. No. 181.)   (A, B) Early blastocysts showing formative and non-formative cells in the inner cell mass.   (C–E) Later arrangement of the formative cells into an upper epiblast and lower hypoblast layer.

These cells form the **mother entoderm cells,** and by mitotic activity they give origin to an entodermal layer which adheres to the underside of the thickened polar area (fig. 176B, C). The polar area then thins out to form the expansive condition shown in figure 176D. A bilaminar, disc-shaped area thus is formed in this immediate region of the blastocyst, and it represents the area occupied by the **formative cells** of the blastula. The edge of this disc of formative cells is attached to the trophoblast or auxiliary cells (fig. 176D). Only the formative cells give origin to the future embryonic body.

c. Eutherian Mammals

The eutherian mammals as a whole present a slightly different picture of blastocyst development from that described above for marsupial species. These differences may be outlined as follows:

(1) During the earliest phases of blastocyst development in most eutherian mammals, a distinct, **inner cell mass** is elaborated at the formative or animal pole (fig. 177A, B). This characteristic is marked in some species (pig, rabbit, man, and monkey) and weaker in others (mink and armadillo). It may be entirely absent in the early blastula of the Madagascan insectivore, *Hemicentetes semispinosus;* however, in the latter, a thickening corresponding to the inner cell mass later

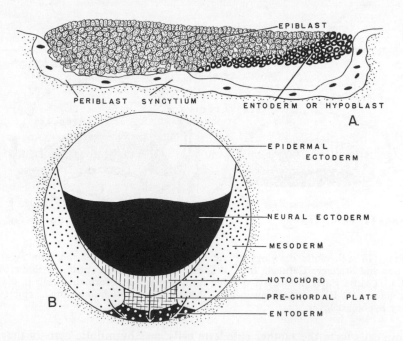

FIG. 179. Presumptive organ-forming areas in the blastoderm of the shark embryo. (A) Median section of the blastoderm of *Torpedo ocellata.* Hypoblast cells are shown in black. Caudal portion of the blastoderm is shown at the right. Cf. (B). (This figure partly modified from Ziegler, '02—see Chap. 6 for complete reference.) (B) Map of the presumptive organ-forming areas of the blastoderm of the shark, *Scyllium canicula.*

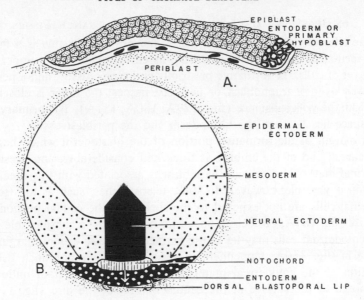

EPIBLAST
ENTODERM OR
PRIMARY
HYPOBLAST

PERIBLAST

A.

EPIDERMAL
ECTODERM

MESODERM

NEURAL ECTODERM

NOTOCHORD

B.

ENTODERM
DORSAL BLASTOPORAL LIP

FIG. 180. Presumptive organ-forming areas of the teleost fish blastoderm. (A) Median section through the late blastoderm of *Fundulus heteroclitus* just previous to gastrulation. Somewhat schematized from the author's sections. Presumptive entoderm or hypoblast is shown exposed to the surface at the caudal end of the blastoderm and, therefore, follows the conditions shown in (B). (D) Presumptive organ-forming areas of the blastoderm of *Fundulus heteroclitus*. Arrows show the direction of cell movements during gastrulation. (Modified from diagram by Oppenheimer, '36.)

appears. Within the inner cell mass, two types of cells are present, namely, **formative** and **trophoblast** (figs. 177B; 178A).

(2) Unlike that of the marsupial mammal, an overlying layer of trophoblast cells, covering the layer of formative cells, always is present (fig. 177B). In some cases (rabbit, pig, and cat) they degenerate (the cells of Rauber, fig. 177C), while in others (man, rat, and monkey) the overlying cells remain and increase in number (fig. 178A–E).

(3) The entodermal cells arise by a separation (delamination) of cells from the lower aspect of the inner cell mass (figs. 177C; 178A), with the exception of the armadillo where their origin is similar to that of marsupials. With these differences, the same essential goal arrived at in the marsupial mammals is achieved, namely, a bilaminar, formative area, the embryonic disc, composed of **epiblast** and **hypoblast layers** (figs. 177D; 178D, E), which ultimately gives origin to the embryonic body. A bilaminar, extra-embryonic, trophoblast area, consisting of extra-embryonic entoderm and ectoderm, also is formed (figs. 177D; 178D, E). The secondary blastocoel originates between the epiblast and hypoblast of the embryonic disc, while below the hypoblast layer is the archenteric space (fig. 178E).

6. Blastulae of Teleost and Elasmobranch Fishes

In the teleost and elasmobranch fishes, the primary blastula is a flattened, disc-shaped structure constructed during its earlier stages of an upper blastoderm layer of cells, the formative or strictly embryonic tissue, and a peripheral and lower layer of trophoblast or periblast tissues; the latter is closely associated with the yolk substance (figs. 179A; 180A; 181A). The primary blastocoelic space lies between the blastoderm and the periblast tissue.

That margin of the formative portion of the blastoderm which lies at the future caudal end of the embryo is thickened considerably, and presumptive entodermal material or primary hypoblast is associated with this area. Its relationship is variable, however. In some teleost fishes, such as the trout, the entodermal cells are not exposed to the surface at the caudal portion of the blastodisc (fig. 181A; Pasteels, '36a). In other teleosts, a considerable portion of the entodermal cells may lie at the surface along the caudal margin of the blastoderm (fig. 180A; Oppenheimer, '36). In the elasmobranch fishes the disposition of the entodermal material is not clear. A portion undoubtedly lies exposed to the surface at the caudal margin of the disc (fig. 179A, B; Vandebroek, '36), but some entodermal cells lie in the deeper regions of the blastoderm (fig. 179A).

Turning now to a consideration of the other presumptive organ-forming areas of the fish blastoderm, we find that the presumptive pre-chordal plate material lies exposed on the surface in the median plane of the future embryo immediately in front of the entoderm and near the caudal edge of the blastoderm. (It is to be observed that, in comparison, the pre-chordal plate lies well forward within the area pellucida of the bird blastoderm.) This condition is found in the shark, *Scyllium,* in *Fundulus,* and in the trout, *Salmo* (figs. 179B; 180B). However, in the trout it lies a little more posteriorly *at the caudal margin* of the disc (fig. 181B). Anterior to the pre-chordal plate is the presumptive notochordal material, and anterior to the latter is a rather expansive region of presumptive neural cells. These three areas thus lie along the future median plane of the embryo, but they exhibit a considerable variation in size and in the extent of area covered in *Scyllium, Fundulus,* and *Salmo* (figs. 179, 180, 181).

Extending on either side of these presumptive organ-forming areas, is an indefinite region of potential mesoderm. In *Salmo,* presumptive mesodermal cells lie along the lateral and anterior portions of the blastoderm edge (fig. 181B). However, in *Scyllium* and in *Fundulus,* it is not as extensive (figs. 179B; 180B). In front of the presumptive neural organ-forming area is a circular region, the presumptive epidermal area.

In their development thus far the three blastulae described above represent a **primary blastular condition,** and the cavity between the blastodisc and the underlying trophoblast or periblast tissue forms a **primary blastocoel.** This condition presents certain resemblances to the early blastocyst in the higher

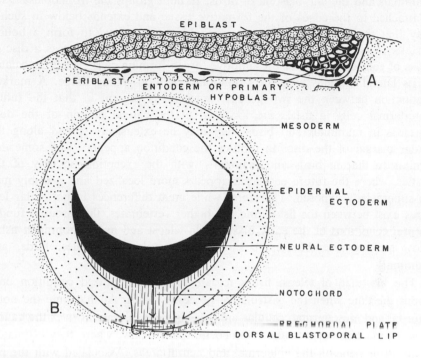

FIG. 181. Presumptive organ-forming areas of the blastoderm of the trout, *Salmo irideus*. (A) Schematized section through blastoderm just previous to gastrulation. Presumptive entoderm (hypoblast) shown in black at caudal end of the blastoderm. Observe that entoderm is not exposed to surface. Cf. (B). (B) Surface view of presumptive organ-forming areas of the blastoderm just before gastrulation.

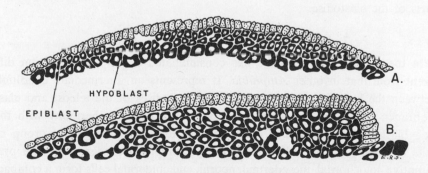

FIG. 182. Late blastoderms of *Gymnophiona*. (Modified from Brauer, 1897.) (A) Late blastoderm of *Hypogeophis alternans*. Entoderm cells in black lie below. (B) Beginning gastrula of *H. rostratus*. Observe blastocoelic spaces in white between the entoderm cells.

369

mammals and the late blastula of birds. In both groups the trophoblast tissue is attached to the edges of the formative tissue and extends below in such a way that the formative cells and trophoblast tissue tend to form a hollow vesicle. In both, the formative portion of the blastula is present as a disc or mass of cells composed of presumptive, organ-forming cells closely associated at its lateral margins with the trophoblast or food-getting tissue. A marked distinction between the two groups, however, is present in that the future entodermal cells in fishes are localized at the caudal margin of the disc, whereas in mammals and birds they may be extensively spread along the under margin of the disc. In reptiles the condition appears to be somewhat similar to that in birds and mammals, with the exception possibly of the turtles, where the future entoderm appears more localized and possibly may be superficially exposed. Therefore, while great differences in particular features exist between the fishes and the higher vertebrates, the essential fundamental conditions of the early blastulae in teleost and in elasmobranch fishes show striking resemblances to the early blastulae of reptiles, birds, and mammals.

The blastulae of teleost fishes remain in this generalized condition until about the time when the gastrulative processes begin. At that time the notochordal and mesodermal, cellular areas begin their migrations over the caudal edge of the blastodisc to the blastocoelic space below, where they ultimately come to lie beneath the epidermal and neural areas. Associated with the migration of notochordal and mesodermal cells, an entodermal floor or **secondary hypoblast** is established below the notochordal and mesodermal cells by the active migration of primary hypoblast cells in an antero-lateral direction. In the elasmobranch fishes there is a similar cell movement from the caudal disc margin, as found in teleost fishes, but, in addition, a delamination of entodermal (and possibly mesodermal cells) occurs from the deeper lying parts of the blastodisc.

7. Blastulae of Gymnophionan *Amphibia*

In the *Gymnophiona,* nature has consummated a blastular condition different from that in other *Amphibia.* It represents an intermediate condition between the blastula of the frog and the blastodiscs of the teleost and elasmobranch fishes and of higher vertebrates (fig. 182). In harmony with the frog blastula, for example, a specialized periblast or food-getting group of cells is absent. On the other hand, the presumptive entoderm and the presumptive notochordal, mesodermal, neural, and epidermal cells form a compact mass at one pole of the egg, as in teleosts, the chick, and mammal. Similar to the condition in the chick and mammal, the entodermal cells delaminate (see Chap. 9) from the under surface of the blastodisc (Brauer, 1897).

Bibliography

Assheton, R. **1896.** An experimental examination into the growth of the blastoderm of the chick. Proc. Roy. Soc., London, s.B. **60**:349.

Baer, K. E., von. **1828–1837.** Über Entwickelungsgeschichte der Thiere. Beobachtung und Reflexion. Bornträger, Königsberg.

Boveri, T. **1892.** Über die Entstehung des gegensatzes zwischen den Geschlechtszellen und den somatischen Zellen bei *Ascaris megalocephala,* etc., in: Sitz. d. gesellsch. d. Morph. u. Physiol. München. vol. **8.**

Brauer, A. **1897,** Beiträge zur Kenntniss der Entwicklungsgeschichte und der Anatomie der *Gymnophionen.* Zool. Jahrb. **10**:389.

Conklin, E. G. **1905.** The organization and cell-lineage of the ascidian egg. J. Acad. Nat. Sc., Philadelphia. **13**:3.

——. **1932.** The embryology of *Amphioxus.* J. Morphol. **54**:69.

——. **1933.** The development of isolated and partially separated blastomeres of *Amphioxus.* J. Exper. Zool. **64**:303.

Duval, M. **1884.** De la formation du blastoderme dans l'oeuf d'oiseau. Ann. d. Sc. Nat., VIᵉ Série. **18**:1.

——. **1889.** Atlas d'embryologie. G. Masson, éditeur. Librairie de l'académie de médicine, Paris.

Flynn, T. T. and Hill, J. P. **1939.** The development of the *Monotremata.* IV. Growth of the ovarian ovum, maturation, fertilization and early cleavage. Trans. Zool. Soc., London, s.A. **24**: Part 6, 445.

—— and ——. **1942.** The later stages of cleavage and the formation of the primary germ layers in the *Monotremata* (preliminary communication). Proc. Zool. Soc., London, s.A. **111**:233.

Haeckel, E. **1866.** Generelle Morphologie. Reimer, Berlin.

——. **1872.** Die Kalkschwämme. Eine Monographie. Reimer, Berlin.

——. **1874.** Vols. 1 and 2 in the English translation, **1910.** The Evolution of Man, translated by J. McCabe. G. P. Putnam's Sons, New York.

Hartman, C. G. **1916.** Studies in the development of the opossum, *Didelphys virginiana.* I. History of early cleavage. II. Formation of the blastocyst. J. Morphol. **27**:1.

——. **1919.** III. Description of new material on maturation, cleavage and entoderm formation. IV. The bilaminar blastocyst. J. Morphol. **32**:1.

Hörstadius, S. **1928.** Über die determination des Keimes bei Echinodermen. Acta Zool. Stockholm. **9**:1.

——. **1937.** Investigations as to the localization of the micromere-, the skeleton-, and the entoderm-forming material in the unfertilized egg of *Arbacia punctulata.* Biol. Bull. **73**:295.

Huxley, T. H. **1849.** On the anatomy and affinities of the family of the *Medusae.* Philos. Tr. Roy. Soc., London, s.B. **139**:413.

——. **1888.** Anatomy of Invertebrated Animals. D. Appleton & Co., New York.

Jacobson, W. **1938.** The early development of the avian embryo. I. Entoderm formation. J. Morphol. **62**:415.

Kionka, H. **1894.** Die Furchung des Hühnereies. Anat. Hefte. **3**:428.

Kleinenberg, N. **1872.** *Hydra.* Eine Monographie. Engelmann, Leipzig.

Kowalewski, A. **1867.** Entwicklungsgeschichte des *Amphioxus lanceolatus.* Mém. Acad. imp d. sc. de St. Petersburg, VIIᵉ Série. **11**: No. 4.

Lankester, R. **1877.** Notes on the embryology and classification of the animal kingdom. Quart. J. M. Sc. **17**:399.

McCrady, E., Jr. **1938.** The embryology of the opossum. Am. Anat. Memoirs, 16, The Wistar Institute of Anatomy and Biology, Philadelphia.

Morgan, T. H. **1934.** Embryology and Genetics. Columbia University Press, New York.

Öllacher, J. **1869.** Untersuchungen über die Furchung und Blätterbildung im Hühnerei. Inst. f. Exper. Path., Wien. **1**:54.

Oppenheimer, J. M. **1936.** Processes of localization in developing *Fundulus*. J. Exper. Zool. **73**:405.

———. **1940.** The non-specificity of the germ layers. Quart. Rev. Biol. **15**:1.

Pander, H. C. **1817.** Beiträge zur Entwickelungsgeschichte des Hühnchens im Eye. Würzburg.

Pasteels, J. **1936a.** Etude sur la gastrulation des vertébrés méroblastiques. I. Téléostéens. Arch. biol., Paris. **47**:205.

———. **1937a.** Etudes sur la gastrulation des vertebrés méroblastiques. II. Reptiles. Arch. biol., Paris. **48**:105.

———. **1937b.** III. Oiseaux. Arch. biol., Paris. **48**:381.

———. **1945.** On the formation of the primary entoderm of the duck *(Anas domestica)* and on the significance of the bilaminar embryo in birds. Anat. Rec. **93**:5.

Patterson, J. T. **1909.** Gastrulation in the pigeon's egg—a morphological and experimental study. J. Morphol. **20**:65.

Peter, K. **1934.** Die erste Entwicklung des Chamäleons *(Chamaeleon vulgaris)* vergleichen mit der Eidechse (Ei, Keimbildung, Furchung, Entodermobildung). Zeit. f. anat. u. Entwicklngesch. Abteil. 2, **102–103**:11.

———. **1938.** Untersuchungen über die Entwicklung des Dotter entoderms. 1. Die Entwicklung des Entoderms beim Hühnchen. 2. Die Entwicklung des Entoderms bei der Taube. Zeit. mikr.-anat. Forsch. **43**:362 and 416.

Spratt, N. T., Jr. **1942.** Location of organ-specific regions and their relationship to the development of the primitive streak in the early chick blastoderm. J. Exper. Zool. **89**:69.

———. **1946.** Formation of the primitive streak in the explanted chick blastoderm marked with carbon particles. J. Exper. Zool. **103**:259.

Vandebroek, G. **1936.** Les mouvements morphogénétiques au cours de la gastrulation chez *Scyllium canicula* Cuv. Arch. biol., Paris. **47**:499.

Vogt, W. **1925.** Gestaltungsanalyse am Amphibienkeim mit örtlicher Vitalfärbung. Vorwort über Wege und Ziele. I. Methodik und Wirkungsweise der örtlichen Vitalfärbung mit Agar als Farbträger. Arch. f. Entwicklngsmech. d. Organ. **106**:542.

———. **1929.** Gestaltungsanalyse, etc. II. Teil. Gastrulation und Mesodermbildung bei *Urodelen* und *Anuren*. Arch. f. Entwicklngsmech. d. Organ. **120**:384.

Wheeler, W. M. **1898.** Caspar Friedrich Wolff and the Theoria Generationis. Biological Lectures, Marine Biol. Lab., Woods Hole, Mass. Ginn & Co., Boston.

Whitman, C. O. **1878.** The embryology of *Clepsine*. Quart. J. M. Sc. **18**:215.

Will, L. **1892.** Beiträge zur Entwicklungsgeschichte der Reptilien. I. Die Anlage der Keimblätter beim Gecko *(Platydactylus facetanus Schreib)*. Zool. Jahrb. **6**:1.

Wilson, E. B. **1892.** The cell lineage of *Nereis*. J. Morphol. **6**:361.

———. **1898.** Cell-Lineage and ancestral reminiscence. Biological Lectures, Marine Biol. Lab., Woods Hole, Mass. Ginn & Co., Boston.

———. **1925.** The Cell in Development and Heredity. 3rd edit. The Macmillan Co., New York.

Wolff, C. F. **1759.** Theoria Generationis. Halle.

———. **1812.** De formatione intestinorum praecipe, etc. Published in Latin in Vols. 12 and 13 of St. Petersburg Commentaries (Acad. Sci. Impt. Petropol. 1768–69) and translated by J. F. Meckel, in Über die Bildung des Darmkanals im bebrüteten Hühnchen, Halle.

Zur Strassen, O. **1896.** Embryonalentwickelung der *Ascaris megalocephala.* Arch. f. Entwicklngsmech. **3**:27, 133.

8

The Late Blastula in Relation to Certain Innate
Physiological Conditions: Twinning

A. Introduction
B. Problem of differentiation
   1. Definition of differentiation; kinds of differentiation
   2. Self-differentiation and dependent differentiation
C. Concept of potency in relation to differentiation
   1. Definition of potency
   2. Some terms used to describe different states of potency
      a. Totipotency and harmonious totipotency
      b. Determination and potency limitation
      c. Prospective potency and prospective fate
      d. Autonomous potency
      e. Competence
D. The blastula in relation to twinning
   1. Some definitions
      a. Dizygotic or fraternal twins
      b. Monozygotic or identical twins
      c. Polyembryony
   2. Basis of true or identical twinning
   3. Some experimentally produced, twinning conditions
E. Importance of the organization center of the late blastula

A. Introduction

In the preceding two chapters the blastula is defined as a morphological entity composed of six, presumptive, organ-forming areas—areas which are poised and ready for the next phase of development or gastrulation. However, the attainment of this morphological condition with its presumptive, organ-forming areas is valid and fruitful in a developmental way only if it has developed within certain physiological conditions which serve as a spark to initiate gastrulation and carry it through to its completion.

The physiological conditions of the blastula are attained, as are its morphological characteristics, through a process of **differentiation.** Moreover, during the development of the blastula, different areas acquire different abilities to undergo physiological change and, hence, possess different abilities or powers of differentiation. To state the matter differently, the various, presumptive, organ-forming areas of the blastula have acquired different abilities not only in their power to produce specific organs of the future body of the embryo, but also in that *some presumptive areas possess this propensity in a greater degree than do other areas.* However, at this point, certain terms in common usage relating to the problem of differentiation are defined in order that a better understanding may be obtained concerning the ability to differentiate on the part of the presumptive, organ-forming areas of the late blastula.

B. Problem of Differentiation

1. Definition of Differentiation; Kinds of Differentiation

The word **differentiation** is applied to that phase of development when a cell, a group of cells, cell product *experiences a change which results in a persistent alteration of its activities.* Under ordinary conditions an alteration in structure or function is the only visible evidence that such a change has occurred.

To illustrate these matters, let us recall the conditions involved in the maturation of the egg. A subtle change occurs within the primitive oogonium which causes it to enlarge and to grow. This growth results in an increase in size and change in structure of both the cytoplasm and the nucleus. A little later, as the egg approaches that condition which is called maturity, observable morphological changes of the nucleus occur which accompany or initiate an invisible change in behavior. These latter changes make the egg fertilizable. Here we have illustrated, first of all, a subtle, invisible, biochemical change in the oogonium which arouses the formation of visible morphological changes in the oocyte and, secondly, a morphological change (i.e., nuclear maturation) which accompanies an invisible physiological transformation.

Another illustration will prove profitable. Let us recall the development of the mammary-gland tissue (fig. 58). Through the action of the lactogenic (luteotrophic) hormone, LTH, the cells of the various acini of the fully developed gland begin to secrete milk. The acini, it will be recalled, were caused to differentiate as a result of the presence of progesterone. Similarly, the various parts of the complicated duct system were stimulated to differentiate from a very rudimentary condition by the presence of estrogenic hormone. Earlier in development, however, the particular area of the body from which the duct rudiments ultimately arose was conditioned by a change which dictated the origin of the duct rudiments from the cells of this area and restricted their origin from other areas.

In the foregoing history of the mammary gland, various types of differentiation are exemplified. The final elaboration of milk from the acinous cells is effected by a change in the activity of the cells under the influence of LTH. The type of change which brings about the functional activities of a structure is called **physiological differentiation.** The morphological changes in the cells which result in the formation of the duct system and the acini are examples of **morphological differentiation.** On the other hand, the invisible, subtle change or changes which originally altered the respective cells of the nipple area and, thereby, *ordained* or *determined* that the cells in this particular locale should produce duct and nipple tissue is an example of **biochemical differentiation or chemodifferentiation.** Chemodifferentiation, morphological differentiation, and physiological differentiation, therefore, represent the three types or levels of differentiation. Moreover, all of these differentiations stem from *a persistent change in the fundamental activities of cells or cell parts.*

It should be observed further that *chemodifferentiation represents the initial step in the entire differentiation process,* for it is this change which *determines or restricts the future possible activities and changes* which the cell or cells in a particular area may experience. Also, in many cases, differentiation appears to arise as a result of stimuli which are applied to the cell or cells externally. That is, internal changes within a cell may be *called forth* by an environmental change applied to the cell from without.

In embryological thinking, therefore, the word differentiation implies a process of becoming something new and different from an antecedent, less-differentiated condition. But beyond this, differentiation also connotes a certain **suitableness** or **purposefulness** of the structure which is differentiated. Such a connotation, however, applies only to **normal embryonic differentiation;** abnormal growths and monstrosities of many kinds may fulfill the first phase (i.e., of producing something new) of differentiation as defined in the first sentence of this paragraph, but they do not satisfy the criteria of purpose and of suitableness within the organized economy of the developing body as a whole. It is important to keep the latter implications in mind, for various structures may appear to be vestigial or aberrant during embryonic development, nevertheless their presence may assume an important, purposeful status in the ultimate scheme which constructs the organization of the developing body.

2. Self-Differentiation and Dependent Differentiation

In the amphibian, very late blastula and beginning gastrula, the presumptive, chordamesodermal area, when undisturbed and in its normal position in the embryo, eventually differentiates into notochordal and mesodermal tissues. This is true also when it is transplanted to other positions. That is, at this period in the history of the chordamesodermal cells the ability resides within the cells to differentiate into notochordal and mesodermal structures. Consequently, these cells are not dependent upon surrounding or external factors to induce or call forth differentiation in these specific directions. Embryonic cells in this condition are described as **self-differentiating** (Roux). Similarly, the entodermal area with its potential subareas of liver, foregut, and intestine develops by itself and this area does not rely upon stimuli from other contiguous cells to realize a specific potency. On the other hand, the presumptive, neural plate region at this time is dependent upon the inducing influence of the chordamesodermal cells during the process of gastrulation for its future realization as neural tissue. This area has little inherent ability to differentiate neural tissue and is described, therefore, as being in a state of **dependent differentiation** (Roux). Furthermore, the presumptive skin ectoderm (i.e., epidermis), if left alone, will proceed to epidermize during gastrulation, but foreign influences, such as transplantation, into the future neural plate area may induce neural plate cells to form from the presumptive skin ectoderm (fig. 183). The differentiation of neural cells from any of the ectodermal cells of the late blastula thus is dependent upon special influencing factors applied to the cells from without.

C. Concept of Potency in Relation to Differentiation

1. DEFINITION OF POTENCY

The word potency, as used in the field of embryology, refers to that property of a cell which enables it to undergo differentiation. From this viewpoint, potency may be defined as *the power or ability of a cell to give origin to a specific kind of cell or structure or to various kinds of cells and structures.*

It is questionable, in a fundamental sense, whether potency actually is gained or lost during development. It may be that the expression of a given kind of potency, resulting in the formation of a specific type of cell, is merely the result of a restriction imposed upon other potentialities by certain modifying factors, while the total or latent potency remains relatively constant. All types of differentiated cells, from this point of view, basically are totipotent; that is, they possess the latent power to give origin to all the kinds of cells and tissues of the particular animal species to which they belong.

The specific potencies which denote the normal development of particular organs undoubtedly have their respective, although often quite devious, connections with the fertilized egg. However, one must concede the origin of abnormal or acquired potency values due to the insinuation of special inductive or modifying factors which disturb the expression of normal potency value. For example, tumors and other abnormal growths and tissue distortions may be examples of such special potencies induced by special conditions which upset the mechanism controlling normal potency expression.

2. SOME TERMS USED TO DESCRIBE DIFFERENT STATES OF POTENCY

a. Totipotency and Harmonious Totipotency

The word **totipotent,** as applied to embryonic development, was introduced into embryological theory by Wilhelm Roux, and it refers to the power or ability of an early blastomere or blastomeres of a particular animal species to give origin to the many different types of cells and structures characteristic of the individual species. Speculation concerning the meaning of totipotency of a single blastomere received encouragement from the discovery by Hans Driesch, in 1891, that an isolated blastomere of the two- or four-cell stage of the cleaving, sea-urchin's egg could give origin to a "perfect larva." Driesch described this condition as constituting an **equipotential state,** while Roux referred to it as a **totipotential condition.** As the word totipotential seems more fitting and better suited to describe the condition than the word equipotential, which simply means equal potency, the word totipotency is used herein. The word **omnipotent** is sometimes used to describe the totipotent condition; as it has connotations of supreme power, it will not be used.

The totipotent state is a concept which may be considered in different ways. In many instances it has been used as described above, namely, as a potency condition that has within it the ability to produce a *perfect* embryo or individual. The word also has been used, however, to describe a condition which is capable of giving origin to all or nearly all the cells and tissues of the body in a haphazard way but which are not necessarily organized to produce a normally formed body of the particular species. Therefore, as a basis for clear thinking, it is well to define two kinds of totipotency, namely, **totipotency** and **harmonious totipotency.** The former term is used to describe the ability of a cell or cell group to give origin to all or nearly all the different cells and tissues of the particular species to which it belongs, but it is lacking in the ability to organize them into an harmonious organism. **Harmonious totipotency,** on the other hand, is used to denote a condition which has the above ability to produce the various types of tissues of the species, but possesses, in addition, *the power to develop a perfectly organized body.*

The fertilized egg or the naturally parthenogenetic egg constitutes an **harmonious totipotential system.** This condition is true also of isolated blastomeres of the two- or four-blastomere stage of the sea-urchin development, as mentioned above, of the two-cell state of *Amphioxus,* or of the first two-blastomere stage of the frog's egg when the first cleavage plane bisects the gray crescent. However, in the eight-cell stage in these forms, potency becomes more limited in the respective cells of the embryo. *Restriction of potency, therefore, is indicated by a restriction of power to develop into a variety of cells and tissues, and potency restriction is a characteristic of cleavage and the blastulative process* (figs. 61; 163A; 163B). When a stage is reached in which the cells of a particular area are limited in potency value to the expression of one type of cell or tissue, the condition is spoken of as one of **unipotency.** A **pluripotent state,** on the other hand, is a condition in which the potency is not so limited, and two or more types of tissues may be derived from the cell or cells.

b. Determination and Potency Limitation

The limitation or restriction of potency, therefore, may form a part of the process of differentiation; as such, it is a characteristic feature of embryonic development. Potency limitation, however, is not always the result of the differentiation process. For instance, in the development of the oocyte in the ovary, the building up of the various conditions, characteristic of the totipotent state, is a feature of the differentiation of the oocyte.

The word **determination** *is applied to those unknown and invisible changes occurring within a cell or cells which effect a limitation or restriction of potency.* As a result of this potency limitation, differentiation becomes restricted to a specific channel of development, denoting a particular kind of cell or structure. Ultimately, by the activities of limiting influences upon the resulting blastomeres during cleavage, the totipotent condition of the mature egg becomes dismembered and segregated into a patchwork or mosaic of general areas of the blastula, each area having a generalized, presumptive, organ-forming potency. As we have already observed, in the mature chordate blastula there are six of these **major, presumptive organ-forming areas** (five if we regard the two mesodermal areas as one). By the application of other limiting influences during gastrulation or the next phase of development, each of these general areas becomes divided into **minor areas** which are limited to a potency value of a particular organ or part of an organ. The process which brings about the determination of individual organs or parts of organs is called **individuation.**

When potency limitation has reduced generalized and greater potency value to the status of a general organ system (e.g., nervous system or digestive system) with the determination (i.e., individuation) of particular organs within such a system, the condition is described as one of **rigid or irrevocable determination.** Such tissues, transplanted to other parts of the embryo favorable for their development, tend to remain limited to an expression of one inherent potency value and *do not give origin to different* kinds of tissues or organs. Thus, determined liver rudiment will differentiate into liver tissue, stomach rudiment into stomach tissue, forebrain material into forebrain tissue, etc.

In many instances determination within a group of cells is brought about because of their position in the developing organism and not because of intrinsic, self-differentiating conditions within the cells. Because their position foreordains their determination in the future, the condition is spoken of as **positional or presumptive determination.** For example, in the late amphibian blastula, the composite ectodermal area of the epiblast will become divided, during the next phase of development, into **epidermal** and **neural areas** as a result of the influences at work during gastrulation, especially the activities of the chordamesodermal area. Therefore, one may regard these areas as already determined, in a *presumptive* sense, even in the late blastula, although their actual determination as definite epidermal and neural tissue will not occur until later.

As stated in the preceding paragraphs, *determination is the result of potency limitation or inhibition.* However, there is another aspect to determination, namely, **potency expression,** which simply means **potency release or development.** Potency expression, probably, is due to an activating stimulus (Spemann, '38). Consequently, the individuation of a particular organ structure within a larger system of organs is the result of two synchronous processes:

(1) *inhibition of potency or potencies* and

(2) *release or calling forth of a specific kind of potency* (Wigglesworth, '48).

Associated with the phenomenon of potency inhibition or limitation is the loss of power for regulation. Consequently, individuation and the loss of regulative power appear to proceed synchronously in any group of cells.

c. Prospective Potency and Prospective Fate

Prospective fate is the end or destiny that a group of cells normally reaches in its differentiation during its normal course of development in the embryo. The presumptive epidermal area of the late blastula differentiates normally into skin epidermis. *This is its prospective fate.* Its **prospective potency,** however, is greater, for under certain circumstances it may be induced, by transplantation to other areas of the late blastula, to form other tissue, e.g., neural plate cells or mesodermal tissues.

d. Autonomous Potency

Autonomous potency is the inherent ability which a group of cells possesses to differentiate into a **definite structure or structures,** e.g., notochord, stomach, or liver rudiments of the late blastula of the frog.

Versatility of autonomous potency is the *inherent ability* which a group of cells possesses to differentiate, *when isolated under cultural conditions outside the embryo,* into tissues not normally developed from the particular cell group in normal development. In the amphibian late blastula this is true of the notochordal and somitic areas of the chordamesodermal area, which may give origin to skin or neural plate tissue under these artificially imposed conditions.

e. Competence

Certain areas of the late amphibian blastula have the ability to differentiate into diverse structures under the stimulus of varied influence. Consequently, we say that these areas have competence for the production of this or that structure. The word **competence** *is used to denote all of the possible reactions which a group of cells may produce under various sorts of stimulations.* The entodermal area of the late amphibian blastula and early gastrula *has great power for self-differentiation but no competence,* whereas the general, neural plate-epidermal area *has competence but little power of self-*

differentiation (see p. 375). On the other hand, the notochord, mesodermal area possesses *both competence and the ability for self-differentiation.*

Competence appears to be a function of a developmental time sequence. That is, the time or period of development is all important, for a particular area may possess competence only at a single, optimum period of development. The word competence is sometimes used to supersede the other terms of **potency** or **potentiality** (Needham, '42, p. 112).

D. The Blastula in Relation to Twinning

1. SOME DEFINITIONS

a. Dizygotic or Fraternal Twins

Fraternal twins arise from the fertilization of two separate eggs in a species which normally produces one egg in the reproductive cycle, as, for example, in the human species. Essentially, fraternal twins are much the same as the "siblings" of a human family (i.e., the members born as a result of separate pregnancies) or the members of a litter of several young produced during a single pregnancy in animals, such as cats, dogs, pigs, etc. Fraternal twins are often called "false twins."

b. Monozygotic or Identical Twins

This condition is known as "true twinning," and it results from the development of two embryos from a single egg. Such twins presumably have an identical genetic composition.

c. Polyembryony

Polyembrony is a condition in which several embryos normally arise from one egg. It occurs regularly in armadillos *(Dasypopidae)* where one ovum gives origin normally to four identical embryos (fig. 186).

2. BASIS OF TRUE OR IDENTICAL TWINNING

The work of Driesch (1891) on the cleaving, sea-urchin egg and that of Wilson (1893) on the isolated blastomeres of *Amphioxus* mentioned above initiated the approach to a scientific understanding of monozygotic or identical twinning. Numerous studies have been made in the intervening years on the developing eggs of various animal species, vertebrate and invertebrate, and from these studies has emerged the present concept concerning the matter of twinning. True twinning appears to arise from four, requisite, fundamental, morphological and physiological conditions. These conditions are as follows:

(1) there must be a sufficient protoplasmic substrate;
(2) the substrate must contain all the organ-forming stuffs necessary to assure totipotency, that is, to produce all the necessary organs;

(3) an organization center or the ability to develop such a center must be present in order that the various organs may be integrated into an harmonious whole; and

(4) the ability or faculty for regulation, that is, the power to rearrange materials as well as to reproduce and compensate for the loss of substance, must be present.

3. Some Experimentally Produced, Twinning Conditions

The isolation of the first two blastomeres in the sea-urchin egg and in *Amphioxus* with the production of complete embryos from each blastomere

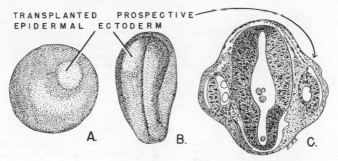

TRANSPLANTED PROSPECTIVE
EPIDERMAL ECTODERM

A. B. C.

Fig. 183 Early gastrula of darkly pigmented *Triton taeniatus* with a small piece of presumptive ectoderm of *T. cristatus* lightly pigmented inserted into the presumptive, neural plate area shown in (A). (B) Later stage of development. (C) Cross section of the later embryo. The lighter eye region shown to the right was derived from the original implant from *T. cristatus*. (After Spemann, '38.)

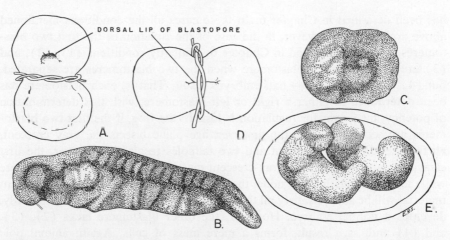

DORSAL LIP OF BLASTOPORE

A. C.

D.

B. E.

Fig. 184. Demonstration that the presence of the organizer region or organization center is necessary for development. (Redrawn from Spemann, '38.) (A) Hair-loop constriction isolates the organizer areas in the dorsal portion of the early gastrula. (B) Later development of the dorsal portion isolated in (A). (C) Later development of ventral portion of gastrula isolated in (A). (D) Constriction of organizer area of early gastrula into two halves. (E) Result of constriction made in (D). Constrictions were made at 2-cell stage.

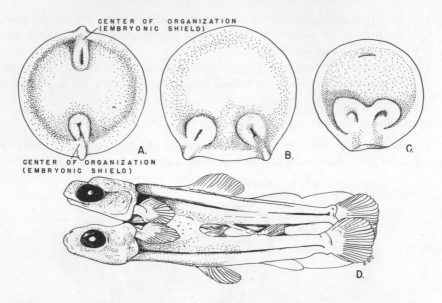

FIG. 185. Twinning in teleost fishes. (After Morgan, '34; *Embryology and Genetics,* Columbia University Press, pp. 102–104. A, B, C from Rauber; D from Stockard.) In certain teleost fishes, especially in the trout, under certain environmental conditions, two or more organization centers arise in the early gastrula.   (A–C) These represent such conditions. If they lie opposite each other as in (A), the resulting embryos often appear as in (D). If they lie nearer each other as in (B) or (C), a two-headed monster may be produced.

has been described in Chapter 6. In these cases all the conditions mentioned above are fulfilled. However, in the case of the isolation of the first two blastomeres in *Styela* described in Chapter 6, evidently conditions (1), (2), and (3) are present in each blastomere when the two blastomeres are separated, but (4) is absent and only half embryos result. That is, each blastomere has been **determined** as either a **right** or **left** blastomere; with this determination of potency, the power for regulation is lost. In the frog, if the first two blastomeres are separated when the first cleavage plane bisects the gray crescent, all four conditions are present and two tadpoles result. If, however, the first cleavage plane separates the gray-crescent material mainly into one blastomere while the other gets little or none, the blastomere containing the gray-crescent material will be able to satisfy all the requirements above, and it, consequently, develops a normal embryo. However, the other blastomere lacks (2), (3), and (4) and, as a result, forms a mere mass of cells. Again, animal pole blastomeres, even when they contain the gray-crescent material, when separated entirely from the yolk blastomeres, fail to go beyond the late blastular or beginning gastrular state (Vintemberger, '36). Such animal pole blastomeres appear to lack requirements (1), (2), and possibly (3) above. Many other illustrations of embryological experiments could be given, establishing

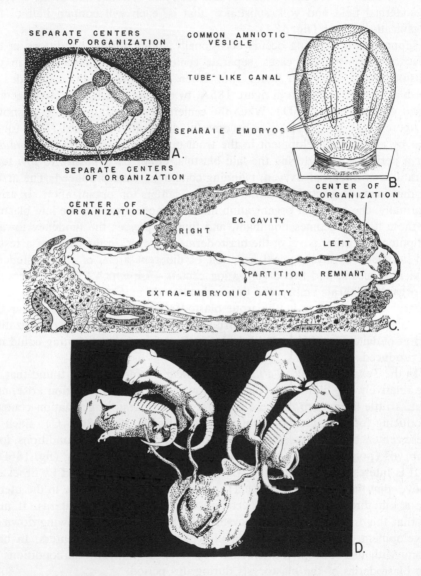

FIG. 186. Polyembryony or the development of multiple embryos in the armadillo, *Tatusia novemcincta*. (After Patterson, '13.) (A) Separate centers of organization in the early blastocyst. (B) Later stage in development of multiple embryos. Each embryo is connected with a common amniotic vesicle. (C) Section through organization centers a and b in (A). The two centers of organization are indicated by thickenings at right and left. (D) Later development of four embryos, the normal procedure from one fertilized egg in this species.

the necessity for the presence of all the above conditions. Successful whole embryos have resulted in the amphibia when the two-cell stage and beginning gastrula is bisected in such a manner that each half contains half of the chorda-mesodermal field and yolk substance; that is, each will contain half of the organization center (fig. 184).

Monozygotic twinning occurs occasionally under normal conditions in the teleost fishes. In these cases, separate centers of organization arise in the blastoderm, as shown in figure 185. When they arise on opposite sides of the blastoderm, as shown in figure 185A, twins arise which may later become fused ventrally (fig. 185D). When the centers of organization arise as shown in figure 185B, C, the embryos become fused laterally. Stockard ('21) found that by arresting development in the trout or in the blastoderm of *Fundulus* for a period of time during the late blastula, either by exposure to low tem-peratures or a lack of oxygen, twinning conditions were produced. The arrest of development probably allows separate centers of organization to arise. Normally, one center of organization makes its appearance in the late blastula of these fishes, becomes dominant, and thus suppresses the tendency toward totipotency in other parts of the blastoderm. However, in the cases of arrested development, a physiological isolation of different areas of the blastoderm evidently occurs, and two organization centers arise which forthwith proceed to organize separate embryos in the single blastoderm. Conditions appear more favorable for twinning in the trout blastoderm than in *Fundulus*. After the late blastular period is past and gastrulation begins, i.e., after one organization center definitely has been established, Stockard found that twinning could not be produced.

In the Texas armadillo, *Tatusia novemcincta*, Patterson ('13) found that, in the relatively late blastocyst (blastula), two centers of organization arise, and that, a little later, each of these buds into two separate organization centers, producing four organization centers in the blastula (fig. 186A–C). Each of these centers organizes a separate embryo; hence, under normal conditions, four embryos (polyembryony) are developed from each fertilized egg (fig. 186D).

It is interesting in connection with the experiments mentioned by Stockard above, that the blastocyst (blastula) in *Tatusia* normally lies free in the uterus for about three weeks before becoming implanted upon the uterus. It may be that this free period of blastocystic existence results in a slowing down of development, permitting the origin of separate organization centers. In har-mony with this concept, Patterson ('13) failed to find mitotic conditions in the blastoderms of the blastocysts during this period.

In the chick it is possible to produce twinning conditions by separating the anterior end (Hensen's node) of the early primitive streak into two parts along the median axis of the developing embryo. Twins fused at the caudal end may be produced under these conditions. In the duck egg, Wolff and Lutz ('47) found that if the early blastoderm is cut through the primitive node

area (fig. 187A), two embryos are produced as in figure 187A'. However, if
the primitive node and primitive streak are split antero-posteriorly, as indicated in figure 187B, two embryos, placed as in figure 187B', are produced.

It is evident, therefore, that in the production of monozygotic twins, condition (3) or the presence of the ability to produce an organization center
is of greatest importance. In the case of the separation of the two blastomeres
of the two-cell stage in *Amphioxus* or of the division of the dorsal lip of the
early gastrula of the amphibian by a hair loop, as shown in figure 184, a
mechanical division and separation of the ability to produce an organization
center in each blastomere *(Amphioxus)* or of the separation into two centers
of the organization center already produced *(Amphibia)* is achieved. Once
these centers are *isolated,* they act independently, producing twin conditions,
providing the substrate is competent. Similar conditions evidently are produced in the duck-embryo experiments of Wolff and Lutz referred to above.

In some teleost blastulae, e.g., *Fundulus* and *Salmo,* during the earlier period
of development, it has been found possible to separate the early blastoderm
into various groups of cells (Oppenheimer, '47) or into quadrants (Luther,
'36), and a condition of totipotency is established in each part. **Totipotency**
appears thus to be a generalized characteristic in certain teleost blastoderms
during the earlier phases of blastular development. Harmonious totipotency,
however, appears not to be achieved in any one part of the blastodisc of
these species during the early conditions of blastular formation. During the

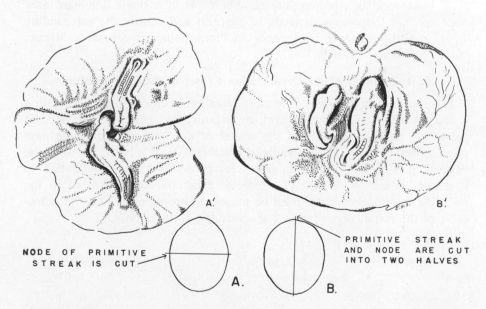

NODE OF PRIMITIVE
STREAK IS CUT

A.

PRIMITIVE   STREAK
AND NODE ARE CUT
INTO   TWO   HALVES

B.

FIG. 187. Isolation of the organization center in the early duck embryo. (From Dalcq,
'49, after Wolff and Lutz.)   (A') Derived from blastoderm cut as in (A).   (B') Derived
from blastoderm cut as in (B).

development of the late blastula, however, the posterior quadrant normally acquires a dominant condition together with a faculty for producing **harmonious totipotency.** The other totipotent areas then become suppressed. These basic conditions, therefore, serve to explain the experiments by Stockard ('21) referred to above, where two organization centers tend to become dominant as a result of isolating physiological conditions which tend to interfere with the processes working toward the development of but one center of organization. This probable explanation of the twinning conditions in the teleost blastoderm suggests strongly that the separation and isolation of separate organization centers is a fundamental condition necessary for the production of **monozygotic or true twinning.**

It becomes apparent, therefore, that, in the development of the trout blastoderm (blastula), the *development of an area which possesses a dominant organization center* is an important aspect of blastulation. In other blastulae, the seat or area of the organization center apparently is established at an earlier period, as, for example, the gray crescent in the amphibian egg which appears to be associated with the organization center during the late blastula state. Similarly, in the teleost fish, *Carassius,* totipotency appears to be limited to one part of the early blastula (Tung and Tung, '43).

It also follows from the analysis in the foregoing paragraphs that in the production of polyembryony in the armadillo or of spontaneous twinning in forms, such as the trout *(Salmo),* a generalized totipotency throughout the early blastoderm is a prerequisite condition. When a single dominant area once assumes totipotency, it tends to suppress and control the surrounding areas, probably because it succeeds in "monopolizing" certain, substrate, "food" substances (Dalcq, '49).

E. Importance of the Organization Center of the Late Blastula

It is also evident that one of the main functions of cleavage and blastulation is the formation of a physiological, or organization, center which must be present to dominate and direct the course of development during the next stage of development. Consequently, the elaboration of a blastocoel with the various, presumptive, organ-forming areas properly oriented in relation to it is not enough. A definite physiological condition entrenched within the so-called organization center must be present to arouse and direct the movement of the major, organ-forming areas during gastrulation.

Bibliography

Butler, E. **1935.** The developmental capacities of regions of the unincubated chick blastoderm as tested in chorioallantoic grafts. J. Exper. Zool. **70**:357.

Dalcq, A. M. **1949.** The concept of physiological competition (Spiegelman) and the interpretation of vertebrate morphogenesis. Experimental Cell Research, Supplement 1: p. 483. Academic Press, Inc., New York.

Driesch, H. **1891.** Entwicklungsmechanische Studien I–II. Zeit. Wiss. Zool. **53**:160.

Holtfreter, J. **1938.** Differenzierungspotenzen isolierter teile der Anuren-gastrula. Roux' Arch. f. Entwick. d. Organ. **138**:657.

Luther, W. **1936.** Potenzprüfungen an isolierten Teilstücken der Forellenkeimscheibe. Arch. f. Entwicklngsmech. d. Organ. **135**:359.

Morgan, T. H. **1934.** Chap. IX in Embryology and Genetics. Columbia University Press, New York.

Needham, J. **1942.** Biochemistry and Morphogenesis. Cambridge University Press, London.

Oppenheimer, J. M. **1947.** Organization of the teleost blastoderm. Quart. Rev. Biol. **22**:105.

Patterson, J. T. **1913.** Polyembryonic development in *Tatusia novemcincta*. J. Morphol. **24**:559.

Spemann, H. **1938.** Embryonic Development and Induction. Yale University Press, New Haven.

Stockard, C. R. **1921.** Developmental rate and structural expression: an experimental study of twins, "double monsters" and single deformities, and the interaction among embryonic organs during their origin and development. Am. J. Anat. **28**:115.

Tung, T. C. and Tung, Y. F. Y. **1943.** Experimental studies on the development of the goldfish. (Cited from Oppenheimer, '47.) Proc. Clin. Physiol. Soc. **2**:11.

Vintemberger, P. **1936.** Sur le développement comparé des micromères de l'oeuf de Rana fusca divisé enhuit (a) Après isolement (b) Après transplantation sur un socle de cellules vitellines. Compt. rend. Soc. de Biol. **122**:927.

Wigglesworth, V. B. **1948.** The role of the cell in determination. Symposia of the Soc. for Exper. Biol. No. II. Academic Press, Inc., New York.

Wilson, E. B. **1893.** *Amphioxus* and the mosaic theory of development. J. Morphol. **8**:579.

Wolff, E. and Lutz, H. **1947.** Embryologie expérimentale—sur la production expérimentale de jumeaux chez l'embryon d'oiseau. Compt. rend. Acad. d. Sc. **224**:1301.

9

Gastrulation

A. Some definitions and concepts
1. Gastrulation
2. Primitive vertebrate body plan in relation to the process of gastrulation
   a. Fundamental body plan of the vertebrate animal
   b. The gastrula in relation to the primitive body plan
   c. Chart of blastula, gastrula, and primitive, body-form relationships (fig. 188)
B. General processes involved in gastrulation
C. Morphogenetic movement of cells
1. Importance of cell movements during development and in gastrulation
2. Types of cell movement during gastrulation
   a. Epiboly
   b. Emboly
3. Description of the processes concerned with epiboly
4. Description of the processes involved in emboly
   a. Involution and convergence
   b. Invagination
   c. Concrescence
   d. Cell proliferation
   e. Polyinvagination
   f. Ingression
   g. Delamination
   h. Divergence
   i. Extension
D. The organization center and its relation to the gastrulative process
1. The organization center and the primary organizer
2. Divisions of the primary organizer
E. Chemodifferentiation and the gastrulative process
F. Gastrulation in various *Chordata*
1. *Amphioxus*
   a. Orientation
   b. Gastrulative movements
      1) Emboly
      2) Epiboly
      3) Antero-posterior extension of the gastrula and dorsal convergence of the mesodermal cells
      4) Closure of the blastopore
   c. Resumé of cell movements and processes involved in gastrulation of *Amphioxus*
      1) Emboly
      2) Epiboly

A. Some Definitions and Concepts

1. Gastrulation

According to Haeckel, the word **gastrula** is the name given to "the important embryonic form" having "the two primary germ-layers," and the word
gastrulation is applied to the process which produces the gastrula. Furthermore, "this ontogenetic process has a very great significance, and is the real
starting-point of the construction of the multicellular animal body" (1874, see
translation, '10, p. 123). Others such as Lankester (1875) and Hubrecht
('06) did much to establish the idea that gastrulation is a process during
which the monolayered blastula is converted into a bilaminar or didermic
gastrula. Haeckel emphasized **invagination** or the infolding of one portion of
the blastula as the primitive and essential process in this conversion, while
Lankester proposed **delamination** or the mass separation of cells as the primitive process. While it was granted that invagination was the main process of
gastrulation in *Amphioxus,* in the *Vertebrata,* especially in reptiles, birds, and
mammals, delamination was considered to be an essential process by many
embryologists. Some, however, maintained that the process of invagination
held true for all the *Chordata* other than the *Mammalia.* It may be mentioned
in passing that Lankester conferred the name "blastopore" upon the opening
into the interior of the blastoderm which results during gastrulation. The
words "blastopore" and "primitive mouth" soon were regarded as synonymous,
for in the *Coelenterata,* the blastopore eventually becomes the oral opening.

The definition of the gastrula as a didermic stage, following the monolayered blastula, is a simple concept, easy to visualize, and, hence, may have
some pedagogical value. However, it is not in accord with the facts unearthed
by many careful studies relative to cell lineage and it does not agree with the
results obtained by the Vogt method (see Chap. 7) applied to the process
of gastrulation in the vertebrate group.

One of the first to define gastrulation in a way which is more consonant
with the studies mentioned in the previous paragraph was Keibel ('01). He
defined gastrulation in the vertebrates ('01, p. 1111) as "the process by
which the entodermal, mesodermal and notochordal cells find their way into
the interior of the embryo." It is to be observed that this definition embodies
the concept of migration of specific, organ-forming areas. We may restate the
concept involved in this definition in a way which includes invertebrates as
well as vertebrates as follows: *Gastrulation is the dynamic process during
which the major, presumptive organ-forming areas of the blastula (Chaps.
6 and 7) become rearranged and reorganized in a way which permits their
ready conversion into the body plan of the particular species.* That is to say,
during the process of gastrulation, the presumptive organ-forming areas of
the blastula undergo axiation in terms of the body organization of the species.
In some animal species, this reorganization of the blastula into the structural

pattern of the gastrula results in the production of a two-layered form, for example, as in *Amphioxus;* in others (actually in most metazoan species) it brings about the formation of a **three-layered condition.** It is apparent, therefore, as observed by Pasteels ('37b, p. 464), that "it is impossible to give a general definition of the gastrula stage." It is obvious, also, that one cannot define gastrulation in terms of simple invagination, delamination, or the production of a two-layered condition. Many processes, involving intricate movements of cell groups, occur as outlined in the succeeding pages of this chapter.

Relative to the process of gastrulation and later development, emphasis should be placed upon the importance of the **blastocoel.** The latter takes its origin largely by the movement of groups of cells in relation to one another during cleavage and blastulation. Therefore, we may enumerate the following events related to the blastocoel during the early phases of embryonic development:

(1) The blastocoel is associated with those movements in the developing blastula which produce the specific cellular configuration of the mature blastula;

(2) during gastrulation, it enables the various, presumptive organ-forming areas of the blastula to be rearranged and to migrate into the particular areas which permit their ready organization and axiation into the scheme of the body form of the particular species; and

(3) in the period of development immediately following gastrulation, it affords the initial space necessary for the tubulation of the major, organ-forming areas.

The events mentioned in (3) will be described in Chapter 10.

2. Primitive Vertebrate Body Plan in Relation to the Process of Gastrulation

In the animal kingdom, each of the major animal groupings has a specific body plan. In the phylum, *Chordata,* the cephalochordate, *Amphioxus,* and the vertebrates possess such a plan. It is necessary at this point to review briefly the rudiments of this primitive or basic body plan.

a. Fundamental Body Plan of the Vertebrate Animal

The vertebrate body essentially is a cylindrical structure with a **head or cephalic end,** a middle **trunk region,** and a **tail or caudal end.** The **dorsum** or **dorsal region** is the uppermost aspect, while the **venter** or **belly** lies below. Also, the body as a whole may be slightly compressed laterally. Viewed in transverse section, the body is composed basically of five hollow tubes, particularly in the trunk area. The **epidermal tube** forms the exterior and within the latter are placed the **neural, enteric,** and **two mesodermal tubes,** all oriented around the median skeletal axis or notochord as indicated in figures 188C and 217G and N.

b. The Gastrula in Relation to the Primitive Body Plan

If one watches a large transport plane preparing to take off at an airfield, the following events may be observed:

(1) The cargo and passengers are boarded, the engines are warmed, and the plane is taxied toward the runway.

(2) Upon reaching the starting end of the runway, the engines are accelerated, and the plane is turned around and headed in the direction of the take-off.

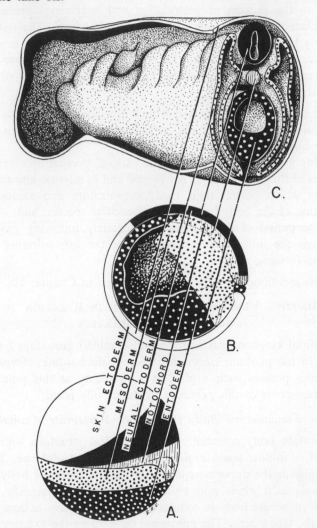

FIG. 188. Relationship between the presumptive organ-forming areas of the blastula (diagram A) and the primitive tubular condition of the developing vertebrate body (diagram C). The gastrula (diagram B) represents an intermediate stage. Consult chart in text.

(3) The engines are further accelerated and the plane is moved down the runway for the take-off into the airy regions.

Similarly, during cleavage and blastulation, the embryonic machine develops a readiness, elaborates the major, organ-forming areas in their correct positions in the blastula, and taxies into position with its engines warming up, as it were. Once in the position of the mature blastula, the various, major, presumptive organ-forming areas *are turned around and reoriented by the gastrulative processes,* and thus, each major, organ-forming area of the gastrula is placed in readiness for the final developmental surge which results in primitive body formation. During the latter process the major, presumptive organ-forming areas in the vertebrate group are molded into the form of elongated tubular structures with the exception of the notochordal area which forms an elongated skeletal axis. (The latter phenomena are described in Chapter 10.)

c. Chart of Blastula, Gastrula, and Primitive Body-form Relationships in the Vertebrate Group
(Fig. 188)

The major, presumptive organ-forming areas are designated by separate numerals.

Blastula	Gastrula	Primitive Body Form
1. Epidermal crescent	1. Part of ectodermal layer	1. External epidermal tube
2. Neural crescent	2. Elongated neural plate a part of ectoderm layer	2. Dorsally placed neural tube
3. Entodermal area	3. Primitive archenteron in rounded gastrulae, such as frog; archenteric layer in flattened gastrulae, such as chick	3. Primitive gut tube
4. Two mesodermal areas	4. Two mesodermal layers on either side of notochord	4. Two primitive mesodermal tubes; one along either side of neural tube, notochord, and gut tube; especially true of trunk region
5. Notochordal crescent	5. Elongated band of cells lying between mesodermal layers	5. Rounded rod of cells lying below neural tube and above entodermal or gut tube; these three structures lie in the meson or median plane of the body

B. General Processes Involved in Gastrulation

Gastrulation is a nicely integrated, dynamic process; one which is controlled largely by intrinsic (i.e., autonomous) forces bound up in the specific, physico-chemical conditions of the various, presumptive, organ-forming areas of the late blastula and early gastrula. These internal forces in turn are correlated with external conditions. One of the important intrinsic factors involves the so-called organization center referred to in Chapter 7. However, before consideration is given to this center, we shall define some of the major processes involved in gastrulation.

There are two words which have come into use in embryology relative to the process of gastrulation, namely, **epiboly** and **emboly.** These words are derived from the Greek, and in the original they denote *motion,* in fact, two different kinds of motion. The word **emboly** is derived from a word meaning to *throw in* or *thrust in.* In other words, it means *insertion.* The word **epiboly,** on the other hand, denotes *a throwing on or extending upon.* These words, therefore, have quite opposite meanings, but they aptly describe the general movements which occur during gastrulation. If, for example, we consider figure 169, these two words mean the following: All the presumptive organ-forming areas below line a–b in (C) during the process of gastrulation are *moved to the inside* by the forces involved in **emboly.** On the other hand, due to the forces concerned with **epiboly,** the presumptive organ-forming materials above line a–b are *extended upon or around* the inwardly moving cells.

Associated with the comprehensive molding processes of epiboly and emboly are a series of subactivities. These activities may be classified under the following headings:

(1) morphogenetic movement of cells,
(2) the organization center and its organizing influences, and
(3) chemodifferentiation.

C. Morphogenetic Movement of Cells

1. IMPORTANCE OF CELL MOVEMENTS DURING DEVELOPMENT AND IN GASTRULATION

The movement of cells from one place in the embryo to another to establish a particular form or structure is a common embryological procedure. This type of cell movement is described as a morphogenetic movement because it results in the generation of a particular form or structural arrangement. It is involved not only in the formation of the blastula where the movements are slow, or in gastrulation where the cell migrations are dynamic and rapid, but also in later development. (See Chap. 11.) In consequence, we may say that cell migration is one of the basic procedures involved in tissue and organ formation.

The actual factors—physical, chemical, physiological, and mechanical—which effect cell movements are quite unknown. However, this lack of knowledge is not discouraging. In fact, it makes the problem more interesting, for cells are **living entities** utilizing physicochemical and mechanical forces peculiar to that condition which we call **living.** The living state is a problem which awaits solution.

At the period when the process of blastulation comes to an end and the process of gastrulation is initiated, there is an urge directed toward cell movement throughout the entire early gastrula. Needham ('42, p. 145) uses the term "inner compulsion" to describe the tendency of the cells of the dorsal-lip area to move inward (invaginate) at this time. Whatever it is called and however it may be described, the important feature to remember is that this tendency to move and the actual movement of the cells represent a living process in which masses of cells move in accordance with the dictates of a precise and guiding center of activity, known as the primary organizer or organization center.

2. Types of Cell Movement During Gastrulation

The following types of cell movement are important aspects of the process of gastrulation.

a. Epiboly

(1) Extension along the antero-posterior axis of the future embryo.
(2) Peripheral expansion or divergence.

b. Emboly

(1) Involution.
(2) Invagination.
(3) Concrescence (probably does not occur).
(4) Convergence.
(5) Polyinvagination.
(6) Delamination.
(7) Divergence or expansion.
(8) Extension or elongation.
(9) Blastoporal constriction.

Note: While cell proliferation is not listed as a specific activity above, it is an important aspect of gastrulation in many forms.

3. Description of the Processes Concerned with Epiboly

Epiboly or ectodermal expansion involves the movements of the presumptive epidermal and neural areas during the gastrulative process. The general migration of these two areas is in the direction of the antero-posterior axis of the future embryonic body in all chordate embryos. In the rounded blastula (e.g., frog, *Amphioxus,* etc.), the tendency to extend antero-posteriorly produces an enveloping movement in the antero-posterior direction. As a result, the presumptive epidermal and neural areas actually engulf and surround the inwardly moving presumptive notochordal, mesodermal, and entodermal areas. (Study fig. 190A–H.) In flattened blastulae the movements of epiboly are concerned largely with antero-posterior extension, associated with peripheral migration and expansion of the epidermal area. (See fig. 202.) The latter movement of the presumptive epidermal area is pronounced in teleost fishes, where the yolk is engulfed as a result of epidermal growth and expansion (figs. 210B; 211D).

The above-mentioned activities, together with cell proliferation, effect spatial changes in the presumptive epidermal and neural areas as shown in figures 189, 190, 191, 198, and the left portion of figure 202A–I. It is to be observed that the **epidermal crescent** is greatly expanded, and the area covered is increased; also, that the **neural crescent** is changed into a shield-shaped area, extended in an antero-posterior direction (figs. 192A; 202I).

4. DESCRIPTION OF THE PROCESSES INVOLVED IN EMBOLY

While forces engaged in epiboly are rearranging the presumptive neural and epidermal areas, the morphogenetic movements concerned with **emboly** move the presumptive chordamesodermal and entodermal areas inward and extend them along the antero-posterior axis of the forming embryo. This inward movement of cells is due to innate forces within various cell groups; some apparently are autonomous (i.e., they arise from forces within a particular cell group), while others are dependent upon the movement of other cell groups.) (See p. 447.) We may classify the types of cell behavior during this migration and rearrangement of the chordamesoderm-entodermal areas as follows:

a. Involution and Convergence

Involution is a process which is dependent largely upon the migration of cells toward the blastoporal lip (e.g., frog, see heavy arrows, fig. 192) or to the primitive streak (e.g., bird, see arrows, fig. 204C–E). The word **involution,** as used in gastrulation, denotes a "turning in" or inward rotation of cells which have migrated to the blastoporal margin. In doing so, cells located along the external margin of the blastoporal lip move over the lip to the inside edge of the lip (see arrows, figs. 191C–E, H; 192B, C). The inturned or involuted cells thus are deposited on the inside of the embryo along the inner margin of the blastopore. The actual migration of cells from the outside surface of the blastula to the external margin of the blastoporal lip is called **convergence.** In the case of the primitive streak of the chick, the same essential movements are present, namely, a convergence of cells to the primitive streak and then an inward rotation of cells through the substance of the streak to the inside (arrows, fig. 204; black arrows, fig. 202). If it were not for the process of involution, the converging cells would tend to pile up along the outer edges of the blastoporal lip or along the primitive streak. Involution thus represents a small but extremely important step in the migration of cells from the exterior to the interior during gastrulation.

b. Invagination

The phenomenon of **invagination,** as used in embryological development, implies an infolding or insinking of a layer of cells, resulting in the formation of a cavity surrounded by the infolded cells (figs. 189, 190, the entoderm). Relative to gastrulation, this process has two aspects:

(1) mechanical or passive infolding of cells, and

(2) active inward streaming or inpushing of cells into the blastocoelic space.

In lower vertebrates, the dorsal-lip area of the blastopore is prone to exhibit the active form of invagination, whereas the entoderm of the lateral- and ventral-lip regions of the blastopore tends to move in a passive manner. The notochordal-canal, primitive-pit area of the primitive streak of higher vertebrates is concerned especially with the active phase of invagination.

c. Concrescence

This term is used in older descriptions of gastrulation. The word denotes the movement of masses of cells toward each other, particularly in the region of the blastopore, and implies the idea of fusion of cell groups from two bilaterally situated areas. It probably does not occur. (However, see development of the feather in Chap. 12.)

d. Cell Proliferation

An increase in the number of cells is intimately concerned with the process of gastrulation to the extent that gastrulation would be impeded without it, in some species more than in others. Cell proliferation in *Amphioxus,* for example, is intimately associated with the gastrulative process, whereas in the frog it assumes a lesser importance.

e. Polyinvagination

Polyinvagination is a concept which implies that individual or small groups of cells in different parts of the external layer of the blastula or blastodisc invaginate or ingress into the segmentation (blastocoelic) cavity. That is, there are several different and separate inward migrations of one or more cells. This idea recently was repudiated by Pasteels ('45) relative to the formation of the entodermal layer in the avian blastoderm. It applies, presumably, to the ingression of cells during the formation of the two-layered blastula in the prototherian mammal, *Echidna* (see p. 364).

f. Ingression

The word **ingression** is suitable for use in cases where a cell or small groups of cells separate from other layers and migrate into the segmentation cavity or into spaces or cavities developed within the developing body. In the primitive-streak area of reptiles, birds, and mammals, for example, mesodermal cells detach themselves from the primitive streak and migrate into the space between the epiblast and hypoblast. Also, in the formation of the two-layered embryo in the prototherian mammal, *Echidna,* the inward migration of small entodermal cells to form the hypoblast may be regarded as cellular ingression (fig. 175D). Ingression and polyinvagination have similar meanings.

g. Delamination

The word **delamination** denotes a mass sunderance or separation of groups of cells from other cell groups. The separation of notochordal, mesodermal, and entodermal tissues from each other to form discrete cellular masses in such forms as the teleost fish or the frog, after these materials have moved to the inside during gastrulation, is an example of delamination (fig. 210E, F).

h. Divergence

This phenomenon is the opposite of **convergence.** For example, after cells have involuted over the blastoporal lips during gastrulation, they migrate and **diverge** to their future positions within the forming gastrula. This movement particularly is true of the lateral plate and ventral mesoderm in the frog, or of lateral plate and extra-embryonic mesoderm in the reptile, bird, or mammal (fig. 192B, C, small arrows).

i. Extension

The elongation of the presumptive neural and epidermal areas externally and of the notochordal, mesodermal, and entodermal materials after they have moved inward beneath the neural plate and epidermal material are examples of **extension.** The extension of cellular masses is a prominent factor in gastrulation in all *Chordata* from *Amphioxus* to the *Mammalia.* In fact, as a result of this tendency to extend or elongate on the part of the various cellular groups, the entire gastrula, in many instances, *begins to elongate in the antero-posterior axis as gastrulation proceeds.* The faculty for elongation and extension is a paramount influence in development of axiation in the gastrula and later on in the development of primitive body form. The presumptive notochordal material possesses great autonomous powers for extension, and hence, during gastrulation it becomes extended into an elongated band of cells.

D. The Organization Center and Its Relation to the Gastrulative Process

1. THE ORGANIZATION CENTER AND THE PRIMARY ORGANIZER

Using a transplantation technic on the beginning gastrula of the newt, it was shown by Spemann ('18) and Spemann and Mangold ('24) that the dorsal-lip region of the blastopore (that is, the chordamesoderm-entoderm cells in this area), when transplanted to the epidermal area of another embryo of the *same stage of development, is able to produce a secondary gastrulative process and thus initiate the formation of a secondary embryo* (fig. 193). Because the dorsal-lip tissue was able thus to organize the development of a second or twin embryo, Spemann and Mangold described the dorsal-lip region of the beginning gastrula as an "organizer" of the gastrulative process. In its normal position during gastrulation this area of cells has since been regarded as the organization center of amphibian development. It is to be observed in this connection that Lewis ('07) performed the same type of experiment but failed to use an embryo of the *same age as a host*. As he used an older embryo, the notochordal and mesodermal cells developed according to their presumptive fate into notochordal and somitic tissue but failed to organize a new embryo.

More recent experiments upon early frog embryos by Vintemberger ('36) and by Dalcq and Pasteels ('37), and upon early teleost fish embryos by other investigators (Oppenheimer, '36 and '47) have demonstrated the necessity and importance of yolk substance in the gastrulative process. This fact led Dalcq and Pasteels ('37) to suggest a new concept of the organization center, namely, that this center is dependent upon two factors: "the yolk and something normally bound to the gray crescent" (i.e., chordamesodermal area).

It was thought at first that the transplanted organizer material actually organized and produced the new embryo itself (Spemann, '18, p. 477). But this idea had to be modified in the light of the following experiment by Spemann and Mangold ('24): Dorsal-lip material of unpigmented *Triton cristatus* was transplanted to an embryo of *T. taeniatus* of the same age. The latter species is pigmented. This experiment demonstrated that the neural plate tissue of the secondary embryo was almost entirely derived from the host and not from the transplanted tissue. Consequently, this experiment further suggested that the **organizer** not only possessed the ability *to organize* but also *to induce* host tissue to differentiate. Induction of neural plate cells from cells which ordinarily would not produce neural plate tissue thus became a demonstrated fact.

The concept of an organizer in embryonic development had profound implications and stimulated many studies relating to its nature. Particularly, intensive efforts were made regarding the kinds of cells, tissues, and other substances which would effect induction of secondary neural tubes. The results of these experiments eventually showed that various types of tissues and tissue substances, some alive, some dead, from many animal species, including the invertebrates, were able to induce *amphibian neural plate and tube formation*. (See Spemann, '38, Chap. X and XI; also see fig. 196A, B and compare with fig. 193.) Moreover, microcautery, fuller's earth, calcium carbonate, silica, etc., have on occasion induced neural tube formation. However, the mere induction of neural tube development should not be confused with the organizing action of normal, living, chordamesoderm-entoderm cells of the dorsal-lip region of the beginning gastrula. The latter's activities are more comprehensive, for the cells of the dorsal-lip area direct and organize the normal gastrulative process as a whole and bring about the organization of the *entire dorsal axial system of notochord, neural tube, somites,* etc. In this series of activities, neural plate induction and neural tube formation merely are *secondary events* of a general organization process.

A clear-cut distinction should be drawn, therefore, between the action of the **dorsal-lip organizer,** in its normal position and capacity, and that of an ordinary inductor which induces secondary neural tube development. The characteristics of the primary organizer or organization center of the early gastrula are:

(a) *its ability for autonomous or self-differentiation* (that is, it possesses the ability to give origin to a considerable portion of the notochord, prechordal plate material, and axial mesoderm of the secondary embryo),

(b) *its capacity for self-organization,*

(c) *its power to induce changes within and to organize surrounding cells, including the induction and early organization of the neural tube.*

As a result of its comprehensive powers, it is well to look upon the organization center (primary organizer) as the area which determines the main features of axiation and organization of the vertebrate embryo. In other words, *it directs the conversion of the late blastula into the axiated gastrular condition* —a condition from which the primitive vertebrate body is formed. Induction is a tool-like process, utilized by this center of activity, through which it effects changes in surrounding cells and thus influences organization and differentiation. Moreover, these surrounding cells, changed by the process of induction, may in turn act as secondary inductor centers, with abilities to organize specific subareas.

An example of the ability of a group of cells, changed by inductive influence, to act as an inducing agent to cause further inductive processes is shown by the following experiment performed by O. Mangold ('32). The right, presumptive, half brain of a neurula of *Ambystoma mexicanum,* the axolotl, was removed and inserted into the blastocoel of a midgastrula of *Triton taeniatus.* Eight days after the implant was made, a secondary anterior end of an embryo was observed protruding from the anterior, ventral aspect of the host larva. An analysis of this secondarily induced anterior portion of an embryo demonstrated the following:

(1) The original implant had developed into a half brain with one eye and one olfactory pit. However,

(2) it also had induced a more or less complete secondary larval head with a complete brain, two eyes, with lenses, two olfactory pits, one ganglion, four auditory vesicles, and one balancer. One of the eyes had become intimately associated with the eye of the implant, both having the same lens.

The series of inductive processes presumably occurred as follows: The implanted half brain induced from the epidermis of the host a secondary anterior end of a neural plate; the latter developed into a brain which induced the lenses, auditory vesicles, etc. from the host epidermis. Thus, the original implant, through its ability to induce anterior neural plate formation from the overlying epidermis, acted as a "head organizer."

The transformation of the late blastula into the organized condition of the late gastrula thus appears to be dependent upon a number of separate inductions, all integrated into one coordinated whole by the "formative stimulus" of the primary organizer located in the pre-chordal plate area of entodermal-mesodermal cells and adjacent chordamesodermal material of the early gastrula.

2. DIVISIONS OF THE PRIMARY ORGANIZER

The **primary organizer** is divisible into two general inductor areas as follows:

(a) **the pre-chordal plate of entomesodermal material,** and
(b) **the chordamesodermal cells** which come to lie posterior to the pre-chordal plate area of the late gastrula.

The pre-chordal plate is a complex of entodermal and mesodermal cells associated at the anterior end of the notochordal cells in the late gastrula. In the beginning gastrula, however, it lies between the notochordal material and the dorsal-lip inpushing of the entoderm in amphibia, and just caudal to the notochordal area in teleosts, elasmobranch fishes, reptiles, and birds (figs. 169; 173A; 179B; 180B). The chordamesodermal portion of the primary organizer is composed of presumptive notochordal cells and that part of the presumptive mesoderm destined to form the somites. The pre-chordal plate is known as the **head organizer,** because of its ability to induce brain structures and other activities in the head region. (The use of the phrase head organizer as a synonymous term for pre-chordal plate is correct in part only, for a portion of the anterior notochord and adjacent mesoderm normally is concerned also with the organization of the head.) On the other hand, the presumptive notochord with the adjacent somitic (somite) material is described as the **trunk or tail organizer** (fig. 191G) because of its more limited inductive power. For example, Spemann ('31) demonstrated that the head organizer transplanted to another host embryo of the same age produced a secondary head with eye and ear vesicles when placed at the normal head level of the host. Also when placed at trunk level, it induced a complete secondary embryo including the head structures. However, the trunk organizer is able to induce head and trunk structures at the head level of the host; but in the trunk region it induces only trunk and tail tissues. (See Holtfreter, '48, pp. 18–19; Needham, '42, pp. 271–272; Spemann, '31, '38. The student is referred also to Huxley and De Beer, '34, Chaps. 6 and 7; and Lewis, '07.)

E. Chemodifferentiation and the Gastrulative Process

In the previous chapter it was observed that certain areas of the amphibian blastula are foreordained to give origin to certain organ rudiments in the future embryo *because of their position and not because of their innate physiological condition*. This condition is true of the future neural plate ectoderm and epidermal ectoderm. During the conversion of the late blastula into the late gastrula, these areas become changed physiologically, and they no longer are determined in a presumptive sense but have undergone changes which make them self-differentiating. This change from a presumptively determined condition to a self-differentiating, fixed state is called **determination** and the biochemical change which effects this alteration is known as **chemodifferentiation** (see Chap. 8).

Chemodifferentiation is an important phenomenon during gastrulation. As a result of the physiological changes involved in chemodifferentiation, restrictive changes in potency are imposed upon many localized cellular areas within the major, organ-forming areas. In consequence, various future organs and parts of organs have their respective fates *rigidly, and irrevocably determined* at the end of gastrulation. The gastrula thus becomes a loose mosaic of specific, organ-forming areas (figs. 194, 205). Consequently, the areas of the beginning gastrula which possess competence (Chap. 8) become more and more restricted as gastrulation proceeds. Chemodifferentiation apparently occurs largely through inductive (evocative) action.

F. Gastrulation in Various *Chordata*

1. *Amphioxus*

a. Orientation

Consult figures 167, 189, and 190 and become familiar with the animal-vegetal pole axis of the egg, the presumptive organ-forming areas, etc.

b. Gastrulative Movements

1) Emboly. As gastrulation begins, a marked increase in mitotic activity occurs in the cells of the dorsal crescent, composed of presumptive notochordal and neural plate cells, and also in the cells of the ventral crescent or future mesodermal tissue. The general ectodermal cells or future epidermis also are active (figs. 167, 189, 190B). The entodermal cells, however, are quiescent (Conklin, '32). Accompanying this mitotic activity, the entodermal plate gradually invaginates or folds inwardly into the blastocoel (figs. 189, 190). In doing so, the upper portion of the entodermal plate moves inward more rapidly and pushes forward toward a point approximately halfway between the polar body (i.e., the original midanimal pole of the egg) and the point which marks the anterior end of the future embryo (observe pointed end of arrow, fig. 189). Shortly after the inward movement of the entodermal plate is initiated, notochordal cells in the middorsal region of the blastopore involute, move inward along with the entoderm, and come to occupy a position in the middorsal area of the forming archenteron (fig. 190C–E). Similarly, mesodermal cells in the upper or dorsal ends of the mesodermal crescent gradually converge dorso-mediad and pass into the roof of the forming gastrocoel (archenteron) on either side of the median area occupied by the notochordal cells (fig. 190F, G). Thus the roof of the gastrocoel is composed of notochordal and mesodermal cells (fig. 195A, B).

2) Epiboly. As the above events come to pass, the potential epidermal and neural cells proliferate actively, and both areas gradually become extended in an antero-posterior direction. In this way the neural ectoderm becomes elongated into a median band which lies in the middorsal region of the gastrula (figs. 190A–H; 247B–F), while the epidermal area covers the entire gastrula externally with the exception of the neural area.

Thus, the general result of this proliferation, infolding, and involution of the presumptive entodermal, notochordal, and mesodermal cells, together with the extension and proliferation of the ectodermal cells is the production of a rudimentary double-layered embryo or gastrula (figs. 189, 190). Ectodermal cells (epidermal and neural) form the external layer (fig. 190G). The internal layer is composed of notochordal cells in the dorso-median area with two narrow bands of mesodermal cells lying along either side of the median notochordal band of cells while the remainder of the internal layer is composed of entodermal cells (figs. 190G; 195A, B). At the blastoporal end of this primitive gastrula are to be found *proliferating notochordal, mesodermal, entodermal, and ectodermal cells.*

3) Antero-posterior Extension of the Gastrula and Dorsal Convergence of the Mesodermal Cells. The processes associated with epiboly bring about an antero-posterior extension of the ectodermal layer of cells. Similarly, the cells which are moved inward by embolismic forces are projected forward toward the future cephalic end of the embryo and become extended along the median embryonic axis. Epiboly and emboly, accompanied by rapid cell proliferation at the blastoporal-lip area, thus *effect an antero-posterior elongation* of the developing gastrula (figs. 189H; 190H).

As the gastrula is extended in the antero-posterior direction, a shift occurs in the position of the mesodermal cells which form the ventral or mesodermal crescent. The ventral crescent becomes divided ventrally into two halves, and each half gradually moves dorsalward along the inner aspect of the lateral blastoporal lips as gastrulation is accomplished. Each arm of the original crescent in this manner converges dorso-mediad toward the median notochordal cells of the dorsal blastoporal lip, and a mass of mesodermal cells comes to lie along either side of the notochordal cells. As a result of this converging movement, entodermal cells of the blastoporal area converge dorso-mediad and come to occupy the ventral lip of the blastopore, together with the externally placed, epidermal cells (fig. 190G, arrow). The blastopore as a whole grows smaller and moves to a dorsal position during the latter changes (fig. 247A–C).

4) Closure of the Blastopore. See Chapter 10, neuralization in *Amphioxus*.

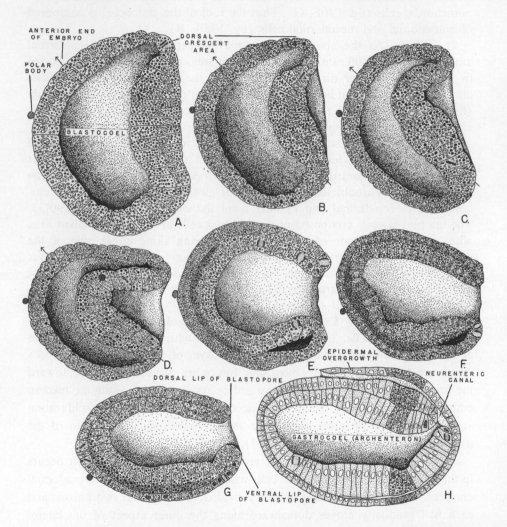

FIG. 189. Gastrulation in *Amphioxus*. (Modified from Conklin, '32.)   (A) Beginning gastrula.   (B) Observe that entodermal (hypoblast layer) is projected roughly in direction of future cephalic end of embryo.   (C–G) Observe continued projection of entoderm toward cephalic end of future embryo. Note also position of polar body. In (F), (G), and (H) the gastrula begins to elongate along the antero-posterior axis of the developing embryo.   (H) End of gastrular condition. Blastopore is closed by epidermal overgrowth, and **neurenteric canal** is formed between archenteron and forming neural tube.

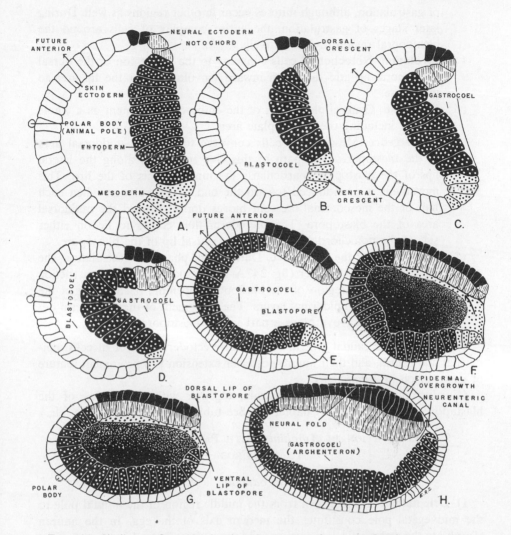

FIG. 190. Similar to fig. 189, showing the presumptive organ-forming areas of the blastula and their position during gastrulation. The position of the respective organ-forming areas in a transverse section through the midregion of gastrula shown in G is depicted in fig. 195A. (Based upon data obtained from Conklin, '32.)

c. Resumé of Cell Movements and Processes Involved in Gastrulation of Amphioxus

1) Emboly:

(a) **Invagination.** The entodermal plate of cells gradually invaginates and folds inward into the blastocoel.

(b) **Proliferation of cells.** This is true particularly of notochordal, meso-dermal, and neural cells near the blastoporal area during initial stages of gastrulation, although mitoses occur in other regions as well. During later stages of gastrulation, the entire complex of cells around the blastoporal region divides actively.

(c) **Involution.** Notochordal cells converge to the midregion of the dorsal blastoporal lip and then turn inward (involute) over the lip area to the inside.

(d) **Extension.** General elongation of the embryonic rudiment as a whole occurs, including the neural plate area.

(e) **Convergence.** Mesodermal cells converge toward the middorsal area of the blastopore. The path of this convergence is along the lateral lips of the blastopore, particularly the inner aspects of the lips. This movement is pronounced toward the end of gastrulation when each half of the mesodermal crescent moves dorsad toward the middorsal area of the blastopore. The mesoderm thus comes to lie on either side of the notochordal material at the dorsal lip of the blastopore.

(f) **Constriction of the blastopore.** During later phases of gastrulation, the blastopore grows smaller (fig. 247A–D), associated with a constriction of the marginal region of the blastoporal opening, particularly of the entodermal and epidermal layers. The movement of the mesoderm described in (e) above plays a part in this blastoporal change.

2) Epiboly. The caudal growth of the entire ectodermal layer of cells, epidermal and neural, and their antero-posterior extension is a prominent feature of gastrulation in *Amphioxus*.

(Further changes in the late gastrula, together with the closing of the blastapore, are described in Chapter 10. See tubulation of neural plate, etc.)

2. GASTRULATION IN *Amphibia* WITH PARTICULAR REFERENCE TO THE FROG

a. Introduction

1) Orientation. A line drawn from the middle region of the animal pole to the midvegetal pole constitutes the median axis of the egg. In the anuran *Amphibia* the embryonic axis corresponds approximately to the egg axis. That is, the midanimal pole of the egg represents the future anterior or anterodorsal end of the embryo, while the midvegetal pole area denotes the posterior region.

As indicated previously (Chap. 7), the very late blastula is composed of presumptive organ-forming areas arranged around the blastocoelic space. The yolk-laden, future entodermal cells of the gut or digestive tube form the hypoblast and are concentrated at the vegetal pole. Presumptive notochordal and mesodermal cells constitute a marginal zone of cells which surrounds the upper region of the presumptive entodermal organ-forming area (fig. 169C–F). The presumptive notochordal area is in the form of a crescent,

whose midportion is located just above the future dorsal lip of the early gastrula, while the mesoderm lies to each side of the notochordal cells, extending
along the margin of the entoderm toward the corresponding mesodermal zone
of the other side (fig. 169D, F). The presumptive neural crescent occupies
a region just dorsal and anterior to the notochordal area. The remainder of
the animal pole is composed of presumptive epidermis. The presumptive
notochordal, neural plate, and epidermal areas are oriented along the general
direction of the future antero-posterior embryonic axis, the notochordal tissue
being the more posterior. Moreover, the midregion of the notochordal and
neural crescents *at this time* lies at the dorsal region of the future embryo
(fig. 194A). The presumptive entodermal area, on the other hand, does not
have the same orientation as that of the above areas. In contrast, its axiation
is *at right angles to the future* embryonic axis (fig. 194A). If one views a
very early gastrula of the anuran amphibian in such a way that the beginning
blastoporal lip is toward the right (fig. 194A), then:

(1) The foregut material lies toward the right at the region of the forming
    blastoporal lip;

(2) the stomach material is slightly to the left of this area; and

(3) the future intestinal area lies to the left and toward the vegetal pole.

Therefore, one aspect of the gastrulative processes is to bring the entodermal area into harmony with the future embryonic axis and, in doing so,
to align its specific, organ-forming subareas along the antero-posterior axis
of the embryo. In other words, the entodermal material must be revolved
about 90 degrees in a counterclockwise direction from the initial position
occupied at the beginning of gastrulation (compare fig. 194A, B).

**2) Physiological Changes Which Occur in the Presumptive Organ-forming
Areas of the Late Blastula and Early Gastrula as Gastrulation Progresses.**
A striking physiological change is consummated in the presumptive organ-
forming areas of the epiblastic portion of the late blastula during the process
of gastrulation. This change has been demonstrated by transplantation experiments. For example, if presumptive epidermis of the very late blastula
and early gastrula is transplanted by means of a micropipette to the presumptive neural area and *vice versa,* the material which would have formed
epidermis will form neural tissue, and presumptive neural cells will form epidermis (fig. 196C, D). (See Spemann, '18, '21; Mangold, '28.)

The experiment pictured in figure 196 involves interchanges between two
presumptive areas within the same potential germ layer, i.e., ectoderm. However, Mangold ('23) demonstrated that presumptive epidermis transplanted
into the dorsal-lip area, i.e., into the presumptive mesodermal area, may invaginate and form mesodermal tissue. The converse of this experiment was
performed by Lopaschov ('35) who found that presumptive mesoderm from
the region of the blastoporal lip transplanted to the neural plate area of a

somewhat older embryo becomes, in some cases, normally incorporated in the neural tube of the host. Similar interchanges of cells of the late blastula have demonstrated that almost any part, other than the presumptive entoderm, can be interchanged without disturbing the normal sequence of events. However, as gastrulation progresses, *interchange from epidermal to neural areas continues to be possible during the early phases of gastrulation (fig. 196C, D) but not at the end of gastrulation. Similar changes occur also in the mesodermal area.* Pronounced physiological changes thus occur in the presumptive organ-forming aᵢeas *of the entire epiblastic region* during gastrulation.

b. Gastrulation

1) Emboly. As gastrulation begins, a small, cleft-like invagination appears in the entodermal material of the presumptive foregut area. This invagination is an active inpushing of entodermal cells which *fold inward and forward toward the future cephalic end of the embryo* (fig. 191B–E). The upper or dorsal edge of the cleft-like depression visible at the external surface forms the **dorsal lip of the blastopore** (fig. 191B). In this connection, study diagrams in figure 197. The **pre-chordal plate cells** are associated with the forming dorsal roof of the archenteron and, therefore, form a part of the invaginated material shortly after this process is initiated.

As the entodermal material migrates inward and the initial dorsal lip is formed, notochordal cells move posteriad to the dorsal lip and involute to the inside in close association with the pre-chordal plate cells. Also, the more laterally situated, notochordal material *converges toward the dorsal lip* and gradually passes to the inside, as gastrulation progresses, where it lies in the mid-dorsal region of the embryo. (See arrows, figs. 188A; 191C, D). Here it begins to elongate antero-posteriorly (i.e., it becomes extended) and forms a narrow band of cells below the forming neural plate (fig. 191C–G).

With the continuance of gastrulation, the entodermal material moves more extensively inward (cf. fig. 191C–E) and the entodermal mass of yolk-laden cells below the site of invagination begins to sink or rotate inwardly. The dorsal blastoporal lip, therefore, widens considerably (fig. 197A, B). In many *Amphibia* the inner surface of the entoderm, as it progresses inward, forms a cup-like structure which actually engulfs the blastocoelic fluid (fig. 191B–D). It is not clear whether this cup-like form is produced by active inward migration of entodermal cells or whether it may be due in part, at least, to constrictive forces at the blastoporal lip.

Synchronized with the events described above, the presumptive somitic mesoderm, located externally along either side of the notochordal area of the early gastrula, migrates (converges) toward the forming dorso-lateral lips of the blastopore (fig. 197A, B, broken arrows). Upon reaching the blastoporal edge, the mesoderm moves over the lip (involutes) to the inside. However, the mesoderm does not flow over the lip to the inside as a part of the entoderm ın a manner similar to the pre-chordal and notochordal cells; rather, upon reaching the edge of the blastopore, it involutes over the lip, then *insinuates itself between the inside entoderm and the external surface layer of cells,* and, in this position, passes inward and forward *between the entoderm and the external layer of cells* (figs. 191H; 198A).

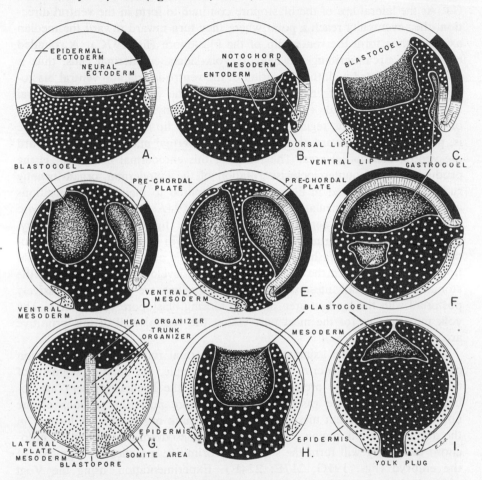

FIG. 191. Migration of the presumptive organ-forming areas of the blastula during gastrulation in the amphibia (with reference particularly to the frog). (See fig. 192.) (A) Late blastula, sagittal section through midplane of future embryo. (B–F) Observe processes of epiboly and emboly. In epiboly, the black (neural) and white (epidermal) areas become extended and gradually envelop (fig. 192A) the inward moving notochord, entoderm, and mesoderm. The processes concerned with emboly bring about the inward migration of the latter presumptive areas. (G) Late gastrular condition, with neural area and upper portion of the epidermal area removed to show relationships of the middle germ layer of chordamesoderm. (H) Horizontal section of middle gastrular condition, showing involution of mesoderm between entoderm and ectoderm. (I) Late gastrula, horizontal section, showing yolk plug, mesoderm, and final engulfment of blastocoelic space by entoderm.

Coincident with the lateral extensions of the original dorsal lip of the blasto-pore to form the lateral lips, a more extensive convergence and involution of presumptive mesoderm located in the lateral portions of the mesodermal cres-cent occurs (fig. 197A, B). The latter mesoderm eventually forms the lateral area of the hypomeric mesoderm of the future embryo (figs. 191G; 198B, C). As the lateral lips of the blastopore continue to form in the ventral direc-tion, they eventually reach a point where they turn inward toward the median axis and thus form the ventral lip of the blastopore (fig. 197C). A rounded blastopore, circumscribing the heavily, yolk-laden, entodermal cells, thus is formed. Associated with the formation of the ventro-lateral and ventral blasto-poral lips is the convergence and involution of the ventro-lateral and ventral mesoderm of the gastrula (fig. 191D–F). Accompanying the inward migration of the entoderm in the region of the dorso-lateral lip of the blastopore, there is, presumably, an inward rotation of the entodermal mass which lies toward the ventral blastoporal area. The result of this entodermal movement is the production of a counterclockwise rotation of the entodermal, organ-forming rudiments, as indicated in figure 194B, compared to their relative positions at the beginning of gastrulation, shown in figure 194A. (This counterclockwise rotation is present to a degree also in *Amphioxus* (fig. 190A–F). In this way, the particular, organ-forming areas of the entoderm become arranged antero-posteriorly in a linear fashion along the embryonic axis. The foregut material now is situated toward the anterior end of the developing embryo, while the stomach, liver, small intestine, and hindgut regions are placed progressively posteriad with the hindgut area near the closing blastopore (fig. 194B). The yolk material lies for the most part within the ventral wall of this primitive archenteron.

Associated with the axiation of the entodermal rudiments is the axiation of the notochord-mesoderm complex. For example, the anterior segment of the notochord and the pre-chordal plate (i.e., the **head organizer**) are lo-cated anteriorly in the gastrula, while the more posterior portions of the notochord and adjacent mesoderm (i.e., the **trunk organizer**) are located in the developing trunk region (fig. 191G). The mesoderm adjacent to the noto-chord eventually will form the somites or primitive mesodermal segments of the embryo (figs. 191G; 217E; 224F). Experimentation, using the Vogt method of staining with vital dyes, has demonstrated that the future, anterior, presumptive somites lie closer to the blastoporal lips in the beginning gastrula, whereas the more posterior, presumptive somites are situated at a greater dis-tance from the blastoporal area. Because of this arrangement, the first or ante-rior pair of presumptive somites moves inward first, the second pair next, etc. The mesoderm of the future somites in this way is arranged along the notochord in an orderly sequence from the anterior to the posterior regions of the gas-trula (fig. 169, somites 1, 2, 3, 4, etc.). Consequently, axiation and extension of the somitic mesoderm occur along with the antero-posterior arrangement of the notochordal material. A similar distribution is effected in other regions of the mesoderm. Therefore, *axiation and antero-posterior extension of the entodermal, notochordal, and mesodermal cells are conspicuous results of the activities which effect emboly.*

2) Epiboly. The above description is concerned mainly with emboly, that is, the inward migration of the notochord-mesoderm-entoderm-yolk complex. Allied with these active events is the downward or caudal migration of the blastoporal lips. This migration is illustrated in figure 191B–E. In this figure it may be observed that, as the marginal zone cells of mesoderm and notochord

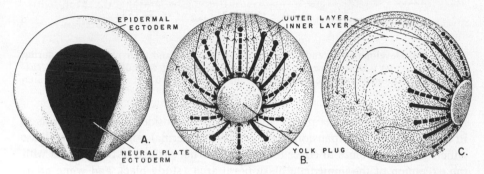

FIG. 192. Movements of the parts of the blastula during gastrulation in amphibia. (Cf. fig. 191.) (A) Results of epiboly. (Cf. fig. 191A–F.) Epidermal and neural areas envelop the other areas during gastrulation. (B) Movements of the areas of the blastula during emboly, as seen from the vegetative pole. Heavy arrows, solid and broken, show the converging movements during emboly; light arrows show the extension and divergence of cells after involution at the blastoporal margin (cf. fig. 191A–F). (C) Similar to (B), as seen from the left side.

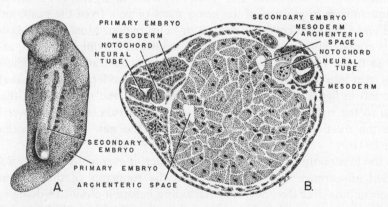

FIG. 193. Induction of a secondary embryo. (From Spemann, '38.) (A) Host embryo shown in this figure is *Triton taeniatus.* A median piece of the upper lip of the blastopore of a young gastrula of *T. cristatus* of approximately the same age as the host was implanted into the ventro-lateral ectoderm of the host. The implanted tissue developed into notochord, somites, etc.; the neural tube was induced from the host ectoderm. (B) Cross section through embryo shown in (A).

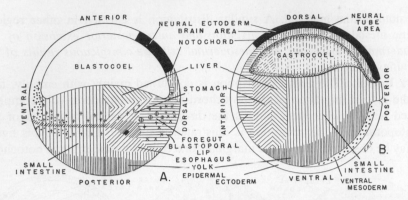

FIG. 194. Developmental tendencies of entodermal area and their reorientation during gastrulation. (A) Developmental tendencies of entodermal area of young anuran gastrula. (B) Counterclockwise rotation of approximately 90° of the entodermal area during gastrulation.

together with the entoderm and yolk pass to the inside, the forces involved in **epiboly** effect the expansion of the purely ectodermal portion of the epiblast which gradually comes to cover the entire external surface of the gastrula with the exception of the immediate blastoporal area (study black and white areas in fig. 191A–E). It may be observed further that the neural crescent now is elongated along the antero-posterior, embryonic axis where it forms a shield-shaped region with the broad end of the shield located anteriorly (fig. 192A).

A study of figure 191E and F shows that a rotation of the entire gastrula occurs in the interim between E and F. This rotation is induced by the inward movement of the entoderm and yolk, depicted in figure 191C–E, with a subsequent shift in position of the heavy mass of yolk from the posterior pole of the embryo to the embryo's ventral or belly region. Most of the blastocoel and its contained fluid is "engulfed" by the inward moving entoderm, as indicated in figure 191C–E, some of the blastocoelic fluid and blastocoelic space passes over into the gastrocoel. The region of the entodermal yolk mass shown to the left in figure 191E, therefore, is more dense and heavier than the area shown to the right. The heavier region of the gastrula seeks the lower level; hence the rotation of the entire gastrula, and the new position assumed in figure 191F.

As the blastopore progressively grows smaller, it eventually assumes a small, rounded appearance (fig. 197A–E), and the remnants of the presumptive mesoderm pass over the lips of the blastopore before it closes. In doing so, the presumptive tail mesoderm converges dorsally and becomes located inside the dorso-lateral portion of the closed blastopore near the lateral aspects of the posterior end of the folding neural plate.

A short while previous to blastoporal closure, the midregion of the neural plate area begins to fold ventrad toward the notochord, while its margins are elevated and projected dorso-mediad. The exact limits of the neural plate thus become evident (fig. 197D).

3) Embryo Produced by the Gastrulative Processes. The general result of epiboly and emboly in the *Amphibia* is the production of an embryo of three germ layers with a rounded or oval shape. The potential skin ectoderm and infolding, neural plate area form the external layer (fig. 192A). Underneath this external layer are the following structural regions of the middle or meso-dermal layer:

(a) Below the developing nerve tube is the elongated band of notochordal cells;

(b) on either side of the notochord is the somitic (somite) mesoderm;

(c) lateral to the somitic area is the mesoderm of the future kidney system; and

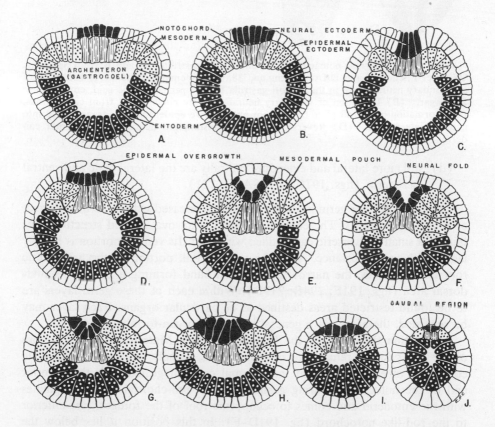

FIG. 195. Placement of the presumptive, organ-forming areas in an embryo of *Amphioxus* of about six to seven somites. (Modified from Conklin, '32.) (A) Section through anterior region. (J) Section through caudal end of embryo. (B–I) Successive sections going posteriorly at different body levels between (A) and (J).

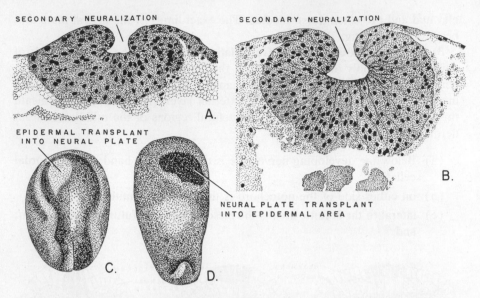

FIG. 196. Ectodermal potencies of the amphibian gastrula. (A and B from Spemann, '38, after Fischer; C and D from Spemann, '38, after Spemann, '18.)   (A) Induction of a secondary neural plate in the axolotl gastrula by five per cent oleic acid, emulsified in agar-agar.   (B) Induction of secondary neural plate by nucleic acid from calf thymus. (C) Formation of neural plate tissue from presumptive epidermal cells transplanted into neural plate region.   (D) Reverse transplant, presumptive neural plate becomes epidermal tissue.

(d) still more lateral and extending ventrally are the lateral plate and ventral mesoderm (figs. 191F–I; 198A–C; 221).

The third or inner germ layer of entoderm is encased within the mesodermal or middle germ layer. The entodermal layer is an oval-shaped structure containing a small archenteric cavity filled with fluid. Its ventral portion is heavily laden with yolk substance. Also, the future trunk portion of the archenteric roof is incomplete, the narrow notochordal band forming a part of its mid-dorsal area (figs. 191F; 194B; 219D). Within each of these germ layers are to be found restricted areas destined to be particular organs. Each layer may be regarded, therefore, as a general mosaic of organ-forming tendencies.

4) Position Occupied by the Pre-chordal Plate Material. Another feature of the late gastrula remains to be emphasized, namely, the pre-chordal plate composed of entodermal and mesodermal cells integrated with the anterior end of the notochord. During gastrulation the pre-chordal plate invaginates with the entoderm and comes to occupy the roof of the foregut, just anterior to the rod-like notochord (fig. 191D–F). In this position it lies below the anterior part of the neural plate area; it functions strongly in the induction and formation of the cephalic structures, including the brain as indicated above. Because of this inductive ability, it is regarded as a principal part of the **head**

organizer (fig. 191E–G). Eventually pre-chordal plate cells contribute to the pharyngeal area of the foregut and give origin to a portion of the head mesoderm, at least in many vertebrate species (Chap. 11, p. 523).

c. Closure of the Blastopore and Formation of the Neurenteric Canal

The closure of the blastopore and formation of the neurenteric canal is described in Chapter 10, p. 471.

d. Summary of Morphogenetic Movements of Cells During Gastrulation in the Frog and Other Amphibia

1) Emboly:

(a) **Invagination.** Invagination in the *Amphibia* appears to consist of two phases: (1) an **active infolding or forward migration** of the future foregut, stomach, etc., areas, and (2) an **insinking and inward rotation** of future intestinal and heavily laden, yolk cells.

(b) **Convergence.** This activity is found in the presumptive, notochordal and mesodermal cells as they move toward the blastoporal lips. A **dorsal convergence** toward the dorsal, blastoporal-lip area is particularly true of the more laterally placed parts of the notochordal crescent and to some extent also of the somitic and lateral plate mesoderm. The tail mesoderm tends to converge toward the dorsal blastoporal area when the blastopore nears closure.

(c) **Involution.** An inward rolling or rotation of cells over the blastoporal lips to the inside is a conspicuous part of notochordal and mesodermal cell migration.

(d) **Divergence.** After the mesodermal cells have migrated to the inside, there is a particular tendency to diverge on the part of the lateral plate and ventral mesoderm. The lateral plate mesoderm diverges laterally and ventrally, while the ventral mesoderm diverges laterally in the ventral or belly area of the gastrula.

(e) **Extension.** The phenomenon of extension or elongation is a characteristic feature of all gastrulative processes in the chordate group. Before arriving at the blastoporal lips, the **converging** notochordal and mesodermal cells may undergo a **stretching or extending movement.** That is, convergence and stretching are two prominent movements involved in the migration of the marginal zone or chordamesodermal cells as they move toward the blastoporal lip. After these materials have involuted to the inside, the chordal cells stretch antero-posteriorly and become narrowed to a cuboidal band in the midline, and the lateral plate mesoderm stretches anteriorly as it diverges laterally. Antero-posterior extension of the somitic mesoderm also occurs.

(f) **Contractile tension or constriction.** A considerable constriction or contraction around the edges of the blastopore occurs as gastrulation progresses. This particularly is true when the blastopore gradually grows smaller toward the end of the gastrulative process (Lewis, '49).

2) Epiboly. Intimately associated with and aiding the above processes involved in emboly are the movements concerned with **epiboly.** These movements result from cell proliferation, associated with a marked antero-posterior extension and expansion of the presumptive epidermal and neural plate areas. These changes are integrated closely with the inward migration of cells of the marginal zone (i.e., chordamesoderm), and the presumptive epidermal and neural areas approach closer and closer to the blastoporal edge, until finally, when mesodermal and notochordal cells have entirely involuted, ectodermal cells occupy the rim of the blastopore as it closes (figs. 192A; 220D).

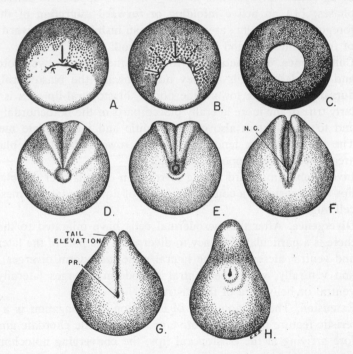

Fig. 197. History of the blastopore and adjacent posterior areas of developing embryo of the frog, *Rana pipiens*. (A) Dorsal lip of blastopore. Arrows show direction of initial invagination to form the dorsal lip. (B) Dorso-lateral and lateral-lip portions of the blastopore are added to original dorsal-lip area by convergence of mesodermal cells (arrows) and their involution at the edge of the lip. Entodermal material is invaginating. (C) Blastopore is complete; yolk plug is showing. (D) Toward the end of gastrulation. Blastopore is small; neural plate area becomes evident as neural folds begin their elevation. (E) Neural folds are slightly elevated; blastopore is very small; size of blastopore at this time is quite variable. (F) Blastopore has closed; neural folds are well developed; neurenteric passageway between neural folds and dorsal evagination of archenteric space into tail-bud area is indicated by N.C. (G) New caudal opening is forming, aided by proctodaeal invagination, PR.; tail rudiment elevation is indicated. (H) Proctodaeal opening and tail rudiment are shown.

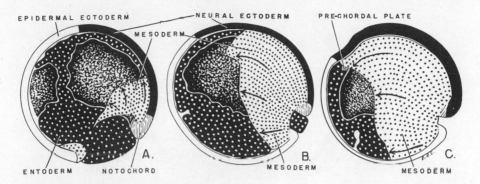

FIG. 198. Anterior extension (migration) of the mesoderm from the blastoporal-lip area after involution at the lip in the urodele, *Pleurodeles*. (A–C) Progressive inward migration of the mantel of mesoderm, indicated by the white area stippled with coarse dots. (A) Early gastrula. (B) Late gastrula. (C) Beginning neurula.

As a result, the presumptive epidermal and neural plate areas literally engulf the inwardly moving cells.

3. Gastrulation in Reptiles

a. Orientation

The reptilian blastoderm, as gastrulation begins, is composed of an upper epiblast and a lower hypoblast as indicated previously in Chapter 7 (fig. 174A–D). The formation of the hypoblast as a distinct layer proceeds in a rapid fashion and *immediately precedes the formation of a large notochordal canal and subsequent cell migration inward*. The two events of entodermal layer (hypoblast) formation and the inward migration of notochordal and mesodermal cells thus are closely and intimately correlated in reptiles. This close relationship is true particularly of the turtle group. The upper layer or epiblast of the reptilian blastoderm is a composite aggregation of presumptive epidermal, neural, notochordal, and mesodermal cells (fig. 174E, F), arranged in relation to the future, antero-posterior axis of the embryo. It is possible that some entodermal material may be located superficially in the epiblast in the turtle as gastrulation begins (Pasteels, '37a).

b. Gastrulation

Immediately following the formation of the hypoblast, the gastrulative phenomena begin with a rather large **inpushing or invagination** involving the notochordal, mesdoermal areas, **particularly the pre-chordal plate and notochordal areas.** This invagination extends downward and forward toward the hypoblast along the antero-posterior embryonic axis, and it produces a pouch-like structure known variously as the **notochordal canal, blastoporal canal, or chordamesodermal canal** (figs. 199A–C; 200A–C). The invaginated noto-

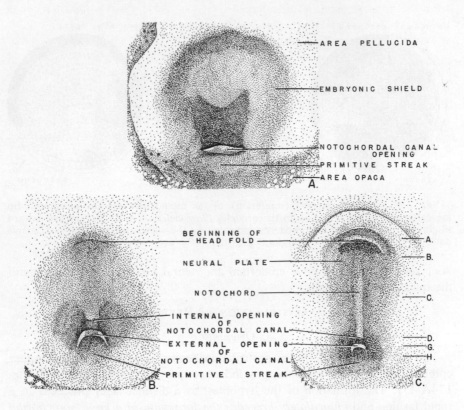

FIG. 199. Surface views of blastoderm of the turtle, *Chrysemys picta,* during gastrulation. Darkened area in the center shows the embryonic shield, the region of the notochordal canal in the area of the primitive plate. (A) Young gastrula. External opening of notochordal canal is wide. (B) Later gastrula. External opening of notochordal canal is horseshoe-shaped; internal opening of canal is indicated by small crescentic light area in front of external opening. (C) Very late gastrula. Notochord is indicated in center; head fold is beginning at anterior extremity of blastoderm.

chordal canal reposes upon the entoderm, and both fuse in the region of contact (fig. 200C). The thin layer of cells in the area of fusion soon disappears, leaving the antero-ventral end of the flattened notochordal canal exposed to the archenteric space below. After some reorganization, the notochord appears as a band, extending antero-posteriorly in the median line, associated with the entoderm on either side (fig. 201B–G). However, at the extreme anterior end of the gastrula, the notochordal material, together with the entoderm and to some extent the overlying ectoderm, presents a fused condition. Within this area the **pre-chordal plate or anterior portion of the head organizer** is located. In this general region of the embryo, foregut, brain, and other head structures eventually arise (fig. 199C). The original, relatively large, notochordal invagination soon becomes a small canal which extends cranio-ventrally from the upper or external opening to the archenteric space which lies below the notochord and entoderm (fig. 200B, E).

Posterior to the opening of the notochordal canal is the thickened primitive plate (primitive streak), composed of converged presumptive mesodermal cells (fig. 199). This converged mass of cells involutes to the inside along the lateral borders of the notochordal canal and also posterior to this opening. However, *most of the mesoderm of the future body of the embryo apparently passes inward with the notochordal material during the formation of the notochordal canal,* where it comes to lie on either side of the median notochordal band between the ectoderm and the entoderm. These general relationships of notochord, ectoderm, mesoderm, and entoderm are shown in figure 201A–H.

The extent to which the original notochordal inpushing is developed varies in different reptilian species. In lizards and snakes its development is more pronounced than in turtles (cf. fig. 200A, D).

During emboly, the presumptive neural plate and epidermal areas are

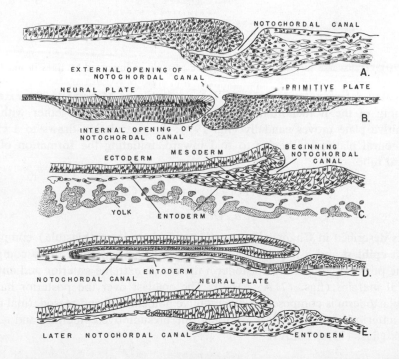

FIG. 200. Sagittal section of reptilian blastoderms to show notochordal inpushing (notochordal canal or pouch). (A) Section of early gastrulative procedure in *Clemmys leprosa.* (After Pasteels, '36b, slightly modified.) (B) Original from slide, *Chrysemys picta,* showing condition after notochordal canal has broken through into archenteric space. (C) Notochordal canal of the lizard, *Platydactylus.* (D) Later stage of (C). (E) After notochordal canal has broken through into archenteric space. (C–E, after Will, 1892.)

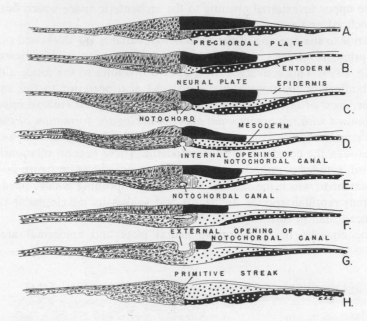

FIG. 201. Transverse sections of the late turtle gastrula as indicated by lines in fig. 199C.

elongated antero-posteriorly by the forces of epiboly. Meanwhile, the external opening of the notochordal canal changes in shape and together with the primitive plate moves caudally (fig. 199). As gastrulation draws to a close, the neural plate area begins to fold inward, initiating the formation of the neural tube.

4. GASTRULATION IN THE CHICK

a. Orientation

As described in Chapter 7, a two-layered blastoderm (blastula) composed of an **epiblast** and a **hypoblast** is present, with the hypoblast more complete at the posterior end of the blastoderm than at its extreme anterior and antero-lateral margins (figs. 171A; 202A). The epiblast over the posterior half of the blastoderm is composed of presumptive notochordal and mesodermal cells, and anteriorly in the epiblast are found the presumptive epidermal and neural areas (figs. 173A; 202A).

b. Gastrulative Changes

1) Development of Primitive Streak as Viewed from the Surface of Stained Blastoderms. The formation of the primitive streak is a progressive affair. Figure 170 pictures a pre-streak blastoderm, and it is to be observed that the entodermal layer below the epiblast is present as an irregular area in the caudal region of the area pellucida. A median, sagittal section through a comparable stage is shown diagrammatically in figure 171A. Figure 203A illustrates an early beginning streak normally found eight hours after incubation of the egg is initiated, while figure 203B presents a medium streak, appearing after about 12 to 13 hours of incubation. In figure 203C, a definite primitive streak appears in which the primitive groove, primitive pit, primitive folds, and Hensen's node (primitive knot) are outlined. This condition occurs after about 18 to 19 hours of incubation. This may be regarded as the mature streak. A later streak after about 19 to 22 hours of incubation is indicated in figure 203D. Observe that the head process or rudimentary notochord extends anteriorly from Hensen's node, while the mesoderm is a deeper-shaded area emanating from the antero-lateral aspect of the streak. The clear proamnion region may be observed at the anterior end of the area pellucida. In the proamnion area, mesoderm is not present at this time between the ectodermal and entodermal layers.

2) Cell Movements in the Epiblast Involved in Primitive-streak Formation as Indicated by Carbon-particle Marking and Vital-staining Experiments. Recent experiments by Spratt ('46), using carbon particles as a marking device, have demonstrated that epiblast cells from the posterior half of the pre-streak blastoderm gradually move *posteriad and mediad* as gastrulation proceeds (figs. 202, 204, black arrows). Before the actual appearance of the streak, mesodermal cells begin to appear between the epiblast and hypoblast at the posterior margin of the area pellucida. (See fig. 202B, involuted mesoderm). As cellular convergence posteriorly toward the median line continues, *the primitive streak begins to form as a median thickening posteriorly in the pellucid area* (fig. 202C, observe posterior median area indicated in white). The rudimentary primitive streak formed in this manner gradually advances anteriorly toward the central region of the pellucid area of the blastoderm (fig. 202D, E). In the thickened area of the developing primitive streak, shown in white at the posterior median portion of the blastoderm in figure 202C, there are about three to four cell layers of epiblast together with about the same number of layers of mesoderm below. At its anterior end the streak is thinner.

The anterior end of this early streak gradually grows forward as a result of cell proliferation in situ and by cells added through convergence of cells from antero-lateral areas (Spratt, '46). Some of the cells at the anterior end of the forming streak may involute or ingress from the epiblast into the space between the hypoblast and epiblast and thus come to lie at the anterior end of the forming streak, while other cells ingress laterally between these two layers (fig. 202C–E, K–O).

As the streak differentiates anteriorly by addition of cells to its anterior end, it also elongates posteriorly by cellular additions to its caudal end. The carbon-marking experiments of Spratt demonstrated further that, during the

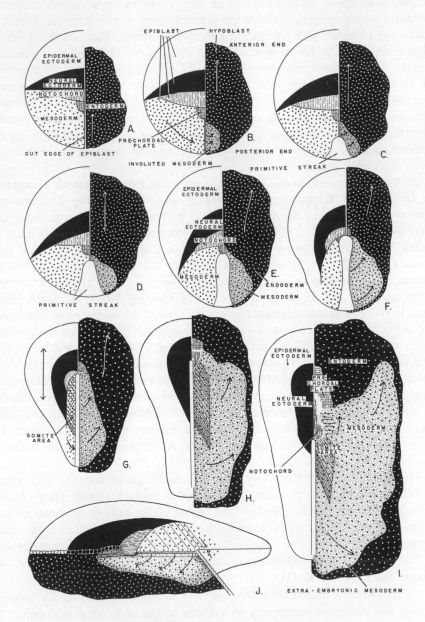

Labels in figure:

A: EPIDERMAL ECTODERM, NEURAL ECTODERM, NOTOCHORD, ENTODERM, MESODERM, CUT EDGE OF EPIBLAST, PRECHORDAL PLATE

B: EPIBLAST, HYPOBLAST, ANTERIOR END, INVOLUTED MESODERM, POSTERIOR END

C: PRIMITIVE STREAK

D: PRIMITIVE STREAK

E: EPIDERMAL ECTODERM, NEURAL ECTODERM, NOTOCHORD, MESODERM, ENDODERM, MESODERM

G: SOMITE AREA

H: NOTOCHORD

I: EPIDERMAL ECTODERM, ENTODERM, PRE-CHORDAL PLATE, NEURAL ECTODERM, MESODERM, SOMITE AREA, EXTRA-EMBRYONIC MESODERM

FIG. 202. *(See facing page for legend.)*

422

formation of the streak up to about the condition present at 20 to 22 hours of incubation (figs. 202I, K; 203D), almost the entire posterior half of the pellucid area, consisting of presumptive pre-chordal plate, notochord, and mesoderm, is brought into the streak and involuted to the inside between the hypoblast and epiblast (figs. 202F–H; 204). This condition of development is often referred to as the "head-process stage" (stage 5, Hamburger and Hamilton, '51). At this stage the approximate, antero-posterior limits of the future embryonic body of the chick, exclusive of the extra-embryonic tissue, are shown by the general area beginning just anterior to the head process and extending for a short distance posterior to Hensen's node (figs. 203D; 205D, E).

As indicated in figure 202, there are two parts to the primitive streak:

(1) the area of Hensen's node and primitive pit concerned with invaginative movements of pre-chordal plate mesoderm and notochordal cells and

(2) the body of the streak.

The former area appears to arise independently in the center of the pellucid area, while the body of the streak is formed at the median, caudal margin of the pellucid area, from whence it grows anteriad to unite with Hensen's node.

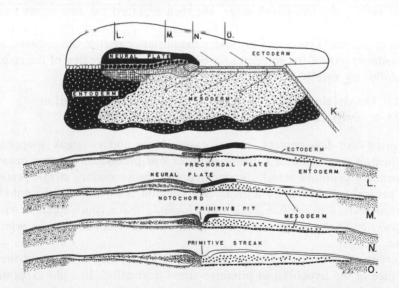

FIG. 202. Migration of cells during gastrulation in the chick. Drawing to the left of the midline represents a surface view; to the right of the midline the epiblast layer has been removed. (A–F) To the left of the midline based on data provided by Spratt, '46. (J) Represents lateral, sectional view of (F)–(G), viewed from the left side. Arrows indicate direction of cell migration. (K) Indicates a left lateral view of (I), with the epiblast cut away midsagitally throughout most of the left side of the blastoderm. (L–O) Transverse sections of (K), as indicated on (K).

The body of the streak serves as the "door" through which migrating meso-dermal cells other than the cells of the pre-chordal plate-notochordal area pass from the epiblast layer downward to the space between the epiblast and hypoblast.

Using the Vogt method of vital staining, Pasteels ('37b) was able to demonstrate morphogenetic movements of cells into the primitive streak area and thence to the inside similar to that described by Spratt (fig. 202G–I).

The evidence derived from the carbon-particle-marking technic and that of vital staining, therefore, strongly suggests that the primitive streak of the chick forms as a result of:

(a) converging movements of the epiblast cells toward the median line of the posterior half of the pellucid area and
(b) cell proliferation in situ within the streak.

3) Cell Movements in the Hypoblast and the Importance of Those Movements in Primitive-streak Formation. The hypoblast or entodermal layer of the blastula appears to play a significant role relative to the formation of the primitive streak in the bird. Various lines of evidence point to this conclusion. For example, Waddington ('33) reported the results of experiments in which he separated the epiblast from the hypoblast of early chick and duck embryos in the early, primitive-streak stage. He then replaced the two layers so that their longitudinal axes were diametrically reversed, that is, the anterior part of the entoderm (hypoblast) lay under the posterior part of the epiblast, while the posterior part of the entoderm lay below the anterior region of the epiblast. The following results were obtained:

(1) The development of the original streak was suppressed; or
(2) a new, secondary, primitive streak was induced.

During later development, in some cases, the secondary streak disappeared; in others, it persisted and a double monster was produced. In other instances the primary primitive streak disappeared and the secondary streak persisted. The general conclusion set forth by Waddington is as follows: the entoderm does not induce the differentiation of a definite tissue, but rather, *it induces the form-building movements which lead to the development of the primitive streak.*

Certain experiments made by Spratt ('46) lend added evidence of the importance of the hypoblast in primitive-streak formation. In eight experiments in which the hypoblast was removed before streak formation, six cases failed to produce a streak, whereas in two instances a beginning streak was formed. It may be that in the latter two cases, the induction of morphogenetic movements within the epiblast cells occurred previous to hypoblast removal. These experiments are too few to permit a definite conclusion; however, they are suggestive and serve to bolster the conclusion made by Waddington. In a second set of experiments performed by Spratt, chick blastoderms in the pre-streak and early-streak stages were inverted and marked with carbon particles. The results showed that the hypoblast moves forward in the median line below the epiblast layer. He also demonstrated that this forward movement of the hypoblast "precedes the anterior differentiation of the primitive streak." Spratt further observed that: When the movement of the hypoblast deviated to the left or to the right, the primitive streak similarly deviated. This evidence "strongly suggests that the hypoblast influences the development of the primitive streak in the overlying epiblast" (Spratt, '46).

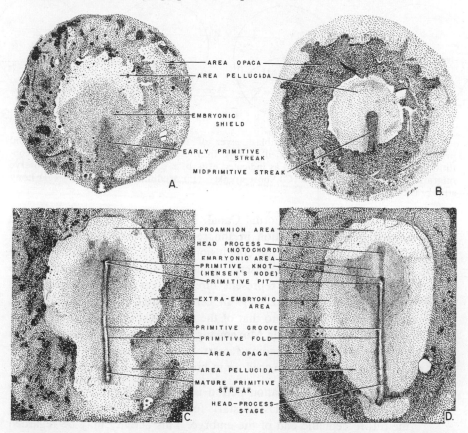

FIG. 203. Surface-view drawings of photographs of developing primitive streak. (From Hamburger and Hamilton, '51, after Spratt.) (A) Initial streak, short, conical thickening at posterior end of blastoderm. (Hamburger and Hamilton, '51, stage 2.) (B) Intermediate streak. Thickened streak area approaches center of area pellucida. (Hamburger and Hamilton, '51, stage 3.) (C) Definitive streak (average length, 1.88 mm.). Primitive groove, primitive fold, primitive pit, and Hensen's node are present. (Hamburger and Hamilton, '51, stage 4.) (D) Head-process stage (19 to 22 hours of incubation). Notochord or head process visible as area of condensed mesoderm extending anteriorly from Hensen's node. Proamnion area is indicated in front portion of area pellucida; head fold is not yet present. (Hamburger and Hamilton, '51, stage 5.)

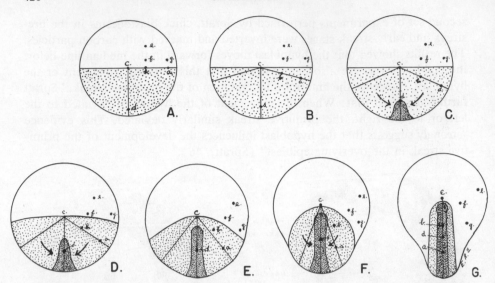

Fig. 204. Movements in the epiblast layer of the chick during gastrulation and primitive-streak formation. (Modified slightly from Spratt, '46.) (A) Pre-streak condition. Carbon particles are placed as indicated at a, b, c, d, e, f, and g. (B–G) Observe migration of carbon particles. (C) Short streak. (E) Medium broad streak. (G) Long streak. (See fig. 203C.)

4) Primitive Pit and Notochordal Canal. If one compares the notochordal canal, formed during gastrulation in the reptilian blastoderm, with that of the primitive pit in the chick, the conclusion is inevitable that the **primitive pit** of the chick blastoderm represents an **abortive notochordal canal.** The lizard, turtle, and chick thus represent three degrees of notochordal canal development (figs. 200A, D; 202J). In certain birds, such as the duck, a notochordal canal very similar to that of the turtle gastrula, is formed.

5) Resumé of Morphogenetic Movements of Cells During Gastrulation in the Chick. In view of the foregoing facts relative to primitive-streak formation, steps in the gastrulative procedure in birds may be described as follows:

(a) Shortly after the incubation period is initiated, hypoblast material at the caudal end of the blastula starts to move in the median line toward the future cephalic end of the embryo. This activity may be regarded as a **gastrulative streaming** of the hypoblast. (This streaming movement probably represents the chick's counterpart of the forward movement of the entodermal area in the dorsal-lip region of the frog embryo.)

(b) After this movement of the hypoblast is inaugurated, cells from the epiblast layer immediately overlying the moving hypoblast pass downward toward the hypoblast. That is, epiblast cells begin to **involute** and come to lie between the epiblast and hypoblast; from this new position the involuted cells migrate laterally and anteriorly between the hypoblast and epiblast.

(c) In conjunction with the foregoing activities, epiblast cells (presumptive mesoderm) from the posterior half of the epiblast of the pellucid area *migrate posteriad, converging from either side toward the median line* (fig. 204A–G).

(d) These converging cells begin to pile up in the posterior median edge of the pellucid area (fig. 204C), where they produce a raphe-like thickening which marks the beginning of the primitive streak (fig. 204C–G). The beginning streak first makes its appearance at about seven to eight hours after the start of incubation in the egg of the chick (fig. 204C).

(e) Once formed, the initial streak grows anteriad in the median line by: (1) cell proliferation in situ, and by the addition of (2) converging cells from the epiblast layer.

(f) Also, the primitive streak apparently grows posteriad by cell proliferation and the addition of converging cells.

(g) When the migrating cells of the epiblast reach the primitive streak, they involute and pass downward to the space between the epiblast and hypoblast. From this new position they move laterad and anteriad on either side of the midline, **diverging** to form a broad, middle layer of mesodermal cells.

(h) As the primitive streak grows anteriad in the epiblast, it eventually approaches the presumptive **pre-chordal plate** and presumptive **notochordal areas.**

(i) The pre-chordal plate and notochordal cells then **invaginate** to form the primitive pit; the latter represents a shallow or vestigial **notochordal canal,** a structure strongly developed in reptiles and some birds, and occasionally in mammals.

(j) Notochordal cells from the notochordal crescent converge to the pit area and probably pass downward in the walls of the pit, whence they ingress and move forward in the median line (fig. 202A–G, J, K). The definitive primitive streak is formed after about 18 to 19 hours of incubation. At about 20 to 22 hours of incubation, the prospective, notochordal material (e.g., the head process) has already invaginated. At this time it represents a mass of cells in the median line *intimately associated with the neural plate ectoderm above the pre-chordal plate cells and the entoderm below* (fig. 202I, K). As the primitive streak recedes posteriad (see p. 431), the notochordal material gradually separates from the surrounding, pre-chordal plate cells and also from the neural plate material. Eventually the notochordal cells become a distinct median mass which elongates rapidly (i.e., **undergoes extension**) as the nodal area and the primitive streak recede caudally (Spratt, '47).

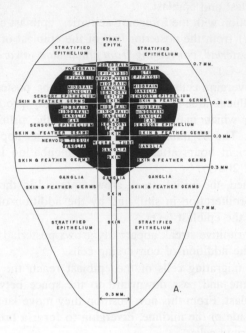

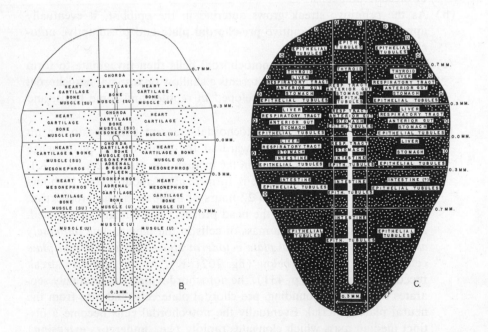

FIG. 205. (See facing page for legend.)

(k) **Somitic mesoderm** (i.e., the mesoderm of the future somites) apparently passes inward between the epiblast and hypoblast from the antero-lateral portions of the primitive streak. It migrates forward and becomes extended along either side of the notochordal cells during the period of primitive-streak recession. The nephric and lateral plate mesoderm involutes along the middle portions of the streak, and this mesoderm becomes **extended** antero-posteriorly. The hypomeric or lateral plate mesoderm also **diverges** laterally. The **extra-embryonic** mesoderm moves inward along the postero-lateral portions of the streak; it migrates laterally and anteriorly (fig. 202I, extra-embryonic mesoderm).

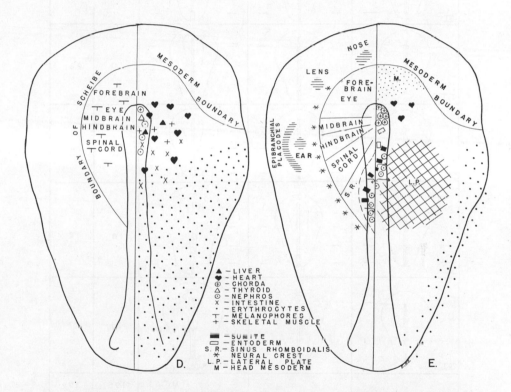

FIG. 205. Three-germ-layered blastoderm or late gastrula of chick, showing the mosaic distribution of developmental tendencies. (A–C after Rawles, '36; D and E after Rudnick, '44, from various sources.) (A–C) The lines transversely placed across embryo are at levels of 0.3 mm. and 0.7 mm. from the center one, considered as 0.0 mm. (A) Ectodermal or external layer; neural plate area is indicated in black, epidermal area in white. (B) Mesodermal or middle germ layer. (C) Entodermal or inner germ layer. (D) Ectodermal layer shown on left, mesodermal and entodermal on right. (E) Superficial or ectodermal layer shown at left, deeper layer, at right. (*Note:* These diagrams should be considered only in a suggestive way; final knowledge relative to exact limits of potencies, especially in the mesodermal layer, should be more thoroughly explored.)

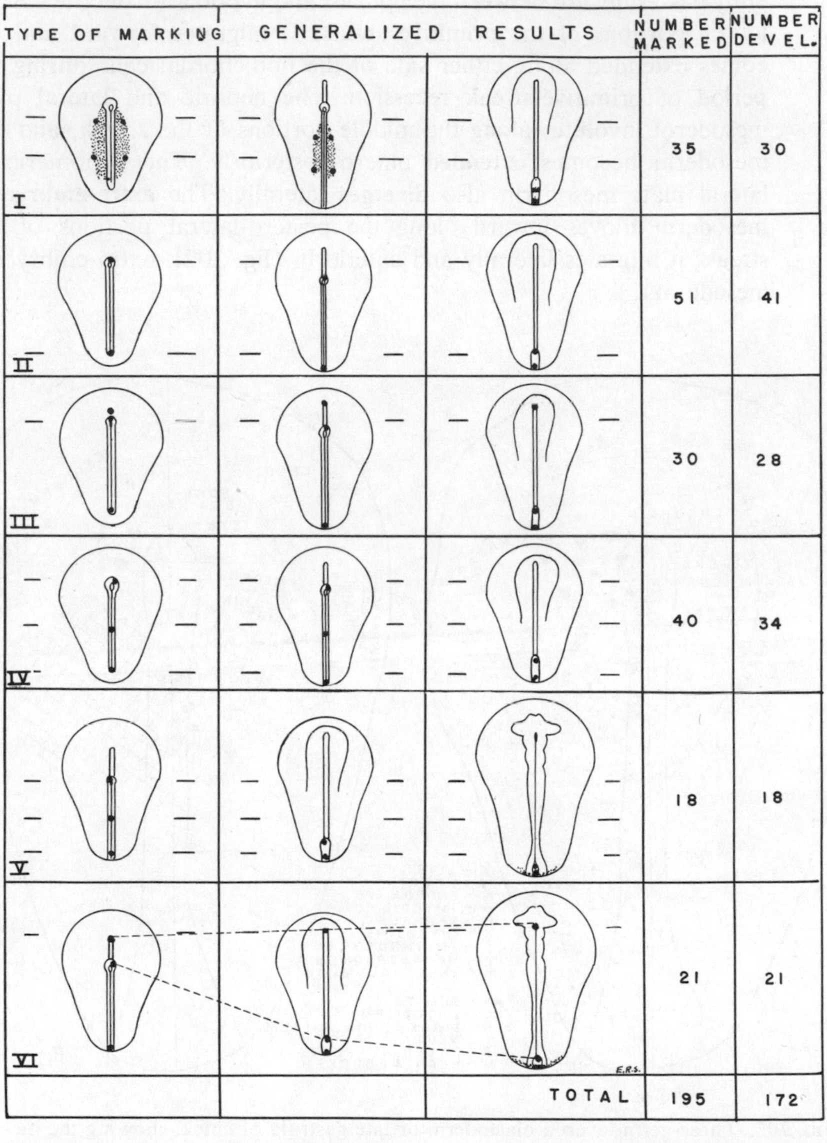

TYPE OF MARKING	GENERALIZED RESULTS		NUMBER MARKED	NUMBER DEVEL.
I			35	30
II			51	41
III			30	28
IV			40	34
V			18	18
VI			21	21
		TOTAL	195	172

FIG. 206. Recession of the primitive streak of the chick and growth of the embryo in front of Hensen's node. Marked cell groups represented by heavy dots; dashes opposite these are reference marks placed on the plasma clot to permit orientation. This diagram based upon 6 different types of carbon-marking experiments with the generalized results 6–15 hours following explantation. In type I, the stippled area is invaginated as indicated. Observe especially type VI, the history of the three areas marked by the three heavy dots placed on the blastoderm at the head-process stage. It is to be observed that the embryo as a whole arises from the area in front of Hensen's node. (After Spratt, '47.)

(l) While the above activities take place, the area pellucida becomes elongated posteriorly. The entire pellucid area thus becomes piriform, i.e., pear-shaped (figs. 202F–I; 203C).

(m) This change in shape of the pellucid area is associated primarily with the activities involved in epiboly which accompany the embolic activities observed above. Epiboly brings about the **elongation** of the presumptive neural crescent, converting it into an elongated band of cells. It also effects the **expansion** and antero-posterior **extension** of the overlying presumptive, neural plate and epidermal cells. The latter behavior is intimately associated with the antero-posterior extension of the notochordal and mesodermal cellular areas mentioned in (j) and (k) on pp. 427, 428.

(n) Most of the gastrulative processes in the chick are completed at about 20 to 22 hours after incubation starts. At this time the blastoderm is in the **head-process stage.** The so-called head process or "notochordal process" represents the rudimentary notochord which projects forward from the primitive streak. (See (j) on p. 427.) At this time the various, specific, organ-forming areas appear to be well established (figs. 202I; 205A–E). (See Rawles, '36; Rudnick, '44.) From this time on the primitive streak regresses caudally, *as the embryo and embryonic tissues develop in front of it.* The caudal regression of the streak is shown in figure 206. Spratt ('47) concludes that as the streak regresses, it becomes shortened by transformation of its caudal end into both embryonic and extra-embryonic ectoderm and mesoderm. Finally, the anterior end of the streak, that is, the primitive knot or Hensen's node together with possibly some condensation of adjacent streak tissue (Rudnick, '44), forms the **end bud.** The latter, according to Homdahl ('26) gives origin to the posterior portion of the embryo caudal to somite 27 and to the tail. The remains of the end bud come to a final resting place at the end of the tail.

5. GASTRULATION IN MAMMALS

a. Orientation

In the mammals, the formative area of the blastocyst (blastula) is located at one pole and is known as the **embryonic or germ disc.** It consists of a lower hypoblast and an upper epiblast. This **embryonic disc** is connected to the non-formative or trophoblast cells around its edges (figs. 176, 177, 178). In some species the embryonic disc is superficial and uncovered by trophoblast cells (pig, cat, rabbit, opossum), while in others, it is sequestered beneath a covering of trophoblast (human, monkey, rat). (See figs. 177, 178.)

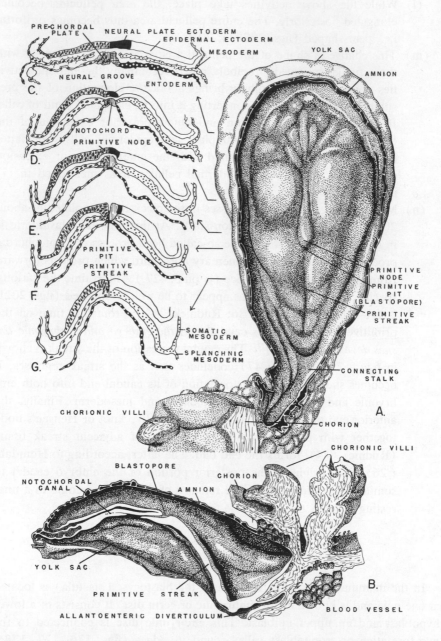

FIG. 207. Three-germ-layer late gastrula of human embryo (pre-somite stage, after Heuser: Contrib. to Embryol. Carnegie Inst., Washington, Publ. 138, 23: 1932). (A) Dorsal view of embryonic disc, amnion removed. (B) Sagittal section through median area of (A). Observe elongated notochordal canal. (C–G) Transverse sections as indicated.

b. Gastrulation in the Pig Embryo

In the pig embryo, two centers of activity are concerned with the formation of the primitive streak, namely, a caudal area of mesodermal proliferation which forms the **body of the primitive streak** and an anterior **primitive knot or Hensen's node.** The similarity of behavior of these two portions of the primitive streak in the chick and pig suggests strongly that their formation by a convergence of superficial epiblast cells occurs in the pig as it does in the chick. Hensen's node, originally described by Hensen (1876) in the rabbit and guinea pig, is a thickened area of the epiblast in the midline near the middle of the embryonic disc. As in the chick, the body of the primitive streak takes its origin at the caudal end of the embryonic disc, where the first appearance of the streak is indicated by a thickening of the epiblast (fig. 209A, B). From this thickened region, cells are budded off between the epiblast and hypoblast, where they migrate distad as indicated by the lightly stippled areas in figure 208. The streak ultimately elongates, continuing to give origin to cells between the hypoblast and epiblast. Eventually, the anterior neck region of the body of the streak merges with Hensen's node (fig. 208E, F). From the anterior aspects of the primitive (Hensen's) node, cells are proliferated off between the epiblast and hypoblast, and a depression or pit, the **primitive pit,** appears just caudal to the node.

The proliferation of cells from the nodal area deposits a median band of cells *which merges anteriorly with the hypoblast below.* More caudally, the hypoblast becomes attached to either side of the median band of cells (fig. 209C). The median band of nodal cells thus forms part of two regions, viz., an anterior, **pre-chordal plate region,** where the nodal cells are merged with hypoblast (entoderm), and an elongated notochordal band or rod of cells extending backward between the hypoblast cells (fig. 209C) to Hensen's node, where it unites with the hypoblast posteriorly (fig. 209D). Unlike the condition in the chick, the notochordal rod, other than in the pre-chordal plate area, is exposed to the archenteric space below (fig. 209C). It simulates strongly that of the reptilian blastoderm as gastrulation draws to a close.

In the meantime, mesodermal cells from the primitive streak migrate forward between the hypoblast and epiblast along either side of the notochord in the form of two wing-like areas (figs. 208H, I; 209C). Other mesodermal cells migrate posteriad and laterad. Consequently, one is able to distinguish two main groups of mesodermal cells:

(1) **formative or embryonic mesoderm,** which remains within the confines of the embryonic or germinal disc and

(2) distally placed **non-formative or extra-embryonic mesoderm.**

The former will give origin to the mesoderm of the embryonic body, while from the latter arises the mesoderm of the extra-embryonic tissues.

In conclusion, therefore, we may assume that, during gastrulation in the

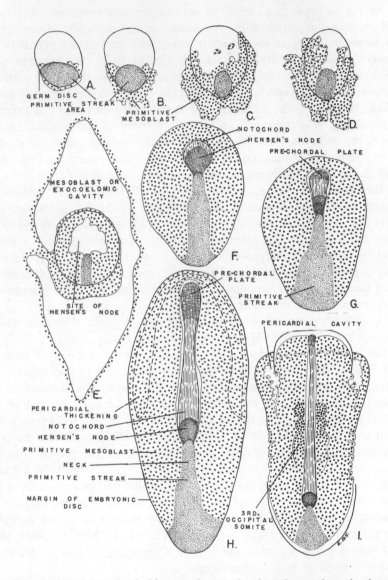

FIG. 208. Development of primitive streak, notochord, and mesodermal migration in the pig. (After Streeter, '27.)   (A) Primitive streak represented as thickened area at caudal end of embryonic (germ) disc. Migrating mesoderm shown in heavy stipple. (B–E) Later stages of streak development. Observe mass migration of mesoderm. The mesoderm outside the germ disc is extra-embryonic mesoderm.   (F) Forward growing, primitive streak makes contact with Hensen's node. (G–I) Observe elongation of notochord accompanied by recession of primitive streak shown in (I). Observe in (I) that an embryo with three pairs of somites has formed anterior to Hensen's node. Compare with Spratt's observation on developing chick, fig. 206, type VI.

434

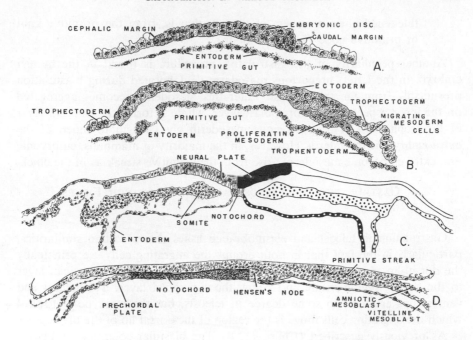

FIG. 209. Longitudinal and transverse sections of the early embryonic (germ) disc of the pig. (C and D after Streeter, '27.) (A) Early, pre-streak, germ disc, showing caudal thickening of epiblast layer. (B) Early streak germ disc, showing thickened caudal edge of disc and beginning migration of mesodermal cells (see fig. 208A). (C) Transverse section through late gastrula, showing three germ layers. Observe that entoderm is attached to either side of median notochordal rod. (D) Longitudinal section through pre-somite, pig blastoderm, showing the relation of notochord to Hensen's node, entoderm, and pre-chordal plate.

pig embryo, emboly and epiboly are comparable and quite similar to these activities in the chick.

c. Gastrulation in Other Mammals

Though the origin of notochordal and pre-chordal plate cells in the pig simulates the origin of these cells in the chick, their origin in certain mammals, such as the mole (Heape, 1883) and the human (fig. 207), resembles the condition found in reptiles, particularly in the lizards, where an enlarged notochordal pouch or canal is elaborated by an invaginative process. Consequently, in reptiles, birds, and mammals, two main types of presumptive prechordal plate-notochordal relationships occur as follows:

(1) In one group **an enlarged notochordal canal or pouch** is formed which pushes anteriad in the midline between the hypoblast and epiblast; and

(2) in others **an abortive notochordal canal or primitive pit** is developed, and the notochordal cells are invaginated and proliferated from the

thickened anterior aspect of the pit, that is, from the primitive knot or primitive node (Hensen's node).

Another peculiarity of the gastrulative procedure is found in the human embryo. In the latter, **precocious mesoderm** is elaborated during blastulation presumably from the trophoblast. Later this mesoderm becomes aggregated on the inner aspect of the trophoblast layer, where it forms the internal layer of the trophoblast. This precocious mesoderm gives origin to much of the **extra-embryonic mesoderm.** However, in the majority of mammals, embryonic and extra-embryonic mesoderm arise from the primitive streak as in the chick.

6. Gastrulation in Teleost and Elasmobranch Fishes

a. Orientation

Gastrulation in teleost and elasmobranch fishes shows certain similarities, particularly in the fact that in both groups the migrating cells use principally the dorsal-lip area of the blastopore as the gateway from the superficial layer to the deeper region inside and below the superficial layer. The lateral and ventral lips are used to some degree in teleosts, but the main point toward which the migrating cells move is the region of the dorsal lip of the blastopore.

As previously described (Chap. 7), the late blastular condition or blasto-disc of elasmobranch and teleost fishes consists of an upper layer of **formative tissue,** or blastodisc (embryonic disc) and a lower layer of **trophoblast or periblast tissue.** The latter is associated closely with the yolk (figs. 179A; 180A; 181A; 210A). In teleost fishes much of the presumptive entodermal, organ-forming area (the so-called primary hypoblast) is represented by cells which lie in the lower region of the caudal portion of the blastodisc (figs. 180A; 181A; 210C). The exact orientation of the hypoblast appears to vary with the species. In *Fundulus,* a considerable amount of the presumptive entoderm appears on the surface at the caudal margin of the blastodisc (fig. 180A, B). (See Oppenheimer, '36.) However, in the trout, *Salmo,* presumptive entoderm lies in the lower areas of the thickened caudal portion of the disc, and the pre-chordal plate of presumptive entomesoderm alone is exposed (fig. 181A, B). (See Pasteels, '36.) The position of the presumptive entoderm in the shark, *Scyllium* (Vandebroek, '36), resembles that of *Fundulus* (fig. 170A), although some entoderm may arise by a process of delamination from the lower area of the blastodisc (fig. 179A).

b. Gastrulation in Teleost Fishes

1) Emboly. As the time of gastrulation approaches, the entire outer edge of the blastodisc begins to thicken and, thereby, forms a ring-like area around the edge of the disc, known as the **germ ring** (figs. 210C; 211B). At the caudal edge of the blastoderm, *the germ-ring thickening is not only more pronounced,* but it also extends inward for some distance toward the center of the blastoderm (fig. 211A, B). This posterior prominence of the germ ring forms the **embryonic shield.**

As gastrulation begins, the entodermal cells of the primary hypoblast at the caudal edge of the embryonic shield stream forward below the epiblast toward the anterior end of the blastodisc (figs. 210A, D). Coincident with this forward movement of the primary hypoblast, a small, crescent-shaped opening

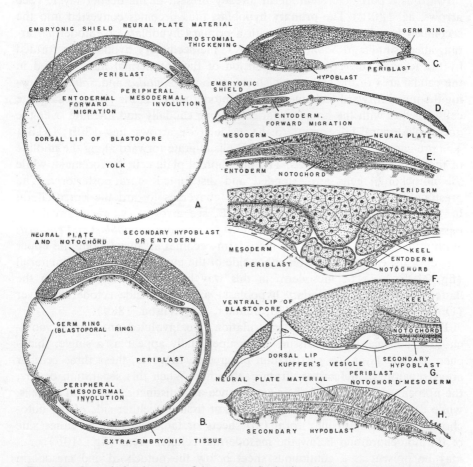

FIG. 210. Gastrulation in teleost fishes. (A) Sagittal section of early gastrula. (Modified slightly from Wilson, 1889.) (B) Midsagittal section through late teleost gastrula. The dorsal and ventral lips of the blastopore are shown approaching each other. (Modified slightly from Wilson, 1889.) (C) Beginning gastrula of early blastoderm of brook trout, *Salvelinus.* Observe inward (forward) migration of primary hypoblast cells and thickened mass of cells which arises at posterior margin. (After Sumner, '03.) (D) Later stage in gastrulation of brook trout. (After Sumner, '03.) (E) Transverse section of late gastrula of brook trout, showing the three germ layers. (After Sumner, '03.) (F) Transverse section through late gastrula of sea bass. (After Wilson, 1889.) (G) Midsagittal section through closing blastopore of sea bass. (After Wilson, 1889.) (H) Longitudinal section through late gastrula of the brook trout. (After Sumner, '03.)

appears at the caudal edge of the embryonic shield; this opening forms the **dorsal lip of the blastopore** (figs. 210A; 211A, B).

In teleost fishes with a primary hypoblast arranged as in *Fundulus* (fig. 180A, B), as the entodermal cells of the hypoblast move anteriad from the deeper portions of the blastodisc, the entodermal cells exposed at the caudal edge of the epiblast move over the blastoporal lip (i.e., involute) and migrate forward as a part of the entoderm already present in the deeper layer. (See arrows, fig. 180B.) The **primary hypoblast** thus becomes converted into the **secondary hypoblast.** In teleosts with a primary hypoblast or entodermal arrangement similar to *Salmo* (fig. 181A), the secondary hypoblast is formed by the forward migration and expansion of the entodermal mass located in the caudal area of the embryonic shield. In both *Fundulus* and *Salmo* following the initial forward movement of the entodermal cells, the pre-chordal plate cells together with the notochordal cells move caudally and involute over the dorsal blastoporal lip, passing to the inside. (See arrows, figs. 180B; 181B.) The pre-chordal plate and notochordal cells migrate forward along the midline of the forming embryonic axis. The pre-chordal plate cells lie foremost, while the notochordal cells are extended and distributed more posteriorly. The presumptive mesoderm in the meantime converges toward the dorso-lateral lips of the blastopore (figs. 180B; 181B, see arrows), where it involutes, passing to the inside *between the entoderm or secondary hypoblast and epiblast.* Within the forming gastrula, the mesoderm becomes arranged along the upper aspect of the entoderm and on either side of the median, notochordal material (fig. 210E, F). The mesoderm in this way becomes inserted between the flattened entoderm (secondary hypoblast) and the outside ectodermal layer (Oppenheimer, '36; Pasteels, '36; Sumner, '03; Wilson, 1889).

During the early phases of gastrulation, the involuted entodermal, notochordal, and mesodermal tissues may superficially appear as a single, thickened, cellular layer. As gastrulation progresses, however, these three cellular areas separate or **delaminate** from each other. When this separation occurs, the notochordal cells make their appearance as a distinct median rod of cells, while the mesoderm is present as a sheet of tissue on either side of the notochord. The entoderm may form two sheets or lamellae, one on either side of the notochord and below the mesodermal cellular areas (fig. 210F) or it may be present as a continuous sheet below the notochord and mesoderm (fig. 210E, H). The entodermal lamellae, when present, soon grow mediad below the notochord and fuse to form one complete entodermal layer (Wilson, 1889).

2) Epiboly. Emboly involves for the most part the movements of cells in the caudal and caudo-lateral areas of the blastoderm, i.e., the **embryonic portion of the germ ring.** However, while the involution of cells concerned with the development of the dorsal, axial region of the embryo occurs, the margins of the blastodisc beyond the dorsal-lip area, that is, the **extra-embryonic,**

germ-ring tissue, together with the presumptive epidermal area, proceeds to expand rapidly. This growth and expansion soon bring about an engulfment of the yolk mass (figs. 210B; 211C–F). The blastoporal-lip area (i.e., edge of germ ring) ultimately fuses at the caudal trunk region (figs. 210G; 211F). As the blastoporal region becomes narrower, a small vesicular outpocketing, known as Kupffer's vesicle, makes its appearance at the ventro-caudal end of the forming embryo at the terminal end of the solid, post-anal gut (fig. 210G). This vesicle possibly represents a vestige of the enteric portion of the neurenteric canal found in *Amphioxus,* frog, etc. A certain amount of mesodermal involution occurs around the edges of the germ ring, in some species more than in others (fig. 210A, B, peripheral mesodermal involution).

As the cellular dispositions involved in extra-embryonic expansion of the epidermal and germ-ring areas are established, the presumptive, neural plate material (figs. 179, 180, 181) becomes greatly extended antero-posteriorly in the dorsal midline (figs. 210A, H; 211E), where it forms into a thickened, elongated **ridge** or **keel.** The latter gradually sinks downward toward the underlying notochordal tissue (fig. 210E, F). Also, by the time that the yolk mass is entirely enveloped, the somites appear within the mesoderm near the notochordal axis, and the developing body as a whole may be considerably delimited from the surrounding blastodermic tissue (fig. 211G). Therefore, if the envelopment of the yolk mass is taken as the end point of gastrulation in teleosts, the stage at which gastrulation is completed does not correspond to the developmental condition found at the termination of gastrulation in the chick, frog, and other forms. That is, the embryo of the teleost fish at the time of blastoporal closure is in an advanced stage of body formation and corresponds more truly with a chick embryo of about 35 to 40 hours of incubation, whereas the gastrulative processes are relatively complete in the chick at about 20 to 22 hours of incubation.

3) Summary of the Gastrulative Processes in Teleost Fishes:

a) EMBOLY:

(1) **Formation of the secondary hypoblast.** The secondary hypoblast forms as a result of the forward migration, expansion, and proliferation of the entodermal cells lying at the caudal margin of the embryonic shield. This forward migration of the entoderm (primary hypoblast) occurs below the upper layer or epiblast and thus produces an underlying entodermal layer or secondary hypoblast.

(2) **Pre-chordal plate and notochordal involution.** As the formation of the secondary hypoblast is initiated, the presumptive pre-chordal plate and notochordal cells *move posteriad and converge toward the dorsal lip* of the blastopore, where they involute and pass anteriad in the median line between the hypoblast and epiblast. The hypoblast or entodermal layer may be separated into two flattened layers or lamellae, one on either side of the notochord in some species. However, there

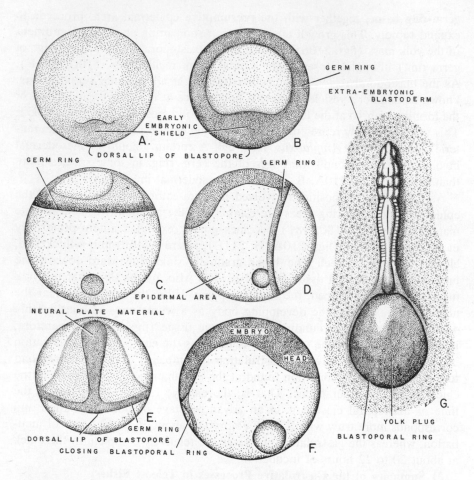

Fig. 211. Gastrulation in teleost fishes. (A–F after Wilson, 1889; G from Kerr, '19, after Kopsch.)   (A) Sea bass, 16 hours, embryonic shield becoming evident, marks beginning of germ ring.   (B) Germ ring well developed. Surface view of blastoderm of 20 hours.   (C) Side view of blastoderm shown in (B).   (D) Side view, 25 hours. (E) Surface view, 25 hours.   (F) Side view, 31 hours.   (G) Late gastrula of trout, *Salmo fario.*

is considerable variation among different species as to the degree of separation of the entodermal layer; in the sea bass it appears to be definitely separated, whereas in the trout it is reduced to a single layer of entodermal cells lying below the notochord. The pre-chordal plate, entoderm, and anterior notochord merge into a uniform mass below the cranial end of the neural plate.

(3) **Mesodermal convergence and involution.** Along with the migration of notochordal cells, the presumptive mesoderm *converges* posteriad to the dorso-lateral lips of the blastopore, where it *involutes and moves*

to the inside on either side of the median, notochordal mass and above the forming, secondary hypoblast.

b) EPIBOLY. The germ-ring tissue and the outer areas of the presumptive epidermal cells gradually grow around the yolk mass and converge toward the caudal end of the developing embryo. Associated with this migration of cells is the anterior-posterior extension of the presumptive neural plate material to form an elongated, thickened, median ridge.

4) Developmental Potencies of the Germ Ring of Teleost Fishes. The germ ring or thickened, marginal area of the teleost late blastula and early gastrula has interested embryologists for many years. It was observed in Chapter 8 that various regions of the marginal area of the blastoderm of the teleost fish have a tendency to form embryos. Luther ('36), working on the trout *(Salmo),* found that all sectors of the blastula were able to differentiate all types of tissue, i.e., they proved to be totipotent. However, in the early gastrula, only the sector forming the embryonic shield and the areas immediately adjacent to it were able to express totipotency. As gastrulation progresses, this limitation becomes more marked. In other words, a generalized potency around the germ ring, present during blastulation, becomes restricted when the embryonic shield of the gastrula comes into prominence. The evidence set forth in the previous chapter indicates that the possibility for twinning in the trout becomes less and less as the gastrular condition nears. The restriction of potency thus becomes a function of a developmental sequence.

In the case of *Fundulus,* Oppenheimer ('38) found that various areas of the germ ring, taken from regions 90 degrees or 180 degrees away from the dorsal blastoporal lip, were able to differentiate many different embryonic structures *if transplanted into the embryonic shield area.* Oppenheimer concludes that: "Since under certain conditions the germ-ring can express potencies for the differentiation of many embryonic organs, it is concluded that its normal role is limited to the formation of mesoderm by the inhibiting action of the dorsal lip." The results obtained by Luther serve to support this conclusion.

c. Gastrulation in Elasmobranch Fishes

In figure 179B the presumptive major organ-forming areas of the blastoderm of the shark, *Scyllium canicula,* are delineated. The arrows indicate the general directions of cell migration during gastrulation. In figure 212A–G are shown surface views of the dorsal-lip area of different stages of blastodermic development in this species, while figure 213A–G presents median, sagittal sections of these blastoderms during inward migration of the presumptive organ-forming cells. It is to be observed that the dorsal-lip region of the blastoderm is the focal area over which the cells involute and migrate to the inside.

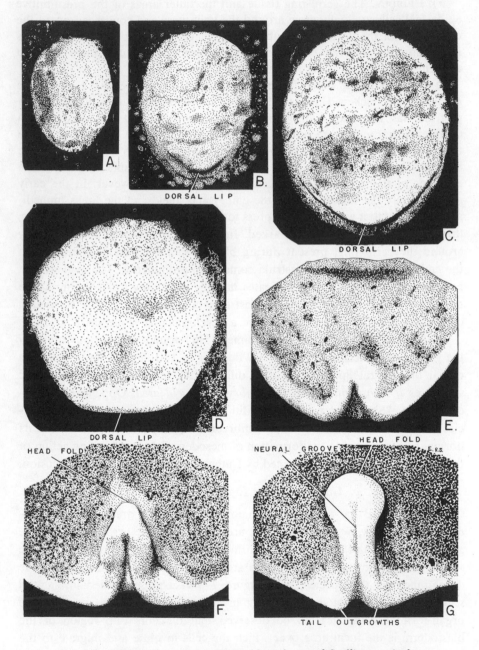

Fig. 212. Surface views of developing blastoderms of *Scyllium canicula*.

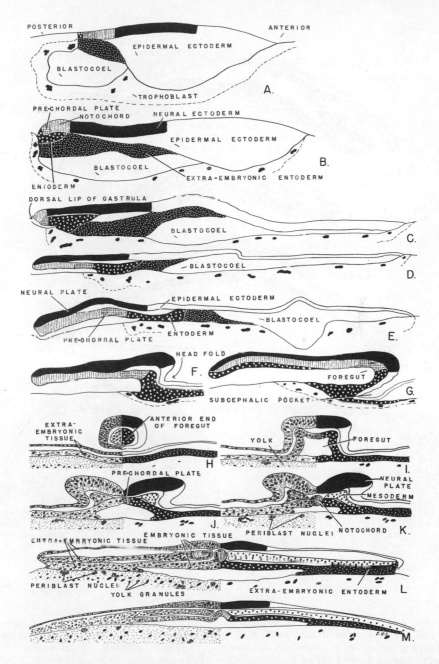

FIG. 213. Sagittal sections of blastoderms shown in figure 212A–G, with corresponding letters, showing migration of presumptive organ-forming areas. (See also fig. 179.)   (B) Dorsal lip is shown to left.   (H–M) Transverse sections of embryo of *Squalus acanthias*, similar to stages shown in 212F and G, for *Scyllium*.   (H) Section through anterior head fold.   (M) Section through caudal end of blastoderm. H–M original drawings from prepared slides.

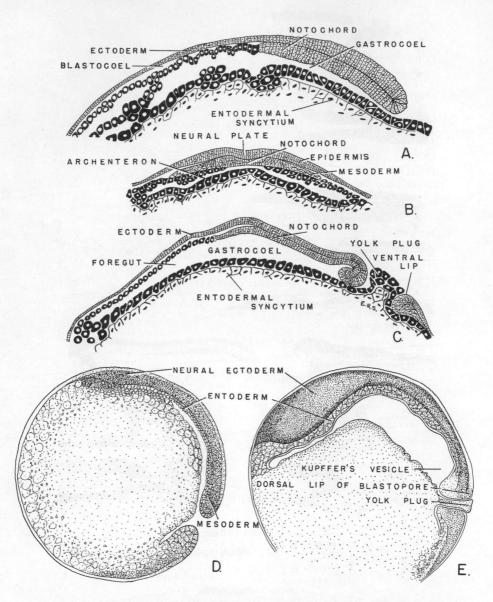

Fig. 214. Gastrulation in the gymnophionan *Amphibia* and in the bony ganoid, *Amia calva*. (A, B, C, after Brauer, 1897; D, E, after Dean, 1896.) Sections A–C through developing embryo of *Hypogeophis alternans*. (A) Middle gastrula, sagittal section. Observe that gastrocoel forms by a separation of the entodermal cells. Blastocoel forms similarly through delamination of entoderm from the overlying epiblast and by spaces which appear between the cells in situ. (B) Transverse section through late gastrula. (C) Sagittal section through late gastrula. (D) Late gastrula of *Amia*. Mass of yolk in center is uncleaved; cellular organization is progressing peripherally around yolk mass. (E) Later gastrula of *Amia*. The blastopore is closing, but a large yolk mass still remains uncleaved.

In figure 213A, B, and C, two general areas of entoderm are shown:

(a) that exposed at the surface (cf. fig. 179), and
(b) the entoderm lying in the deeper areas of the blastoderm (cf. fig. 179, cells in black).

According to Vandebroek, '36, the deeper lying entoderm is extra-embryonic entoderm (in fig. 213, this deeper entoderm is represented as a black area with fine white stipple), whereas the entoderm exposed at the caudal portion of the blastoderm in figure 179A and B, and figure 213A is embryonic entoderm.

The later distribution of the major presumptive organ-forming areas of the shark blastoderm is shown in figure 213E–M. In figure 213, observe the periblast tissue connecting the blastoderm with the yolk substrate.

As the notochordal, entodermal, and mesodermal cells move inward during emboly, the presumptive epidermal and neural areas become greatly expanded externally by the forces of epiboly as shown in figures 213B–E, and 213H. (Compare the positions of these two areas in fig. 179B.)

The general result of the gastrulative processes in the shark group is to produce a blastoderm with three germ layers similar to that shown in figure 213L and M. The notochordal and pre-chordal plate cells occupy the median area below the neural plate as shown in figure 213E and F; the mesoderm and entoderm lie on either side of the median notochord as shown in figure 213M. A little later the entoderm from either side of the notochord grows mediad to establish a complete floor of entoderm below the notochord as represented in figure 213L.

7. INTERMEDIATE TYPES OF GASTRULATIVE BEHAVIOR

In certain forms, such as the ganoid fish, *Amia,* and in the *Gymnophiona* among the *Amphibia,* the gastrulative processes present distinct peculiarities. In general, gastrulation in the bony ganoid fish, *Amia calva,* presents a condition of gastrulation which is intermediate between that which occurs in the teleost fishes and the gastrulative procedures in the frog or the newt. For example, a blastodisc-like cap of cells is found at the end of cleavage in the bony ganoid. This cap gradually creeps downward around the yolk masses which were superficially furrowed during the early cleavages. This process resembles the cellular movement occurring during epiboly in teleost fishes. In addition, the entodermal, notochordal, and mesodermal materials migrate inward in much the same way as occurs in the teleost fishes, although the formation of the primitive archenteron resembles to a degree the early invaginative procedure in the frog. However, a distinctive process of entodermal formation occurs in *Amia,* for some of the entodermal cells arise as a separation from the upper portion of the yolk substance where yolk nuclei are found. (See fig. 214D, E; consult Eycleshymer and Wilson, '06.)

The gastrulative processes in the gymnophionan *Amphibia* are most pe-

culiar, particularly the behavior of the entoderm. But little study has been
devoted to the group; as a result, our knowledge is most fragmentary. Elusive
and burrowing in their habits and restricted to a tropical climature, they do
not present readily available material for study. Brauer, 1897, described blastulation and gastrulation in *Hypogeophis alternans*. Our information derives
mainly from this source.

In some respects gastrulation in *Hypogeophis* is similar to that in teleost
and bony ganoid fishes, while other features resemble certain cellular activities
in other *Amphibia* and possibly also in higher vertebrates. For example, the
blastoderm behaves much like the flat blastoderm of teleost fishes, for a dorsal
blastoporal lip or embryonic portion of the germ ring is formed toward which
the notochordal and mesodermal materials presumably migrate, involute, and
thus pass to the inside below the epiblast layer (fig. 214A, B). Also, the rapid
epiboly of the presumptive epidermal area around the yolk material (or yolk
cells) is similar to that of teleost fishes and of the bony ganoid, *Amia* (fig.
214C–E). However, the behavior of the entodermal cells differs markedly
from that of teleosts. In the first place, there is a double delamination whereby
the solid blastula is converted into a condition having a blastocoel and a gastrocoel (fig. 214A). These processes occur concurrently with the gastrulative phenomena. Blastocoelic formation resembles somewhat the delaminative
behavior of the entoderm in reptiles, birds, and mammals, for the entodermal
layer separates from the deeper areas of the epiblast layer. The formation of
the gastrocoel (archenteron) is a complex affair and is effected by a process
of hollowing or space formation within the entodermal cell mass as indicated
in figure 214A. The arrangement of the entodermal cells during later gastrulative stages resembles the archenteron in the late gastrula of other *Amphibia*.
The archenteron possesses a heavily yolked floor, with the roof of the foregut
region complete, but that of the archenteron more posteriorly is incomplete,
exposing the notochord to the archenteric space (fig. 214A–C).

G. The Late Gastrula as a Mosaic of Specific, Organ-forming
Territories

It was observed above that the presumptive organ-forming areas of the late
blastula become distributed in an organized way along the notochordal axis
during gastrulation. Further, while an interchangeability of different parts of
the epiblast of the late blastula is possible without upsetting normal development, such exchanges are not possible in the late gastrula. For during gastrulation, **particular areas** of the epiblast become individuated by activities or
influences involved with **induction** or **evocation.** (The word "evocation" was
introduced by Waddington and it has come to mean: "That part of the morphogenetic effect of an organizer which can be referred back to the action of
a single chemical substance, the evocator." See Needham, '42, p. 42.) As a

result, the gastrula emerges from the gastrulative process as a general mosaic of self-differentiating entities or territories. (See Spemann, '38, p. 107.)

It necessarily follows, therefore, that *the production of specific areas or territories of cells, each having a tendency to differentiate into a specific structure, and the axiation of these areas along the primitive axis of the embryo are two of the main functions of the gastrulative process.* In figure 205A–E, diagrams are presented relative to the chick embryo showing the results of experiments made by Rawles ('36), Rudnick ('44), and others. (See Rudnick, '44.) These experiments were made to test the developmental potencies of various limited areas of the chick blastoderm. A considerable overlapping of territories is shown, which stems, probably, from the fact that transplanted pieces often show potencies which are not manifested in the intact embryo. Therefore, these maps should be regarded not with finality but merely as suggesting certain developmental tendencies.

H. Autonomous Theory of Gastrulative Movements

Our knowledge concerning the dynamics of gastrulation in the *Chordata* is based largely on the classical observations of cell movement made by Conklin ('05) in *Styela,* the same author ('32) in *Amphioxus,* Vogt ('29) in various *Amphibia,* Oppenheimer ('36) in *Fundulus,* Pasteels ('36, '37b) in trout and chick, Vandebroek ('36) in the shark, and Spratt ('46) in the chick. For detailed discussions, concerning the morphodynamics of the gastrulative period, reference may be made to the works published by Roux (1895), Spemann ('38), Pasteels ('40), Waddington ('40), and Schechtman ('42).

The theory popularly held, regarding the movements of the major presumptive organ-forming areas of the late blastula, is that a strict autonomy is present among the various groups of cells concerned with the gastrulative process. Spemann ('38) p. 107, describes this theory of autonomy as follows:

Each part has already previously had impressed upon it in some way or other direction and limitation of movement. The movements are regulated, not in a coarse mechanical manner, through pressure and pull of the single parts, but they are ordered according to a definite plan. . . . After an exact patterned arrangement, they take their course according to independent formative tendencies which originate in the parts themselves.

There are some observations, on the other hand, which point to an interdependence of the various cell groups. For example, we have referred to the observations of Waddington ('33) and Spratt ('46) which suggest that the movements of the mesoderm in the bird embryo are dependent upon the *inductive influence of the entoderm.* Similarly, Schechtman ('42) points out that presumptive notochordal material does not have the power to invaginate (involute) to the inside when transplanted to the presumptive ectodermal

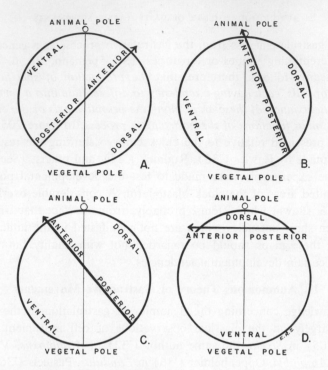

FIG. 215. Direction of entodermal projection in relation to egg polarity during gastrulation in various *Chordata*. (A) *Amphioxus*. (B) Frog. (C) Urodele amphibia. (D) Chick. For diagrammatic purposes, the positions to the right of the median egg axis in the diagrams arbitrarily are considered as clockwise positions, whereas those to the left are regarded as counterclockwise.

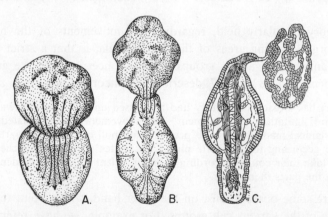

FIG. 216. Exogastrulation in the axolotl *(Amphibia)*. (From Huxley and De Beer, '34, after Holtfreter: Biol. Zentralbl., 53: 1933.) (A, B) Mass outward or exogastrular movements of entoderm and mesoderm, resulting in the separation of these organ-forming areas from the epidermal, neural areas shown as a sac-like structure in upper part of figure. (C) Section of (B). Exogastrulation of this character results when the embolic movements of gastrulation are directed outward instead of inward. Observe that neural plate does not form in the ectodermal area.

area, but it does possess the autonomous power to elongate into a slender column of cells.

I. Exogastrulation

It was demonstrated by Holtfreter ('33) and also by others that embryos may be made to exogastrulate, i.e., the entoderm, notochord, and mesoderm evaginate to the outside instead of undergoing the normal processes involved in emboly (fig. 216). For example, in the axolotl, *Ambystoma mexicanum,* if embryos are placed in a 0.35 per cent Ringer's solution, exogastrulation occurs instead of gastrulation, and the entodermal, mesodermal and noto-chordal areas of the blastula lie outside and are attached to the hollow ecto-dermal vesicle. The exogastrulated material, therefore, never underlies the ectodermal cells but comes to lie outside the neural plate and skin ectodermal areas of the gastrula (fig. 216B).

Therefore, the phenomenon of exogastrulation indicates strongly that the presumptive, neural plate and epidermal areas of the late blastula and early gastrula are dependent upon the normal gastrulative process for their future realization in the embryo. Exogastrulation also clearly separates the parts of the forming gastrula which are concerned with **emboly** from those which are moved by the forces of **epiboly.** That is, *exogastrulation results when the forces of epiboly are separated from the forces normally concerned with emboly.* Normal gastrulation is concerned with a precise and exact correlation of these two sets of forces.

J. Pre-chordal Plate and Cephalic Projection in Various Chordates

It is evident from the descriptions presented in this chapter that the initial invaginative movements in gastrulation begin in the region of the dorsal lip of the blastopore in *Amphioxus,* fishes, and *Amphibia.* This initial movement of cells in the region of the dorsal lip consists in the projection forward, toward the future head region of the embryo, of foregut entoderm, pre-chordal plate mesoderm, and notochordal cells. The foregut entoderm, pre-chordal meso-derm, and the anterior extremity of the notochord come to lie beneath the anterior portion of the neural plate. The complex of anterior foregut entoderm and pre-chordal mesoderm lies in front of the anterior limits of the notochord —hence, the name **pre-chordal plate.** As such it represents, as previously observed, *a part of the head organizer* (see p. 401), the complete organization of the vertebrate head being dependent upon anterior chordal (notochordal), as well as pre-chordal, factors.

In higher vertebrates a different situation prevails during gastrulation. As observed in Chapter 7, the late blastula consists of a lower hypoblast and an upper epiblast *in a flattened condition,* the hypoblast having separated from the lower parts of the epiblast. The separation of the hypoblast occurs shortly before the gastrulative rearrangement of the major, presumptive, organ-forming areas begins. The organization of the blastoderm (blastula) is such that presumptive pre-chordal plate mesoderm and notochordal areas lie far anteriorly toward the midcentral part of the epiblast. In other words, a contiguous relationship between presumptive pre-chordal entoderm (i.e., anterior foregut entoderm) and presumptive pre-chordal mesoderm and the presumptive notochord at the caudal margin of the blastula does not exist. Consequently, a different procedure is utilized in bringing the foregut entoderm, pre-chordal mesoderm, and anterior notochord together. That is, the head-organizer materials must be assembled together in one area underneath the cephalic portion of the neural plate. This is accomplished by two methods:

(1) The use of a large invaginative process, **the notochordal canal,** which projects pre-chordal plate mesoderm and notochord cranio-ventrad toward the foregut entoderm in the hypoblast below, as described in figure 200 relative to the reptiles or in figure 207B of the human embryo and

(2) the use of another and less dramatic method for getting the head-organizer materials together, the vestigial invaginative process which produces the primitive pit and Hensen's nodal area.

The latter mechanism succeeds in getting pre-chordal plate mesoderm and notochord down between the epiblast and hypoblast and forward to unite with the anterior part of the foregut entoderm. (See Adelmann, '22, '26; Pasteels, '37b.)

It is not clear whether the invaginative behavior which produces the primitive pit or notochordal canal is an autonomous affair or whether it may be dependent upon the inductive activities of the entoderm below. More experimentation is necessary to decide this matter. The work of Waddington ('33), however, leads one to conjecture that inductive activities may be responsible.

Regardless of the factors involved, **cephalogenesis** or the genesis of the head is dependent upon the assemblage of anterior foregut, pre-chordal mesoderm, and anterior notochordal cells beneath the cephalic portion of the neural plate as described on page 401.

K. Blastoporal and Primitive-streak Comparisons

From the considerations set forth above, it is clear that the area of the notochordal canal or primitive pit (i.e., Hensen's nodal area) corresponds to the general region of the dorsal lip of the blastopore of lower vertebrates, whereas the dorso-lateral and lateral lips of the blastopore of lower forms correspond to the body of the primitive streak in higher vertebrates (Adelmann, '32).

Bibliography

Adelmann, H. B. **1922.** The significance of the prechordal plate: an interpretative study. Am. J. Anat. **31**:55.

——. **1926.** The development of the premandibular head cavities and the relations of the anterior end of the notochord in the chick and robin. J. Morphol. **42**:371.

——. **1932.** The development of the prechordal plate and mesoderm of *Amblystoma punctatum*. J. Morphol. **54**:1.

Brauer, A. **1897.** I. Beiträge zur Kenntniss der Entwicklungsgeschichte und der Anatomie der Gymnophionen. Zool. Jahrb. **10**:389.

Conklin, E. G. **1905.** The organization and cell-lineage of the ascidian egg. J. Acad. Nat. Sc., Philadelphia. **13**:5.

——. **1932.** The embryology of *Amphioxus*. J. Morphol. **54**:69.

——. **1933.** The development of isolated and partially separated blastomeres of *Amphioxus*. J. Exper. Zool. **64**:303.

Dalcq, A. and Pasteels, J. **1937.** Une conception nouvelle des bases physiologiques de la morphogénèse. Arch. biol., Paris. **48**:669.

Dean, B. **1896.** The early development of *Amia*. Quart. J. Micr. Sc. New Series. **38**:413.

Eycleshymer, A. C. and Wilson, J. M. **1906.** The gastrulation and embryo formation in *Amia calva*. Am. J. Anat. **5**:133.

Haeckel, E. **1874.** Anthropogenie oder Entwickelungsgeschichte des Menschen. Vols. 1 and 2 in English translation, **1910,** The evolution of man, translated by J. McCabe. G. P. Putnam's Sons, New York.

Hamburger, V. and Hamilton, H. L. **1951.** A series of normal stages in the development of the chick embryo. J. Morphol. **88**:49.

Heape, W. **1883.** The development of the mole *(Talpa europea)*. The formation of the germinal layers and early development of the medullary groove and notochord. Quart. J. Micr. Sc. **23**:412.

Hensen, V. **1876.** Beobachtungen über die Befruchtung und Entwicklung des Kaninchens und Meerschweinchens. Zeit. f. anat. u. Entwicklngesch. **1**:213.

Holtfreter, J. **1933.** Die totale Exogastrulation, eine Selbstablösung des Ektoderms vom Entomesoderm. Entwicklung und funktionelles Verhalten nervenloser Organe. Roux' Arch. f. Entwick. d. Organ. **129**:669.

——. **1948.** Concepts on the mechanism of embryonic induction and its relation to parthenogenesis and malignancy. Symposia of the Soc. Exper. Biol. No. II, p. 17. Growth in Relation to Differentiation and Morphogenesis. Academic Press, Inc., New York and Cambridge University Press, England.

Holmdahl, D. E. **1926.** Die erste Entwicklung des Körpers bei den Vögeln und Säugetieren, inkl. dem Menschen I–V. Morph. Jahrb. **54**:333; **55**:112.

Hubrecht, A. A. W. **1906.** The gastrulation of the vertebrates. Quart. J. Micr. Sc. **49**:403.

Huxley, J. S. and De Beer, G. R. **1934.** The Elements of Experimental Embryology. Cambridge University Press, London.

Keibel, F. **1901.** Gastrulation und Keimblattbildung der Wirbelthiere. See chap. 10 of Ergebnisse der Anatomie und Entwickelungsgeschichte. Wiesbaden.

Kerr, J. G. **1919,** Textbook of Embryology. Vol. II. Vertebrata with the Exception of the *Mammalia*. Macmillan & Co., Ltd., London.

Lankester, R. **1875.** On the invaginate planula, or diploblastic phase of Paludina vivipara. Quart. J. Micr. Sc. **15**:159.

Lewis, W. H. **1907.** Transplantation of the lips of the blastopore in *Rana palustris*. Am. J. Anat. **7**:137.

——. **1949.** Gel layers of cells and eggs and their role in early development. Lecture Series, Rosco B. Jackson Memorial Laboratories, Bar Harbor, Maine.

Lopaschov, G. **1935.** Die Umgestaltung des präsumtiven Mesoderms in Hirnteile bei Tritonkeimen. Zool. Jahrb. (Abt. f. allg. Zool. u. Physiol.) **54**:299.

Luther, W. **1936.** Potenzprüfungen an isolierten Teilstücken der Forellenkeimscheibe. Arch. f. Entwicklngsmech. d. Organ. **135**:359.

Mangold, O. **1923.** Transplantationsversuche zur Frage der Spezifität und der Bildung der Keimblätter. Arch. f. Entwicklngsmech. d. Organ. **100**:198.

————. **1928.** Neue Experimente zur Analyse der frühen Embryonal entwicklung des Amphibienkeims. Naturwissensch. **16**:387.

————. **1928.** Probleme der Entwicklungsmechanik. Naturwissensch. **16**:661.

————. **1932.** Autonome und komplementäre Induktionen bei Amphibien. Naturwissensch. **20**:371.

Morgan, T. H. and Hazen, A. P. **1900.** The gastrulation of *Amphioxus.* J. Morphol. **16**:569.

Needham, J. **1942.** Biochemistry and Morphogenesis. Cambridge University Press, London.

Nicholas, J. S. **1945.** Blastulation, its role in pregastrular organization in *Amblystoma punctatum.* J. Exper. Zool. **100**:265.

Oppenheimer, J. M. **1936.** Processes of localization in developing *Fundulus.* J. Exper. Zool. **73**:405.

————. **1938.** Potencies for differentiation in the teleostean germ ring. J. Exper. Zool. **79**:185.

————. **1947.** Organization of the teleost blastoderm. Quart. Rev. Biol. **22**:105.

Pasteels, J. **1936.** Etudes sur la gastrulation des vertébrés méroblastiques. I. Téléostéens. Arch. biol., Paris. **47**:205.

————. **1937a.** Etudes sur la gastrulation des vertébrés méroblastiques. II. Reptiles. Arch. biol., Paris. **48**:105.

————. **1937b.** Etudes sur la gastrulation des vertébrés méroblastiques. III. Oiseaux. IV. Conclusions generales. Arch. biol., Paris. **48**:381.

————. **1940.** Un aperçu comparatif de la gastrulation chez les chordés. Biol. Rev. **15**:59.

————. **1945.** On the formation of the primary entoderm of the duck *(Anas domestica)* and on the significance of the bilaminar embryo in birds. Anat. Rec. **93**:5.

Rawles, M. E. **1936.** A study in the localization of organ-forming areas in the chick blastoderm of the head-process stage. J. Exper. Zool. **72**:271.

Roux, W. **1895.** Gesammelte Abhandlungen über Entwicklungsmechanik der Organismen. II. Engelmann, Leipzig.

Rudnick, D. **1944.** Early history and mechanics of the chick blastoderm. Quart. Rev. Biol. **19**:187.

Rugh, R. **1951.** The Frog, Its Reproduction and Development. The Blakiston Co., Philadelphia.

Schechtman, A. M. **1934.** Unipolar ingression in *Triturus torosus:* a hitherto undescribed movement in the pregastrular stages of a urodele. University of California Publ., Zoöl. **39**:303.

————. **1935.** Mechanism of ingression in the egg of *Triturus torosus.* Proc. Soc. Exper. Biol. & Med. **32**:1072.

————. **1942.** The mechanism of amphibian gastrulation. I. Gastrulation-promoting interactions between various regions of an anuran egg *(Hyla regilla).* University of California Publ., Zoöl. **51**:1.

Spemann, H. **1918.** Über die Determination der ersten Organanlagen des Amphibienembryo. I–VI. Arch. f. Entwicklngsmech. d. Organ. **43**:448.

————. **1921.** Die Erzeugung tierischer Chimaren durch heteroplastische embryonale Transplantation zwischen *Triton cristatus* und *T. taeniatus.* Arch. f. Entwicklngsmech. d. Organ. **48**:533.

————. **1931.** Über den Anteil von Implantat und Wirtskeim an der Orientierung und Beschaffenheit der induzierten Embryonalanlage. Arch. f. Entwicklngsmech. d. Organ. **123**:389.

————. **1938.** Embryonic Development and Induction. Yale University Press, New Haven.

———— and Mangold, H. **1924.** Über Induktion von Embryonalanlagen durch Implantation artfremder Organisatoren. Arch. f. mikr. Anat. **100**:599.

Spratt, N. T., Jr. **1942.** Location of organ-specific regions and their relationship to the development of the primitive streak in the early chick blastoderm. J. Exper. Zool. **89**:69–101.

———. **1946.** Formation of the primitive streak in the explanted chick blastoderm marked with carbon particles. J. Exper. Zool. **103**:259.

———. **1947.** Regression and shortening of the primitive streak in the explanted chick blastoderm. J. Exper. Zool. **104**:69.

Streeter, G. L. **1927.** Development of the mesoblast and notochord in pig embryos. Carnegie Inst., Washington, Publ. No. 380. Contrib. to Embryol. **19**:73.

Sumner, F. B. **1903.** A study of early fish development. Arch. f. Entwicklngsmech. d. Organ. **17**:92.

Vandebroek, G. **1936.** Les mouvements morphogénétiques au cours de la gastrulation chez *Scyllium canicula.* Arch. biol., Paris. **47**:499.

Vintemberger, P. **1936.** Sur le développement comparé des micromeres de l'oeuf de *Rana fusca* divise en huit: (a) Après isolement. (b) Après transplantation sur un socle de cellules vitellines. Compt. rend. Soc. de biol. **122**:127.

Vogt, W. **1929.** Gestaltungsanalyse am Amphibienkeim mit örtlicher Vitalfärbung. II. Teil: Gastrulation und mesodermbildung bei Urodelen und Anuren. Roux' Arch. f. Entwick. d. Organ. **120**:385.

Waddington, C. H. **1933.** Induction by the entoderm in birds. Arch. f. Entwicklngsmech. d. Organ. **128**:502.

———. **1940.** Organizers and genes. Cambridge University Press, London.

Will, L. **1892.** Beiträge zur Entwicklungsgeschichte der Reptilien. Zool. Jahrb. **6**:1.

Wilson, H. V. **1889.** The embryology of the sea bass *(Serranus atrarius).* Bull. U. S. Fish Comm. **9**:209.

10

Tubulation and Extension of the Major Organ-forming Areas: Development of Primitive Body Form

A. Introduction
   1. Some of the developmental problems faced by the embryo after gastrulation
      a. Tubulation
      b. Increase in size and antero-posterior extension of the tubulated, major organ-forming areas
      c. Regional modifications of the tubulated areas
   2. Common, vertebrate, embryonic body form
   3. Starting point for tubulation
   4. Developmental processes which accomplish tubulation
      a. Immediate processes
      b. Auxiliary processes
   5. Blastocoelic space and body-form development
   6. Primitive circulatory tubes or blood vessels
   7. Extra-embryonic membranes
B. Tubulation of the neural, epidermal, entodermal, and mesodermal, organ-forming areas in the vertebrate group
   1. Neuralization or the tubulation of the neural plate area
      a. Definition
      b. Neuralizative processes in the *Vertebrata*
         1) Thickened keel method
         2) Neural fold method
      c. Closure of the blastopore in rounded gastrulae, such as that of the frog
      d. Anterior and posterior neuropores; neurenteric canal
   2. Epidermal tubulation
      a. Development of the epidermal tube in *Amphibia*
      b. Tubulation of the epidermal area in flat blastoderms
   3. Formation of the primitive gut tube (enteric tubulation)
      a. Regions of primitive gut tube or early metenteron
      b. Formation of the primitive metenteron in the frog
      c. Formation of the tubular metenteron in flat blastoderms
   4. Tubulation (coelom formation) and other features involved in the early differentiation of the mesodermal areas
      a. Early changes in the mesodermal areas
         1) Epimere; formation of the somites
         2) Mesomere
         3) Hypomere
      b. Tubulation of the mesodermal areas

A. Introduction

1. Some of the Developmental Problems Faced by the Embryo After Gastrulation

a. Tubulation

One of the main problems, confronting the embryo immediately following gastrulation, is the **tubulation of the major organ-forming areas,** namely, epidermal, neural, entodermal, and the two, laterally placed, mesodermal areas. The epidermal, neural, and entodermal areas eventually form elongated, rounded tubes, whereas the mesodermal tubes are flattened. The epidermal and neural tubes extend the entire length of the developing embryo (fig. 217A–C), while the entodermal tube normally terminates at the beginning of the tail (fig. 217B, C), although in some instances it may extend even to the tail's end (fig. 217A). Anteriorly, the entodermal tube ends along the ventral aspect of the developing head (fig. 217A, C). The two mesodermal tubulations are confined mainly to the trunk region of the embryo, but in the early embryo of the shark they continue forward into the head almost to the posterior limits of the developing eyes (fig. 217D). The condition of the mesodermal tubes in the *Amphibia* resembles to a degree that in the shark embryo (fig. 217B, E).

An important concept to grasp is that *the tubulations of the respective areas occur synchronously or nearly so.* It is true that the initial stages of the epidermal and entodermal tubulations slightly precede the other tubulations in

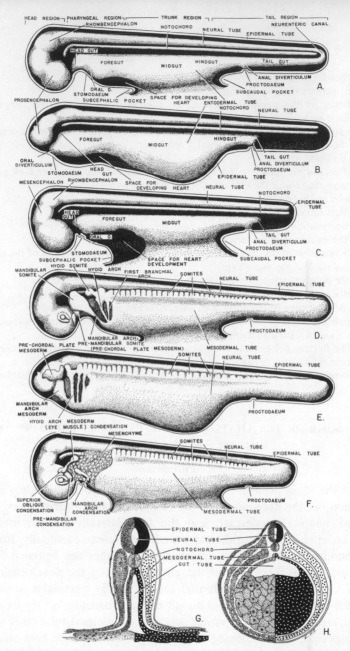

FIG. 217. Primary tubes (tubulations) of the primitive vertebrate body. (A) Schematic representation of epidermal, neural, and entodermal tubes in the early embryo of the shark. Observe that a well-developed, post-anal or tail gut continues to the end of the tail. (B) Gut, neural, and epidermal tubes in the amphibian type. (C) Gut, neural, and epidermal tubes in the chick and mammal type. (D) Mesodermal tube in the shark embryo. (E) Mesodermal tube in the amphibian embryo. (F) Mesodermal condition in the early bird and mammal embryo. (G) Transverse section of shark embryo, showing tubulations of major organ-forming areas and primary coelomic conditions. (H) Transverse section of frog embryo shortly after closure of neural tube, showing the five fundamental body tubes oriented around the notochord.

Amphioxus, in the frog, and in forms having rounded gastrulae, while in the chick the neural area is precocious. Viewed in their totality, however, the tubulations of all of the major organ-forming areas are simultaneous processes with the exception of the notochord which does not become tubulated but continues as an elongated rod of cells.

b. Increase in Size and Antero-posterior Extension of the Tubulated, Major Organ-forming Areas

Another goal to be achieved by the embryo during the immediate, post-gastrular period is an increase in size, together with an antero-posterior extension of the major organ-forming areas. These changes are associated with tubulation, *and they aid in producing the elongated, cylindrical form typical of the chordate body.*

c. Regional Modifications of the Tubulated Areas

As tubulation of the various major organ-forming areas progresses, specific, organ-forming areas or fields (see end of chapter), located along the respective primitive body tubes, begin to express themselves and develop in a specialized manner. Thus, regional differentiation of the major organ-forming areas, comprising each primitive body tube, is another feature of the post-gastrular period. As a result, localized areas along each of the body tubes show changes in shape, and specific, individualized structures begin to make their appearance. For example, the neural tubulation develops the primitive parts of the brain at its anterior end, while the posterior portion of the neural tube, caudal to the brain area, begins to form the spinal cord. Thus, the primitive brain becomes a specific peculiarity of the head region. Also, the epidermal tubulation at its cranial end contributes definite structures peculiar to the head. In the pharyngeal region, special developmental features arise in the entodermal tube together with the epidermal tube and the mesoderm. In the trunk region, modifications of the entodermal and mesodermal tubes give origin to many of the structural conditions peculiar to this area, while in the tail, the neural and epidermal tubulations together with activities of the mesoderm account for the characterstic structures of the tail appendage. These special developmental features of the respective, tubulated, organ-forming areas, which arise in specific areas along the antero-posterior axis of the embryo, *occur in much the same way throughout the vertebrate group with the result that common or generalized structural conditions of the tubulated organ-forming areas appear in all vertebrate embryos.* That is, the primitive brains of all vertebrate embryos up to a certain stage of development resemble each other in a striking manner; the contributions of the epidermal tubulation to the head also resemble each other, and the early development of the pharyngeal and trunk regions is similar. As a result, the early morphogenesis

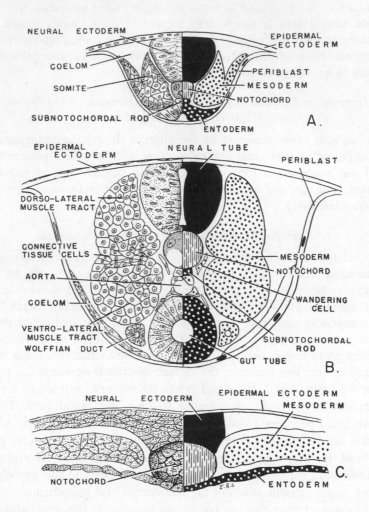

FIG. 218. Solid keel of neural ectoderm in teleost and bony ganoid fishes. (A and B after H. V. Wilson, 1889; C after Dean, 1896.) (A) Neural ectoderm separating from epidermal ectoderm. (B) Neural tube completely separated from epidermal ectoderm. (C) Late gastrular condition of *Amia calva*.

of the respective body tubes tends to follow a similar procedural plan throughout the entire vertebrate series.

2. COMMON, VERTEBRATE, EMBRYONIC BODY FORM

As a result of the changes outlined above and the tendency to form common, generalized, structural conditions during the early phases of development, a common, generalized, primitive embryonic body form is developed in the embryos of all vertebrate species in which the rudiments of various, future, organ systems conform to generalized, basic plans. After the generalized plan of a particular system is established, it is modified in later development to fit the requirements of the habitat in which the particular species lives. In the cephalochordate, *Amphioxus,* a similar body form also develops, although it is considerably modified.

The common, generalized, primitive embryonic body form of all vertebrate embryos possesses the following characteristics:

(1) It is an elongated structure, cylindrical in shape, and somewhat compressed laterally.

(2) It is composed of **five, basic, organ-forming tubes,** oriented around a primitive axis, the notochord (fig. 217).

(3) It possesses the following regions: (a) **head,** (b) **pharyngeal area,** (c) **trunk,** and (d) **tail** (figs. 217, 226, 227, 230, 238, 244, 246).

In Chapter 11 and the following chapters, various details of these common regions and other features will be considered. In this chapter, we are concerned mainly with tubulation and antero-posterior extension of the major organ-forming areas in relation to body-form development.

3. Starting Point for Tubulation

The starting point for tubulation of the major organ-forming areas and subsequent, primitive, body formation is the gastrula, which, as observed in Chapter 9, exists in two forms, namely, **rounded** and the **flattened gastrulae** (figs. 219, 232). Many heavily yolked embryos, such as the embryo of *Necturus maculosus,* although they form a rounded gastrula, are faced with some of the problems of the flattened gastrulae (fig. 227). The rounded gastrulae, found in the frog, *Amphioxus,* etc., differ from the flattened gastrulae present in the bird, reptile, mammal, and teleost and elasmobranch fishes, mainly by the fact that, at the beginning of tubulation and body formation, the epidermal and gut areas already are *partially tubulated* in the rounded gastrulae. That is, *in the rounded blastoderm, the initial stages of tubulation occur in these two major organ-forming areas during gastrulation.* This means that the ventral portion of the trunk area in rounded gastrulae is circumscribed by intact cellular layers of the embryonic trunk region, with yolk material contained within the cell layers, while, in flattened gastrulae, the ventro-lateral portions of the trunk region are spread out flat, the yolk not being surrounded by the future, ventro-lateral walls of the embryonic trunk region. These conditions are illustrated in figures 219B and C and 234A–F.

The developmental problems faced by these two groups of gastrulae, therefore, are somewhat different. Moreover, tubulation of the organ-forming areas and the development of body form in *Amphioxus* varies considerably from that of the rounded gastrulae of the vertebrate group. For this reason, tubulation in *Amphioxus* is considered separately.

Regardless of differences, however, **all vertebrate gastrulae,** rounded and flattened, possess three fundamental or basic regions, to wit, (1) a **cephalic or head region,** containing the rudiments of the future head and pharyngeal structures, (2) a **trunk region,** wherein lie the undeveloped fundaments of the trunk, and (3) an **end-bud or tail rudiment,** containing the possibilities of the future tail.

4. DEVELOPMENTAL PROCESSES WHICH ACCOMPLISH TUBULATION

a. Immediate Processes

The term, immediate processes, signifies the events which actually produce the hollow tubular condition. In the case of the epidermal, enteric, and neural tubulations, the immediate process is mainly one of *folding the particular,*

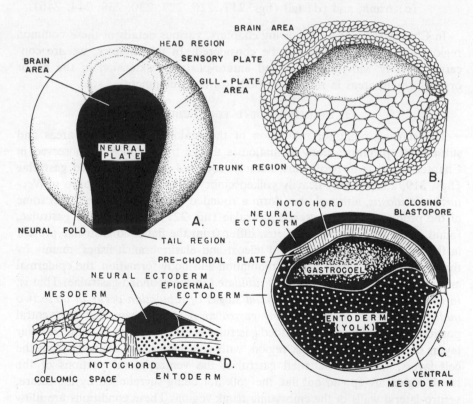

FIG. 219. Relationships of the major presumptive organ-forming areas at the end of gastrulation in the anuran amphibia. (A) External view of gastrula, showing the ectodermal layer composed of presumptive epidermis (white) and presumptive neural plate (black), as viewed from the dorsal aspect. (B) Diagrammatic median sagittal section of condition shown in (A). (C) Same as (B), showing major organ-forming areas. (D) Section through middorsal area of conditions (B) and (C), a short distance caudal to foregut and pre-chordal plate region. Observe that the notochord occupies the middorsal area of the gut roof.

organ-forming area into a hollow tubular affair. With respect to the mesodermal areas, the immediate process is an *internal splitting (delamination),* whereby the mesodermal area separates into an outer and an inner layer with a space or cavity appearing between the two layers. In the case of the teleost fishes, a process of internal separation of cells appears to play a part also in the neural tubulation.

b. Auxiliary Processes

Aiding the above activities which produce tubulation are those procedures which extend the tubulated areas into elongated structures. These auxiliary processes are as follows:

(1) The cephalic or head rudiment, with its contained fundaments of the developing head region, grows forward as a distinct outgrowth. This anterior protrusion is known as the **cephalic or head outgrowth** (figs. 223A, B; 232I–L).

(2) The trunk rudiments enlarge and the trunk region as a whole undergoes **antero-posterior extension** (figs. 225A; 233).

(3) The tail-bud area progresses caudally as the **tail outgrowth** and forms the various rudimentary structures associated with the tail (figs. 225; 230F; 238).

(4) A **dorsal upgrowth** (arching) movement occurs, most noticeable in the trunk area. It serves to lift the dorsal or axial portion of the trunk up above the yolk-laden area below, and the developing body tubes and primitive body are projected dorsalward (figs. 221, 224, 241).

(5) In embryos developing from rounded gastrulae, a ventral contraction and reshaping of the entire ventro-lateral areas of the primitive trunk region are effected as the yolk is used up in development. This results in a *gradual retraction of this area* which eventually brings the ventro-lateral region of the trunk into line with the growing head and tail regions (cf. figs. 220, 223, 225 on the development of the frog, and 227 on the development of *Necturus*).

(6) In embryos developing from flattened gastrulae, a constriction of the ventral region of the developing trunk comes to pass. This constriction is produced by an ingrowth toward the median line of entodermal, mesodermal, and epidermal cellular layers in the form of folds, the **lateral body folds.** Upon reaching the midline, the cellular layers fuse as follows: The entodermal layer from one side fuses with the entodermal layer of the other; the mesodermal layers fuse similarly; and, finally, the epidermal layer from one side fuses with the epidermal layer of the opposite side. The result is a general fusion of the respective body layers from either side, as shown in figure 241C and D, which establishes the ventral region of the trunk. A complete fusion throughout the extent of the ventral body wall does not take place

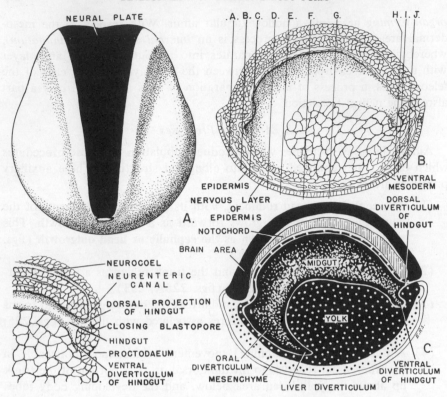

Fig. 220. Beginning neural fold stage of frog embryo from prepared material. (A) Beginning neural fold stage as seen from dorsal view. (B) Sagittal section near median plane of embryo similar to that shown in (A). (C) Same as (B), showing organ-forming areas. (D) Midsagittal section of caudal end of frog embryo slightly younger than that shown in fig. 223B. Observe that the blastopore practically is closed, while the dorsal diverticulum of the hindgut connects with the neurocoel to form the neurenteric canal. Observe, also, ventral diverticulum of hindgut.

until later in development, and, as a result, a small opening remains, the **umbilicus,** where the embryonic and extra-embryonic tissues are continuous. This discontinuity of the embryonic layers permits the blood vessels to pass from the embryonic to the extra-embryonic regions. (*Note:* In the teleost fishes, although a typical, flattened, gastrular form is present, the formation of the ventral body wall of the trunk through a general retraction of tissues resembles that of the rounded gastrulae mentioned above.)

5. Blastocoelic Space and Body-form Development

During the terminal phases of gastrulation in such forms as *Amphioxus* and the frog, the blastocoel, as a spacious cavity, disappears for the most part. Its general area is occupied by cells which migrated into the blastocoel during gastrulation. However, the disappearance of the blastocoelic space is more apparent than real. For, while most of the original blastocoelic space is thus occupied and obliterated, a part of the original blastocoel does remain as an extremely thin, potential area between the outside ectoderm and the mesoderm-entoderm complex of cells. In flattened blastoderms, as in the chick, the actual space between the ectoderm, mesoderm, and entoderm is considerable (fig. 234E, F). To sum up: Though the blastocoelic space appears to disappear during the terminal phases of gastrulation, a residual or potential space remains between the three germ layers, more pronounced in some species than in others. This residual space gradually increases during the tubulation processes of the major organ-forming areas. In doing so, it permits not only the tubulation of these areas within the outside ectoderm, but *it allows important cell migrations to occur between the various body tubes*.

6. PRIMITIVE CIRCULATORY TUBES OR BLOOD VESSELS

Accompanying the tubulations of the epidermal, neural, entodermal, and the two mesodermal areas on either side of the notochord, is the formation

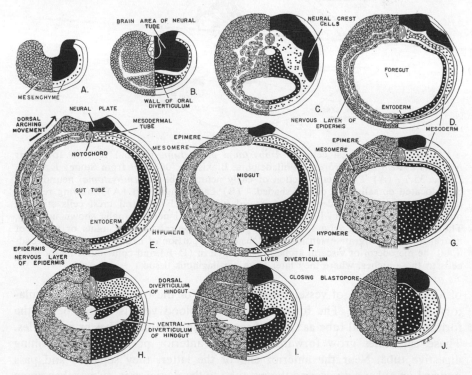

FIG. 221. Transverse sections through early neural fold embryo of the frog as shown in fig. 220A and B. (A–J) Sections are indicated in fig. 220B by lines A–J, respectively. Observe that the dorsal arching (dorsal upgrowth) movement of the dorsally situated tissues accompanies neural tube formation.

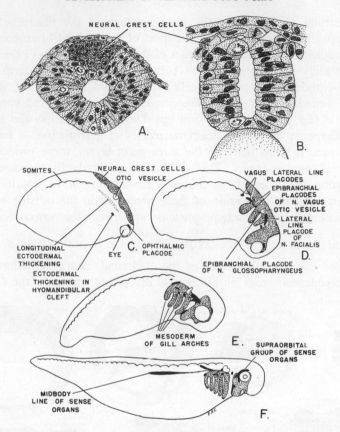

FIG. 222. Neural crest cells in *Ambystoma punctatum*. (A and B from Johnston: *Nervous System of Vertebrates,* Philadelphia, Blakiston, '06; C–F from Stone: J. Exper. Zool., '35.) (A) Transverse section of early neural tube of *Ambystoma,* neural crest cells located dorsally and darkly shaded. (B) Later stage than (A), showing relation of neural crest cells, epidermis, and neural tube. (C–F) Neural crest cells stippled, placodes of special lateral line sense organs and cranial nerve ganglia shown in black. The neural crest cells arise from dorsal portion of neural tube at points of fusion of neural folds and migrate extensively. A considerable portion of neural crest cells descends upon the mesoderm of visceral arches as indicated in (D–F) and contributes mesodermal cells to these arches, where they later form cartilaginous tissue.

of a delicate system of vessels which function for the transport of the circulatory fluid or blood. The formation of these blood vessels begins below the forming entodermal tube as **two, subenteric (subintestinal) tubes or capillaries.** These capillaries grow forward below the anterior portion of the forming digestive tube. Near the anterior end of the latter, they separate and pass upward on either side around the gut tube to the dorsal area, where they come together again below the notochord and join to form the rudiments of the dorsal aortae. The latter are two delicate **supraenteric capillaries** which extend from the forming head area caudally toward the trunk region. In the latter region, each rudiment of the dorsal aorta sends a small, vitelline blood vessel laterally into that portion of the gut tube or yolk area containing the yolk or other nutritional source. In the yolk area, each joins a plexus of small capillaries extending over the surface of the yolk substance. These capillaries in turn connect with other capillaries which join ultimately each of the original subintestinal blood capillaries. Below the anterior or foregut portion of the entodermal tube, the two subintestinal blood vessels fuse and thus form the beginnings of the future heart (figs. 234–237; 332). The further development of this system of primitive vessels is described in Chapter 17.

7. Extra-embryonic Membranes

Associated with the development of body form and tubulation of the major, organ-forming areas, is the elaboration of the very important extra-embryonic membranes. As the essential purpose at this time is to gain knowledge of the changes concerned with tubulation of the major organ-forming areas and the development of primitive body form, consideration of these membranes is deferred until Chapter 22. The latter chapter is concerned with various activities relating to the care and nutrition of developing embryos of various vertebrate species.

B. Tubulation of the Neural, Epidermal, Entodermal, and Mesodermal, Organ-forming Areas in the Vertebrate Group

1. Neuralization or the Tubulation of the Neural Plate Area

a. Definition

The separation of the neural plate material from the skin ectoderm, its migration inward, and its formation into a hollow tube, together with the segregation of the accompanying neural crest cells, is called **neuralization.**

b. Neuralizative Processes in the Vertebrata

Neuralization is effected by two general procedures in the vertebrate subphylum.

1) Thickened Keel Method. In teleost, ganoid, and cyclostomatous fishes, the neural plate material becomes aggregated in the form of a **thickened, elongated ridge or keel** along the middorsal axis of the embryo (figs. 210F; 218C). This keel separates from, and sinks below, the overlying skin ectoderm (fig. 218A). Eventually the keel of neural cells develops a lumen within its central area and thus gradually becomes transformed into an elongated tube, coincident with the tubulations of the other major organ-forming areas (fig. 218B). In the cyclostomatous fish, *Petromyzon planeri,* although neuralization closely resembles the condition in teleost fishes, in certain respects the behavior of the neuralizative changes represents an intermediate condition

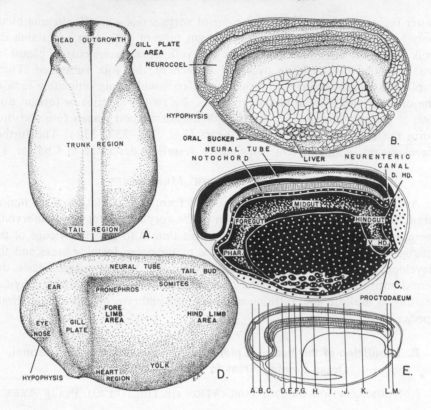

FIG. 223. Early neural tube stage of the frog, *Rana pipiens,* 2½ to 3 mm. in length. (A) Dorsal view. (B) Midsagittal section of embryo similar to (A). (C) Same as (B), showing organ-forming areas. Abbreviations: V. HD. = ventral hindgut diverticulum; D. HD. = dorsal hindgut diverticulum; PHAR. = pharyngeal diverticulum of foregut. (D) Later view of (A). (E) See fig. 224.

between the keel method of the teleost and neural fold method of other vertebrates described below (Selys–Longchamps, '10).

2) Neural Fold Method. In the majority of vertebrates, the neural (medullary) plate area folds inward (i.e., downward) to form a **neural groove.** This neural groove formation is associated with an **upward and median movement** of the epidermal layers, attached to the lateral margins of the neural plate, as these margins fold inward to form the neural folds. A change of position in the mesoderm also occurs at this time, for the upper part which forms the somites *shifts laterad from the notochordal area* to a position between the forming neural tube and the outside epidermis. This mesodermal migration permits the neural tube to invaginate downward to contact the notochordal area. Also, *this change in position of the somitic mesoderm is a most important factor in neuralization and neural tube development as mentioned at the end of this chapter. (Note:* In this stage of development, the embryo is often de-

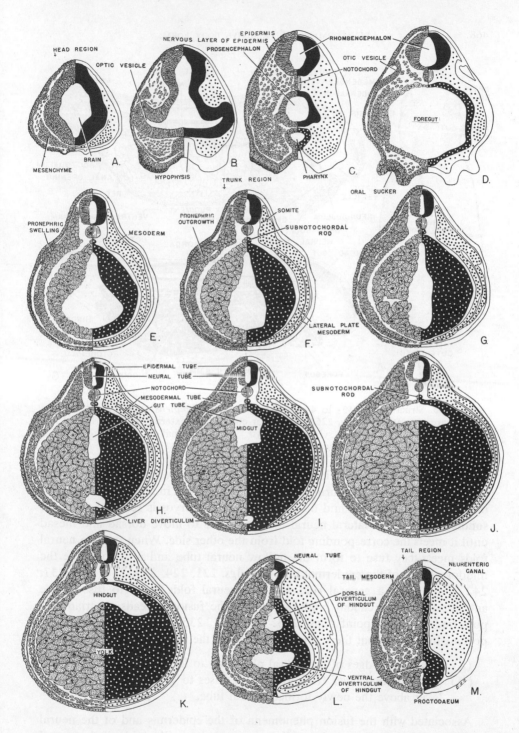

FIG. 224. Transverse sections through frog embryo shortly after closure of the neural tube, as indicated in fig. 223E. This embryo is slightly older than that shown in 223A–C.

467

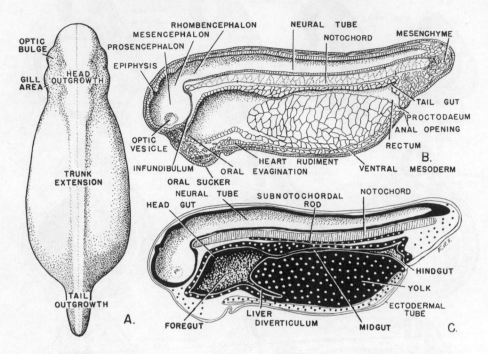

FIG. 225. Structure of 3½- to 4-mm. embryo of *Rana pipiens* (about eight pairs of somites are present). (See fig. 226A and B for comparable external views of lateral and ventral aspects of 5-mm., *Rana sylvatica* embryo.)   (A) External dorsal view.   (B) Mid-sagittal view.   (C) Same, showing major organ-forming areas.

scribed as a **neurula,** especially in the *Amphibia*. However, in the bird and the mammal, the embryo during this period is described in terms of the number of somitic pairs present, and this stage in these embryos is referred to as the **somite stage.**) Each lateral neural fold continues to move dorsad and mesad until it meets the corresponding fold from the other side. When the two neural folds meet, they fuse to form the hollow neural tube and also complete the middorsal area of the epidermal tube (cf. figs. 221, 224, 233, 234, 236, 237, 242, 245A). As a general rule, the two neural folds begin to fuse in the anterior trunk and caudal hindbrain area. The fusion spreads anteriad and posteriad from this point (figs. 223, 229, 233, 235, 242, 245A). It is important to observe that there are two aspects to the middorsal fusion process:

(a) The lateral edges of the neural plate fuse to form the neural tube; and
(b) the epidermal layer from either side fuses to complete the epidermal layer above the newly formed neural tube.

Associated with the fusion phenomena of the epidermis and of the neural tube, **neural crest cells** are given off or segregated on either side of the neural tube at the point where the neural tube ectoderm separates from the skin ectoderm (figs. 221C–E; 234B; 236B). The neural crest material forms a longitudinal strip of cells lying along either side of the dorsal portion of the neural tube. As such, it forms the **neural or ganglionic crest.** In some vertebrate embryos, as in the elasmobranch fish, *Torpedo,* and in the urodele, *Ambystoma,* the cells of the neural crest are derived from the middorsal part of the neural tube immediately after the tube has separated from the skin ectoderm (epidermis). (See fig. 222A, B.) In other vertebrates, such as the frog, chick, and human, the neural crest material arises from the general area of junction of neural plate and skin ectoderm as fusion of the neural folds is consummated (fig. 234B).

The neural crest gives origin to ganglionic cells of the dorsal root ganglia of the spinal nerves and the ganglia of cranial or cephalic nerves as described in Chapter 19. Pigment cells also arise from neural crest material and migrate extensively within the body, particularly to the forming derma or skin, peritoneal cavity, etc., as set forth in Chapter 12. A considerable part of the mesoderm of the head and branchial area arises from neural crest material (fig. 222C–F). (See Chapters 11 and 15.)

As the neural plate becomes transformed into the neural tube, it undergoes extension and growth. Anteriorly, it grows forward into the cephalic outgrowth, in the trunk region it elongates coincident with the developing trunk, while posteriorly it increases in length and forms a part of the tail outgrowth.

c. Closure of the Blastopore in Rounded Gastrulae, such as that of the Frog

Neuralization and the infolding of the neural plate cells begins in the frog and other amphibia before the last vestiges of the entoderm and mesoderm have completed their migration to the inside. As mentioned above, the neural folds begin, and fusion of the neural tube is initiated in the anterior trunk region. From this point, completion of the neural tube continues anteriad and posteriad. As the neural tube proceeds in its development caudally, it reaches ultimately the dorsal lip of the now very small blastopore. As the neural tube sinks inward at the dorsal blastoporal lip, the *epidermal attachments to the sides of the infolding neural tube fuse in a fashion similar to the fusion of the edges of the neural tube to complete the dorsal epidermal roof.* Associated with this epidermal fusion at the dorsal lip of the blastopore is the fusion of the epidermal edges of the very small blastopore. The extreme caudal end of the archenteron or **blastoporal canal** in this manner is closed off from the outside (fig. 220D), and the posterior end of the archenteron (the future hindgut area), instead of opening to the outside through the blastoporal canal, now opens into the caudal end of the neural tube. In this way, a canal is formed connecting the caudal end of the future hindgut with the neural tube. This neurenteric union is known as the **neurenteric canal.**

It is to be observed in connection with the closure of the blastopore and

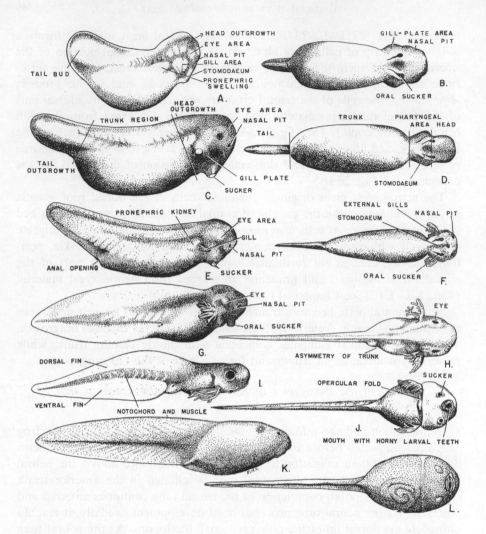

FIG. 226. External views of embryos of *Rana sylvatica* and *Rana pipiens*. (A to J after Pollister and Moore: Anat. Rec., 68; K and L after Shumway: Anat. Rec., 78.) (A, B) Lateral and ventral views of 5-mm. stage. Muscular movement is evident at this stage, expressed by simple unilateral flexure; tail is about one-fifth body length. (Pollister and Moore, stage 18.) (C, D) Lateral and ventral views of 6-mm. stage. Primitive heart has developed and begins to beat; tail equals one-third length of body. (Pollister and Moore, stage 19.) (E, F) Similar views of 7-mm. stage. Gill circulation is established; hatches; swims; tail equals one-half length of body. (Pollister and Moore, stage 20.) (G, H) Ten-mm. stage, lateral and dorsal views. Gills elongate; tail fin is well developed and circulation is established within; trunk is asymmetrical coincident with posterior bend in the gut tube; cornea of eyes is transparent; epidermis is becoming transparent. (Pollister and Moore, stage 22.) (I, J) Eleven-mm. stage, true tadpole shape. Opercular fold is beginning to develop and gradually growing back over gills. (K, L) Eleven-mm. stage of *R. pipiens* embryo. Observe that opercular folds have grown back over external gills and developing limb buds; opercular chamber opens on left side of body only. Indicated in fig. 257B.

the formation of the neurenteric canal that two important changes occur in the future hindgut area of the archenteron at this time, namely, the posterior dorsal end of the archenteron projects dorso-caudally to unite with the neural tube (fig. 220D), while the posterior ventral end of the archenteron moves ventrad toward the epidermis where it meets the epidermal invagination, the **proctodaeum** (fig. 220D).

d. Anterior and Posterior Neuropores; Neurenteric Canal

The fusion of the neural folds in the middorsal area proceeds anteriad and posteriad from the anterior somitic and hindbrain region as described above. At the anterior end of the forebrain when fusion is still incomplete, an opening from the exterior to the inside of the neural canal is present; it forms the **anterior neuropore** (figs. 229D; 231L; 235B; 242E–G; 245B). When fusion is complete, this opening is obliterated. The caudal end of the neural tube closes in a similar manner, and a **posterior neuropore** is formed (figs. 242E, G; 245). In the chick, as in the mammal, the posterior neuropore at first is a wide, rhomboidal-shaped trough, known as the **rhomboidal sinus.** The anterior end of the primitive streak is included within the floor of this sinus rhomboidalis (fig. 235A, B). The point of posterior neuroporal closure is at the base of the future tail in most vertebrates (fig. 245D), but, in the elasmobranch fishes, this closure is effected after the tail rudiments have grown caudally for some distance (fig. 229B–E).

The vertebrate tail arises from a mass of tissue, known variously as the **tail bud, caudal bud, or end bud,** and the posterior end of the neural tube comes to lie in the end-bud tissues (figs. 225, 238C). The end bud grows caudally and progressively gives origin to the tail. It consists of the following:

(a) the epidermal tube (i.e., the ectodermal covering of the end bud); within this epidermal layer are
(b) the caudal end of the neural tube;
(c) the caudal end of the notochord;
(d) mesoderm in the form of a mass of rather compact mesenchyme surrounding the growing caudal ends of the notochord and neural tube; and
(e) a caudal growth from the **primitive intestine or gut.**

This extension of the gut tube into the tail is called, variously, **the tail gut, caudal gut or post-anal gut.** It varies in length and extent of development in embryos of different vertebrate species. In some species it is joined to the neural tube; in others it is not so united. For example, the tail gut is as long as the trunk portion of the gut in the young shark embryo of 8 to 10 mm. in length, and at the caudal extremity it is confluent with the neural tube (figs. 217A; 229F). The confluent terminal portions of the neural and gut tubes form the **neurenteric canal.** This well-developed neurenteric canal extends

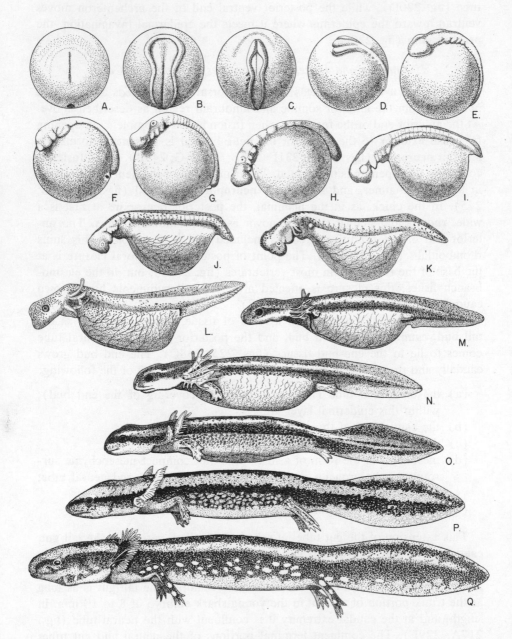

FIG. 227. (*See facing page for legend.*)

around the caudal end or base of the notochord. In the developing frog on the other hand, the confluence between the neural and gut tubes is present only during the initial stages of tail formation, and it thus represents a transient relationship (fig. 223B, C). Consequently, as the tail bud in the frog embryo grows caudally, the neurenteric connection is obliterated and the tail gut disappears. On the other hand, in the European frog, *Bombinator,* the condition is intermediate between frog and shark embryos (fig. 228). True neurenteric canals within the developing tail are never formed in the reptile, chick, or mammal, although a tail or post-anal gut, much abbreviated, develops in these forms. (See paragraph below.) In teleost fishes, Kupffer's vesicle possibly represents a small and transient attempt to form a neurenteric canal (fig. 210G). However, the tail gut here, with the exception of the terminally placed Kupffer's

---

FIG. 227. Stages of normal development of *Necturus maculosus.* (Slightly modified from Eycleshymer and Wilson, aided by C. O. Whitman; Chap. 11 in *Entwicklungsgeschichte d. Wirbeltiere,* by F. Keibel, '10.) (A) Stage 15, 14 days, 19 hours after fertilization. Blastopore is circular and reduced; neural groove is indicated in center of figure. (B) Stage 18, 17 days, 2 hours old. Blastopore is an elongated, narrow aperture between caudal ends of neural folds; neural folds prominent and neural groove is deeper. (C) Stage 21, 18 days, 15 hours old, 3 or 4 pairs of somites. Neural folds are widely separated in head region, narrower in trunk, and coalesced in tail area. (D) Stage 22, 20 days, 10 hours, 6 pairs of somites, length about 6 mm. Observe head has three longitudinal ridges, the middle one represents developing brain, while lateral ones are common anlagen of optic vesicles and branchial arches. (E) Stage 23, 21 days, 2 hours, 10 to 12 pairs of somites, 7 mm. long. Head projects forward slightly above egg contour; end of tail is prominent; large optic vesicles protrude laterally from head area; branchial arch region is caudal to optic vesicle enlargement; anus is below tip of tail. (F) Stage 24, 22 days, 17 hours, 16 to 18 pairs of somites, 8 mm. long. Anterior half of head is free from egg contour; optic vesicles and mandibular visceral arch are well defined. (G) Stage 25, 23 days, 10 hours, 20 to 22 pairs of somites, 9 mm. long. Head is free from egg surface; tail outgrowth is becoming free; mandibular, hyoid, first branchial and common rudiment of second and third branchial arches are visible. Otic vesicle lies above hyoid arch and cleft between hyoid and first branchial arches. (H) Stage 26, 24 days, 22 hours, 23 to 24 pairs of somites, length—10 mm. Head and caudal outgrowths are free from egg surface; heart rudiment is shown as darkened area below branchial arches; cephalic flexure of brain is prominent. (I) Stage 27, 26 days, 26 to 27 myotomes, length—11 mm. Outline of body is straighter; nasal pits and mouth are well defined, mandibular arches are long; heart is prominent below branchial arches; anterior limb buds are indicated; faint outlines of posterior limb buds are evident. (J) Stage 28, 30 days, 8 hours, 30 to 31 myotomes, length—13 mm. Trunk of embryo is straight, head and tail are depressed; surface of yolk is covered by dense network of capillaries; vitelline veins are prominent; pigment appears below epidermis; anterior limb bud projects dorsally; nuchal or neck flexure is prominent above heart and limb-bud area. (K) Stage 29, 36 days, 16 hours, 36 to 38 myotomes, length—16 mm. Mandibular arches are forming lower jaw; nuchal and tail flexures are straightening; eye and lens are well defined; anlagen of gill filament are present on gill bars; pigment cells are evident on head areas; vitelline veins are prominent; yolk-laden, ventro-lateral portion of trunk is becoming elongated and contracted toward dorsal region of embryo. (L) Stage 30, 40 days, 20 hours, 44 to 46 myotomes, length—18 mm. Fore and hind limb buds are prominent; nasal openings are small. (M) Stage 31, larva 49 days, 21 mm. (N) Stage 32, larva 61 days, 25 mm. (O) Stage 33, larva 70 days, 28 mm. (P) Stage 34, larva 97 days, 34 mm. (Q) Stage 35, young adult form, 126 days, 39 mm.

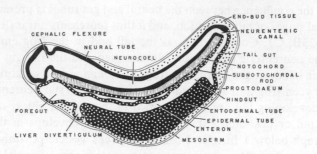

FIG. 228. Sagittal section, showing organ-forming areas of *Bombinator* embryo. (After O. Hertwig: *Lehrbuch der Entwicklungsgeschichte des Menschen und der Wirbeltiere.* 1890. Jena, G. Fischer.) Observe elongated tail gut.

vesicle, is a solid mass of cells. Thus, the shark and *Bombinator* embryos, on the one hand, and the frog, chick, or mammal embryo, on the other, represent two extremes in the development of the tail gut in the vertebrate group.

In the reptiles, also in some birds, such as the duck, in the human embryo, and certain other mammals, **a transient notochordal-neural canal** is present which connects the enteron or gut tube with the caudal area of the forming neural tube (figs. 200B, E; 207B; 231G–K). This canal is occasionally referred to as a neurenteric canal. However, it is best to view this condition as a special type of development within the above group, for it is not strictly comparable to the neurenteric canal formed in the developing tail of the embryos of the frog, shark, etc., where the neurenteric canal is formed *by a definite union between neural and tail-gut tubes* as they project caudalward into the tail rudiment.

2. Epidermal Tubulation

The formation of the external, epidermal, tubular layer of the vertebrate body is a complex procedure. Its development differs considerably in the **rounded** type of gastrula of the *Amphibia* from that in the **flattened** gastrula of the chick or mammal.

a. Development of the Epidermal Tube in Amphibia

In the frog and other *Amphibia,* tubulation of the epidermal area of the blastula begins during gastrulation. At the end of gastrulation, the changes involved in epiboly have transformed the ectodermal area of the blastula into an oval-shaped structure, surrounding the internally placed mesoderm and entoderm (fig. 219). The neural plate material occupies the middorsal area of this oval-shaped, ectodermal layer, while the future epidermal area forms the remainder. Following gastrulation, the anterior end of this oval-shaped structure, in harmony with the forming neural tube, begins to elongate and grows forward as the **head outgrowth** (figs. 220, 223, 225). A cylindrical, epidermal covering for the entire head, in this manner, is produced as the cranial or brain portion of the neural plate folds inward (invaginates). A similar outgrowth in the tail area proceeds posteriorly, although here the neural tube grows caudally by proliferative activity within the epidermal tube instead of folding into the epidermal tube as it does in the cephalic outgrowth (figs. 223, 225). Coincident with these two outgrowths, the trunk area, with its ventral, yolk-filled, entodermal cells, elongates antero-posteriorly as the neural plate folds inward. It also grows larger in harmony with the head and tail outgrowths. As these activities continue, yolk substance is used up, and

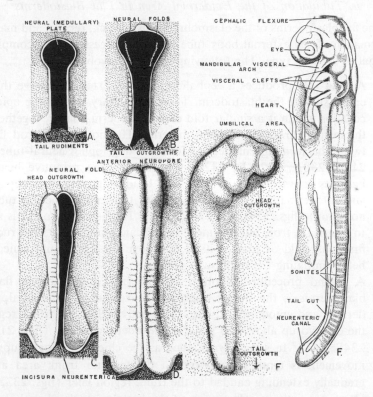

Fig. 229. Early stages of tubulation of neural and epidermal organ-forming areas with resultant body-form development in the shark, *Squalus acanthias* (drawn from prepared slides). Neural area shown in black; epidermal area is stippled white; neural folds are outlined in white around edges of black area. (Consult also fig. 230.) (A) Embryonic area is raised upward; neural plate is flattened; bilateral tail outgrowths are indicated. (B) Embryo is considerably elevated from extra-embryonic blastoderm; brain area is much expanded; trunk region of neural groove is pronounced. (C) Neuralization is considerably advanced; tail rudiments are converging. (D) Neural and epidermal areas are well tubulated; tail rudiments are fusing. (E) Young *Squalus* embryo, lying on left side; tail rudiments are fused into single caudal outgrowth. The body now consists of a flexed cephalic outgrowth, trunk region, and tail outgrowth. (F) *Squalus* embryo of about 10 mm. in length.

the ventro-lateral region of the trunk is retracted. A cylindrical shape of the trunk region thus is established, bringing the trunk area into harmony with the head and tail outgrowths. (Study particularly fig. 227.) *The epidermal area of the late gastrula thus becomes converted into an elongated, epidermal tube which forms the external covering or primitive skin* (see Chap. 12) *for the developing body.* In Amphibia, this primitive epidermal tube is two layered, consisting of an outer epidermal ectoderm and an inner neural ectoderm (figs. 221, 224). (See Chap. 12.) In the newly hatched larva, the epidermis is extensively ciliated in all anuran and urodele *Amphibia.*

b. Tubulation of the Epidermal Area in Flat Blastoderms

In the flat blastoderms of the elasmobranch fish, chick, reptile, and mammal, the formation of the external body tube involves processes more complicated than that of the frog type. The following steps are involved:

(1) A **head fold** produces a cephalic epidermal extension above the general tissues of the blastoderm. This rudimentary fold of the epidermis contains within it a similar fold of the entodermal layer, together with the invaginating, neural plate material. The notochordal rod lies between the forming entodermal fold and developing neural tube (figs. 213F; 230A; 232I–L; 242B, C). Shortly, the primitive head fold becomes converted into a cylindrical head outgrowth of the epidermal and entodermal layers, associated with the forming neural tube and notochord (figs. 229C, D; 230C; 233). The general process is similar to that in the frog, but it is more complicated in that the head rudiment first must fold or project itself up above the extra-embryonic areas, before initiating the outgrowth process.

(2) A second procedure involved in epidermal tubulation in flattened blastoderms is the **dorsal upgrowth movement** of epidermal, mesodermal, and entodermal tissues. This activity lifts the trunk region of the embryo up above the general blastodermic tissues (figs. 213H–J; 234B; 241). In some forms, such as the chick, the dorsal upgrowth movement is more pronounced in the anterior trunk area at first, gradually extending caudad to the trunk region later (figs. 233, 235). However, in the pig, human, and shark embryos, the dorsal elevation extends along the entire trunk area, coincident with the head outgrowth, and thus quickly lifts the embryonic body as a whole up above the extra-embryonic tissues (figs. 229, 230, 242, 245).

(3) The **tail outgrowth,** in reptiles, birds, and mammals, begins in a manner similar to that of the head region, and a tail fold first is developed which later becomes a cylindrical projection, bounded externally with epidermal cells, within which are found the notochord, tail mesoderm, and tail portions of neural and gut tubes (figs. 238C; 239K, L; 245B).

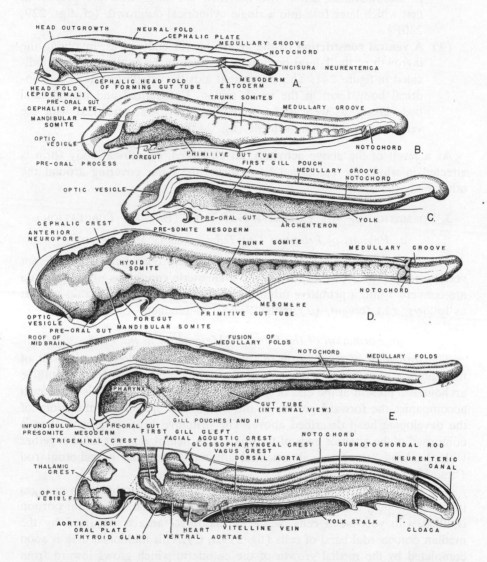

FIG. 230. Sagittal sections of early elasmobranch embryos. (Slightly modified from Scammon. See Chap. 12 in *Entwicklungsgeschichte d. Wirbeltiere,* by F. Keibel.) (A) Graphic reconstruction from sagittal sections of embryo of 2 mm., seen from left side (condition roughly comparable to stage between fig. 229A and B). Observe that neural plate is broad and flattened with slight elevation of neural folds. (B) Reconstruction of embryo of 2.7 mm., viewed from left side, showing mesoderm, forming gut, neural tubes, etc. (Consult (C) below.) (C) Same as (B) with mesoderm removed. Observe primitive gut and neural tubes. *Note:* (B) and (C) are comparable to stage shown in surface view in fig. 229C. (D, E) Same as (B) and (C), embryo 3.5 mm. in length. (This embryo is comparable to fig. 229D.) (F) Same as (D) with mesoderm removed, showing primitive vascular tubes and neural crest cells.

In elasmobranch fishes, two flattened tail outgrowths are present at first which later fuse into a single cylindrical outgrowth (cf. figs. 229; 230F).

(4) A **ventral constriction** of the ventro-lateral body areas, involving the ingrowth of the lateral body folds, occurs in the trunk region as indicated in figure 241. This movement aids the establishment of a cylindrical body form in the trunk region. Entodermal and mesodermal body layers, as well as the epidermal layer, are concerned with the ventral constrictive movement (fig. 241B, C).

As a result of the above activities, an elongated, cylindrical body form is effected in which the epidermal layer forms the outer covering around the other body tubes.

3. FORMATION OF THE PRIMITIVE GUT TUBE (ENTERIC TUBULATION)

a. Regions of Primitive Gut Tube or Early Metenteron

The details of formation of the enteric tube vary considerably in different vertebrate species. However, in all, the **archenteric conditions** of the gastrula are converted into a **primitive tubular metenteron,** having three main regions as follows: (1) foregut, (2) midgut, and (3) hindgut.

b. Formation of the Primitive Metenteron in the Frog

The formation of the **foregut** in the frog naturally follows as a result of the anterior growth and extension of the cephalic portion of the primitive archenteron present at the end of gastrulation (fig. 220B, C). This outgrowth accompanies the forward growth of the neural and epidermal tubulations of the developing head described above. The primitive head outgrowth thus is composed of the anterior ends of the epidermal, neural, and gut tubes together with the head mesoderm, all oriented around the median notochordal rod (figs. 221B, C; 223B, C).

The **midgut** area of the primitive metenteron forms in relation to changes in the developing trunk region. At the end of gastrulation, its ventral portion is filled with yolk-laden cells, while its middorsal area is occupied by the median notochordal band of cells (fig. 219B, C). This middorsal area is soon completed by the medial growth of the entoderm which grows inward from either side below the notochord (fig. 219D). Accompanying the completion of the roof portion of the midgut, the entire midgut area becomes extended antero-posteriorly (figs. 220B, C; 223B, C; 225B, C). Associated with these changes, the middorsal area of the midgut moves dorsad toward the notochord, forming a dorsal, trough-like region of the gut (fig. 224). It is to be observed in this connection that the neural tube invaginates toward the notochordal rod, whereas the roof of the gut evaginates (i.e., in a sense it invaginates) toward the same notochordal area. This dorsal folding of the gut tube in the

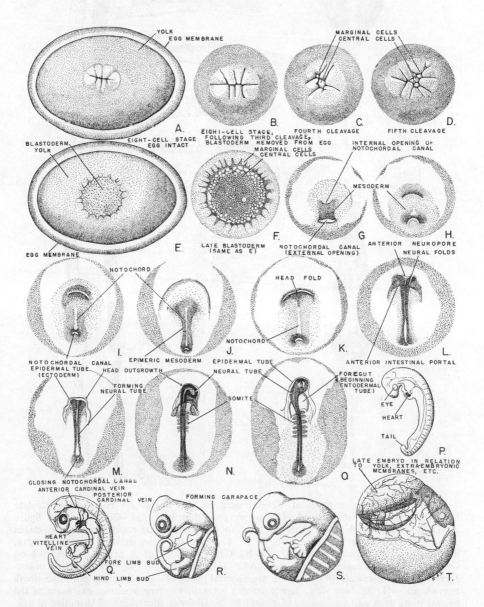

FIG. 231. Series of diagrams, showing stages in the development of the turtle. (A–F) Cleavage stages after Agassiz. (G–J) Stages of gastrulation, drawn from slide preparations. (K–T) Stages during development of body form. (P, Q, T from Agassiz; the others are original.) (See L. Agassiz, 1857, Cont. Nat. Hist. of U. S. A., Vol. II.)

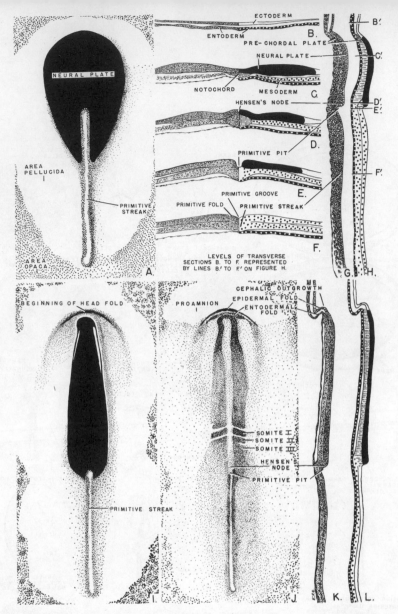

FIG. 232. Early post-gastrular development in the chick. (A–H represent a late head-process stage—stage 5 of Hamburger and Hamilton, '51. Compare with figure 203D. I–L show the beginnings of the head fold—intermediate condition between stages 7 and 8 of Hamburger and Hamilton, '51.)   (A) Surface view, showing primitive streak, neural plate, and epidermal areas.   (B–F) Cross sections of A at levels indicated on G.   (G) Median sagittal section of (A).   (H) Same, showing presumptive, organ-forming areas of entoderm notochord, pre-chordal plate, neural plate, and primitive-streak mesoderm.   (I) Surface view, demonstrating a marked antero-posterior extension of the neural plate area and beginnings of neural folds. Observe shortening of primitive streak.   (J) Drawing of stained specimen.   (K) Median sagittal section of (J).   (L) Same, showing major organ-forming areas. In (G) and (H) the entoderm, notochord, and overlying neural ectoderm are drawn as separate layers. Actually, however, at this stage, the three layers are intimately associated.

480

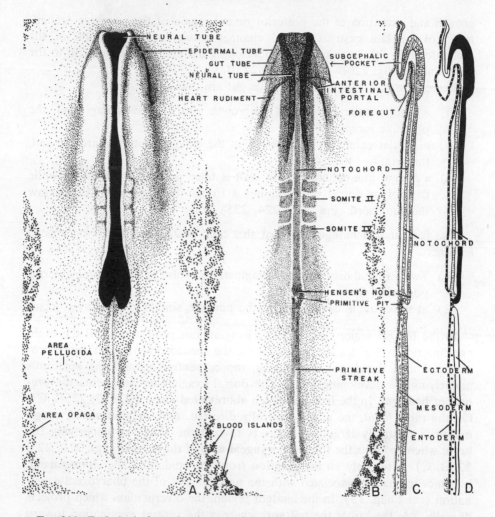

FIG. 233. Early body-form development in chick of 3 to 4 pairs of somites. (Approximately comparable to Hamburger and Hamilton, '51, stage 8, 26 to 29 hours of incubation.) (A) Surface view, unstained specimen. (B) Stained, transparent preparation. Observe blood islands in caudal part of blastoderm. (C) Median sagittal section. (D) Same as (C), showing organ-forming layers.

direction of the notochord is much more pronounced in the flattened blastoderms than in the rounded blastoderms of the frog, salamander, etc. (cf. figs. 224; 237). (*Note:* Associated with the dorsal invagination of the roof of the midgut in the frog, is the detachment of a median rod of entodermal cells from the middorsal area of the gut. This median rod of cells comes to lie between the notochord and the roof of the midgut. It is known as the **subnotochordal rod** (fig. 225C). (See Chapter 15.)

The development of the rudimentary **hindgut** is consummated by caudal growth and extension of the posterior or tail region of the primitive archenteron of the late gastrula. These changes result in an extension of the archenteron in the direction of the developing tail and the area ventral to the tail (compare fig. 220B–D with figs. 223B, C; 225B, C).

Three general areas of the primitive gut are thus established:

(a) a tubular enlargement and outgrowth into the developing head, the primitive foregut,

(b) a tubular extension and growth in the caudal region toward the tail, the primitive hindgut, and

(c) a midgut area whose ventral wall is filled with yolk substance, while its roof or dorsal wall assumes a trough-like form extending below the notochord (figs. 223, 224, 225).

The foregut and hindgut areas at this time present the following special features:

(1) Two terminal diverticula or evaginations evolve at the extreme anterior portion of the foregut; and

(2) at the extreme caudal end of the hindgut, similar evaginations occur.

In the foregut region, one of these evaginations projects toward the brain and anterior end of the notochord, while the second diverticulum, more pronounced than the dorsal evagination, moves ventrad toward the epidermis underlying the developing brain. The dorsal evagination represents the **pre-oral** or **head gut**. In the frog it is much abbreviated (figs. 220B, C; 225B, C). On the other hand, the antero-ventrally directed, **oral, or pharyngeal, evagination** is relatively large and projects toward the ectoderm underlying the brain where it forms the future **pharyngeal area of the foregut** (figs. 220; 223; 225B, C). Ultimately an **invagination** from the epidermis, the **stomodaeum,** becomes intimately associated with the anterior end of the pharyngeal evagination (see Chap. 13). In the hindgut region, the diverticulum which projects dorsally into the tail is the **tail gut,** whereas the ventral evagination toward the epidermis below the tail represents the future **rectal and cloacal areas** of the hindgut (figs. 220; 223; 225B, C). It shortly becomes associated with an invagination of the epidermis, the **proctodaeum** (fig. 223B, C). As previously mentioned, the tail gut may be well developed, as in the European frog, *Bombinator* (fig. 228), or quite reduced, as in the frog, *Rana* (fig. 225).

c. Formation of the Tubular Metenteron in Flat Blastoderms

The development of the cylindrical gut tube in those vertebrate embryos which possess flattened gastrulae is an involved, complicated affair. The developmental mechanics are not clearly understood. For example, it is not clear whether the embryonic layers, lying in front of the head fold in figure 232G and H, are folded slightly backward in figures 232K and L and still farther

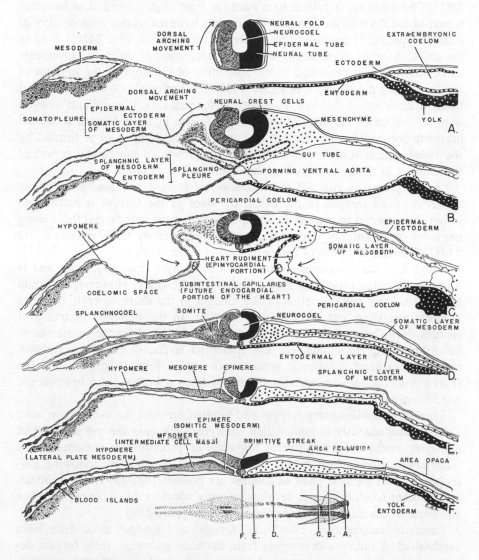

FIG. 234. Transverse sections of chick embryo with five pairs of somites. (This embryo is slightly older than that shown in fig. 233; a topographical sketch of this developmental stage is shown at the bottom of the figure with level of sections indicated.) Observe that a dorsal arching (dorsal upgrowth) movement of the dorsal tissues is associated with neural tube formation. See A and B.

483

caudad in figure 233C and D by autonomous activities within this tissue, or whether the actively growing head outgrowth proceeds so rapidly that it mechanically causes the area in front of the head fold to rotate backward under the developing foregut and thus contribute to the foregut floor. It is obvious, however, that the entodermal material, lying in front of the head fold of the embryo, is folded backward, at least slightly, and thus becomes a part of the floor of the foregut. The extent, however, varies considerably in different species. It appears to be greater in the mammal (fig. 242C) than in the chick. Another example suggesting the integration of different movements of cellular layers is presented in the formation of the floor of the hindgut of the developing pig embryo. In figure 242C, the rudiments of the foregut and hindgut areas are established. However, in figure 242G, it is difficult to evaluate how much of the floor of the hindgut in this figure is formed by actual ingrowth forward from point "a" and to what extent the floor is formed by the rapid extension of tissues and backward growth of the caudal region of the embryo as a whole, including the allantoic diverticulum.

Special processes also aid the formation of foregut and hindgut in many instances. For example, in the chick, the floor of the foregut is established in part by a medial or inward growth and fusion of the entodermal folds along the sides of the anterior intestinal portal, as indicated by the arrows in figure 234C. A similar ingrowth of entoderm occurs in the shark embryo (fig. 213J). although here the entoderm grows in as a solid layer from either side and is not present in the form of a lateral fold, as in the chick. However, it should be observed that the formation of the hindgut in the shark embryo arises by a most interesting and extraordinary method. In the flattened gastrulae of reptiles, birds, and mammals, the hindgut is established by the formation of tail folds, involving entodermal and epidermal layers. In the shark embryo, on the other hand, an enteric groove with enteric folds is formed, and the folds eventually move ventrad and fuse to form a hollow tube beneath the notochord of the developing tail.

Though the rudimentary foregut and hindgut areas of the metenteron arise almost simultaneously in mammalian embryos, such as in the pig and human embryos, in the chick a different sequence of procedure is present. In the latter species the foregut begins its development immediately following gastrulation when the **first pairs of somites** are present (fig. 233). The hindgut, on the other hand, begins its development at a considerably later period when the embryo has attained **many pairs of somites** (fig. 238).

Once the rudimentary, pouch-like, foregut and hindgut areas have been established in embryos developing from flattened gastrulae, their further development assumes morphogenetic features similar to those in the frog embryo. For example, the foregut possesses an antero-dorsal prolongation toward the brain, the **pre-oral** or **head gut,** while slightly posterior to the pre-oral gut, the future **pharyngeal area** makes contact ventrally with the **stomodaeal in-**

vagination from the epidermal (ectodermal) tube (fig. 242G). Similarly, the caudal region of the hindgut rudiment contacts the **proctodaeal invagination** of the epidermal tube, while a **tail gut extension** continues into the tail (fig. 217).

The formation of definitive walls of the midgut area in embryos developing from the flattened gastrular condition (including the higher mammals which do not possess large amounts of yolk substance) occurs as follows:

(1) Where the entoderm of the midgut terminates on either side of the notochord at the end of gastrulation, it grows mesad from either side

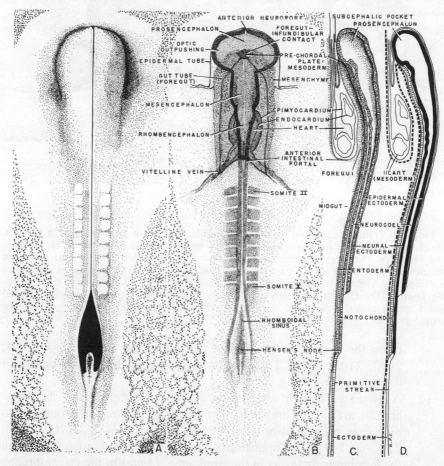

FIG. 235. Chick embryo of 9 to 10 pairs of somites. (Approximating Hamburger and Hamilton, '51, stage 10; 33 to 38 hours of incubation.)   (A) Surface view, unstained. (B) Stained preparation.   (C) Median sagittal section. Observe the following: heart is bent slightly to the right; three primary brain vesicles are indicated; foregut touches infundibular outgrowth of prosencephalon; first indication of downward bending of the head outgrowth, i.e., the cephalic (cranial) flexure is evident. (D) Same, showing major organ-forming areas.

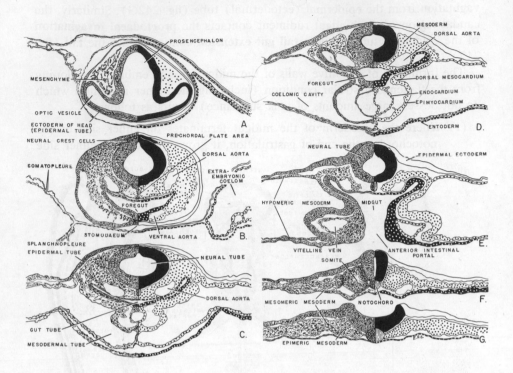

FIG. 236. Transverse sections through chick embryo of about 12 to 13 pairs of somites, about 38 hours of incubation. (Approximately between stages 10 to 11 of Hamburger and Hamilton, '51, slightly older than that shown in fig. 235.) Observe that the optic vesicles are constricting at their bases; heart is bent slightly to the right; anterior neuropore is evident. (A) Optic vesicles. (B) Stomodaeal area. (C) Anterior end of developing heart. (D) Caudal extremity of forming heart. (E) Anterior intestinal portal and forming caudal portion of the heart. (F) Well-developed somites. (G) Open neural groove.

> below the notochord to complete the roof of the midgut (figs. 201D; 209C; 210F; 213). This process is similar to that which occurs in the *Amphibia* (cf. fig. 219D).
>
> (2) A dorsal arching or evagination of the entoderm toward the notochordal area, comparable to that found in the frog and other *Amphibia,* is present also. A study of figures 213H–J; 217G; 234B; 237E–G; 241B–D demonstrates the marked dorsal upgrowth of all the forming body layers in the trunk area. (*Note:* In the elasmobranch fishes, a subnotochordal rod of cells of entodermal origin is formed similar to that in the frog and other *Amphibia.*)
>
> (3) The **ventro-lateral walls** of the midgut area, in contrast to those found in the frog, are established largely by actual ingrowth of the entoderm, mesoderm, and ectoderm with subsequent fusion in the median line

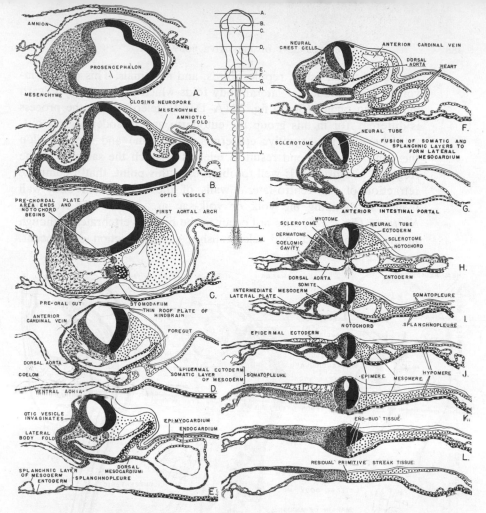

Fig. 237. Chick embryo of 17 to 19 pairs of somites. (Approximating Hamburger and Hamilton, '51, stage 13, 48 to 52 hours of incubation, sections indicated on outline drawing.) Head lies partly on left side; auditory pits are deep; cervical flexure is evident in region of rhombencephalon; cephalic flexure is marked; stomodaeum is a deep indentation touching foregut between the first pair of aortal arches; head fold of amnion reaches back to anterior part of rhombencephalon (hindbrain). (A) Anterior (telencephalic) portion of prosencephalon, showing closed neuropore; amnion is indicated. (B) Optic vesicles. (C) Anterior end of foregut, showing anterior extremity of stomodaeal invagination and first (mandibular) pair of aortal arches; notochord ends and pre-chordal plate area begins at about this section. (D) Anterior end of heart (ventral aorta); observe thin roof plate of neural tube, characteristic of the later myelencephalic (medulla) portion of rhombencephalon or hindbrain. (E) Otic (auditory) pits and anterior region of ventricular portion of heart. (F) Caudal limits of forming heart, dorsal mesocardium, neural crest cells. (G) Caudal end of heart, showing converging (vitelline) veins of the heart, sclerotome given off to notochordal area, lateral mesocardium forming. (H) Anterior trunk area, showing differentiation of somite and typically flattened condition of ectoderm, mesoderm, and entoderm. (I) Caudal trunk area, showing undifferentiated somite (epimeric mesoderm), intermediate mesoderm (mesomere), and lateral plate mesoderm (hypomere). (J) Similar to (I). (K) Caudal trunk region, showing closing neural tube. (L) Area of Hensen's node. (M) Primitive streak.

487

in elasmobranch fishes, reptiles, birds, and mammals. This process involves the formation of lateral body folds which fold mesially toward the median plane. (Study fig. 241A–D.) In teleost fishes the process is different, for in this group the entoderm and mesoderm grow outward beneath the primitive epidermis (ectoderm) and soon envelop the yolk. Thus, the end result in teleosts is much the same as in the frog and *Necturus*. It is well to observe, at this point, that a complete retraction of the ventro-lateral walls of the midgut and body-wall tissues surrounding the yolk or yolk-sac area, as in the frog and *Necturus* (fig. 227), does not occur in the higher vertebrates, although in the elasmobranch and teleost fishes such retraction does occur.

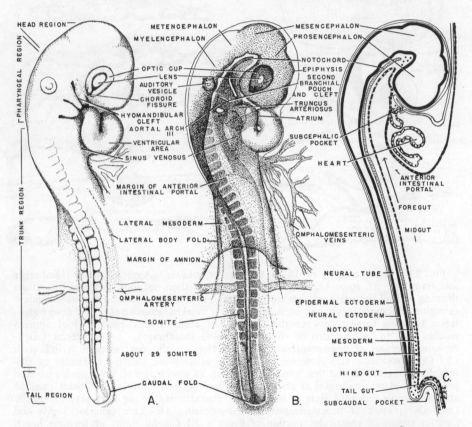

FIG. 238. Chick embryo of about 27 to 28 pairs of somites. (Corresponding approximately to Hamburger and Hamilton, '51, stage 16, 51 to 56 hours of incubation.) Forebrain (prosencephalon) is divided into telencephalon and diencephalon; epiphysis is appearing on roof of diencephalon; cephalic and cervical flexures are pronounced; tail bud is short; anterior part of body is rotated to the left back to about the thirteenth pair of somites; amnion now covers anterior three fifths of body; heart shows strong ventricular loop; three pairs of aortal arches can be seen. (A) External view. (B) Transparent wholemount. (C) Sagittal section, diagrammatic.

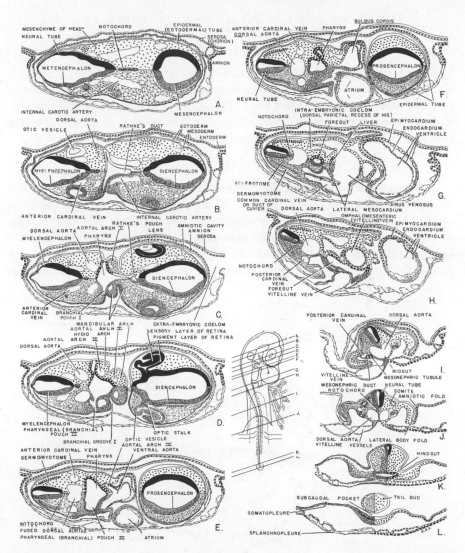

FIG. 239. Sections through chick embryo of age indicated in fig. 238. Level of sections is shown on diagram.

(See Chap. 22.) In the elasmobranch fishes, this retraction of tissues contributes little to the formation of the wall of the enteron or to that of the body. However, in teleosts such contribution is considerable.

At this point reference should be made to figures 238C on the chick, 242C and G on the pig, and 245B on the early human embryo to gain a visual image of the developing foregut, midgut, and hindgut areas of the primitive metenteron. Compare with the frog (fig. 225C).

4. TUBULATION (COELOM FORMATION) AND OTHER FEATURES INVOLVED IN THE EARLY DIFFERENTIATION OF THE MESODERMAL AREAS

The differentiation of the mesodermal areas is an all-important feature of embryonic development, for the mesoderm contributes much to the substance of the developing body. (See Chaps. 11 and 15.) While the neural, enteric, and epidermal tubes are being established, radical changes occur within the two mesodermal layers on either side of the notochord as follows:

a. Early Changes in the Mesodermal Areas

1) Epimere; Formation of the Somites. The longitudinal mass of paraxial mesoderm which lies along the side of the notochord forms the **epimere** (figs. 221F, G; 234E, F). The two epimeres, one on either side of the notochord, represent the future **somitic mesoderm** of the trunk area. In the early post-gastrula, the epimeric mesoderm, together with the notochord, lies immediately below the neural plate. However, as neuralization is effected, the

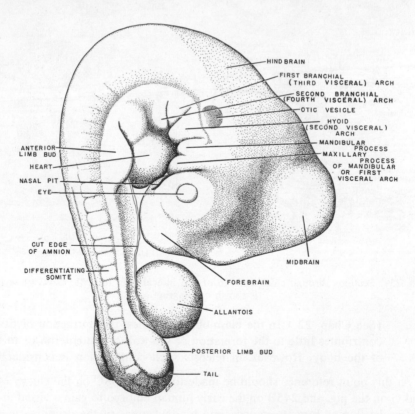

FIG. 240. Chick embryo of about 72 to 75 hours of incubation, about stage 20 of Hamburger and Hamilton, '51.

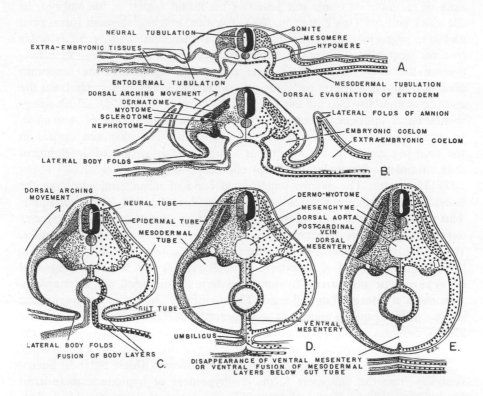

FIG. 241. Formation of ventral body wall, differentiation of somites, formation of dorsal and ventral mesenteries, embryonic and extra-embryonic coelom, etc., in chick embryo. (A) Dorsal upgrowth is evident as neural tube, somites, and forming entodermal (gut) tube are projected upward above the level of the extra-embryonic tissues. Observe heavy line at left, denoting general region of demarcation between embryonic and extra-embryonic tissues. (B) Separation of differentiating somite from nephrotome; sclerotomic mesenchyme is migrating from somite to notochordal-neural area; lateral body folds are migrating mediad to form ventral wall of trunk region; lateral folds of amnion are migrating dorsad. (C–E) Dorsal upgrowth movement lifts embryonic body above extra-embryonic tissues below; fusion of ventral, body-wall layers begins. (C) Body layers are meeting in midventral line. (D, E) Fusion of ventral body-wall layers, disappearance of ventral mesentery.

epimeric mesoderm on either side of the notochord gradually moves laterally and dorsally and comes to lie along the lateral aspects of the notochord and neural tube. During this migration, each epimere increases in thickness and becomes segmented into small oblong blocks of cells called **somites** (figs. 231N; 233B; 234D; 245A). A somite which forms in the epimere on one side of the notochord always has a corresponding somite in the epimere on the other side of the notochord. Somites thus form in pairs, *each pair representing a primitive segment of the developing body*. This primitive segmentation is a fundamental characteristic of the vertebrate body. It begins in the general area of the anterior trunk and posterior hindbrain region of the embryo. In the chick embryo (see Patterson, '07), the most anterior segment forms first, and later segmentation progresses in a caudal direction. This probably holds true for most other vertebrates. However, in elasmobranch fishes, segmentation of the epimeric mesoderm also extends forward from the hindbrain area into the head region presenting a continuous series of somites from the eye region caudally into the tail (fig. 217D). (Study figs. 217D, 230D.) Segmentation of epimeric mesoderm appears in the head region of *Amphibia*. In many higher vertebrates, three pairs of somitic condensations appear in the area just caudal to the eye but at a slightly later period of development than that of the elasmobranch fishes (fig. 217D–F).

2) Mesomere. The narrow longitudinal band of mesoderm, adjoining the lateral border of the epimere, is the **mesomere** (figs. 221F, G; 230D; 234E, F). This mesoderm ultimately gives origin to much of the excretory (kidney) tissue and ducts and to certain of the reproductive ducts of many vertebrates. (See Chap. 18.) Because of the origin of nephric tissue from its substance, this longitudinal band of mesoderm generally is referred to as the **urogenital or nephrotomic mesoderm.** Synonymous terms often used are **intermediate mesoderm or intermediate cell mass.** The mesomere undergoes a segmentation similar to the epimeric area in its more anterior portion where the pronephric kidney develops in higher vertebrates, while in lower vertebrates, such as the shark embryo, it may be more extensively segmented.

3) Hypomere. The remainder of the mesoderm which extends lateroventrally from the mesomere forms the **hypomere or hypomeric mesoderm.** It also is called the **lateral plate mesoderm or lateral plate mesoblast.** This portion of the mesoderm does not become segmented in present-day vertebrates. (Compare with the condition in *Amphioxus* described on p. 505.)

b. Tubulation of the Mesodermal Areas

Coincident with the formation of the somites, a cavity begins to appear within the mesoderm. This cavity or primitive coelomic space separates the mesoderm into two layers, an outer layer near the ectoderm and an inner layer close to the neural, notochordal, and entodermal cells. This hollowing process within the mesodermal layer is known as **coelom formation or tubulation of the mesoderm.** In many embryos of the lower vertebrates, there is a strong tendency for the coelomic space to form throughout the entire lateral mass of mesoderm from the epimeric area ventrad into the lateral plate mesoderm. For example, in elasmobranch (shark) embryos of about 3 to 4 mm. in length and also in many early post-gastrular amphibia, the following features of the primitive coelom are found in the trunk region of each mesodermal mass:

(1) The mesoderm possesses a cavity, continuous dorso-ventrally from the epimere into the lateral plate (figs. 217G, H; 221E). When the epimere (and to some extent the nephrotomic region as well) under-

goes segmentation, the coelomic space within these areas becomes segregated within the segments and, thus, is present in a discontinuous condition.

(2) The early coelomic cavity in the shark and amphibian embryo, therefore, may be divided into three parts: (a) the **myocoelic** portion within the epimeric mesoderm, (b) the **nephrocoel** within the nephrotomic mesoderm, and (c) the **splanchnocoel** contained within the hypomeric or lateral plate mesoderm. *While the myocoelic and nephrocoelic regions of the primitive coelom may become segmented and discontinuous, that within the splanchnocoel is continuous antero-posteriorly in the trunk region.*

The coelomic cavities contained within the somites of the shark and amphibian embryo are soon lost. The coelomic cavity or nephrocoel within the nephrotome is concerned with the development of the lumen within the tubules and ducts of the excretory (urinary) system, while the splanchnocoels give origin to the **coelomic cavity proper of the adult.** The lateral wall of the splanchnocoel near the primitive epidermis is known as the **somatopleural mesoderm,** and the inner or medial wall associated with the gut tube and developing heart tissues constitutes the **splanchnopleural layer.** The epidermis and somatopleural mesoderm together form the **somatopleure,** while the entoderm and splanchnopleural mesoderm form the **splanchnopleure.**

In the embryos of higher vertebrates, the coelomic space of the somitic portion of the primitive coelom (i.e., the myocoels) is less pronounced and appears somewhat later in development than in the shark and amphibian embryo, but it does tend to appear. This is true also of the nephrocoel or coelomic cavity within the nephrotome. (See Chap. 18.) The coelomic condition or splanchnocoel within the hypomere forms similarly in all vertebrates. These matters will be described more in detail in Chapter 20.

C. Notochordal Area

The notochord is the elongated, median band of cells of the gastrula which lies between the two mesodermal areas. The notochord thus may be regarded as a specialized, median portion of the middle germ layer of mesodermal tissue. During gastrulation and shortly after, there may be a tendency for the notochordal material in certain forms to canalize or tubulate. Later, the notochordal material becomes converted into a definite rod of notochordal cells which represents the primitive skeletal axis of the embryo. The notochord and its relation to the early skeletal system are discussed in Chapter 15.

D. Lateral Constrictive Movements

While the neural, epidermal, and entodermal tubulations are in progress, a lateral constriction or invagination of the body wall occurs on either side in all vertebrate embryos from the fishes to the mammals. These constrictions are effected at the level of the notochord and lower margin of the somitic area from the anterior trunk region caudally into the tail. As a result, a transverse section of the early vertebrate body appears pyriform or pear shaped, with the neck of the pear directed dorsally (fig. 241C). The **constriction line** is shown typically in the developing embryo of *Necturus* (fig. 227) where it extends from the lower aspect of the head outgrowth along the lower boundary of the somitic area to the base of the tail. A line, drawn across the body from the general area of the two lateral constrictions and passing through the notochord, divides the embryonic body into an upper or **epaxial** (epiaxial) **region** above the level of the notochord and a lower or **hypaxial** (hypoaxial) **region** below the level of the notochord.

E. Tubulation of the Neural, Epidermal, Entodermal, and Mesodermal, Organ-forming Areas in *Amphioxus*

1. COMPARISON OF THE PROBLEMS OF TUBULATION IN THE EMBRYO OF *Amphioxus* WITH THAT OF THE EMBRYOS IN THE SUBPHYLUM *Vertebrata*

a. End-bud Growth

In *Amphioxus,* the procedures involved in tubulation of the major organ-forming areas and development of primitive body form differ from those in the vertebrate group. For example, in the latter group, the basic rudiments of the head, pharyngeal, trunk, and tail regions appear to be well established at the end of gastrulation. During tubulation of the major organ-forming areas, these subregions become extended in an antero-posterior direction and the rudiments of specific structures begin to express themselves. This is especially true of the head, pharyngeal, and trunk regions. The vertebrate tail, however, arises from an end-bud tissue which progressively lays down the various parts of the tail by means of a proliferative growth in the caudal direction. On the other hand, in *Amphioxus,* only a small portion of the anterior end of the future body is laid down during gastrulation. Further development of the epidermal, neural, enteric, and mesodermal cellular areas together with the notochord are dependent upon cell proliferation at the caudal end of the late gastrula and later embryo. Much of the body of *Amphioxus,* therefore, is formed by a caudal proliferative growth of end-bud cells, somewhat comparable to the end-bud growth of the tail in the vertebrate group.

b. Position Occupied by the Notochord and Mesoderm at the End of Gastrulation

A second feature of difference in the developing embryo of *Amphioxus* from that of the vertebrate embryo lies in the arrangement of the notochord-mesoderm complex of cells in the late gastrula. In the late gastrula of

Amphioxus, this potential, third germ layer forms a part of the entodermal roof, although the studies of Conklin ('32) have demonstrated that notochord and mesoderm are distinct cellular entities even in the blastula. In contrast to this condition, the notochord and the mesoderm already are segregated as a middle germ layer between the ectoderm and the entoderm in the late vertebrate gastrula. The gastrula of *Amphioxus,* therefore, has the added problem of segregating the notochordal and mesodermal cells from the entoderm during tubulation of the major organ-forming areas.

2. Neuralization and the Closure of the Blastopore

In the late gastrula of *Amphioxus,* a longitudinal middorsal plate of cells, the **neural plate,** elaborated by cell division and extension during gastrulation, represents the future central nervous system (fig. 247E). As the period of gastrulation comes to its end, the blastopore decreases greatly in size (fig. 247A–D). The archenteric opening also moves dorsally, coincident with a shifting of the caudal end of the archenteron in such a way that it projects in a dorso-caudal direction (figs. 189G, H; 247H). This movement of the archenteron is associated with the migration of the mass of mesodermal cells from the two lateral areas of the blastoporal lips (fig. 247A, B) to the dorso-medial portion of the blastopore (fig. 247C), where the mesoderm comes to lie on either side of the notochord below the neural plate (fig. 247C). As these changes occur, the dorsal area of the gastrula near the blastopore becomes flattened with a subsequent depression of the neural plate (fig. 247C, D). In sagittal section, the gastrula now appears oval in shape and considerably elongated in the antero-posterior direction (fig. 189G, H); in transverse view, it is triangular, especially at the caudal end (fig. 247D).

As the above changes are brought about, the ectoderm of the ventral lip of the blastopore grows dorsad, while that of the lateral lips grows mediad. In this way, the opening of the blastopore is closed by the coming together and fusion of these ectodermal (epidermal) growths (fig. 247D–F). However, the archenteron does not lose its connection, at this time, with the outside environment of the embryo for two reasons.

(1) As observed above, the caudal end of the archenteron previously had shifted in such a manner that it now projects dorso-caudally; and

(2) synchronized with the epidermal growth which closes the blastoporal opening (fig. 248A), the neural plate sinks downward, becoming detached along its margin from the epidermal area (fig. 248B–D).

The downward sinking of the neural plate and its detachment from the epidermal layer begins at the dorsal lip of the blastopore and spreads anteriad. (Compare fig. 248D with 248B and C.) Consequently, as the epidermal growth along the lateral lips of the blastopore reaches the area of the sinking neural

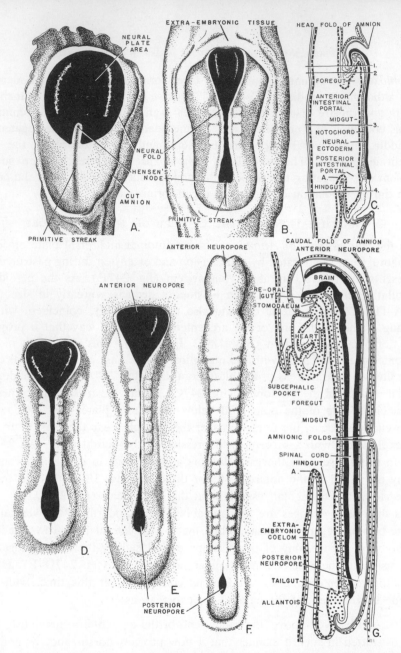

FIG. 242. Early development of the pig embryo (B, C, and G from Patten: *Embryology of the Pig,* Philadelphia, Blakiston; A is from Streeter: Carnegie Inst. Publ. No. 380, Contrib. to Embryol. 100; D, E, and F from Heuser and Streeter: Carnegie Inst. Publ. No. 394, Contrib. to Embryol. 109. All figures have been modified). (A) Early, neural groove stage. Neural area is shown in black; amnion is cut away as indicated. (B) Four-somite stage. (C) Median sagittal section, approximating the stage of development shown in (B). Observe foregut, midgut, and hindgut areas. (D) Embryo of about six pairs of somites. (E) Embryo of about 7 to 8 pairs of somites. (F) Eighteen pairs of somites. (G) Sagittal sectional diagram of embryo slightly younger than (F), showing neural and gut tubes, amnion, allantois, and forming heart.

plate in the region of the dorsal blastoporal lip, it continues forward along the epidermal margins of the insinking neural plate, growing mesad and fusing in the midline over the neural plate (fig. 247E–G). In this way, the epidermal growth forms a covering for the neural plate. It follows, therefore, that the posterior end of the archenteron will now open into the space between the neural plate and its epidermal covering. This new passageway between the epidermal-neural plate cavity and the archenteron is the beginning of the **neurenteric canal** (figs. 247H; 248A).

The flattened neural plate, canopied by the epidermal overgrowth, then begins to fold itself into the form of a tube. In doing so, its lateral edges swing gradually toward the middorsal line, as shown in figure 195. The actual grooving and tubulation of the neural plate starts at a point about midway along the embryo at the stage of development shown in figure 247F. It proceeds anteriorly and posteriorly from this point. At its extreme anterior end, the neural tube remains open to the surface as the **anterior neuropore** (figs. 247H; 249A–D). Eventually the caudal end of the neural plate becomes tubulated, and a definite canal is formed, connecting neural and enteric tubes. This canal is the **neurenteric canal.** The neurenteric canal disappears between the stage of development shown in figure 249C and that shown in figure 249D. The continued caudal growth of the neural tube is accomplished by cell proliferation from the posterior end of the tube and neurenteric canal area.

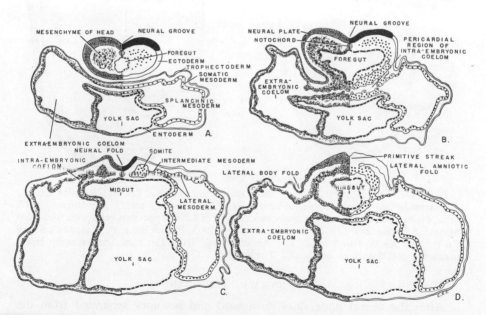

FIG. 243. Sections of pig embryo of about stage shown in fig. 242 (B) and (C). (Modified from Patten: *Embryology of the Pig,* 3d Ed., Philadelphia, Blakiston, '48.) (A) Line 1, fig. 242C.   (B) Line 2, fig. 242C.   (C) Line 3, fig. 242C.   (D) Line 4, fig. 242C.

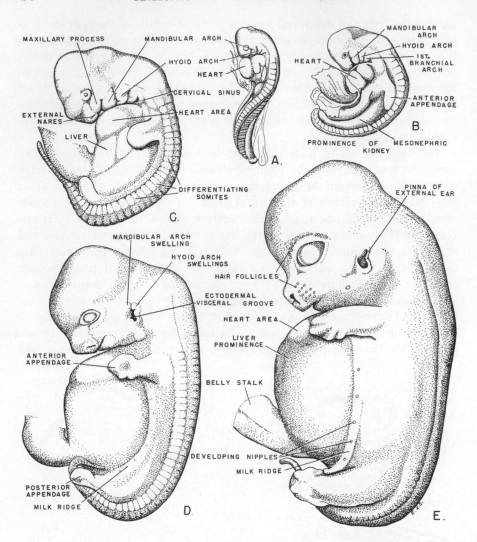

FIG. 244. Development of body form in the pig embryo. (A and B from Keibel: *Normentafel zur Entwicklungsgeschichte des Schweines (Sus scrofa domesticus)*. 1897. Jena, G. Fischer. C, D, and E slightly modified from Keibel, previous reference, and from Minot: *A Laboratory Text-book of Embryology*. 1903. Philadelphia, P. Blakiston's Son & Co.) (A) About 4 to 5 mm. (B) About 6 mm. (C) Ten mm. (crown-rump measurement). (D) Fifteen mm. (E) Twenty mm.

3. Epidermal Tubulation

After the neural plate sinks downward and becomes separated from the outside epidermis, the medial growth of the epidermis over the neural plate completes the middorsal area of the primitive epidermal tube (fig. 247E–H). It then comes to enclose the entire complex of growing and elongating neural,

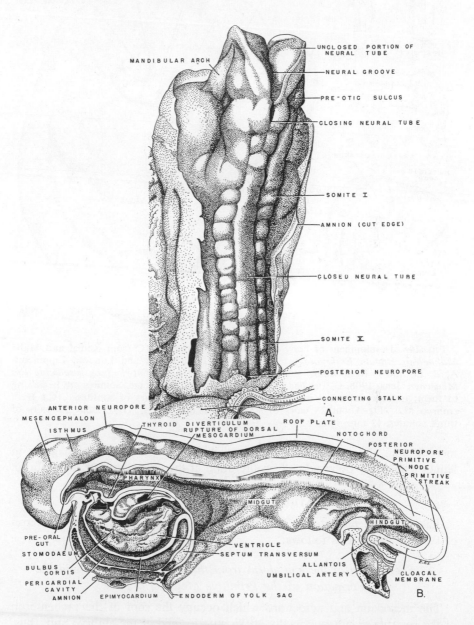

FIG. 245. Human embryo of ten somites. (After G. W. Corner: Contrib. to Embryol. Carnegie Inst., Washington, Publ. No. 394, 112.) (A) Dorsal view. (B) Median, sagittal section of model.

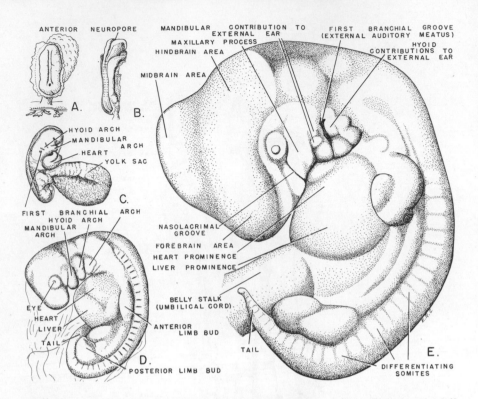

Fig. 246. Development of body form in human embryo. (C from Keibel and Mall: *Manual of Human Embryology,* Vol. I, 1910. Philadelphia and London, Lippincott. A, B, D, and E from Keibel and Elze: *Normentafel zur Entwicklungsgeschichte des Menschen.* Jena, 1908. G. Fischer.) (A) Early neural fold stage. Somites are beginning to form; notochordal canal is evident. (B) About nine pairs of somites. (C) His's embryo M. (D) About 23 pairs of somites, 4-5 mm. long. (E) About 35 pairs of trunk somites, 12 mm. long.

mesodermal, and entodermal tubes and with them it continues to grow in length principally by rapid cell proliferation at the caudal end of the embryo.

4. Tubulation of the Entodermal Area

The primitive metenteron of *Amphioxus* is derived from the archenteron of the late gastrula as follows.

a. Segregation of the Entoderm from the Chordamesoderm and the Formation of the Primitive Metenteric Tube

The mesoderm and notochord which occupy the roof of the archenteron of the gastrula evaginate dorsally at the anterior end of the embryo and, thus, become separated from the entoderm. (Compare fig. 195 with fig. 250A.) This separation of notochord and mesoderm by dorsal evagination from the entoderm continues slowly in a caudal direction from the anterior end until an embryonic condition is reached approximating about 13 to 14 pairs of mesodermal segments. At this level, the notochord and mesoderm become completely separated from the entoderm. As a result, the enteric or gut tube from this point in its growth posteriad is a separate entity. (See tubulation of mesoderm on p. 505. Anterior to the fourteenth somite, after the notochord and mesoderm separate from the entoderm, the latter grows medially from either side to complete the entodermal roof below the evaginated notochord and mesoderm (fig. 250A). A primitive metenteric tube thus is formed, as shown in figure 249C, whose only opening is that which leads by way of the neurenteric canal (fig. 249A, C) into the neurocoel of the neural tube and from thence to the outside through the anterior neuropore.

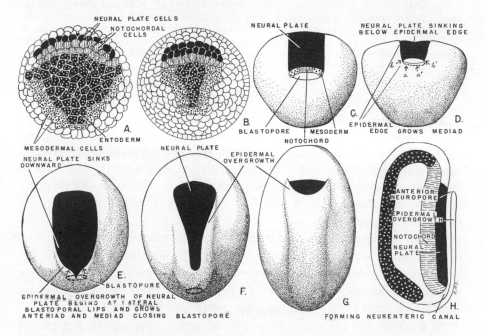

FIG. 247. Closure of the blastopore and epidermal overgrowth of neural plate in *Amphioxus* (original diagrams, based on data supplied by Conklin, '32). (A) Vegetal pole view of early stage of gastrulation, showing general areas occupied by notochordal, entodermal, and mesodermal cells. (B) Same view of gastrula, one hour later, showing triangular form of blastopore. (C) Posterior view of late gastrula. Blastopore is now ovoid in shape and dorsally placed. Gastrula is triangular in transverse section with dorsal surface flattened. (D) Same view, later. Slight epidermal upgrowth, indicated by arrows (a and a') merges with ingrowing epidermal edges along lateral lips of blastopore (b and b') which spreads along epidermal edges of neural plate. (E) Dorsal view a brief period later than (D). Epidermal ingrowth from lateral blastoporal lips is now closing the blastoporal opening, shown in broken lines, and also is proceeding craniad along edges of sinking neural plate. (See fig. 248.) (F, G) Later stages of epidermal overgrowth of neural plate. (H) Sagittal section of (G).

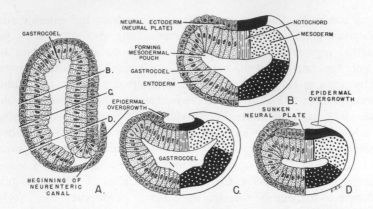

FIG. 248. Sinking of neural plate and epidermal overgrowth of neural plate in *Amphioxus*. (Slightly modified from Conklin, '32.)　(A) Sagittal section of embryo comparable to that shown in fig. 247F.　(B, C, D) Sections through embryo as shown by lines B, C, D, respectively, on (A). Observe that the neural plate begins to sink downward from region of closed blastopore and proceeds forward from this point.

b. Formation of the Mouth, Anus, and Other Specialized Structures of the Metenteron

At the anterior end of the metenteron, a broad, dorsal outgrowth occurs which continues up on either side of the notochord and becomes divided into **right and left dorsal diverticula** (fig. 249B, H). The left diverticulum remains small and thick-walled and later fuses with an ectodermal invagination to form the **pre-oral pit,** described as a sense organ. The right diverticulum, however, increases greatly in size, becomes thin-walled, and gives origin to the so-called **head cavity.**

The **mouth** develops at a time when the larva acquires about 16 to 18 pairs of mesodermal segments or somites (fig. 249D). It appears when the overlying epidermis about halfway up on the left side of the body fuses with the entoderm, a fusion which occurs just posterior to the forming pre-oral pit (left diverticulum). (See black oval fig. 249D, and fig. 249F.)

At the time that the mouth forms, the entoderm opposite the first pair of somites pushes ventrally and fuses with the ectoderm. This area of fusion finally perforates and forms the **first gill slit.** The gill slit, once formed, moves up on the right side of the body (fig. 249E). The entodermal area from which the first and later gill slits make their appearance is known as the **branchial rudiment** (fig. 249D).

At the caudal end of the larva, following the degeneration of the neurenteric canal, a small area of entoderm fuses with the ectoderm and forms the **anal opening.** The **anus** is first ventral in position, but later moves up to the left side as the caudal fin develops (fig. 249E, G).

5. TUBULATION OF THE MESODERM

Tubulation of the mesoderm and the formation of a continuous antero-posterior coelom in *Amphioxus* differs considerably from that found in the subphylum *Vertebrata*. This fact becomes evident in tracing the history of the mesoderm from the time of its segregation from the entoderm of the late

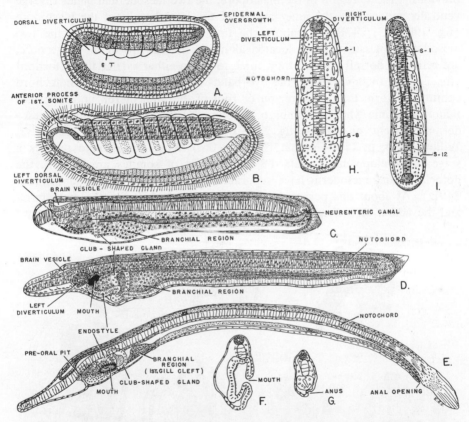

FIG. 249. Various stages of development of *Amphioxus*. (A from Kellicott, '13, and Conklin, '32; B from Kellicott, '13, slightly modified; C–I, slightly modified from Conklin, '32.) (A) Six-somite stage, comparable to fig. 247G and H. The animal hatches about the time that two pairs of somites are present. (B) Nine-somite stage. The larva at this stage swims by means of cilia which clothe the entire ectodermal surface. (C) About fourteen pairs of somites are present at this stage. Neurenteric canal is still patent. (D) About 16 to 18 pairs of somites. Neurenteric canal is degenerating; mouth is formed. (E) About 20 to 22 pairs of somites. Anal opening is established between this stage and that shown in (D). (F) Transverse section, showing oral opening, looking from anterior end of animal. (G) Same through anal area. (H) Frontal section of a 24-hour larva near dorsal side showing notochord, somites (S-1, S-8, etc.) and undifferentiated tissue at caudal end. Neural tube shown at anterior end. Nine pairs of somites are present. (I) Frontal section of a 38-hour larva at the level of the notochord showing section through the neural tube at the anterior and posterior ends, i.e., in region where larva bends ventralwards. Thirteen pairs of somites are present with muscle fibrillae along the mesial borders of the somites.

gastrula and later embryo to the stage where a continuous antero-posterior coelomic space is formed, comparable to that found in the vertebrates.

The mesoderm of the late gastrula of *Amphioxus* is present as a dorso-median band of cells on either side of the notochord, and together with the notochord, occupies the dorsal area or roof of the archenteron as mentioned previously. In the region of the blastopore, the two mesodermal bands diverge ventrally and occupy the inner aspect of the lateral walls of the blastopore (fig. 190F, G; 247B). At about the time of blastoporal closure, the two mesodermal masses of cells, located along the lateral lips of the blastopore, are retracted dorsally, where they come to lie on either side of the notochord (fig. 247C). In this position the two bands of mesoderm and the notochord continue to form the dorsal region or roof of the archenteron until approximately the time when the embryo is composed of 13 to 14 pairs of mesodermal segments or somites (fig. 249C). (See Hatschek, 1893, pp. 131, 132; Willey, 1894, p. 115; Conklin, '32, p. 106.) When the embryo reaches a stage of development wherein 15 to 16 pairs of somites are present, the notochord and mesoderm have separated entirely from the entoderm (fig. 249D). At about this period the **neurenteric canal** between the metenteron and the neural tube disappears (fig. 249C, D).

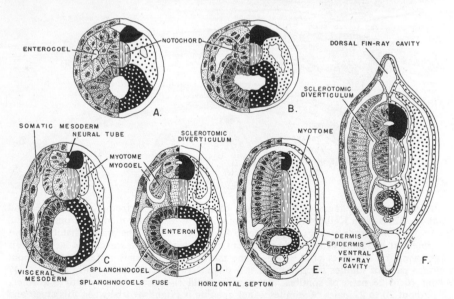

Fɪɢ. 250. Differentiation of somites in *Amphioxus*. (A and B from Conklin, '32; C, E, and F after Hatschek, 1888 and 1893; D from MacBride, 1898; all figures are modified.) (A) Somites shortly after separation from entoderm. (B) Later stage, the somites grow ventrally. (C) Somitic wall begins to differentiate into a thickened, dorsal, myotomic area, located near notochord and neural tube, and thinner somatic and visceral areas. (D) Horizontal septum formed which separates dorso-myotomic portion of somite from splanchnocoelic area below. (E, F) Later stages in differentiation of myotome and myocoelic diverticulum. (See text.)

The formation of a continuous, antero-posterior, coelomic cavity in *Amphioxus* may be described as follows. The **mesodermal bands** on either side of the notochord of the post-gastrular embryo become converted into **mesodermal grooves** as each mesodermal band folds inwards or evaginates into the residual blastocoelic space between the archenteron and the outside ectoderm (fig. 195). Beginning at the anterior end, these longitudinal grooves of mesoderm soon become divided into distinct segments or **somites** by the appearance of transverse divisions (fig. 249A, B, H). The first and second pairs of somites are formed at the anterior ends of the mesodermal grooves at about the time that the embryo hatches and swims about by means of ciliary action.

Eventually each somite becomes entirely constricted from the notochord and entoderm. In this segregated condition the somite forms a rounded structure retaining within itself a portion of the original archenteric cavity (fig. 250A). Hence, the cavity within the somite is called an **enterocoel** and represents the beginnings of the coelomic cavity of later development, at least in the anterior 13 or 14 pairs of somites. (*Note:* It is to be observed in this connection that the primitive somite in *Amphioxus* is not comparable to the primitive somite of the vertebrate embryo. In the latter, the somite represents merely a segment of the epimeric mesoderm, whereas in *Amphioxus* it is the entire mesoderm in each half of a particular segment of the embryo.)

After hatching, the mesodermal bands continue to form into grooves as the embryo elongates, and, synchronously, successive pairs of somites are formed. At about the time 8 to 10 pairs of somites are present (fig. 249B, H), the **enterocoels** of the first two pairs of somites have become entirely separated from the archenteron. The enterocoels of the following six pairs of somites are small and are not as evident at first as those of the first two pairs. Ultimately a definite enterocoel is found, however, in each somite.

Posterior to the eighth or ninth pairs of somites, the forming mesodermal grooves do not show the enterocoelic pouches as plainly as the more anterior somites. Slit-like mesodermal grooves tend to be present, however, and, when the somite is entirely free from the archenteron, this slit-like cavity expands into the enterocoelic space of the somite. As the region of the fourteenth pair of somites is approached, the slit-like mesodermal groove becomes more and more indefinite. Posterior to the fourteenth or fifteenth pair of somites, the somites originate from a solid mesodermal band on either side of the notochord. An enterocoelic origin of the cavity within each somite, therefore, is not possible caudal to this area, and the coelomic space arises by a hollowing-out process similar to coelomic cavity formation in the vertebrate group.

At about the time when eight pairs of somites are established, a shift of the mesoderm on either side of the embryo produces a condition wherein the somites of either side may be slightly intersegmental in relation to the somites on the other side (fig. 249H).

During its later development, each somite grows ventrally (fig. 250B). That portion of the somite contiguous to the notochord and neural tube thickens and forms the **myotome.** The region of the somite near the epidermal ectoderm is called the **somatic or parietal mesoderm,** while that associated with the entoderm forms the **visceral or splanchnic mesoderm** (fig. 250C).

As the myotome enlarges, the coelomic space becomes more and more displaced ventrally, and most of it comes to lie on either side of the enteron (metenteron). (See fig. 250D.) This ventral coelomic space forms the **splanchnocoel,** while the dorsal space, lateral to the **myotome,** is known as the **myocoel.** Eventually, the splanchnocoels of each pair of somites push ventrally to the lower portion of the enteron, where they ultimately fuse (fig. 250D–F). Gradually the splanchnocoels of each segment fuse antero-posteriorly and in this way a **continuous, antero-posterior, splanchnocoelic space below and around the gut tube** is formed. **Tubulation** or the formation of a continuous, antero-posterior, coelomic cavity thus is effected by **fusion of the splanchnocoels** of the respective somites on either side (fig. 250F). A horizontal septum, the **intercoelomic membrane** also appears, separating the myocoels above from the splanchnocoelic cavity below (fig. 250D).

6. Later Differentiation of the Myotomic (Dorsal) Area of the Somite

While the above events are taking place in the ventral portion of the somite, the upper, **myotomic region** undergoes profound modification.

As shown in figure 250D, the myotomic portion of the somite has two unequally developed areas:

(1) a medial muscular portion, the **myotome** and
(2) the laterally placed, thin-walled, parietal part which surrounds the coelomic space, or **myocoel.**

The muscular portion enlarges rapidly and, as seen in figure 250E and F, forms the **muscle plate or myotome of the adult.** These muscle plates very early assume the typical > shape characteristic of the adult. On the other hand, the myocoelic portion contributes important **connective or skeletal tissue** to the framework of the body. In each segment, the wall of the myocoel gives origin to three diverticula as follows:

(a) a **lower sclerotomic diverticulum,**
(b) a **ventral diverticulum,** and
(c) a **dorsal sclerotomic diverticulum.**

The **lower sclerotomic diverticulum** (fig. 250D, E) extends up between the myotome and the medially placed notochord and nerve cord, as diagrammed in figure 250F. Its walls differentiate into two parts:

(1) an inner layer which, together with a similar contribution from the somite on the opposite side, wraps around the notochord and nerve cord and, subsequently, gives origin to a **skeletogenous sheath of connective tissue** which enswathes these structures; and

(2) an outer layer which covers the mesial (inner) aspect of the myotome with a **fascia or connective tissue covering.**

The outer surface of the myotome does not have a covering of fascia.

The **ventral diverticulum** extends between the lateral wall of the splanchnocoel and the epidermal layer of the body wall (fig. 250E, F) and separates the parietal wall of the splanchnocoel from the epidermal wall (fig. 250F). This ventral diverticulum or **dermatomic fold,** together with the external or parietal wall of the myocoel above, forms the **dermatome.** The inner and outer layers of the ventral diverticulum gradually fuse to form the cutis or dermal layer of the integument or skin in the ventro-lateral portion of the body, whereas the parietal wall of the myocoel above gives origin to the same dermal layer in the body region lateral to the myotome. The **dorsal sclerotomic diverticula** form the **fin-ray cavities** in the dorsal fin. These cavities become entirely isolated from the rest of the myocoelic spaces. Several **fin-ray cavities** occupy the breadth of a single myotome. The dorsal myotomic portion of the somite thus differentiates into three main structural parts:

(a) the muscular **myotome,**
(b) the mesial **sclerotome** or skeletogenous tissue, and
(c) the latero-ventral **dermatome** or dermal tissue of the skin.

7. NOTOCHORD

The notochord arises as a middorsal evagination of the primitive archenteron up to about the stage of about 13 to 14 pairs of somites (fig. 195). Posterior to this region it takes its origin by proliferative growth from a separate mass of notochordal tissue, lying above the gut and between the two mesodermal masses of cells. Its origin posterior to the general area of the thirteenth to fourteenth body segments, therefore, has no relation to the entoderm. It rapidly develops into a conspicuous skeletal rod, lying below the neural tube and between the mesodermal somites and resting in a slight depression along the dorsal aspect of the metenteron or entodermal tubulation (fig. 249E, H). It continues forward in the head region, anterior to the brain portion of the neural tube (fig. 249E).

(The student is referred to the following references for further details relative to the early development of *Amphioxus:* Cerfontaine, '06; Conklin, '32;

Hatschek, 1893; Kellicott, '13; MacBride, 1898, '00, '10; Morgan and Hazen, '00; and Willey, 1894.)

F. Early Development of the Rudiments of Vertebrate Paired Appendages

Two pairs of appendages, placed at the anterior (pectoral) and posterior (pelvic) extremities of the trunk, are common to all vertebrate groups. However, all vertebrates do not possess two pairs of paired appendages. Certain lizards of the genera *Pygopus* and *Pseudopus* have only a posterior pair of appendages, while in certain other vertebrates the opposite condition is found, the anterior pair being present without posterior appendages. The latter condition is found in certain teleost and ganoid fishes; the amphibian, *Siren lacertina;* the lizard, *Chirotes;* and among the mammals, the *Sirenia and Cetacea*. Again, some vertebrates are entirely apodal, e.g., cyclostomatous fishes and most snakes, although the boa constrictors and pythons possess a pair of rudimentary posterior appendages embedded in the skin and body wall. Some have rudimentary appendages only in the embryo, as the legless amphibians of the order *Gymnophiona,* and certain lizards. Consequently, the presence of embryonic rudiments of the paired appendages is a variable feature when the entire group of vertebrates is considered.

The rudiments of the paired appendages also are variable, relative to the time of their appearance in the vertebrate group as a whole. They are more constant in the *Amniota,* i.e., reptiles, birds, and mammals, in time of appearance than in the *Anamniota,* i.e., fishes and amphibia. In the reptiles, birds, and mammals, the limb buds arise when primitive body form is being evolved. In the anuran amphibia, the anterior rudiments may appear and go on to a high degree of differentiation before the appearance of the posterior pair of appendages. For example, in the frog, *Rana pipiens,* the posterior limb buds first make their appearance a brief period before the beginning of metamorphosis of the tadpole into the adult form. However, the anterior limb buds differentiate earlier but remain concealed beneath the operculum until they become visible during the later stages of metamorphosis. In urodele amphibia, the fore limb bud is not covered by an operculum, and it is visible at the time of its initial appearance which occurs before the hind limb rudiment arises (fig. 227J–L).

In the majority of vertebrates, the limb rudiment first makes its appearance as an *elongated, dorso-ventrally flattened fold of the epidermis, containing a mass of mesodermal cells within,* as shown, for example, in the chick and mammalian embryos (figs. 240, 244, 246). The contained mesodermal cells may be in the form of epithelial muscle buds derived directly from the myotomes (e.g., sharks) or as a mass of mesenchyme (chick, pig, human). (See Chap. 16.) The early limb-bud fold may be greatly exaggerated in certain elasmobranch fishes, as in the rays, where the anterior and posterior fin folds fuse together for a time, forming one continuous lateral body fold. On the other hand, in the lungfishes (the *Dipnoi*) and in amphibia (the *Anura* and *Urodela*), the appendage makes its first appearance, not as an elongated fold of the lateral body wall, flattened dorso-ventrally, but as a rounded, knob-like projection of the lateral body surface (fig. 227K–M).

G. The Limb Bud as an Illustration of the Field Concept of Development in Relation to the Gastrula and the Tubulated Embryo

In Chapter 9 it was observed that the major presumptive organ-forming areas are subdivided into many local, organ-forming areas at the end of gastrulation. In the neural and epidermal areas, this subdivision occurs during gastrulation through influences associated with **local inductive action.** At the end of the gastrular period, therefore, each local area within the major organ-forming area possesses the tendency to give origin to a specific organ or a part of an organ. The restricted, localized areas within each major organ-forming area represent the **individual, or specific, organ-forming fields.** During tubulation, the major organ-forming areas with their individuated, organ-forming fields are molded into tubes, and, thus, the individual fields become arranged along each tube. Consequently, *each tube possesses a series of individual, organ-forming areas or fields, distributed antero-posteriorly along the tube.*

As a result of the close association of cells and substances during gastrulation and tubulation, many specific organ-forming fields *are related to more than one of the body tubes. Specific organ-forming fields, therefore, may have intertubular relationships.* For example, the **lens field** is located in the epidermal tube, but, in many species, its origin as a lens field is dependent upon influences emanating from the **optic vesicle of the neural tube** (see Chap. 19). Another example of an association between the parts of two contiguous tubes is the limb-bud field in the urodele, *Ambystoma punctatum.* As the limb-bud field in this species illustrates various aspects and properties of an organ-forming field, it will be described below in some detail.

The presumptive anterior limb disc or limb field of *Ambystoma* is determined as a specific limb-forming area in the middle gastrular stage (Detwiler, '29, '33). Later on in the embryo, it occupies a circular-shaped area within trunk segments three to six. According to Harrison ('18) and Swett ('23), its properties as a field mainly are resident in the cells of the somatic layer of the mesoderm in this area. If, for example, the somatic layer of mesoderm in this area is transplanted to another area, a well-developed limb will result. Also, the mesoderm of the dorsal half of the field forms a greater part of the limb than the other parts, with the anterior half of the limb disc next in importance. It appears, therefore, that the limb-forming potencies are greatest in the dorso-anterior half of the limb field and become less postero-ventrally. Moreover, not "all of the cells which are potentially limb forming go into the limb" (Swett, '23). As demonstrated by Harrison ('18) half discs (half fields), left intact in the developing embryo or removed and transplanted to other areas, develop into normal limbs.

The above experiments of Harrison, together with those of Detwiler ('29, '33) suggest that while the limb field is irreversibly determined at an early stage to form limb tissue, the exact determination of the various parts within the field is absent at the earlier phases of development. One kind of precise determination is present, however, for the first digit-radial aspect (i.e., the pre-axial aspect) of the limb appears to arise only from the anterior end of the field, whether the field is allowed to develop intact or is split into two parts. That is, if it is split into two portions, the anterior extremity of the posterior portion, as well as the original anterior part of the limb field, develops the pre-axial aspect of the limb. This antero-posterior polarization is present from the first period of field determination. On the other hand, the dorso-ventral polarity is not so determined; for if the transplanted limb disc is rotated 180 degrees (i.e., if it is removed and reimplanted in its normal place dorsal side down) it will develop a limb with the dorsal side up but with the antero-posterior axis reversed (Harrison, '21). In these cases the first digit-radial aspect will appear ventral in position. This result indicates that the pre-axial aspect of the limb becomes oriented always toward the ventral aspect of the limb. However, the experiments of Swett ('37, '39, '41) tend to show that the reversal of the dorso-ventral axis occurs only when implanted *below the myotomes;* for when the rotated limb field is implanted in the somitic (myotomic) area, it will remain inverted. Factors other than those resident within the limb field itself, probably factors in the flank area, appear thus to **induce** the normal dorso-ventral axis when the limb disc is implanted in its normal site.

In the descriptions given above, the importance of the somatic layer of mesoderm as the seat of the limb-forming factors is emphasized. It is obvious, however, that the epidermal covering of the limbs derived from the epidermal tubulation also is important in limb formation. For example, epidermal importance is suggested by the experiments of Saunders ('49) on the developing limb bud of the chick wherein it was found that the **apical ridge of ectoderm,** located at the apex of the early limb bud, is essential for normal limb development.

Individual, or specific, organ-forming fields which appear in the gastrula and early tubulated embryo thus are generalized areas determined to form individual organs. As development proceeds, two main limitations are imposed upon the field:

(1) The cellular contribution of the field actually entering into the organ becomes restricted; and

(2) specific parts of the field become progressively determined to form specific parts of the organ.

It is obvious, therefore, that the fields of influence which govern the development of specific organs may be much more extensive in cellular area than the actual cellular contributions which take part in the formation of the specific organ structures. Experiments on the forming limb of *Ambystoma* also have demonstrated that a particular area of the field is stronger in its limb-forming potencies than other regions of the field. This property probably is true of other fields as well.

(For a detailed discussion of the field concept in embryonic development, reference should be made to Huxley and DeBeer, '34, Chaps. 8 and 9; Weiss, '39, p. 289 ff.)

H. Cephalic Flexion and General Body Bending and Rotation in Vertebrate Embryos

The anterior end of the neural tubulation is prone to assume a bent or flexed contour whereby the anterior end of the neural tube is directed downward toward the ventral aspect of the embryo. This general behavior pattern is strong in vertebrate embryos with the exception of the teleost fishes. In teleost fishes this bending habit is slight. As the later development of the head progresses in other vertebrate embryos, the neural tube shows a pronounced **cephalic (cranial) flexure** in the region of the midbrain, in some species more than in others. (See Chap. 19.) An additional bending occurs in the posterior hindbrain area. The latter flexure is the **cervical or nuchal flexure** (figs. 231, 238, 240, 244, 246).

Aside from the acute bending which takes place in the formation of the cephalic and the nuchal flexures, there is a definite tendency for many vertebrate embryos to undergo a **general body bending,** with the result that the anterior part of the body and the caudal portion of the trunk and tail may be depressed in a ventral direction (figs. 222C–E; 227; 229F; 238; 240; 244; 246). In the frog embryo, at hatching, the opposite tendency may prevail for a brief period, and the dorsal trunk region may appear sagging or hollowed (fig. 226A, C).

In addition to these bending movements, in the embryos of higher vertebrates, a rotation or twisting (torsion) of the developing body along the antero-posterior axis is evident. In the chick embryo, for example, the head region begins to rotate toward the right at about 38 hours of incubation. Gradually this torsion continues caudally (figs. 237, 238, 239, 260). At about 70 to 75 hours, the rotational movement reaches the tail region, and the embryo then comes to lie on its left side throughout its length (fig. 240). In exceptional embryos, the rotational movement is toward the left, and the embryo comes to lie on its right side. Similar movements occur in the pig and other mammals.

This rotational movement is advantageous, particularly in long-bodied *Amniota,* such as the snakes, where it permits the developing embryo to coil in spiral form within the extra-embryonic membranes. The coiling tendency, however, is not alone confined to the snake group, for the habits of general body bending, referred to above, essentially is a coiling tendency. Viewed thus, the rotation or torsion of the developing body along its median axis is a generalized behavior pattern which permits and aids the coiling habit so prevalent among the embryos of higher vertebrates. It may be observed further that the coiling behavior is a common attitude during rest not only among snakes but also among the adults of many higher vertebrates.

I. Influences Which Play a Part in Tubulation and Organization of Body Form

In Chapter 9,   it was pointed out that the **pre-chordal plate material,** that is, organizer material which invaginates first during gastrulation and which comes to lie in the future head region, induces the organization of certain head structures and itself may form a part of the pharyngeal wall and give origin to head mesoderm, etc. On the other hand, the trunk-organizer material (notochord and somitic mesoderm) which moves to the inside, following the pre-chordal plate material, organizes the trunk region. The following series of experiments based upon work by Spemann, '31, sets forth the inductive properties of these two cellular areas:

Experiment

---

1. **Head-organizer** material, taken from one embryo and placed at head level of a host embryo, will induce a secondary head, having eyes and ear vesicles

2. **Head-organizer** material, transplanted to trunk and tail levels in host embryos, induces a complete secondary embryo, including head

3. **Trunk-organizer** material (i.e., notochord and somitic mesoderm), placed at head level in host embryo, induces a complete secondary embryo, including the head structures

4. **Trunk-organizer** material, placed at future trunk or tail levels in host embryos, induces trunk and tail structures only

---

The many influences which play a part in the organization of the vertebrate head and body constitute an involved and an unsolved problem. The extreme difficulty of this general problem has long been recognized. (See Kingsbury and Adelmann, '24.) The above-mentioned work of Spemann represents a beginning attempt to analyze this aspect of development and to understand the factors involved. It demonstrates that the organization of the neural tube and other axial areas is dependent upon specific cellular areas which migrate inward during gastrulation. However, this is but one aspect of the problem. As observed in the series of experiments above, **trunk-organizer material** is able to organize a complete secondary embryo, including the head, when

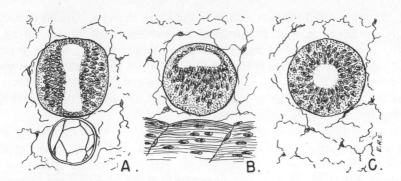

FIG. 251. Dependency of neural tube formation upon surrounding tissues. (A) Effect of notochord without myotomes. (B) Effect of myotomes without notochord. (C) Absence of notochord and myotomes.

placed at **head level in the host** but can only organize trunk and tail structures when placed **in trunk and tail areas of the host.** In other words, there exists a mutual relationship between the *level* of the host tissues and the transplanted organizer material of the trunk organizer in effecting the formation of a head at the head level.

Another forceful example of the interrelationship of developing parts and formative expression of body structures is shown by the work of Holtfreter ('33) on the development of the neural tube. This work demonstrates that the form of the neural tube is dependent upon influences in its environment, as shown in figure 251. The presence of the later developing notochord determines a thin ventral floor of the neural canal, whereas the contiguous myotome determines a thick wall of the neural tube. Normally, in development, the notochord lies below the neural tube, while the somites with their myotomic parts come to lie lateral to the tube. That is to say, *the normal bilateral symmetry of the neural tube is dependent upon the relationship, in their normal positions, of the notochord and the myotomes.*

The behavior of the developing neural tube, relative to the notochord and the myotomes, demonstrates the importance of the migration of the somitic mesoderm from a position contiguous and lateral to the notochord at the beginning of neuralization to one which is lateral to the forming neural tube as neuralization and differentiation of the neural tube progresses.

A further illustration of the probable influence of the notochordal area in morphogenesis and organization of body form is the behavior of the developing metenteron or enteric tube. As observed previously, the gut tubulation tends to invaginate or arch upward toward the notochord not only in embryos developing from flattened gastrulae but also in amphibia. The movement of the entoderm toward the notochord strikingly resembles the behavior of the neural plate ectoderm during the formation of the neural tube. This comparison becomes more striking when one considers the manner of enteron formation in the tail and hindgut regions in the shark embryo, *Squalus acanthias,* already mentioned, p. 484. In this species the entoderm of the developing tail actually invaginates dorsad and closes in a manner similar to the forming neural tube. That is to say, in the developing tail of the shark, two invaginations toward the notochord are evident, one from the dorsal side, which involves the formation of the neural tube, and the other from the ventral side, effecting the developing enteric tube.

The above facts suggest, therefore, that one of the main organizing influences at work during tubulation and primitive body formation emanates from the pre-chordal plate area, the notochord, and the epimeric portion of the mesoderm. From this general area or center, a chain of acting and interacting influences extends outward, one part acting upon another, to effect the formative expression of the various parts of the developing body.

J. Basic Similarity of Body-form Development in the Vertebrate Group of Chordate Animals

In the earlier portion of this chapter, differences in the general procedures concerned with tubulation and primitive body formation in round and flattened gastrulae were emphasized. However, basically all vertebrate embryos show the same tendency of the developing body to project itself upward and forward in the head region, dorsally in the trunk area and dorso-posteriad in the tail region. Literally, the embryonic body tends to lift itself up out of, and above, the area which contains the yolk and extra-embryonic tissues. This proneness to move upward and to protrude its developing head end forward and its caudal end backward is shown beautifully in the development of the embryos of the shark (figs. 229, 230), the mud puppy (fig. 227), the chick (fig. 235C), and the pig (fig. 242). The embryo struggles to be free from its bed of yolk and extra-embryonic tissue, as it were, and it reminds one of the superb imagery employed by the poet, John Milton, in his immortal poem, *Paradise Lost,* where he describes the development of the lion thus:

> The grassy clods now calv'd; now half appear'd
> The tawny lion, pawing to get free
> His hinder parts, then springs as broke from bonds,
> And rampant shakes his brinded mane.

In summary, therefore, although it appears that rounded and flattened gastrulae in the vertebrate group may have slightly different substrative conditions from which to start, they all employ essentially similar processes in effecting tubulation of the respective, major organ-forming areas and in the development of primitive body form.

Bibliography

Cerfontaine, P. **1906.** Recherches sur le developpement de *l'Amphioxus*. Arch. biol., Paris. **22**:229.

Conklin, E. G. **1932.** The embryology of *Amphioxus*. J. Morphol. **54**:69.

Dean, B. **1896.** The early development of *Amia*. Quart. J. Micr. Sc. (New Series) **38**:413.

Detwiler, S. R. **1929.** Transplantation of anterior limb mesoderm from *Amblystoma* embryos in the slit blastopore stage. J. Exper. Zool. **52**:315.

————. **1933.** On the time of determination of the antero-posterior axis of the forelimb in *Amblystoma*. J. Exper. Zool. **64**:405.

Hamburger, V. and Hamilton, H. I. **1951.** A series of normal stages in the development of the chick embryo. J. Morphol. **88**:49.

Harrison, R. G. **1918.** Experiments on the development of the forelimb of *Amblystoma*, a self-differentiating equipotential system. J. Exper. Zool. **25**:413.

————. **1921.** On relations of symmetry in transplanted limbs. J. Exper. Zool. **32**:1.

Hatschek, B. **1888.** Uber den Schechtenbau von Amphioxus. Anat. Anz. **3**:662.

Hatschek, B. **1893.** The *Amphioxus* and its development. Translated by J. Tuckey. The Macmillan Co., New York.

Holtfreter, J. **1933.** Der Einfluss von Wirtsalter und verschiedenen Organbezirken auf die Differenzierung von angelagertem Gastrulaektoderm. Arch. f. Entwicklngsmech. d. Organ. **127**:619.

Huxley, J. S. and De Beer, G. R. **1934.** The Elements of Experimental Embryology. Cambridge University Press, London.

Kellicott, W. E. **1913.** Outlines of Chordate Development. Henry Holt & Co., New York.

Kingsbury, B. F. and Adelmann, H. B. **1924.** The morphological plan of the head. Quart. J. Micr. Sc. **68**:239.

MacBride, E. W. **1898.** The early development of *Amphioxus*. Quart. J. Micr. Sc. **40**:589.

————. **1900.** Further remarks on the development of *Amphioxus*. Quart. J. Micr. Sc. **43**:351.

————. **1910.** The formation of the layers in *Amphioxus* and its bearing on the interpretation of the early ontogenetic processes in other vertebrates. Quart. J. Micr. Sc. **54**.279.

Morgan, T. H. and Hazen, A. P. **1900.** The gastrulation of *Amphioxus*. J. Morphol. **16**:569.

Needham, J. **1942.** Biochemistry and Morphogenesis. Cambridge University Press, London.

Patterson, J. T. **1907.** The order of appearance of the anterior somites in the chick. Biol. Bull. **13**:121.

Saunders, J. W. **1949.** An analysis of the role of the apical ridge of ectoderm in the development of the limb bud in the chick. Anat. Rec. **105**:567.

Selys–Longchamps, M. de. **1910.** Gastrulation et formation des feuillets chez *Petromyzon planeri*. Arch. biol., Paris. **25**:1.

Spemann, H. **1931.** Über den Anteil von Implantat und Wirtskeim an der Orientierung und Beschaffenheit der induzierten Embryonalanlage. Arch. f. Entwicklngsmech. d. Organ. **123**:389.

Swett, F. H. **1923.** The prospective significance of the cells contained in the four quadrants of the primitive limb disc of *Amblystoma*. J. Exper. Zool. **37**:207.

————. **1937.** Experiments upon delayed determination of the dorsoventral limb axis in *Amblystoma punctatum* (Linn.). J. Exper. Zool. **75**:143.

————. **1939.** Further experiments upon the establishment and the reversal of prospective dorsoventral limb-axis polarity. J. Exper. Zool. **82**:305.

————. **1941.** Establishment of definitive polarity in the dorsoventral axis of the forelimb girdle in *Amblystoma punctatum* (Linn.). J. Exper. Zool. **86**:69.

Weiss, P. **1939.** Principles of Development. Henry Holt & Co., New York.

Willey, A. **1894.** *Amphioxus* and the Ancestry of the Vertebrates. The Macmillan Co., New York.

11

Basic Features of Vertebrate Morphogenesis

A. Introduction
 1. Purpose of this chapter
 2. Definitions
   a. Morphogenesis and related terms
   b. Primitive, larval, and definitive body forms
    1) Primitive body form
    2) Larval body form
    3) Definitive body form
 3. Basic or fundamental tissues
B. Transformation of the primitive body tubes into the fundamental or basic condition of the various organ systems present in the primitive embryonic body
 1. Processes involved in basic system formation
 2. Fundamental similarity of early organ systems
C. Laws of von Baer
D. Contributions of the mesoderm to primitive body formation and later development
 1. Types of mesodermal cells
 2. Origin of the mesoderm of the head region
   a. Head mesoderm derived from the anterior region of the trunk
   b. Head mesoderm derived from the pre-chordal plate
   c. Head mesoderm contributed by neural crest material
   d. Head mesoderm originating from post-otic somites
 3. Origin of the mesoderm of the tail
 4. Contributions of the trunk mesoderm to the developing body
   a. Early differentiation of the somites or epimere
   b. Early differentiation of the mesomere (nephrotome)
   c. Early differentiation and derivatives of the hypomere
    1) Contributions of the hypomere (lateral plate mesoderm) to the developing pharyngeal area of the gut tube
    2) Contributions of the hypomere (lateral plate mesoderm) to the formation of the gut tube and heart structures
    3) Contributions of the hypomere (lateral plate mesoderm) to the external (ectodermal or epidermal) body tube
    4) Contributions of the hypomere or lateral plate mesoderm to the dorsal body areas
    5) Contributions of the lateral plate mesoderm to the walls of the coelomic cavity
 5. Embryonic mesenchyme and its derivatives

516

E. Summary of later derivatives of presumptive, major, organ-forming areas of the late blastula and gastrula
  1. Neural plate area (ectoderm)
  2. Epidermal area (ectoderm)
  3. Entodermal area
  4. Notochordal area
  5. Mesodermal areas
  6. Germ-cell area
F. Metamerism
  1. Fundamental metameric character of the trunk and tail regions of the vertebrate body
  2. Metamerism and the basic morphology of the vertebrate head
G. Basic homology of the vertebrate organ systems
  1. Definition
  2. Basic homology of vertebrate blastulae, gastrulae, and tubulated embryos

A. Introduction

1. PURPOSE OF THIS CHAPTER

In this chapter, the basic morphogenetic features which give origin to the later organ systems are emphasized. These features arise from the stream of morphogenetic phenomena which come down from the fertilized egg through the periods of cleavage, blastulation, gastrulation, and tubulation. This chapter thus serves to connect the developmental processes, outlined in Chapters 6 to 10, with those which follow in Chapters 12 to 21. As such, it emphasizes certain definitions and basic structural features involved in the later morphogenetic activities which mold the adult body form.

2. DEFINITIONS

a. Morphogenesis and Related Terms

The word **morphogenesis** means the development of form or shape. It involves the elaboration of structural relationships. The morphogenesis of a particular shape and structure of a cell is called **cytomorphosis** or **cytogenesis** and is synonymous with the term **cellular differentiation,** considered from the structural aspect. In the *Metazoa,* the body is composed of groups of cells, each cellular group possessing cells of similar form and function. That is, each cell group is similarly differentiated and specialized. A cellular group, composed of cells similar in form (structure) and function, is called a **tissue.** **Histology** is the study of tissues, and the word **histogenesis** relates to that phase of developmental morphology which deals with the genesis or development of tissues. An **organ** is an anatomical structure, produced by an association of different tissues which fulfills one or several specialized functions. For example, the esophagus, stomach, liver, etc., are organs of the body. During development, each of the major organ-forming areas, delineated in

Chapters 6, 7, 9 and 10, produce several specific organs. **Organogenesis** is concerned with the formation of these specific organs. A group of organs which are associated together to execute one general function form an **organ system.** The digestive system, for example, has for its general function that of obtaining nourishment for the body. It is composed of a series of organs integrated toward this end. The nervous system, similarly, is an assemblage of specific organs devoted to the discharge of nervous functions. So it is with the other systems of the organism. **System development** is concerned with the genesis of such systems. The association of various systems, integrated together for the maintenance of the body within a particular habitat, constitutes the **organism.** Finally, the organism acquires a particular **body form** because of the form, structure, and activities assumed by its organ systems as a result of their adaptation to the functional necessities of the particular habitat in which the organism lives. It should be urged further that this nice relationship between form and structure, on the one hand, and functional requirements, on the other, *is a fundamental principle of development from the egg to the adult.* It is a principle intimately associated with the morphogenesis of the organ systems described in Chapters 12 to 21.

During development from the egg to the adult form, three major types of body form are evolved in the majority of vertebrate species.

b. Primitive, Larval, and Definitive Body Forms (see fig. 255)

1) Primitive Body Form. The condition of primitive or generalized, embryonic body form is attained when the embryo reaches a state in which its developing organ systems resemble the respective developing organ systems in other vertebrate embryos at the same general period of development. (See p. 520.) Superficially, therefore, the general structure of the primitive embryonic body of one species resembles that of the primitive embryonic bodies of other vertebrate species. Such comparable conditions of primitive, body-form development are reached in the 10 to 15-mm. embryo of the shark, *Squalus acanthias,* of the frog embryo at about 5 to 7 mm., the chick at about 55 to 96 hrs. of incubation, the pig at 6 to 10 mm., and the human at 6 to 10 mm.

2) Larval Body Form. Following primitive body form, the embryo gradually transforms into a larval form. The larval form is present in the period between primitive body form and definitive body form. *The larval period is that period during which the basic conditions of the various organ systems, present in primitive body form, undergo a metamorphosis in assuming the form and structure of the adult or definitive body form.* In other words, during the larval period, the basic or generalized conditions of the various organ systems are changed into the adult form of the systems, and *the larval period thus represents a period of transition.* Embryos which develop in the water (most fishes, amphibia) tend to accentuate the larval condition, whereas those which develop within the body of the mother (viviparous teleosts, sharks, mammals) or within well-protected egg membranes (turtle, chick) slur over the larval condition.

The larval stage in non-viviparous fishes (see Kyle, '26, pp. 74–82) and in the majority of amphibia is a highly differentiated condition in which the organs of the body are adapted to a free-living, watery existence. The tadpole of the frog, *Rana pipiens,* from the 6-mm. stage to the 11-mm. stage, presents a period during which the primitive embryonic condition, present at the time of hatching (i.e., about 5 mm.), is transformed into a well-developed larval stage capable of coping with the external environment. From this time on to metamorphosis, the little tadpole possesses free-living larval features. Another example of a well-developed, free-living, larval stage among vertebrates is that of the eel, *Anguilla rostrata.* Spawning occurs in the ocean depths around the West Indies and Bermuda. Following the early embryonic stage in which primitive body form is attained, the young transforms into a form very unlike the adult. This form is called the *Leptocephalus.* The *Leptocephalus* was formerly classified as a distinct species of pelagic fishes. After many months in the larval stage, it transforms into the adult form of the eel. The latter migrates into fresh-water streams, the American eel into streams east of the Rockies and the European eel into the European streams (Kyle, '26, pp. 54 58). The larval stages in most fishes conform more nearly to the adult form of the fish.

The embryo of *Squalus acanthias* at 20 to 35 mm. in length, the chick embryo at 5 to 8 days of incubation, the pig embryo of 12- to 18-mm. length, and the human embryo of 12 to 20-mm. length may be regarded as being in the stage of larval transition. The young opossum, when it is born, is in a late larval state. It gradually metamorphoses into the adult body form within the marsupium of the mother (Chap. 22).

3) Definitive Body Form. The general form and appearance of the adult constitute definitive body form. The young embryo of *Squalus acanthias,* at about 40 mm. in length, assumes the general appearance of the adult shark; the frog young, after metamorphosis, resembles the adult frog (Chap. 21), the chick of 8 to 13 days of incubation begins to simulate the form of the adult bird; the pig embryo of 20 to 35 mm. gradually takes on the body features of a pig, and the human fetus, during the third month of pregnancy, assumes the appearance of a human being. The transformation of the larval form into the body form of the adult is discussed further in Chapter 21 in relation to the endocrine system.

3. Basic or Fundamental Tissues

Through the stages of development to the period when the primitive or generalized, embryonic body form is attained, most of the cells which take part in development are closely associated. In the primitive embryonic body, this condition is found in all the five primitive body tubes and in the notochord. These closely arranged cells form the **primitive epithelium.** In the developing head and tail regions, however, mesoderm is present in the form of loosely aggregated cells, known as **mesenchyme.** While the cells of the epithelial variety are rounded or cuboidal in shape *with little intercellular substance or space* between the cells, mesenchymal cells tend to assume stellate forms and to *have a large amount of intercellular substance* between them. The primitive vascular or blood tubes are composed of epithelium in the sense that the cells are closely arranged. However, as these cells are flattened and show specific peculiarities of structure, this tissue is referred to as **endothelium.** Also, while the cells of the early neural tube show the typical epithelial features, they soon undergo marked changes characteristic of developing **neural tissue.** The primitive or generalized, embryonic body thus is composed of four fundamental tissues, viz., **epithelial, mesenchymal, endothelial,** and **neural tissues.**

B. Transformation of the Primitive Body Tubes into the Fundamental or Basic Condition of the Various Organ Systems Present in the Primitive Embryonic Body

1. PROCESSES INVOLVED IN BASIC SYSTEM FORMATION

As the primitive body tubes (epidermal, neural, enteric, and mesodermal) are established, they are modified gradually to form the basis for the various organ systems. While the notochordal axis is not in the form of a tube, it also undergoes changes during this period. The morphological alterations, which transform the primitive body tubes into the basic or fundamental structural conditions of the systems, consist of the following:

(a) extension and growth of the body tubes,

(b) saccular outgrowths (evaginations) and ingrowths (invaginations) from restricted areas of the tubes,

(c) cellular migrations away from the primitive tubes to other tubes and to the spaces between the tubes, and

(d) unequal growth of different areas along the tubes.

As a result of these changes, the primitive neural, epidermal, enteric, and mesodermal tubes, together with the capillaries or blood tubes and the notochord, experience a state of gradual differentiation which is directed toward the production of the particular adult system to be derived from these respective basic structures. *The primitive body tubes, the primitive blood capillaries, and the notochord thus come to form the basic morphological conditions of the future organ systems.* The basic structural conditions of the various systems are described in Chapters 12 to 21.

2. FUNDAMENTAL SIMILARITY OF EARLY ORGAN SYSTEMS

The general form and structure of each primitive embryonic system, as it begins to develop in one vertebrate species, exhibits a striking resemblance to the same system in other vertebrate species. This statement is particularly true of the gnathostomous vertebrates (i.e., vertebrates with jaws). Consequently, we may regard the initial generalized stages of the embryonic or rudimentary systems as fundamental or basic plans of the systems, morphologically if not physiologically. *The problem which confronts the embryo of each species, once the basic conditions of the various systems have been established, is to convert the generalized basic condition of each system into an adult form which will enable that system to function to the advantage of the particular animal in the particular habitat in which it lives.* The conversion of the basic or primitive condition of the various systems into the adult form of the systems constitutes the subject matter of Chapters 12 to 21.

The basic conditions of the various organ systems are shown in the structure of shark embryos from 10 to 20 mm. in length, frog embryos of 5 to 10 mm., chick embryos from 55 to 96 hrs., pig embryos from 6 to 10 mm., crown-rump length, and human embryos of lengths corresponding to 6 to 10 mm. That is to say, *the basic or generalized conditions of the organ systems are present when primitive or generalized embryonic body form is developed.* It is impossible to segregate any particular length of embryo in the above-mentioned series as the ideal or exact condition showing the basic condition of the systems, as certain systems in one species progress faster than those same systems in other species. However, a study of embryos of these designations serves to provide an understanding of the basic or fundamental conditions of the various systems (figs. 257–262; also fig. 347A).

C. Laws of von Baer

As indicated above, the species of the vertebrate group as a whole tend to follow strikingly similar (although not identical) plans of development during blastulation, gastrulation, tubulation, the development of the basic plan of the various systems and primitive body form. As observed in the chapters which follow, the fundamental or basic plan of any particular, organ-forming system, in the early embryo of one species, is comparable to the basic plan of that system in other species throughout the vertebrate group. However, after these basic parallelisms in early development are completed, divergences from the basic plan begin to appear during the formation of the various organ systems of a particular species.

The classical statements or laws of Karl Ernst von Baer (1792–1876) describe a tendency which appears to be inherent in the developmental procedure of any large group of animals. This developmental tendency is for generalized structural features to arise first, to be remodeled later and supplanted by features specific for each individual species. To interpret these laws in terms of the procedure principle mentioned in Chapter 7, it may be assumed that general, or common, developmental procedures first are utilized, followed by specific developmental procedures which change the generalized conditions into specific conditions.

The laws of von Baer (1828–1837, Part I, p. 224) may be stated as follows:

(a) The general features of a large group of animals appear earlier in development than do the special features;

(b) after the more general structures are established, less general structures arise, and so on until the most special feature appears;

(c) each embryo of a given adult form of animal, instead of passing through or resembling the adult forms of lower members of the group, diverges from the adult forms, because

(d) the embryo of a higher animal species resembles only the embryo of the lower animal species, not the adult form of the lower species.

D. Contributions of the Mesoderm to Primitive Body Formation and Later Development

The mesoderm is most important to the developing architecture of the body. Because the mesoderm enters so extensively into the structure of the many organs of the developing embryo, it is well to point out further the sources of mesoderm and to delineate the structures and parts arising from this tissue.

1. TYPES OF MESODERMAL CELLS

Most of the mesoderm of the early embryo exists in the form of **epithelium** (see p. 519). As development proceeds, much of the mesoderm loses the close arrangement characteristic of epithelium. In doing so, the cells separate and assume a loose connection. They also may change their shapes, appearing stellate, oval, or irregular, and may wander to distant parts of the body. This loosely aggregated condition of mesoderm forms the primitive **mesenchyme.** Though most of the mesoderm becomes transformed into mesenchyme, the inner layer of cells of the original hypomeric portion of the mesodermal tubes retains a flattened, cohesive pattern, described as **mesothelium.** Mesothelium comes to line the various body cavities, for these cavities are derived directly from the hypomeric areas of the mesodermal tubes (Chap. 20).

2. ORIGIN OF THE MESODERM OF THE HEAD REGION

The primary cephalic outgrowth (Chap. 10), which later forms the head structures, contains two basic regions, namely, the **head proper** and the **pharyngeal or branchial region.** During its early development, the heart lies at the ventro-caudal extremity of the general head region; it recedes gradually backward as the head and branchial structures develop. The exact origin of the mesoderm which comes to occupy the head proper and pharyngeal areas varies in different gnathostomous vertebrates. The general sources of the head mesoderm may be described in the following manner.

a. Head Mesoderm Derived from the Anterior Region of the Trunk

The mesoderm of the branchial area in lower vertebrates, such as the sharks and, to some degree, the amphibia, represents a direct anterior extension of the mesoderm of the trunk (figs. 217D, E; 230D; 252E). It is divisible into two parts: (1) a ventro-lateral region, the hypomeric or lateral plate mesoderm, and (2) a dorsal or somitic portion. The latter represents a continuation into the head region of the epimeric (somitic) mesoderm of the trunk. That portion of the mesoderm of the branchial area which may be regarded specifically as part of the mesoderm of the head proper is the mesoderm associated with the mandibular and hyoid visceral arches, together with the hyoid and mandibular somites located at the upper or dorsal ends of the hyoid and mandibular visceral arches (fig. 217D, E).

In the higher vertebrates (reptiles, birds, and mammals), the mesoderm of the branchial region appears early, not as a continuous epithelium, as in the shark and amphibian embryo, but as a mass of mesenchyme which wanders into the branchial area from the anterior portion of the developing trunk region (figs. 217F; 233B; 234B). This mesenchyme assumes branchial region characteristics, for it later condenses to form the mandibular, hyoid, and more posteriorly located, visceral arches. Also, mesenchymal condensations appear which correspond to the pre-otic head somites formed in the early shark embryo. For example, in the chick, there is an abducent condensation, which corresponds to the hyoid somite of the shark embryo, and a superior oblique condensation corresponding probably to the mandibular somite of the shark embryo (cf. fig. 217D, F). (See also Adelmann, '27, p. 42.) Both of these condensations give origin to eye muscles (Chap. 16). Somewhat similar condensations of mesenchyme which form the rudiments of eye muscles occur in other members of the higher vertebrate group.

b. Head Mesoderm Derived from the Pre-chordal Plate

The term **pre-chordal plate mesoderm** signifies that portion of the head mesoderm which derives from the pre-chordal plate area located at the anterior end of the foregut. The pre-chordal plate mesoderm is associated closely with the foregut entoderm and anterior extremity of the notochord in the late blastula and gastrula in the fishes and amphibia. However, in reptiles, birds, and mammals, this association is established secondarily with the foregut entoderm by means of the notochordal canal and primitive-pit invaginations during gastrulation. (See Chap. 9 and also Hill and Tribe, '24.)

(*Note:* It is advisable to state that Adelmann, '32, relative to the 19-somite embryo of the urodele *Ambystoma punctatum,* distinguishes between a **pre-chordal mesoderm,** which forms the core of the mandibular visceral arch, and the **pre-chordal plate mesoderm,** which earlier in development is associated with the dorsal anterior portion of the foregut entoderm. See figure 252E.)

During the period when the major organ-forming areas are being tubulated,

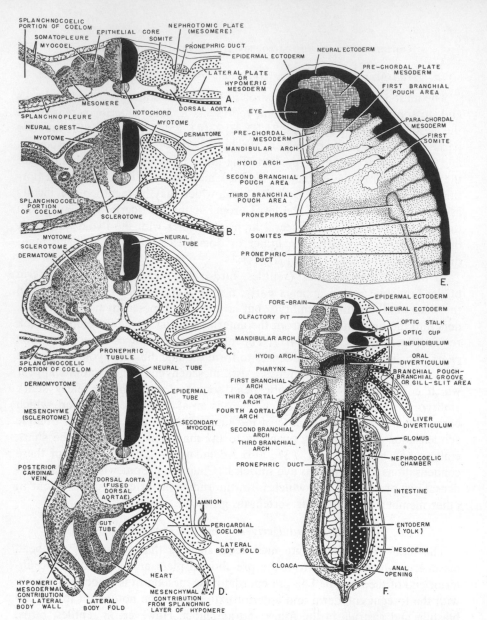

FIG. 252. Mesodermal contributions to developing body. (A–D) Sections through developing chick of 48–52 hrs. of incubation. (A) Section through somites of caudal trunk area showing primitive area of mesoderm and coelomic spaces. (B) Section through anterior trunk area depicting early differentiation of somite. (C) Section through trunk area posterior to heart revealing later stage of somite differentiation than that shown in B. (D) Section through developing heart area. Observe dermomyotome, sclerotomic mesenchyme, and mesenchymal contributions of hypomere to forming body substance. (E) Mesodermal contributions to anterior end of developing embryo of Ambystoma of about 19 somites. (Redrawn and modified from Adelmann: 1932, J. Morphol. 54.) (F) Frontal section of early post-hatching larva of *Rana pipiens* showing mass of mesoderm lying between gut, epidermal and neural tubes, together with the contributions of the mesoderm to the visceral arches.

the pre-chordal plate mesoderm separates as a mass of mesenchyme from the antero-dorsal aspect of the foregut, anterior to the cephalic terminus of the notochord (fig. 232G, H). It migrates forward as two groups of mesenchyme connected at first by an interconnecting bridge of mesenchyme. Eventually these two mesenchymal masses become separated and each forms a dense aggregation of mesodermal cells over the mandibular visceral arch and just caudal to the eye (fig. 252E). In the shark embryo and in the chick it gives origin to the **pre-mandibular somites** (condensations) which probably give origin to the eye muscles innervated by the oculomotor or third cranial nerves. In *Ambystoma,* Adelmann ('32, p. 52) describes the pre-chordal plate meso-derm as giving origin to "the eye muscles" and "probably much of the head mesenchyme ahead of the level of the first (gill) pouch, but its caudal limit cannot be exactly determined." Thus it appears that a portion of the head mesoderm in the region anterior to the notochordal termination is derived from the pre-chordal plate mesoderm in all vertebrates.

c. Head Mesoderm Contributed by Neural Crest Material

A conspicuous phase of the development of the head region in vertebrate embryos is the extensive migration of neural crest cells which arise in the mid-dorsal area as the neural tube is formed (Chap. 10; fig. 222C–F). Aside from contributing to the nervous system (Chap. 19), a portion of the neural crest material migrates extensively lateroventrally and comes to lie within the forming visceral (branchial) arches, contributing to the mesoderm in these areas (figs. 222C–F; 230D, F). Also, consult Landacre ('21); Stone ('22, '26, and '29); and Raven ('33a and b). On the other hand, Adelmann ('25) in the rat and Newth ('51) in the lamprey, *Lampetra planeri,* were not able to find evidence substantiating this view. However, pigment cells (melano-phores) of the skin probably arise from neural crest cells in the head region of all vertebrate groups.

d. Head Mesoderm Originating from Post-otic Somites

There is good evidence that the musculature of the tongue takes its origin in the shark embryo and lower vertebrates from cells which arise from the somites of the trunk area, immediately posterior to the otic (ear) vesicle, from whence they migrate ventrad to the hypobranchial region and forward to the area of the developing tongue (fig. 253). In the human embryo, Kingsbury ('15) suggests this origin for the tongue and other hypobranchial musculature. However, Lewis ('10) maintains that, in the human, the tongue musculature arises from mesenchyme in situ.

3. Origin of the Mesoderm of the Tail

In the *Amphibia,* the tail mesoderm has been traced by means of the Vogt staining method to tail mesoderm in the late blastular and early gastrular stages. At the time of tail-rudiment formation, this mesoderm forms two bilateral masses of cells located within the "tail bud" or "end bud." These cellular masses proliferate extensively as the tail bud grows caudally and give origin to the mesoderm of the tail. Similarly, in other vertebrates, the mesoderm of the future tail is present as mesenchyme in the terminal portion of the tail bud. These mesenchymal cells proliferate, as the tail grows caudalward, and leave behind the mesoderm, which gradually condenses into the epithelial masses or segments (myotomes) along either side of the notochord and neural tube.

4. Contributions of the Trunk Mesoderm to the Developing Body

The mesoderm of the trunk area contributes greatly to the development of the many body organs and systems in the trunk region. Details of this contribution will be described in the chapters which follow, but, at this point, it is well to survey the initial activities of the mesodermal tubes of the trunk area in producing the vertebrate body.

a. Early Differentiation of the Somites or Epimere

The somites (figs. 217, 237, 252) contribute much to the developing structure of the vertebrate body. This fact is indicated by their early growth and differentiation. For example, the ventro-mesial wall of the fully developed somite gradually separates from the rest of the somite and forms a mass of mesenchymal cells which migrates mesad around the notochord and also dorsad around the neural tube (fig. 252A–C). The mesenchyme which thus arises from the somite is known as the **sclerotome.** In the somite of the higher vertebrates just previous to the origin of the sclerotome, a small epithelial core of cells becomes evident in the myocoel; this core contributes to the sclerotomic material (fig. 252B). As a result of the segregation of the sclerotomic tissue and its migration mesad to occupy the areas around the notochord and nerve cord, the latter structures become enmeshed by a primitive **skeletogenous mesenchyme.** The notochord and sclerotomic mesenchyme are the foundation for the future axial skeleton of the adult, including the vertebral elements and the caudal part of the cranium as described in Chapter 15.

After the departure of sclerotomic material, myotomic and dermatomic portions of the somite soon rearrange themselves into a hollow structure (fig. 252C, D), in which the myotome forms the inner wall and the dermatome the outer aspect. This composite structure is the **dermomyotome,** and the cavity within, the **secondary myocoel.** In many vertebrates (fishes, amphibia, reptiles, and birds), the dermatome gives origin to cells which migrate into the region of the developing dermis (Chap. 12) and contributes to the formation of this layer of the skin.

b. Early Differentiation of the Mesomere (Nephrotome)

The differentiation of the nephrotome or intermediate mesoderm will be considered later (Chap. 18) in connection with the urogenital system.

c. Early Differentiation and Derivatives of the Hypomere

The lateral-plate mesoderm (hypomere), figure 252A, performs an extremely important function in embryological development. The cavity of the hypomere **(splanchnocoel)** and the cellular offspring from the hypomeric mesoderm, which forms the wall of this cavity, give origin to much of the structural material and arrangement of the adult body.

1) Contributions of the Hypomere (Lateral Plate Mesoderm) to the Developing Pharyngeal Area of the Gut Tube. The developing foregut (Chap. 13) may be divided into four main areas, namely, (1) head gut, (2) pharyngeal, (3) esophageal, and (4) stomach areas. The head gut is small and represents a pre-oral extension of the gut; the pharyngeal area is large and expansive and forms about half of the forming foregut in the early embryo; the esophageal segment is small and constricted; and the forming stomach region is enlarged. At this point, however, concern is given specifically to the developing foregut in relation to the early development of the pharyngeal region.

In the pharyngeal area the foregut expands laterally. Beginning at its anterior end, it sends outward a series of paired, pouch-like diverticula, known as the branchial (pharyngeal or visceral) pouches. These pouches push outward toward the ectodermal (epidermal) layer. In doing so, they separate the lateral plate mesoderm which synchronously has divided into columnar masses or cells (fig. 252E, F). Normally, about four to six pairs of **branchial (pharyngeal) pouches** are formed in gnathostomous vertebrates, although in the cyclostomatous fish, *Petromyzon,* eight pairs appear. In the embryo of the shark, *Squalus acanthias,* six pairs are formed, while in the amphibia, four to six pairs of pouches may appear (fig. 252F). In the chick, pig, and human, four pairs of pouches normally occur (figs. 259, 261). Also, invaginations or inpushings of the epidermal layer occur, the **branchial grooves (visceral furrows);** the latter meet the entodermal outpocketings (figs. 252F, 262B).

The end result of all these developmental movements in the branchial area is to produce elongated, dorso-ventral, paired columns of mesodermal cells (figs. 252E; 253), the **visceral or branchial arches,** which alternate with the branchial-groove-pouch or gill-slit areas (figs. 252F; 253). The most anterior pair of visceral arches forms the **mandibular visceral arches;** the second pair forms the **hyoid visceral arches;** and the succeeding pairs form the **branchial (gill) arches** (figs. 239C, D; 240; 244; 246; 252E; 253). The branchial arches with their mesodermal columns of cells will, together with the contributions from the neural crest cells referred to above, give origin to the connective, muscle, and blood-vessel-forming tissues in this area.

2) Contributions of the Hypomere (Lateral Plate Mesoderm) to the Formation of the Gut Tube and Heart Structures. Throughout the length of the forming gut tube, from the oral area to the anal region, the lateral plate mesoderm (mesoblast) contributes much to the forming gut tube. This is occasioned to a great extent posterior to the pharyngeal area by the fact that the inner or mesial walls of the two hypomeres enswathe the forming gut tube as they fuse in the median plane (fig. 241), forming the dorsal and ventral mesenteries of the gut. However, in the heart area, due to the dorsal displacement of the foregut, the dorsal mesentery is vestigial or absent while the ventral mesentery is increased in extent. Each mesial wall of the hypomeric mesoderm, forming the ventral mesentery in the region of the developing heart, becomes cupped around the primitive blood capillaries, coursing anteriad in this area to form the rudiments of the developing heart. The ventral mesentery in the heart area thus gives origin to the dorsal mesocardium, the ventral mesocardium, and the rudimentary, cup-shaped, epimyocardial structures around the fusing blood capillaries (figs. 236C–D; 254A). The primitive blood capillaries soon unite to form the rudiment of the future endocardium of the heart, while the enveloping epimyocardium establishes the rudiment of the future muscle and connective tissues of the heart (Chap. 17).

On the other hand, in the region of the stomach and continuing posteriorly to the anal area of the gut, the movement mediad of the mesial walls of the two lateral plate (hypomeric) mesodermal areas occurs in such a way as to

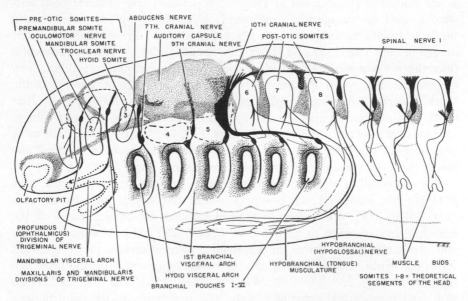

Fig. 253. Diagram illustrating the basic plan of the vertebrate head based upon the shark, *Scyllium canicula*. (Modified from Goodrich: 1918, Quart. Jour. Micros. Science, 63.)

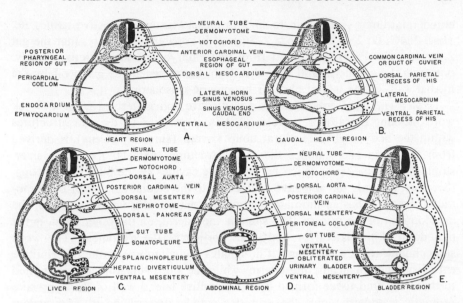

FIG. 254. Diagrams illustrating the contributions of the mesial or splanchnic layers of the hypomeres to the developing heart and gut structures in reptiles, birds, and mammals. Sections are drawn through the following regions: (A) Through primitive tubular heart anterior to sinus venosus. (B) Through caudal end of sinus venosus and lateral mesocardia.   (C) Through liver region. (D) Through region posterior to liver.   (E) Through posterior trunk in region of urinary bladder.

envelop or enclose the gut tube. This enclosure readily occurs because in this region of the trunk, the gut tube lies closer to the ventral aspect of the embryo than in the heart area. Consequently, a dorsal mesentery above and a ventral mesentery below the primitive gut tube are formed (fig. 254C). The dorsal and ventral mesenteries may not persist everywhere along the gut (fig. 254D). The degree of persistence varies in different vertebrates; these variations will be mentioned later (Chap. 20) when the coelomic cavities are discussed. However, there is a persistence of the ventral mesentery below the stomach and anterior intestinal area of all vertebrates, for here the ventral mesentery (i.e., the two medial walls of the lateral plate mesoderm below the gut) contributes to the development of the liver and the pancreas. These matters are discussed in Chapter 13.

Aside from the formation of the dorsal and ventral mesenteries by the inward movement and fusion of the medial walls of the lateral plate mesoderm above and below the primitive enteron or gut tube, that part of the medial walls of the lateral plate mesoderm which envelops the primitive gut itself is of great importance. This importance arises from the fact that the entoderm of the gut only forms the lining tissue of the future digestive tract and its various glands, such as the liver, pancreas, etc., whereas mesenchymal contributions from the medial wall of the lateral plate mesoderm around the entodermal lining give origin to smooth muscle tissue, connective tissue, etc. (figs. 254C, D; 258; 260; 262; 278C). It is apparent, therefore, that the gut throughout its length is formed from two embryonic contributions, namely, one from the entoderm and the other from the mesenchyme given off by the medial walls of the lateral plate or hypomeric mesoderm.

(*Note:* The word **splanchnic** is an adjective and is derived from a Greek word meaning entrails or bowels. That is, it pertains to the soft structures within the body wall. The plural noun **viscera** (singular, **viscus**) is derived from the Latin and signifies the same structures, namely, the heart, liver, stomach, intestine, etc., which lie within the cavities of the body. It is fitting, therefore, to apply the adjective **splanchnic** to the medial portion of the hypomere because it has an intimate relationship with, and is contributory to, the development of the viscera. The **somatic** mesoderm, on the other hand, is the mesoderm of the lateral or body-wall portion of the hypomere. The word **splanchnopleure** is a noun and it designates the composite tissue of primitive entoderm and splanchnic mesoderm, while the word **somatopleure** is applied to the compound tissue formed by the primitive lateral wall of the hypomere (somatic mesoderm) plus the primitive ectoderm overlying it. The coelom proper or **splanchnocoel** is the space or cavity which lies between the splanchnic and somatic layers of the lateral plate or hypomeric mesoderm. During later development, it is the cavity in which the entrails lie.

3) Contributions of the Hypomere (Lateral Plate Mesoderm) to the External (Ectodermal or Epidermal) Body Tube. The somatopleural mesoderm gives origin to a mass of cellular material which migrates outward to lie along the inner aspect of the epidermal tube in the lateral and ventral portions of the developing body (fig. 252A, D). In the dorsal and dorso-lateral regions of the body, contributions from the sclerotome and dermatome apparently aid in forming this tissue layer. The layer immediately below the epidermis constitutes the embryonic rudiment of the **dermis.** (See Chap. 12.)

4) Contributions of the Hypomere or Lateral Plate Mesoderm to the Dorsal Body Areas. Many cells are given off both from splanchnic and somatic layers of the hypomeric mesoderm to the dorsal body areas above and along either side of the dorsal aorta (fig. 254), contributing to the mesenchymal "packing tissue" in the area between the notochord and differentiating somite, extending outward to the dermis.

5) Contributions of the Lateral Plate Mesoderm to the Walls of the Coelomic Cavities. The pericardial, pleural, and peritoneal cavities are lined, as stated above, by an epithelial type of tissue called **mesothelium** (fig. 254A–E). These coelomic spaces (see Chap. 20) are derived from the fusion of the two primitive splanchnocoels or cavities of the two hypomeres. External to the mesothelial lining of the coelomic spaces, there ultimately is developed a fibrous, connective tissue layer. Thus, mesothelium and connective tissue form,

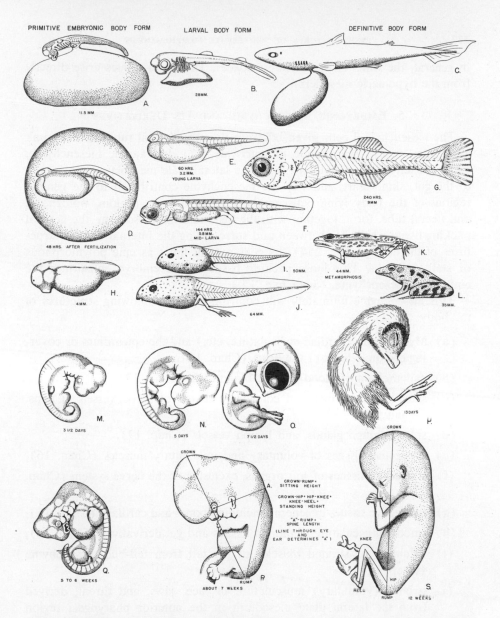

PRIMITIVE EMBRYONIC BODY FORM   LARVAL BODY FORM   DEFINITIVE BODY FORM

A. 11.5 MM.

B. 28MM.

C.

D. 48 HRS. AFTER FERTILIZATION

E. 60 HRS. 3.2 MM. YOUNG LARVA

F. 144 HRS. 5.8 MM. MID-LARVA

G. 240 HRS. 9MM

H. 4 MM.

I. 50MM.

J. 64 MM.

K. 44 MM. METAMORPHOSIS

L. 35MM.

M. 3 1/2 DAYS

N. 5 DAYS

O. 7 1/2 DAYS

P. 13 DAYS   CROWN

Q. 5 TO 6 WEEKS

R. CROWN   ABOUT 7 WEEKS   RUMP

CROWN-RUMP = SITTING HEIGHT

CROWN-HIP + HIP-KNEE + KNEE-HEEL = STANDING HEIGHT

"A"-RUMP = SPINE LENGTH (LINE THROUGH EYE AND EAR DETERMINES "A")

S. CROWN   KNEE   HIP   HEEL   RUMP   12 WEEKS

FIG. 255. This figure illustrates different types of body form in various vertebrates during embryonic development. A, D, H, M, and Q show primitive embryonic body form in the developing shark, rock fish, frog, chick, and human. B, larval form of shark; E and F, larval forms of rock fish; I and J, larval forms of frog; N and O, larval forms of chick; R, larval form of human. C, G, K, L, P, and S represent definitive body form in the above species. (Figures on rockfish development (*Roccus saxatilis*) redrawn from Pearson: 1938, Bull. Bureau of Fisheries, U. S. Dept. of Commerce, vol. 49; figures on chick redrawn from Hamburger and Hamilton: 1951, J. Morphol., vol. 88; figure Q, of developing human embryo, redrawn and modified from model based upon Normentafeln of Keibel and Elze: 1908, vol. 8, G. Fischer, Jena; Dimensions of human embryos in R and S, from Mall: Chap. 8, vol. I, Human Embryology, by F. Keibel and F. P. Mall, 1910, Lippincott, Philadelphia.)

531

in general, the walls of the coelomic spaces. These two tissues arise directly from the hypomeric mesoderm.

5. EMBRYONIC MESENCHYME AND ITS DERIVATIVES

The mesenchymal cells given off from the mesodermal tubes of the trunk area, namely, (1) sclerotomic mesenchyme, (2) dermatomic mesenchyme, (3) mesenchymal contributions from the lateral plate mesoblast (hypomere) to the gut, skin, heart, and (4) the mesenchyme contributed to the general regions of the body lying between the epidermal tube, coelom, notochord, and neural tube, form, together with the head and tail mesoderm, the general packing tissue which lies between and surrounding the internal tubular structures of the embryo (fig. 254). Its cells may at times assume polymorphous or stellate shapes. This loose packing tissue of the embryo constitutes the **embryonic mesenchyme.** (See Chap. 15.)

This mesenchyme ultimately will contribute to the following structures of the body:

(a) Myocardium (cardiac musculature, etc.) and the epicardium or covering coelomic layer of the heart (Chap. 17),

(b) endothelium of blood vessels, blood cells (Chap. 17),

(c) smooth musculature and connective tissues of blood vessels (Chaps. 16 and 17),

(d) spleen, lymph glands, and lymph vessels (Chap. 17),

(e) connective tissues of voluntary and involuntary muscles (Chap. 16),

(f) connective tissues of soft organs, exclusive of the nerve system (Chap. 15),

(g) connective tissues in general, including bones and cartilage (Chap. 15),

(h) smooth musculature of the gut tissues and gut derivatives (Chap. 16),

(i) voluntary or striated muscles of the tail from tail-bud mesenchyme (Chap. 16),

(j) striated (voluntary) musculature of face, jaws, and throat, derived from the lateral plate mesoderm in the anterior pharyngeal region (Chap. 16),

(k) striated (voluntary) extrinsic musculature of the eye (Chap. 16),

(l) intrinsic, smooth musculature of the eye (Chap. 16),

(m) tongue and musculature of bilateral appendages, derived from somitic muscle buds (sharks) or from mesenchyme possibly of somitic origin (higher vertebrates) (Chap. 16), and

(n) chromatophores or pigment cells of the body from neural crest mesenchyme (Chap. 12).

E. Summary of Later Derivatives of the Major Presumptive Organ-forming Areas of the Late Blastula and Gastrula

1. Neural Plate Area (Ectoderm)

This area gives origin to the following:

(a) Neural tube,

(b) optic nerves and retinae of eyes,

(c) peripheral nerves and ganglia,

(d) chromatophores and chromaffin tissue (i.e., various pigment cells of the skin, peritoneal cavity, etc., chromaffin cells of supra-renal gland),

(e) mesenchyme of the head, neuroglia, and

(f) smooth muscles of iris.

2. Epidermal Area (Ectoderm)

This area gives origin to:

(a) Epidermal tube and derived structures, such as scales, hair, nails, feathers, claws, etc.,

(b) lens of the eye, inner ear vesicles, olfactory sense area, general, cutaneous, sense organs of the peripheral area of the body,

(c) stomodaeum and its derivatives, oral cavity, anterior lobe of pituitary, enamel organs, and oral glands, and

(d) proctodaeum from which arises the lining tissue of the anal canal.

3. Entodermal Area

From this area the following arise:

(a) Epithelial lining of the primitive gut tube or metenteron, including: (1) epithelium of pharynx; epithelium pharyngeal pouches and their derivatives, such as auditory tube, middle-ear cavity, parathyroids, and thymus; (2) epithelium of thyroid gland; (3) epithelial lining tissue of larynx, trachea, and lungs, and (4) epithelium of gut tube and gut glands, including liver and pancreas,

(b) most of the lining tissue of the urinary bladder, vagina, urethra, and associated glands,

(c) Seessel's pocket or head gut, and

(d) tail gut.

4. Notochordal Area

This area:

(a) Forms primitive antero-posterior skeletal axis of all chordate forms,

(b) aids in induction of central nerve tube,

(c) gives origin to adult notochord of *Amphioxus* and cyclostomatous fishes and to notochordal portions of adult vertebral column of gnathostomous fishes and water-living amphibia, and

(d) also, comprises the remains of the notochord in land vertebrates, such as "nucleus pulposus" in man.

5. MESODERMAL AREAS

These areas give origin to:

(a) Epimeric, mesomeric, and hypomeric areas of primitive mesodermal tube,

(b) epimeric portion also aids in induction of central nerve tube,

(c) muscle tissue, involuntary and voluntary,

(d) mesenchyme, connective tissues, including bone, cartilage,

(e) blood and lymphoid tissue,

(f) gonads with exception of germ cells, genital ducts, and glandular tissues of male and female reproductive ducts, and

(g) kidney, ureter, musculature and connective tissues of the bladder, uterus, vagina, and urethra.

6. GERM-CELL AREA

This area gives origin to:

(a) Primordial germ cells and probably to definitive germ cells of all vertebrates below mammals and

(b) primordial germ cells of mammals and possibly to definitive germ cells.

F. Metamerism

1. FUNDAMENTAL METAMERIC CHARACTER OF THE TRUNK AND TAIL REGIONS OF THE VERTEBRATE BODY

Many animals, invertebrate as well as vertebrate, are characterized by the fact that their bodies are constructed of a longitudinal series of similar parts or **metameres.** As each metamere arises during development *in a similar manner* and from similar rudiments along the longitudinal or antero-posterior axis of the embryo, each metamere is homologous with each of the other metameres. This type of homology in which the homologous parts are arranged serially is known as **serial homology. Metamerism** is a characteristic feature of the primitive and later bodies of arthropods, annelids, cephalochordates, and vertebrates.

In the vertebrate group, the mesoderm of the trunk and tail exhibits a type of segmentation, particularly in the epimeric or somitic area. Each pair of somites, for example, denotes a primitive body segment. The nervous system

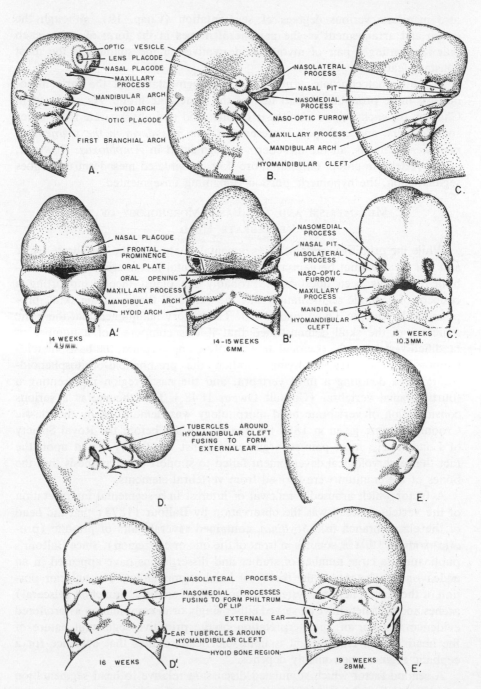

Labels in figure:

A.
- OPTIC VESICLE
- LENS PLACODE
- NASAL PLACODE
- MAXILLARY PROCESS
- MANDIBULAR ARCH
- HYOID ARCH
- OTIC PLACODE
- FIRST BRANCHIAL ARCH

B.
- NASOLATERAL PROCESS
- NASAL PIT
- NASOMEDIAL PROCESS
- NASO-OPTIC FURROW
- MAXILLARY PROCESS
- MANDIBULAR ARCH
- HYOMANDIBULAR CLEFT

C.

A'.
- NASAL PLACODE
- FRONTAL PROMINENCE
- ORAL PLATE
- ORAL OPENING
- MAXILLARY PROCESS
- MANDIBULAR ARCH
- HYOID ARCH
- 14 WEEKS 4.9 MM.

B'.
- NASOMEDIAL PROCESS
- NASAL PIT
- NASOLATERAL PROCESS
- NASO-OPTIC FURROW
- MAXILLARY PROCESS
- MANDIBLE
- HYOMANDIBULAR CLEFT
- 14-15 WEEKS 6MM.

C'.
- 15 WEEKS 10.3 MM.

D.
- TUBERGLES AROUND HYOMANDIBULAR CLEFT FUSING TO FORM EXTERNAL EAR

E.

D'.
- NASOLATERAL PROCESS
- NASOMEDIAL PROCESSES FUSING TO FORM PHILTRUM OF LIP
- EXTERNAL EAR
- EAR TUBERCLES AROUND HYOMANDIBULAR CLEFT
- HYOID BONE REGION
- 16 WEEKS

E'.
- 19 WEEKS 28MM.

FIG. 256. Developmental features of the human face. Modified slightly from models by B. Ziegler, Freiburg, after Karl Peter.

535

also manifests various degrees of segmentation (Chap. 19), although the origin and arrangement of the peripheral nerves in the form of pairs, each pair innervating a pair of myotomic derivatives of the somites, is the most constant feature.

In the cephalochordate, *Amphioxus,* the segmentation of the early mesoderm is more pronounced than that of the vertebrate group. As observed in Chapter 10, each pair of somites is distinct and entirely separate from other somitic pairs, and each pair represents *all the mesoderm in the segment or metamere.* That is, all the mesoderm is segmented in *Amphioxus.* However, in the vertebrate group, only the more dorsally situated mesoderm undergoes segmentation, the hypomeric portion remaining unsegmented.

2. METAMERISM AND THE BASIC MORPHOLOGY OF THE VERTEBRATE HEAD

While the primitive, metameric (segmental) nature of the vertebrate trunk and tail areas cannot be gainsaid, the fundamental metamerism of the vertebrate head has been questioned. Probably the oldest theory supporting a concept of cephalic segmentation was the **vertebral theory** of the skull, propounded by Goethe, Oken, and Owen. This theory maintained that the basic structure of the skull demonstrated that it was composed of a number of modified vertebrae, the occipital area denoting one vertebra, the basisphenoid-temporo-parietal area signifying another, the presphenoid-orbitosphenoid-frontal area denoting a third vertebra, and the nasal region representing a fourth cranial vertebra. (Consult Owen, 1848.) This theory, as a serious consideration of vertebrate head morphology was demolished by the classic Croonian lecture given in 1858 by Huxley (1858) before the Royal Society of London. His most pointed argument against the theory rested upon the fact that embryological development failed to support the hypothesis that the bones of the cranium were formed from vertebral elements.

A factor which aroused a renewal of interest in a segmental interpretation of the vertebrate head was the observation by Balfour (1878) that the head of the elasmobranch fish, *Scyllium,* contained several pairs of pre-otic (pro-otic) somites (that is, somites in front of the otic or ear region). Since Balfour's publication, a large number of studies and dissertations have appeared in an endeavor to substantiate the theory of head segmentation. The anterior portion of the central nervous system, cranial nerves, somites, branchial (visceral) arches and pouches, have all served either singly or in combination as proffered evidence in favor of an interpretation of the primitive segmental nature of the head region. However, it is upon the head somites that evidence for a cephalic segmentation mainly depends.

A second factor which stimulated discussion relative to head segmentation was the work of Locy (1895) who emphasized the importance of so-called neural segments or **neuromeres** (Chap. 19) as a means of determining the

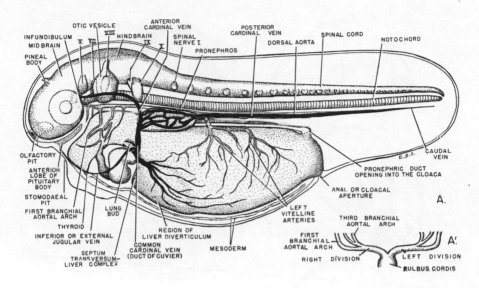

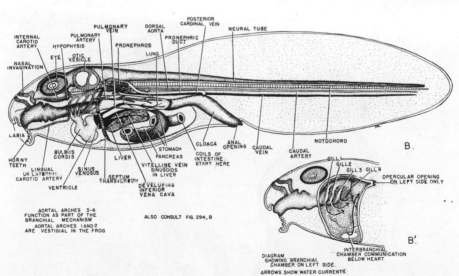

FIG. 257. Drawings of early frog tadpoles showing development of early systems. (A) Frog tadpole (*R. pipiens*) of about 6–7 mm. It is difficult to determine the exact number of vitelline arteries at this stage of development and the number given in the figure is a diagrammatic representation. (A′) Shows right and left ventral aortal divisions of bulbus cordis. (B) Anatomy of frog tadpole of about 10–18 mm. See also figures 280 and 335.

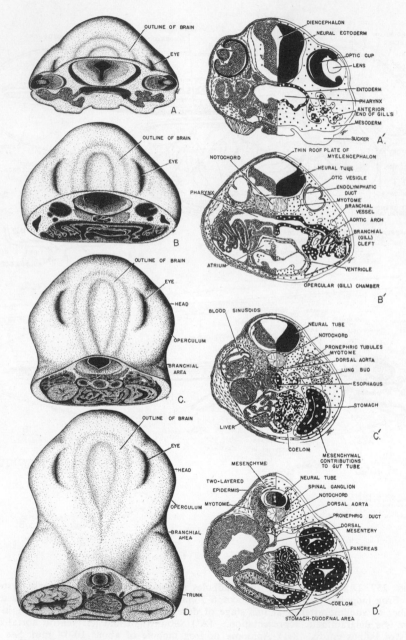

FIG. 258. Sections and stereograms of *Rana pipiens* tadpole of 10 mm.

538

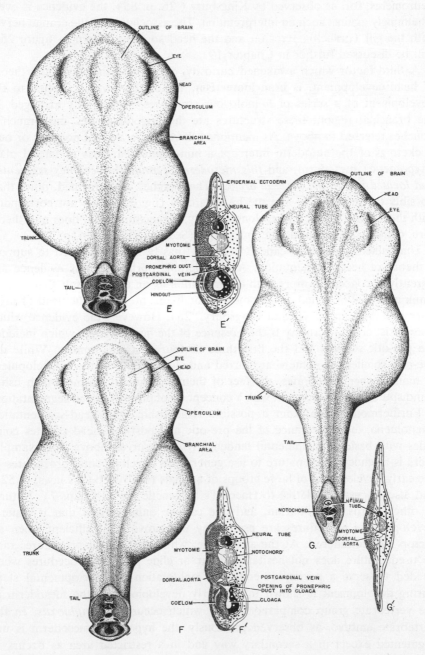

Labels in image E/E′:
OUTLINE OF BRAIN
EYE
HEAD
OPERCULUM
BRANCHIAL AREA
TRUNK
TAIL
EPIDERMAL ECTODERM
NEURAL TUBE
MYOTOME
DORSAL AORTA
PRONEPHRIC DUCT
POSTCARDINAL VEIN
COELOM
HINDGUT
E
E′

Labels in image (right, G/G′):
OUTLINE OF BRAIN
HEAD
EYE
TRUNK
TAIL
NEURAL TUBE
NOTOCHORD
MYOTOME
DORSAL AORTA
G.
G′.

Labels in image F/F′:
OUTLINE OF BRAIN
EYE
HEAD
OPERCULUM
BRANCHIAL AREA
TRUNK
TAIL
NEURAL TUBE
MYOTOME
NOTOCHORD
DORSAL AORTA
POSTCARDINAL VEIN
OPENING OF PRONEPHRIC DUCT INTO CLOACA
COELOM
CLOACA
F
F′

FIG. 258—(*Continued*) Sections and stereograms of *Rana pipiens* tadpole of 10 mm.

539

primitive segmental structure of the vertebrate brain. It is to be observed that the more conservative figure 253, taken from Goodrich, does not emphasize neuromeres, for, as observed by Kingsbury ('26, p. 85), the evidence is over-whelmingly against such an interpretation. The association of the cranial nerves with the gill (branchial) region and the head somites, shown in figure 253, will be discussed further in Chapter 19.

A third factor which awakened curiosity, concerning the segmental theory of head development, is **branchiomerism.** The latter term is applied to the development of a series of homologous structures, segmentally arranged, in the branchial region; these structures are the visceral arches and branchial pouches referred to above. As mentioned there, the branchial pouches or out-pocketings of the entoderm interrupt a **non-segmented mass** of lateral plate (hypomeric) mesoderm, and *this mesoderm secondarily becomes segmented and located within the visceral arches*. These arches when formed, other than possibly the mandibular and the hyoid arches (fig. 253), do not correspond with the dorsal somitic series. Consequently, "branchiomerism does not, there-fore, coincide with somitic metamerism." (See Kingsbury, '26, p. 106.)

Undoubtedly, much so-called "evidence" has been accumulated to support a theory of head segmentation. A considerable portion of this evidence ap-parently is concerned more with segmentation as an end in itself than with a frank appraisal of actual developmental conditions present in the head (Kings-bury and Adelmann, '24 and Kingsbury, '26). However, the evidence which does resist critical scrutiny is the presence of the head somites which includes the pre-otic somites and the first three or four post-otic somites. While the pre-otic somites are somewhat blurred and slurred over in their development in many higher vertebrates, the fact of their presence in elasmobranch fishes is indisputable and consistent with a conception of primitive head segmentation.

Furthermore, aside from a possible relationship with head-segmentation phenomena, the appearance of the pre-otic and post-otic head somites coin-cides with basic developmental tendencies. As observed above, for example, there is a tendency for nature to use generalized developmental procedures in the early development of large groups of animals (see von Baer's laws, p. 522, and also discussion relative to Haeckel's biogenetic law in Chap. 7). Nature, in other words, is utilitarian, and one can be quite certain that if general developmental procedures are used, they will prove most efficient when all factors are considered. At the same time, while generalized procedures may be used, nature does not hesitate to mar or elide parts of procedures when needed to serve a particular end. The obliteration of developmental steps during development is shown in the early development of the mesoderm in the vertebrate group compared to that which occurs in *Amphioxus*. In the vertebrate embryo, as observed previously, the hypomeric mesoderm is un-segmented except in a secondary way and in a restricted area as occurs in branchiomerism. However, in *Amphioxus,* early segmentation of the mesoderm is complete dorso-ventrally, including the hypomeric region of the mesoderm. It becomes evident, therefore, that the suppression of segmentation in the hypomeric area in the vertebrate embryo achieves a precocious result which the embryo of *Amphioxus* reaches only at a later period of development. Presumably in the vertebrate embryo, segmentation of the epimeric mesoderm is retained because it serves a definite end, whereas segmentation of the hypomeric mesoderm is deleted because it also leads to a necessary end result in a direct manner.

When applied to the developing head region, this procedure principle means this: A primitive type of segmentation does tend to appear in the pre-otic area as well as in the post-otic portion of the head, as indicated by the pre-otic and post-otic somites, and secondarily there is developed a branchial metam-

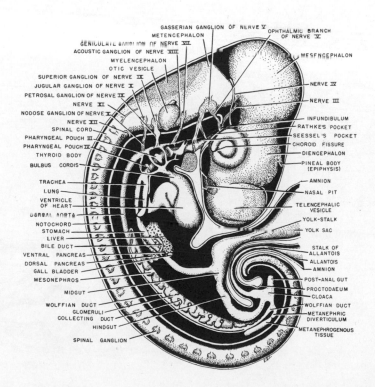

Fig. 259. Chick embryo reconstruction of about 100 hrs. of incubation with special reference to the nervous and urinary systems. See also fig. 336D.

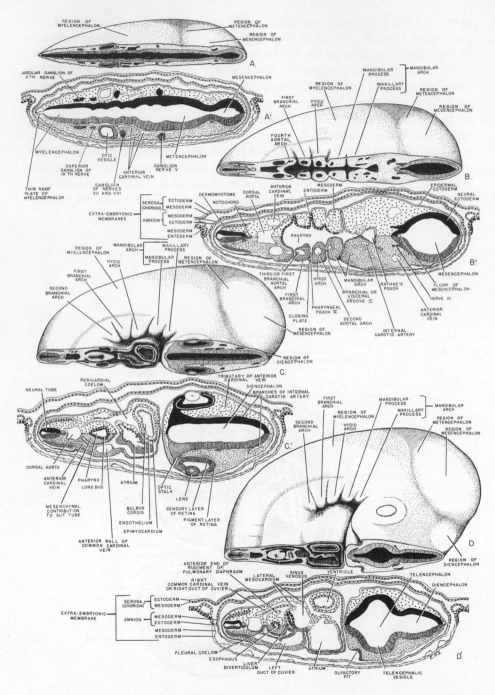

FIG. 260. Sections and stereograms of chick embryo of about 72 hrs. incubation. Reference should be made also to fig. 336D.

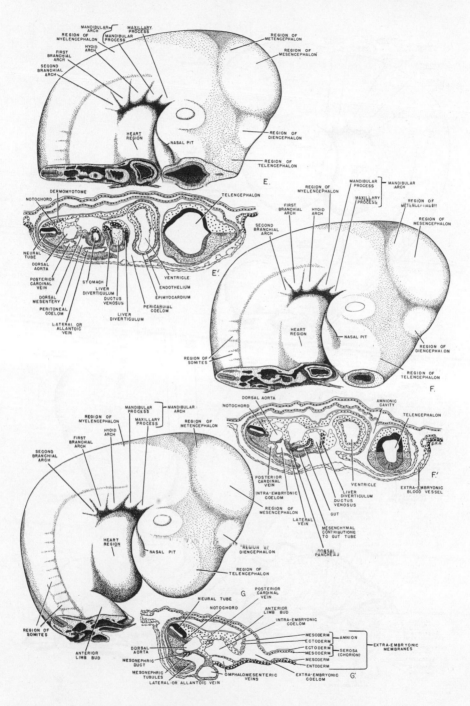

FIG. 260—(Continued) Sections and stereograms of chick embryo of about 72 hrs. incubation. Reference should be made also to fig. 336D.

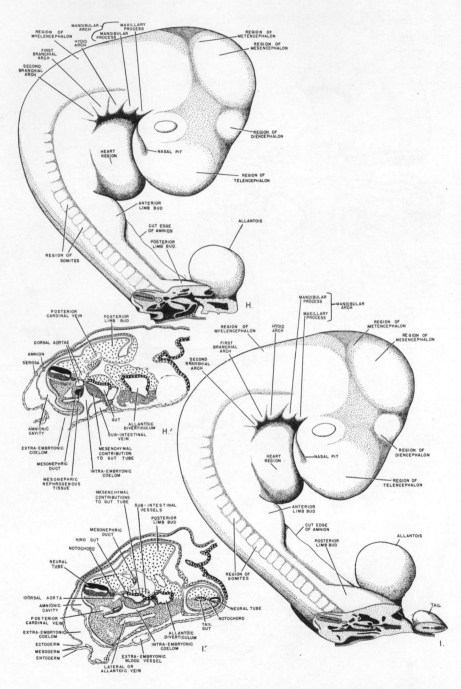

FIG. 260—*(Continued)* Sections and stereograms of chick embryo of about 72 hrs. incubation. Reference should be made also to fig. 336D.

erism (branchiomerism). However, all these segmental structures serve a definite end. In other areas, head development proceeds in a manner which obscures segmentation, for the probable reason that segmentation does not fit into the developmental pattern which must proceed directly and precociously to gain a specific end dictated by problems peculiar to head development.

(*Note:* For a critical analysis of the supposed facts in favor of segmentation, together with a marshaling of evidence against such an interpretation, consult Kingsbury and Adelmann ('24) and for a favorable interpretation of the segmental nature of the head region, see Goodrich ('18) and Delsman ('22). Figure 253 is taken from Goodrich ('18), and the various structures which favor a segmental interpretation of the head region are shown.)

G. Basic Homology of the Vertebrate Organ Systems

1. DEFINITION

Homology is the relationship of agreement between the structural parts of one organism and the structural parts of another organism. An agreeable relationship between two structures is established if:

(1) the two parts occupy the same relative position in the body,

(2) they arise in the same way embryonically and from the same rudiments, and

(3) they have the same basic potencies.

By basic potency is meant the potency which governs the initial and fundamental development of the part; it should not be construed to mean the ability to produce the entire structure. To the basic potency, other less basic potencies and **modifying factors** may be added to produce the adult form of the structure.

2. BASIC HOMOLOGY OF VERTEBRATE BLASTULAE, GASTRULAE, AND TUBULATED EMBRYOS

In Chapters 6 and 7, the basic conditions of the vertebrate blastula were surveyed, and it was observed that the formative portion of all vertebrate blastulae presents a basic pattern, composed of major presumptive organ-forming areas oriented around the notochordal area and a blastocoelic space. During gastrulation (Chap. 9), these areas are reoriented to form the basic pattern of the gastrula, and although round and flattened gastrulae exist, these form one, generalized, basic pattern, composed of three germ layers arranged around the central axis or primitive notochordal rod. Similarly, in Chapter 10, the major organ-forming areas are tubulated to form an elongated embryo, composed of head, pharyngeal, trunk, and tail regions. As tubulation is effected in much the same manner throughout the vertebrate series and as the pre-chordal plate mesoderm, foregut entoderm, notochord, and somitic meso-

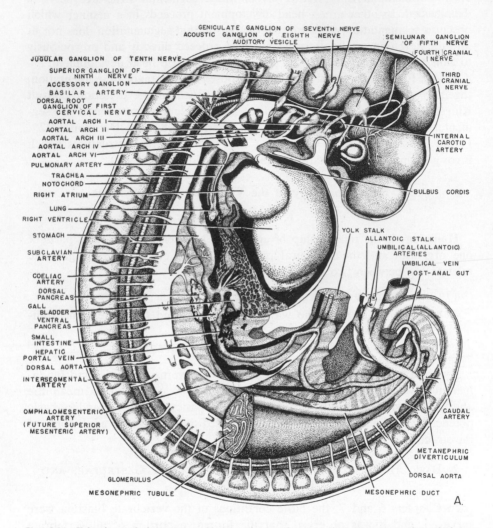

GENICULATE GANGLION OF SEVENTH NERVE
ACOUSTIC GANGLION OF EIGHTH NERVE
AUDITORY VESICLE
SEMILUNAR GANGLION OF FIFTH NERVE
FOURTH CRANIAL NERVE
JUGULAR GANGLION OF TENTH NERVE
SUPERIOR GANGLION OF NINTH NERVE
ACCESSORY GANGLION
BASILAR ARTERY
DORSAL ROOT GANGLION OF FIRST CERVICAL NERVE
AORTAL ARCH I
AORTAL ARCH II
AORTAL ARCH III
AORTAL ARCH IV
AORTAL ARCH VI
PULMONARY ARTERY
TRACHEA
NOTOCHORD
RIGHT ATRIUM
LUNG
RIGHT VENTRICLE
STOMACH
SUBCLAVIAN ARTERY
COELIAC ARTERY
DORSAL PANCREAS
GALL BLADDER
VENTRAL PANCREAS
SMALL INTESTINE
HEPATIC PORTAL VEIN
DORSAL AORTA
INTERSEGMENTAL ARTERY
OMPHALOMESENTERIC ARTERY (FUTURE SUPERIOR MESENTERIC ARTERY)
GLOMERULUS
MESONEPHRIC TUBULE
THIRD CRANIAL NERVE
INTERNAL CAROTID ARTERY
BULBUS CORDIS
YOLK STALK
ALLANTOIC STALK
UMBILICAL (ALLANTOIC) ARTERIES
UMBILICAL VEIN
POST-ANAL GUT
CAUDAL ARTERY
METANEPHRIC DIVERTICULUM
DORSAL AORTA
MESONEPHRIC DUCT
A.

FIG. 261. Drawings of pig embryos of about 9.5 to 12 mm.   (A) Reconstruction of about 9.5 to 10 mm. pig embryo with special emphasis on the arterial system.

derm appear to be the main organizing influence throughout the series (Chap. 10), the conclusion is inescapable that the tubulated embryos of all vertebrates are homologous basically, having the same relative parts, arising in the same manner, and possessing the same basic potencies within the parts. To this conclusion must be added a caution, namely, that, although the main segments or specific organ regions along each body tube of one species are homologous with similar segments along corresponding tubes of other species, variations may exist and non-homologous areas may be insinuated or homologous areas may be deleted along the respective tubes. Regardless of this possibility, a basic homology, however, appears to exist.

During later development through larval and definitive body-form stages, a considerable amount of **molding** or **plasis** by environmental and intrinsic factors may occur. An example of plasis is given in the development of the forelimb rudiment of the fish, frog, bird, and pig. In the definitive form, these structures assume different appearances and are adapted for different func-

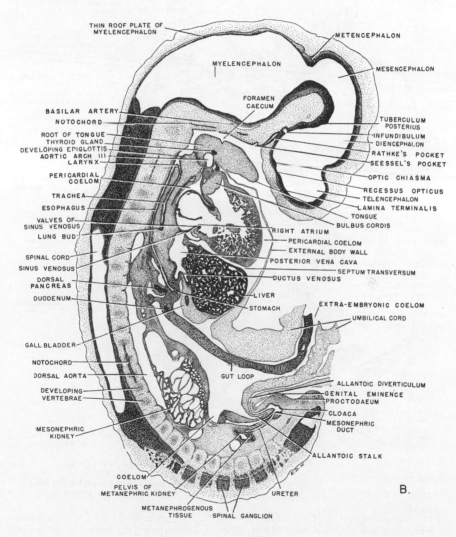

Fig. 261—*(Continued)* (B) Median sagittal section of 10 mm. embryo.

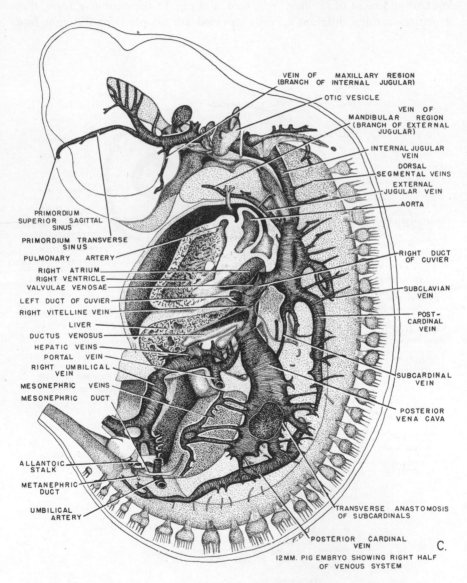

VEIN OF MAXILLARY REGION
(BRANCH OF INTERNAL JUGULAR)

OTIC VESICLE

VEIN OF
MANDIBULAR REGION
(BRANCH OF EXTERNAL
JUGULAR)

INTERNAL JUGULAR
VEIN

DORSAL
SEGMENTAL VEINS

EXTERNAL
JUGULAR VEIN

AORTA

PRIMORDIUM
SUPERIOR SAGITTAL
SINUS

PRIMORDIUM TRANSVERSE
SINUS

PULMONARY ARTERY

RIGHT ATRIUM
RIGHT VENTRICLE
VALVULAE VENOSAE
LEFT DUCT OF CUVIER
RIGHT VITELLINE VEIN
LIVER
DUCTUS VENOSUS
HEPATIC VEINS
PORTAL VEIN
RIGHT UMBILICAL
VEIN
MESONEPHRIC VEINS
MESONEPHRIC DUCT

RIGHT DUCT
OF CUVIER

SUBCLAVIAN
VEIN

POST-
CARDINAL
VEIN

SUBCARDINAL
VEIN

POSTERIOR
VENA CAVA

ALLANTOIC
STALK

METANEPHRIC
DUCT

UMBILICAL
ARTERY

TRANSVERSE ANASTOMOSIS
OF SUBCARDINALS

POSTERIOR CARDINAL
VEIN

C.

12 MM. PIG EMBRYO SHOWING RIGHT HALF
OF VENOUS SYSTEM

FIG. 261—*(Continued)* (C) Lateral view of 12 mm. embryo showing venous system. (C is redrawn and modified from Minot: 1903, A Laboratory Text-book of Embryology, Blakiston, Philadelphia.)

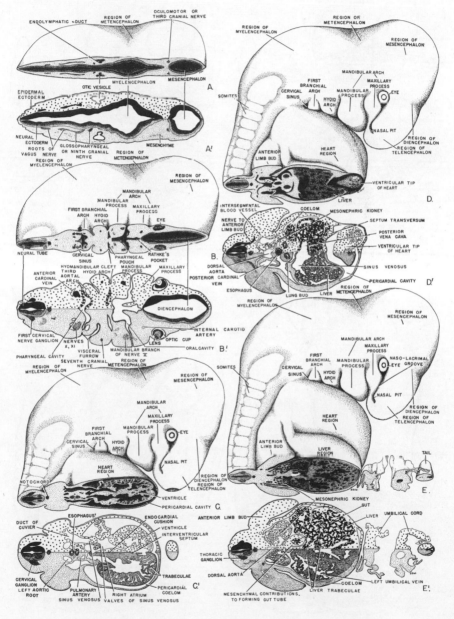

FIG. 262. Sections and stereograms of 10 mm. pig embryo.

549

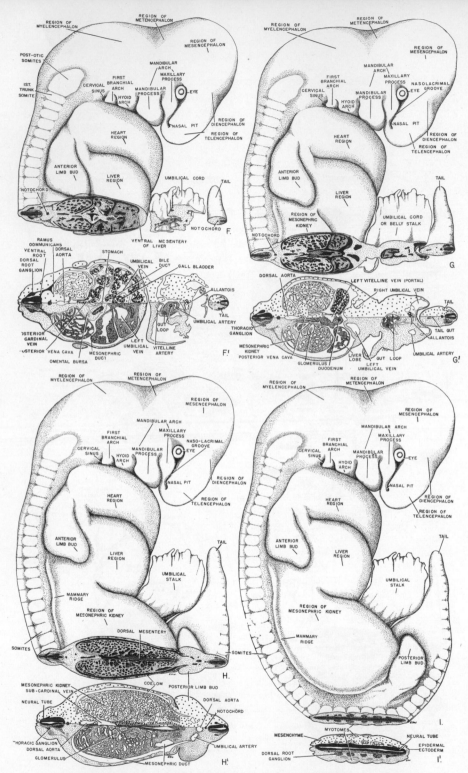

Fig. 262—*(Continued)* Sections and stereograms of 10 mm. pig embryo.

tional purposes. Basically, however, these structures are homologous, although **plasis** produces adult forms which appear to be different.

A further statement should be added, concerning that type of molding or plasis of a developing structure which produces similar structures from conditions which have had a different genetic history. For example, the bat's fore limb rudiment is molded to produce a structure resembling superficially that of the bird, although modern bats and birds have arisen through different lines of descent. Similarly, the teeth of certain teleost fishes superficially resemble the teeth of certain mammals, an effect produced from widely diverging lines of genetic descent. These molding effects or **homoplasy,** which produce superficially similar structures as a result of adaptations to certain environmental conditions, are called **convergence, parallelism,** and **analogy.** An example of experimental homoplasy is the induction of eye lenses in the embryo by the transplantation of optic-cup material to a place in the epidermis which normally does not produce a lens.

(*Note:* For a discussion of homology, homogeny, plasis, convergence, etc., see Tait, '28.)

Bibliography

Adelmann, H. B. **1925.** The development of the neural folds and cranial ganglia of the rat. J. Comp. Neurol. **39**:19

——. **1927.** The development of the eye muscles of the chick. J. Morphol. **44**:29.

——. **1932.** The development of the prechordal plate and mesoderm of *Amblystoma punctatum.* J. Morphol. **54**:1.

Baer, K. E. von. **1828–1837.** Über Entwickelungsgeschichte der Thiere. Beobachtung und Reflexion. Erster Theil, **1828**; Zweiter Theil, **1837.** Königsberg, Bornträger.

Balfour, F. M. **1878.** Monograph on the development of elasmobranch fishes. Republished in 1885 in The Works of Francis Maitland Balfour, edited by M. Foster and A. Sedgwick, vol. 1. The Macmillan Co., London.

Delsman, H. C. **1922.** The Ancestry of Vertebrates. Valkoff & Co., Amersfoort, Holland.

Goodrich, E. S. **1918.** On the development of the segments of the head of *Scyllium.* Quart. J. Micr. Sc. **63**:1.

Hill, J. P. and Tribe, M. **1924.** The early development of the cat (*Felis domestica*). Quart. J. Micr. Sc. **68**:513.

Huxley, T. H. **1858.** The Croonian lecture —on the theory of the vertebrate skull. Proc. Roy. Soc., London, s.B. **9**:381.

Kingsbury, B. F. **1915.** The development of the human pharynx. I. Pharyngeal derivatives. Am. J. Anat. **18**:329.

——. **1924.** The significance of the so-called law of cephalocaudal differential growth. Anat. Rec. **27**:305.

——. **1926.** Branchiomerism and the theory of head segmentation. J. Morphol. **42**:83.

—— and Adelmann, H. B. **1924.** The morphological plan of the head. Quart. J. Micr. Sc. **68**:239.

Kyle, H. M. **1926.** The Biology of Fishes. Sidgwick and Jackson, Ltd., London.

Landacre, F. L. **1921.** The fate of the neural crest in the head of urodeles. J. Comp. Neurol. **33**:1.

Lewis, W. H. **1910.** Chapter 12. The development of the muscular system in Manual of Human Embryology, edited by F. Keibel and F. P. Mall. J. B. Lippincott Co., Philadelphia.

Locy, W. A. **1895.** Contribution to the structure and development of the vertebrate head. J. Morphol. **11**:497.

Newth, D. R. **1951.** Experiments on the neural crest of the lamprey embryo. J. Exper. Biol. **28**:17.

Owen, R. **1848.** On the archetype and homologies of the vertebrate skeleton. John Van Voorst, London.

Raven, C. P. **1933a.** Zur Entwicklung der Ganglienleiste. I. Die Kinematik der Ganglienleistenentwicklung bei den Urodelen. Arch. f. Entwlngsmech. d. Organ. **125**:210.

————. **1933b.** Zur Entwicklung der Ganglienleiste. III. Die Induktionsfähigkeit des Kopfganglienleistenmaterials von *Rana fusca.*

Stone, L. S. **1922.** Experiments on the development of the cranial ganglia and the lateral line sense organs in *Amblystoma punctatum.* J. Exper. Zool. **35**:421.

————. **1926.** Further experiments on the extirpation and transplantation of mesectoderm in *Amblystoma punctatum.* J. Exper. Zool. **44**:95.

————. **1929.** Experiments showing the role of migrating neural crest (mesectoderm) in the formation of head skeleton and loose connective tissue in *Rana palustris.* Arch. f. Entwicklngsmech. d. Organ. **118**:40.

Tait, J. **1928.** Homology, analogy and plasis. Quart. Rev. Biol. **III**: 151.

PART IV

Histogenesis and Morphogenesis
of the Organ-Systems

For definitions of cytogenesis, histogenesis, etc., see Chap. 11; for histogenesis and morphogenesis of the organ systems, see Chaps. 12–21. The events described in Chapters 12–21 occur, to a great extent, during the *so-called larval period* or *period of transition*. During this period of development, the basic conditions of the various organ-systems which are present at the end of primitive embryonic body formation *are transformed into the structural features characteristic of definitive or adult body form.* In other words, during this phase of development, the basic, generalized morphological conditions of the various organ-systems of the embryo are rearranged and transformed into the adult form of the systems. As a result, the body as a whole assumes the definitive or adult form.

12

The Integumentary System

A. Introduction
  1. Definition and general structure of the vertebrate integument or skin
  2. General functions of the skin
  3. Basic structure of the vertebrate skin in the embryo
     a. Component parts of the developing integument
     b. Origin of the component parts of the early integument
        1) Origin of the epidermal component
        2) Origin of the dermal or mesenchymal component
        3) Origin of chromatophores
B. Development of the skin in various vertebrates
  1. Fishes
     a. Anatomical characteristics of the integument of fishes
     b. Development of the skin in the embryo of the shark, *Squalus acanthias*
        1) Epidermis
        2) Dermis
        3) Development of scales and glands
     c. Development of the skin in the bony ganoid fish, *Lepisosteus (Lepidosteus) osseus.*
     d. Development of the skin in the teleost fish
  2. Amphibia
     a. Characteristics of the amphibian skin
     b. Development of the skin in *Necturus maculosus*
     c. Development of the skin in the frog, *Rana pipiens*
  3. Reptiles
     a. Characteristics of the reptilian skin
     b. Development of the turtle skin
  4. Birds
     a. Characteristics of the avian skin
        1) Kinds of feathers
        2) General structure of feathers
           a) Pluma or contour feather
           b) Plumule or down feather
           c) Filoplume or hair feather
           d) Distribution of feathers on the body
     b. Development of the avian skin
        1) Development of the epidermis, dermis, and nestling down feather

A. Introduction

1. DEFINITION AND GENERAL STRUCTURE OF THE VERTEBRATE INTEGUMENT OR SKIN

The word integument means a cover. The word applies specifically to the external layer of the body which forms a covering for the underlying structures. The integument also includes the associated structures developed therefrom, such as hair, feathers, scales, claws, hoofs, etc. The latter are important features of the body covering. The skin is continuous with the digestive and urogenital tracts by means of mucocutaneous junctions at the lips, anus, and external genitalia.

The integument is composed of two main parts, an outer **epidermis** and an underlying **corium** or **dermis.** Below the latter is a third layer of connective tissue which connects or binds the corium to the underlying body tissues. This third layer forms the **superficial fascia** (tela subcutanea or hypodermis). The superficial fascia is continuous with the **deep fascia** or the connective tissue which overlies muscles, bones, and tendinous structures of the body (fig. 272H).

2. General Functions of the Skin

The integument acts as a barrier between other body tissues and the external environment. Modifications of the integument serve also as an external skeleton or exoskeleton in many vertebrates. In warm-blooded forms, the skin is associated intimately with the regulation of body temperature. The hypodermal portion of the skin often serves to store reserve fatty substances. The presence of fat functions as a buffer against mechanical injury from without, as reserve food, and as an aid in temperature regulation in warm-blooded species. Still another and very important function of the skin is its intimate association with the end organs of the peripheral nervous system by means of which the animal becomes acquainted with changes in the external environment. (See Chap. 19.)

3. Basic Structure of the Vertebrate Skin in the Embryo

a. Component Parts of the Developing Integument

In all vertebrates, the integument arises from a primitive embryonic integument which at first is composed of the cells of the epidermal tube only, i.e., the primitive epidermis. Later this rudimentary condition is supplemented by a condensation of mesenchymal cells below the epidermis. Following this contribution, the primitive skin is composed of two main cellular layers:

(1) a primitive epidermal (ectodermal) layer of one or two cells in thickness and
(2) an underlying mesenchymal layer.

The former gives origin to the epidermis, while the latter is the fundament of the dermis. A little later, **chromatophores** or pigment cells, presumably of neural crest origin, wander into the primitive dermis and become a conspicuous feature of this layer. In the development of the vertebrate group as a whole, these two **basic layers** serve as the basis for the later development of the integument. As a result, these two layers undergo characteristic modifications which enable the skin to fulfill its specific role in the various vertebrate species. The marked differences in later development of these two integumentary components in different vertebrate species are associated with the needs and functions of the skin in the adult form.

b. Origin of the Component Parts of the Early Integument

1) Origin of the Epidermal Component. The epidermal component descends directly from the primitive epidermal (ectodermal) organ-forming area of the late blastula, which, as we have seen, becomes greatly extended during gastrulation and, in the post-gastrular period, is tubulated into the elongated, cylinder-like structure. The primitive epidermal tube thus forms the initial skin or outer protective investment of the developing body.

The wall of the primitive epidermal tube at first may be composed of a single layer of cells of one cell in thickness, as in the shark, chick, pig, opossum, or human (figs. 263A; 269A; 272A). However, in teleost fishes and amphibia, the primitive epidermal tube is composed of two layers of cells. For example, in the sea bass, the wall of the primitive epidermal tube is composed of two layers, the outer layer being thin and made up of much-flattened cells and the lower layer being two cells in thickness (fig. 264A, B). In the anurans and urodeles, the wall of the primitive epidermal tube is composed of two layers, each of one cell in thickness (fig. 267A, D). The lower layer in the frog, salamander, and teleost often is referred to as the inner ectodermal or nervous layer. It is the germinative layer and thus forms the inner or lower portion of the **stratum germinativum** of the later epidermis (fig. 267A, D). The outer layer is densely pigmented and forms the **periderm.**

In the embryo of the shark, chick, and mammal, the single-layered condition of the primitive epidermal tube soon becomes transformed into a double-layered condition, the outer layer or **periderm** being composed of much-flattened cells (figs. 263B; 269B; 272B). In all vertebrates, therefore, the

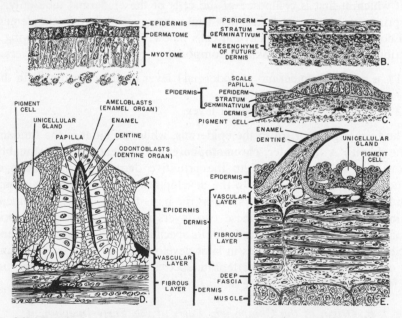

FIG. 263. Developing skin of *Squalus acanthias*. (A) Section through differentiating somite and epidermis of 10-mm. embryo. (B) Integument of 34-mm. embryo. (C) Section of skin, showing beginning of scale formation in 60-mm. embryo. (D) Scale development in 145-mm. embryo. (E) Later stage of placoid scale, projecting through epidermal layer of skin.

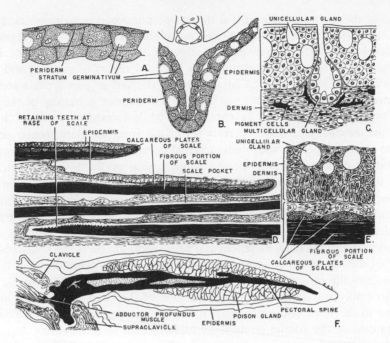

FIG. 264. Diagrams pertaining to the skin of bony fishes. (A and B after H. V. Wilson: Bull. U. S. Fish Commission, Vol. 9, 1889, reprint, 1891; C after Kingsley: Comp. Anat. of Vertebrates, 1912, P. Blakiston's Son & Co., Phila.; F from Reed; Am. Nat., 41.) (A) Section of ectoderm (primitive epidermis) of 39-hr. embryo of *Serranus atrarius,* the sea bass. (B) Epidermis of sea-bass embryo of 59 hrs. (C) Skin of the lungfish, *Protopterus.* (D) Integument of teleost fish with special reference to scales. (E) Higher power of epidermal and dermal tissue overlying scale in D. (F) Poison gland along pectoral spine of *Schilbeodes gyrinus.*

primitive epidermal layer of the skin eventually is composed of two simple cellular layers, an outer protective **periderm,** and a lower, actively proliferating **stratum germinativum.** It is to be observed further that the periderm in the recently hatched frog embryo possesses ciliated cells (fig. 267H, I). These cilia, as in *Amphioxus* (fig. 249B), are used for locomotor purposes, and also function to bathe the surface with fresh currents of water. As such, they probably play a part in external respiration.

The periderm forms a protective covering for the actively dividing and differentiating cells below. In the mammals, the periderm occasionally is called the **epitrichium,** as it eventually comes to rest upon the developing hair. In *Amphioxus,* there is no periderm, and the epidermal tube (epidermis) remains as a single layer of one cell in thickness (fig. 250E, F).

2) Origin of the Dermal or Mesenchymal Component. In *Amphioxus,* the thin lateral and ventro-lateral walls of the myotome give origin to the dermatome which comes to lie beneath the epidermal wall. From the dermatome arises the dermis or connective-tissue layer of the skin (fig. 250E, F). The origin of the embryonic dermis in the vertebrate group is more obscure than in *Amphioxus,* for in the vertebrates its origin varies in different regions of the developing body. Moreover, the origin of the dermal mesenchyme is not the same in all species. For example, in the head region of the frog and other amphibia, the dermal portion of the skin is derived in part from wandering mesenchyme of the head area, at least in the anterior extremity of the head and posteriorly to the otic or ear region, while immediately caudal to this area the mesenchyme of the dermis is derived from the dermatomic portion of the somite, together with mesenchymal contributions of the outer wall of the lateral plate mesoderm. In the trunk region of the body, mesenchyme from the dermatomic portion of the somite wanders off to form the embryonic connective-tissue layer of the skin in the dorso-lateral region of the embryo. In the middorsal region, sclerotomic mesenchyme appears to contribute to the dermal area. However, the dermal layer in the latero-ventral region of the body is derived from mesenchymal cells whose origin is the somatopleural layer of the hypomere (lateral plate mesoderm). The dermal layer in the tail arises from the mesenchyme within the developing end bud (tail bud).

The embryonic dermis in the head region of the chick arises from mesenchyme in the head and pharyngeal areas. In the cervico-truncal region, the dermatome of the somite contributes mesenchyme to the forming dermis on the dorso-lateral portion of the body wall (Engert, '00; Williams, '10; fig. 269C), whereas latero-ventrally the mesenchyme of the future dermis springs from the lateral wall of the hypomere. That portion of the developing dermis overlying the neural tube appears to receive contributions from the sclerotomic mesenchyme. The mesenchyme which forms the dermal layer of the skin in the tail descends from the mesoderm of the end bud (tail bud).

In the shark embryo, the origin of the embryonic dermis is similar to that of the amphibia. In the mammalian embryo, a small portion of the dermal tissue may arise from the dermatome; however, the greater part arises in the head and pharyngeal area from the mesenchyme within these areas, in the mid-dorsal region of the trunk from sclerotomic mesenchyme, and in the latero-ventral region of the trunk from the outer wall of the lateral plate. In the tail region, the tissue of the dermis derives from tail-bud mesoderm. Bardeen ('00) concluded that the dermatome in pig and man gives origin to muscle tissue. However, Williams ('10) doubted this conclusion. The fact remains that the exact fate of the dermatome or cutis plate of the somite in mammals, and even in the lower vertebrates, is not clear.

3) Origin of Chromatophores. Chromatophores or pigment-bearing cells occur in relation to the epidermis and the dermis. Dermal chromatophores are numerous in vertebrates from man down to the fishes. Pigment also appears in the epidermal cells, hair, feathers, and certain epidermal scales. This pigment is derived from melanoblasts or chromatophores which lie in the basal area of the epidermis or in the zone between the epidermis and the dermis

(Dushane, '44). Experimental embryology strongly suggests that these chromatophores are derived from the neural crest cells which in turn take origin from the primitive ectoderm in association with the neural tube at the time of neural tube closure. From the neural crests, the mesenchymal cells, which later give origin to chromatophores, migrate extensively throughout the body and to the skin areas (Dushane, '43, '44; Eastlich and Wortham, '46).

B. Development of the Skin in Various Vertebrates

1. Fishes

a. Anatomical Characteristics of the Integument of Fishes

The epidermal layer of the skin of fishes is soft, relatively thin, and composed of stratified squamous epithelium (figs. 263E; 264E; 265). Cornification of the upper layers is absent in most instances. However, in those fishes which come out of the water and spend considerable time exposed to the air, cornification of the surface cells occurs (Harms, '29). Unicellular mucous glands are abundant, and multicellular glands also are present (fig. 264C). A slimy mucous covering overlies the external surface of the epidermis. Poison glands may occur in proximity to protective spines or other areas (fig. 264F).

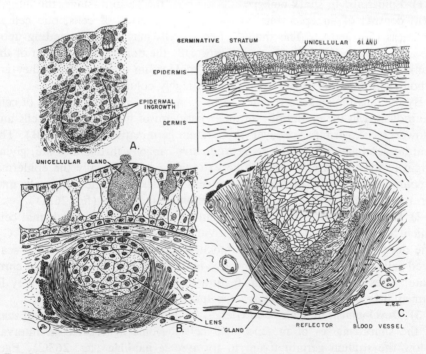

FIG. 265. Development of phosphorescent organ in *Porichthys notatus*. (From Greene: J. Morphol., 15.)   (A) Rudiment, separating from epidermis.   (B) Section of ventral organ of free-swimming larva.   (C) Section of fully developed ventral organ.

The dermal layer of fishes is a fibrous structure of considerable thickness. The layer of dermal tissue, immediately below the epidermis, is composed of loosely woven, connective-tissue fibers, copiously supplied with blood vessels, mesenchymal cells, and chromatophores. Below this rather narrow region is a thick layer, containing bundles of fibrous connective tissue. Between the latter and the muscle tissue is a thin, less fibrous, subcutaneous layer (fig. 263E).

Scales are present generally throughout the group and are of dermal origin in most species. However, both layers of the skin contribute to scale formation in the shark and ganoid groups of fishes. Scales are absent in some fishes as, for example, in cyclostomes and certain clasmobranchs, such as *Torpedo*. In certain teleosts, the scales are minute and are embedded in the skin. This condition is found in the family *Anguillidae* (eels).

Highly specialized, phosphorescent organs are developed in deep-sea fishes as ingrowths of masses of cells from the epidermis. (Consult Green, 1899.) These epidermal ingrowths (fig. 265A) separate from the epidermal layer and become embedded within the dermis (fig. 265B, C).

b. Development of the Skin in the Embryo of the Shark, Squalus acanthias

1) Epidermis. In shark embryos up to about the 15-mm. stage, the integument consists of an epidermis composed of one layer of cells, one cell in thickness (fig. 263A). The shapes of these cells may vary, depending upon the area of the body. In some areas, especially the dorso-lateral region of the trunk, they are flattened, while along the middorsum of the embryo they are cuboidal. In the pharyngeal area they are highly columnar.

By the time the embryo reaches 25 to 35 mm. in length, two layers of cells are indicated in the epidermis, an outer periderm of much-flattened cells and a lower, basal, germinative layer, the stratum germinativum (fig. 263B). The stratum germinativum retains its reproductive capacity throughout life, giving origin to the cells which come to lie external to it. Eventually the epidermis is composed of a layer of cells, several cells in thickness. The outer cells may form a thin squamous layer, covering the external surface (fig. 263D).

2) Dermis. The dermis gradually condenses from loose mesenchymal cells which lie below the stratum germinativum of the epidermis (fig. 263B, C). The dermis gradually increases in thickness and becomes composed of scattered cells, intermingled with connective-tissue fibers. Deeply pigmented chromatophores become a prominent feature of the dermal layer, where they lie immediately below the germinative stratum (fig. 263D, E).

3) Development of Scales and Glands. In the formation of the placoid scale of the shark, masses of mesenchymal cells become aggregated at intervals below the stratum germinativum to form **scale papillae** (fig. 263C). Each papilla gradually pushes the epidermis outward, especially the basal layer (fig. 263D). The cells of the outer margin of the papilla give origin to **odontoblasts**

or cells which secrete a hard, bone-like substance, resembling the **dentine** of the teeth of higher vertebrates (fig. 263D). This substance is closely related to bone. The cells of the basal epidermal layer, overlying the dentine-like substance, then form an enamel organ, composed of columnar **ameloblasts** which produce a hard, enamel-like coating over the outer portion of the conical mass of dentine (fig. 263D). As this scale or "tooth-like" structure increases in size, it gradually pushes the epidermis aside and projects above the surface as a placoid scale (fig. 263E). Some are small, while others are large and spine-like. Many different shapes and sizes of scales are formed in different areas of the body (Sayles and Hershkowitz, '37).

As the epidermis increases in thickness, unicellular glands appear within the epidermal layer (fig. 263D). These glands discharge their secretion of mucoid material externally, producing a slimy coating over the surface of the skin. Multicellular glands appear at the bases of the spines which develop at the anterior margins of the dorsal fins and in the epidermis overlying the claspers of the pelvic fins of the male.

c. Development of the Skin in the Bony Ganoid Fish, Lepisosteus (Lepidosteus) osseus

The development of the epidermis and dermis in *Lepisosteus* is similar to that of the shark embryo. Consideration, therefore, is confined to the development of the characteristic ganoid scale.

In the formation of the ganoid scale of *Lepisosteus,* a different mechanism is involved than in that of the placoid scale of the shark embryo. Most of the scale is of dermal origin; the epidermal contribution of enamel substance is small and restricted to the outer surface of the spines of the scale (fig. 266D-F).

The scale first appears as a thin calcareous sheet, secreted by the dermal cells in the outer portion of the dermis (fig. 266A). Unlike the formation of dentine in the shark skin, the calcareous material comes to enclose some of the scleroblasts **(osteoblasts)** or bone-forming cells (fig. 266B). This process continues as the scale increases in mass, and the scleroblasts become distributed as bone cells within the hard, bony substance of the scale. These cells occupy small spaces or **lacunae** within the bone-like substance, and small canals **(canaliculi)** traverse the hard substance of the scale to unite with similar canals from neighboring, bone-cell cavities (Nickerson, 1893, p. 123).

Spine-like projections (fig. 266F) appear on the surface of the bony scales. These spines are secondarily developed and form in a manner similar to the placoid scale of the elasmobranch fish. That is, a dermal papilla is formed externally to the already-formed dermal scale. This papilla pushes outward into the epidermal layer, and a dentine-like substance appears on its outer surface (fig. 266D). As development of the spine proceeds, this cap of dentine gradually creeps basalward and unites secondarily with the dentine of the

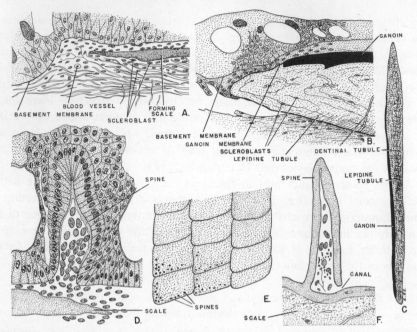

FIG. 266. Formation of the scale in *Lepisosteus (Lepidosteus) osseus*. (After Nickerson: Bull. Mus. Comp. Zool. at Harvard College, 24.) (A) Section through posterior end of scale of fish, 150 mm. long. (B) Section through posterior end of decalcified scale of fish, 300 mm. long. (C) Section through scale of fish, 300 mm. long. (D) Section showing developing spine. (E) Outlines of scales viewed from surface. (F) Section of scale spine attached to scale.

scale (fig. 266F). The papillary cells thus become entirely enclosed within the spines of dentine, with the exception of a small canal, leading to the exterior, at the base of the spine (fig. 266F). As the dentine-like spine develops, an enamel-like substance is deposited upon its outer surface by the epidermal cells.

Another characteristic of scale formation in *Lepisosteus* is the deposition of **ganoin** upon the outer surface of the scale (fig. 266B, C). This ganoin appears to have many of the characteristics of the enamel. It previously was considered to have been formed by the lower layer of epidermal cells, but Nickerson (1893) concluded that it is of dermal origin. The outer, ganoin-covered surface of the scale eventually lies exposed to the exterior in the adult condition and, therefore, is not covered by epidermal tissue.

Much of the external surface of the body of the bony ganoid fish, *Lepisosteus osseus* (common garpike), is covered with these plate-like scales, and, consequently, the epidermal layer of the skin tends to be pushed aside by this form of scaly armor. In *Amia calva* the epithelial (epidermal) covering is retained, and **cycloid scales,** similar to those of teleosts, are developed. The "ganoid" scales of *Amia* lack ganoin. They protect the head (fig. 316D).

d. Development of the Skin in the Teleost Fish

The early development of the epidermis and dermis in the teleost embryo resembles that of the shark embryo, and a soft glandular epidermis eventually is formed which overlies a thick, connective-tissue-layered dermis, containing numerous scale pockets, each containing a scale (fig. 264D, E). Consideration is given next to the development of the teleostean scale.

The development of the scale in teleost fishes is a complicated affair (Neave, '36, '40). It arises in the superficial area of the dermis in relation to an aggregation of cells. This aggregation of cells forms a **dermal pocket or cavity.** The latter contains a fluid or gelatinous substance. The scale forms within this cavity. A homogeneous scale rudiment of compact, connective-tissue fibers, the **fibrillary plate,** is established within the gelatinous substance of the scale pocket. A little later, **calcareous or bony platelets** are deposited upon this fibrous scale plate. The scale continues to grow at its periphery and, thus, stretches the dermal cavity. At the posterior margins of the scale, the dermal cavity becomes extremely thin. Further growth of the scale posteriorly pushes the epidermis outward, but the epidermis and the thin dermal cavity wall normally retain their integrity (fig. 264D).

The mature scale consists of a hard fibrous substrate, upon the upper posterior margins of which are embedded calcified plates. These calcified plates fuse together basally as development proceeds. Most of the scale is embedded deeply in the tissue of the dermal or scale pocket. At the anterior, deeply embedded end of the scale, small, hook-like, retaining barbs or teeth develop along the inner margins of the scale which serve to fasten the scale within the pocket (fig. 264D).

2. AMPHIBIA

a. Characteristics of the Amphibian Skin

The amphibian skin is soft, moist, and slimy. It is devoid of scales, with the exception of the *Gymnophiona* which possess patches of small scales embedded within pouches in the dermal layer of the skin (fig. 267J). However, some of the *Gymnophiona* lack scales entirely. Unicellular and multicellular glands of epidermal origin are a prominent feature of the amphibian skin (fig. 267F, G). Specialized poison glands also are present (Noble, '31, p. 133). Glands are developed in some species which attract the members of the opposite sex during the breeding season. In *Cryptobranchus,* the epidermal layer may be invaded by capillaries which penetrate almost to the surface of the skin in the region of the respiratory folds, located along the lateral sides of the body (Chap. 14). Cornification of the outer epidermal cells is the rule during later stages of development, in some species more than in others. For example, the development of a cornified layer is characteristic of the skin of toads, whose wart-like structures on the dorsal surface of the body represent areas of considerable cornification. Horny outgrowths of the epidermis are common in certain species.

The dermal layer in general is delicate and characterized by the presence of many pigment cells (chromatophores) of various kinds. The scales within the skin of the *Gymnophiona* are of dermal origin. In frogs, the dermis is

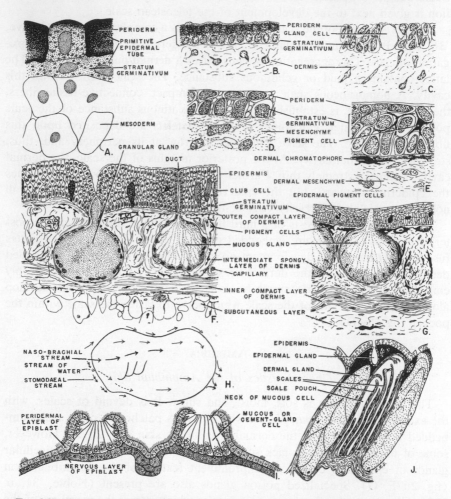

FIG. 267. Developing integument of amphibia. (A after Field: Bull. Mus. Comp. Zool. at Harvard College, 21; F after Dawson: J. Morphol., 34; H and I after Assheton: Quart. J. Micr. Sc., 38; J from Kingsley, 1925: The Vertebrate Skeleton, Blakiston, Philadelphia, after Sarasins.)   (A) Section of skin of frog embryo in neural plate stage.   (B) Section of skin of 10-mm. frog embryo.   (C) Skin of 34-mm. frog embryo.   (D) Skin of *Necturus* embryo, 6 mm. long.   (E) Skin of *Necturus* embryo, 20 mm. long.   (F) Structure of mature skin of *Necturus*.   (G) Structure of skin of *Rana pipiens* of section through head shortly after metamorphosis.   (H) Frog embryo, 3 mm. long, showing water streams produced by cilia.   (I) Semidiagrammatic figure through suckers of frog embryo, 6 to 7 mm. long.   (J) Section of skin of the Gymnophionan, *Epicrium*.

separated from the deeper areas of the body along the dorso-lateral region of the trunk by the presence of large lymph spaces.

b. Development of the Skin in Necturus maculosus

The newly formed, epidermal tube of a 6-mm. embryo of *Necturus* consists of two layers of epidermal cells, an outer periderm and an inner stratum germinativum (fig. 267D). In the ventro-lateral region of the trunk, however, these two layers are flattened greatly and may become so attenuated that only one layer of flattened cells is present. Unicellular glands appear in the head region and represent modifications of cells of the outer ectodermal (peridermal) layer.

In larvae of 18 to 20 mm. in length, the epidermis is 3 to 4 cells in thickness, with the outer layer considerably flattened (fig. 267E). The dermis consists of a mass of mesenchymal cells, with large numbers of chromatophores lying near the epidermis. Chromatophores also lie extensively within the epidermal layer; some even approach the outer periphery. According to Eycleshymer ('06), some of the pigment cells of the epidermis represent modified epithelial cells, while others appear to invade the epidermis from the dermis. Dawson ('20) believed these epidermal pigment cells to be entirely of an epidermal origin in *Necturus*. Dushane ('43, p. 124) considered the origin of epidermal pigment cells in *Amphibia* in general to be uncertain but suggested "that these cells also come from the neural crest" via the dermal mesenchyme.

Later changes in the developing skin consist in an increase in the number of epithelial cells and in a great increase in the thickness of the dermis, with the formation of bundles of connective-tissue fibers. Associated with these changes, two types of multicellular alveolar glands arise as invaginations into the dermis from the stratum germinativum. One type of gland is the granular or poison gland, and the other is the mucous gland. The latter type is more numerous (fig. 267F). Mixed glands, partly mucous and partly granular, also may appear (Dawson, '20). Large club-shaped cells or unicellular glands may be observed in the lower epidermal areas, while flattened cornified elements lie upon the outer surface of the epidermis.

The dermis is arranged in three layers as follows:

(a) a thin, outer, compact layer between the lower epidermal cells and the dermal chromatophores,

(b) below this outer compact layer, the intermediate spongy layer, containing some elastic, connective-tissue fibers as well as white fibers, and

(c) below the spongy layer, the inner compact layer.

The chromatophores located in the outer part of the dermal layer are of different kinds (see p. 591).

c. Development of the Skin in the Frog, Rana pipiens

The development of the skin of the common frog resembles closely that of *Necturus*. The primitive epidermal tube consists of two layers of ectodermal cells, an outer periderm and a lower nervous layer or stratum germinativum (fig. 267A). The cells of the periderm contain pigment granules, and unicellular glands also are present, particularly in the head region. At the 10-mm. stage, the outer, pigmented, peridermal layer begins to flatten, while the stratum germinativum assumes the normal characteristics of the reproductive stratum of the epidermis (fig. 267B). The cells are cuboidal and closely arranged. A condensation of mesenchyme, immediately below the thin epidermal layer, represents the rudiment of the future dermis. Chromatophores are prevalent in the dermal area. In figure 267C are shown the characteristics of the skin of the head area of the 34-mm. tadpole, while figure 267G represents the skin of the head region of the newly metamorphosed frog. In this area of the body, the dermis is compact and dense, but in the dorso-lateral area of the trunk, large lymph spaces are present in the dermis.

3. REPTILES

a. Characteristics of the Reptilian Skin

Most reptiles are land-frequenting animals. The land type of habitat dictates the development of a mechanism which keeps the lower layers of the epidermis soft and moist. The problem of epidermal drying is not encountered to any great extent in the fishes and most amphibia because of the moist conditions under which they live. To circumvent the drying effects imposed upon land-living animals, the outer layers of the skin become cornified. A superficial or outer **stratum corneum,** therefore, becomes a prominent feature of the epidermis of reptiles, birds, and mammals.

Aside from its role of protecting the lower epidermal layers of cells against loss of moisture, the cornified layer also functions as a protective mechanism against mechanical injury. Foot pads, friction ridges, and all calloused structures are evidence of this function. The cornified stratum represents flattened, dead, epithelial cells, infiltrated with a protein substance, **keratin,** present abundantly in all horny structures, such as claws, scales, etc.

Both epidermal and dermal layers are thickened considerably in reptiles, while epidermal glands, so prominent in fishes and amphibia, are absent, with the exception of certain specialized regions in the oral and anal areas, between the carapace and plastron of some turtles, and between the scales in certain areas of the skin of crocodiles and alligators.

b. Development of the Turtle Skin

The turtle is an example of an armored animal, possessing a "shell" consisting of a **dermal skeleton,** the carapace, and the plastron, composed of a

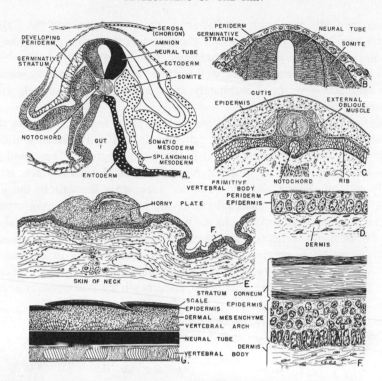

FIG. 268. Development of turtle skin. (A) Section through turtle embryo, showing early division of epidermis into periderm and germinative stratum. (B) Section showing two-layered condition of epidermis in slightly older embryo. (C) Section through dorsal area of embryo, 11 mm. long. (D) Higher power drawing of epidermis of 11-mm. embryo. (E) Section of skin of turtle, after hatching, to show horny plates. (F) Higher power sketch of skin shown in square in (E). (G) Section of skin of turtle just before hatching, showing epidermal scales of carapace, dermal mesenchyme, and vertebrae.

series of interlocking bony paltes, associated with an outer cover, the **epidermal skeleton,** composed of horny scutes. The latter comprises the so-called tortoise shell of commerce. The dorsal carapace and ventral plastron are united along their lateral edges by a bony ridge, and the carapace is firmly fused with the vertebrae and ribs of the endoskeleton. The skin of the head, neck, tail, and legs is fortified with thick horny plates placed at intervals (fig. 268E). Between these horny plates, the stratum corneum is highly developed (fig. 268F).

At the 11- to 15-mm. stage, the condensation of dermal mesenchyme already is thickened greatly in the dorsal region of the embryo in the future carapace area. This thickened condition and the intimate association of the mesenchyme with the trunk vertebrae and ribs are shown in figure 268C. The rudiment of the plastron begins to appear in the ventral region at this time.

After the young hatch from the egg, ossifications occur within the dermal mesenchyme of the carapace and plastron. The bony ossifications of the carapace gradually fuse with the flattened trunk vertebrae and the flattened ribs. In figure 268G is shown a longitudinal section through a part of the mid-dorsal area of a turtle just before hatching. It is to be observed that the epidermal horny scales or scutes are well formed, while the dermal mesenchyme of the carapace is wrapped intimately around the flattened, dorsal, spinous processes of the vertebrae.

Epidermal scales and thickened horny skin pads, together with an armor of bone, in turtles, demonstrate the types of dermal and epidermal differentiations which form a protective coat in the reptilian group. The "shed skin" of the snake represents a sheet of horny epidermal scales which is periodically cast off. New scales are reformed repeatedly throughout the life of snakes. The rattles on the terminal end of the tail in the rattlesnake represent horny rings, developed proximal to the horny spine, prevalent as the end piece of the tail of many serpents. Lizards are well protected with thick epidermal scales, and in some species these scales are reinforced with dermal bony plates. The crocodiles are tough-skinned animals, possessing thick epidermal scales; the dorsal scales are supported underneath by corresponding dermal

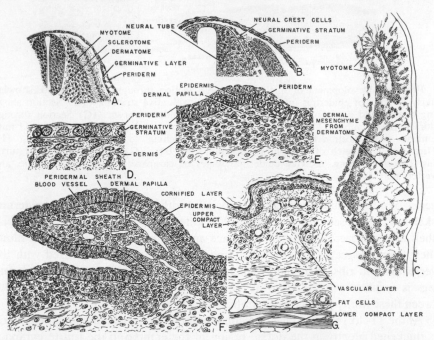

FIG. 269. Development of skin in the chick. (C after Williams: Am. J. Anat., 11.) (A) Epidermis of 48-hr. chick. (B) Epidermis of 72-hr. chick. (C) Dermal mesenchyme, arising from dermatome of embryo of 40 somites. (D) Skin of chick embryo, incubation six days. (E) Skin of eight-day embryo, showing beginning of feather rudiment. (F) Eleven-day embryo, feather rudiment. (G) Section of mature skin between feather outgrowths. Observe that the epidermis is thin, and that the dermis is composed of two compact layers separated by a vascular layer.

bony plates. Horny claws develop upon the digits of the appendages in turtles, crocodiles, and lizards.

4. Birds

a. Characteristics of the Avian Skin

The skin of the bird is more delicate than that of the reptile. The epidermal layer is thin with a highly cornified external surface. The dermis is composed of an outer compact layer below the epidermis, and beneath the latter is a vascular layer. Below the vascular layer is another compact layer of connective-tissue fibers, and between this layer and the deep fascia is the characteristic adipose (fatty) layer (fig. 269G). Extensive cutaneous glands are not developed. However, the two **uropygial** or preening glands at the base of the tail are common to most birds, although they are not present in the ostriches. In certain gallinaceous birds, such as the common fowl, modified sebaceous glands are present around the ear. Scales, resembling the reptilian type, are developed on the distal parts of the legs, while feathers present a feature characteristic of the avian skin.

1) Kinds of Feathers. Feathers are of many kinds, but they may be grouped under three major categories:

(1) **plumae** (plumous or pennaceous feathers), the most perfectly constructed type of feather, filling the role of contour feathers,

(2) **plumules** (plumulae or plumulaceous feathers), making up the under feather coat or down, and

(3) **filoplumes** or hair feathers.

Of all the epidermal structures developed in the vertebrate group, feathers appear to be the most ingeniously constructed. They possess to a high degree the qualities of lightness, strength, and toughness which serve to protect a delicately constructed skin from cold, moisture, and abrasion.

2) General Structure of Feathers: a) Pluma or Contour Feather. The plumous feather consists of a **rachis (shaft or scape)** and a **vane.** The proximal portion of the rachis or shaft is the **quill** or **calamus.** The latter is hollow but may contain a small amount of loose pith. It has an opening, the **inferior umbilicus,** at its base. The quill resides in a **feather follicle,** a deep pit surrounded by epidermal tissue projecting downward into the dermal part of the skin (fig. 270D, E). Above the quill is the expanded "feathery" portion of the feather, called the **vane.** At the junction of the quill and the vane is a small opening, the **superior umbilicus,** to which is attached, in some contour feathers, a secondary, smaller shaft, the **aftershaft** or **hyporachis,** together with a group of irregularly placed barbs.

The shaft of the vane of the feather is semisolid, with its interior filled with a mass of horny, air-filled cavities. Extending outward from the shaft in this area are lateral branches or **barbs** (fig. 270E). The barbs form two

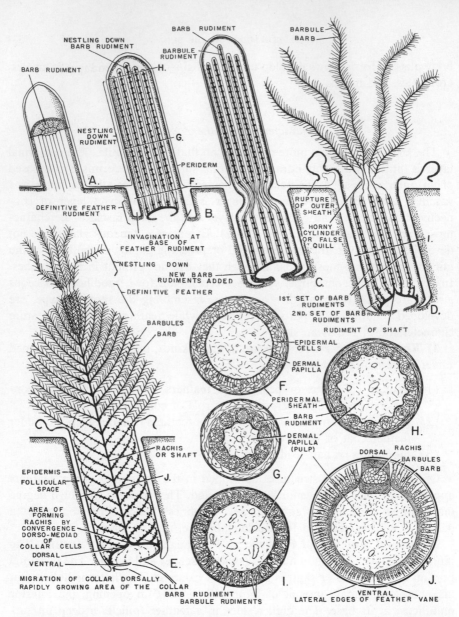

FIG. 270. Diagrams of developing feathers in chick. (A) Nestling, down-feather rudiment of chick of about 12 days of incubation. (B) Feather rudiment, 12 to 14 days of incubation, showing beginning of definitive feather rudiment. (C) Nestling down rudiment and definitive feather rudiment of chick shortly before hatching. (D) Relation of nestling down feather to definitive feather shortly after hatching. (E) Later stage in definitive feather development; nestling down feather is attached to distal end of first definitive feather. (F–H) Cross sections of nestling down rudiment diagrammatically shown in (B). (I) Cross section of definitive feather rudiment shown in (D). (J) Cross section of definitive rudiment shown in (E). It is to be noted that the sheath around the developing feather extends for a considerable distance beyond the surface of the skin during development. This area is shortened considerably in E for diagrammatic purposes. F–I based on data from Jones ('07).

572

rows, one on either side of the shaft. From the barbs, smaller branches extend outward; the latter are the **barbules** (fig. 270E). An interlocking system of hooks, the **barbicels,** enables the barbule of one barb to connect with a barbule of the next barb. If these interlocking hooks are disrupted mechanically, the bird restores them while preening its feathers.

b) PLUMULE OR DOWN FEATHER. The **plumules** or **down feathers** form an inner feathery coat which lies below the contour feathers in the adult bird. They constitute the main insulating portion of the feather coat. In the down feathers of the adult, the barbs arise in bouquet fashion at the distal end of the quill. On the other hand, the nestling or first down feathers of the chick or newly hatched birds of other species do not possess a quill, for the barbs are attached to the distal ends of the apical barbs of the definitive feather (fig. 270F). Therefore, two types of down feathers are found:

(1) the nestling down feather without a quill and
(2) the later down feather which possesses a quill.

The barbules in down feathers do not interlock, and a vane is not formed (fig. 270D, E).

c) FILOPLUME OR HAIR FEATHER. The **filoplume** or **hair feather** possesses a long slender shaft which generally is deprived of barbs, although a tuft of barbs may be present at the distal end.

d) DISTRIBUTION OF FEATHERS ON THE BODY. Feathers are not evenly distributed over the surface of the body but arise in certain definite areas or feather tracts, the **pterylae.** Between the pterylae are the **apteria** or areas where the number of feathers are reduced or absent altogether. When feathers are present in an apterium, they consist mainly of a scanty distribution of downy and filoplumous feathers.

b. Development of the Avian Skin

1) Development of the Epidermis, Dermis, and Nestling Down Feather. When the epidermal tube in the chick embryo begins to form, it consists of a single layer of cells of one cell in thickness. As development proceeds, this single-layered condition becomes transformed into a double layer, so that at 48 to 72 hours of incubation a two-layered epidermis is realized. This condition consists of an outer layer or periderm, considerably flattened, and an inner layer or stratum germinativum (fig. 269A, B). At 96 hours of incubation in most parts of the developing integument, a primitive dermis is present as a loose aggregate of mesenchyme below the two-layered epidermis. The origin of a part of this mesenchyme from the dermatome is shown in figure 269C. At six days of incubation, mesenchyme is present as a definite dermal condensation (fig. 269D).

Between the sixth and eighth days of incubation, the epidermis and dermis increase in thickness, and small, mound-like protuberances begin to appear in certain areas (fig. 269E). Each elevation is produced by a mass of cells, known as the **dermal papilla,** which pushes the epidermal layer outward (fig. 269E). The initial dermal papillae represent the beginnings of the feather rudiments. At eleven days of incubation, many feather rudiments have made their appearance. Each rudiment consists of a central, mesenchymal (dermal) core or pulp, surrounded externally by epidermal cells. The dermal pulp is supplied copiously with small blood vessels (fig. 269F). The epidermal cells at this time are beginning to be arranged into longitudinal columns of cells. These longitudinal cellular columns represent the initial stages of barb-rudiment development (fig. 270A). This condition of the developing feather marks the beginning of the first or the "nestling down" feathers.

At 12 to 14 days of incubation, the feather rudiment increases considerably in length and begins to invaginate into the dermal layer at its base (fig. 270B). This invagination of the base of the feather rudiment marks the beginning of definitive feather formation (Jones, '07). In the developing feather from 14 to 17 days of incubation, two general regions are indicated. These regions of the developing feather are:

(a) a region from the surface of the skin to the distal end of the feather germ where the barbs and barbules of the nestling down are being formed (fig. 270B) and

(b) a proximal region below the surface of the skin where the barbs and barbules of the definitive feather begin to differentiate (fig. 270B).

After the seventeenth day, the differentiation of the definitive feather proceeds rapidly (fig. 270C, D).

From the fourteenth to the seventeenth days, the barbs of the nestling down feathers elongate slightly by adding new ridge material at the basal end of each ridge (fig. 270B, C). The length of the barb rudiments of the down feather thus increases as the feather rudiment grows outward from the surface of the skin. As the barb rudiments elongate, they differentiate into the barbs and barbules (fig. 271B, C). (See Davies, 1889; Strong, '02.) At about eighteen days of incubation, such a feather may be removed, and the distal portion of the horny sheath may be ruptured with a needle. Following the rupture of the horny sheath, the enclosed barbs will spread out as shown in the distal part of the developing feather in figure 270D.

At eighteen to twenty days of incubation, feather development in the chick may be represented as shown in figure 270C and D. A distal or nestling-down-feather region and a proximal definitive-feather area are present. Barbs and barbules of the definitive feather differentiate in the proximal area. A real quill is not established at the base of the nestling down feather, although a horny cylinder may intervene between the base of the down feather and the barbs of the definitive feather (fig. 270D). (See Jones, '07.) Thus, in the chick and most birds, the first or nestling down feather and the succeeding definitive feather are developed as one continuous process, and cannot be regarded as two separate feather growths (Jones, '07, p. 17). When the chick hatches, the outer horny sheath around the differentiated down feather dries and cracks open, and the barbs and barbules of the down feather spread out into fuzzy tufted structures (fig. 270D). Later, as the definitive feather emerges from the surface of the skin, the down-feather barbs appear as delicate tufts, attached to the distal ends of the barbs of the definitive feather (fig. 270E).

2) Development of the Contour Feather. The development of the contour feather is more complicated than that of the nestling down feather described above. Its development may be divided into early or primary and later or secondary phases (Lillie and Juhn, '32). The formation of barbs during the early phase consists in the elaboration of barb and barbule rudiments without a shaft rudiment. This type of development resembles somewhat that of the down feather. The secondary phase of contour–feather development is concerned with the formation of a shaft, as well as the barb and barbule rudiments.

a) FORMATION OF BARBS DURING THE PRIMARY OR EARLY PHASE OF CONTOUR-FEATHER FORMATION. During the first phase of contour-feather formation, the barbs are formed in two different orders. The first order of barb rudiments arises more or less simultaneously (Lillie and Juhn, '32); they are practically of the same size, about equal in number on either side, and dorsally placed. After this first set of barb rudiments is formed, a second order of barb rudiments arises in seriatim with the youngest barb rudiments, located more ventrally. (See first and second sets of barb rudiments in fig. 270D.) Both of these sets of barb rudiments eventually give origin to the barbs at the apical or distal end of the feather. As a shaft is not formed during the period when these two sets of barb rudiments are developing, i.e., during the first phase of definitive, contour-feather formation, these barbs later become associated with the forming shaft as the latter develops during the next or second phase of feather formation.

b) SECONDARY PHASE OF CONTOUR-FEATHER FORMATION. Following the formation of the barb rudiments mentioned above, the second phase of feather formation is initiated. It consists in the formation of the shaft and the further development of barb ridges and barbules. The development of the shaft is effected by the migration dorsalward of the collar cells (fig. 270E), which produces a continuous concrescence and fusion in the middorsal line of the two dorsal ends of the barb-bearing collar. This fusion of the collar cells forms the rudiment of the shaft as indicated in figure 270D. This concrescence of cells, however, establishes only the rudiment of the shaft, for it is apparent that the development of the shaft results from two sets of processes:

(1) the concrescence of a segment of the shaft rudiment at a particular point in the middorsal line of the feather rudiment and

(2) the elongation and growth of the rudiment material thus established.

As the shaft is laid down progressively from apex to base, the continuous concrescence of the collar cells and gradual formation of the shaft rudiment along the middorsal plane of the feather germ bring about the formation of the shaft (Lillie, '40; Lillie and Juhn, '32, '38), beginning at its apex and progressing baseward.

As the collar material is fed into the developing shaft rudiment dorsally, the bases of the barbs, which are located in the collar or germinative ring, are carried continuously dorsalward and eventually become located along the sides of the shaft (fig. 270E). Also, the first set of barbs, which was formed in the first phase of contour-feather formation, becomes attached along either side of the developing shaft in the same way that the later barbs become attached.

In the formation of the barb, the apical or distal end of the barb is laid down by cellular contributions from the collar. Following this, more basal or proximal portions of the barb are elaborated by cellular deposition from the collar cells. The base of the barb thus remains attached to the collar as the barb rudiment elongates, while the apex maintains its position in the midventral line. As the base of the barb and the collar material to which it is attached move dorsalward toward the forming shaft, as observed in the previous paragraph, the base of the barb comes in contact with and fuses with the rachis or shaft, whereas the ventral extremity, i.e., the distal end of the barb, remains associated with the mesodermal pulp along the ventral aspect of the developing feather (fig. 271A). The barb thus comes to form a half spiral around the developing feather within the external horny sheath (fig. 270E). As successive barb rudiments are laid down, the previously formed barbs are moved progressively distad along with the mesodermal core.

c) FORMATION OF THE BARBULES AND THE FEATHER VANE. During the period when the barbs are being formed, the side branches of the barbs or **barbules** are developed by the formation of groups of cells along either side of the barb (fig. 271B, C). Each of these groups of barbule cells differentiates into a barbule. A barbule thus represents a group of cells, specialized to form an elongated structure as shown in figure 271D. After the distal end of the feather extends markedly beyond the surface of the skin, the horny sheath breaks, and the barbs and barbules expand to form the vane of the feather. In doing so, the barbules interlock by means of **barbicels** which develop on the barbules, located on the side of the barbs facing toward the apex of the feather (fig. 271D).

d) LATER DEVELOPMENT OF THE FEATHER SHAFT. During its development, the shaft gradually enlarges in the direction of the base of the feather. When the feather approaches its mature length, the shaft has enlarged to the extent that it comes to occupy the entire basal portion of the feather rudiment. As the last condition develops, barb formation becomes less exact until finally it is suppressed altogether. When this stage is reached, the contained dermal pulp within the base of the shaft begins to atrophy, starting at the end

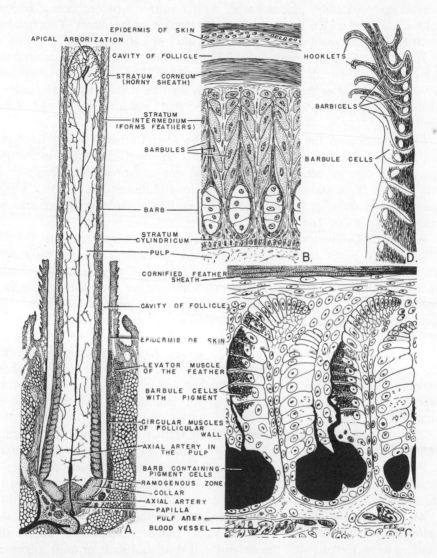

EPIDERMIS OF SKIN
APICAL ARBORIZATION
CAVITY OF FOLLICLE
HOOKLETS
STRATUM CORNEUM
(HORNY SHEATH)
BARBICELS
STRATUM
INTERMEDIUM
(FORMS FEATHERS)
BARBULES
BARBULE CELLS
BARB
STRATUM
CYLINDRICUM
PULP
B.
D.
CORNIFIED FEATHER
SHEATH
CAVITY OF FOLLICLE
EPIDERMIS OF SKIN
LEVATOR MUSCLE
OF THE FEATHER
BARBULE CELLS
WITH PIGMENT
CIRCULAR MUSCLES
OF FOLLICULAR
WALL
AXIAL ARTERY IN
THE PULP
BARB CONTAINING
PIGMENT CELLS
RAMOGENOUS ZONE
COLLAR
AXIAL ARTERY
PAPILLA
PULP AREA
BLOOD VESSEL
A.

FIG. 271. Diagrams of feather development. (A from F. R. Lillie: Physiol. Zoöl., 13; C and D redrawn from Strong: Bull. Mus. Comp. Zool. at Harvard, '40.) (A) Semidiagrammatic drawing of the pulp (papilla) of a regenerating feather. The axial artery of the feather is shown traversing the pulp to the distal end. The veins of the pulp (not shown) consist of a series of central and peripheral veins which connect with venous sinuses at the base of the pulp and, from thence, communicate with the cutaneous veins. (B) Part of transverse section of a feather follicle, showing the developing barbs and barbules. (C) Transverse section of a feather rudiment of the tern, *Sterna hirundo*. Pigment cells, within the barb substance, send out processes which distribute melanin to the cells of the developing barbule. (D) Middle portion of wing-feather barbule, showing pigment within individual barbule cells together with the distal barbicels with their hooklets; cornification is not complete.

nearest the proximally placed barbs. As a result, a series of horny, hollow cells are formed within the base of the developing feather shaft. This hollow, basal end of the feather shaft forms the quill or calamus. The quill has a proximal umbilicus or opening through which the dermal pulp extends into the interior of the quill in the intact feather (fig. 271A). A distal umbilicus, from which the after feather emerges, may also be present in some feathers at the point where the ventral groove of the shaft meets the upper end of the quill.

3) Formation of the After Feather. The after feather emerges from the upper end of the quill of the contour feather. It is well developed in the unspecialized, contour feather but may be absent or represented merely by a few barbs in flight and tail feathers of the fowl (Lillie and Juhn, '38). For a description of the after feather and its distribution in birds, reference may be made to Chandler ('16).

As observed above, when the rachis or shaft reaches a certain size, the development of barbs tends to be suppressed. A stage is reached ultimately when the barbs are irregular and not well formed. Consequently, the barbs near the quill lose all tendency to form a vane and are placed in an irregular fashion along the shaft. As this distortion of barb development occurs dorsally, some of the developing barbs on the ventral side of the enlarged shaft become physiologically and morphologically isolated from those which are moving dorsad in the normal fashion along the collar. As a result, they remain on the ventral surface and, in this position, they endeavor to form a twin feather. In doing so, they become attached in their isolated position to the ventral aspect of the forming quill. The superior umbilicus marks this point of attachment.

The degree of development of the after feather varies from the presence of a few barbs to a condition where a well-formed, miniature, secondary feather is developed. The secondary or after feather in this condition possesses a secondary rachis or aftershaft, known as the **hyporachis,** and is attached to the main rachis at the superior umbilicus.

4) Development of the Later Down and Filoplumous Feathers. The development of the later down or undercoat feather is similar to that of the nestling down feather, with the exception that a basal shaft or quill is formed to which the barbs become attached at the distal end of the quill. In the formation of the hair feather or filoplume, an elongated shaft of small diameter is formed to which a few small barbs may be attached at the distal end.

5. MAMMALS

a. Characteristics of the Mammalian Skin

The adult skin of mammals is characterized by a highly cornified, outer layer of the epidermis, together with the presence of numerous glands and hair. Hair, a distinguishing feature of the mammalian skin, is present in all species, with the exception of the *Cetacea* (whales) and the *Sirenia* (sea cows). Various types of horny structures are associated with the epidermis, while the dermis may develop plates of bone in certain instances. Both epidermis and dermis are of considerable thickness.

b. Development of the Skin

1) Development of the Skin in General. As in other vertebrates, the primitive mammalian integument is formed by the epidermal tube which, when first developed, consists of a single layer, one cell in thickness (fig. 272A). Later it becomes double layered, having an external flattened **periderm** and an inner **stratum germinativum.** As in other vertebrates, the germinative stratum is the reproductive layer. Mesenchyme condenses below the germinative stratum, and the rudiment of the future dermis is formed (fig. 272B).

In the further development of the epidermal layer, a third layer of cells, the **stratum intermedium,** appears between the periderm and the stratum germinativum (fig. 272C). The stratum germinativum or deep layer of Malpighi may appear to be several cells in thickness as development proceeds. The cells of the germinative stratum, in contact with the dermal surface, are cuboidal or cylindrical (fig. 272C, D). During later development, the epidermis becomes highly stratified, and the outer or external layer is converted into a cornified layer, the **stratum corneum** (fig. 272D). Cornification occurs first on the future contact surfaces of the appendages, such as the volar surface of the hand, plantar surface of the foot, and foot pads of the cat, dog, etc. Pigment granules (melanin) appear in the deepest layers of the epidermis in the region of the basal, cylindrical cells of the stratum germinativum during later fetal development and after parturition (birth).

In the meantime, the dermal mesenchyme increases in thickness, and various types of connective-tissue fibers, white and elastic (see Chap. 15), appear in the intercellular substance between the mesenchymal cells. Pigment cells make their appearance in the dermis during later fetal development. These cells descend, probably, from cells of neural crest origin, although other mesenchymal cells possibly may contribute to the store of pigment-forming cells. Fat cells occur in the deeper layers of the dermis.

2) Development of Accessory Structures Associated with the Skin: a) Development of the Hair. The first indication of hair development is the formation of a localized thickening and invagination of the epidermal layer, particularly the germinative stratum (fig. 272E). This thickened mass of epidermal cells pushes inward, accompanied by an increase in the number of epidermal cells in the area of invagination (fig. 272F). Adjacent mesenchymal cells of the dermis respond to this epidermal activity by aggregating about the invaginating mass (fig. 272E, F). As the germinative stratum with its central core of cells continues to push downward in tangential fashion

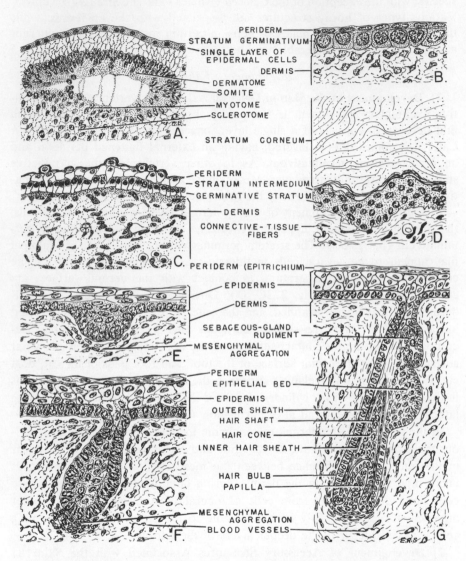

PERIDERM
STRATUM GERMINATIVUM
SINGLE LAYER OF
EPIDERMAL CELLS
DERMIS
DERMATOME
SOMITE
MYOTOME
SCLEROTOME
A.
B.

STRATUM CORNEUM

PERIDERM
STRATUM INTERMEDIUM
GERMINATIVE STRATUM
DERMIS
CONNECTIVE-TISSUE
FIBERS
C.
D.

PERIDERM (EPITRICHIUM)
EPIDERMIS
DERMIS
SEBACEOUS-GLAND
RUDIMENT
MESENCHYMAL
AGGREGATION
E.

PERIDERM
EPITHELIAL BED
EPIDERMIS
OUTER SHEATH
HAIR SHAFT
HAIR CONE
INNER HAIR SHEATH
HAIR BULB
PAPILLA
MESENCHYMAL
AGGREGATION
BLOOD VESSELS
F.
G.
E.R.S.D

FIG. 272. Diagrams of developing hair. (A from Johnson: Carnegie Inst., Washington, Publ. No. 226, Contrib. to Embryol., 6; C and D from Pinkus, Chap. 10, The development of the integument, Keibel and Mall, 1910, Vol. I, Lippincott, Phila.) (A) Section through epidermis of 24-somite human embryo. (B) Section through developing skin of 15-mm. cat embryo. (C) Section through 85-mm. human embryo, showing three-layered epidermis. (D) Human skin, eight months, showing well-developed stratum corneum. (E) Early hair germ in human skin. (F) Later hair germ in human skin. (G) Still later hair germ, showing hair cone, sebaceous-gland rudiment, and epithelial bed. Observe that the hair cone arises as a result of the proliferative activity of the cells of the epithelial or hair matrix which overlies the mesenchymal papilla. Compare with fig. 273A.

580

into the dermis, the surrounding mesenchyme forms a delicate, enveloping, connective-tissue sheath around the epidermal downgrowth (fig. 272G).

As development continues, the distal portion of the germinative stratum forms a bulbous enlargement, the **hair bulb.** The mesenchymal rudiment of the **papilla** pushes into this bulb at its distal end to form the beginnings of the knob-like, definitive papilla of the future hair (fig. 272G). The **hair rudiment** then is formed by the proliferation of the epidermal cells, immediately overlying the knob-like papilla. The epithelial cells, overlying the papilla, form the **epithelial matrix** of the bulb (fig. 272G). The cells of the matrix soon produce a central core within the hair follicle, known as the **hair cone** (fig. 272G). The latter is a conical mass of cells which extends upward from the bulb into the center of the cellular material of the epidermal downgrowth. The hair cone thus gives origin to the beginnings of the **hair shaft** and the **inner hair (epithelial) sheath** (fig. 272G). The peripheral cells of the original epithelial downgrowth, which now surround the hair shaft and inner hair sheath, form the **outer sheath** (fig. 272G).

When the growing shaft of the hair reaches the level of the epidermal layer of the skin, it follows along a **hair canal** or opening in the epidermal layer and finally erupts at the surface of the skin.

As the foregoing changes are effected, two epithelial growths appear along the lower surface of the obliquely placed, hair follicle (fig. 272G). The upper growth is the rudiment of the **sebaceous gland** which with certain exceptions generally is associated with hair development. The lower epithelial outgrowth forms the **epithelial bed.** This bed represents reserve epithelial material for future hair generations. The **arrector pili** muscle arises from adjacent mesenchymal cells and becomes attached to the side of the follicle (figs. 272G; 273). This muscle functions to make the hair "stand on end," so noticeable in the neck-shoulder area of an angered dog.

The first hair to be developed is known as the **down hair, fine hair** or **lanugo.** In the human, the body is generally covered with lanugo by the seventh to eighth fetal month. It tends to be cast off immediately before birth or shortly thereafter. The lanugo corresponds somewhat to the nestling down of the chick, for the replacing hairs develop from the same follicles as the down hairs after the follicles have been reorganized from cells derived from the epithelial bed. However, some replacing hairs appear to arise from new hair follicles.

The hair on the face of the human female, exclusive of the eyebrows, nostrils, and eyelids, and also on the neck and trunk is of the fine-haired variety and resembles the lanugo of the fetus, whereas hair on the face of the human male is of the fine-haired type, exclusive of the eyebrows, eyelids, nostrils, and beard. Hair on various other regions of the male body may be of the fine-haired or lanugo variety.

b) STRUCTURE OF THE MATURE HAIR AND THE HAIR FOLLICLE. The general structure of the mature hair and its follicle is as follows: The hair itself consists of a **shaft** and a **root** (fig. 273A). The hair shaft is composed, when viewed in transverse section, of three regions of modified cells or products (fig. 273B). The innermost, central (axial) portion of the shaft is the **medulla.** It is composed of shrunken, cornified cells separated by air spaces. Surrounding the medulla, is the **cortex,** constructed of a dense horny substance interspersed with air vacuoles. External to the latter is the **cuticle,** made up of thin, cornified, epithelial cells with irregular outlines. The cuticle is transparent and glassy in texture. The pigment or coloring substance is contained within the cortical and medullary portions of the hair. Hair color is dependent upon two main factors:

(1) the nature and quantity of pigment present and
(2) the amount of air within the cortex and medulla.

In some hairs, a distinct medullary portion may be absent.

While the shaft of the hair represents a cornified modification of epidermal

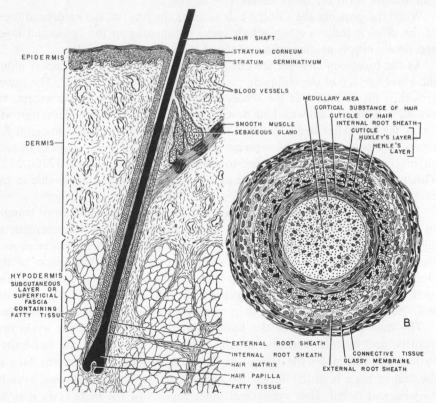

FIG. 273. Diagrams of hair and follicle. (B redrawn from Maximow and Bloom, 1942, A Textbook of Histology. Saunders, Phila., slightly modified.) (A) Diagrammatic representation of the hair shaft and follicle in relation to skin. (B) Transverse section of hair shaft and follicle in skin of a pig embryo.

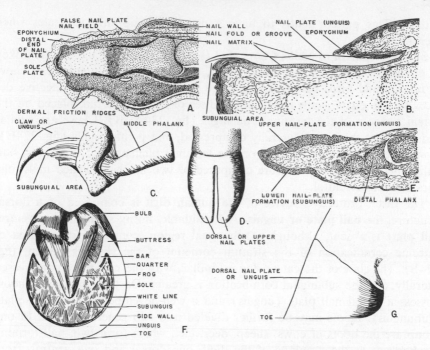

FIG. 274. Diagrams of nails, claws and hoofs. (A redrawn and modified from Pinkus, Chap. 10. *The Development of the Integument,* from Keibel and Mall, 1910, Vol. I, Lippincott, Phila.)   (A) Longitudinal section of index finger of human fetus of 8.5 cm.   (B) Longitudinal section of human finger, showing relationships of fully developed nail plate.   (C) Claw of the cat,   (D) Cloven hoof of the pig.   (E) Developing hoof of pig.   (F) Uncleft hoof of horse, lateral view.   (G) Uncleft hoof of horse, ventral view.

cells, the root contains the cells in a viable condition before transformation into the cornified state. The root of the hair consists of the **hair papilla,** composed of dermal mesenchymal cells, blood vessels, nerve fibers, and a cup-shaped **epithelial matrix** which overlies the papilla (fig. 273A). The hair shaft and the **internal root sheath** are derived from the modification of the cells of the hair matrix. The internal root sheath is composed of the **inner sheath cuticle,** together with **Huxley's and Henle's layers** (fig. 273D). The internal sheath disappears in the upper regions of the follicle near the entrance of the sebaceous gland. External to the internal root sheath is the **external root sheath.** The latter represents the wall of the epithelial follicle and is the downward continuation of the epidermal layer of the skin around the root of the hair. The external root sheath thus forms a pocket-like structure, extending from the distal margin of the hair matrix to the epidermis of the surface skin. A sheath of dermal cells and fibers lies around the external root sheath and acts as the skeletal support of the hair.

During development, hair first appears in the region of the eyebrows and around the mouth. Later it develops over the surface of the body in a regular pattern. This pattern tends to have a definite relationship to scales when present.

3) Development of Nails, Claws, and Hoofs. Resembling and closely linked to epidermal scales are the nails, claws, and hoofs of mammals. The claws of reptiles and birds belong to the same category of terminal protective devices for the digits. Nails are flattened discs of horny material, placed on the dorsal surfaces of the terminal phalanges (fig. 274A, B). Claws are similar and represent thickened, laterally compressed, and pointed nails (fig. 274C). Hoofs are composite structures on the terminal phalanges of the digits, but, unlike nails and claws, they are composed of two much-thickened nails, one dorsal and one ventral.

The distal protective device of the human digit is composed of a dorsal structure, the **nail plate or unguis.** A formidable, horny **subunguis or ventral nail plate** is absent, although a subungual region, consisting of an area of extreme cornification of the stratum corneum of the skin, is present (fig. 274B). The claw of the cat or dog is similar, with the nail plate compressed laterally, and the subungual cornification is greater. On the other hand, hoofs possess a dorsal nail plate (unguis) and a well-developed ventral nail plate (subunguis). Hoofs may be further divided into two general groups. In one group are the hoofs of cows, sheep, deer, etc., which form two, nail-forming mechanisms at the terminus of the digit, one dorsal and one ventral, from which the dorsal and ventral nail plates arise. In the other group are the hoofs of horses, donkeys, zebras, etc., which develop a dorsal, nail-developing mechanism, forming the dorsal nail plate, and two ventral, nail-producing structures. One of the latter generative devices gives origin to the frog and the other to the ventral nail plate. Thus, embryologically, nails and claws belong to one group, whereas hoofs form another.

A better appreciation of the above-mentioned facts relative to claws, nails, and hoofs can be gained by considering the development of a relatively simple, terminal structure of the digit, the human finger nail.

The nails on the terminal digits of the developing human finger begin to form when the embryo (fetus) is about three months old. In doing so, a thickened epidermal area arises on the dorsal aspect of the terminal end of the digit. This general, thickened, epidermal area constitutes the **nail field.** The proximal portion of the nail field then invaginates in a horizontal direction, passing inward into the underlying mesenchyme toward the base of the distal phalanx. This invaginated epidermal material forms the **nail fold or groove,** and it lies within the mesenchyme, paralleling the overlying epidermis (fig. 274A). The nail fold, when viewed from above, is a crescent-shaped affair with the outer aspect of the crescent facing distally; it may be divided into a deeper layer, the **nail matrix,** and a more superficial layer. The nail matrix is confined almost entirely within the nail fold or groove. The distal edge of the **lunula** marks its greatest extension distally along the nail field.

At about the fifth month, the upper cells of the nail matrix begin to keratinize, and the keratinized cells gradually fuse into the compact **nail plate.** As new material is added to the nail plate from the cells of the matrix, the distal portion of the plate is pushed progressively toward the end of the digit (fig. 274A). Although that portion of the nail field between the terminal end of the digit and the lunula takes no part in the formation of the cornified material of the nail plate, the underlying dermis below the nail field does form elongated ridges which push upward into the epidermis of the nail field. These ridges secondarily modify the already-formed nail plate by producing fine, longitudinal lines or ridges.

The claw or nail plate of the cat is compressed laterally to form a narrow, sickle-shaped structure. Three main factors are responsible for this peculiar form of the nail plate in the cat. One factor is the laterally compressed form of the distal phalanx. This condition results in a nail-fold invagination which is laterally compressed. The nail matrix thus is elliptical in shape, dorso-ventrally, instead of flattened as in the human finger. A second factor responsible for the extreme, claw-shaped form of the nail plate in the cat is the more rapid growth in the middorsal portion than in the lateral areas of the nail plate. This discrepancy in growth results in the highly pointed mid-region at the distal end of the nail plate. Ventrally, the two lateral sides of the nail plate tend to approach each other. The area between these two sides is filled with a cornified mass of subungual material. A final factor governing the extreme pointedness of the cat's claw is the fact that the claw-distal-phalanx arrangement, relative to the middle phalanx and tendons, makes the claw retractile when not in use, thus preserving its pointed distal end (fig. 274C).

The dog's claw or nail on the ordinary digits is compressed laterally less than that of the cat, with the result that the subungual cornification is broader and more pronounced and the distal end of the claw not as pointed. However, the claws upon the vestigial first digit, the so-called dewclaws, are pointed and cat-like. The fact that the claw of the dog is non-retractile is a factor in reducing its pointedness, for it, unlike the cat's retractile claw, is worn down continually.

The cloven hoof of the pig or cow is produced by the formation of two nail plates, one dorsal and one ventral, around each of the distal phalanges of the third and fourth digits (fig. 274E). The dorsal nail plate is rounded from side to side and meets the lower nail plate ventrally, with which it fuses along the lateral and distal portions of the lower plate. The unsplit hoof of the horse is produced by a somewhat similar arrangement of dorsal and ventral nail plates around the hoof-shaped phalanx of the third digit (fig. 274F, G). A third nail plate or growth center produces the **frog** or **cuneus.**

4) Development of Horns. The horns of cattle arise as two bony outgrowths, one on either side of the head, from the area of the parietofrontal bones of the skull. In most instances the frontal bone alone is involved. Each bony outgrowth pushes the epidermis before it. The epidermis then responds by producing a highly keratinized, horny substance around the outgrowing bone. The result is the formation around the bony outgrowth of an unbranched cone (or horn) of cornified epidermal material (fig. 275A). This type of horn grows continuously until the mature size is reached. If removed, this type of horn will not regenerate. Horns of this structure are found in sheep, goats, cattle, and antelopes.

The horns of the pronghorn, *Antilocapra americana,* are somewhat similar to those of cattle, with the exception that the external, keratinized, slightly branched, horny covering, overlying the bony core, is shed yearly, to be replaced by a new horny covering (fig. 275B).

On the other hand, the antlers of the deer offer a different developmental procedure. A new bony core is formed each spring which grows and forms the mature antler. As this hard, bony antler matures during late summer and early autumn, the outside covering of epidermis (i.e., the velvet) eventually atrophies and drops off, leaving the very hard, branched, bony core or antler as a formidable fighting weapon for use during the breeding season (fig. 275C). When the latter period is past, the level of the male sex hormone falls in the blood stream, which brings about a deterioration of the bony tissue of the antler near the skull. This area of deterioration continues until the connection to the frontal bone becomes most tenuous, and the antlers fall off, i.e., are shed. (See Chap. 1, p. 27.)

The horns of the giraffe are simple, unbranched affairs which retain the velvet or epidermal covering around a bony core. The horns of the rhinoceros are formidable, cone-shaped, median structures (one or two), composed of a keratinized, hair-like substance. These horns are located on the nasal and frontal bones. (For a discussion of horns in the Mammalia, see Anthony, '28, '29.)

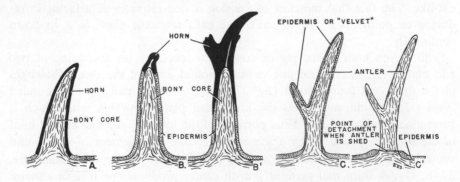

FIG. 275. Horns of mammals.   (A) Cow.   (B) Prong-horn antelope.
(C) White-tailed deer.

5) Development of the Skin Glands. Three types of glands develop in relation to the skin in mammals:

(1) **sebaceous or oil glands,**
(2) **sudoriferous or sweat glands,** and
(3) **mammary or milk glands.**

a) SEBACEOUS GLANDS. **Sebaceous glands** generally are associated with the hair follicles (figs. 272G; 273A), but in some areas of the body this association may not occur. For example, in the human, sebaceous glands arise independently as invaginations of the epidermis in the region of the upper eyelids, around the nostrils, on the external genitals, and around the anus. When the sebaceous gland arises with the hair follicle, it generally takes its origin from the lower side of the invaginated hair follicle, although this condition may vary (fig. 272G). The sebaceous-gland rudiment originates as an outpushing of the germinative stratum and differentiates into a simple or compound alveolar type of gland. The secretion originates as fatty material within the more centrally located cells of the gland, with subsequent degeneration of these cells and release of the oily substance. Since the secretion forms as a result of alteration of the gland cells themselves, this type of gland is classified as an **holocrine gland.** New cells are formed continuously from that portion of the gland connected with the germinative stratum. The oil produced is discharged to the surface of the skin through the opening of the hair follicle when a relationship with the hair is present. If not connected with a hair follicle, the gland has a separate opening through the epidermal layer.

b) SUDORIFEROUS GLANDS. **Sweat** or **sudoriferous glands** most often develop independently of hair follicles, but in certain areas they form on the sides of these follicles. Whenever formed, they represent solid, elongated ingrowths of the epidermis into the dermis. Later these cellular cords coil at their distal ends to form simple, coiled, tubular glands (fig. 276).

The outer wall of the forming sweat gland develops so-called myoepithelial cells; the latter presumably have the ability to contract. The cells lining the lumen of the gland secrete (excrete) the sweat, the distal ends of the cells being discharged with the exudate. Hence, this type of gland is called an **apocrine gland.** The secretion is watery and contains salts, wastes, including urea, and occasionally some pigment granules and fat droplets. In the cat, dog, and other carnivores, sweat glands are reduced in number.

c) MAMMARY GLANDS. **Mammary glands** are characteristic of the mammals. The first indication of mammary-gland development is the formation of the **milk or mammary ridges** (fig. 241D, E). These ridges represent elevations of the epidermis, extending along the ventro-lateral aspect of the embryo from the pectoral area posteriad into the inguinal region. The ridges are developed in both sexes and represent a generalized condition of development. In the human embryo, the mammary ridge is well developed only in the

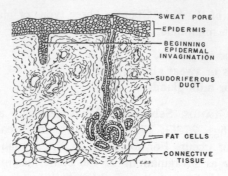

FIG. 276. Diagram of sudoriferous (sweat) gland.

pectoral region, but it is extensive in the pig, dog, and cat. In the cow, horse, deer, etc., its greatest development is in the inguinal area.

Only very restricted areas of each mammary ridge on either side are utilized in mammary-gland development. In the pig or dog embryo, a series of localized thickenings begin to appear along the ridge. In the sheep, cow, and horse, these thickenings are confined to the inguinal region, whereas in the primates and the elephant, they are found in the pectoral area. In the human, one thickening in each ridge generally appears, although occasionally several may arise. These thickenings represent the beginnings of the nipples and result from increased proliferations of cells (fig. 277B). Eventually, each thickened portion of the ridge becomes bulbous and sinks inward into the dermis (fig. 277C). Gradually, solid cords of cells push out from the lower rim of the solid epidermal mass into the surrounding dermal tissue (fig. 277D). These cords of cells represent the rudiments of the mammary-gland ducts. Secondary outpushings appear at the distal ends of the primary ducts. Later, lumina appear in the primary ducts. Further development of these ducts, with the formation of the terminal rudimentary acini, occurs during late fetal stages, resulting in the formation of an infantile state. This condition is found at birth in the human, dog, cat, etc. Under the influence of hormones present in the blood stream of the mother (see Chap. 2, p. 103), these acini may secrete the so-called "witch's" milk in the newborn human male and female. While the occurrence of this type of milk secretion is not uncommon, the gland as a whole is in a rudimentary, undeveloped state. It remains in this infantile condition until the period of sexual development when, in the female, the mammary-gland ducts and attendant structures begin to grow and develop under the influence of estrogen, the female sex hormone. (See Chap. 2.) It should be observed that the rounded condition of the developing breast in the human female at the time of puberty (fig. 277F) is due largely to the accumulation of fat and connective tissue and not to a great extension of the duct system of the glands, although some duct extension does occur at this time.

As the original epithelial thickening of the nipple rudiment sinks inward,

the center of the thickened area moves downward to a greater extent than the
margins. Some disintegration of the central cells also occurs. As a result, a
slight cavity or crater-like depression is formed in the middle of the epithelial
mass of the rudiment (fig. 277C). In the cow and rat, this depressed area
continues in this state, while the edges of the cavity and adjacent integument
grow outward to form the nipple (fig. 277E). This type of nipple is called
an **inversion nipple.** The ducts of the gland thus open into the bottom of the
nipple (teat or mammilla). In the human, the original depression and the
openings of the primary ducts of the gland gradually are elevated outward
to form the type of nipple or mammilla indicated in figure 277A. This type
of nipple is called an **eversion nipple.**

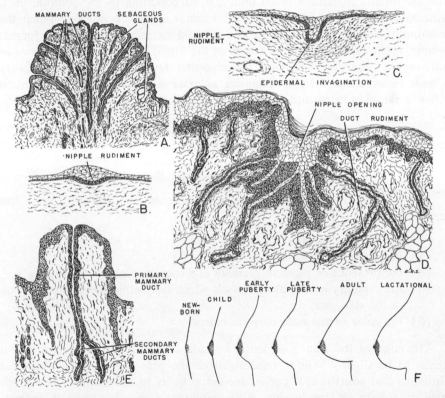

FIG. 277. Diagrams showing mammary-gland development. (A) Human nipple
showing mammary duct openings. (Modified from Maximow and Bloom, A Textbook of
Histology, after Schaffer, 1942, Saunders, Phila.)   (B) Transverse section of early nipple
rudiment of 20-mm. pig embryo.   (C) Transverse section through developing nipple of
pig embryo of 70 mm., showing epidermal invagination into the dermal area of the skin.
(D) Section through nipple of mammary gland of human male fetus, eight months old.
(After Pinkus, Keibel and Mall: *Manual of Human Embryology*, Vol. I, 1910, Lippincott,
Phila.)   (E) Section through developing nipple of newborn rat. (Redrawn and modified
from Myers, '16, Am. J. Anat., 19.)   (F) Development of human mammary gland from
birth to maturity.

As indicated above, the distribution of nipples and mammary glands along the ventral abdominal wall varies greatly in different mammalian species. In lemurs and fruit bats, the mammary glands are developed in the axillary region; in the human and in primates, they are pectoral; in the cat, they are best developed in the pecto-abdominal area; in the dog and pig, they are mainly well developed in the abdominal and inguinal areas; in the cow and horse, inguinal nipples only appear; and in whales, the mammary glands are located near the external genitals.

The development of supernumerary mammary glands, i.e., **hypermastia,** is rare, but the formation of extra nipples, i.e., **hyperthelia,** is common in both male and female. In female mammals, such as the bitch, it is not uncommon for the breasts to remain in an undeveloped condition in the pectoral area, whereas those in the inguinal and abdominal areas are normal. When the mammary glands continue in an undeveloped or regressed state as, for example, in the anterior pectoral region of the bitch, the condition is known as **micromastia.** On the other hand, the abnormal development of the mammary glands to an abnormal size is known as **macromastia.** The latter condition often is found in cattle and occasionally in the bitch and human.

C. Coloration and Pigmentation of the Vertebrate Skin and Accessory Structures

1. Factors Concerned with Skin Color

The color of the skin and its accessory structures is dependent upon five main factors:

(1) the color of the skin itself,
(2) its opacity or translucency,
(3) the presence of pigment granules and special, pigment-bearing cells,
(4) the capillary bed of blood vessels which lies within the dermal portion of the skin, and
(5) the color of the accessory structures.

The color of the skin itself varies considerably in different species, but it tends to be slightly yellow, resulting from the presence of fatty tissue, fat droplets, and constitutent, connective-tissue fibers in the dermis. The property of opacity or translucency is an important factor for upon it depends transmission of light waves through the skin from deeper lying structures, such as blood vessels, pigment droplets, pigment-bearing cells, etc. The presence of definite types of pigment granules within or between the cells of the epidermis and dermis determines the course and kind of light waves which are reflected. The richness or paucity of blood vessels, ramifying through the dermal area, also affects the skin's color in many instances.

The color of the accessory structures, particularly the structures derived from the epidermis, greatly conditions the color pattern of the species. The color of these accessory structures is dependent upon three main factors:

(1) presence or absence of pigment,
(2) presence of air, and
(3) iridescence.

Pigment and air are dominant factors, for example, in the color exhibited by hair and feathers. The presence of air diminishes and distorts the effects of the pigment which may be present. The property of iridescence is to be distinguished from the color effects due to the presence of certain pigments; the latter absorb light rays and reflect them, whereas iridescence is dependent upon the diffraction of light waves from irregular surfaces. Iridescence is important in the color effects produced by the plumage of a bird or the skin surface of many fish, reptiles, and amphibia.

2. COLOR PATTERNS

In the vertebrates whose manner of life dictates a close association of the body with the environmental substrate, the underparts have less color than the parts exposed to the light rays coming from above. Also, within the general, colored areas, there are certain spots, lines bars, and dark and light regions which follow a definite pattern more or less peculiar to the variety, subspecies, or species. These color patterns tend to be fixed and are determined by the heredity of the animal. Consequently, they are related to the genic complex in some way. However, in many species the tone of the color patterns may be changed from time to time by changing environmental conditions as mentioned on page 594.

3. MANNER OF COLOR-PATTERN PRODUCTION

a. Role of Chromatophores in Producing Skin-color Effects

Work in experimental embryology has demonstrated fairly conclusively that the pigments necessary for color formation are elaborated principally by certain cells known as **chromatophores.** Chromatophores are pigment-bearing and pigment-elaborating cells. Various cells may produce pigment, but chromatophores are cells specialized in the function of pigment elaboration.

The distribution and activities of chromatophores vary in the different vertebrate groups. For example, in fishes, amphibia, and many reptiles, three or probably four kinds of chromatophores are present in the dermis, namely, **melanophores, lipophores, guanophores,** and (possibly) **allophores** (Nobel, '31, p. 141). By their presence and arrangement, the chromatophores produce specific color patterns. Moreover, the expansion and contraction of the pigmented cytoplasm of some or all the chromatophores effects changes in color, for the contracted or expanded state determines the types of light rays which will be absorbed or reflected. The rapid color changes in certain tree frogs and lizards are due to this type of chromatophoric behavior. The slower changes of color in other amphibia and fishes also are due to this type of chromatophoric activity. It thus appears that dermal chromatophores are responsible largely for the color effects found in the lower vertebrates. On the other hand, in the bird group and in mammals, the chromatophores present are mainly of one type, known as a **melanophore.** Melanophores produce pigments, known as **melanins** (Dushane, '44, p. 102). The melanin granules, elaborated by the bird melanophore, have a wide range of color from yellow through orange to reddish-brown to dark brown. The melanophores in the bird deposit the melanin-pigment granules within the feather as it develops (fig. 271C). Melanophores also deposit melanins in the bill of the male sparrow at breeding time under the influence of the male sex hormone (Witschi and Woods, '36). Hair color in mammals is due, mainly, to pigmented granules deposited in the hair by melanophores. The skin color of various races of the human species is determined largely by the amount of melanin deposited within the lower epidermal layers by melanophores resident in the upper dermal area. In other words, the color of the skin and its appendages in the higher vertebrate groups is due, to a considerable extent, to diffuse granules deposited in the epidermis and epidermal structures by melanophores, whereas, in lower vertebrates, dermal chromatophores are responsible for color pattern and color change.

b. Activities of Other Substances and Structures in Producing Color Effects of the Skin

In the common fowl, the presence of carotenoids (lipochromes) in the Malpighian layer (stratum germinativum) mainly is responsible for the color of the face, legs, and feet. Orange-red, lipochromic droplets have been found in the germinative stratum of the head of the pheasant, and *these droplets plus the capillaries in the dermis produce a brilliant red coloration* (Dushane, '44, p. 102). The color of the combs and wattles of the common fowl is conceded generally to be due to the presence of a rich capillary plexus in the dermis alone. In the ear regions of the fowl, the blood capillaries are reduced in the dermis, and the presence of certain crystals of unknown chemical composition produces a double refraction of the light waves. Hence, the ear region appears white in reflected light.

c. Genic Control of Chromatophoric Activity

The transplantation of small pieces of epidermis and its adhering mesoderm from one early chick embryo to another is possible. Under these conditions, the donor tissue with its donor melanophores governs the color pattern of the feathers developed in the area of the transplant (Willier and Rawles, '40). That is, melanophores from a Black Minorca embryo, transplanted to a White Leghorn embryo, will produce a Black Minorca color pattern, in the White

Leghorn in the area of transplant, at least during the development of nestling down and juvenile feathers. Barred Rock melanophores produce barred feather patterns in White Leghorn, New Hampshire Red, Black Minorca, etc. These results demonstrate that the introduced melanophore produces the color pattern in the feather in the immediate area of the implant.

Various genetic studies (see Dushane, '44, for references) have demonstrated that the Barred Rock factor is dominant, and that it is sex-linked. For example, if a Barred Rock hen is crossed with a Rhode Island Red cock, the F_1 male will contain two sex chromosomes, one from each parent. That chromosome from the female parent will have a Barred Rock factor, whereas that from the male parent will not. The F_1 cock, therefore, is heterozygous for barring, and, as the barring factor is dominant, the F_1 cock will show barred feathers. The F_1 female, however, derives its single sex chromosome from the male parent; as this chromosome does not contain the barring factor, the F_1 female is black.

Willier ('41) presents evidence concerning the transplantation of melanophores from F_1 heterozygous males and F_1 heterozygous females of this Barred Rock cross. Transplanted melanophores from an F_1 male into White Leghorn hosts always produce barred contour feathers in either sex, whereas F_1 female melanophores transplanted to White Leghorn hosts always produce non-barred or black regions. Danforth ('29) demonstrated that the barring factor in the skin of the male donor at hatching, when transplanted to a female host at hatching which lacked the barring factor, produces barred feathers in the female host in the area of the transplant. The results obtained by Danforth suggest that the barring gene acts independently of the sex hormone, although the feather type present in the graft assumes the female characters of the host and, hence, is affected by the female sex hormone. The results of these experiments by Willier and Danforth suggest that the barring gene in poultry acts directly upon the melanophore and not upon the environment in which the melanophore functions. (For extensive description, references, and discussion of these phenomena, consult Danforth, '29; Willier, '41; and Dushane, '44.)

d. Examples of Hormonal Control of Chromatophoric Activity

In the indigo bunting, the male resembles the female during the non-breeding season. During the breeding season, however, the male develops a brilliant, purple-colored, highly iridescent plumage. Castration experiments and gonadotrophic hormone administration suggest that this nuptial plumage is dependent, not upon the male sex hormone, but upon *gonadotrophic hormones elaborated by the pituitary gland* in the male. In the female, however, the presence of the female sex hormone inhibits the effects of the pituitary gonadotrophins; hence, she retains the sexually quiescent type of plumage (Domm, '39, p. 285). Also, in certain cases where the color of the bird's bill is a sex-dimorphic character appearing during the breeding season only, it has been shown that the pigmentation of the bill is dependent upon the presence of the male sex hormone (Domm, '39).

e. Environmental Control of Chromatophoric Activity

The above-mentioned instances of color-pattern development are concerned with the elaboration and deposition of pigment within the epidermis and epidermal structures. On the other hand, other observations demonstrate that the contraction and expansion of chromatophores and, hence, the production of different tones of color patterns, may be effected by a variety of environmental stimuli in lower vertebrates. In some cases this may be due to direct stimulation of the chromatophores by light or darkness or by changes in temperature; in other instances the causative factor is a secretion from certain glands, such as the pituitary or adrenal glands. The latter secretions in some forms appear to be aroused by light waves to the eye, from whence the stimulation is relayed through the nervous system to the respective gland or glands. In still other instances the light waves to the eye may cause a direct stimulation of the chromatophores by means of nerve fibers which reach the chromatophores. Other examples suggest that certain **neurohumoral substances,** elaborated by the terminal fibers of the nerves some distance away from the chromatophore, slowly diffuse to the chromatophore, causing its expansion or contraction (Noble, '32, pp. 141–147; Parker, '40).

Bibliography

Anthony, H. C. **1928; 1929.** Horns and antlers, their evolution, occurrence, and function in the *Mammalia*. Bull. New York Zool. Soc. **31; 32.**

Bardeen, C. R. **1900.** The development of the musculature of the body wall in the pig. Johns Hopkins Hosp. Rep. **9**:367.

Chandler. A. C. **1916.** A study of the structure of feathers with reference to their taxonomic significance. University of California Publ., Zoöl. **13**:243.

Danforth, C. H. **1929.** Genetic and metabolic sex differences. J. Hered. **20**:319.

Davies, H. R. **1889.** Die Entwicklung der Feder und ihre Beziehungen zu anderen Integumentgebilden. Morph. Jahrb. **15**:560.

Dawson, A. B. **1920.** The integument of *Necturus maculosus*. J. Morphol. **34**:487.

Domm, L. V. **1939.** Chap. V. Modifications in sex and secondary sexual characters in birds in Sex and Internal Secretions by Allen, Danforth, and Doisy. 2d ed. The Williams & Wilkins Co., Baltimore.

Dushane, G. P. **1943.** The embryology of vertebrate pigment cells. Part I. Amphibia. Quart. Rev. Biol. **18**:109.

———. **1944.** The embryology of vertebrate pigment cells. Part II. Birds. Quart. Rev. Biol. **19**:98.

Eastlick, H. L. and Wortham, R. A. **1946.** An experimental study on the feather-pigmenting and subcutaneous melanophores in the silkie fowl. J. Exper. Zool. **103**:233.

Engert, H. **1900.** Die Entwicklung der ventralen Rumpfmuskulatur bei Vögeln. Morph. Jahrb. **29**:169.

Eycleshymer, A. C. **1906.** The development of chromatophores in *Necturus*. Am. J. Anat. **5**:309.

Greene, C. W. **1899.** The phosphorescent organs in the toad-fish, *Porichthys notatus* Girard. J. Morphol. **15**:667.

Harms, J. W. **1929.** Die Realisation von Genen und die consecutive Adaption. I. Phasen in der Differenzierung der Anlagenkomplexe und die Frage der Landtier-werdung. Zeit. Wiss. Zool. **133**:211.

Jones, L. **1907.** The development of nestling feathers. Oberlin College Lab. Bull. No. 13.

Lillie, F. R. **1940.** Physiology of development of the feather. III. Growth of the mesodermal constituents and blood circulation in the pulp. Physiol. Zoöl. **13**:143.

——— and Juhn, M. **1932.** The physiology of development of feathers. I. Growth rate and pattern in the individual feather. Physiol. Zoöl. **5**:124.

——— and ———. **1938.** Physiology of development of the feather. II. General principles of development with special reference to the after-feather. Physiol. Zoöl. **11**:434.

Neave, F. **1936.** The development of the scales of *Salmo*. Tr. Roy. Soc. Canada. **30**:550.

———. **1940.** On the histology and regeneration of the teleost scale. Quart. J. Micr. Sc. **81**:541.

Nickerson, W. S. **1893.** The development of the scales of *Lepidosteus*. Bull. Mus. Comp. Zool. at Harvard College. **24**:115.

Noble, G. K. **1931.** The Biology of the Amphibia. McGraw-Hill Book Co., Inc., New York.

Parker, G. H. **1940.** Neurohumors as chromatophore activators. Proc. Am. Acad. Arts & Sc. **73**:165.

Sayles, L. P. and Hershkowitz, S. G. **1937.** Placoid scale types and their distribution in *Squalus acanthias*. Biol. Bull. **73**:51.

Strong, R. M. **1902.** The development of color in the definitive feather. Bull. Mus. Comp. Zool. at Harvard College. **40**:146.

Williams, L. W. **1910.** The somites of the chick. Am. J. Anat. **11**:55.

Willier, B. H. **1941.** An analysis of feather color pattern produced by grafting melanophores during embryonic development. Am. Nat. **75**:136.

——— and Rawles, M. E. **1940.** The control of feather color pattern by melanophores grafted from one embryo to another of a different breed of fowl. Physiol. Zoöl. **13**:177.

Witschi, E. and Woods, R. P. **1936.** The bill of the sparrow as an indicator for the male sex hormone. II. Structural basis. J. Exper. Zool. **73**:445.

13

The Digestive System

A. Introduction
  1. General structure and regions of the early digestive tube or primitive metenteron
     a. Definition
     b. Two main types of the early metenteron
  2. Basic structure of the early metenteron (gut tube)
     a. Basic regions of the primitive metenteron
        1) Stomodaeum
        2) Head gut or Seessel's pocket
        3) Foregut
        4) Midgut
        5) Hindgut
        6) Tail gut (post-anal gut)
        7) Proctodaeum
     b. Basic cellular units of the primitive metenteron
  3. Areas of the primitive metenteron from which evaginations (diverticula) normally arise
     a. Stomodaeum
     b. Pharynx
     c. Anterior intestinal or pyloric area
     d. Junction of midgut and hindgut
     e. Cloacal and proctodaeal area
B. Development of the digestive tube òr metenteron
  1. General morphogenesis of the digestive tube
  2. Histogenesis and morphogenesis of special areas
     a. Oral cavity
        1) General characteristics of the stomodaeal invagination
        2) Rudiments of the jaws
        3) Development of the tongue
        4) Teeth
           a) General characteristics
           b) Development of teeth in the shark embryo
           c) Development of teeth in the frog tadpole
           d) Development of the egg tooth in the chick
           e) Development of teeth in mammals
        5) Formation of the secondary palate
        6) Formation of the lips
        7) Oral glands

596

A. Introduction

1. General Structure and Regions of the Early Digestive Tube or Primitive Metenteron

a. Definition

The word **metenteron** is applied to the gut tube which is developed from the archenteric conditions of the gastrula. The term **primitive metenteron** may be applied to the gut tube shortly after it is formed, that is, shortly after tubulation of the entoderm to form the primitive gut tube has occurred, while the word metenteron, unqualified, is applicable to the tubular gut, generally, throughout all stages of its development following the gastrular state.

b. Two Main Types of the Early Metenteron

Two types or morphological forms of early vertebrate metenterons are developed immediately after the gastrular stage. In one type, such as is found in the frog and other amphibia, ganoids, cyclostomes, and lungfishes, the walls of the gut tube are complete, and the yolk material is enclosed principally within the substance of the midgut area of the tube (fig. 217). In the second

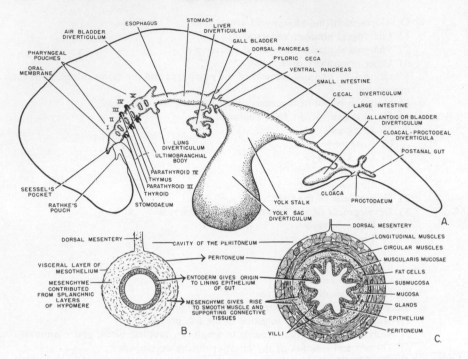

Fig. 278. Diagrams showing basic features of digestive-tube development in the vertebrates. (A) The regions of the primitive gut where outgrowths (diverticula) normally
occur. (B) Basic cellular features of the gut tube. (C) Contributions of the basic
cellular composition to the adult structure of the digestive tract. Consult Fig. 293 for
actual structure of mucous layer in esophagus, stomach, and intestines.

type, on the other hand, most of the yolk material lies outside the confines of
the primitive gut tube (fig. 217), and the midgut region of the primitive tube
is open ventrally, the ventro-lateral walls of the tube being incomplete. The
latter condition is found in elasmobranch fishes, reptiles, birds, and primitive
mammals. In higher mammals, although yolk substance is greatly reduced,
the arrangement is similar to that of the latter group. The teleost fishes represent a condition somewhat intermediate between these two major groups.

2. Basic Structure of the Early Metenteron (Gut Tube)

(Consult figs. 278A; 279A; 280A; 281A; and 282B.)

a. Basic Regions of the Primitive Metenteron

The primitive vertebrate metenteron possesses the following regions.

1) Stomodaeum. The stomodaeum lies at the anterior extremity of the gut
tube, and represents an ectodermal contribution to the entodermal portion of
the primitive gut. It results from an invagination of the epidermal tube directed
toward the **oral evagination** of the foregut. The membrane, formed by the

apposition of the oral evagination of the foregut and the stomodaeal invagination of the epidermal tube, constitutes the **oral or pharyngeal membrane.** Ectoderm and entoderm thus enter into the composition of the pharyngeal membrane. This membrane normally atrophies.

2) Head Gut or Seessel's Pocket. This structure represents the extreme anterior end of the foregut which projects forward toward the anterior end of the notochord and brain. It extends cephalad beyond the region of contact of the stomodaeum with the oral evagination of the foregut. During its earlier period, the head gut is intimately associated with the anterior end of the

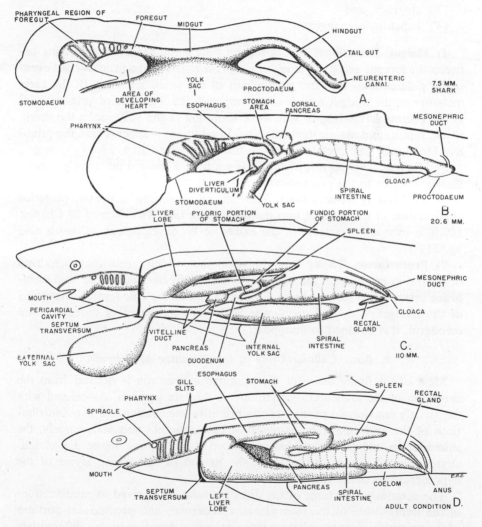

FIG. 279. Morphogenesis of the digestive structures in the dog fish, *Squalus acanthias.* See also Figs. 291C and 296A.

notochord and the pre-chordal plate mesoderm. The head gut ultimately degenerates. Its significance probably lies in its function as a part of the head organizer.

3) Foregut. The foregut comprises the anterior portion of the primitive metenteron from the region of the stomodaeum and Seessel's pocket, posteriorly to the intestinal area where arise the liver and pancreatic diverticula. It is divisible into four general regions:

(1) pharyngeal area,
(2) esophagus,
(3) stomach, and
(4) hepatopyloric segment.

4) Midgut. The midgut area of the gut tube is the general region lying between the foregut and hindgut regions. This segment of the primitive gut eventually differentiates into the greater part of the small intestine. In the early metenteron, the midgut area is concerned with the digestion of yolk material in such forms as the frog or with the elaboration of the yolk sac in the shark, chick, reptile, and mammalian embryos. In addition, it appears that the primitive blood cells also are elaborated in this area. (See Chap. 17.)

5) Hindgut. This portion of the early gut tube is located posteriorly, immediately anterior to the proctodaeum.

6) Tail Gut (Post-anal Gut). The tail gut represents a dorsal, posterior continuation of the hindgut into the developing tail. As indicated in Chapter 10, it is extremely variable in the extent of its development. (Consult also fig. 217.)

7) Proctodaeum. The epidermal invagination, which meets the proctodaeal or ventral evagination of the hindgut, forms the proctodaeum. The **anal membrane** results when the proctodaeal inpushing meets the entodermal outpushing of the hindgut. The anal membrane is double, composed of entoderm and ectoderm. It is destined to disappear.

b. Basic Cellular Units of the Primitive Metenteron

Most of the lining tissue of the primitive metenteron is derived from the entoderm of the archenteric conditions of the late gastrula. Associated with the strictly entodermal portion of the primitive metenteron are two contributions of the epidermal tube as observed on pages 598 and 600, namely, the **stomodaeum** and the **proctodaeum.** Added to this lining tissue are mesenchymal contributions, derived from the medial or splanchnic layers of the hypomeric mesoderm (fig. 278B).

The glandular structures of the digestive tube are derived as modifications of the lining tissue of the stomodaeal, entodermal, and proctodaeal portions of the primitive gut tube, whereas muscular and connective tissues differentiate from mesenchyme (fig. 278C).

3. Areas of the Primitive Metenteron from which Evaginations (Diverticula) Normally Arise

Certain areas of the primitive metenteron tend to produce outgrowths (evaginations; diverticula). The following comprise these areas (fig. 278A).

a. Stomodaeum

In the middorsal area of the stomodaeum, a sac-like diverticulum or Rathke's pouch, invaginates dorsally toward the infundibulum of the diencephalic portion of the brain. It remains open for a time and thus retains its connection with the oral epithelium. Later, however, it loses its connection with the oral cavity and becomes firmly attached to the infundibulum of the brain. It eventually forms the anterior lobe of the hypophysis or pituitary gland. (See chapters 1, 2, and 21.) Other diverticula of the oral (stomodaeal) cavity occur. These evaginations form the rudiment of the oral glands and will be discussed on page 617.

b. Pharynx

The **pharyngeal area or pharynx** represents the anterior portion of the foregut, interposed between the stomodaeum or oral cavity and the esophagus. This general region has four main functions:

(1) **external respiration,**
(2) **food passage (alimentation),**
(3) **endocrine-gland formation,** and
(4) development of **buoyancy structures.**

In most vertebrates, five or six pairs of lateral outgrowths, known as the **visceral or branchial pouches** are formed. A **ventral outpocketing** or outpocketings also occur in all vertebrates. The **thyroid-gland diverticulum** is the most constantly formed ventral outgrowth, but lung and air-bladder evaginations are conspicuous in most vertebrate species. **Dorsal** and **dorso-lateral air-bladder evaginations** occur in many fishes.

c. Anterior Intestinal or Pyloric Area

The anterior intestinal area of the primitive gut, immediately caudal to the stomach region, is characterized by a tendency to form diverticula. Various types of outgrowths occur here, the most constant of which are the hepatic (liver) and the pancreatic evaginations. In lower vertebrates, such as teleost, ganoid, and some elasmobranch fishes, blind digestive pockets, the **pyloric ceca,** may be formed in this area.

d. Junction of Midgut and Hindgut

At the junction of the developing small and large intestines, outgrowths are common in many of the higher vertebrates. The diverticula which occur here

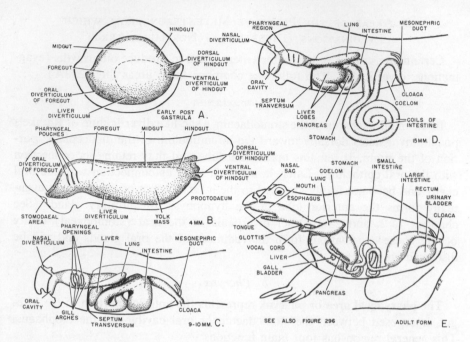

FIG. 280. Morphogenesis of the digestive tract in the frog, *Rana pipiens.* (See Chap. 10.)

may be large and pouch-like, as in certain mammals, or slender and elongated, as in birds.

e. Cloacal and Proctodaeal Area

The most prominent cloacal diverticula occur ventrally. Ventral urinary bladders arise in this area in many vertebrates. The allantoic diverticulum (Chap. 22) is a prominent outgrowth of the ventral wall of the cloaca. In the chick, the **bursa of Fabricius** projects dorsally from the area between the cloaca proper and the proctodaeum. Dorsal urinary bladders occur in fishes, arising as dorsal diverticula within this general area. The anal glands of certain mammals, such as the dog, represent proctodaeal evaginations.

B. Development of the Digestive Tube or Metenteron

The following descriptions pertain mainly to the developing shark, frog, chick, and human embryos. Other forms are mentioned incidentally to emphasize certain aspects of digestive-tube development.

1. General Morphogenesis of the Digestive Tube

The general morphological changes of the developing digestive tubes of the shark, frog, chick, and human are shown in figures 279–282.

2. Histogenesis and Morphogenesis of Special Areas

a. Oral Cavity

1) General Characteristics of the Stomodaeal Invagination. The oral cavity arises as a simple stomodaeal invagination in most vertebrates. However, in the toadfish, *Opsanus (Batrachus) tau,* two stomodaeal invaginations occur which later fuse to give origin to a single oral cavity (Platt, 1891). In *Amphioxus,* the mouth originates on the left side of the head as shown in figure 249D and F; later, it migrates ventrally to a median position. In cyclostomes, the original invagination becomes partly everted secondarily, so that the pituitary invagination eventually lies on the upper portion of the head (fig. 283A, B).

2) Rudiments of the Jaws. In the shark embryo, the mandibular visceral arches bend to form U-shaped structures on either side of the forming oral cavity and *thus give origin to the primitive framework of the upper and lower jaws* (fig. 253). This condition holds true for other lower vertebrates, including the *Amphibia.* In the chick, the mandibular arch bends similarly to that in the shark embryo, but only the proximal portion of the upper jaw is present. The anterior or distal portion is displaced by mesenchyme from the head area (fig. 240). The latter condition is true also of the mammals (fig. 261). Regardless of whether or not all the jaw framework on either side of the forming oral cavity is derived from the original mandibular arch, the fact remains that in the formation of the jaws, a U-shaped, mesenchymal framework on either side is established in all the gnathostomous or jaw-possessing vertebrates.

3) Development of the Tongue. The "tongue" of the shark is essentially a fold of the oral membrane of the floor of the mouth, which overlies the basal (hypobranchial) portion of the hyoid visceral arch. A true, flexible tongue, however, is never developed in the shark or other fishes. Flexible, protrusile tongues are found almost entirely in forms which inhabit the land, where they are used for the acquisition and swallowing of food. The protrusile tongue, therefore, is a digestive-tract structure primarily, and its use in communication in the human and other species is a secondary adaptation.

The tongue generally develops from folds or growths, associated with the floor of the oral cavity and anterior branchial region. These lingual growths are associated with the ventral or lower jaw portions of the hyoid and mandibular visceral arches and the ventral area between these arches. However, in the frog, the tongue arises from a mass of tissue at the anterior portion of the floor of the mouth between the mandibular visceral arches. It is protruded from the oral cavity largely by the flow of lymph into the base of the tongue.

The tongue of the chick and other birds is developed as a fleshy, superficially cornified structure, overlying the anterior portion of the greatly modified hyoid apparatus. It arises from the **tuberculum impar,** a swelling located in the floor of the pharyngeal area between the first and second visceral arches,

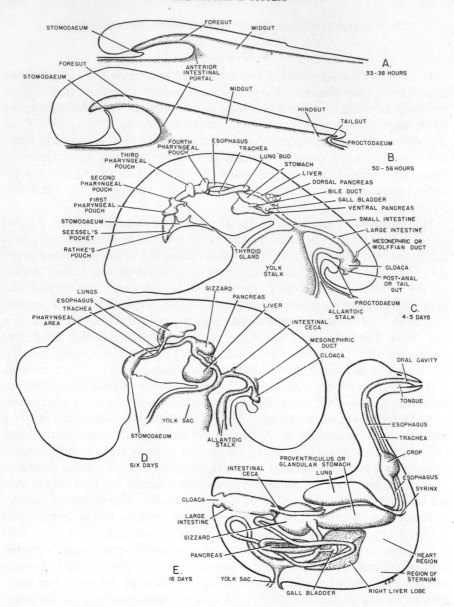

FIG. 281. Morphogenesis of the gut structures in the chick, *Gallus (domesticus) gallus*.

and the **copula protuberance** which forms as a result of swellings on the lower ends of the second and third visceral arches and the intervening area. The copula forms the root of the tongue; the tuberculum impar contributes the middle portion; and the anterior part of the tongue arises from folds which grow forward from the anterior portion of the tuberculum impar (fig. 284).

In the human and pig embryos, the anterior portion or body of the tongue arises through the fusion of two **ventro-medial swellings of the mandibular arches** (fig. 285B). The root of the tongue takes its origin from areas of elevated tissue upon the ventral ends of the hyoid arches and in the adjacent area between the hyoid and first branchial visceral arches (fig. 285B). This elevated tissue is known as the **copula.** A small, insignificant area, the **tuberculum impar,** emerges from the medio-ventral area between the mandibular and hyoid visceral arches (fig. 285B). Stages in tongue development in the human embryo are shown in figure 285A–E.

4) Teeth: a) GENERAL CHARACTERISTICS. Teeth are of two types:

(1) horny teeth and

(2) bony or true teeth.

Horny teeth are found in cyclostomatous fishes, the larval stages of frogs and toads, and in the prototherian mammal, *Ornithorhynchus*.

Most vertebrates possess true or bony teeth, although they are absent in some fishes (e.g., the sturgeon, pipefishes, and sea horses), turtles, and birds. Among the mammals, certain whales lack teeth, and, in *Ornithorhynchus,* vestigial bony teeth are formed before hatching, to be lost and supplanted by cornified epidermal teeth. Teeth are lacking also in the edentates, *Myrmecophaga* and *Munis.*

True or bone-like teeth have essentially the same general structure in all vertebrates. A tooth possesses three general areas (fig. 286E):

(1) **crown,**

(2) **neck,** and

(3) **root.**

The crown projects from the surface of epithelium overlying the jaw or oral cavity, while the root is attached to the jaw tissue. The neck is the restricted area lying between the root and the crown.

Teeth generally are composed of two substances, **enamel** and **dentine.** Some teeth, however, lack enamel. Examples of the latter are the teeth of sloths and armadillos. The tusks of elephants also represent greatly modified teeth without enamel. Some teeth have the enamel only on the anterior aspect, such as the incisors of rodents.

Teeth may be attached to the jaw area in various ways. In sharks, the teeth are embedded in the connective tissue overlying the jaws (fig. 287F), whereas in most teleosts, amphibia, reptiles, birds, and mammals, they are connected to the jaw itself (fig. 287A–D). In many vertebrates, such as crocodilians and mammals, the tooth is implanted in a **socket** or **alveolus** within the jaw tissue (fig. 287C, D). In other forms, the tooth is fused (i.e., ankylosed) to the upper surfaces of the jaw (fig. 287A, B). A tooth inserted within a socket or alveolus of the jaw is spoken of as a **thecodont tooth,** while those teeth

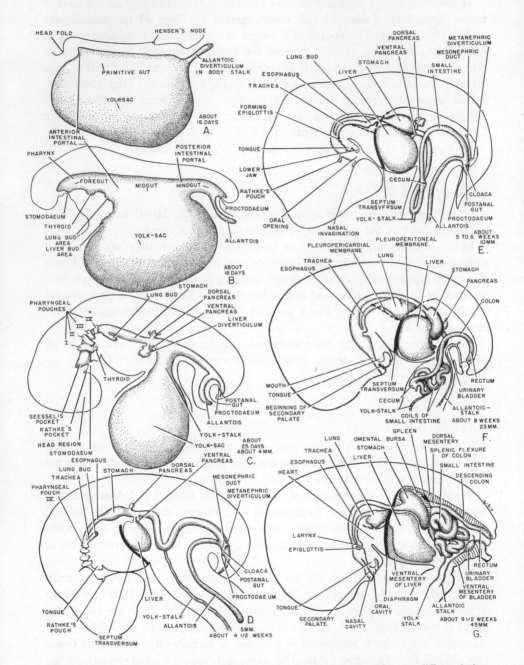

FIG. 282. Morphogenesis of the digestive tract in the human. Observe differentiation of the cloaca in E–G, and the mesenteric supports including the omental bursa in G. (Based upon data from various sources.)

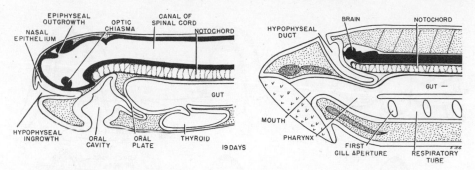

FIG. 283. Partial eversion of the oral cavity during development in the embryo of Petromyzon. *(Left)* Longitudinal section of the head region in 19-day embryo. (Redrawn and modified from Kingsley, 1912, Comparative Anatomy of Vertebrates, Blakiston, Phila.) *(Right)* Median longitudinal section of head region of adult Petromyzon. (Redrawn and modified from Neal and Rand, 1936, Comparative Anatomy, Blakiston, Phila.)

fused to the surface of the jaw are referred to either as **acrodont or pleurodont teeth.** If the tooth is ankylosed to the upper edge of the jaw, as in many teleosts and snakes, it falls within the **acrodont** group (fig. 287B), but if it is attached to the inner surface of the jaw's edge, as in the frog and *Necturus,* it is of the **pleurodont** variety (fig. 287A).

In most vertebrates, all the teeth of the dentition are similar and thus form a **homodont** dentition. In some teleosts, some reptiles, and in most mammals, the teeth composing the dentition are specialized in various areas. Such localized groups of specialized teeth within the dentition assume different shapes to suit specific functions. Consequently, the conical, **canine** teeth are for tearing; the **incisor** teeth are for biting or cutting; and the flat-surfaced, **lophodont** and **bunodont** teeth are for grinding and crushing. A dentition composed of teeth of heterogeneous morphology is a **heterodont** dentition.

b) DEVELOPMENT OF TEETH IN THE SHARK EMBRYO. The development of teeth in the shark embryo is identical with that of the placoid scale previously described. However, the teeth of the shark are larger and more durably constructed than the placoid scale and they are developed from a dental lamina of epithelial cells which grows downward along the inner aspect of the jaw. From this epithelium, a continuous series of teeth is developed as indicated in figure 287E and F. Within the oral cavity and pharyngeal area, ordinary placoid scales are found. Teeth are continuously replaced throughout life in the shark from the dental lamina. The word **polyphyodont** is applied to a condition where teeth are replaced continuously.

c) DEVELOPMENT OF TEETH IN THE FROG TADPOLE. The mouth of the frog tadpole possesses prominent upper and lower lips (fig. 287H). Inside these lips are rows of horny epidermal teeth. Three or four rows are inside the upper lip, and four rows are found inside the lower lip. These horny teeth represent cornifications of epidermal cells. They are sloughed off and

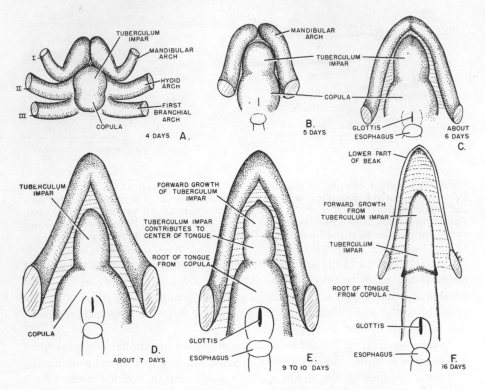

FIG. 284. Development of the tongue in the chick embryo.

replaced continuously until the time of metamorphosis when they are dispensed with. The permanent teeth begin to form shortly before metamorphosis from an epithelial ridge (dental lamina) which grows inward into the deeper tissues around the medial portion of the upper jaw. The teeth develop from an enamel organ and dental papilla in a manner similar to that of the developing shark or mammalian tooth. After the young tooth is partially formed, it moves upward toward the jaw, where its development is completed and attachment to the jaw occurs. Teeth are replaced continuously during the life of the frog.

d) DEVELOPMENT OF THE EGG TOOTH IN THE CHICK. Modern birds do not develop teeth. However, an ingrowth of epithelium does occur which suggests a rudimentary condition of the **dental lamina** of the shark, amphibian, and mammalian embryo (fig. 287I). It is possible that this represents the rudiment of a basic condition for tooth development, one which is never realized, for the sharp edge of the horny beak takes the place of teeth. The **egg tooth** is a conical prominence, developed upon the upper anterior portion of the upper horny jaw (fig. 287J). It is lost shortly after hatching. It appears to function in breaking the shell at hatching time.

e) DEVELOPMENT OF TEETH IN MAMMALS. As the oral cavity in the pig or in the human embryo is formed, the external margins or primitive jaw area of the oral cavity soon become differentiated into three general areas (fig. 288A):

(1) an external **marginal elevation,** the rudiment of the labium or lip,

(2) slightly mesial to the lip rudiment, a depressed area, the **labial** or **labiogingival groove,** and

(3) internal to this epithelial ingrowth, the **gingiva** or gum elevation.

The latter overlies the developing jaw. From the mesial aspect of the labial groove, an epithelial thickening forms which pushes inward into the tissue of the gum or gingiva. This thickened ridge of epithelium forms the **dental lamina** (ledge). (See fig. 288B, C.)

After the dental ledge is formed, epithelial buds arise at intervals along the ledge. These epithelial buds form the rudiments of the **enamel organs.** Each enamel organ pushes downward into the mesenchyme of the gum and eventually forms a cup-shaped group of cells, enclosing a mass of mesenchyme,

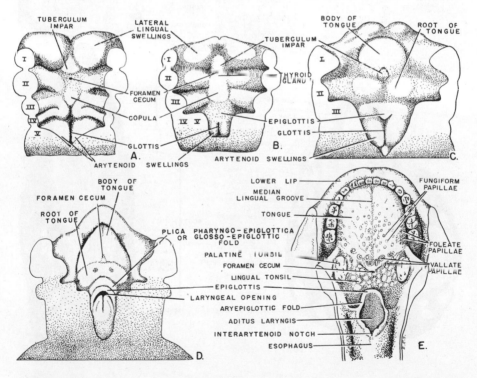

FIG. 285. Development of the tongue in the human embryo. (A–D drawn and modified from Ziegler models. (A) Fourth week. (B) About fifth week. (C) 6th to 7th week; 10 mm. (D) 7th week; 14 mm. (E) Adult condition. Observe that the mandibular lingual swellings give origin to the body of the tongue, while the copula forms the root of the tongue.

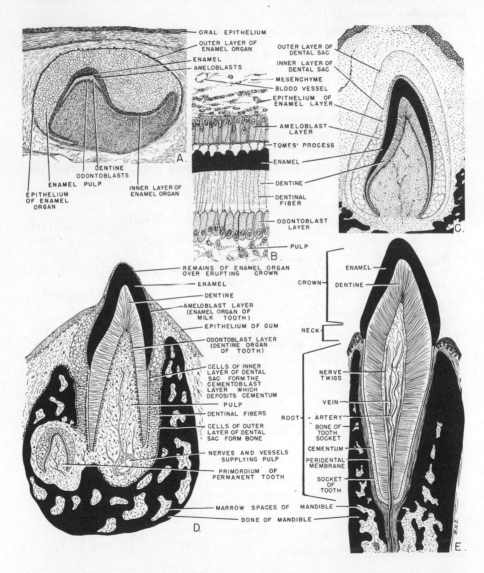

ORAL EPITHELIUM
OUTER LAYER OF ENAMEL ORGAN
ENAMEL
AMELOBLASTS

OUTER LAYER OF DENTAL SAC
INNER LAYER OF DENTAL SAC
MESENCHYME
BLOOD VESSEL
EPITHELIUM OF ENAMEL LAYER
AMELOBLAST LAYER
TOMES' PROCESS
ENAMEL
DENTINE
DENTINAL FIBER
ODONTOBLAST LAYER
PULP

DENTINE
ODONTOBLASTS
ENAMEL PULP
INNER LAYER OF ENAMEL ORGAN
EPITHELIUM OF ENAMEL ORGAN

A.
B.
C.

REMAINS OF ENAMEL ORGAN OVER ERUPTING CROWN
ENAMEL
DENTINE
AMELOBLAST LAYER (ENAMEL ORGAN OF MILK TOOTH)
EPITHELIUM OF GUM
ODONTOBLAST LAYER (DENTINE ORGAN OF TOOTH)
CELLS OF INNER LAYER OF DENTAL SAC FORM THE CEMENTOBLAST LAYER WHICH DEPOSITS CEMENTUM
PULP
DENTINAL FIBERS
CELLS OF OUTER LAYER OF DENTAL SAC FORM BONE
NERVES AND VESSELS SUPPLYING PULP
PRIMORDIUM OF PERMANENT TOOTH
MARROW SPACES OF MANDIBLE
BONE OF MANDIBLE

ENAMEL
CROWN
DENTINE
NECK
NERVE TWIGS
VEIN
ARTERY
ROOT
BONE OF TOOTH SOCKET
CEMENTUM
PERIDENTAL MEMBRANE
SOCKET OF TOOTH

D.
E.

FIG. 286. Development of thecodont teeth. (A) Early stage of developing premolar of human. (B) Cellular relationships of tooth-forming area greatly magnified. (C) Later stage in tooth development showing dental sac. (D) Vertical section of erupting milk tooth. (E) Vertical section of canine tooth, in situ. (Redrawn and modified from Morris, 1942, Human Anatomy, Blakiston, Phila. After Toldt.)

the **dental papilla** (fig. 288D, E). The enamel organ differentiates into three layers (fig. 288E):

(1) an **inner enamel layer,** surrounding the dental papilla,
(2) an **outer enamel layer,** and
(3) between these two layers, a mass of epithelial cells, giving origin to the **enamel pulp.**

The cells of the enamel pulp eventually form a stellate reticulum.

Development thus far serves to establish the basic mechanisms for tooth development. Further development of the tooth may be divided into two phases:

(1) formation of the **dentine** and **enamel** and
(2) development of the **root** of the tooth and its union with the **alveolus** or **socket** of the jaw.

The initial phase of tooth formation begins when the inner cells of the inner enamel layer of the enamel organ become differentiated into columnar epithelial cells. These cells form the **ameloblasts** (fig. 288E, F). Following this change in the cells of the inner enamel layer, the mesenchymal cells, facing the ameloblasts, become arranged into a layer of columnar **odontoblasts** (fig. 288F). The odontoblasts then begin to deposit the **dentine** of the tooth. The initial phase of formation of dentine consists first in the elaboration of an organic substance or **matrix.** The organic matrix then becomes impregnated with inorganic calcareous materials to form the **dentine,** a hard, bone-like substance. As the dentinal layer becomes thicker, the odontoblasts recede toward the dental pulp of the papilla. However, the odontoblasts do not withdraw entirely from the dentine already formed, as elongated, extremely fine extensions from the odontoblasts continue to remain within the dentine to form the **dentinal fibers** (fig. 286B).

Dentine is deposited by the odontoblasts; the ameloblasts deposit the enamel layer in the form of a cap, surrounding the dentine (fig. 286A, B). In doing so, a slight amount of organic substance is first deposited, and then the ameloblast constructs in some way a prismatic column of hard calcareous material at right angles to the dentinal surface (fig. 286B). The columnar prisms thus deposited around the dentine form an exceedingly hard cap for the dentine. As in the formation of the dentine, the elaboration of enamel begins at the crown or distal end of the tooth and proceeds rootward.

The development of the root of the tooth and its union with the jaw socket (alveolus) is a complicated procedure. This phase of tooth development is accomplished as follows: The mesenchyme, with its contained blood vessels and nerves of the dental papilla, lies within the developing dentinal layer of the forming tooth. At the base of the tooth (i.e., the end of the tooth opposite the crown), the mesenchyme of the dental papilla is continuous with

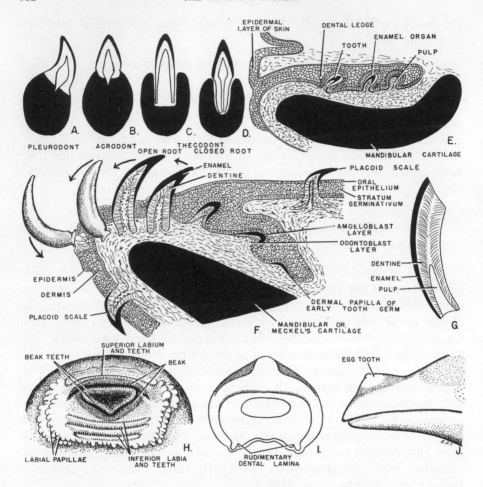

FIG. 287. Tooth development and arrangement in various vertebrates.   (A–D) Tooth relationships with the jaw. (Redrawn and modified from Rand, 1950, The Chordates, Blakiston, Phila. After Wilder.)   (E) Dental ledge and developing teeth in the dog shark, *Acanthias*. (Redrawn and modified from Rand, 1950, The Chordates, Blakiston, Phila. After Kingsley.)   (F) Section of the shark's lower jaw indicating a continuous replacement of teeth, i.e., a polyphyodont condition. (Redrawn and modified from Rand, 1950, The Chordates, Blakiston, Phila.)   (G) Incisor tooth of rodent. (Redrawn and modified from Rand, 1950, The Chordates, Blakiston, Phila. After Zittel.)   (H) Horny teeth of 12 mm. frog tadpole.   (I) Rudimentary dental lamina in upper jaw of chick. (Redrawn from Lillie, 1930, The Development of the Chick, Holt & Co., N. Y.)   (J) Anterior portion of upper jaw of 18-day chick showing egg tooth.

the mesenchyme surrounding the developing tooth. Around the base, sides, and crown of the tooth, this mesenchyme condenses and forms the outer and inner layers of the **dental sac** (fig. 286C). The latter is a connective-tissue sac which surrounds the entire tooth, continuing around the outside of the outer enamel cells of the enamel organ. As the dentine and enamel are deposited, the process of deposition proceeds downward from the crown toward the developing root of the tooth. However, in the root area, the cellular layers of the enamel organ are compressed against the dentine, where they form the **epithelial sheath.** The sheath eventually disintegrates and disappears. The formation of enamel thus becomes restricted to the upper or crown part of the tooth, the root portion consisting only of dentine. As the root area of the tooth lengthens downward, the tooth as a whole moves upward. Finally, the crown of the tooth erupts to the outside through the tissues of the gum (fig. 286D). The eruption, completion, and shedding of the **milk** or **deciduous teeth** in the human body occur apparently as shown in the following table.

THE MILK DENTITION

Median incisors	6th to 8th month
Lateral incisors	8th to 12th month
First molars	12th to 16th month
Canines	17th to 20th month
Second molars	20th to 24th month

THE PERMANENT DENTITION

First molars	7th year
Median incisors	8th year
Lateral incisors	9th year
First premolars	10th year
Second premolars	11th year
Canines	13th to 14th year
Second molars	13th to 14th year
Third molars	17th to 40th year

This table is taken from McMurrich, J. Playfair. 1922. Keibel and Mall, *Manual of Human Embryology,* page 354, Lippincott, Philadelphia.

At about the time of eruption, the tooth becomes *cemented* into the alveolus or socket of the jaw in the following manner:

(1) The **inner layer of the dental sac** (fig. 286D) forms a layer of **cemento-blasts** which deposit a coating of **cementum** over the dentine of the root (fig. 286E). This occurs only after the epithelial sheath (enamel-layer cells around the root) has been withdrawn or otherwise has disappeared.

(2) The **cells of the outer layer of the dental sac** become active in forming spongy bone.

(3) As the tooth reaches maturity, the two bony surfaces, i.e., the cementum of the root and the spongy bone of the jaw socket, gradually begin to approach each other. Then, as more cementum is deposited and more spongy bone is formed, the space between the cementum and the spongy bone of the alveolus becomes extremely narrow (fig. 286E).

(4) Finally, the dental-sac tissue between these two bony surfaces forms the **peridental membrane, a thin, fibrous, connective-tissue layer whose fibers are attached to the cementum and to the spongy bone of the socket.** In other words, the **cemental bone** of the root and the **spongy bone** of the socket become sutured together by means of the interlocking fibers of the peridental membrane. This type of suture, which

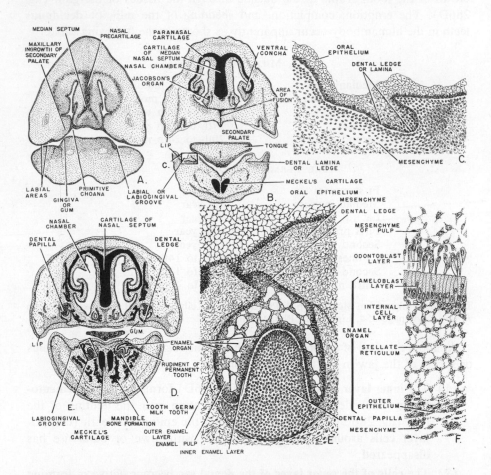

Fig. 288. Tooth development in the pig.   (A) Upper and lower jaw region of 18 mm. pig embryo showing labial and gum areas with the labial groove insinuated between.   (B) Section through snout and upper and lower jaws of 30-mm. pig embryo showing formation of nasal passageways, secondary palate, lip, gum, and jaw regions, and ingrowing dental ledge.   (C) High-powered drawing of dental ledge shown in square C in figure B.   (D) Section similar to B in 65-mm. pig embryo.   (E) Enlargement of area marked E in D showing dental papilla and enamel organ.   (F) Drawing showing juxtaposition of inner layer of enamel organ (the ameloblast layer) and the odontoblast cells which differentiate from the mesenchyme of the dental papilla.

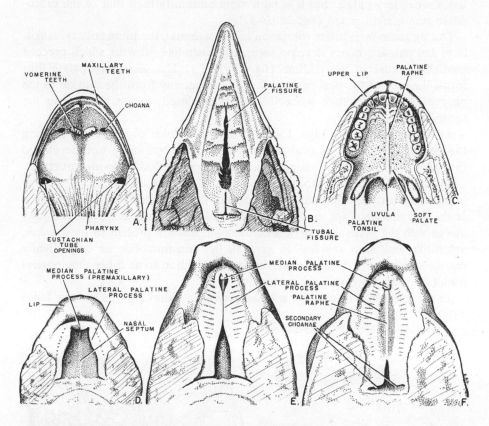

FIG. 289. Palatal conditions in frog, chick, and mammal. (A) Frog, adult. (B) Chick, 16-day embryo. (C) Human adult. (Redrawn and modified from Morris, 1942, Human Anatomy, Blakiston, Phila.) Only the anterior or hard palate is supported by bone, the soft palate being a fleshy continuation of the palate caudally toward the pharyngeal area. (D–F) Stages in development of the palate in the pig. (D) 20.5 mm. (E) 26.5 mm. (F) 29.5 mm.

is formed between the root of the tooth and the walls of the alveolar socket, is called a **gomphosis** (fig. 286E).

The permanent teeth, which supplant the deciduous teeth, develop in much the same manner as the deciduous teeth. Man, like the majority of mammals, develops two sets of teeth and, consequently, is **diphyodont.** Some mammals, such as the mole, *Scalopus,* never cut the permanent teeth, while the guinea pig sheds its deciduous teeth in utero.

5) Formation of the Secondary Palate. In the fishes and the amphibia, a secondary palate, separating the oral cavity from an upper respiratory passage-way, is not formed. The formation of a secondary palate begins in the turtle group and is well developed in the crocodilians and mammals. The bird also has a secondary palate, but it is built more tenuously than that of the crocodilian-mammalian group (fig. 289A–C).

During secondary-palate formation in the mammal, the premaxillary, maxillary, and palatine bones develop secondary plate-like growths which proceed medially to fuse in the midline (fig. 289D–F). The secondary palate thus forms the roof of the oral cavity—the air passageway from the outside to the pharynx being restricted, when the mouth is closed, to the area above the secondary palate.

6) Formation of the Lips. Lips are ridge-like folds of tissue surrounding the external orifice of the oral cavity. They are exceptionally well developed in mammals, where they are present in the form of fleshy mobile structures. They are absent in the prototherian mammal, *Ornithorhynchus,* as well as in birds and turtles, where the horny edges of the beak displace the fleshy folds at the oral margin. Lips are much reduced in sharks, where the toothed jaws merge with the general epidermis of the skin, but are present in most fishes, amphibia, and most reptiles. In general, lips are immobile or only slightly mobile structures in the lower vertebrates, although in some fishes they possess a mobility surpassed only in mammals.

In the formation of the lips, a **labial groove** or insinking of a narrow ledge

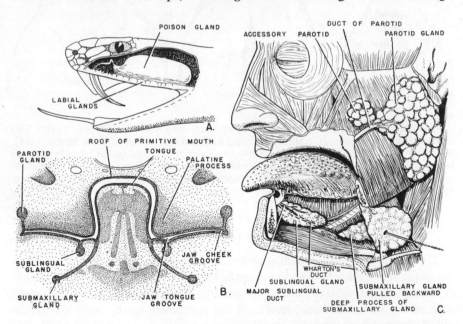

FIG. 290. Oral glands. (A) Poison and labial glands of the rattlesnake, *Crotalus horidus.* (Redrawn from Kingsley, 1912, Comparative Anatomy of the Vertebrates, Blakiston, Phila.)   (B) Loci of origin of salivary glands in human embryo. (Redrawn from Arey, 1946, Developmental Anatomy, Saunders, Phila.)   (C) Position of mature salivary glands in human. (Redrawn and modified from Morris, 1942, Human Anatomy, Blakiston, Phila.)

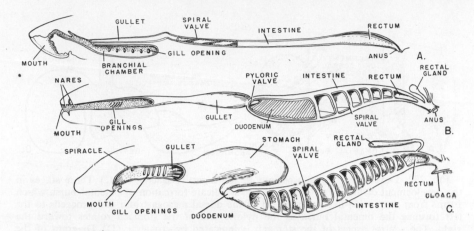

FIG. 291. Diagrams of intestinal tracts in various fishes. (Redrawn from Dean, 1895, Fishes, Living and Fossil, Macmillan, N. Y.) (A) Petromyzon, the cyclostome. (B) Protopterus, the lungfish. (C) The shark.

of epidermal cells occurs along the edge of the forming mouth. The labial groove then divides the edge of the forming mouth into an **outermost lip margin** and the **gum or jaw region** (fig. 288A). In forms where the lip is mobile, the lip region becomes highly developed and the muscle tissue which invades this area comes to form the general mass of the lip.

7) Oral Glands. Mouth glands are present throughout the vertebrate series. Mucus-secreting glands are the predominant type, but specialized glands, producing special secretions, appear in many instances. The cyclostomatous fish, for example, possesses a specialized gland which secretes an **anticoagulating substance** to prevent coagulation and stoppage of blood flow in the host fish to which it may be temporarily attached by its sucker-like mouth. Meanwhile, it rasps the host's flesh with its horny teeth and "sucks" the flowing blood. **Salivary glands** (i.e., glands forming the saliva) make their appearance in the amphibia. Such glands may be found on the amphibian tongue, where, as **lingual glands,** they secrete mucus and a watery fluid. **Intermaxillary glands** are present on the amphibian palate. The **poison glands** of the Gila monster and of snakes represent specialized oral glands (fig. 290A). Salivary glands are present also below the tongue and around the lips and palate in snakes. Birds, in general, possess salivary glands of various sorts. The mammals are characterized by the presence of highly developed, salivary glands, among which are the **parotid, sublingual,** and **submaxillary glands.** Unlike most of the salivary glands in other vertebrates, the mammalian salivary glands, in many species, secrete mucus and a watery fluid, **together with a starch-splitting enzyme, ptyalin.**

The submaxillary and sublingual glands in mammals arise as evaginations of the oral epithelium in the groove between the forming lower jaw and the

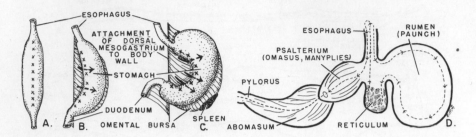

Fig. 292. Developing stomach regions of the digestive tract. (A–C) Three stages in the development of the pig's stomach. Arrows indicate formation of omental bursa which forms from the pocket-like enlargement of the dorsal mesogastrium and proceeds to the left forming the omental bursa as the pyloric end of the stomach rotates toward the right. The ventral aspect of the stomach is indicated by crosses. (D) Diagram of the ruminant stomach. The abomasum corresponds to the glandular stomach of the pig or human; the other areas represent esophageal modifications. (Redrawn from Kingsley, 1912, Comparative Anatomy of the Vertebrates, Blakiston, Phila.)

developing tongue. The place of origin is near the anterior limits of the tongue. Two of these epithelial outpushings occur on either side (fig. 290B). The sub-maxillary-gland and sublingual-gland ducts open at the side of the frenulum of the tongue (fig. 290C). The parotid glands arise as epithelial evaginations, at the angle of the mouth, from the groove which separates the forming jaw and the lip (fig. 290B, C).

The various oral glands, such as the palatine, labial, tongue, and cheek glands of mammals and lower vertebrates, the poison glands of snakes, etc., arise as epithelial buds which grow out from the developing oral cavity in a manner similar to those of the parotid, submaxillary, and sublingual glands of mammals. The original epithelial outgrowths may branch and rebranch many times to produce large, compound, alveolar glands, as in the parotid, sub-maxillary, and sublingual glands of mammals and the poison glands of snakes.

b. Development of the Pharyngeal Area

1) Pharyngeal Pouches and Grooves. The pharynx is that region of the early digestive tube which lies between the oral cavity and the esophagus. In adult vertebrate species, the pharyngeal area is much modified and differentially developed. However, in the early embryo, it tends to assume a generalized sameness throughout the vertebrate series.

The early formation of the pharynx results from a series of outpocketings of the entoderm of the foregut, associated with a corresponding series of epidermal inpushings; the latter tend to meet the entodermal outgrowths. As a result of these two sets of movements, the one outward and the other inward, the lateral plate mesoderm becomes isolated into dorso-ventral columns, the **branchial or visceral arches,** between the series of outpocketings and inpushings (figs. 252F; 260; 262). The entodermal pouches or outpocketings are called the **branchial, pharyngeal, or visceral pouches,** while the epidermal (ectodermal) inpushings form the **visceral or branchial grooves (furrows).** The mesodermal columns constitute the **visceral arches.**

The number of branchial pouch-groove relationships, thus established, varies in different vertebrate species. In the cyclostomatous fish, *Petromyzon,* there are seven; in *Squalus acanthias,* the shark, there are six. The latter number is present typically in a large number of fishes. In most frogs and salamanders, there are five, pouch-groove relationships with a vestigial sixth; in the chick, pig, and human, there are four. (In reptiles, birds, and mammals, the fourth pouch on either side may represent a fusion of two or three pouches.) The number of visceral arches, of course, varies with the number of pouch-groove relationships produced, the first pair of arches being formed just anterior to the first pair of pouches. The first pair of arches are called the **mandibular visceral arches;** the second pair constitute the **hyoid visceral arches;** and the remaining pairs form the **branchial arches.**

Within each visceral arch, three structures tend to differentiate:

(1) a **skeletal arch,**
(2) a **muscle column,** associated with the skeletal arch, and
(3) the **aortal arch,** a blood vessel.

In all water-living vertebrates, including those species which spend the larval period in the water, the entoderm of the branchial pouch and ectoderm of the branchial groove tend to fuse intimately and perforate to form the branchial or visceral clefts, with the exception of the first, pouch-groove relationship. The latter is variable. In the amphibia, the first pouch does not perforate but becomes associated with the developing ear. In land forms, on the other hand, the pouches, as a rule, remain imperforate or weakly so. As a rule, they continue unperforated in mammals. The ectoderm and entoderm of the branchial-pouch-groove relationships is very thin in the chick, and openings (?) may appear in the more anterior pouches. (*Note:* The relation of these pouches to respiration is discussed in the following chapter.)

2) Pharyngeal Glands of Internal Secretion. An important developmental function of the pharynx is the formation of masses of epithelial cells from various parts of the entodermal wall which serve as endocrine glands. These glands are the thyroid, parathyroid, thymus, and ultimobranchial bodies. The places of origin of these cellular masses and their part in the formation of the endocrine system are discussed in Chapter 21.

3) Other Respiratory Diverticula. One of the primary functions of the pharyngeal area is respiration. In most water-living vertebrates, the pharyngeal pouches are adapted for respiratory purposes. However, in many water-dwelling species and in all land forms, a median ventral outpushing occurs which de-

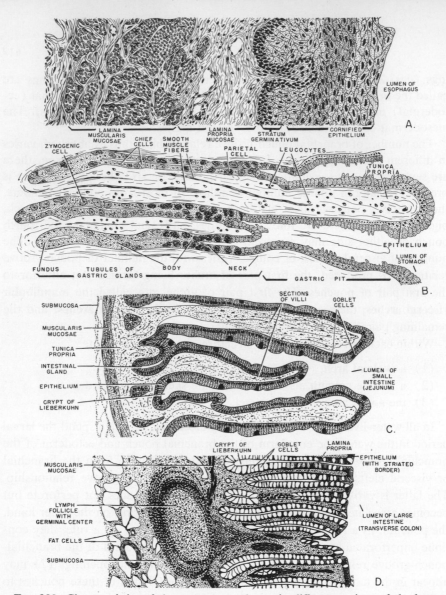

FIG. 293. Characteristics of the mucous membrane in different regions of the human digestive tract: (A and D) redrawn and modified from Maximow and Bloom, A Textbook of Histology, Saunders, Philadelphia; (B and C) redrawn from Bremer, A Textbook of Histology, Blakiston, Philadelphia. (A) Esophageal area. Stratified squamous epithelium together with esophageal and cardiac glands are characteristic. The *esophageal glands* are located in the submucous layer and are of the tubulo-alveolar variety. The *cardiac glands* are found in the upper and lower esophageal regions and are confined to the mucous layer. (B) Stomach region. The mucous layer of the stomach is featured by the presence of many glands composed of simple and branched tubules. These glands open into the bottom of the gastric pits which in turn form small, circular openings at the mucosal surface. (C) The mucosal walls of the small intestine present many finger-like processes, the *villi,* between the bases of which the intestinal glands or *crypts of Lieberkühn* project downward toward the *lamina muscularis mucosae.* (D) The mucosa of the large intestine is devoid of villi, and the glands of Lieberkühn are longer and straighter than in the small intestine.

velops into the lungs or into structures which function as air bladders and lungs. (See Chap. 14.)

c. Morphogenesis and Histogenesis of the Esophagus and the Stomach Region of the Metenteron

The esophageal and stomach areas of the gut develop from that segment of the foregut which extends from the pharyngeal area caudally to the area of the developing gut tube from which the liver and pancreatic diverticula arise. In *Amphioxus* and certain of the lower vertebrates, a true stomach is not differentiated within this portion of the foregut. This condition is found in the cyclostome, *Petromyzon,* in the lungfish, *Protopterus,* and various other forms (fig. 291A, B). In these species, this segment of the gut merely serves to transport food caudally to the **intestine,** and the histogenesis of its walls resembles that of the esophagus. On the other hand, a true stomach is developed in all other vertebrate species. The functions of the stomach are to store food, to break it up into smaller pieces, and to digest it partially. As such, the stomach comprises that segment of the digestive tract which lies between the esophagus and intestine. It is well supplied with muscular tissue, is capable of great distention, and possesses glands for enzyme secretion.

In development, therefore, the foregut area between the primitive pharynx and the developing liver becomes divided into two general regions in most vertebrates:

(1) a more or less constricted, esophageal region, and
(2) a posteriorly expanded, stomach segment (figs. 279–282).

The latter tends to expand and to assume a general, V-shaped form, the portion nearest the esophagus comprising the **cardiac region,** and the part nearest the intestine forming the **pyloric end.**

Many variations in esophageal-stomach relationships are elaborated in different vertebrate species. In the formation of the stomach of the pig or human, for example, a generalized, typical, vertebrate condition may be assumed to exist. In these forms, the stomach area of the primitive gut gradually enlarges and assumes a broad, V-shaped form, with its distal or pyloric end rotated toward the right (fig. 292A–C). Eventually, the entodermal lining tissue shows four structural conditions:

(a) There is an **esophageal area** near the esophagus, where the character of the epithelial lining resembles that of the esophagus.
(b) A **cardiac region** occurs, where the epithelium is simple, columnar in form, and contains certain glands.
(c) There is a **fundic region,** capable of being greatly expanded. The internal lining of the fundic area produces numerous, simple, slightly branched, tubular glands, wherein **pepsin** is secreted by the **chief cells** and **hydrochloric acid** by the **parietal cells** (fig. 293).

(d) The **pyloric area** is the last segment of the stomach and is joined to the intestine. It has numerous glands, producing a mucus-like secretion.

The pig's stomach resembles closely that of the human.

If we compare the general morphogenesis of the stomach in the pig or human with that of the shark, frog, chick, or the cow, the following differences exist.

The shark stomach is composed mainly of fundic and pyloric segments (fig. 279C). The stomach of the frog closely resembles that of the pig (fig. 280F). Unlike the pig, however, the frog is able to evert the stomach by muscular action projecting it forward through the mouth to empty its contents. In the chick (fig. 281E), an area of the esophagus expands into a **crop** which functions mainly as a **food-storage organ.** A glandular stomach **(proventriculus),** comparable to the fundus of the pig, is formed posterior to the crop, while, still more caudally, a highly muscular **gizzard or grinding organ** is elaborated.

In the cow or sheep, an entirely different procedure of development produces a greatly enlarged, distorted, esophageal portion of the stomach. This esophageal area of the stomach comprises the **rumen,** the **reticulum** or honeycomb stomach, and the **omasum (psalterium)** or manyplies stomach. The distal end of the stomach of the cow or sheep is the **abomasum** or true stomach, comparable to that of the human or pig described above (fig. 292D).

d. Morphogenesis and Histogenesis of the Hepato-pancreatic Area

The hepato-pancreatic area of the digestive tract is a most important one. Its importance springs not only from the development of indispensable glands but also from the relationship of the liver to the developing circulatory system (Chap. 17) and the division and formation of the coelomic cavity. (See Chap. 20.)

1) Development of the Liver Rudiment. The liver begins in all vertebrates as a midventral outpushing of the primitive metenteron, immediately caudal

---

FIG. 294. Development of the liver and pancreatic rudiments. (Diagrams C–E, redrawn from Lillie, 1930, The development of the chick, Holt, N. Y. F redrawn from Thyng, 1908, Am. J. Anat.) (A) Developing liver rudiment in 10 mm. embryo of the dogshark, *Squalus acanthias*. (B) Developing liver in tadpole of *Rana pipiens*. (See also Figs. 221, 223, 225, 280.) (C) Developing liver rudiments in the 3rd-day chick. (D) Developing liver in early 4th-day chick. (E) Developing liver in late 4th-day chick. (F) Hepatic evagination in 7.5 mm. human embryo. (G) Relation of the fully developed liver to associated structures in various vertebrates. (G1) *Squalus acanthias*. The liver is suspended from the posterior surface of the septum transversum by the coronary ligament. (G2 and G3) Frog, *Rana pipiens*. G2 transverse view; G3 sagittal view. (G4 and G5) 16-20 day chick, *Gallus domesticus*. G4 transverse view. Observe that the liver lobes and peritoneal cavity have grown forward on either side of the heart and have separated the heart and pericardial cavity from the ventro-lateral body walls. G5 is a left ventral view of the heart, pericardial cavity, and liver. Left lobe of the liver is removed. Observe that the septum transversum is applied to the posterior wall of the parietal pericardium. G6 Mammal. The septum transversum has been completely displaced by developing diaphragmatic tissue. The liver is suspended from the caudal surface of the diaphragm by the coronary ligament.

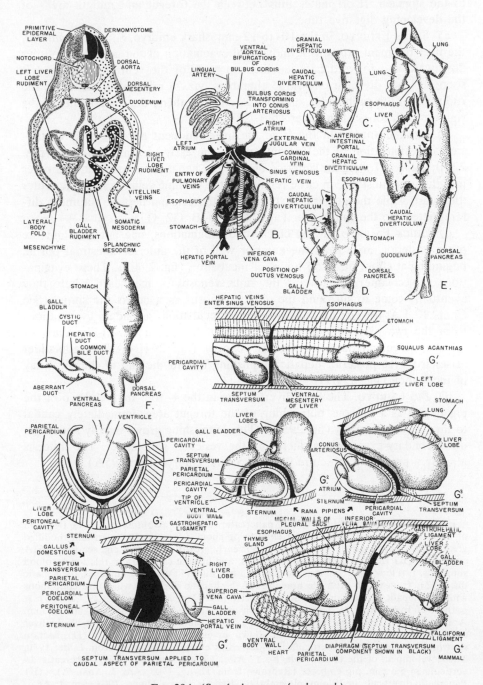

FIG. 294. *(See facing page for legend.)*

to the stomach. It originates thus between the foregut and midgut areas of the developing digestive tube.

a) SHARK EMBRYO. In the 10- to 12-mm. shark embryo, *Squalus acanthias,* the liver rudiment arises as a midventral evagination of the gut which pushes downward and forward between the two parts of the ventral mesentery. It soon becomes divisible into three chambers, viz., a **midventral chamber,** the rudiment of the **gallbladder,** and **two lateral chambers,** the fundaments of the right and left lobes of the liver (figs. 279B; 294A).

b) FROG EMBRYO. In the frog, the liver rudiment appears as a ventro– caudal prolongation of the foregut area at the early, neural fold stage (figs. 220B; 223B). Later, the anterior end of the hepatic rudiment differentiates into the liver substance in close relation to the vitelline veins as the latter enter the heart, while the posterior extremity of the original hepatic rudiment dif- ferentiates into the gallbladder (figs. 280; 294B, G2, G3).

c) CHICK EMBRYO. In the chick, two evaginations, one anterior and the other posterior, arise from the anterior wall of the anterior intestinal portal, beginning at about 50 to 55 hours of incubation (fig. 294C). These evagina- tions project anteriorly toward the sinus venosus of the heart, where they eventually come to surround the ductus venosus as it enters the sinus. (See Chap. 17.) At the end of the fourth day of incubation, secondary evaginations from the two primary outgrowths begin to produce a basket-like mass of tubules which surround the ductus venosus (fig. 294E). The gallbladder arises from the posterior hepatic outpushing toward the end of the third day of incubation (fig. 294D).

d) PIG EMBRYO. The liver diverticulum in the 4- to 5-mm. embryo of the pig begins as a bulbous outpushing of the foregut area, immediately caudal to the forming stomach (fig. 295E). This outpushing grows rapidly and sends out secondary evaginations, including the vesicular gallbladder. The latter is already a prominent structure in the 5.5-mm. embryo (fig. 295A).

FIG. 295. Development of liver and pancreatic rudiments *(Continued).* (A) Diagram of early hepatic diverticulum in pig embryo of about 5.5 mm. (Redrawn and modified greatly from Thyng, 1908, Am. J. Anat.) For early growth of liver in pig, see Figs. 261A and 262. (B) Hepatic ducts, hepatic tubules, and hepatic canaliculi in relation to blood sinusoids. It is to be observed that the common bile duct (1) gives off branches, the hepatic ducts (2), from which arise the branches of the hepatic duct (3) which are continuous with the hepatic tubules or hepatic cord cells (4). Compare with Fig. 295C. (C) A portion of liver lobule of human. (Redrawn and modified from Maximow and Bloom, A Text-book of Histology, Saunders, Phila.) Blood sinusoids are shown in black; liver cells in stippled white; bile canaliculi shown in either white or black. (D) Section showing three pancreatic diverticula in 5-day chick embryo. (Redrawn from Lillie, 1930, The development of the chick, Holt, N. Y. After Choronschitsky.) (E) Pancreatic di- verticula in 5.5 mm. pig embryo. (Redrawn from Thyng, 1908, Am. J. Anat. 7.) (F) Pancreatic diverticula in 20 mm. pig embryo. (Redrawn from Thyng, 1908, Am. J. Anat. 7.) (G) Pancreatic acini and islet of Langerhans.

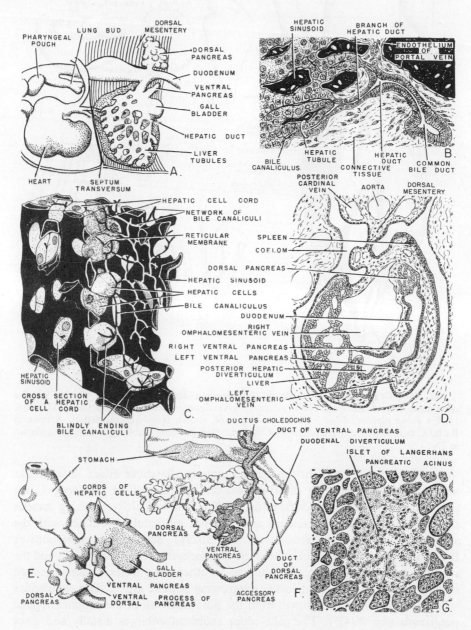

FIG. 295. (*See facing page for legend.*)

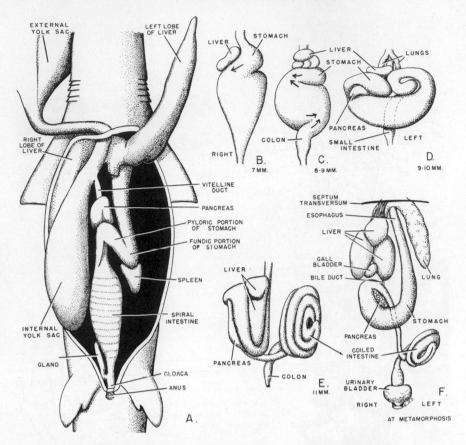

FIG. 296. Development of coils in the digestive tracts in the dog shark, *Squalus acanthias,* and in the frog, *Rana pipiens.* (A) *Squalus acanthias* embryo of 110 mm. (B–F) *Rana pipiens,* digestive tube development, shown from ventral aspect. Arrows in B and C denote primary movements of the primitive gut tube resulting in condition shown in D.

e) HUMAN EMBRYO. In the human embryo, the liver arises in a similar manner to that of the pig embryo from the ventral wall of the foregut, just posterior to the forming stomach (fig. 294F). The hepatic outpushing invades the area of the ventral mesentery and becomes intimately associated with the substance of the septum transversum (fig. 362H). Secondary evaginations or **liver cords** ramify extensively within the mesenchyme of the mesentery, and the vitelline or omphalomesenteric veins, as in other vertebrates, become broken up into sinusoids, surrounding the outgrowing hepatic cords. The gallbladder arises as a secondary outgrowth from the posterior wall of the original hepatic outgrowth (fig. 294F). The gallbladder rudiment enlarges distally and gives origin to the cystic duct which joins the common bile duct.

2) Histogenesis of the Liver. As the liver pushes out into the ventral mesentery, it tends to project forward below the forming stomach and the caudal limits of the heart (figs. 295A; 362H). Within the ventral mesentery, secondary evaginations or epithelial cords of entodermal cells sprout from the primary entodermal evagination of the entodermal lining of the gut (fig. 295A). These epithelial or **liver cords** grow in between the paired vitelline veins, and the veins become changed into a mass of capillary-like **sinusoids.** The liver cords come to lie in the interstices between the vitelline sinusoids (fig. 295B).

As the liver cords grow within the ventral mesentery, mesenchymal cells, given off from the medial surfaces of the mesentery, come to surround the liver cords and give origin to the connective-tissue substance of the liver. The outer surface of the ventral mesentery retains its integrity and functions as the peritoneal covering of the growing liver.

It is apparent that the growth of the epithelial (liver) cords progresses dichotomously, branching into a tree-like system of branches from the original hepatic diverticulum of the gut tube, thus forming the parenchyma of the liver (Bloom, '26). The proximal portion of the original hepatic diverticulum forms the **common bile duct,** or **ductus choledochus,** whereas the larger branches of the hepatic cords develop lumina and form the duct system. The gallbladder represents an original diverticulum from the common-bile-duct rudiment. The liver cords appear to be hollow from the beginning. The bile capillaries thus apparently develop directly within the liver cords. The liver-cord cells probably assume their typical cuboidal shape under the influence of the surrounding young connective tissue and branches from the portal vein (Bloom, '26). The ultimate relationship between hepatic cell cords, liver sinusoids, and bile ductules is shown in figure 295C.

In the majority of vertebrates, as the liver substance increases within the ventral mesentery below the stomach area, it expands the ventral mesentery enormously until the liver, with its coating of ventral mesentery, fills the coelomic space below the gut tube and posterior to the heart. The developing liver thus comes in contact with the ventral and lateral body walls and becomes fused to these walls. The anterior face of the liver, eventually, forms a partition across the coelomic cavity just caudal to the heart (figs. 261; 295A). The anterior face of the liver substance gradually separates and forms a primitive partition across the body cavity. This partition is the **primary septum transversum** (fig. 295A). (See also Chap. 20.)

As the liver rudiment develops in the pig embryo, the septum transversum forms essentially as described above, i.e., it develops as a modification of the ventral mesentery covering the anterior face of the liver. However, in the human embryo, the primary septum transversum develops precociously, forming a partition across the ventral area of the coelomic cavity between the developing heart and liver (fig. 362F–H). When the hepatic cords in the human embryo grow forward within the ventral mesentery, they secondarily become related to the previously formed, primitive septum transversum along the caudal aspect of the septum. The ends achieved in the human and pig embryos are much the same, therefore, and the anterior face of the developing liver and the septum transversum are intimately associated.

3) Development of the Rudiments of the Pancreas: a) SHARK EMBRYO. In the embryo of *Squalus acanthias,* the shark, the pancreas arises as a **dorsal diverticulum** of the gut a short distance posterior to the gallbladder and hepatic outpushings (fig. 279B). It grows rapidly and, in the 18- to 20-mm. embryo, it is a much-branched gland with its pancreatic duct entering the duodenum slightly anterior to the beginning coils of the spiral valve.

b) FROG EMBRYO. In the frog, the pancreas arises from three diverticula, one dorsal and two ventral, near the liver rudiment (Kellicott, '13, p. 167). The dorsal diverticulum is solid and separates from the gut tissue. The two ventral diverticula arise together from the ventral portions of the gut but soon branch into two rudiments. As these rudiments enlarge and branch, they eventually unite with the dorsal diverticulum of the pancreas, and the three fuse to form one gland. The proximal portion of the original, ventral, pancreatic outpushing remains as the pancreatic duct and empties into the duodenum close to the bile duct.

c) CHICK EMBRYO. As in the frog, three pancreatic diverticula arise in the

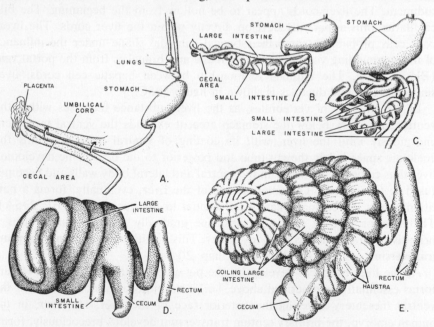

FIG. 297. Developing coils in the digestive tube of the pig. (A) 12 mm. embryo. (B) 24 mm. embryo. (C) 35 mm. embryo. (D) Cecum and large intestine showing coils in 120 mm. embryo. (E) Coiling of large intestine of young adult pig. Observe *haustra* or *lateral diverticula* of colonic wall. (All figures redrawn and modified from Lineback, 1916, Am. J. Anat. 16.)

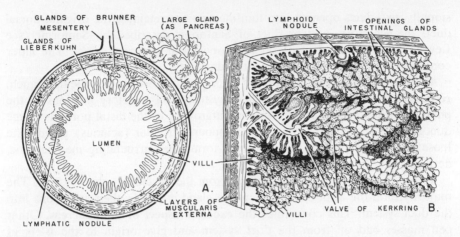

FIG. 298. Structural composition of walls of human digestive tract. (A) Diagrammatic representation of digestive tract structure. (B) Portion of wall of small intestine showing folds of mucosa. (A and B redrawn from Maximow and Bloom, 1942, A Textbook of Histology, Saunders, Phila. B after Braus.)

chick. The dorsal one appears first as an outpushing into the dorsal mesentery at the end of the third and early fourth days of incubation (fig. 295D). The two ventral diverticula arise during the end of the fourth and early fifth days of incubation as two lateral diverticula of the posterior hepatic evaginations close to the latter's origin from the duodenum. The three diverticula fuse into one pancreatic mass, but tend to retain the proximal portions of the original outpushings as pancreatic ducts. Two or even all three may persist in the adult.

d) PIG EMBRYO. Two pancreatic diverticula make their appearance in the pig embryo. One, the ventral pancreatic diverticulum, arises from the proximal end of the hepatic evagination, while the other, the dorsal diverticulum, emerges as a separate dorsal outpushing from the duodenal area approximately opposite the hepatic diverticulum (fig. 295E). In the 20-mm. embryo of the pig, these two diverticula proceed in development as shown in figure 295F. At about the 24-mm. stage, the duct of the ventral pancreas is obliterated, the dorsal pancreatic duct (duct of Santorini) remaining ordinarily as the pancreatic duct of the adult (Thyng, '08).

e) HUMAN EMBRYO. Dorsal and ventral pancreatic evaginations occur in the human embryo in a manner similar to that in the pig. Both fuse into one mass, although the dorsal pancreas grows much faster and forms much of the bulk of the pancreatic tissue. The ventral pancreas swings dorsally as the stomach and duodenal area of the intestine are rotated toward the right side of the peritoneal cavity. In doing so, the dorsal pancreas appropriates the duct of the ventral pancreas proximally toward the intestine, while distally it retains its own duct. This combined duct, or **duct of Wirsung,** first observed by Wirsung in 1642 (see Lewis, '12), is the pancreatic duct of the adult. Occasionally, two ducts opening into the intestine are retained, the original dorsal duct, the accessory duct or duct of Santorini, described by Santorini (see Lewis, '12), and the duct of Wirsung or ventral pancreatic duct. The latter condition appears to be normal in the dog.

4) Histogenesis of the Pancreas. The original pancreatic diverticula branch, rebranch, and form an elaborate duct system. The secretory portions of the pancreas or the acini arise as terminal outgrowths of the distal portions of the duct system. The pancreas thus is a compound alveolar (acinous) gland. The loose connective tissue of the pancreas forms the surrounding mesenchyme, derived from the mesenteric tissue.

Two types of secretory cells bud off from the developing duct system. The majority form the acini of the pancreatic gland and pour their secretions into the duct system. This constitutes the **exocrine aspect of the pancreas.** Other cell masses bud off from the duct system and give origin to the **islets of Langerhans.** The latter form the **endocrine portion of the pancreas** (fig. 295G).

e. Morphogenesis and Histogenesis of the Intestine

1) Morphogenesis of the Intestine in the Fish Group. In the fishes, the intestinal rudiment of the digestive tube does not undergo extensive elongation during development. A relatively short tube is formed as shown in figure 279C, although some coiling of the intestine does occur in teleost fishes. A distinct, small and large division of the intestine is not formed; intestinal and rectal areas only are developed. Specialized rectal outgrowths develop in sharks (fig. 279C), while, in teleost fishes, pyloric evaginations or cecae are formed.

2) Morphogenesis of the Intestine in Amphibia, Reptiles, Birds, and Mammals. The development of the intestine in this group of vertebrates involves considerable elongation and coiling (figs. 280, 281, 282). Two general divisions of the intestine are formed, a **small intestine,** developed from the midgut portion of the primitive metenteron, and a **hindgut** or **colon,** derived from the hindgut portion of the gut tube. A **rectal area** is formed at the caudal end of the hindgut. There is a tendency also for enlargements or extensions to occur in the area of junction between the small intestine and colon in the birds and mammals.

3) Torsion and Rotation of the Intestine During Development. Twisting and rotation of the stomach and intestine is a general feature of alimentary-tract development. In the shark embryo, the stomach is rotated in such a way that its pyloric end is pulled upward toward the liver, forming a J-shaped structure (fig. 296A). Also, the duodenal and valvular areas of the intestine are rotated vertically, and the place of attachment of the dorsal mesentery moves into a ventro-lateral position.

The developing stomach and intestine of the frog embryo presents a remarkable and precise rotative procedure. In the early stages, the primitive metenteron is a simple tube, continuing from the forming stomodaeum caudad to the proctodaeum (fig. 280B). At the 6- to 7-mm. stage, the stomach-liver area begins to rotate toward the right as indicated in figure 296B. At about 7 to 9 mm., the stomach-liver area is projected to the right and anteriad, while the midgut and hindgut regions move toward the left (see arrows, fig. 296C). At the stage of development when the larvae approximate 10 mm. in length, the stomach and intestinal areas are arranged as in figure 296D. Through the larval stages to the time of metamorphosis, the midgut or small intestinal area becomes greatly extended and coiled as shown in figure 296E. At the time of metamorphosis, the small intestine becomes greatly reduced in relative length (fig. 296F).

The chick embryo manifests similar gastrointestinal torsion. The duodenal area of the intestine and the gizzard are pulled forward toward the liver, while the small intestine becomes coiled and lies to a great extent in the umbilical stalk, to be retracted later into the abdominal area.

At the 10-mm. stage in the pig, the digestive tract consists of a simple tubular structure as shown in figure 297A (Lineback, '16). In this figure, the pyloric-duodenal area is projected forward toward the liver, where the pyloric-duodenal area eventually is tied to the liver on the right side of the peritoneal cavity, with the result that the forming stomach lies transversely across the upper part of the abdominal cavity. The cecal and large intestinal areas are rotated around the small intestine (see arrow, fig. 297A), when the latter lies herniated within the umbilical cord. In figure 297B is shown the condition in the 24-mm. pig. It is to be observed that there is now a half rotation of the large intestine around the small intestine, the latter being considerably coiled, while in figure 297C a complete rotation of 360 degrees is shown.

Aside from these rotational movements, extensive coiling of the gut tube occurs, especially in the higher vertebrates. For example, the small intestine of the frog becomes coiled extensively during the larval period (fig. 296E). Reference to figure 297D and E shows a similar coiling of the large intestine of the pig.

Rotational movements of the intestine in the human embryo also occur. For example, in the human embryo of about 23 mm., a condition is present, comparable to that of the pig embryo of 24 mm., and the future large intestine has been rotated 180 degrees around the small intestine as shown in figure 282F. Unlike the pig, however, a complete rotation of the gut is not effected. Also, the large intestine does not later form into a double coil as in the pig. In the human embryo soon after the intestine is retracted from its herniated position in the umbilical cord (fig. 282G), the cecal area of the large intestine becomes fixed to the right side of the peritoneal cavity near the crest of the ilium (Hunter, '28). The ascending, transverse, and descending portions of the large intestine are then developed (fig. 364G, H).

4) **Histogenesis of the Intestine.** During histogenesis of the intestine, two

prominent modifications of the internal lining or mucous membrane tend to occur:

  (a) Small finger-like projections or **villi** are formed which project inwardly into the lumen (fig. 298A); and
  (b) the internal lining may project inwardly in the form of extensive elongated **folds.**

In many fishes, such as the sharks, lungfishes, ganoids, and cyclostomes, elaborate folds of the mucosa, known as the **spiral folds** or **valves,** are formed (fig. 291C). Similarly, in higher vertebrates, elongated folds may occur, such as the **valves of Kerkring** in the human and pig small·intestine (fig. 298B).

Another conspicuous feature of the early histogenesis of the entodermal layer is the formation of epithelial membranes and plugs. The **pharyngeal membrane** is formed by the stomodaeal ectoderm and pharyngeal epithelial layers. The **proctodaeal membrane** is similarly constructed. This structure serves as a temporary blocking device between external and internal media. Under normal conditions these membranes degenerate and disappear, although occasionally they may persist. Epithelial plugs, temporarily obliterating the lumen of the digestive tract, appear with regularity in many vertebrates. Such temporary obstruction, for example, may appear in the developing digestive tract of the chick or in the human esophagus, duodenum, and other areas of the digestive tract.

f. Differentiation of the Cloaca

As previously observed, the caudal end of the intestine expands into the cloaca, an enlarged area which eventually receives the urinary products as well as the intestinal substances. The differentiation of this area is considered in Chapter 18.

C. Physiological Aspects of the Developing Gut Tube

Within the developing digestive tubes of the shark, reptiles, birds, and mammals, a brownish-green, pigmented material appears during the latter phases of embryonic development. This material is composed of cells, bile pigments, mucus, etc. It is discharged during the period just before or after parturition. Fetal swallowing of ammionic fluid, gastrointestinal motility, the presence of enzymes, fetal digestion and absorption, and defecation are well-established facts in the physiology of the developing digestive tract of the mammalian fetus (Windle, '40, Chap. VII).

Bibliography

Bloom, W. **1926.** The embryogenesis of human bile capillaries and ducts. Am. J. Anat. **36**:451.

Hunter, R. H. **1928.** A note on the development of the ascending colon. J. Anat. **62**:297.

Kellicott, W. E. **1913.** Outlines of Chordate Development. Henry Holt & Co., New York.

Lewis, F. T. **1912.** Development of the Pancreas. Vol. II. Human Embryology by Keibel and Mall. J. B. Lippincott Co., Philadelphia.

Lineback, P. E. **1916.** The development of the spiral coil in the large intestine of the pig. Am. J. Anat. **20**:483.

Platt, J. B. **1891.** Further contribution to the morphology of the vertebrate head. Anat. Anz. **6**:251.

Thyng, F. W. **1908.** Models of the pancreas in embryos of the pig, rabbit, cat and man. Am. J. Anat. **7**:489.

Windle, W. F. **1940.** Physiology of the Fetus. W. B. Saunders Co., Philadelphia.

14

Respiratory and Buoyancy Systems

A. Introduction
  1. External and internal respiration
  2. Basic structural relationships involved in external respiration
    a. Cellular relationships
    b. Sites or areas where external respiration is accomplished
    c. Main types of organs used for respiration
B. Development of bronchial or gill respiratory organs
  1. Development of gills in fishes
    a. Development of gills in *Squalus acanthias*
    b. Gills of teleost fishes
    c. External gills
  2. Development of gills in *Amphibia*
    a. General features
    b. Development of gills in *Necturus maculosus*
    c. Development of gills in the larva of the frog, *Rana pipiens*
      1) Development of external gills
      2) Formation of the operculum
      3) Internal gills
      4) Resorption and obliteration of gills
C. Development of lungs and buoyancy structures
  1. General relationship between lungs and air bladders
  2. Development of lungs
    a. Development of lungs in the frog and other *Amphibia*
    b. Lung development in the chick
      1) General features of lung development
      2) Formation of air sacs
      3) Formation of the bronchi and respiratory areas of the chick's lung
      4) Trachea, voice box, and ultimate position of the bird's lung in the body
      5) Basic cellular composition of the trachea, lungs, and air sacs
    c. Development of lungs in the mammal
      1) Origin of the lung rudiment
      2) Formation of the bronchi
      3) Formation of the respiratory area of the lung
      4) Development of the epiglottis and voice box
      5) Cellular composition
      6) Ultimate position of the mammalian lung in the body
  3. Development of air bladders
  4. Lunglessness

A. Introduction

1. EXTERNAL AND INTERNAL RESPIRATION

Respiration consists of two phases: (1) **external** and (2) **internal. External respiration** enables the organism to acquire oxygen from its external environment and to discharge carbon dioxide into this environment. **Internal respiration** is the utilization of oxygen and the elimination of carbon dioxide by the cells and tissues of the organism. The formation of the structural mechanisms related to external respiration, in many vertebrates, is associated intimately with buoyancy functions. The development of **external respiratory and buoyancy mechanisms** is discussed in this chapter.

2. BASIC STRUCTURAL RELATIONSHIPS INVOLVED IN EXTERNAL RESPIRATION

a. Cellular Relationships

In effecting external respiration, it is necessary for blood capillaries to come into a close relationship with a moist or watery medium containing sufficient amounts of oxygen and a lowered content of carbon dioxide. The mechanisms permitting this relationship vary in different vertebrates. In lower vertebrates, blood capillaries in the gills or in the skin are brought near the watery medium containing oxygen, while, in higher vertebrates, lungs are used for this purpose. In lower vertebrates, an epithelial layer of cells is always interposed between the blood stream and the oxygen-containing fluid. Small amounts of mesenchyme or connective tissue may interpose also (fig. 299B & C). However, in the air capillaries of the lungs of birds (fig. 307C) and in the air cells (alveoli) of mammalian lungs (figs. 299A; 309G), the surrounding blood capillaries may be exposed intimately to the air-fluid mixture containing oxygen, and the barrier of epithelium between the blood capillaries and the air mixture may be greatly reduced if not entirely absent.

h. Sites or Areas Where External Respiration Is Accomplished

External respiration is achieved in various areas in the embryos and adults of different vertebrate species. In the early shark embryo, external gill filaments, attached to the pharyngeal area, serve as a mechanism for effecting external respiration (fig. 299D), whereas, in the chick and reptile embryo, allantoic contacts with surface membranes of the egg are important (fig. 299E). In the frog tadpole, the flattened tail region is a factor, as well as the presence of gills and lungs associated with the pharyngeal area. The embryos of higher mammals utilize allantoic-placental relationships for this phase of respiration (see Chap. 22). Similarly, in adult vertebrate species, various areas of the body are used as respiratory mechanisms, such as a moist skin (fig. 299B), gills, lungs, vascular villosities, or papillae (fig. 299F). The skin is most im-

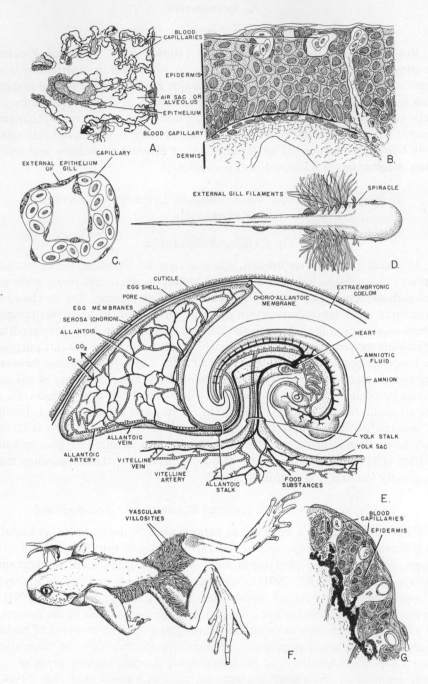

Labels in figure:

BLOOD CAPILLARIES
EPIDERMIS
AIR SAC OR ALVEOLUS
EPITHELIUM
BLOOD CAPILLARY
DERMIS
A.
B.

CAPILLARY
EXTERNAL EPITHELIUM OF GILL
C.

EXTERNAL GILL FILAMENTS
SPIRACLE
D.

CUTICLE
EGG SHELL
PORE
EGG MEMBRANES
SEROSA (CHORION)
ALLANTOIS
CO₂
O₂
CHORIO-ALLANTOIC MEMBRANE
EXTRAEMBRYONIC COELOM
HEART
AMNIOTIC FLUID
AMNION
ALLANTOIC VEIN
ALLANTOIC ARTERY
VITELLINE VEIN
VITELLINE ARTERY
ALLANTOIC STALK
YOLK STALK
YOLK SAC
FOOD SUBSTANCES
E.

VASCULAR VILLOSITIES
BLOOD CAPILLARIES
EPIDERMIS
F.
G.

Fig. 299. (See facing page for legend.)

636

portant in the amphibian group as a respiratory mechanism (Noble, '31, pp. 162, 174–175). However, considering the vertebrate group in its entirety, *the branchial or pharyngeal area is the particular part of the developing body devoted to the formation of adult respiratory mechanisms.*

c. Main Types of Organs Used for Respiration

Two main types of respiratory organs are developed in the vertebrate group:

(1) **branchial organs or gills** in water-living forms and
(2) **pulmonary organs or lungs** in land-frequenting species.

Both of these organs represent pharyngeal modifications.

B. Development of Branchial or Gill Respiratory Organs

As observed in the previous chapter, p. 618, the invaginating **branchial grooves** and the outpocketing **branchial pouches** come together in apposition in the early embryos of all vertebrate species, and, in water-living forms, varying numbers of these pouch-groove relationships perforate to form the gill slits. In cyclostomatous fishes (fig. 301A, B), the number of perforations is six or more pairs; in elasmobranch and teleost fishes, there are five or six pairs (fig. 301C, D); and in amphibia, two or three pairs become perforated. In general, the first pair of branchial-pouch-groove areas is concerned with the formation of the **spiracular openings** or with the **auditory mechanisms.** However, in some species it may be vestigial. In water-inhabiting species, the succeeding pairs of pouch-groove areas and their accompanying visceral arches may develop gill structures. (See p. 669, visceral skeleton.)

Two types of gill mechanisms are developed in the vertebrate group:

(1) **internal gills** in fishes and
(2) **external gills** in amphibia and in lung fishes.

In all cases, *gill development involves a modification of visceral-arch structure.* This modification involves the external surface membranes and blood vessels of the arches. The first two pairs of visceral arches, the **hyoid** and **mandibular,** are utilized generally throughout the vertebrate series in jaw and tongue formation (see Chap. 13). On the other hand, the third and succeeding pairs of visceral arches are potentially **branchial** or gill-bearing **arches** in

---

FIG. 299. Structural relationships of respiratory surfaces. (A after Clements, '38; B after Noble, '31; E after Patten: Am. Scientist, vol. 39, '51; F and G after Noble, '25; C and D original.) (A) Respiratory surface in air sac of pig, 18 hrs. after birth. Capillaries are exposed to air surface. (B) Section through epidermis of respiratory, integumentary folds along the sides of the body of *Cryptobranchus alleganiensis.* (C) Transverse section of external gill filament of *Rana pipiens.* (D) External gill filaments of *Squalus acanthias.* (E) The allantoic-egg-surface relationship of the developing chick embryo. (F) Respiratory villosities or "hair" of *Astylosternus robustus,* the hairy frog. (G) Section through skin of vascular villosity shown in (F).

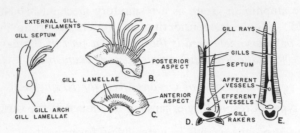

Fig. 300. Respiratory surface relationships in fishes. (A–C original; D and E after Romer: *The Vertebrate Body,* 1949, Philadelphia, Saunders.) (A–C) External gill filaments and developing gill lamellae on gill arch of shark embryo, *Squalus acanthias.* (D) Section of gill arch of a shark. (E) Section of gill arch of a teleost fish.

water-living forms. In reptiles, birds, and mammals, the potency for gill formation by these arches ostensibly is lost.

1. DEVELOPMENT OF GILLS IN FISHES

a. Development of Gills in Squalus acanthias

As the developing gill arch of *Squalus acanthias* enlarges, the lateral portion extends outward as a flattened membrane, the **gill septum** (fig. 300A). On the posterior surface of the early gill arch, the covering epithelium produces elongated structures, the **external gill filaments.** Each gill filament contains a capillary loop which connects with the afferent and efferent branchial arteries (see Chap. 17). These filaments are numerous and give the branchial area a bushy appearance when viewed externally (fig. 300B). The epithelial covering on the anterior face of the gill arch, in the meantime, produces elongated, lamella-like folds, the **gill lamellae** or **gill plates** (fig. 300C). During later embryonic life, the external gill filaments are retracted and resorbed as gill lamellae are developed at the basal area of the filaments. The gill arch thus comes to have a series of gill lamellae or plates developed on anterior and posterior surfaces, i.e., the surfaces facing the gill-slit passageway. The gill plates on each surface of the gill arch form a **demibranch,** and the two demibranchs constitute a **holobranch** or complete gill.

Meanwhile, internal changes occur within the branchial arch. The original aortal (vascular) arch becomes divided into efferent and afferent aortal arteries, with capillaries interposed between the two (fig. 341A–D). Afferent capillaries bring blood from the afferent portion of the aortal arch to the gill lamellae, while efferent capillaries return the blood to the efferent segment of the aortal arch. Associated with these changes, a skeletal support for the gill arch and gill septum is formed (fig. 315C and D). It is to be observed that the branchial or gill rays extend outward between the lamellae and thus form a series of supports for the gill septum and lamellae. Musculature is developed also in relation to each gill arch (fig. 327B).

b. Gills of Teleost Fishes

Gill development in teleost fishes is similar to that of *Squalus acanthias,* but the gill septum is reduced, more in some species than in others (fig. 300D, E). An **operculum** or external covering of the gills, supported by a bony skeleton, also is developed. The operculum forms an armor-like, protective door, hinged anteriorly, which may be opened and closed by opercular muscles (fig. 301D).

c. External Gills

Aside from the formation of external gill filaments as mentioned above (fig. 300B), true external gills, resembling those of *Amphibia,* occur in most of the dipnoan (lung) fishes and *Polypterus* in the larval stages (fig. 302A).

2. Development of Gills in Amphibia

a. General Features

The gills of *Amphibia* occur only in the larval condition and in some adults which retain a complete aquatic existence, such as the mud puppy, *Necturus maculosus,* and the axolotl, *Ambystoma mexicanum.* In other adult amphibia which have not renounced a continuous watery existence, such as *Amphiuma* and *Cryptobranchus,* the larval gills also are lost. *Cryptobranchus* relies largely upon the skin as a respiratory mechanism (fig. 299B). External gills are formed in the larval stage of all amphibia, and, in some, they present a bizarre appearance (Noble, '31, Chaps. III and VII). In the frog tadpole, external gills are formed first, to be superseded later by an internal variety.

The amphibian external gill is a pharyngeal respiratory device which differs

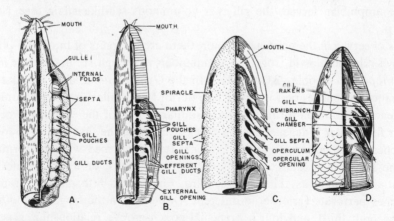

FIG. 301. Gill arrangement in various fishes. (After Dean: *Fishes, Living and Fossil,* 1895, New York and London, Macmillan and Co.)   (A) *Polistotrema (Bdellostoma).* (B) Hagfish, *Myxine.*   (C) Shark.   (D) Teleost.

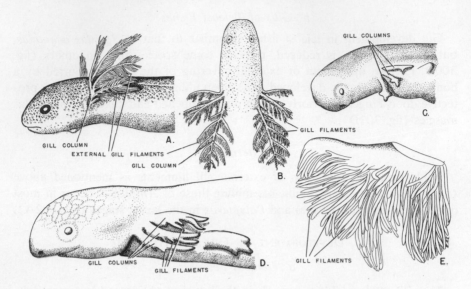

FIG. 302. External gills. (A after Kerr: Chap. 9, *Entwicklungsgeschichte der Wirbeltiere,* by Keibel, Jena, G. Fischer; B from Noble, '31; C–E original.) (A) Larval form of *Lepidosiren paradoxa.* (B) Larval form of *Pseudobranchus striatus.* (C, D) Early developmental stages of *Necturus maculosus.* (E) Gill filaments on gill of adult *Necturus.*

considerably from that found in most fishes. In many species, the gill is a columnar musculo-connective tissue structure with side branches, projecting outward from a restricted area of the branchial arch (fig. 302B). Gill filaments or cutaneous vascular villosities extend outward from the tree-like branches of the central column. The exact pattern differs with the species. In some amphibian larvae, the gill is a voluminous sac-like affair (see Noble, '31, p. 61).

As observed in the previous chapter, there are five pairs of branchial-pouch-groove relationships in frogs and salamanders, although six may occur in the *Gymnophiona* (Noble, '31, p. 159). In the *Gymnophiona,* also, the first pair of branchial pouches perforates to the exterior for a while during embryonic life and each perforation forms a spiracle similar to that of the sharks and certain other fish. Later it degenerates. In other *Amphibia,* the first pair of branchial pouches never perforates to the exterior. It is concerned with the formation of the Eustachian tubes, as in most frogs and toads, or it degenerates and eventually disappears. The second, third, fourth, and fifth pairs of branchial pouches perforate variously in different *Amphibia.* In the frog, *Rana pipiens,* the second, third, and fourth branchial-pouch-groove relationships generally perforate, and sometimes the fifth does also. In *Necturus maculosus,* the third and fourth pairs normally perforate.

b. Development of Gills in Necturus maculosus

The gills of *Necturus* arise at about the 10- to 14-mm. stage as fleshy columnar outgrowths from a limited region of the third, fourth, and fifth visceral arches (i.e., the first, second, and third branchial bars or gill arches). (See fig. 302C.) These outgrowths are at first conical in shape (fig. 227) but later become compressed laterally. Epidermal outgrowths or gill filaments arise from the sides of these outgrowing gill columns (fig. 302C, D). (See Eycleshymer, '06.) As the larva grows and matures, the development of gill filaments from the sides of the gill columns becomes profuse (fig. 302E). During the elaboration of the gill column and gill filaments, the original aortal (vascular) arch becomes separated into two main components, the afferent artery from the ventral aorta to the gill column and an efferent artery from the gill column to the dorsal aorta (Chap. 17).

c. Development of Gills in the Larva of the Frog, Rana pipiens

1) **Development of External Gills.** As stated on p. 639, two types of gills are developed in the frog larva, external and internal. The external gills are developed as follows: At about the 5-mm. stage, the gill-plate area on either side of the embryo begins to be divided into ridges by vertical furrows (fig. 303A). Eventually, three ridges appear. These ridges represent the third, fourth, and fifth visceral arches (i.e., the first, second, and third branchial arches). From the upper external edges of these arches, a conical protuberance begins to grow outward, beginning first on the first branchial arch. Ultimately, three pairs of these fleshy columns are formed (fig. 303B). From these gill columns, finger-like outgrowths, the gill filaments, arise. An abortive type of gill may form also in relation to the fourth branchial arch. The gill column and the filaments possess the ability to expand and contract.

2) **Formation of the Operculum.** At approximately the 9- to 10-mm. stage, an oro-pharyngeal opening is formed by rupture of the pharyngeal membrane. At this time, also, the **opercular membranes** arise. Each **operculum** arises as a fold of tissue along the caudal edge of the hyoid or second visceral arch. This opercular fold on either side grows backward over the gill area. Eventually, the two opercula fuse ventrally and laterally with the body wall to form a gill chamber for the gills (fig. 303C). On the right side the fusion of the operculum with the body wall is complete. However, on the left side the fusion of the operculum in the mid-lateral area of the body wall is incomplete and a small opening remains as the **opercular opening** (fig. 257B').

3) **Internal Gills.** During the above period of opercular development, the external gills become transformed into internal gills, and branchial clefts form between the gill arches. In doing so, the external gill columns gradually shrink, and small, delicate, gill filaments sprout from the outer edges of the gill arches (fig. 303D). External respiration is achieved now not by a movement of the gill in the external medium, as previously, but by the passage of water into

the mouth, through the gill slit, over the gill filament, and, from thence, through the opercular opening to the exterior. Both types of gill filaments, external and internal, fundamentally are similar.

4) Resorption and Obliteration of Gills. The resorption of gills is a phenomenon associated with metamorphosis in dipnoan fishes and in *Amphibia,* although certain species of *Amphibia,* as indicated on p. 639, retain certain larval characteristics in the adult condition. Most species metamorphose into an adult form which necessitates many changes in body structure (Noble, '31, p. 102). This transformation has been related to the thyroid hormone (Chap. 21). In frogs, toads, and salamanders, the thyroid hormone produces degeneration and resorption of gills, the branchial clefts fuse, and the larval branchial skeleton is changed into the adult form (fig. 317).

An interesting feature of gill resorption in the anuran tadpole is that the degenerating gills produce a cytolytic substance which brings about the formation of the hole in the operculum through which the foreleg protrudes during metamorphosis (Helff, '24; Noble, '31, p. 103).

C. Development of Lungs and Buoyancy Structures

1. GENERAL RELATIONSHIP BETWEEN LUNGS AND AIR BLADDERS

The functions of buoyancy and external respiration are related closely. Lungs and air bladders (sacs) constitute a series of pharyngeal diverticula associated with these functions (fig. 304A–F). (For an historical approach to the work on developing lungs, see Flint, '06; for studies on air bladders, consult Goodrich, '30.) Air bladders (sacs) are a characteristic feature of

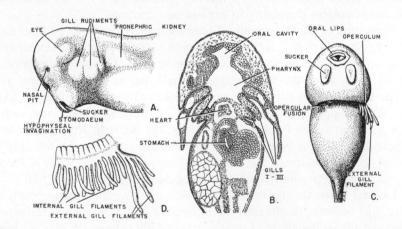

FIG. 303. Gill development in the tadpole of *Rana pipiens*. (All drawings are original.) (A) Five- to six-mm. tadpole. (B) Frontal section of 7-mm. tadpole. (C) External, ventral view of 10-mm. tadpole, showing opercular fold covering gill area. (D) Gill bar, internal and external gill filaments of 10- to 11-mm. stage.

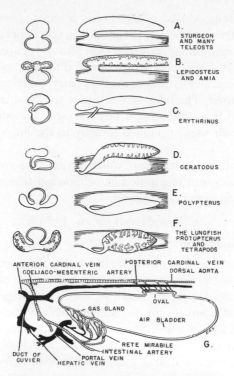

A. STURGEON AND MANY TELEOSTS

B. LEPIDOSTEUS AND AMIA

C. ERYTHRINUS

D. CERATODUS

E. POLYPTERUS

F. THE LUNGFISH PROTOPTERUS AND TETRAPODS

ANTERIOR CARDINAL VEIN — COELIACO-MESENTERIC ARTERY — POSTERIOR CARDINAL VEIN — DORSAL AORTA — OVAL — GAS GLAND — AIR BLADDER — RETE MIRABILE — INTESTINAL ARTERY — DUCT OF CUVIER — PORTAL VEIN — HEPATIC VEIN — **G.**

FIG. 304. Swim-bladder and lung relationships. (A–F slightly modified from Dean: *Fishes, Living and Fossil*, 1895, New York and London, Macmillan and Co.; G after Goodrich, '30.)   (A–E) Sagittal and transverse sections of swim-bladder relationships. (F) Lung relationship of *Dipnoi* and *Tetrapoda*.   (G) Diagram of physoclistous swim bladder of teleost fish.

most teleost and ganoid fishes. In elasmobranch and cyclostomatous fishes, the air bladder is absent. Two main types of air bladders are found:

(1) a **physoclistous** type (fig. 304G), in which a direct connection with the pharyngeal area is lost (e.g., the toadfish, *Opsanus tau*), and

(2) a more primitive **physostomous** variety (fig. 304A–E), retaining a pharyngeal or **pneumatic duct** (e.g., the common pike or pickerel, *Esox lucius*).

One function of the air bladder presumably is to alter the density of the fish in such a way as to keep its density as a whole equal to the surrounding water at various levels (Goodrich, '30, p. 586). Buoyancy, therefore, is one of the main functions of the air bladder.

The air bladders of fishes, in some cases at least, have both respiratory or lung and buoyancy functions (Goodrich, '30, pp. 578–593). In the bony ganoid fishes, *Amia calva* and *Lepisosteus osseus* (fig. 304B), the air bladder apparently has a primary function of external respiration and, therefore, may be regarded as a lung which secondarily is associated with the function of buoyancy. The latter condition is found also in the Dipnoi (lungfishes).

The lung of the mud puppy, *Necturus maculosus,* is capable of considerable extension, particularly in the antero-posterior direction, is devoid of air cells within, and, hence, probably serves the buoyancy function as much or more than that of respiration. The lungs of sea turtles are capable of great distension and aid the animal in maintaining a position near the surface of the water. In the bird group, **air sacs** are united directly to the lungs, as sac-like extensions of the latter.

Thus, the formation of structures which assume the responsibility for the functions of buoyancy and respiration is a characteristic feature of pharyngeal development in most vertebrate species.

2. DEVELOPMENT OF LUNGS

a. Development of Lungs in the Frog and Other Amphibia

In the 5- to 6-mm. embryo of *Rana pipiens,* the lungs arise as a solid evagination of the midventral area of the pharynx at the level of the fifth branchial pouches and over the developing heart. At the 7-mm. stage from this evagination, two lung rudiments begin to extend caudally below the developing esophagus (fig. 305). In the 10-mm. embryo, the lungs extend backward from a common tracheal area above the heart and liver area (fig. 258D). At this time, the entodermal lung buds are surrounded by a mass of mesenchyme and coelomic epithelium. The entodermal lining eventually becomes folded to form larger and smaller air chambers.

In *Necturus,* the development of lungs is similar to that of the frog, but the inner surface of the lungs remains quite smooth. The tracheal area of the frog and *Necturus* shows little differentiation and represents a comparatively short chamber from the lungs to the glottis. In some urodeles, the trachea is well differentiated, possessing cartilaginous, supporting structures (e.g., *Amphiuma, Siren*).

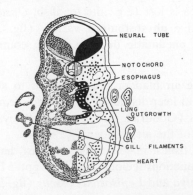

FIG. 305. Lung rudiment of 7-mm. of frog tadpole. (Cf. fig. 258.)

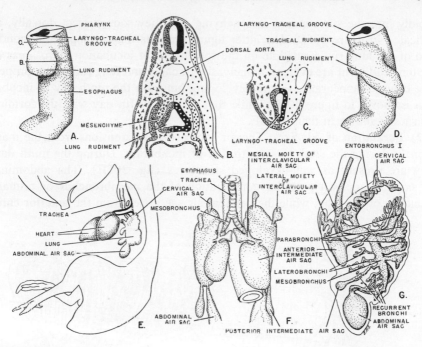

FIG. 306. Lung development in the chick. (All figures, with the exception of A, were redrawn from Locy and Larsell: '16, Am. J. Anat., vols. 19, 20; A original.) (A) External view of lung rudiment during third day of incubation. (B) Transverse section through pharynx and lung pouches of embryo of 52 to 53 hrs. of incubation. (C) Section slightly anterior to (B), showing laryngotracheal groove. (D) Lateral view of lung outgrowth of chick at close of fourth day of incubation. (E) Diagram of dissection, exposing left lung of 9-day embryo. Air sacs are now evident; observe relation of heart to lungs. (F) Ventral view of lungs and air sacs of 12-day embryo. (G) Diagram of lateral view of bronchi of 9-day embryo. Four ectobronchi, from which parabronchi are arising, are shown at right of figure.

b. Lung Development in the Chick

1) General Features of Lung Development. The development of lungs in the chick differs greatly from that in the *Amphibia* and other vertebrates. (For a thorough description of the developing lung of the chick, reference should be made to Locy and Larsell, '16, a and b.)

Lung development begins during the first part of the third day of incubation in the form of ventro-lateral, ridge-like enlargements of the pharynx, immediately posterior to the fourth pair of branchial (visceral) pouches. These evaginations arise from a ventral, groove-like trough of the pharyngeal floor (fig. 306A). The entire area of the pharyngeal floor, where the lung rudiments begin to develop, gradually sinks below the pharyngeal-esophageal level, and its remaining connection with the pharynx proper is the laryngotracheal groove in the floor of the pharynx (fig. 306B, C).

After the lung and tracheal rudiments are formed, they extend backward rapidly into the surrounding mesenchyme and they soon project dorsally, as indicated in figure 306D. The latter figure presents the developmental condition of the lung rudiments late on the fourth day of incubation. Two areas of the lung rudiment are evident, namely, the tracheal and lung rudiments proper. The external appearance of the developing lungs on the ninth day of incubation is shown in figure 306E, while that of the twelfth day with the forming air sacs is shown in figure 306F.

2) Formation of Air Sacs. The air sacs arise as extensions from the main bronchi during the sixth to seventh day of incubation. During the ninth day, they are present as well-developed structures (fig. 306E). The abdominal air sac appears as a posterior continuation of the **mesobronchus** or primary bronchus of the lung, while the cervical air sac arises from the **anterior ento-**

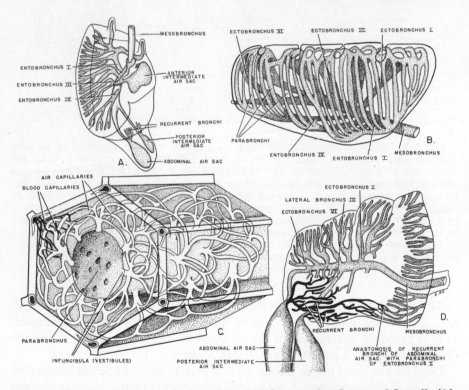

Fig. 307. Lung development in the chick. (All figures, after Locy and Larsell: '16, Am. J. Anat., vols. 19, 20.) (A) Diagram of dissection of lung of 9½-day embryo, designed to show entobronchi and air-sac connections with bronchial tree. (B) Diagram of mesial aspect of adult lung, showing parabronchial connections between entobronchi and ectobronchi. Dorsal and lateral bronchi are not shown. (C) Simplified diagram to show air capillaries in relation to infundibula and parabronchus. (Blood capillaries added to one sector of figure represent a modification of the original figure.) (D) Diagram of lateral surface of right lung of 15-day embryo, showing recurrent bronchi of abdominal and posterior intermediate air sacs. Anastomoses of recurrent bronchi are also shown.

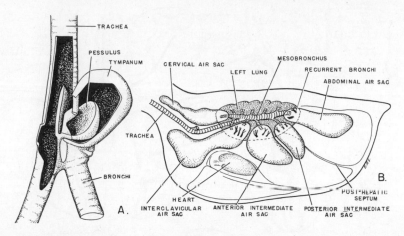

FIG. 308. Respiratory structures in adult birds. (A after Kingsley, '12, *Comparative Anatomy of Vertebrates*, Philadelphia, P. Blakiston's Son & Co.; B slightly modified from Goodrich, '30.) (A) Syrinx or voice box of canvasback, *Aythya*. (B) Diagram of left side view of lungs and air sacs of an adult bird.

bronchus, an outgrowth of the mesobronchus at the anterior extremity of the lung. The **anterior intermediate, posterior intermediate,** and the **interclavicular air sacs** take their origins from the ventral surface of the lungs and represent outgrowths from the **entobronchi** (figs. 306G, 307A). The interclavicular air sac arises from the fusion of four moieties, two from each lung. The air sacs lie among the viscera and send out slender diverticula, some of which may enter certain bones (fig. 308B).

3) Formation of the Bronchi and Respiratory Areas of the Chick's Lung. Internally, the primary bronchial division of each lung passes into the lung's substance where it continues as the mesobronchus. The mesobronchus thus represents a continuation of the main or primary bronchial stem of the lung and is a part of the original entodermal outpushing from the pharynx. From the mesobronchus, the **ectobronchi** and **entobronchi** arise as diverticula (fig. 307A, B). The **parabronchi or lung pipes** develop as connections between the ectobronchi and entobronchi (fig. 307B). The parabronchi constitute the respiratory areas of the lung, for the parabronchi send off from their walls elongated diverticula, the **infundibula or vestibules.** The vestibules are branched distally (fig. 307C) and anastomose with each other to form the **air capillaries.** The **blood capillaries** (fig. 307C) ramify profusely between the air capillaries. It is not clear that the air capillaries possess definite cellular walls throughout.

As indicated in figure 307D, other or **recurrent bronchi** are formed as air passages which arise from the air sacs and grow back into the lungs, where they establish secondary connections with the other bronchi. *The air sacs thus represent expanded parts of the bronchial circuits of the lungs which not only*

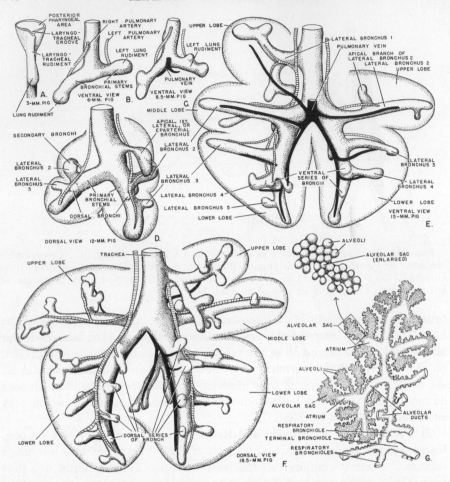

FIG. 309. Lung development in the mammal. (A–F modified from Flint, '06; G modified from Maximow and Bloom, '42, *A Textbook of Histology,* Philadelphia, Saunders.) (A–F) Development of the bronchial tree in the pig.   (G) Terminal respiratory relationships in the human lung. Respiratory bronchioles arise from terminal divisions of the terminal bronchiole; from the respiratory bronchiole arise the alveolar ducts which may terminate in spaces, the atria; from the atrium the alveolar sacs arise; and the side walls of each alveolar sac contain the terminal air sacs or alveoli.

provide buoyancy but effect a more thorough utilization of the available air by the respiratory areas of the lungs. That is, all the air passing through the respiratory parts of the lung is active, moving air. (See Locy and Larsell, 16b, pp. 42–43; Goodrich, '30, pp. 600–607.)

4) Trachea, Voice Box, and Ultimate Position of the Bird's Lung in the Body. The trachea of the bird's lung is an elongated structure, reinforced by cartilage rings or plates in the tracheal wall. The voice box of the bird is developed at the base of the trachea in the area of the tracheal division into the two major bronchi. It is an elaborate structure, consisting of a number of folds of the mucous membrane together with an enlargement of this particular area. This structure is known as the **syrinx** (fig. 308A). The morphological structure of the syrinx varies from species to species. The ultimate position of the bird's lung in the body is shown in figure 308B.

5) Basic Cellular Composition of the Trachea, Lungs, and Air Sacs. It is obvious from the description above that the entire lining tissue and the respiratory membrane of the bird's respiratory and air-sac system are derived from the original entodermal evagination, whereas the muscle, connective, and other tissues are formed from the surrounding mesenchyme.

c. Development of Lungs in the Mammal

1) Origin of the Lung Rudiment. The first indication of the appearance of the lungs in the pig and human embryo is the formation of a midventral trough or furrow in the entoderm of the pharynx, the **laryngotracheal groove.** This groove forms immediately posterior to the fourth branchial (visceral) pouch, approximately at the stage of 3 to 4 mm. in both pig and human. In the human, about the fourth week, and 3-mm. pig, the laryngotracheal groove deepens, and its posterior end gradually forms a blind, finger-like pouch which creeps posteriorly below the esophageal area as a separate structure (fig. 309A). Thus, the original laryngotracheal groove is restricted to the cephalic end of the developing lung rudiment, where it forms a slit-like orifice in the midventral floor of the pharynx at about the level of the fifth visceral (i.e., third branchial) arch.

2) Formation of the Bronchi. As the caudal end of the original lung rudiment grows caudad, it soon bifurcates into **left and right bronchial stems** as shown in figure 309B. Each **primary or stem bronchus** is slightly enlarged at the distal end. As the stem bronchi of the right and left lung buds continue to grow distally, evaginations or **secondary bronchi** arise progressively from the primary bronchi as indicated in figure 309C–E. While this statement holds true for the human embryo, the **apical bronchus** (i.e., eparterial bronchus because this lobe of the lung comes to lie anterior to the pulmonary artery) in the pig arises directly from the trachea as shown in figure 309D. Each of these secondary bronchi forms the main bronchus for the upper and middle lobes of the lungs (fig. 309D, E). From each lobular bronchus, other bronchial buds arise progressively and dichotomously, with the result that the bronchial system within each lobe of the lung becomes complex, simulating the branches upon the limb of a tree. Considerable variation may exist in the formation of the various bronchi in different individuals.

3) Formation of the Respiratory Area of the Lung. This growth of bronchial buds of the pulmonary tree continues during fetal life and for a considerable time after birth. The large bronchi give rise to smaller bronchi, and, from the latter, bronchioles of several orders originate. Finally, the **terminal bronchioles**

arise. Fifty to eighty terminal bronchioles have been estimated to be present for each lobule of the human lung (Maximow and Bloom, '42, p. 465). From each of the terminal bronchioles, a varying number of **respiratory bronchioles** arise, which in turn give origin to the **alveolar ducts,** and, from the latter, arise the **alveolar sacs** and **alveoli.** Each alveolus represents a thin-walled compartment of the alveolar sac (fig. 309G). The exact cellular structure of the terminal air compartments or alveoli is not clear. In the frog lung, a layer of flattened epithelium is present. However, in the lung of the bird and the mammal, this epithelial lining may not be complete, and the wall of the alveolus may be formed, in part at least, by the endothelial cells of the surrounding capillaries (fig. 299A; Palmer, '36; Clements, '38).

4) Development of the Epiglottis and Voice Box. The **epiglottis** is the structure which folds over the **glottis** and thus covers it during deglutition. The glottis is the opening of the trachea into the pharynx. An epiglottis is found only in mammals. It arises as a fold in the pharyngeal floor in the area between the third and fourth visceral arches. It grows upward and backward in front of the developing glottis (fig. 310A–C). In the meantime, the arytenoid swellings or ridges appear on either side of the glottis.

The larynx or voice box is an oval-shaped compartment at the anterior end of the trachea in mammals. It is supported by cartilages derived from the visceral arches (Chap. 15). The vocal cords arise as transverse folds along the lateral sides of the laryngeal wall.

5) Cellular Composition. The epithelial lining of the larynx, trachea, bronchi, etc., is derived from the entodermal outpushing, whereas the sur-

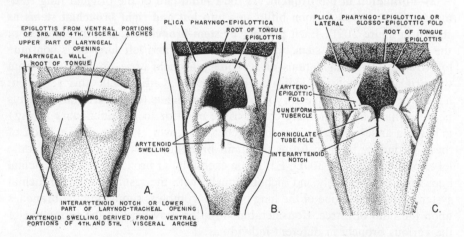

FIG. 310. Development of the epiglottis and entrance into the larynx in the human embryo. (Consult also fig. 285.) (All figures slightly modified from Keibel and Mall: *Manual of Human Embryology,* vol. II, '12, Philadelphia, Lippincott.) (A) About 16-mm., crown-rump length, 7 to 8 weeks. (B) About 40-mm., crown-rump length, 9 to 10 weeks. (C) Late fetal condition.

rounding mesenchyme gives origin to the cartilage, muscle, and connective tissue present in these structures.

6) Ultimate Position of the Mammalian Lung in the Body. See Chapter 20.

3. DEVELOPMENT OF AIR BLADDERS

It is difficult to draw a clear distinction between air bladders of *Pisces* and the lungs of *Tetrapoda*. Air bladders and gills appear to be the standard arrangement for most fishes. It is probable, therefore, that the function of external respiration rests mainly upon the **branchiae** or gills in all fishes other than the *Dipnoi,* while the function of buoyancy is the responsibility of the air bladder. In some fishes (*Dipnoi* and ganoids), the functions of buoyancy and respiration converge into one structure, the air bladder or lung, as they do in many *Tetrapoda.*

In development, air bladders, like the lungs of all *Tetrapoda,* arise as diverticula of the posterior pharyngeal area. In most cases, the air bladder arises as a dorsal diverticulum (fig. 304A, B), while, in other instances, its origin appears to be from the lateral wall (fig, 304C). In *Salmonidae, Siluridae,* etc., for example, it arises from the right wall, while in *Cyprinidae, Characinidae,* etc., it takes its origin from the left wall. The air bladder generally is a single structure (fig. 304A, C, D), but in some cases it is double or bilobed (fig. 304E).

Generally speaking, the air bladder receives blood from the dorsal aorta or its immediate branches (fig. 304G), but in Dipnoi and *Polypterus,* the blood supply to the air bladder comes from the pulmonary arteries as it does in *Tetrapoda.*

4. LUNGLESSNESS

Many urodele amphibia have reduced or lost their lungs entirely. In many cases the reduced condition of the lungs or absence of lungs is compensated for by the development of **buccopharyngeal respiration.** The latter type of respiration depends upon an extreme vascularization of the pharyngeal and caudal mouth epithelium and rapid throat movements which suck the air in and then expel it. In *Aneides* (Autodax) *lugubrus,* a land form, these throat movements may reach 120 to 180 movements per minute (Ritter and Miller, 1899). Lungless aquatic salamanders also practice buccopharyngeal respiration, although, in *Pseudotriton ruber,* cutaneous respiration evidently is resorted to (Noble, '25).

Bibliography

Clements, L. P. **1938.** Embryonic development of the respiratory portion of the pig's lung. Anat. Rec. **70**:575.

Eycleshymer, A. C. **1906.** The growth and regeneration of the gills in the young *Necturus.* Biol. Bull. X: 171.

Flint, J. M. 1906. The development of the lungs. Am. J. Anat. 6:1.

Goodrich, E. S. 1930. Studies on the Structure and Development of Vertebrates. Macmillan and Co., London.

Helff, O. M. 1924. Factors involved in the formation of the opercular leg perforation in anuran larvae during metamorphosis. Anat. Rec. 29:102.

Locy, W. A. and Larsell, O. 1916a. The embryology of the bird's lung. Based on observations of the domestic fowl. Part I. Am. J. Anat. 19:447.

——— and ———. 1916b. The embryology of the bird's lung. Based on observations of the domestic fowl. Part II. Am. J. Anat. 20:1.

Maximow, A. A. and Bloom, W. 1942. A Textbook of Histology. W. B. Saunders Co., Philadelphia.

Noble, G. K. 1925. The integumentary, pulmonary and cardiac modifications correlated with increased cutaneous respiration in the Amphibia; a solution to the "hairy frog" problem. J. Morphol. & Physiol. 40:341.

———. 1931. The Biology of the Amphibia. McGraw-Hill Book Co., Inc., New York.

Palmer, D. W. 1936. The lung of a human foetus of 170 mm. C. R. length. Am. J. Anat. 58:59.

Ritter, W. E. and Miller, L. 1899. A contribution to the life history of Autodax lugubris Hallow., a Californian salamander. Am. Nat. 33:691.

15

The Skeletal System

A. Introduction
  1. Definition
  2. Generalized or basic embryonic skeleton; its origin and significance
      a. Basic condition of the skeletal system
      b. Origin of the primitive ghost skeleton
          1) Notochord and subnotochordal rod
          2) Origin of the mesenchyme of the early embryonic skeleton
      c. Importance of the mesenchymal packing tissue of the early embryo
B. Characteristics and kinds of connective tissues
  1. Connective tissue proper
      a. Fibrous types
          1) Reticular tissue
          2) White fibrous tissue
          3) Elastic tissue
      b. Adipose tissue
  2. Cartilage
      a. Hyaline cartilage
      b. Fibrocartilage
      c. Elastic cartilage
  3. Bone
      a. Characteristics of bone
      b. Types of bone
      c. Characteristics of spongy bone
      d. Compact bone
C. Development of skeletal tissues
  1. Formation of the connective tissue proper
      a. Formation of fibrous connective tissues
      b. Formation of adipose or fatty connective tissue
  2. Development of cartilage
  3. Development of bone
      a. Membranous bone formation
      b. Endochondral and perichondrial (periosteal) bone formation
          1) Endochrondral bone formation
          2) Perichondrial (periosteal) bone formation
      c. Conversion of cancellous bone into compact bone
D. Development (morphogenesis) of the endoskeleton
  1. Definitions

2. Morphogenesis of the axial skeleton
   a. General features of the skeleton of the head
      1) Neurocranium or cranium proper
      2) Visceral skeleton or splanchnocranium
      3) Development of the skull or neurocranium
      4) Vicissitudes of the splanchnocranium
   b. Ossification centers and the development of bony skulls
   c. Development of the axial skeleton
      1) Axial skeleton of the trunk
         a) Notochord
         b) Vertebrae
         c) Divisions of the vertebral column
         d) Ribs
         e) Sternum
      2) Axial skeleton of the tail
   d. Development of the appendicular skeleton of the paired appendages
      1) General features
      2) Development of the skeleton of the free appendage
      3) Formation of the girdles
   e. Growth of bone
   f. Formation of joints
      1) Definitions
      2) Ankylosis (synosteosis) and synarthrosis
      3) Diarthroses
      4) Amphiarthroses
   g. Dermal bones

A. Introduction

1. Definition

The word **skeleton** is used commonly to denote the hard, supporting framework of the body, composed of bone and cartilage. In this restricted sense it is employed to refer particularly to the internal or **endoskeleton** (see p. 668). The word has a broader meaning, however, for the skeletal system includes not only the bony and cartilaginous materials of the deeper-lying, internal skeleton but also the softer, pliable connective tissues as well. Thus, the skeletal tissues in a comprehensive sense may be divided as follows:

(1) the **soft skeleton,** composed of pliable connective tissues which bind together and support the various organs of the body and

(2) the **hard or firm skeleton,** formed of bone, cartilage, and other structures which protect and sustain, and give rigidity to the body as a whole. The exoskeletal structures described in Chapter 12 in reality are a part of the hard, protective skeleton of the vertebrate body.

(*Note:* Blood and lymph are often classified as a part of the connective tissues. See Maximow and Bloom, '42, p. 39.)

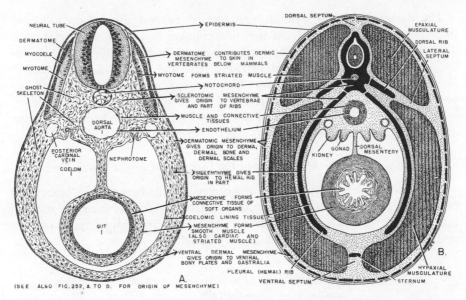

FIG. 311. (A) Diagram showing basic mesenchymal packing tissue around the various body tubes and notochord. (B) Contribution of embryonic mesenchyme to adult skeletal tissue.

2. GENERALIZED OR BASIC EMBRYONIC SKELETON; ITS ORIGIN AND SIGNIFICANCE

a. Basic Condition of the Skeletal System

The generalized or basic skeleton of the embryo which has achieved primitive body form is composed of the **notochord** or primitive skeletal axis, together with the **mass of mesenchyme** which comes to fill the spaces between the epidermal, neural, enteric, mesodermal, and primitive circulatory tubes. Because of the delicate nature of the mesenchymal cells and the coagulable intercellular substance between them, this primitive skeleton sometimes is referred to as the "ghost skeleton" (fig. 311A).

b. Origin of the Primitive Ghost Skeleton

1) Notochord and Subnotochordal Rod. As observed in Chapters 9 and 10, the notochord becomes segregated as a distinct entity during gastrulation and embryonic body formation. It soon comes to form a rod-like structure, surrounded by a primitive notochordal membrane. The notochordal axis extends from the pituitary body (hypophysis) and diencephalic region of the brain caudally to the end of the tail (fig. 217). In many of the lower vertebrates, a second rod of cells, the **hypochord** or **subnotochordal rod,** evaginates and segregates from the roof of the gut in the trunk region of the embryo during tubulation and early body-form development; it comes to lie immediately below the notochord (fig. 228). The subnotochoral rod soon degenerates.

The notochord never extends cranialward beyond the hypophysis and infundibular downpushing from the diencephalon in any of the vertebrates. This meeting place of the hypophysis, notochord, and infundibulum is a constant feature of early vertebrate structure from the cyclostomatous fishes to the mammals. In *Amphioxus,* however, the notochord projects anteriad beyond the limits of the "brain" (fig. 249D, E).

2) Origin of the Mesenchyme of the Early Embryonic Skeleton. The origin of mesenchyme in the early embryo is set forth in Chapter 11, page 520.

c. Importance of the Mesenchymal Packing Tissue of the Early Embryo

The mass of mesenchymal cells which comes to lie between the embryonic body tubes not only forms the primitive skeletal material of the early embryo but it also serves as a reservoir from which later arise many types of cells and tissues, as indicated in the following diagram:

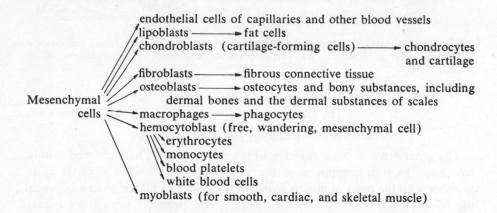

In regard to the skeletal system, it is pertinent to point out the fact that *wherever mesenchyme exists, the possibility for connective tissue development also exists.*

B. Characteristics and Kinds of Connective Tissues

Connective tissues, other than adipose tissue, are characterized by *the presence of intercellular substances which become greater in quantity than the cellular units themselves.* In consequence, the various types of connective tissue are classified in terms of the intercellular substance present. Excluding the blood, **three main categories** of connective tissues are found:

(1) **connective tissue proper,**
(2) **cartilage,** and
(3) **bone.**

1. Connective Tissue Proper

The connective tissues proper may be divided into

(a) **fibrous types** and
(b) fatty or **adipose tissue.**

a. Fibrous Types

1) Reticular Tissue. This type of connective tissue possesses stellate cells, between which are found delicate aggregations of fibrils and a fluid-like, intercellular substance (fig. 312B).

2) White Fibrous Tissue. White fibrous tissue contains bundles or sheets of white, connective-tissue fibers (i.e., collagenous fibers), placed between the cells. Some elastic fibers may be present (fig. 312C, D). Collagenous fibers yield gelatin upon boiling with water and are not digested readily by trypsin (Maximow and Bloom, '42).

3) Elastic Tissue. Elastic connective tissue is similar to the white fibrous variety but contains a large percentage of elastic tissue fibers which extend under stress but contract again when tension is released (fig. 312E). Elastic fibers are resistant to boiling water and are digested readily by trypsin (Maximow and Bloom, '42). Elastic tissue may have a yellowish tinge when viewed macroscopically.

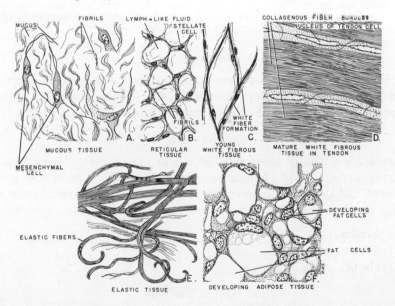

FIG. 312. Types of soft connective tissues. (A, D, and E redrawn from Bremer, 1936, *Textbook of Histology,* Philadelphia, Blakiston; B and C redrawn from Keibel and Mall, 1910, *Manual of Human Embryology,* vol. I, Philadelphia. Lippincott; F redrawn from Bell, '09.)

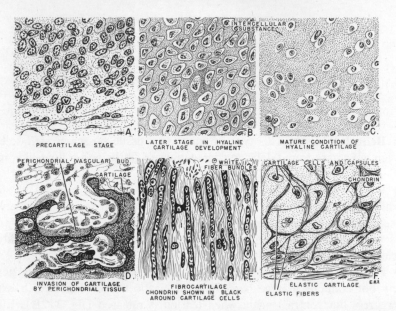

FIG. 313. Types of cartilaginous tissue. (A–C) Development of hyaline cartilage. (D) Destruction of cartilage by perichondrial vascular bud preparatory to ossification. The cartilage spicules may be infiltrated with calcium salt at this period. (Redrawn from Bremer, 1936, *Textbook of Histology,* Philadelphia, Blakiston.) (E) Fibrocartilage, from area of tendinous union with bone. (F) Elastic cartilage from human larynx. (Redrawn and modified from Bremer, 1936, *Textbook of Histology,* Philadelphia, Blakiston.)

b. Adipose Tissue

Adipose tissue contains a fibrous network of white and elastic fibers, between which fat cells develop. Eventually, the fibrous connective tissue is displaced and pushed aside by the fat-containing elements (fig. 312F).

2. CARTILAGE

Cartilage is a type of connective tissue with a solid intercellular substance. The latter is composed of a fibrous framework filled with an amorphous ground substance. Unlike bone, the intercellular substance may be readily cut with a sharp instrument. Three main types of cartilage are found:

(1) **hyaline,**
(2) **fibrous,** and
(3) **elastic.**

a. Hyaline Cartilage

Hyaline cartilage (fig. 313A–C) is the most widespread variety of cartilage. It is characterized by a solid, amorphous, ground substance, slightly bluish in appearance, easily bent and capable of being cut with a sharp instrument.

The amorphous ground substance or **chondrin** is reinforced by fibers of the collagenous (white) variety, but the quantity of fiber present is much less than in fibrous or elastic cartilage. The **chondrocytes** (i.e., the cartilage cells) lie within **capsules.** Canaliculi apparently do not connect one capsule with another. This type of cartilage forms a considerable part of the temporary axial and appendicular skeleton of the developing organism and remains as the adult axial and appendicular skeleton in cyclostomatous and elasmobranch fishes. In the adults of other vertebrates, it is supplemented to various degrees by bone.

b. Fibrocartilage

Fibrocartilage (fig. 313E) is a transitional form between white fibrous connective tissue and cartilage. It contains bundles of collagenous fibers, placed parallel to each other. Between the fibrous bundles, cartilage capsules are present, containing cartilage cells (chondrocytes). A small amount of amorphous ground substance or chondrin is present, particularly around the cell capsules. Some types of fibrocartilage contain more of the amorphous ground substance than other types. Fibrocartilage is found in the intervertebral discs between the vertebrae, in the area between the two pubic bones in mammals, and in certain ligaments, such as the ligamentum teres femoris.

o. Elastic Cartilage

Elastic cartilage (fig. 313F) differs from the hyaline variety by the pres-ence of an interstitial substance which contains branching and interlacing fibers of the elastic variety. The elastic fibers penetrate through the amorphous substance in all directions. While hyaline cartilage is bluish in color, the color of elastic cartilage is yellowish. It is found in the external ear of mammals, in the mammalian epiglottis, Eustachian tubes, the tubes of the external auditory meatus, etc.

3. BONE

a. Characteristics of Bone

Bone forms the greater part of the adult skeleton of all vertebrates above the cyclostomatous and elasmobranch fishes. In teleost fishes and in land-frequenting vertebrates, it tends to displace most of the cartilaginous sub-stance of the skeleton. The interstitial substance of bone is composed of a fundamental fibrous material similar to that of connective tissue. These fibers are called **osteocollagenous fibers.** A small amount of amorphous ground substance also is present. The interstices of this fibrous and amorphous sub-strate are infiltrated with mineral salts, particularly calcium salts, to form the bony substance. The latter is formed in layers, each layer constituting a **lamella.** The bone cells or **osteocytes** are present in small cavities or **lacunae** between the lamellae. The lacunae are connected with each other by small

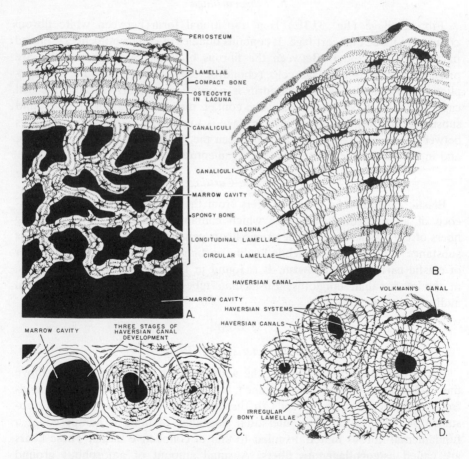

FIG. 314. Types and development of bone. (A) Compact and cancellous (spongy) bone. (B) Diagram showing structure of compact bone. (Redrawn and slightly modified from Maximow and Bloom, 1942, *A Textbook of Histology*, Philadelphia, Saunders.) (C) Stages in conversion of marrow canal or space of spongy bone into an Haversian system by deposition of concentric layers of bony lamellae. (D) Haversian systems of compact bone from thin, ground section. (Redrawn and modified from Bremer, 1936, *Textbook of Histology*, Philadelphia, Blakiston.)

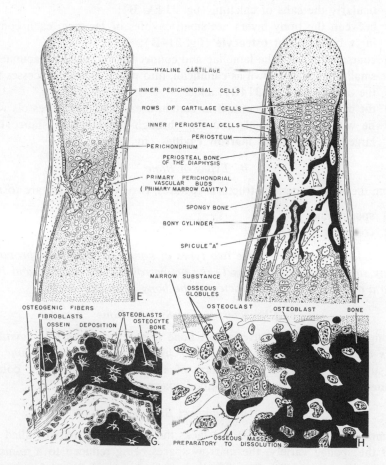

Labels in figure:
- HYALINE CARTILAGE
- INNER PERICHONDRIAL CELLS
- ROWS OF CARTILAGE CELLS
- INNER PERIOSTEAL CELLS
- PERIOSTEUM
- PERICHONDRIUM
- PERIOSTEAL BONE OF THE DIAPHYSIS
- PRIMARY PERICHONDRIAL VASCULAR BUDS (PRIMARY MARROW CAVITY)
- SPONGY BONE
- BONY CYLINDER
- SPICULE "A"
- E.
- F.
- MARROW SUBSTANCE
- OSSEOUS GLOBULES
- OSTEOGENIC FIBERS
- FIBROBLASTS
- OSTEOBLASTS
- OSSEIN DEPOSITION
- OSTEOCYTE BONE
- OSTEOCLAST
- OSTEOBLAST
- BONE
- G.
- A OSSEOUS MASS PREPARATORY TO DISSOLUTION
- H.

FIG. 314—*(Continued)* Types and development of bone. (E) Diagram showing invasion of cartilage by perichondrial vascular buds, preparatory to deposition of bony substance on cartilaginous spicules produced by erosion of cartilage (compare with fig. 313, D). (F) The formation of spongy bone within, by deposition of bony substance on cartilaginous spicules. See spicule "A." Compact bone is deposited on outer surface of cartilaginous replica of future bone by periosteal osteoblasts, forming bony cylinder of compact bone. (Redrawn and modified from Bremer, 1936, *Textbook of Histology*, Philadelphia, Blakiston.) (G) Formation of membrane bone from jaw of pig embryo. (Redrawn and modified from Bremer, 1936, *Textbook of Histology*, Philadelphia, Blakiston.) (H) Bone destruction and resorption. Observe osseous globules within substance of osteoclast. (From Jordan, '21, Anat. Rec., 20.)

661

channels or **canaliculi** which course through the lamellae. Some of the canaliculi join larger channels within the bony substance which contain blood vessels. Bony substance in the living animal, therefore, is living tissue, constructed of the following features (fig. 314):

(1) **Bony layers** or **lamellae** are present, composed of a **ground substance** of fibrous and amorphous materials infiltrated with **mineral salts,** particularly the salts of calcium (fig. 314A, B);

(2) between the bony layers are small cavities or **lacunae,** each containing a bone cell or **osteocyte** (fig. 314B);

(3) coursing through the lamellae and connecting the various lacunae, are small channels, known as **canaliculi,** into which extend processes from the osteocytes (fig. 314B); and

(4) the canaliculi make contact in certain areas with blood vessels which lie within small canals coursing through the bony substance or in larger spaces, called **marrow cavities** (fig. 314A, B).

b. Types of Bone

From these fundamental structural features, two types of bone are formed:

(1) **spongy** and
(2) **compact.**

The difference between these two types of bone rests upon the proportion of bony substance to blood-vessel area or marrow cavity present, and is not due to a difference in the character of the bony substance itself.

c. Characteristics of Spongy Bone

Spongy bone differs from compact bone in that *large marrow cavities or spaces are present between an irregular framework of compact bone.* The bony substance present is in the form of a meshwork of irregular columns or **trabeculae** between the marrow-filled spaces (fig. 314A).

d. Compact Bone

Compact bone (fig. 314A, B, D) lacks the widespread, marrow-filled cavities of the spongy variety, the marrow spaces being reduced to a minimum. This is accomplished by the utilization of a structural unit known as the **Haversian system,** named after Clopton Havers, an English anatomist who discovered the system during the latter part of the seventeenth century while investigating the blood supply of bone. The bony walls of the shafts of long bones are composed largely of many Haversian systems, associated side by side as shown in figure 314D. Irregular layers (lamellae) lie between the various systems.

The Haversian system is composed of a very narrow canal or lumen, the **Haversian canal,** around which are placed concentrically arranged bony plates (lamellae) with their associated lacunae, osteocytes, and canaliculi (fig. 314B–D). Blood vessels from the marrow cavity within the bone or from the surface of the bone via **Volkmann's canals** (fig. 314D) pass into the Haversian canals, thus supplying nourishment and other life-maintaining features to the canaliculi and through the latter to the osteocytes. Compact bone thus restricts the marrow cavity to a central area, and the Haversian and Volkmann canals convey the blood supply into the compact bony substance which surrounds the central marrow cavity. In general, the Haversian systems are formed parallel with the long axis of the bone. **Circumferential lamellae** surround the external surface of the bone around the Haversian systems. Inner circumferential lamellae also are present lining the marrow cavities of long bones.

C. Development of Skeletal Tissues

1. FORMATION OF THE CONNECTIVE TISSUE PROPER

a. Formation of Fibrous Connective Tissues

In the early embryo, following the ghost-skeleton stage, two types of connective tissues are found:

(1) **Mucoid or loose connective tissue** is located in Wharton's jelly in the umbilical cord of mammals and in other parts of the embryo. This embryonic type of connective tissue is characterized by the presence of large mesenchymal cells whose processes contact the processes of other surrounding mesenchymal cells (fig. 312A). Within the meshwork formed by these cells and their processes, mucus or a jelly-like substance is present. Very delicate fibrils may lie within this jelly.

(2) A second type of early embryonic connective tissue is **reticular tissue.** It contains stellate mesenchymal cells whose processes contact each other (fig. 312B). Very delicate bundles of fibrils may be present which are closely associated with the cells.

The foregoing, connective-tissue conditions of the early embryo eventually are replaced by the mature forms of connective tissue. In this process the reticular type of connective tissue appears to form an initial or primary stage of connective-tissue development. For example, in the development of **white fibrous tissue,** a delicate network of fine fibrils appears within the ectoplasmic ground substance between the primitive mesenchymal cells, thus forming a kind of reticular tissue (fig. 312A, B). With the appearance of fibrils between the mesenchymal cells, the latter may be regarded as **fibroblasts.** Following this reticular stage, the ectoplasmic ground substance becomes more fibrillated and parallel bundles of white fibers arise, probably by the direct chemical transformation of the earlier fibrils into white or collagenous fibers (fig. 312C). (See Bardeen, '10, p. 300.) It is probable that the elastic connective tissue with its elastic fibers arise in a similar manner, with the exception that elastic fibers are formed instead of collagenous fibers.

The matter of fiber formation within connective tissues has been the subject of much controversy. The older view of Flemming (Mall, '02, p. 329) maintains that the fibers arise within the peripheral area of the cytoplasm of the cell from whence they are thrown off into the intercellular space where they continue to grow. However, most observers now agree that the fibrils arise from an intercellular substance, i.e., from the substance lying between the fibroblasts, but the manner by which this intercellular substance itself arises is questionable. Some observers, such as Mall ('02) and Jordan ('39), set forth the interpretation that the intercellular substance is derived from a syncytial ectoplasm which becomes separated from the early mesenchymal cells. Baitsell ('21) and Maximow ('29), however, consider the intercellular substance to be a secretion product of the mesenchymal cells which have become fibroblasts. The observations of Stearns ('40) on living material in a transparent chamber of the rabbit's ear suggest that the ground substance is exuded by the surface of the fibroblasts and that the fibers then develop within this exudate.

b. Formation of Adipose or Fatty Connective Tissue

Adipose tissue is fibrous connective tissue which contains certain specialized cells of mesenchymal origin, the **lipoblasts.** The latter have the ability to produce lipoidal substances and to store these substances within the confines of their own boundaries. Adipose or fatty tissue arises in fibrous connective tissues in various parts of the body in proximity to blood capillaries.

Lipogenesis or the formation of the fatty substance is an unsolved problem. Two main types of fat are formed, **white** and **brown.** The process of lipogenesis in white fat, according to Schreiner ('15) who studied the process in detail in the hagfish embryo, *Myxine glutinosa,* consists at first in liberation of small buds from the nucleolus within the nucleus. These buds pass through the nuclear membrane into the cytoplasm as **granules** or **chromidia.** In the cytoplasm these granules appear as **mitochondria.** The latter increase in number by division. The secondary granules then separate and each gives origin to a **liposome** which liquefies and expands into a small fat globule. Regardless of the exact method by which the small fat globules arise, when once formed, the small globules coalesce to form the large fat globule, typical of white fat, which ultimately pushes the nucleus and cytoplasm of the lipoblast to the periphery (fig. 312F). (See Bell, '09.) Lipoblasts in the mature condition are fat cells or **lipocytes.**

The above type of fat-cell formation occurs in the subcutaneous areas of the embryo. In the human embryo it begins at about the fourth month. However, aside from the common type or white-fat formation, another kind of fat-cell development occurs in certain restricted areas of the body in the so-called brown fat tissue found in certain **adipose glands.** It is referred to as brown fat because a brownish pigment may be present in certain mammals. During brown-fat formation, mesenchymal cells become ovoid in shape and develop a highly granular cytoplasm. These granules give origin to small fat globules which remain distinct for a time and do not readily fuse to form the large fat globule, characteristic of white fat. However, they ultimately may coalesce and become indistinguishable from the ordinary lipocyte found in white fat. In man, this type of fat disappears shortly after birth; in the cat, it is present until maturity when it transforms into the ordinary type or white fat; and in the rat, it persists throughout life (Sheldon, '24). In the woodchuck, this type of fat forms the **hibernating gland** (Rasmussen, '23). In mice and other rodents, the presence of a small amount of brownish pigment is evident in this type of fat. In the young monkey, hibernating-gland tissue is found in the cervical, axillary, and thoracic areas (Sheldon, '24).

2. Development of Cartilage

The formation of cartilage is an interesting process. During the initial stage of cartilage development, mesenchymal cells withdraw their processes, assume a rounded appearance, and become closely aggregated. This condition is known as the **pre-cartilage stage** (fig. 313A). Gradually the pre-cartilage condition becomes transformed into cartilage by the appearance of the **intercellular substance,** characteristic of cartilage between the cells (fig 313B, C). As in the case of the connective tissues described on page 664, two schools of thought explain the appearance of this intercellular substance:

(a) as a modification of the ectoplasm which separates from the **chondroblasts** and

(b) as a secretion of these cells.

In **hyaline cartilage,** the homogeneous, amorphous, ground substance is predominant, together with a small number of fibrils; in **fibrocartilage,** a large number of **white, connective-tissue fibers** and a smaller amount of the amorphous substance is deposited; and in **elastic cartilage, elastic, connective-tissue fibers** are formed in considerable numbers. The mesenchyme, immediately surrounding the mass of cartilage, forms the specialized tissue, known as the **perichondrium.** The perichondrial layer, as the name implies, is the tissue immediately surrounding the cartilage. It connects the cartilage with the surrounding connective tissue and mesenchyme. The inner cells of the perichondrium transform into chondroblasts and deposit cartilage; in this manner the cartilage mass increases in size by addition from without. The latter form of growth is known as **peripheral growth.** On the other hand, an increase within the mass of cartilage already formed is the result of **interstitial growth.** Interstitial growth is effected by an increase in the number of cells within the cartilage and by a deposition of intercellular substance between the cells. The increase in the intercellular substance separates the chondroblasts from each other, and the mass of cartilage expands as a whole. These two types of growth are important processes involved in the increase in size of many body structures. Cartilage formation in the human embryo begins during the fifth and sixth weeks.

3. DEVELOPMENT OF BONE

Bone develops as the result of the calcification of previously established fibrous or cartilaginous connective tissues. The transformation of fibrous connective tissue into bone is called **membranous** or **intramembranous** bone formation, and the process which transforms cartilage into bone constitutes **endochondral** or **intracartilaginous** bone development. Membranous bone formation occurs in the superficial areas of the body, particularly in or near the dermal area of the skin whereas cartilaginous bone formation is found more deeply within the substance of the body and its appendages.

a. Membranous Bone Formation

Membranous bone formation occurs as follows (fig. 314G): Thin spicules or bars of a compact intercellular substance, known as **ossein,** gradually come to surround collagenous (osteogenic) fibers which lie between fibroblast cells. Later, these spicules of ossein become calcified by the action of specialized cells, called **osteoblasts,** which surround the osseinated fibrils. Osteoblasts may represent transformed fibroblasts or, more directly, transformed mesenchymal cells. With the *deposition of the bone salts, the tissue is converted from ossein into bone.* Thus, spicules of ossein and connective tissue fibers serve as the basis for bone deposition and become converted into bony spicules. These spicules are converted next into bony columns (trabeculae) by the formation of layers (lamellae) of compact bone around the original bony spicule. Such bony columns or trabeculae are characteristic of spongy bone (fig. 314A). Some of the bone-forming cells become enclosed within the lacunar spaces in the bone during the above process and are left behind as bone cells or **osteocytes** (fig. 314A). The osteocytes within their respective lacunae tend to be located *between* the layers of bony material (fig. 314A–D).

After the primary trabeculae of spongy bone are formed, the surrounding mesenchyme, which encloses the site of bone formation, becomes converted into a membranous structure, known as the **periosteum.** The cells of the inner layer of periosteum are transformed into osteoblasts and begin to deposit successive layers of compact bone around the initial framework of spongy bone (peripheral growth). The latter activity results in an increase in diameter of the bony area.

The first bone thus formed occurs in a restricted area. As the bone grows, the previously formed bone is torn down and resorbed, while new compact bone is built up around the area occupied by the spongy bone. Either by the formation of new cellular entities or by the fusion of osteoblasts, multinucleated giant cells appear which aid in the dissolution of the previously formed bone. These multinucleate cells are known as **osteoclasts** (fig. 314H). The marrow-filled spaces between the trabeculae of spongy bone contain blood spaces (sinusoids), developing red blood cells, looser connective tissues, and fat cells (fig. 314H). When the trabeculae of spongy bone are resorbed, the marrow-filled area increases in size.

b. Endochondral and Perichondrial (Periosteal) Bone Formation

While membranous bone development utilizes collagenous fibrils and ossein as a foundation upon which the osteoblasts deposit bone salts, endochondral that is, intracartilaginous bone development employs small spicules or larger masses of cartilage as a basis for calcification. The small columns or spicules of cartilage are produced as a result of erosion and removal of cartilage. This erosion of cartilage is produced by perichondrial cells and vascular tissue which invade the cartilaginous substance from the perichondrium.

1) Endochondral Bone Formation. Endochondral bone formation occurs as follows:

(a) The initial step in erosion of cartilage is the migration within the cartilage, in a manner not understood, of the scattered cartilage cells. This migration brings about the arrangement of the cartilage cells and their capsules into elongated rows (fig. 314F). Some deposition of calcium within the cartilaginous matrix occurs at this time.

(b) As this realignment of the cartilage cells is effected, vascular buds from the inner layer of the perichondrium invade the cartilage, eroding the cartilaginous substance and forming **primary marrow cavities** (figs. 313D; 314E, F). Large multinucleate cells or **chondroclasts** make their appearance at this time and aid the process of dissolution of cartilage.

(c) Following this procedure, osteoblasts arise within the peripheral areas of each vascular bud and begin to deposit bone matrix upon the small spicules of calcified cartilage which remain. (See spicule "a," fig. 314F.) The continual deposition of bone salts around these spicules converts the greatly eroded cartilaginous mass into spongy or cancellous bone (fig. 314F).

2) Perichondrial (Periosteal) Bone Formation. As cancellous bone is formed within the cartilaginous mass, the surrounding perichondrium of the original cartilage now becomes the periosteum, and the cells of the inner layer of the periosteum deposit circumferential layers of compact bone (perichondrial or periosteal bone formation) around the periphery of the cancellous bone (fig. 314F). The latter action forms a cylinder of compact bone around the spongy variety and around the cartilage which is being displaced (fig.

314F). The **primary marrow spaces,** established by the original invasion of
the perichondrial vascular buds, merge to form the **secondary marrow areas**
of the developing bone. This merging process is effected by the dissolution
of previously formed bony spicules or trabeculae.

c. Conversion of Cancellous Bone into Compact Bone

Spongy or cancellous bone is converted into compact bone by the deposition
of layers of compact bone between the trabeculae or columns of spongy bone,
thus obliterating the marrow cavities around the trabeculae of the cancellous bone and converting the intervening areas into Haversian systems
(fig. 314C, D).

D. Development (Morphogenesis) of the Endoskeleton

1. DEFINITIONS

For pedagogical purposes, the hard, skeletal tissues may be divided into
the **external skeleton** or **exoskeleton** and the **internal skeleton** or **endoskeleton.**
The exoskeleton comprises all the hard, protective structures which are derived from the mesenchyme of the dermis and from the epithelium of the
epidermis, described in Chapter 12. The exoskeleton as a whole will not be
described further.

Excluding the exoskeleton and the softer, connective-tissue portion of the
skeletal tissues, we shall proceed with a description of the morphogenesis of
the main skeletal support of the vertebrate body, the endoskeleton. The endoskeleton is composed of the **axial skeleton** and the **appendicular skeleton.**
The axial skeleton is composed of the **skeleton of the head,** the **skeleton of
the trunk,** and the **skeleton of the tail.** The skeleton of the appendages is
made up of the **pectoral and pelvic girdles** and the **bony supports for the
appendages.**

2. MORPHOGENESIS OF THE AXIAL SKELETON

a. General Features of the Skeleton of the Head

The **cranium** or skeleton of the head comprises:

(1) the protective parts for the **special sense organs** and the **brain,** and
(2) the skeleton of the **oral area** and **anterior end of the digestive tract.**

That portion of the cranium which protects the brain and its associated,
special sense organs may be called the **skull, cranium proper, or neurocranium**
(fig. 315D), whereas that which surrounds the anterior portion of the digestive
tract and pharyngeal area is known as the **visceral skeleton** or **splanchnocranium** (fig. 315D).

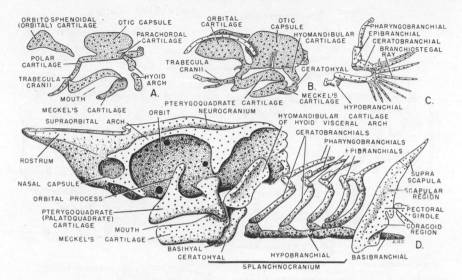

FIG. 315. Developmental stages of the chondrocranium in the dogfish, *Squalus acanthias.* (A and B redrawn from El-Toubi, '49, Jour. Morph., 84.) (A) Early developmental stage, 37-mm. embryo, lateral view. (B) Intermediate stage, 45-mm. embryo, lateral view. (C) Branchiostegal (gill support) rays attached to ceratobranchial segment of gill arch. (D) Adult stage of chondrocranium (neurocranium plus splanchnocranium), lateral view.

1) Neurocranium or Cranium Proper. The neurocranium is present in three main forms in the vertebrate group:

(1) a complete cartilaginous cranium without dermal reinforcing bones, as in cyclostomatous and elasmobranch fishes (fig. 315D),

(2) an inner cartilaginous cranium, associated with an outer or surrounding layer of bony plates, as in *Amia* (fig. 316C, D), the adult skull of *Necturus* and the frog being similar but slightly more ossified (fig. 317B, C), and

(3) an almost entirely ossified cranium, in teleosts, reptiles, birds, and mammals (figs. 318C; 319C, D, E).

Various degrees of intermediate conditions exist between the above groupings.

2) Visceral Skeleton or Splanchnocranium. The splanchnocranium or visceral skeleton consists of a number of cartilaginous or bony arches which tend to enclose the anterior portion of the digestive tube (fig. 315D). They are present in pairs, one arch on one side, the other arch on the other side. The first two pairs are related to the skull in gnathostomes. The succeeding pairs of visceral arches are associated with the branchial or gill apparatus in fishes and in certain amphibia, such as *Necturus.*

3) Development of the Skull or Neurocranium. The neurocranium of all vertebrates from the fishes to the mammals possesses a beginning cranial con-

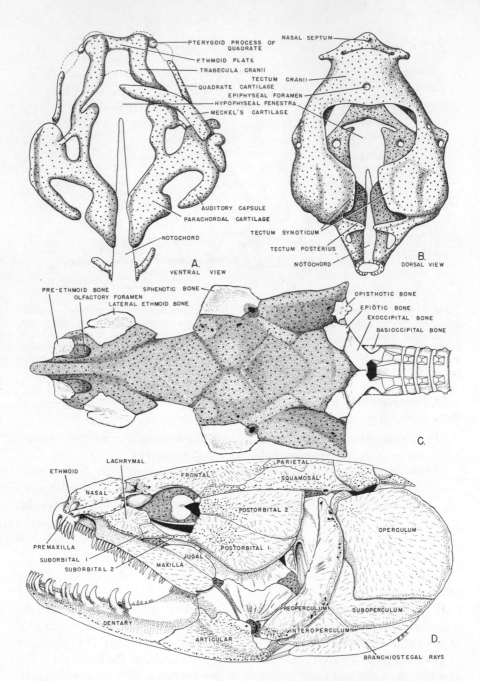

Fig. 316. Developmental stages of neurocranium of the bowfin, *Amia calva*. (A and B redrawn from De Beer, '37, after Pehrson; C and D from Allis, 1897, J. Morph., 12.) (A) Ventral view of 9.5-mm. stage. (B) Dorsal view of 19.5-mm. stage. (C) Cartilaginous neurocranium of adult stage. (D) Dermal (membrane) bones overlying neurocranium of adult stage. Cartilage = coarse stipple; bone = fine stipple.

dition in which dense mesenchyme, the so-called **desmocranium,** comes to surround the brain and its appendages. The membranous cranium is more pronounced in the basal areas of the brain. This pre-cartilage stage is followed by formation of cartilage which results in the development of a **chondric neurocranium.** A complete cartilaginous neurocranium is not formed in all vertebrate groups, although *the ventro-lateral areas of all vertebrate skulls are laid down in cartilage.* This basic, chondrocranial condition exists as the first step in skull formation, and it consists of three main regions, composed of cartilaginous rudiments (figs. 316A, 320):

(1) The **basal plate area** is composed of a pair of **parachordal cartilages** on either side of the anterior extremity of the notochord, together with the **otic capsules,** surrounding the otic(ear) vesicles.

(2) A **trabecular** or **pre-chordal plate area** lies anterior to the notochord. This area begins at the infundibular-hypophyseal fenestra and extends forward below the primitive forebrain. Two elongated cartilages, the **trabecula cranii** (fig. 320A) or a single elongated cartilage (fig. 320B), the **central stem or trabecular plate,** develop in the basal area of this region. With the trabecular area are associated the **sphenolateral, orbital** or **orbitosphenoidal cartilages** and the **optic capsules.** The latter are placed in a position lateral to the orbitosphenoidal cartilages.

(3) A **nasal capsular** or **ethmoidal plate area,** associated with the developing olfactory vesicles, later arises in the anterior portion of the trabecular region (figs. 316A, 319A).

This fundamental cartilaginous condition of the vertebrate skull or neurocranium is followed by later conditions which proceed in three ways: (a) In the elasmobranch fishes, an almost complete roof of cartilage is developed, and the various cartilaginous elements fuse to form the cartilaginous neurocranium (fig. 315). This neurocranium enlarges but never becomes ossified. (b) In the ganoid fish, *Amia,* the frog, *Rana,* the mud puppy, *Necturus,* etc., the basic, ventrolaterally established, cartilaginous neurocranium is converted into a more or less complete chondrocranium by the formation of a roof and the complete fusion of the various cartilaginous elements (figs. 316A–C; 317A, B). In these forms, the cartilaginous cranium becomes ossified in certain restricted areas. In addition to this cartilaginous neurocranium, superficial, membrane bones (dermal bones) are added to the partially ossified chondrocranium. These membrane bones come to overlie and unite with the partly ossified cartilaginous skull (figs. 316D; 317C). (Consult also Table 1.) The adult skull or neurocranium in these forms thus is composed of a chondrocranial portion and an osteocranial part, the osteocranial part arising from cartilaginous and membranous sources. (c) In reptiles, birds, mammals, and in many teleost fishes, the basic ventro-lateral regions of the cartilaginous neurocranium only are formed (figs. 318A, B; 319A, B). This basic chondrocranium undergoes considerable ossification, forming cartilage bones, which replaces the cartilage of the chondrocranium. These cartilage bones are supplemented by superficially developed membrane bones which become closely associated with the cartilage bones. The adult skulls of these vertebrates are highly ossified structures, composed of cartilage and membrane bones. (See Tables 2 and 3.) A few cartilaginous areas persist in the adult skull, more in teleost fishes than in the reptiles, birds, and mammals (Kingsley, '25 and De Beer, '37).

4) Vicissitudes of the Splanchnocranium. The early visceral skeleton, established in the embryo, experiences many modifications in its development in the different vertebrate groups.

In the elasmobranch fishes, the first visceral (mandibular) arch on either side gives origin to an upper jaw element, composed of the **palatoquadrate (pterygoquadrate) cartilage,** and a lower jaw element or **Meckel's cartilage**

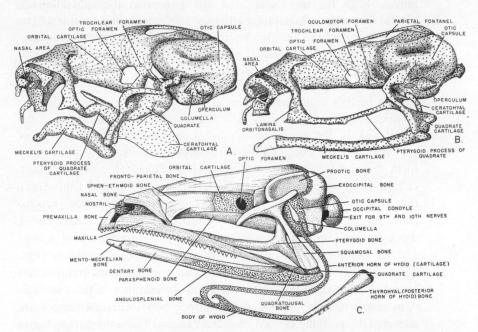

FIG. 317. Developmental stages of neurocranium in the frog. (A and B redrawn from De Beer, '37, after Pusey; C, redrawn and modified from Marshall, 1893, *Vertebrate Embryology,* New York, Putnam's Sons.) (A) Intermediate condition between larval and adult form. (B) Adult form of cartilaginous cranium, present after metamorphosis. (C) Adult neurocranium composed of membrane and cartilage bones associated with basic cartilaginous neurocranium (see Table 1). Cartilage = coarse stipple; bone = fine stipple.

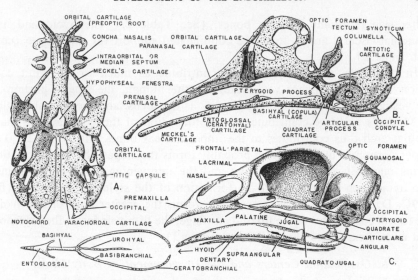

FIG. 318. Developmental stages of bird neurocranium. (A and B redrawn from De Beer, '37, from De Beer and Barrington.) (A) Dorsal view of 8½-day stage of *Anas* (duck). (B) Lateral view of 14-day stage of *Anas*. (C) Lateral view, adult stage of *Gallus* (chick). Cartilage = coarse stipple; bone = fine stipple.

(fig. 315D). Each second visceral (hyoid) arch in the shark forms on each side an upper **hyomandibula,** attached to the otic capsule by fibers of connective tissue, a **ceratohyal part,** and a lower **basihyal element** (fig. 315D). The basihyal portion of the two hyoid arches forms a basis for the so-called tongue. The succeeding branchial arches form supports for the gills and develop cartilaginous **branchial rays** which extend out into the gill area (fig. 315C). Each branchial arch on each side divides into four cartilages, namely, the upper *pharyngobranchial,* and the lower *hypobranchial,* the *epibranchial* and the *ceratobranchial* elements. The last two elements lie between the first two, and the ceratobranchial element is articulated with the hypobranchial element (fig. 315D).

The visceral skeleton in ganoid and teleost fishes arises similarly to that in elasmobranchs but becomes largely ossified in the adult (fig. 316).

In the frog, the well-developed, visceral skeleton of the late larva becomes greatly modified during metamorphosis and the acquisition of adulthood. The hyoid arch persists in cartilage. The mandibular arch contributes to the formation of the upper and lower jaws. The lower jaw in the metamorphosed frog consists of Meckel's cartilages, reinforced by membrane bones, the **dentaries** and the **angulospenials.** The pterygoquadrate cartilages remain as cartilage and are reinforced by the **pterygoid, quadratojugal, squamosal, maxillae** and **premaxillae,** to form the upper jaw (fig. 317B, C and Table 1).

In birds, the first visceral or **mandibular arch** contributes to the formation of the **quadrate** and **articulare** at the angle of the jaw. These two bones on either side represent cartilage bones. (See Table 2.) The hyoid and first branchial-visceral arches form the complicated support for the tongue (consult Table 2).

In mammals, the visceral arches contribute as much to the adult condition as in other higher vertebrates. In the human, the caudal portion of the vestigial upper jaw rudiment persists as the **incus,** and the caudal portion of Meckel's cartilage contributes to the formation of the **malleus.** The mandibular arch thus contributes to the important ear bones (fig. 319C-2). The upper portion of the hyoid arch probably forms the **stapes;** the ventral portion forms one half of the **hyoid bone;** and the intervening tissue of the primitive hyoid arch contributes to the formation of the **stylohyal structures** (fig. 319C, D). The third arch on each side forms the greater horn of the hyoid; the fourth contributes to the **thyroid cartilage;** the fifth pair forms the **arytenoid and cricoid cartilages** (fig. 319C and Table 3).

b. Ossification Centers and the Development of Bony Skulls

The formation of the bony crania of all vertebrates entails the use of **centers of ossification** which involve methods of bone formation previously described. As a rule, one ossification center arises in a single bone, with the exception of those bones, such as the human frontal, sphenoid, or occipital bones, which result from the fusion of two or more bones. In these instances separate centers of ossification are developed in each individual bone. The exact number of ossification centers in all bones has not been exactly determined.

c. Development of the Axial Skeleton

1) Axial Skeleton of the Trunk: a) NOTOCHORD. The notochord is one of the basic structural features of the chordate group of animals. It will be recalled (Chapters 9 and 10) that the primitive notochordal band of cells is the physiological instrument which effects much of the early organization of the developing body of the vertebrate embryo. Aside from this basic, apparently universal function in vertebrate development, the notochord later functions as a prominent feature in the development of the median skeletal axis. In the cyclostomatous fishes, a persistent, highly developed notochord, enclosed in elastic, and fibrous, connective-tissue sheaths, is found in the adult. The enveloping, connective-tissue sheaths establish a covering for the nerve cord above and for the blood vessels immediately below the notochord. Vertebrae are not developed, but in the cyclostomes *(Petromyzontia)* paired cartilaginous rods lie along either side of the nerve cord above (Goodrich, '30, pp. 27, 28). In the Dipnoi and in the cartilaginous ganoids, such as *Acipenser sturio,* the notochord persists unconstricted by vertebral elements although supplemented by these structures. In the shark group and in teleost fishes in general, as well as in certain Amphibia, such as *Necturus,* the notochord is continuous but constricted greatly by the developing vertebral centra. In

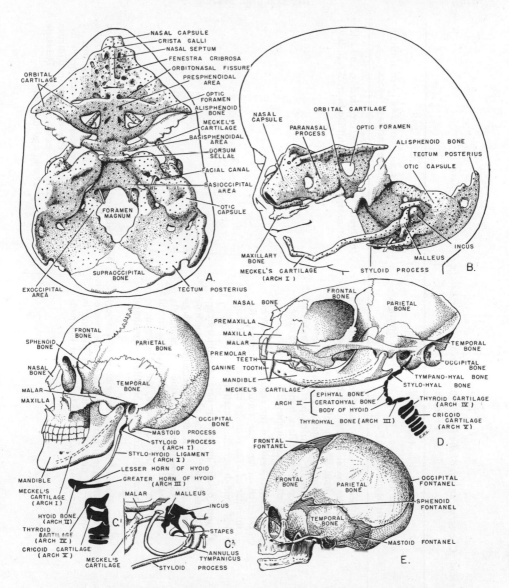

FIG. 319. Developmental stages of mammalian neurocranium and splanchnocranium. (A) Human chondrocranium at end of third month viewed from above (from Keibel and Mall, 1910, *Manual of Human Embryology,* vol. I, after Hertwig's model). (B) Same, lateral view, slightly modified. (C-1) Lateral view of adult skull showing visceral arch (splanchnocranial) derivatives. (C-2) Auditory ossicles (see fig. 319B). Malleus derived from caudal end of Meckel's cartilage in lower jaw portion of mandibular visceral arch; incus from caudal end of maxillary process of mandibular arch; stapes from upper or hyomandibular portion of hyoid visceral arch. (D) Lateral view of cat skull and visceral arch (splanchnocranial) derivatives. (E) Human cranium, lateral view, at birth showing fontanels (from Morris, '42, *Human Anatomy,* Philadelphia, Blakiston). Cartilage = coarse stipple; bone = fine stipple.

675

TABLE 1*

Embryonic Chondrocranium of the Frog (Rana fusca) and Its Relation to the Adult Skull
(See fig. 317)

Basic embryonic chondrocranium	Adult Skull	Adult Skull
	Cartilage bones, i.e., bones developed from a cartilaginous base	Membrane bones, i.e., bones of dermal origin, associated with the cartilage bones
A. Neurocranium	*Note:* persistence of chondrocranium in adult includes nasal capsule, trabecular and basal plates, hind portion of otic capsules, tectum synoticum, quadrate cartilage, and considerable part of anterior part of hypobranchial skeleton. The cartilage bones which do appear arise after metamorphosis	Membrane bones arise before, during, and after metamorphosis (consult De Beer, '37, p. 209)
1. Occipital region	**Exoccipitals** ossify in the region of the occipital arch around the foramen magnum. Remainder of area remains cartilaginous. Occipital condyles continue cartilaginous	
2. Otic capsular (auditory) region	**Prootic** ossifies in anterior part of auditory capsule and part of basal plate in the immediate area. Rest of otic capsule remains cartilaginous. **Columella auris** ossifies in its middle region as the **mediostapedial** bone, its lateral portion or extra-columella, the attachment to the operculum, and the operculum, remaining cartilaginous	
3. Orbitotemporal region (= trabecular region plus anterior portion of basal plate area)	**Sphenethmoid** bone (os en ceinture of Cuvier) represents the orbitosphenoids of other vertebrates. A distinct presphenoid is present in certain anurans. Rest of area is cartilaginous	**Frontals** and **parietals** arise over vacuity in roof of chondrocranium and fuse to form the **frontoparietal,** covering upper part of brain case. **Parasphenoid** appears below hypophyseal fenestra. **Prevomer** (paired) arises beneath floor of nasal capsule. **Palatine** connects pterygoid and maxilla

4. Nasal (olfactory) capsular and anterior trabecular area	Remains cartilaginous together with anterior trabecular region	Nasal bones come to overlie roof of nasal capsule. **Intranasal** or **septomaxilla** forms part of roof of nasal capsule. May be regarded as a lacrimal bone
5. Optic (eye) capsule	**Sclerotic coat** of eyeball persists in cartilage	
B. Splanchnocranium		
1. Mandibular or visceral arch I on each side		
a. Pterygoquadrate part	Remains cartilaginous	**Pterygoid** ossifies along medio-ventral surface of pterygoquadrate. **Squamosal** arises along the dorsal and medial surface of quadrate portion of pterygoquadrate. **Quadratojugal** ossifies on outer surface of quadrate cartilage. It grows forward to the maxilla. **Premaxilla** and **maxilla** form upper jaw
b. Meckel's cartilage	Meckel's cartilage, with the exception of anterior extremity which ossifies as **mentomeckelian**, remains cartilaginous	**Dentary** and **angulare** (angulosplenial) arise in relation to Meckel's cartilage and reinforce it externally
2. Hyoid or visceral arch II on each side	Hyoid tends to persist in cartilage together with hypobranchial plate. Posterior horn of hyoid ossifies as **thyrohyal**	
3. Branchial arches on each side	Disappear with exception of hypobranchial area which contributes to hypobranchial plate	

* Based largely on data supplied by De Beer, '37.

TABLE 2*

Embryonic Chondrocranium of the Chick and Its Relation to the Adult Skull

Basic embryonic chondrocranium	Adult Skull	Adult Skull
	Cartilage bones, i.e., bones developed from a cartilaginous base	Membrane bones, i.e., bones of dermal origin, associated with the cartilage bones
A. Neurocranium	Most cartilage bones arise at beginning of 3rd week of incubation	Most membrane bones begin to ossify during middle of 2nd week of incubation
1. Occipital region		
a. Tectum synoticum	**Supraoccipital**	
b. Occipital arch	**Exoccipitals**	
c. Caudal part of basal plate	**Basioccipital**	
2. Otic capsular (auditory) region		
a. Prootic area	**Prootic** forms anterior half of auditory capsule	**Squamosal** arises laterally in region of auditory capsule and posterior orbital area
b. Periotic area	**Opisthotic** ossifies in wall of posterior semicircular canal and fuses with prootic to form **periotic**	
c. Epiotic area	**Epiotic** arises in dorsal wall of posterior semicircular canal; it fuses with supraoccipital	
3. Orbitotemporal region = trabecular region plus anterior portion of basal plate area)	**Basisphenoid** arises in caudal part of trabecular area. **Presphenoid** arises in interorbital area and caudal part of nasal septum. **Pleurosphenoid** ossifies in posterior orbital cartilage	**Frontal** arises in posterior nasal and orbital area. **Lacrimal** (prefrontal) arises in orbitonasal area. **Parasphenoid** and paired lateral wings of **basitemporals** lie below basisphenoid. **Palatine** arises ventro-laterally to interorbital septum and articulates with premaxilla and parasphenoid

4. Nasal (olfactory) capsular and anterior trabecular areas	Bony ethmoidal structures	**Nasal** arises in dorsal and lateral surfaces of nasal capsule. **Prevomer** arises as two bones which later fuse, underlying the nasal septum. **Parietal** is small and arises over posterior part of nasal capsular area
5. Optic (eye) capsule	Forms **sclerotic capsule** of the eye (remains cartilaginous)	**Sclerotic bones** or platelets lie on rim of sclerotic cartilage
B. Splanchnocranium		
1. Mandibular or visceral arch I on each side a. Pterygoquadrate part	**Quadrate bone** arises in substance of pterygoquadrate cartilage and comes to occupy the whole of it	**Premaxilla** arises as two bones which fuse. **Maxilla** is a slender bone, arising in ventral area of nasal capsule; it sends a zygomatic process backward toward the quadrate. **Pterygoid bone** arises over pterygoid process of pterygoquadrate cartilage and articulates firmly with quadrate bone. **Jugal** is a small bone, joining zygomatic process of maxilla and extending toward the quadrate. **Quadratojugal** joins jugal to quadrate.
b. Meckel's cartilage	**Articulare** arises in caudal end of Meckel's cartilage	Membrane bones of lower jaw, the **dentary**, **splenial**, **angular**, and **supra-angular** supplant Meckel's cartilage.
2. Hyoid or visceral arch II on each side	Upper part probably forms the **columella** and **stapes.** Lower part of hyoid arch or ceratohyals form the **os entoglossum**, or entoglossal bone of the **tongue** and possibly the **basihyal** which unites the entoglossal bone with the greater horn of the hyoid apparatus	
3. Branchial arches on each side	Branchial arch I (visceral arch III) forms **greater horn of hyoid**, composed of **basibranchial** and **ceratobranchial** bony segments joined by cartilage	

* Based largely on data supplied by De Beer, '37.

TABLE 3*

Human Embryonic Chondrocranium and Its Relation to the Adult Skull

Basic embryonic chondrocranium	Adult Skull	Adult Skull
A. Neurocranium	Cartilage bones, i.e., bones developed from a cartilaginous base	Membrane bones, i.e., bones of dermal origin, associated with the cartilage bones
	For time of origin, consult De Beer, '37, pp. 363, 364	For time of origin, consult De Beer, '37, pp. 363, 364
1. Occipital region		
a. Tectum synoticum	**Supraoccipital, squamous inferior portion**	Dorsal part of **supraoccipital** or **squamous superior portion** = **interparietal** of cat
b. Occipital arch around neural foramen	**Exoccipitals**	
c. Posterior part of basal plate	**Basioccipital**	
2. Otic capsular (auditory) region		
a. Prootic area	**Prootic** gives origin to anterior, dorsal, and lateral walls of auditory capsule	Squamous part of **temporal; tympanic ring**
b. Periotic area	**Periotic** gives origin to much of petrous portion of the temporal bone	
c. Epiotic area	**Epiotic** gives origin to mastoid process of temporal bone	
3. Orbitotemporal region = trabecular region plus anterior portion of basal plate area)	**Presphenoid** and its **orbitosphenoidal** wings; **basisphenoid** and basal areas of its **alisphenoidal** wings	**Frontal; parietals; palatines; pterygoid** processes and squamous portion of alisphenoidal wings

4. Nasal (olfactory) capsular and anterior trabecular areas — **Maxilloturbinal; ethmoturbinals; cribriform plate; nasal septum, in part** — **Nasal; lacrimal; vomer; premaxillary and maxillary processes**

5. Optic (eye) capsule — **Sclerotic coat of the eye (remains cartilaginous)**

B. Splanchnocranium

1. Mandibular or visceral arch I on each side
   a. Quadrate part — **Incus** — **Premaxillary; maxillary; zygomatic**
   b. Meckel's cartilage (caudal end) — **Malleus** — **Dentary**

2. Hyoid or visceral arch II on each side — **Stapes; body and lesser horn of hyoid; styloid process of temporal; stylohyoid ligament**

3. Branchial arches on each side
   a. Arch III — **Greater horn of hyoid**
   b. Arch IV — **Thyroid cartilage (half of)**
   c. Arch V — **Cricoid and arytenoid cartilages (half of)**

* Based largely on data supplied by De Beer, '37.

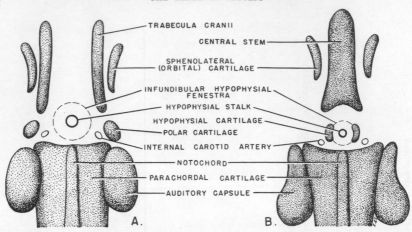

FIG. 320. Diagrams of basic cartilaginous underpinning or foundation of the vertebrate neurocranium. (Somewhat modified from De Beer, '37, after De Beer and Woodger.) (A) Pisces. (B) Placental mammals. It is to be observed that the trabecula cranii in the fish is represented by the central stem or trabecular plate in the mammal.

most amphibia and in the reptiles, birds, and mammals, the notochord tends to be entirely displaced by the vertebrae, and its residual remains are restricted within or between the vertebrae. In mammals, the residual remainder of the notochord constitutes the **nucleus pulposus** (pulpy nucleus) near the center of the fibrocartilage of the intervertebral disc. In the human, according to Terry, '42, p. 288, the pulpy nucleus forms a "pivot round which the bodies of the vertebrae can twist or incline."

b) VERTEBRAE. Vertebrae, the distinct segments of which the spinal column consists, arise from sclerotomic mesenchyme, derived from the ventro-mesial aspects of the various somites (fig. 252A–D). Potentially, this sclerotomic mesenchyme *in each primitive segment* becomes segregated into eight masses, four on either side of the notochord. These eight masses or blocks of mesenchyme form the **arcualia.** The arcualia become arranged in relation to the notochord and the developing intermuscular septa as indicated in figure 321A. These masses are designated as **basidorsals** and **basiventrals, interdorsals** and **interventrals.** Thus there are two basidorsals, two basiventrals, two interdorsals, and two interventrals.

During the formation of the vertebra in mammals, the sclerotomic masses within a primitive body segment become associated about the notochordal axis as indicated in figure 321J–L. It is to be observed that the arteries from the dorsal aorta lie in an intersegmental position. This position represents the area of the myoseptal membrane, shown in figure 321A. As the sclerotomic masses increase in substance, each mass on each side of the notochord becomes divisible into an anterior area, in which the mesenchymal cells are less dense, and a posterior area, where the cells are closely aggregated (fig. 321J). The less dense mesenchymal mass represents the rudiment of the **interdorsal vertebral element,** while the posterior dense mass of mesenchyme is the **basidorsal element.** As development proceeds, the basidorsal mass of cells from one segment and the interdorsal mass of the next posterior segment on either side of the notochord move toward each other and align themselves in the intersegmental area as shown in figure 321K, L. The basidorsal element thus comes to lie along the anterior portion of the intersegmental area, and the interdorsal rudiment occupies the posterior part of this area. The four vertebral elements, two on either side of the notochord in the intersegmental area, form the basic vertebral rudiments, although rudimentary basiventral and interventral elements possibly are present. The intersegmental artery eventually comes to lie laterally to the forming vertebra.

Once these basic rudiments of the vertebra are established, the vertebra begins to form. In doing so, there is an increase in the number of mesenchymal cells present, and the sclerotomic masses move toward and around the notochord in the intersegmental position. The two dense basidorsal elements from either side expand dorsally around the neural tube as the two interdorsal rudiments coalesce to form the body of the centrum (fig. 321M). Laterally, the rudiment of the rib arises as a condensation of mesenchyme continuous with the forming neural arch and centrum. The rib element continues to grow ventro-laterally, particularly in the thoracic area (fig. 321N). In the lateral growth of the rib rudiment, surrounding mesenchyme is organized and incorporated into the growing structure of the rudiment.

Once the vertebral rudiment is established as a dense mass of mesenchyme, the pre-cartilage stage of cartilage development occurs (fig. 313A). The pre-cartilage stage is followed soon by cartilage (fig. 313B, C). Later, centers of ossification arise as indicated in figure 321O, and the cartilaginous condition becomes converted into a bony condition. Secondary centers of ossification, forming bony epiphyses, ultimately arise after birth at the anterior and posterior ends of each centrum. When the ultimate size of the vertebra is attained, the epiphyseal cartilages between the epiphyses and the centrum of each vertebra become ossified, and the epiphyses thus unite with the centrum. The intervertebral discs of fibrocartilage form in the segmental position between the vertebrae.

It is to be observed that the intersegmental arrangement of the vertebrae permits direct passage of the spinal nerves to the developing musculature within each segment and also permits the musculature of each segment to attach itself to two successive vertebrae. The latter feature is particularly advantageous in lateral bending movements, so prominent in the swimming movements of water-dwelling forms.

See legend, fig. 321, for vertebral development in various vertebrates.

c) DIVISIONS OF THE VERTEBRAL COLUMN. In fishes, two main divisions of the vertebral column are recognizable, the **caudal region** where the ver-

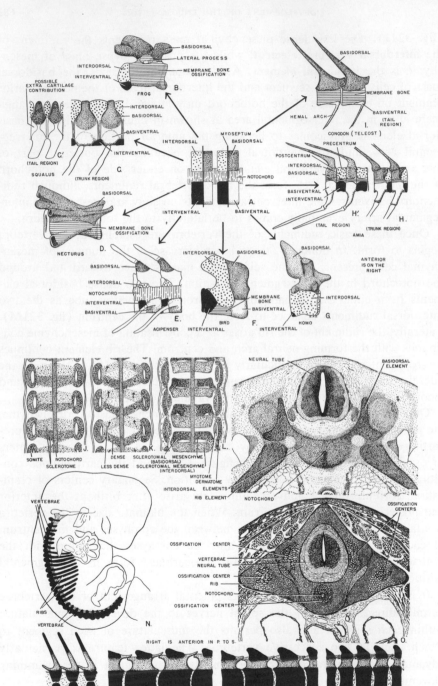

FIG. 321. *(See facing page for legend.)*

Fig. 321. Development of vertebrae. The vertebral column in the phylum Vertebrata is a variable structure. In the early embryo the primitive notochord serves as the primitive axis. Later this structure develops fibrous sheaths in fishes and amphibia. The notochord plus its surrounding sheaths serves as the only axial support in the embryo and adult stages of *Amphioxus* and Cyclostomes. However, in all true vertebrates, the notochord is supplemented during later embryonic stages by vertebral rudiments known as **arcualia** (fig. 321, A). Eight arcualia are present typically in each vertebral segment. The arcualia begin as mesenchymal condensations from the sclerotome (see fig. 252, A–D), and later are transformed into cartilaginous masses. In the elasmobranch fishes the cartilaginous arcualia fuse to form the vertebra as described below, but in most vertebrates they undergo ossification.

I. The Formation of Vertebrae in Fishes. In certain instances among the fishes, the arcualia are merely saddled on to the notochord and its sheaths. This condition is found, for example, in the lung fishes and cartilaginous ganoid fishes (fig. 321, E). A vertebral centrum is not developed in these instances.

In the elasmobranch fishes the vertebra is formed essentially from that group of arcualia known as the **basalia**, that is, the **basidorsals** and **basiventrals.** These rudiments **invade the fibrous sheath** from above and below on either side and form the neural arch and centrum as indicated in fig. 321, C. The **interbasalia**—that is, the **interdorsals and interventrals**—lie between the vertebrae. The notochord is constricted greatly in the region of the centrum but is disturbed little in the areas between the centra. That is, the centrum is hollowed out or deeply concave at either end. This form of centrum is found in all **amphicoelous vertebrae** (fig. 321, P). In the tail region (fig. 321, C'), there are two vertebrae per muscle segment. This condition is known as **diplospondyly.** Other cartilaginous elements may enter into the formation of the centrum as indicated in fig. 321, C'.

The diplospondylous condition in the tail region of *Amia* presumably is developed as indicated in fig. 321, H'. In the trunk region of *Amia* the arcualia associate to form the vertebrae as in fig. 321, H. A certain amount of membrane bone may enter into the composition of the centra in *Amia*. In the teleost fishes (fig. 321, I), the basidorsals form the neural arches, but the centrum is developed almost entirely from the ossification of fibrous connective tissue membrane (i.e., membrane bone formation). The basiventrals form the area of attachment of the pleural ribs and also form the hemal arches.

II. Development of Vertebrae in Amphibia. In the frog (fig. 321, B), the neural arch of each vertebra appears to arise as the result of fusion and ossification of two basidorsal arcualia. Ossification spreads from the neural arch downward into the developing centrum. The centrum, however, develops as a result of **perichordal ossification** which arises within the membranous connective tissue *around the notochord*. The rudimentary interdorsals and interventrals probably grow inward into the intercentral spaces to obliterate the notochord between the centra. The interdorsal-interventral complex fuses ultimately with the caudal end of the centrum, to form a rounded knob which articulates with the concave end of the next posterior vertebra. That is, the vertebrae in the frog are **procoelous** (fig. 321, Q). The urostyle of the frog probably represents a fusion of rudimentary vertebrae caudal to the ninth or sacral vertebra. Vestigial notochordal remains may exist in the center of each bony centrum.

The development of the vertebrae in *Necturus* (fig. 321, D), resembles that of the frog, with the exception that the bony centrum arises from a perichordal ossification which is entirely independent of the neural arch. Also, the notochord remains continuous, being constricted in the region of the bony centrum, but relatively unconstricted in the area between the centra. That is, the vertebrae are of the **amphicoelous** type (fig. 321, P). The basiventral arcualia unite to form the hemal arches in the tail.

III. Development of Vertebrae in the Chick and Mammals. The development of the vertebra in the chick is a complicated affair, as the vertebra is composed of a complex of fused arcualia associated with a perichordal ossification (see fig. 321, F). The vertebrae are **heterocoelous,** their ends being partly procoelous and opisthocoelous. In mammals tebrae possess hemal arches and the **trunk region** without hemal arches but with ribs. The amphibia begin to show a third division, the **cervical area** or anterior portion of the trunk region in which the vertebrae do not possess ribs. This area is limited to one vertebra, the **axis.** In the amphibia, also, a **sacral region** begins to make its appearance. It is only slightly differentiated in water-abiding forms but well developed in the *Anura.* The caudal vertebral area in the *Anura* generally is fused to form the **coccyx** or **urostyle.** The reptilian vertebral column manifests great variability in the different orders. The turtles show **cervical, trunk, and tail regions,** with the trunk vertebrae fused with the bony plates of the **carapace.** In snakes, a short **cervical area,** a greatly elongated **trunk region,** and a **caudal area** are present. Some of the snakes possess the largest number of vertebrae among verterbates, the number reaching several hundreds. Sacral vertebrae are absent in snakes. The lizards and crocodilians show conditions closely resembling the amphibia. In the birds, **caudal, synsacral, thoracic, and cervical regions** are present, while, in mammals, **cervical, thoracic, lumbar, sacral, and caudal regions** exist.

d) RIBS. Ribs are not found in cyclostomatous fishes. In the gnathostomes, two types of ribs may be present:

(1) **dorsal ribs** and
(2) **ventral or pleural ribs.**

FIG. 321—*(Continued)*

the vertebra appears to arise from two basidorsal and two interdorsal arcualia as indicated in fig. 321, G. The origin of the basidorsal and interdorsal vertebral rudiments from the sclerotomic mesenchyme are shown in figure 321, J–M. The vertebrae are of the **acoelous (amphiplatyan)** type (fig. 321, S). The **chevron bones** and hemal arches in the tail region of many mammals represent basiventral elements. Fig. 321, M–O, shows the rib outgrowths from the developing vertebrae. Observe centers of ossification in the vertebra in fig. 321, O.

Fig. 321, A, presents a lateral view of the so-called arcualia in relation to the notochord and the myosepta (myocommata). According to this theory of the development of the vertebrae, the arcualia form the main rudiments from which future vertebrae arise.   (B) The adult frog vertebrae showing probable contributions of arcualia.   (C and C') Probable contributions of the arcualia to trunk and tail vertebrae of *Squalus acanthias*.   (D) The adult vertebrae of *Necturus maculosus*.   (E) The role played by the arcualia in forming the axial supporting structure in *Acipenser sturio*. (Redrawn and modified from Goodrich, Vertebrate Craniata, 1909.)   (F) The composite origin of the vertebra in the bird. (Redrawn from Piiper, 1928. Phil. Trans. Series B, 216.)   (G) Probable contributions of the arcualia to vertebra formation in man.   (H) Probable contributions of the arcualia in the formation of trunk and caudal vertebrae in *Amia calva*.   (I) Same for the teleost, *Conodon nobilis*.   (J–L) The origin and early development of the sclerotomic mesenchyme in the mammal.   (M) shows vertebral and costal development in a 15-mm. pig embryo.   (N) presents vertebral and costal development in a human embryo of 11 mm. The vertebral and rib rudiments are in the mesenchymal stage at this period. (Redrawn from Bardeen, 1910. Keibel and Mall, Vol. I, Human Embryology, Lippincott, Phila.)   (O) is a drawing of developing vertebra in the 22-mm. opossum embryo.   (P, Q, R, and S) are diagrams of amphicoelous, procoelous, opisthocoelous and slightly biconcave amphiplatyan (acoelous) vertebrae. (Redrawn and modified from Kingsley, '25.)

Ribs develop in relation to the basidorsal and basiventral elements and extend outward in the myosepta. The dorsal rib appears typically in the position between the epaxial and hypaxial divisions of the primitive skeletal musculature, whereas the pleural rib lies in close relationship to the coelomic cavity (fig. 311B). It is questionable whether or not the hemal arch, when present, is homologous with the ventral or pleural ribs. The shark, *Squalus acanthias,* has dorsal ribs. This condition is true also of all *Tetrapoda.* In *Amia,* the ribs are of the pleural variety, whereas, in most teleosts, pleural ribs are present, supplemented by dorsal or *epipleural ribs.*

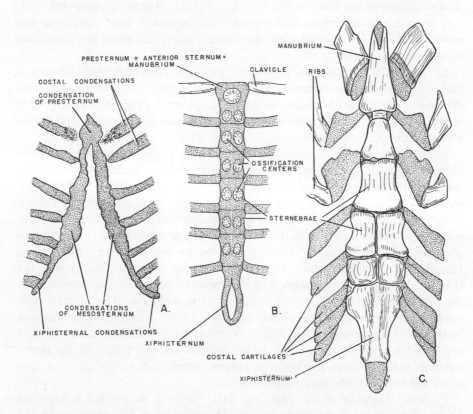

FIG. 322. Development of the sternum in the mammal. (A and C redrawn from Hanson, '19, Anat. Rec., 17; B redrawn from Kingsley, '25.) (A) Diagrammatic reconstruction of sternum of 24-mm. pig embryo. The two precartilaginous condensations of the mesosternum are united anteriorly with the presternal condensation. The rib or costal condensations are approaching and uniting with the sternal condensations. (B) Schematic representation of sternal rudiments in the mammal. The mesosternal cartilages have segmented into cartilaginous segments or **sternebrae.** Bilateral centers of ossification arise in each sternebra which later form the bony sternebra. (C) Sternum of old boar, weight 450 lbs. It is to be observed that the sternebrae have remained distinct, and in two of the sternal segments anterior to the xiphisternum the two centers of ossification produce a dual condition within the sternal segment. In the human and certain other mammals the sternebrae fuse to form the **gladiolus** or **corpus sterni.**

As indicated above, ribs may be considered as outward extensions or processes of the vertebrae. In the frog, the much-abbreviated ribs become firmly ossified to the basidorsal elements of the vertebrae and extend outward as the transverse processes. However, in most vertebrates, they are articulated with the vertebrae by means of lateral extensions or processes from the vertebrae.

Chondrification of the rib occurs separately from the chondrification of the vertebra, and articulations develop between the rib and the vertebrae (fig. 321O). Similarly, when ossification develops, a separate center of ossification arises in the body of the rib (fig. 321O). However, epiphyseal centers arise in the tubercular and capitular heads, which later unite with the shaft of the rib. The student is referred to Kingsley, '25, for a full discussion of vertebrae and ribs.

e) STERNUM. A *sternum connected with the ribs,* and thus forming *a part of the protective thoracic basket,* is found only in reptiles, birds, and mammals. A sternum is absent in the gymnophionan Amphibia (Apoda), is reduced to a midventral cartilaginous series of bars in *Necturus,* and forms a part of the pectoral girdle in the frog (fig. 323C).

In its formation in the mammal, the sternum begins as a bilateral series of mesenchymal aggregations between the ventro-mesial ends of the clavicular and costal concentrations of mesenchyme (fig. 322A). These mesenchymal aggregations move toward the midline, form pre-cartilage, and then form cartilage. The median cartilaginous mass at the anterior end forms the **presternum** or **episternum;** the portion between the rib elements forms the **mesosternum,** and the posterior free area is the **metasternum** or **xiphisternum** (fig. 322B). In forms which have a clavicle, the latter articulates with the episternum. The anterior portion of the mesosternum unites ultimately with the presternum to form the rudiment of the **manubrium.** The mesosternum segments into blocks or **sternebrae,** while the caudal free end of the sternum forms the **xiphisternum** (fig. 322C). Centers of ossification arise in these areas and convert them to bone. In the human, the sternebrae of the mesosternum unite to form the body or **corpus sterni,** but, in the cat, pig, and many other mammals, they remain distinct.

2) Axial Skeleton of the Tail. The axial skeleton of the tail is modified greatly from that of the trunk region. In water-living vertebrates, the tail forms a considerable portion of the body. As the tail is used for swimming purposes, the contained vertebrae are developed to serve this end. In consequence, rib processes are reduced or lost entirely, and hemal arches for the protection of the caudal blood vessels are strongly developed features. Another feature subserving the swimming function is the tendency toward **diplospondyly,** i.e., the development of two vertebral centra per segment (fig. 321H'). In land forms, the tail tends to be reduced. However, in the armadillo, kangaroo, etc., the tail is a formidable structure, and hemal-arch

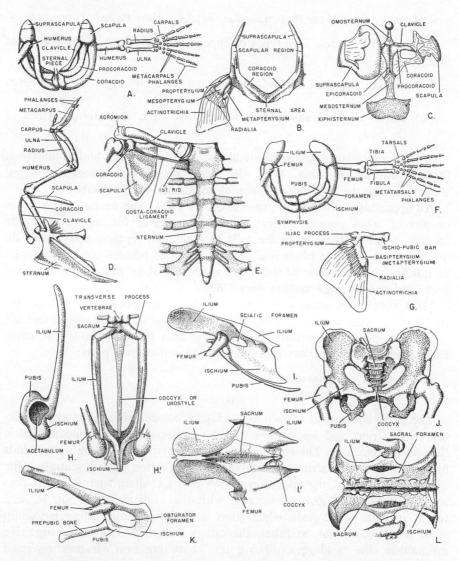

FIG. 323. Pectoral and pelvic girdles. (A) Diagrammatic pectoral girdle of Tetrapoda (modified from Kingsley, '25). (B) Pectoral girdle of *Squalus acanthias*. (C) Pectoral girdle of the frog, *Rana* (redrawn from Kingsley, '25, after Parker). Observe that clavicle is a small bony bar superimposed upon procoracoid; suprascapula removed on right side. (D) Pectoral girdle of the bird, *Gallus*. (E) Human pectoral girdle. (F) Diagrammatic representation of pelvic girdle in Tetrapoda (modified from Kingsley, '25). (G) Pelvic girdle in *Squalus acanthias*. (H) Pelvic girdle in *Rana catesbiana*. (I) Pelvic girdle in *Gallus* (chick). (J) Pelvic girdle in human. (K) Pelvic girdle in *Didelphys* (opossum). (L) Dorsal view of sacrum and pelvic girdle in the armadillo, *Tatusia*.

689

structures for the protection of blood vessels are developed in the intervertebral area.

d. Development of the Appendicular Skeleton of the Paired Appendages

1) General Features. Two types of appendages are found in the vertebrate group:

(1) **median unpaired appendages** which take their origin in the median plane and

(2) **paired bilateral appendages** which arise from the lateral surface of the body.

Median appendages appear in the fishes, aquatic urodeles, and in the larval form of anuran amphibia. They also occur in the crocodilian and lizard groups, among the reptiles, and, among mammals, in the whales.

All appendages arise as outgrowths of the body. The median appendages or fins of fishes possess separate skeletal structures for support, but the median, fin-like structures in the tails of amphibia, reptiles, and whales do not acquire a separate internal skeleton. All fishes possess a median caudal or **tail fin** at the terminus of the tail, a median **anal fin** posterior to the anal area, and **one or more median dorsal fins.**

Most vertebrates possess two pairs of bilateral appendages (Chap. 10, p. 508), one pair located anteriorly in the pectoral or breast region and the other pair situated posteriorly in the pelvic area just anterior to the anus. Each paired appendage has a skeleton composed of two parts:

(1) a **girdle component** and

(2) a **limb component.**

The girdle component of each appendage is associated with the axial skeleton of the trunk and also with the girdle component of the appendage on the contralateral side. The entire girdle of each pair of appendages thus tends to form a U-shaped structure with the closed portion placed ventrally (fig. 323A–K). In fishes, the open dorsal area of the U-shaped girdle in the pectoral area may be closely associated with the axial skeleton, but, in land forms, it is the pelvic girdle which joins the axial skeleton. This relationship is to be expected, for, in fishes, the tail is the more important propulsive mechanism, the head region being the "battering ram" insinuating itself through the water. As a result, the skull, anterior vertebrae, and the pectoral girdle ofttimes form a composite structure as, for example, in many teleost fishes. In land-living vertebrates, on the other hand, the main propulsive force is shifted anteriorly from the tail region and is assumed to a great extent by the posterior pair of appendages. In consequence, the pelvic girdle acquires an intimate relationship with the axial skeleton, and a fusion of vertebrae to form the **sacrum** occurs. The sacrum serves as the point of articulation between the pelvic girdle and the axial skeleton and is most highly developed in those species which use the hind limbs vigorously in support and propulsion of the body (fig. 323I, L).

Two main types of bilateral appendages are found in the vertebrate group:

(1) the **ichthyopterygium** of *Pisces* and
(2) the **cheiropterygium** of *Tetrapoda.*

The former is flattened dorso-ventrally, and assumes the typical flipper or fin shape, while the latter is an elongated, cylindrical affair.

2) Development of the Skeleton of the Free Appendage. The paired appendages arise either as a dorso-ventrally flattened fold of the epidermal portion of the skin, or as a cylindrical outgrowth of the epidermis. (See Chap. 10.) Within the epidermal protrusion, is a mass of mesenchyme (figs. 262D, E; 324A). As development proceeds, condensations of mesenchyme, centrally placed, begin to foreshadow the outlines of the future skeletal structures of the limb (fig. 324A, C, D). This mesenchyme gradually becomes more compact to form a pre-cartilage stage, to be followed by a cartilaginous condition.

The pattern, which these cartilages of the limb assume, varies greatly in the two types of limbs mentioned above. In the ichthyopterygium (fig. 323B, G), they assume a radially arranged pattern, extending out from the point of attachment to the girdle, whereas, in the cheiropterygium (fig. 323A), they assume the appearance characteristic of the typical limb of the *Tetrapoda.*

In the tetrapod limb, such as that of the hog, chick, or human, elongated, cylindrically shaped bones begin to make their appearance in mesenchyme (fig. 324A–E). Following the cartilaginous condition, a center of ossification arises in the **shaft** or **diaphysis** of each developing bone, transforming the cartilage into bone (figs. 314E, F; 324E). Cancellous or spongy bone is formed centrally within the shaft, while compact bone is deposited around the periphery of the shaft (fig. 314E, F). Later, the cancellous bone of the shaft is resorbed, and a compact bony cylinder, containing a relatively large marrow cavity, is formed. Separate centers of ossification, the **epiphyses,** arise in the distal ends of the bones (fig. 324I). Each epiphysis is separated from the bone of the shaft by means of a cartilaginous disc, the **epiphyseal cartilage** (fig. 324I). At maturity, however, the bony epiphysis at each end of the bone becomes firmly united with the shaft or **diaphysis** by the appearance of an ossification center in the epiphyseal cartilage (fig. 324J). Internally, the ends of the long bones tend to remain in the cancellous or spongy condition, whereas the shaft is composed of compact bone with an enlarged central marrow cavity (fig. 324J). For later changes of the bony substance involved in the growth of bone, see growth of bone, p. 693.

3) Formation of the Girdles. The typical tetrapod pectoral girdle (fig. 323A) is composed of a sternal midpiece, three lateral columns, extending

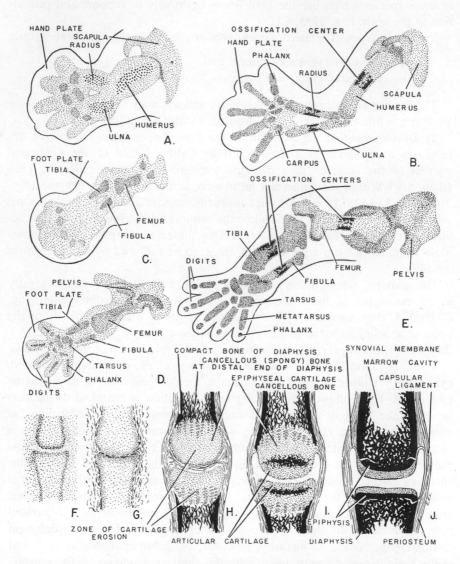

FIG. 324. Development of long bones of the appendages. (B and E have been modified to show conditions present in the fore- and hind appendages at about 8 weeks. For detailed description of limb development consult Bardeen, '05, Am. J. Anat., 4; Lewis, '02, Am. J. Anat., 2.) (A) Forelimb at 11 mm. (B) Forelimb at about eighth week, showing centers of ossification in humerus, radius and ulna. (C) Hindlimb at 11 mm. (D) Hindlimb at 14 mm. (E) Hindlimb at about eighth week, showing centers of ossification in femur, tibia, and fibula.

The heavy strippling in A, C, D represent centers of chondrification; the black areas in B and E portray ossification centers within cartilaginous form of the long bones.

F–J represent stages in joint development.

692

dorsad from the sternal area on either side, the **clavicle, procoracoid,** and **coracoid** to which is attached dorsally the **scapula.** Often a **suprascapula** is attached to the scapula. The pelvic girdle of the *Tetrapoda,* on the other hand (fig. 323F), is composed of two lateral columns on either side. The anterior column is called the **pubis,** and the posterior column is the **ischium.** An **ilium** is attached to the dorsal ends of the pubis and ischium on either side. **Epipubic** and **hypoischial** midpieces are sometimes present at the midventral ends of the pubic and ischial columns in some species.

As in the development of the skeleton of the free appendage, all the rudiments of these structures are laid down in cartilage and later ossify, with the exception of the clavicle which may be of intramembranous origin (Hanson, '20a and '20b). The clavicles are more strongly developed in man, whereas the coracoidal elements are vestigial (fig. 323E). In the cat, the coracoidal and clavicular elements are reduced. However, in the chick and frog, the coracoidal elements are dominant (fig. 323C, D). In the pelvic girdle, the iliac, pubic, and ischial elements are constant features in most *Tetrapoda.* In the shark, a single coracoid-scapula unit is present in the pectoral girdle and the pelvic girdle is reduced to a small transverse bar of cartilage (fig. 323B, G).

e. Growth of Bone

Bone once formed is not a static affair, for it is constantly being remodeled and enlarged during the growth period of the animal. In this process, bone is destroyed and resorbed by the action of multinucleate giant cells, called **osteoclasts,** or specialized, bone-destroying cells and is rebuilt simultaneously in peripheral areas by **osteoblasts** from the surrounding **periosteal tissue.**

To understand the processes involved in bone growth, let us start with the conditions found in the primitive shaft of a long bone (fig. 314F). Within the bony portion of the shaft, there is a network of cancellous bone, and, peripherally, there are lamellae of compact bone. The following transformative activities are involved in the growth of this bone:

(1) Within the bone, the cancellous columns of bony substance are destroyed by osteoclasts, the bony substance is resorbed, the marrow spaces are enlarged, while, peripherally, **circumferential lamellae** are deposited around the bones beneath the periosteum.

(2) Distally, cartilage is converted into cancellous bone while outer circumferential lamellae are fabricated beneath the periosteum. The bony substance thus creeps distally, lengthening the shaft of the bone.

(3) As the bone increases in length, some of the bony substance, forming the wall of the shaft or **diaphysis** is destroyed. This alteration is effected to a degree by vascular buds which grow into the bony substance from the **periosteum** around the outer surface of the bone and from the **endosteum** which lines the marrow cavities. These vascular

buds erode the bony substance with the aid of osteoclasts and produce elongated channels in the bone, channels which tend to run length-wise along the growing bone. Once these channels are made, osteo-blasts lay down bony lamellae in concentric fashion, converting the channel into an Haversian system. (Consult Maximow and Bloom, '42, pp. 141–145.) The Haversian systems thus tend to run parallel to the length of the bone. The Haversian canals open into the central marrow cavity of the bone in some of the Haversian systems, whereas others, through Volkmann's canals, open peripherally.

(4) While the foregoing processes are in progress, circumferential lamellae are laid down around the bone. The bone's diameter thus grows by the erosion of its bony walls (including previously established Haver-sian systems) and by the formation of new bony substance externally around the diaphysial area which is destroyed and resorbed. New Haversian systems and new circumferential lamellae in this way super-sede older systems and lamellae.

At the distal ends of the bone within the spaces of the cancellous bone, **red marrow** is found. In the shaft or diaphysis, however, the contained marrow cavity is filled with **yellow bone marrow,** composed mainly of fat cells.

The distal growth of elongated, cylindrically shaped bones, such as the phalanges or the long bones of the limbs, is possible, while epiphyseal carti-lage remains between the shaft of the bone and the bony epiphysis at the end of the bone. The maintenance and growth of the epiphyseal cartilage is prerequisite to the growth of these bones, for the increase in the length of the bony shaft involves the conversion of cartilage nearest to the bony shaft into cancellous bone. A bony cylinder of compact bone is then formed around the cancellous bone. When, however, the epiphyseal cartilage ceases to maintain itself, and it in turn becomes ossified, uniting the epiphysis to the bony shaft, growth of the bone in the distal direction comes to an end. Growth in the length of a vertebra also involves the epiphyseal cartilages lying between the bony ends of the centrum and the epiphyses. Increase in size of the diameter of the vertebra results from the destruction and resorption of bone already formed and the deposition of compact bone around the periphery.

In the case of flattened bones of cartilaginous origin such as the scapula or the pelvic-girdle bones, growth in the size of the bone is effected by the conversion of peripherally situated cartilage into bone, and by the destruction and resorption of bone previously formed and its synchronous replacement external to the area of destruction. On the other hand, in the growth of flat bones of membranous origin, the bone increases in size along its margins at the expense of the connective tissue surrounding the bone. Growth in the diameter of membrane bones is similar to that of cartilage bone, namely, destruction, resorption, and deposition of new bone at the surface.

f. Formation of Joints

1) Definitions. The word **arthrosis** is derived from a Greek word meaning a joint. In vertebrate anatomy, it refers to the point of contact or union of two bones. When the contact between two bones results in a condition where the bones actually fuse together to form one complete bone, the condition is called **ankylosis** or **synosteosis.** If, however, the point of contact is such that the bones form an immovable union, it is called a **synarthrosis;** if slightly movable, it forms an **amphiarthrosis;** and where the contact permits free mobility, it is known as a **diarthrosis.** Various degrees of rapprochement between bones, therefore, are possible.

2) Ankylosis (Synosteosis) and Synarthrosis. In the development of the bones of the vertebrate skull, two types of bone contact are effected:

(1) **ankylosis** and
(2) **synarthrosis.**

In the human **frontal bone,** for example, two bilaterally placed centers of ossification arise in the connective-tissue membrane, lying below the skin in the future forehead area. These two centers increase in size and spread peripherally until two frontal bony areas are produced, which are separated in the median plane at birth. Later on in the first year following birth, the two bones become **sutured** (i.e., form a synarthrosis) in the midsagittal plane. Beginning in the second year and extending on into the eighth year, the suture becomes displaced by actual fusion of bone, and **ankylosis** occurs. In the cat, however, the two frontal bones remain in the sutured condition (synarthrosis). The **temporal bone** in the human and other mammals is a complex bone, arising by the ultimate fusion (ankylosis) of several bones. In the human at birth, three separate bones are evident in the temporal bone:

(1) a **squamous portion,**
(2) a **petrous portion,** and
(3) a **tympanic part.**

The squamous and the tympanic bones are of membranous origin, whereas the petrous portion arises through the ossification of the cartilaginous otic capsule. The fusion of these three bones occurs during the first year following birth. The **occipital bone** is another bone of complex origin. Five centers of ossification are involved, viz., a **basioccipital,** two **exoccipitals,** a **squamous inferior,** and a **squamous superior.** The last arises as a membrane bone; the others are endochondral. Ultimate fusion of these entities occurs during the early years of childhood and is completed generally by the fourth to sixth years. In the cat, the squamous superior remains distinct as the **interparietal bone.** Finally, the sphenoid bone in the human represents a condition derived from many centers of ossification. According to Bardeen, '10, fourteen centers of ossification arise in the sphenoidal area, ten of them arising in the orbitotemporal region of the primitive chondrocranium. At birth, two major portions of the sphenoid bone are present, the **presphenoid** and the **basisphenoid,** being separated by a wedge of cartilage. Ultimate fusion of these two sphenoid bones occurs late in childhood (Bardeen, '10). In the adult cat, they remain distinct. The maxillary bone in the human arises as a premaxillary and a maxillary portion; later these bones fuse to form the adult maxilla. In the cat, on the other hand, these two bones remain distinct. (Consult also Table 3.)

The history of the human skull, therefore, is one of gradual fusion (ankylosis) of bones. In many parts, however, fusion does not occur, and definite sutures (synarthroses) are established between the bones, as in the case of the two parietals, the parietal and the occipital, the frontal and the parietals, etc.

The formation of the association between the parietal bones and neighboring bones establishes an interesting developmental phenomenon, known as the **fontanels.** The fontanels are wide, membranous areas between the developing parietal and surrounding bones which, at birth, are not ossified. These membranous areas are the **anterior fontanel,** in the midline between the two parietals and two frontal bones, and the **posterior fontanel,** between the parietals and the occipital bones. The **lateral fontanels** are located along the latero-ventral edges of the parietal and neighboring bones (fig. 319E).

3) Diarthrosis. A **diarthrosis** or movable joint is established at the distal ends of the elongated, cylindrically shaped bones of the body. Diarthroses are present typically in relation to the bones of the appendages. As the bones of the appendages form, there is a condensation of the mesenchyme in the immediate area of the bone to be formed. At the ends of the bone, the mesenchyme is less dense than in the area where the rudimentary bone is in the process of formation (fig. 324A–E). As a result, the area between bones is composed of mesenchyme less compact and less dense than in the areas where bone formation is initiated (fig. 324F, G). This mesenchyme at the ends of the bones thus forms a delicate membrane, tying the bony rudiments together, and, as such, forms a rudimentary **synarthrosis.** As development proceeds, the miniature bone itself becomes more dense, and, eventually, cartilage is formed. The latter later is displaced gradually by bone (fig. 324E). The areas between the ends of the respective developing bones become, on the contrary, less dense, and a space within the mesenchyme is developed between the ends of the forming bones (fig. 324H). As this occurs, connective tissue, continuous with the periosteum, forms around the outer edges of the ends of the bones, tying the ends of the bones together (fig. 324H, I). A cavity, the joint cavity, thus is formed at the ends of the bones, bounded by the cartilage at the ends of the bones and peripherally by connective tissues or ligaments which tie the ends of the bones together along their margins. The membrane which lines the joint cavity is known as the **synovial mem-**

brane, and the cartilaginous discs at the ends of the bones form the **articular cartilages** (fig. 324H, J).

4) Amphiarthrosis. The term **amphiarthrosis** refers to a condition intermediate between synarthrosis and diarthrosis. This condition occurs for example in the area of the **pubic symphysis.**

g. Dermal Bones

As observed in figure 311A, the primitive mesenchyme of the ghost skeleton of the embryo underlies the epidermal tube, as well as enmeshing the neural, gut, and coelomic tubes. As mentioned previously, wherever mesenchyme exists, a potentiality for bony or bone-like structures also exists. Consequently, it is not surprising that various types of dermal armor or exoskeletal structures in the form of bone, dermal scales, and bony plates are developed in various vertebrates in the dermal area, as described in Chapter 12. Aside from the examples exhibited in Chapter 12, other important bony contributions to the skeleton of vertebrates may be regarded as essentially dermal in origin. Among these are the membrane bones of the skull (Tables 1, 2, and 3). These bones sink inward and become integrated with the basic chondrocranial derivatives to form a part of the endoskeleton. Other examples of membrane bones of dermal origin are the **gastralia** or abdominal ribs of the Tuatera *(Sphenodon)* and the *Crocodilia,* the formidable, dermal, bony armor of the *Edentata,* e.g., the armadillo, and the bony plates on the head, back, and appendages in certain whales (Kingsley, '25, p. 17). All these examples of dermal armor or exoskeletal structures form an essential protective part of the entire hard or bony skeleton of vertebrate animals.

Bibliography

Baitsell, G. A. **1921.** A study of the development of connective tissue in the *Amphibia.* Am. J. Anat. **28**:447.

Bardeen, C. R. **1910.** Chap XI. The development of the skeleton and of the connective tissues. Human Embryology. Edited by Keibel and Mall. J. B. Lippincott Co., Philadelphia.

Bell, E. T. **1909.** II. On the histogenesis of the adipose tissue of the ox. Am. J. Anat. **9**:412.

De Beer, G. R. **1937.** The development of the vertebrate skull. Oxford University Press, Inc., Clarendon Press, New York.

Goodrich, E. S. **1930.** Studies on the structure and development of vertebrates. Macmillan and Co., London.

Hanson, F. B. **1919.** The development of the sternum in *Sus scrofa.* Anat. Rec. **17**:1.

————. **1920a.** The development of the shoulder-girdle of *Sus scrofa.* Anat. Rec. **18**:1.

————. **1920b.** The history of the earliest stages in the human clavicle. Anat. Rec. **19**:309.

Jordan, H. E. **1939.** A study of fibrillogenesis in connective tissue by the method of dissociation with potassium hydroxide, with special reference to the umbilical cord of pig embryos. Am. J. Anat. **65**:229.

Kingsley, J. S. **1925.** The Vertebrate Skeleton. P. Blakiston's Son & Co., Philadelphia.

Lewis, W. H. **1922.** Is mesenchyme a syncytium? Anat. Rec. **23**:177.

Mall, F. P. **1902.** On the development of the connective tissues from the connective-tissue syncytium. Am. J. Anat. **1**:329.

Maximow, A. **1929.** Über die Entwicklung argyrophiler und kollagener Fasern in Kulturen von erwachsenem Säugetiergewebe. Jahrb. f. Morph. u. Mikr. Anat. Abt. II. **17**:625.

———— and Bloom, W. **1942.** A Textbook of Histology. W. B. Saunders Co., Philadelphia.

Rasmussen, A. T. **1923.** The so-called hibernating gland. J. Morphol. **38**:147.

Shaw, H. B. **1901.** A contribution to the study of the morphology of adipose tissue. J. Anat. & Physiol. **36**: (New series, 16) :1.

Sheldon, E. F. **1924.** The so-called hibernating gland in mammals: a form of adipose tissue. Anat Rec. **28**:331.

Stearns, M. L. **1940.** Studies on the development of connective tissue in transparent chambers in the rabbit's ear. Part II. Am. J. Anat. **67**:55.

Schreiner, K. E. **1915.** Über Kern- und Plasmaveränderungen in fettzellen während des fettansatzes. Anat. Anz. **48**:145.

Terry, R. J. **1942.** The articulations. Morris' Human Anatomy, Blakiston, Philadelphia.

16

The Muscular System

A. Introduction

1. DEFINITION

The muscular system produces mobility of the various body parts. As such, it is composed of cells specialized in the execution of that property of living matter which is known as **contractility.** Since contractility is a generalized property of living matter, it may occur without the actual differentiation of muscular tissue. In the developing heart of the chick, for example, contractures begin to occur as early as 33 to 38 hours of incubation before muscle cells, as such, have differentiated (Patten and Kramer, '33).

2. GENERAL STRUCTURE OF MUSCLE TISSUE

Muscle cells are elongated, fibrillated structures, known as **muscle fibers.** They contain many elongated **fibrils,** called **myofibrils,** extending longitudinally along the muscle fiber. The myofibrils may possess a series of **cross striations** in the form of light and dark transverse bands as in **skeletal or striated muscle** and **cardiac muscle,** or the transverse bands may be absent as in **smooth muscle** (fig. 325A–C). In smooth muscle, the myofibrils are extremely fine, whereas in striated muscle they are seen readily under the microscope.

a. Skeletal Muscle

In skeletal muscle, the muscle fibers are elongated, cylinder-shaped structures; the ends are rounded; and a row of nuclei extend along the periphery of the muscle fiber or cell, and are more numerous at the ends of the cell than in the central portion. The cell, as a whole, is filled with myofibrils, embedded in a matrix of **sarcoplasm.** The latter contains fat droplets, glycogen, interstitial granules, amino acids, mitochondria, and Golgi substances. The surrounding cell membrane is a delicate structure and is known as the **sarcolemma.**

The myofibrils are composed of dark and light transverse bands, a dark band alternating with a light band. The bands are arranged along the myofibrils in such a manner that the dark band of one fibril is at the same level as the dark bands of other fibrils. The light bands are arranged similarly. This arrangement presents the effect shown in figure 325A.

Two types of muscle fibers are found in skeletal muscle. In one type, the **red or dark fiber,** there is an abundance of sarcoplasm with fewer myofibrils. The myofibrils possess weaker transverse markings or striations. In the second type, the **pale or white fiber,** there is less of the sarcoplasm present with a larger number of highly differentiated myofibrils, having well-defined transverse striations. This muscle fiber is larger in transverse diameter than the red type. In many animals, such as man, these two sets of fibers are intermingled in the various skeletal muscles, but in some, such as the breast muscles of the common fowl, the white fibers constitute most of the muscle. Also, in the **M. quadratus femoris** of the cat or the **M. semitendinosus** of the rabbit, the red fiber predominates. In general, the more continuously active muscles contain the greater number of red fibers, while the less continuously active contain pale fibers. Pale fibers react more quickly and thus contract more readily than the red fibers. However, they are exhausted more rapidly.

Connective tissue, mostly of the white fibrous variety, associates the muscle fibers (cells) into groups called muscles. Muscles, such as the **Mm. biceps brachii, biceps femoris, sartorius, rectus abdominis,** etc., are a mass of associated muscle fibers, tied together by connective-tissue fibers.

The surrounding connective tissue of a particular muscle is known as the **external perimysium** (fig. 325D). The external perimysium extends centralward into the muscle and separates it into smaller bundles of fibers, or **fasciculi.** Thus each fasciculus is a group of muscle fibers, surrounded by the **internal perimysium.** The perimysium around each fasciculus extends into the fasciculus between the muscle cells, where its fibers become associated with the sarcolemma of each muscle fiber (cell).

The connection between the muscle fibers and their tendinous attachment has attracted considerable interest. One view holds that the myofibrils pass directly into the tendinous fibers. An alternative and more popular view maintains, however, that it is the sarcolemma which attaches directly to the tendinous fibers. Hence, the pull of the muscle is transmitted through the sarcolemmas of the various muscle cells to the tendon.

b. Cardiac Muscle

Cardiac muscle is characterized by the presence of alternating dark and light bands as in skeletal muscle. The striations are not as well developed, however, as in skeletal muscle, nor is the sarcolemma around the muscle fibers as thick. Another distinguishing feature of cardiac muscle is the fact that the fibers anastomose and thus form a syncytium, although M. R. Lewis ('19) questions this interpretation. Still another characteristic structure of cardiac muscle is the presence of the **intercalated discs** (fig. 325C). These discs are heavy transverse bands which extend across the fiber at variable distances from one another. A final feature which distinguishes cardiac muscle is the central location of the nuclei within the anastomosing fibers.

c. Smooth Muscle

Smooth muscle fibers are elongated, spindle-shaped elements which may vary in length from about 0.02 mm. to 0.5 mm. The larger fibers are found in the pregnant uterus. The diameter across the middle of the fiber approximates 4 to 7 μ. This middle area contains the single nucleus. The fiber tapers gradually from the middle area and may terminate in a pointed or slightly truncate tip (fig. 325B).

Smooth muscle cells may contain two kinds of fibrils:

(1) **fine myofibrils,** presumably concerned with contraction phenomena, within the cytoplasm and

(2) **myoglial** or border fibrils, coarser than the myofibrils, in the peripheral areas of the cell.

The myoglial fibrils are not usually demonstrable in adult tissues.

A connective-tissue mass of fibers between the smooth muscle fibers which binds the fibers into bundles as in skeletal muscle is not readily demonstrated. It may be that a kind of adhesiveness or stickiness (Lewis, W. H., '22) associates these muscle fibers into a mass, within which each muscle cell is a distinct entity and not part of a syncytium. However, around the muscle bundles, elastic and white fibers (Chap. 15) seem to hold the muscle tissue in place and some elastic fibers may be present between the cells, especially in blood vessels.

B. Histogenesis of Muscle Tissues

1. SKELETAL MUSCLE

The primitive embryonic cell which gives origin to the later muscle cells is called a **myoblast.** The myoblasts which give origin to skeletal muscle fibers are derived from two sources:

(1) **mesenchyme** and

(2) **myotomes.**

(See Chap. 11 for origin of mesenchyme and myotomes; also consult fig. 252.)

In striated-muscle-fiber formation, the myoblasts begin to elongate and eventually produce cylinder-like structures. As the cell continues to elongate, the nuclei increase in number, and, hence, the myoblast becomes converted into a multinuclear affair in which the nuclei at first lie centrally along the axis of the cell. Later, the myofibrils increase, and the nuclei move peripherally.

As the myofibrils grow older, dark and light areas appear along the fibrils. These dark and light bands are shown in figure 325E. Observe that the light band is bisected by the slender membrane, known as **Krause's membrane,** shown in the figure as the dark line, Z., and the dark band is bisected by **Hensen's membrane.**

2. CARDIAC MUSCLE

The musculature of the vertebrate heart takes its origin from the two mesial walls of hypomeric mesoderm (i.e., the splanchnic layers of mesoderm) which come to surround the **endocardial primordia** or primitive blood capillaries coursing anteriad below the foregut (Chap. 17). These two enveloping layers of mesoderm give origin to the **epicardium** and **myocardium** of the heart, and in consequence they are referred to as the **epimyocardial rudiment.** From the surfaces of the two layers of hypomeric mesoderm which face the primitive blood capillaries, mesenchymal cells are given off. These mesenchymal cells constitute the **myocardial primordium.** The outer wall of each hypomeric layer of mesoderm, however, retains its epithelial character and eventually gives origin to the epicardium or **coelomic covering** of the heart. The mesenchymal cells which form the myocardial primordium surround the two endocardial rudiments (blood capillaries) and later form an aggregate of coalesced cells, i.e., a **syncytium.** The future heart musculature arises from this syncytium.

As the mass of the myocardial syncytium increases in size, the nuclei become irregularly scattered, and myofibrils make their appearance. The number of myofibrils rapidly increases, and dark bands of **anisotropic substance** (i.e., substance which is doubly refractive under polarized light) alternate with lighter bands of **isotropic substance.** Z lines soon appear which bisect the lighter segment of the myofibrils.

The myofibrils increase, and the myocardial syncytium gradually becomes drawn out into elongated strands of cytoplasm which appear to anastomose (fig. 325C). The nuclei are scattered within these strands. As the myofibrils

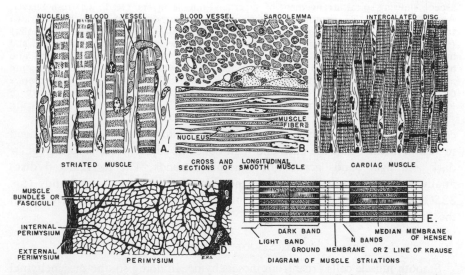

FIG. 325. Structure of the three types of muscle tissue. (All figures redrawn from Bremer (1936), *Textbook of Histology,* Philadelphia, Blakiston.) (A) Skeletal or striated muscle fibers. Observe that nuclei lie at the periphery of the muscle fibers. (B) Smooth muscle fibers. Upper part of figure shows fibers cut transversely, while lower part represents a longitudinal view of separate fibers. (C) Cardiac muscle. Observe that the fibers appear to anastomose; intercalated discs shown as dark, transverse bands. (D) Connective tissue contributions to skeletal muscle tissue. (E) Diagram of muscle striations. (After Heidenhain.)

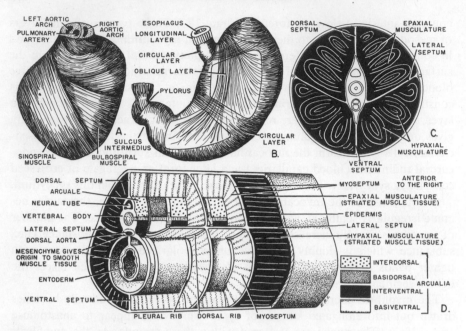

FIG. 326. Arrangement of muscle tissues. (A) Ventricles of alligator heart, ventral aspect, showing spiral arrangement of superficial muscle layers. (Redrawn from Shaver, Anat. Rec., 29.) (B) Arrangement of smooth muscle layers of the stomach. (Redrawn from Bremer, 1936, *Textbook of Histology,* Philadelphia, Blakiston, after Spalteholz.) (C) Transverse section of tail of *Squalus acanthias* showing arrangement of epaxial and hypaxial muscle groups. (D) Primitive arrangement of myotomes into epaxial and hypaxial groups in relation to the myocommata or myosepta. Observe that the myoseptum attaches to the middle of the vertebra. (Redrawn and modified from Goodrich, *Vertebrate Craniata,* 1909, New York, Macmillan Co., and Kingsley, *Comparative Anatomy of Vertebrates,* 1912, Philadelphia, Blakiston.)

continue to increase, they become aggregated into groups and are arranged in such a manner that the dark and light bands of adjacent fibrils form regular dark and light bands across the muscular strands. The **intercalated discs** finally make their appearance here and there across the muscle strands (fig. 325C). In some areas, there are no nuclei within the muscle strand between the intercalated discs.

3. SMOOTH MUSCLE

Smooth muscle cells arise from mesenchyme. In doing so, the mesenchymal cells lose their stellate shapes, elongate, and eventually become spindle shaped. Accompanying these changes, the nuclei experience some extension in the direction of the elongating cells (fig. 325B). Fibrils appear in the cytoplasm, first at the periphery in the form of coarse fibers, to be followed somewhat later by the true myofibrils of finer texture. It is possible that the coarser fibrils, the so-called myoglial fibers, represent bundles of myofibrils. The myofibrils in smooth muscle fibers do not assume anisotropic (dark) and isotropic (light) bands or cross striations. Increase in the number of muscle fibers (cells) appears to occur by the mitotic division of existing fibers and also by the transformation of other mesenchymal cells.

C. Morphogenesis of the Muscular System

1. MUSCULATURE ASSOCIATED WITH THE VISCERA OF THE BODY

The musculature associated with the viscera of the body is of the smooth type with the exception of cardiac muscle and anterior part of the esophagus. Smooth and cardiac musculature are under involuntary control. The smooth muscle tissue of the digestive tract is derived from mesenchyme, which arises from the inner or splanchnic layers of the hypomeres, while that of the urinary and genital systems takes its origin from nephrotomic mesoderm and contributions from the splanchnic layers of the two hypomeres (fig. 311A, B). The smooth muscle tissue associated with many of the blood vessels of the body arises from mesenchymal sources in the immediate area of the blood vessels.

The arrangement of muscle tissue in various parts of the digestive tract, blood vessels, and urinary and reproductive ducts is generally in the form of circular and longitudinal layers (fig. 325B). On the other hand, the myocardium or muscle tissue of the heart is an association of layers or sheets which tend to be wound in complex spirals. Particularly is this true of the ventricular portion of the heart (fig. 326A). Also, in the stomach, the arrangement of the muscle layers is complex, being composed of an outer longitudinal layer, a middle circular layer, and an inner, somewhat spirally arranged, oblique layer (fig. 326B). The general pattern of arrangement of smooth and cardiac muscle tissues shows much similarity throughout the vertebrate group.

2. MUSCULATURE OF THE SKELETON

The skeletal musculature is striated and under voluntary control. It is that musculature which moves various parts of the endoskeleton and integumental structures, enabling the animal to adapt itself to surrounding environmental conditions. The development of skeletal musculature will be described under the following headings:

(a) development of trunk and tail muscles,
(b) development of muscles of the head-pharyngeal area,
(c) development of the musculature of the paired appendages, and
(d) development of the panniculus carnosus in Mammalia.

a. Development of Trunk and Tail Muscles

1) Characteristics of Trunk and Tail Muscles in Aquatic and Terrestrial Vertebrates. In endeavoring to understand the development of the trunk and tail musculature in the vertebrate group as a whole, it is important that one consider the environment in which the various species live, for *the trunk and tail musculature is adapted to the general functions of moving the animal in its particular habitat*. We may recognize three main environmental adaptations:

(1) **natatorial,**
(2) **terrestrial,** and
(3) **aerial.**

a) NATATORIAL ADAPTATIONS. Animals, adapted to swimming, possess a different arrangement of the musculature of the trunk and tail regions than do terrestrial and aerial forms. A transverse section through the tail of the dogfish, *Squalus acanthias,* demonstrates that the musculature is arranged around the vertebrae in a definite pattern. A **horizontal skeletogenous septum** extends outward from either side, dividing the muscles on each side of the vertebra into **epaxial and hypaxial groups,** and **dorsal and ventral septa** are present in the middorsal and midventral areas (fig. 326C).

Viewed laterally, the muscles are divided by transverse membranes, the muscle septa, myosepta, or **myocommata** (figs. 326D; 327A). The position of the myocomma corresponds to the intermyotomic (intersegmented) area observed in Chapter 15. Each myocomma is attached to the vertebral body (really several vertebral bodies). The myotomes (fig. 326D) lie in the segmented position between the myocommata and are attached to the latter. In the tail, both these groups of muscles are attached to the myocommata and the vertebrae, but, farther forward in the trunk, it is the epaxial group which is associated directly with the myocommata and the vertebrae, the hypaxial group being less direct in its contact with the vertebral column. (See fig. 311B.) In figure 327B, the myotomes and myosepta (myocommata) have a Z-shaped appearance because of a secondary modification during development.

It is evident, therefore, that in the shark, the skeletal muscles of the trunk and tail exist in the form of segments, each segment being divided into an upper epaxial and lower hypaxial component. This arrangement of the muscles and the attachment of the fibers to the myosepta, and thus through the myoseptum to the vertebra, produces a mechanism exceedingly well adapted to the side-to-side movement of the vertebral column so necessary during natation. The conditions present in the sharks are comparable to those of other fishes, and, in all, the epaxial musculature is exceedingly well developed.

b) TERRESTRIAL ADAPTATIONS. In the land-frequenting vertebrates, there is less development of and dependence upon the tail region and the dorsal or epaxial musculature for locomotive purposes. In consequence, the epaxial musculature is segregated on either side of the vertebrae in a dorsal position, while the hypaxial musculature and its derivatives in the bilateral appendages are expanded ventrally. The suppression of epaxial muscle development is carried to an extreme form in the **aerial adaptations** of the bird. In nonaquatic forms the tail musculature is greatly reduced, and in some forms is almost non-existent.

A consideration of the effect that locomotive habits have upon musculature development may be shown by a brief comparison of the musculature in a water-living amphibian, such as *Necturus,* and in a land-going adventurer, such as the frog. In *Necturus,* the dorsal (epaxial) musculature, the primitive **M. dorsalis trunci,** is more like that of the fish, with the muscle fibers attached to the myocommata (fig. 327C), although, contrary to the piscine condition, the muscle fibers close to the vertebrae are attached directly to the vertebrae, where they form short bundles. In the frog, the attachment of the epaxial musculature to the vertebrae is more extensive. Bundles of muscle fibers, the **Mm. intertransversarii,** pass between the vertebral transverse processes, while **Mm. interneurales** connect the transverse processes and spinous processes, respectively, of the vertebrae. A separate muscle, the **M. longissimus dorsi,** extending from the head to the urostyle, separates from the above-mentioned dorsal muscles (fig. 327D). Although a slight suggestion of myocommata may be present, there is little functional relationship of the myocommata to the vertebrae. Laterally, **Mm. coccygeo-sacralis and coccygeo-iliacus** also are present as differentiations of the dorsal musculature (fig. 327D). Therefore, a definite formation of special and individual muscles occurs in the dorsal or epaxial musculature of the frog, whereas in *Necturus,* the dorsal musculature tends to resemble the segmental myotomic condition of the fish. It is to be observed that the dorsal musculature of the frog is adapted to a land-going existence, while the dorsal musculature of *Necturus* is suited to swimming movements.

A further land adaptation is shown in many salamanders, such as the various species of *Desmognathus,* where the dorsal trunk musculature differentiates in the neck region into several muscles which insert upon the skull. The latter muscles permit lateral movements of the head.

Turning to the **hypaxial musculature,** we find that this musculature in *Necturus* also approaches the condition in fishes. Let us examine this musculature in more detail. In the midventral abdominal area, the fibers assume a primitive, strictly segmental, antero-posterior direction. These muscle bundles form the **M. rectus abdominis.** Along the lateral side of the body wall, the myosepta (myocommata) are retained between the segmented muscles. However, two layers of muscle fibers are present, an outer thick **M. obliquus externus,** whose fibers run postero-ventrally, and an inner thin layer, the **M. obliquus internus,** with fibers coursing antero-ventrally. Turning now to the frog, we find that a segmented **rectus abdominis** (M. rectus abdominis) is present. In each lateral body wall, an outer **external oblique muscle** (M. obliquus externus superficialis) runs postero-ventrally, while an **internal transverse muscle** (M. transversus) courses antero-ventrally (fig. 327D). In *Necturus* and the frog, therefore, the primitive myotomic condition of the hypaxial musculature of the shark is disrupted, and the myotomes tend to split into layers or sheets of muscles. This splitting is slight in *Necturus* and marked in the frog. Also, in the frog, the myocommata are displaced as a part of the muscular-skeletal mechanism, with the exception of the rectus abdominis muscle whose segmentation possibly is a secondary development.

In mammals (fig. 327E), the epaxial musculature is differentiated into a complex of muscles, extending from the sacral area anteriorly into the cervical region and connecting the various vertebrae with each other and the vertebral column with the ribs. The epaxial musculature in the trunk area of the bird is much less developed than it is in the mammal. The hypaxial musculature in both bird and mammal becomes separated into distinct layers, such as the external, internal oblique, and transversus muscles. **External and internal intercostal muscles** are present between the ribs. In the midventral area, the rectus abdominis muscle tends to retain its primitive segmentation.

It is noteworthy to observe that the external and internal intercostal muscles in the mammal appear much the same as the lateral body muscles in *Necturus,* particularly if we keep in mind the fact that ribs grow out into the myoseptal (myocommal) area (fig. 326D). The external intercostal muscles run postero-ventrally, while the internal intercostals pass antero-ventrally from one rib to the next (fig. 327E). The intercostal musculature of the mammal thus retains the primitive, segmented condition.

c) AERIAL ADAPTATIONS. The musculature of the bird is a highly differentiated organization of structures in which the primitive myotomic plan is greatly distorted. The epaxial musculature is reduced greatly over the trunk region, although well developed in the cervical area. Hypaxial musculature is present in the form of external and internal oblique, and transverse muscle layers. Very short rectus abdominis muscles are to be found. Aside from the intrinsic muscles of the limbs, a large percentage of the volume of the hypaxial

---

FIG. 327. Development of branchial and somitic muscles in various vertebrates. (A) Basic areas of the embryo from which skeletal muscle develops. The skeletal muscles of the limb buds are portrayed as masses of mesenchyme represented in this figure as stippled areas in the two limb buds. The origin of this mesenchyme varies in different vertebrates (see text). (B) Skeletal muscular development in the shark. The muscle tissue derived from the hyoid visceral arch is shown in black with white lines. Muscle tissue derivatives from the mandibular visceral arch are shown anterior to the black-white line areas of the hyoid musculature. (C) Same for *Necturus maculosus*. (D) Same for the frog. (E) Epaxial muscles and intercostal part of hypaxial muscles of cat. External intercostals mostly removed. The "masseter muscle," a derivative of the mandibular visceral arch tissue of the embryo, also is shown. (E') Superficial facial and platysma muscle distribution in the cat. These muscles are derivatives of the hyoid visceral and mesenchyme. (E") External pterygoid muscle in the cat, another derivative of the branchial arch mesenchyme. (F) Anterior muscles of the goose. The muscles derived from the primitive hyoid visceral arch are shown in black with white lines. (Adapted from Huber, 1930, Quart. Rev. Biol., vol. 5, and from Fürbringer, 1888, Morphologie und Systematik der Vögel, van Holkema, Amsterdam.) (F') The temporal and masseter muscles in the common fowl. These muscles are derived from the mandibular visceral arch.

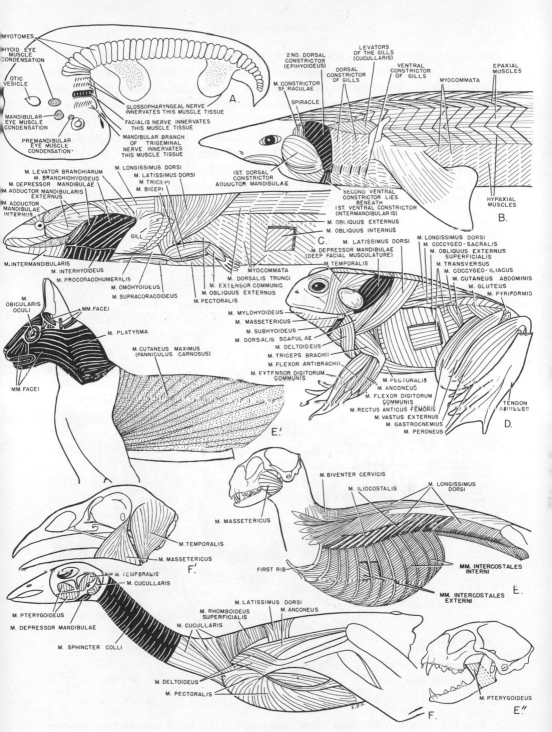

FIG. 327. (*See facing page for legend.*)

musculature of the bird is contained within the pectoral muscles (fig. 327F). As such the pectoral musculature represents an extreme adaptation to the flying habit. A somewhat similar adaptation is found among mammals, in the bat group. Myotomic metamerism is much less evident in the bird than in any other group of vertebrates, and the only remains of it appear in the intercostal muscles and some of the deeper muscles of the cervical area.

2) Development of Trunk and Tail Musculature: a) GENERAL FEATURES OF MYOTOMIC DIFFERENTIATION IN THE TRUNK. The muscles of the trunk are derived from the primitive myotomes. As described previously, Chapters 11, 12, and 15, the primitive body segment or somite differentiates into the

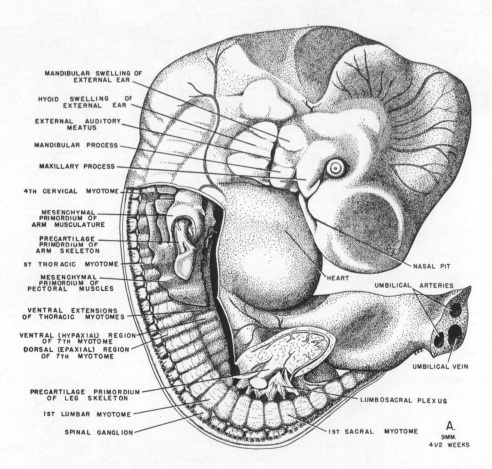

FIG. 328. Muscle development in the human embryo. (A and B redrawn from Bardeen and Lewis, 1901, Am. J. Anat., 1.) (A) Early division of truncal myotomes into dorsal (epaxial) and ventral (hypaxial) regions.

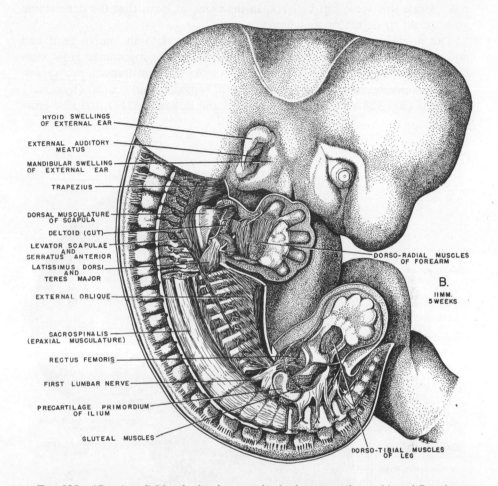

HYOID SWELLINGS
OF EXTERNAL EAR

EXTERNAL AUDITORY
MEATUS

MANDIBULAR SWELLING
OF EXTERNAL EAR

TRAPEZIUS

DORSAL MUSCULATURE
OF SCAPULA

DELTOID (CUT)

LEVATOR SCAPULAE
AND
SERRATUS ANTERIOR

LATISSIMUS DORSI
AND
TERES MAJOR

EXTERNAL OBLIQUE

SACROSPINALIS
(EPAXIAL MUSCULATURE)

RECTUS FEMORIS

FIRST LUMBAR NERVE

PRECARTILAGE PRIMORDIUM
OF ILIUM

GLUTEAL MUSCLES

DORSO-RADIAL MUSCLES
OF FOREARM

B.
11MM.
5 WEEKS

DORSO-TIBIAL MUSCLES
OF LEG

Fig. 328—*(Continued)* Muscle development in the human embryo. (A and B redrawn from Bardeen and Lewis, 1901, Am. J. Anat., 1.) (B) Differentiation of myotomal derivatives in 11-mm. embryo. Observe that the dorsal division of the spinal nerves is distributed to the epaxial musculature, while the lateral division of the ventral rami passes to the intercostal areas.

sclerotome, myotome, and dermatome (fig. 252). After the sclerotome has departed toward the median plane, the myotome and dermatome reconstruct the dermo-myotome which has a myocoelic cavity within (fig. 311A). The inner layer or myotome gives origin to the muscle fibers of the later myotome. The fate of the dermatome or cutis plate is not definite in all vertebrates. In lower vertebrates it is probable that most of the dermatome gives origin to dermal mesenchyme (Chap. 12). However, in mammals, according to Bardeen ('00) in his studies relative to the pig and human, the dermatome or cutis plate gives origin to muscle cells. On the other hand, Williams ('10) does not tolerate this view, but believes, in the chick at least, that the dermatome gives origin to dermal mesenchyme.

The primitive position of the myotome is lateral to the nerve cord and notochord. As development progresses, the individual myotomes grow ventrally toward the midventral line (fig. 327A). As this downgrowth progresses, each myotome becomes separated into dorsal (epaxial) and ventral (hypaxial) segments (fig. 328A). As indicated above and in figure 326D, the ribs grow

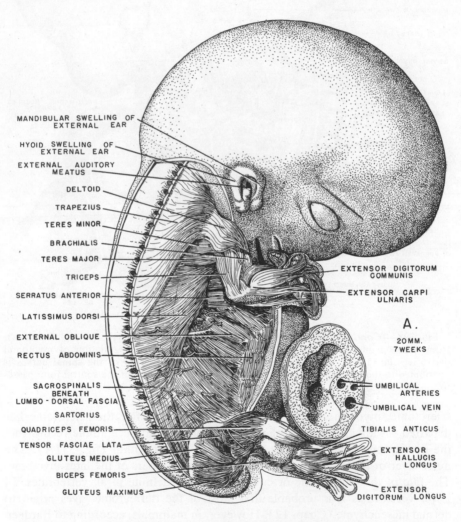

Fig. 329. Later development of musculature in human embryo. (A after Bardeen and Lewis, 1901, Am. J. Anat., 1.) (A) Limb and superficial trunk musculature of 20-mm. human embryo.

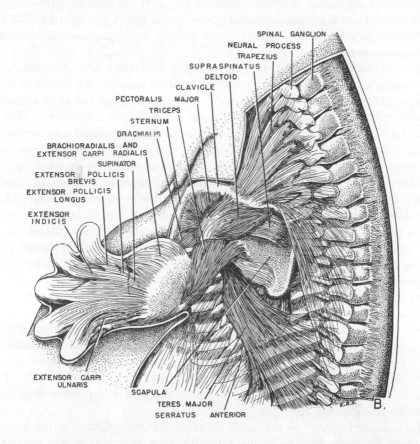

SPINAL GANGLION
NEURAL PROCESS
TRAPEZIUS
SUPRASPINATUS
DELTOID
CLAVICLE
PECTORALIS MAJOR
TRICEPS
STERNUM
BRACHIALIS
BRACHIORADIALIS AND EXTENSOR CARPI RADIALIS
SUPINATOR
EXTENSOR POLLICIS BREVIS
EXTENSOR POLLICIS LONGUS
EXTENSOR INDICIS
EXTENSOR CARPI ULNARIS
SCAPULA
TERES MAJOR
SERRATUS ANTERIOR

B.

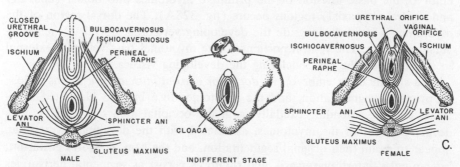

CLOSED URETHRAL GROOVE
BULBOCAVERNOSUS
ISCHIOCAVERNOSUS
ISCHIUM
PERINEAL RAPHE
LEVATOR ANI
SPHINCTER ANI
GLUTEUS MAXIMUS
MALE

CLOACA
INDIFFERENT STAGE

URETHRAL ORIFICE
VAGINAL ORIFICE
BULBOCAVERNOSUS
ISCHIOCAVERNOSUS
ISCHIUM
PERINEAL RAPHE
SPHINCTER ANI
LEVATOR ANI
GLUTEUS MAXIMUS
FEMALE
C.

FIG. 329—(*Continued*) Later development of musculature in human embryo. (B after Lewis, 1902, Am. J. Anat., 1.) (B) Developing forelimb musculature of human embryo (lateral aspect of limb). (C) Differentiation of cloacal musculature in human embryo.

713

out in the area occupied by the myocommata or connective tissue partitions between the myotomes, and thus ribs and myocommata are correlated intimately with myotomic differentiations in all lower vertebrates. However, in reptiles, birds, and mammals, the outgrowing ribs travel downward within the connective tissue between the myotomes, but the development of the mycommata are suppressed.

b) DIFFERENTIATION OF THE MYOTOMES IN FISHES AND AMPHIBIA. In the fishes, as the ventral myotomic progression occurs, the differentiating muscle fibers become united anteriorly and posteriorly to the myocommata. In *Necturus* and in amphibian larvae, in general, this relationship also is established, but, in addition, the myotomes become separated into sheets or layers. In the frog during metamorphosis, this *splitting* of myotomes and the *segregation* of separate layers and bundles of distinct muscles is carried further. Also in the frog, a marked *migration* of separate bundles of muscle fibers occurs, while the *fusion* of parts of separate myotomes is indicated in the development of the M. longissimus dorsi which superficially appears to be segmented (fig. 327D). There is a pronounced tendency, therefore, in the development of the frog musculature for the primitive myotomic plan to be distorted and myotomes fuse, split, degenerate or migrate to serve the required functional purpose of the various muscles.

c) DIFFERENTIATION OF THE TRUNCAL MYOTOMES IN HIGHER VERTEBRATA AND PARTICULARLY IN THE HUMAN EMBRYO. The principles of myotomic modification by fusion, splitting into separate components, migration of parts of myotomes away from the primitive position, and degeneration of myotomic structure as exemplified in the developing musculature of the frog, are utilized to great advantage in reptiles, birds and mammals. The end to be served in all instances is the adaptation of a particular muscle or muscles to a definite function.

In the development of the adult form of the musculature in the human embryo, the basic division of the primitive myotomes into dorsal (epaxial) and ventral (hypaxial) regions occurs (fig. 328A). The dorsal region of the myotomes is located alongside the developing vertebrae, dorsal to the transverse processes. The ventral portions of the myotomes pass ventrally external to and between the ribs, enclosing the developing viscera.

In a slightly older embryo, the *dorsal or epaxial musculature* begins to lose its primitive segmentation, and the myotomes fuse into an elongated myotomic column, extending caudally from the occipital area (fig. 328B). The deeper portions of the myotomes, associated with the developing vertebrae, appear to retain their original segmentation, and the **Mm. levatores costarum, interspinales, intertransversarii,** and **rotatores** persist as segmental derivatives of the myotomes. The outer layer of the dorsal or epaxial musculature splits lengthwise into an outer muscle group, the dorsally placed **Mm. longissimus dorsi and spinalis dorsi,** and a latero-ventral **Mm. iliocostalis** group (fig.

328B). (See Lewis, W. H., '10.) Between the above two major groups of muscles derived from the epaxial muscle column are other epaxial derivatives such as the **semispinalis** and **multifidus** muscles.

The *ventral or hypaxial portions* of the myotomes overlying the developing ribs fuse into a continuous mass, while the medial portions of the myotomes lying between the ribs give origin to the **Mm. intercostales interni and externi.** The ventral ends of the fused myotomes on either side of the midventral line split off longitudinally to form the **M. rectus abdominis** which becomes an elongated sheet, extending from the anterior pectoral area caudal to the differentiating pelvic girdle. The tendency toward segmentation of the two rectus abdominis muscles probably represents a secondary process in man. *Tangential splitting* of the fused thoracic and abdominal myotomes and migration of the fibers give origin to the **Mm. obliquus abdominis externus, obliquus abdominis internus, transversus abdominis, serratus posterior superior, and serratus posterior inferior.**

The *deep or subvertebral muscles* below the vertebral column in the dorsal area are derived from two sources. The **Mm. longus colli and longus capitis** arise from the migration of myotomic tissue to the ventral vertebral surfaces in the neck region, whereas the **Mm. iliopsoas** appear to be derived from the musculature of the hind limb (Lewis, W. H., '10).

d) Muscles of the Cloacal and Perineal Area. The muscle tissue of the cloaca forms a circle of constricting muscular bands which surround the cloacal opening. These muscular bands are derived from myotomic tissue of the posterior truncal region.

In the higher mammals, the primitive cloacal opening becomes divided during development into **anterior urogenital and posterior anal openings,** and the cloacal musculature is divided into the musculature associated with the urethra, external genital structures, and the anal sphincter (fig. 329C).

e) Development of the Musculature of the Tail Region. The musculature of the tail arises from the tail-bud mesoderm of the early embryo. This mesenchyme condenses to form myotomic concentrations which later divide into epaxial and hypaxial segments as in the truncal region of the body. These myotomic segments are well developed in all fishes and in the adults of amphibia other than the Anura. In fishes the enlarged condition of the epaxial and hypaxial muscles of the tail region coincides with the elongation of neural spines and hemal processes of the tail vertebrae where they serve the function of moving the caudal fin from side to side. Three main types of caudal fin skeletal arrangement in fishes (see fig. 331B–D) act as the framework for the fin which serves the relatively enormous propulsive force generated by the tail musculature.

In *Necturus,* in *Cryptobranchus,* and in other water-dwelling amphibians, and also in crocodilians, whales, etc., the tail musculature is developed to serve the natatorial function which requires a lateral movement of the tail.

On the other hand, the prehensile or grasping movement of the tail of the opossum, or the tails of western-hemisphere monkeys necessitates an extreme adaptation on the part of individual muscle bundles and their attachment to the caudal vertebrae. Similar specializations are found in the writhing tail of the cat group. The wagging movement of the tail of the dog or the swishing motion of the tails of cows, horses and other mammals is the result of the activities of the **Mm. abductor caudae internus and abductor caudae externus** which appear to be derivatives of the hind-limb musculature.

b. Development of Muscles of the Head-pharyngeal Area

1) Extrinsic Muscles of the Eye. The extrinsic muscles of the eyeball are one of the most constant features of vertebrate morphology. Six muscles for each eye are found in all gnathostomes, innervated by three cranial nerves as follows:

(1) M. rectus superior—cranial nerve III,
(2) M. rectus internus or anterius—cranial nerve III,
(3) M. rectus inferior—cranial nerve III,
(4) M. rectus externus (posterius or lateralis)—cranial nerve VI,
(5) M. obliquus superior—cranial nerve IV, and
(6) M. obliquus inferior—cranial nerve III.

To these muscles may be added the **Mm. retractor oculi** of many mammals and the **Mm. quadratus** and **pyramidalis** of birds.

In the shark group, the muscles of the eye arise from three pre-otic somites or *head cavities,* namely, the **pre-mandibular, mandibular** and **hyoid somites** (figs. 253, 327A). The pre-mandibular somite, innervated by the **oculomotorius** or third cranial nerve, gives origin to all of the rectus muscles with the exception of the **Mm. rectus externus.** The **Mm. obliquus inferior** also arises from the pre-mandibular somite. From the mandibular somite, innervated by the **trochlearis** or fourth cranial nerve, arises the **Mm. obliquus superior,** while the hyoid somite gives origin to the **Mm. rectus externus** (Balfour, 1878; Platt, 1891; Neal, '18). A derivation of eye muscles from three pre-otic somites or mesodermal condensations has been described in the gymnophionan amphibia by Marcus ('09), in the turtle by Johnson ('13), in the chick by Adelmann ('26, '27), and in the marsupial mammal, *Trichosurus,* by Fraser ('15). For extensive references regarding the eye-forming somites or mesodermal condensations, see Adelmann ('26, and '27).

Various disagreements, concerning the presence or absence of the various head somites and the origin of the eye muscles therefrom, are to be found in the literature. Regardless of this lack of uniformity of agreement, it is highly probable that the premuscle masses of tissue which give origin to the eye muscles in the gnathostomous vertebrates, in general, adhere closely to the pattern of the eye-muscle development from three pre-otic pairs of somites as manifested in the shark embryo.

2) **Muscles of the Visceral Skeleton and Post-branchial area:** a) Tongue and Other Hypobranchial Musculature. As indicated in figures 253 and 327A, a variable number of **post-otic** or **met-otic somites** are concerned with the composition of the head of the gnathostomous vertebrate. In the dogfish, *Squalus acanthias,* about six pairs of post-otic somites contribute to the structure of the head (De Beer, '22). For most vertebrates, about three pairs of post-otic somites, a conservative estimate, appear to enter into the head's composition. The hypobranchial musculature in the elasmobranch embryo arises as myotomal buds from the myotomes of posterior head area. These muscle buds migrate ventrad from these myotomes to the hypobranchial region as indicated in figure 253. Associated with this migration of myotomal material is the migration and distribution of the **hypoglossal nerve,** compounded from the ventral roots of post-otic spinal nerves to this area (fig. 253). In the human, W. H. Lewis ('10) favors the view that the tongue musculature arises in situ from the hypobranchial mesenchyme, but Kingsbury ('15) suggests the post-otic origin of the tongue musculature for all vertebrates. Regardless of its origin, the tongue musculature is innervated by ventral nerve roots of post-otic segments in higher vertebrates, i.e., the **hypoglossal or twelfth cranial nerve.** The tongue musculature becomes associated with the basihyal portion of the hyoid arch, which acts as its support. In mammals, the **sternohyoid, sternothyroid,** and **omohyoid** muscles are innervated also by the hypoglossal or twelfth cranial nerve. These muscles probably arise from the post-otic myotomes in a manner similar to the tongue musculature.

b) Musculature of the Mandibular Visceral Arch. The mesoderm, associated with this arch, gives origin to the muscles of mastication, and as a result these muscles are innervated by special visceral motor fibers located in the **trigeminal or fifth cranial nerve.** In the shark, the muscles arising from the mandibular visceral arch tissue are the **adductor mandibulae** and the **first ventral constrictor** muscles (fig. 327B); in the frog, the **temporal, masseter, pterygoid,** and **mylohyoid** muscles; in the chick, the **pterygotemporal, temporal,** and **digastric** muscles; and, in mammals, the **temporal, masseter, pterygoid,** anterior portion of the **digastric, mylohoid, tensor tympani,** and **tensor veli palatini** muscles (fig. 327D, E', E", F, F').

c) Musculature of the Hyoid Visceral Arch. The musculature, which develops from mesenchyme associated with the embryonic hyoid arch, becomes distributed as indicated in figures 327 and 330. It is to be observed that, in the adult shark (fig. 327B), this musculature functions in relation to the hyoid arch. In the adult frog (fig. 327D), it is represented by deep facial musculature or the **depressor mandibulae** and **subhyoideus** muscles. In the adult goose (fig. 327F), it is present as the **M. sphincter colli,** which represents superficial facial musculature, and the **M. depressor mandibulae** or deep facial musculature. In mammals (figs. 327E′; 330A–D), the muscles derived from the hyoid arch is distributed over the cervico-facial area as many separate muscles. The musculature derived from the hyoid arch is innervated by the seventh or facial cranial nerve. Reference may be made to the extensive review of the literature by Huber ('30, a and b), relative to the facial musculature in vertebrates.

d) MUSCULATURE OF THE FIRST BRANCHIAL ARCH. The musculature of the first branchial arch is innervated by the **glossopharyngeal or ninth cranial nerve.** In the shark, the muscle tissue arising from the first branchial arch becomes the constrictor musculature of this arch, but, in the mammal, it gives origin to the **stylopharyngeus** muscle and to the **constrictors** of the pharynx.

e) MUSCLES OF THE SUCCEEDING VISCERAL ARCHES. In the shark, these muscles contribute to the constrictor muscles of the gill arches and are under the domain of the vagus or tenth cranial nerve. In the mammal, this muscle tissue becomes associated with the **larynx** and with the constrictors of the **pharynx.**

f) MUSCLES ASSOCIATED WITH THE SPINAL ACCESSORY OR ELEVENTH CRANIAL NERVE. The **sternocleidomastoid** and **trapezius musculature** in the human, according to W. H. Lewis ('10), arises from a premuscle mass associated at the caudal end of the pharyngeal area below the post-otic myotomes (fig. 336A). With the musculature arising from this premuscle mass, the **spinal accessory or eleventh cranial nerve** becomes associated. The trapezius musculature migrates extensively over the scapular area (fig. 329A).

g) MUSCULATURE OF THE MAMMALIAN DIAPHRAGM. The striated musculature of the mammalian diaphragm appears to arise from the ventral portions of the myotomes in the midcervical area. In the human, this diaphragmatic musculature is innervated by the ventral roots of cervical nerves IV and V, while, in the cat, cervical nerves V and VI are involved. These ventral rami give origin to the **phrenic nerve,** which later migrates posteriad with the diaphragmatic musculature together with the developing diaphragm during the division of the coelomic cavities (Chap. 20).

c. Development of the Musculature of the Paired Appendages

Two main theories have arisen relative to the origin of the paired appendages. One is the *gill-arch theory* of Gegenbauer (1876) and the *fin-fold* or *lateral-fold theory* of Balfour (1881). According to the theory of Gegenbauer, the limb girdles are modified gill arches, and the limb tissue itself represents a modification of the gill septa and supporting gill rays. The pelvic limbs were produced, according to this theory, by a backward migration of the gill arch involved. The lateral-fold theory, on the other hand, postulated that the paired limbs were derived from longitudinal fin folds. The endoskeleton within the

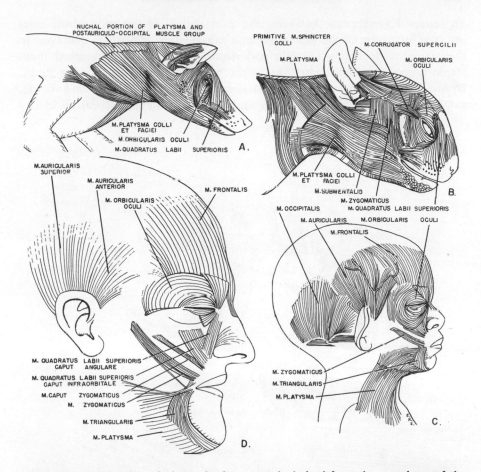

FIG. 330. Facial and cervical muscles in mammals derived from the mesoderm of the hyoid arch. (Redrawn from Huber, 1930, Quart. Rev. Biol., 5.) (A) Opossum *(Didelphys).* (B) Cat *(Felis).* (C) New-born baby (white) human. (D) Adult (white) human.

fold arose as a support for the fold in a manner similar to the median fins. The latter theory has the greatest number of adherents today.

The early development of the rudiments of the paired appendages and the properties of the limb field are discussed in Chapter 10, page 508. Relative to the developing limb, the exact origin of the cells which go to make up its intrinsic musculature has been the object of much study. In the elasmobranch and teleost fishes, muscle buds from the myotomes in the vicinity of the developing fin fold unquestionably contribute dorsal and ventral premuscle masses of cells to the limb, which give origin respectively to

1) the *dorsal, elevator and extensor muscles,* and
2) the *ventral depressor* and *adductor* muscles of the fin.

In tetrapod vertebrates, however, the exact origin of the cells which enter into the formation of the limb's intrinsic musculature is open to question. In the amphibia, including *Urodela* and *Anura*, Field (1894) described myotomic processes which contribute to the musculature of the anterior limbs. Byrnes (1898), working experimentally with the same group, and W. H. Lewis ('10b) deny this conclusion and affirm the somatopleural or in situ

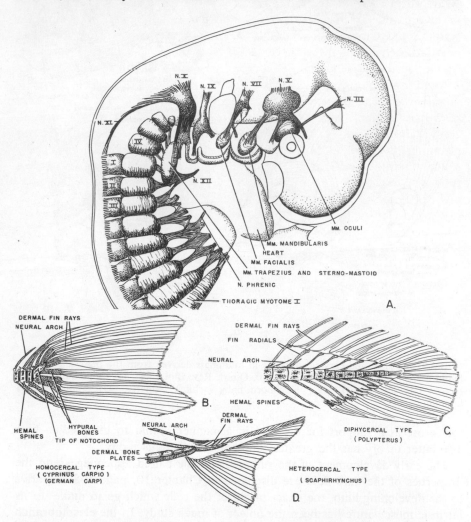

Fig. 331. (A) Innervation of premuscle masses in head and pharyngeal areas, and of myotomes in the cervical and caudal head regions of 7-mm. human embryos. Four post-otic (occipital) myotomes and the premuscle mass of the trapezius and sterno-mastoid muscles are shown just back of the tenth cranial nerve. The first cervical myotome and spinal nerve are shown just posterior to the fourth occipital myotome. (Redrawn from W. H. Lewis, 1910, chap. 12 in *Manual of Human Embryology*, vol. I, by F. Keibel and F. P. Mall, Philadelphia, Lippincott.) (B, C, D) Types of caudal fins in fishes.

origin of the limb musculature and connective tissues. Similar affirmations and denials are found in the literature, relative to origin of the intrinsic limb muscles in higher vertebrates, including man. For example, Ingalls ('07) described myotomic cell migrations into the developing human limb, whereas W. H. Lewis ('10a) was not able to subscribe to this view.

Although actual muscle tissue from the myotomes to the limb buds cannot be traced in all cases, the fact remains that the nerve supply to a myotome or to a particular group of muscle-forming cells appears to be a constant feature. For example, the facial musculature, which is derived from the hyoid arch mesenchyme of the embryo as set forth above, retains its innervation by the facial or seventh cranial nerve, even though the muscle migrates far forward from its original site of development. The innervation of the trapezius muscle by the spinal accessory nerve is another example of this same fidelity of the nerve supply to the original site of the origin of the muscle-forming cells. Mall (1898, p. 348) describes this relationship between the nerves and myotomes as follows: "As the segmental nerves appear, each is immediately connected with its corresponding myotome, and all of the muscles arising from a myotome are always innervated by branches of the nerve which originally belonged to it." (See fig. 331A.)

The development of the musculature of the tetrapod limb involves two main premuscle masses of tissue:

(1) An **intrinsic mass of muscle-forming mesenchyme** within the developing limb which condenses to form separate muscle-forming associations of cells around the developing skeleton of the limb. Each of these cellular associations then proceeds to differentiate into a particular muscle or closely integrated group of muscles (figs. 328B; 329A and B). That is, the intrinsic mass of muscle-forming tissue gives origin to the intrinsic musculature of the limb.

(2) An **extrinsic mass of premuscle tissue** which ultimately gives origin to the musculature which attaches the limb and its girdle to the axial skeleton. This premuscle tissue arises from two sources:

(a) Premuscle tissue from the limb bud which migrates from the limb bud proximally toward the axial skeleton. In the forelimb, the pectoral, latissimus dorsi, and teres major muscles develop from this mass of tissue, while in the hind-limb the caudo-femoralis, iliopsoas, piriformis, and certain of the gluteal muscles appear to arise from muscle-forming tissue which extends axially to unite the limb with the axial skeleton.

(b) Premuscle tissue which arises outside the limb bud mesenchyme. The muscles which arise from this tissue serve to attach the limb girdle to the axial skeleton. From premuscle tissue of this type arise the Mm. trapezius, sternocleidomastoideus, rhomboidei, levator scapulae, serratus anterior, and omohyoideus.

d. Panniculus Carnosus

There are two groups of skeletal "skin muscles," that is, muscles under voluntary control which move the skin and skin structures. One group is the **mimetic or facial musculature,** described on page 717 and originating from the primitive hyoid mesoderm; the other is the **panniculus carnosus,** found only in the *Mammalia* and derived embryologically from the tissue which forms the pectoral musculature. The facial musculature is innervated by cranial nerve VII or the **facial** nerve, while the panniculus carnosus receives its innervation from the **anterior thoracic** nerves (fig. 327E′).

The panniculus carnosus is highly developed in the guinea pig and porcupine and, although less developed in the rabbit, cat, dog, and horse, it forms a prominent muscular layer. The fibers may be divided into two groups:

(a) fibers which arise and insert in the superficial fascia of the skin and
(b) fibers that arise in the superficial fascia of the back and thigh and converge toward the greater tuberosity of the humerus, where they insert.

For extensive references and descriptions, see Langworthy ('24 and '25).

Bibliography

Adelmann, H. B. **1926.** The development of the premandibular head cavities and the relations of the anterior end of the notochord in the chick and robin. J. Morphol. **42**:371.

———. **1927.** The development of the eye muscles of the chick. J. Morphol. **44**:29.

Balfour, F. M. **1878.** A monograph on the development of elasmobranch fishes. Chap. X in The Works of Francis Maitland Balfour. Edited by M. Foster and A. Sedgwick. Vol. 1, 1885. Macmillan and Co., London.

———. **1881.** On the development of the skeleton of the paired fins of elasmobranchii, considered in relation to its bearings on the nature of the limbs of the *Vertebrata*. Chap. XX in The Works of Francis Maitland Balfour. Edited by M. Foster and A. Sedgwick. Vol. 1, 1885. Macmillan and Co., London.

Bardeen, C. R. **1900.** The development of the musculature of the body wall in the pig. Johns Hopkins Hospital Reports. **9**:367.

Byrnes, E. F. **1898.** Experimental studies on the development of limb-muscles in *Amphibia.* J. Morphol. **14**:105.

De Beer, G. R. **1922.** The segmentation of the head in *Squalus acanthius.* Quart. J. Micr. Sc. **66**:457.

Field, H. H. **1894.** Die Vornierenkapsel, ventrale Musculatur und Extremitätenanlagen bei den Amphibien. Anat. Anz. **9**:713.

Fraser, E. A. **1915.** The head cavities and development of the eye muscles in *Trichosurus vulpecula* with notes on some other marsupials. Proc. Zool. Soc., London, sA. 299.

Gegenbaur, C. **1876.** Zur morphologie der Gliedmaassen der Wirbelthiere. Morph. Jahrb, **2**:396.

Huber, E. **1930a.** Evolution of facial musculature and cutaneous field of Trigeminus. Part I. Quart. Rev. Biol. **5**:133.

———. **1930b.** Evolution of facial musculature and cutaneous field of Trigeminus. Part I. Quart. Rev. Biol. **5**:389.

Ingalls, N. W. **1907.** Beschreibung eines menschlichen Embryos von 4:9mm. Arch. f. mikr. Anat. u. Entwicklngsgesch. **70**:506.

Johnson, C. E. **1913.** The development of the prootic head somites and eye muscles in *Chelydra serpentina*. Am. J. Anat. **14:**119.

Kingsbury, B. F. **1915.** The development of the human pharynx. Part I. The pharyngeal derivatives. Am. J. Anat. **18:**329.

Langworthy, O. R. **1924.** The panniculus carnosus in cat and dog and its genetical relationship to the pectoral musculature. J. Mammalogy. **5:**49.

————. **1925.** A morphological study of the panniculus carnosus and its genetical relationship to the pectoral musculature in rodents. Am. J. Anat. **35:**283.

Lewis, M. R. **1919.** The development of cross-striations in the heart muscle of the chick embryo. Johns Hopkins Hosp. Rep. **30:**176.

Lewis, W. H. **1910a.** Chap. 12, Development of the Muscular System in Human Embryology. Edited by Keibel and Mall. J. B. Lippincott Co., Philadelphia.

————. **1910b.** The relation of the myotomes to the ventrolateral musculature and to the anterior limbs in Amblystoma. Anat. Rec. **4:**183.

————. **1922.** The adhesive quality of cells. Anat. Rec. **23:**387.

Mall, F. P. **1898.** Development of the ventral abdominal walls in man. J. Morphol. **14:347.**

Marcus, H. **1909.** Beiträge zur Kenntnis der Gymnophionen. III. Zur Entwicklungsgeschichte des Kopfes. I Teil. Morph. Jahrb. **40:**105.

Neal, H. V. **1918.** The history of the eye muscles. J. Morphol. **30:**433.

Patten, B. M. and Kramer, T. C. **1933.** The initiation of contraction in the embryonic chick heart. Am. J. Anat. **53:**349.

Platt, J. B. **1891.** A contribution to the morphology of the vertebrate head, based on a study of *Acanthias vulgaris*. J. Morphol. **5:**79.

Williams, L. W. **1910.** The somites of the chick. Am. J. Anat. **11:**55.

17

The Circulatory System

A. Introduction
  1. Definition
  2. Major subdivisions of the circulatory system
B. Development of the basic features of the arteriovenous system
  1. The basic plan of the arteriovenous system
  2. Development of the primitive heart and blood vessels associated with the primitive gut
  3. Formation of the primitive blood vessels associated with the mesodermal and neural areas
  4. Regions of the primitive vascular system
C. Histogenesis of the circulatory system
  1. The heart
  2. Formation of the primitive vascular channels and capillaries
  3. Later development of blood vessels
    a. Arteries
    b. Veins
    c. Capillaries
  4. Hematopoiesis (Hemopoiesis)
    a. Theories of blood-cell origin
    b. Places of blood-cell origin
      1) Early embryonic origin of blood cells
      2) Later sites of blood-cell formation
      3) Characteristics of development of the erythrocyte
      4) Characteristics of various white blood cells
        a) Granulocytes
        b) Lymphoid forms
D. Morphogenesis of the circulatory system
  1. Introduction
  2. Transformation of the converging veins of the early embryonic heart into the major veins which enter the adult form of the heart
    a. Alteration of the primitive converging veins of the heart in the shark, *Squalus acanthias*
    b. Changes in the primitive converging veins of the heart in the anuran amphibia
      1) The vitelline veins
      2) Lateral (ventral abdominal) veins
      3) Formation of the inferior vena cava
      4) Formation of the renal portal system
      5) Precaval veins

A. Introduction

1. DEFINITION

Living matter in its active state depends for its existence upon the beneficent flow of fluid materials through its substance. This passage of materials consists of two phases:

(1) the inflow of fluid, containing food materials and oxygen, and
(2) the outflow of fluid, laden with waste products.

In the vertebrate group as a whole, the inflow of materials to the body substance occurs through the epithelial membranes of the digestive, integumentary, and respiratory systems, while the outflow of materials is effected through the epithelial membranes of the excretory, respiratory, and skin surfaces. The passage of materials through the substance of the body lying between these two sets of epithelial membranes is made possible by (a) the blood and (b) a system of blood-conveying tubes or vessels. These structures form the **circulatory system.**

2. Major Subdivisions of the Circulatory System

The circulatory system is composed of two major subdivisions:

(1) the **arteriovenous system,** composed of the heart, arteries, and veins together with the blood vessels and capillaries of smaller dimensions intervening between the arteries and veins, and

(2) the **lymphatic system,** made up of lymph sacs, and lymphatic vessels together with specialized organs such as the **spleen, tonsils, thymus gland,** and **lymph nodes.** In larval and adult amphibia pulsating **lymph hearts** are a part of the lymphatic system. Lymph hearts are present also in the tail region of the chick embryo.

The lymphatic vessels parallel the vessels of the arteriovenous system, and one of their main functions appears to be to drain fluid from the small spaces within tissues as well as larger spaces, such as the various divisions of the coelomic cavity.

The blood within the arteriovenous system is composed of a fluid substance or **plasma** together with **red blood corpuscles or erythrocytes, white blood cells** of various types, and **blood platelets.** The latter are small protoplasmic bodies which may represent cytoplasmic fragments of the giant, bone-marrow cells or **megakaryocytes.** The blood within the lymphatic system is composed of a **vehicle** the **lymph fluid,** similar to the plasma of the arteriovenous blood system, together with various **white blood corpuscles.**

B. Development of the Basic Features of the Arteriovenous System

1. The Basic Plan of the Arteriovenous System

The primitive circulatory system is constructed of three main parts:

(1) two sets of simple **capillary tubes,** bilaterally developed on either side of the median line (fig. 332),

(2) a local modification of these tubes which forms the **rudimentary heart,** and

(3) **blood cells and fluid** contained within the tubes.

2. Development of the Primitive Heart and Blood Vessels Associated with the Primitive Gut

The primitive vascular tubes or capillaries form below the anterior region of the developing metenteron or gut tube in relation to the yolk sac or yolk-containing segment of the gut. Two sets of identical tubes begin to form, one set on either side of the median plane of the embryo (fig. 332A and B). Simultaneous with the formation of these primitive, **subintestinal blood capillaries,** the splanchnic layers of the two hypomeric portions of the mesodermal tubes grow mesiad to cup around the blood capillaries in the area *just posterior* *to the forming pharyngeal area of the gut tube* (figs. 234; 236D, E; 332F–M). This encirclement of the primitive blood capillaries by the splanchnic layers of the hypomeric mesoderm produces the rudimentary **tubular heart,** composed within of two **fused subintestinal capillaries** and without of modified **fused portions of the hypomeric mesoderm.** The modified portions of the hypomeric mesoderm form the **epimyocardial** rudiment of the heart, while the fused capillaries within establish the rudimentary **endocardium** (fig. 332F–M).

Proceeding anteriad from the area of primitive tubular heart, the blood capillaries establish the **primitive ventral aortae** (fig. 332A).

From the primitive ventral aortae, the two capillaries move forward toward the anterior end of the foregut where they diverge and pass dorsally, one on either side of the foregut, as the **first or mandibular pair of aortal arches.** In the dorsal area of the foregut the two primitive aortal arches pass inward toward the median plane and each aortal arch joins a primitive capillary which runs antero-posteriorly along the upper aspect of the developing gut tube. These two **supraintestinal blood vessels** are the rudiments of the future **dorsal aorta** and they are known as the **dorsal aortae.** They lie above the primitive gut and below the notochord. In the region where the mandibular pair of aortal arches joins the dorsal aortae, each primitive dorsal aorta sends a capillary sprout toward the developing eye region and the brain. This capillary forms the rudiment of the anterior end of the **internal carotid artery.** About the midregion of the developing midgut, each of the **dorsal aortae** sends off a lateral branch which connects with a series of capillaries in the yolk or yolk-sac area of the deveoping midgut. The vessels which diverge from the dorsal aorta to the yolk-sac region form the rudiments of the two **vitelline arteries.** The capillary network in the yolk region or yolk-sac area of the midgut in turn connect with the two subintestinal capillaries, previously mentioned, which enter the forming heart. The two latter blood vessels constitute the **vitelline veins** (fig. 332B). Meanwhile, successive pairs of aortal arches are formed posterior to the first pair, connecting the ventral aortae with the dorsal aortae (fig. 332D). These aortal arches pass through the substance of the visceral arches, as mentioned in Chapters 14 and 15.

3. FORMATION OF THE PRIMITIVE BLOOD VESSELS ASSOCIATED WITH THE MESODERMAL AND NEURAL AREAS

The system of blood vessels described above (fig. 232A) is developed in relation to the primitive gut tube. Very shortly, however, another system of vessels is established dorso-laterally to the mesodermal tubes. This second system of blood capillaries forms the beginning of the **cardinal system** (fig. 232B). The cardinal system is composed of **two anterior cardinal veins** which begin as a series of small capillaries on either side over the forming brain; from whence these veins proceed backward, one on either side over the branchial mesoderm, and lateral to the forming somites. These vessels eventually proceed latero-ventrad in their development along the outer lateral aspect of the somatopleural mesoderm to the caudal regions of the forming heart, where they turn ventrad along the outer aspect of the somatopleural layer of the hypomere. In the region where the anterior cardinal veins turn ventrad toward the heart region, each anterior cardinal vein is joined by a **posterior cardinal vein.** The latter proceeds forward from the posterior end of the developing embryo, lying along the outer aspect of the nephrotomic portion of the hypomere below the primitive epidermal tube (fig. 332B). The union of the anterior and posterior cardinal veins on either side forms the **common cardinal vein.** The latter travels postero-ventrally along the outer aspect of the somatopleure until it reaches the upper limits of the caudal region or **sinus venosus** of the developing heart. In this area, the splanchnopleural layer (epimyocardium) and the endocardial layer of the developing sinus venosus, *bulge laterad to fuse with the somatopleural layer of the hypomere.* This area of contact between the epimyocardial layer of the sinus venosus and somatopleural mesoderm produces a bridge across the coelomic space. The two posterior, dorso-lateral regions of the **sinus venosus** thus extend dorso-laterad on either side across the coelomic space to join the somatopleure. Each common cardinal vein perforates through the somatopleure in this area and empties into the sinus venosus at a point lateral to the entry of the two vitelline veins (fig. 332C). This bridge established across the coelomic cavity from the somatopleure of the body wall to the splanchnopleure of the heart forms a **lateral mesocardium** on either side. The two lateral mesocardia

---

FIG. 332. Early development of primitive vascular system including tubular heart. (The diagrams included in this figure should be studied together with descriptions in Chapter 10 relative to tubulation of the major organ-forming areas of the early embryo.) (A) Diagram of the early bilaterally developed vascular tubes (capillaries) which form in relation to the primitive gut tube. This system of capillaries constitutes the first or early *vitelline system* of developing circulatory structures. (B) The *cardinal or primary venous system* is added to the primitive vitelline system. (C) The area of union between the early vitelline and cardinal systems at the caudal end of the heart. (D) The basic (fundamental) condition of the vascular system. (E) Two diagrams showing the union of the vitelline and cardinal systems distally between the somites and near the nerve cord. The three vascular tubules to the left in this drawing show an early relationship of the intersegmental arteries and veins, and the drawing of the three vascular tubules to the right depict a later stage of this developmental relationship. (F–M) Stages in the development of the early tubular heart in shark, frog, and chick embryos. As the mammal is similar to the chick it is not included. (F–H) Early development of the heart in *Squalus acanthias.* (F) The lower, mesial edges of the hypomeric mesoderm begins to cup around the primitive subintestinal capillaries. (G) Later stage. (H) A transverse section through the heart which is now in the form of a straight tube comparable to that shown in Fig. 339A. (I–K) Early stages in the development of the frog heart. Observe that the ventral areas of the two hypomeres become confluent and later form a trough-like cup around the forming subintestinal capillaries below the foregut. (Redrawn from Kellicott, 1913. Outlines of Chordate Development, Henry Holt, N. Y.) (L–M) Early development of the chick heart. (L) At about 26 hrs. of incubation. (M) About 30 hrs. of incubation.

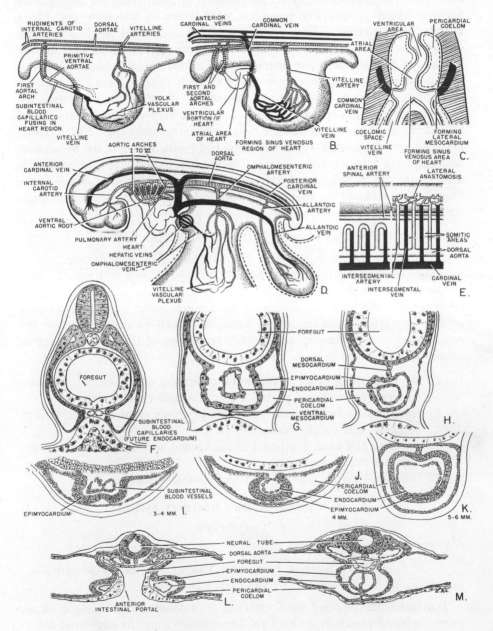

FIG. 332. *(See facing page for legend.)*

represent the initial stages in the development of the various coelomic divisions of the primitive coelomic space (Chap. 20).

As the cardinal and intestinal systems of the primitive vascular system become joined together centrally via the common cardinal veins, the two systems become joined peripherally by means of a series of **intersegmental blood vessels.** The latter arise from the dorsal aortae and travel dorsally between the somites and myotomes to the central nerve tube (fig. 232E). In the nerve-tube area, the primitive **intersegmental arteries** become continuous with the rudiments of the **intersegmental veins** which course laterad to join the anterior and posterior cardinal veins. When the above vascular channels are well established, another set of veins is formed between the somatopleural mesoderm of the hypomere and the developing integument (figs. 332D; 336C, D). The last veins course along the lateral body wall, arising in the pelvic area and emptying into the sinus venosus of the heart. In fishes and amphibia, these veins are called **lateral veins,** but in reptiles, birds, and mammals, they are denominated the **allantoic or umbilical veins** as they drain principally the allantoic area of the embryo.

4. REGIONS OF THE PRIMITIVE VASCULAR SYSTEM

The primitive morphological plan of the vascular system, as outlined above, is a basic condition strikingly comparable in all vertebrate embryos. In view of the later changes of this fundamental vascular plan necessitated by the adaptation of the vascular system to the environmental conditions existing within the various habitats of the adult, it is well to demarcate, for the purposes of later discussion, certain definite regions of the primitive arteriovenous system. These regions are (fig. 332D):

(1) the **converging veins of the heart,** composed of the lateral, common cardinal, anterior and posterior cardinal, and vitelline veins,

(2) the **primitive heart,** made up of the primitive sinus venosus, atrium, ventricle, and bulbus cordis,

(3) the **branchial area,** composed of the ventral aortae, aortal arches, and adjacent dorsal aortae, and,

(4) the **dorsal aortae** (later aorta) and **efferent branches.**

C. Histogenesis of the Circulatory System

1. THE HEART

Consult Chap. 16.

2. FORMATION OF THE PRIMITIVE VASCULAR CHANNELS AND CAPILLARIES

Two principal theories have emerged to account for the origin of the primitive blood vessels in the embryo. These theories are the **angioblast theory** and the **local origin theory.**

The **angioblast theory** rests upon the assumption that a special **vascular tissue,** called **the angioblast** by Wilhelm His, develops in the area of the yolk sac. This angioblast tissue, according to the angioblast theory, forms a vascular rudiment within which the **endothelium,** or flattened epithelial cells peculiar to blood capillaries, is developed. This endothelium produces the primitive capillaries of the yolk area, and, further, it grows into the developing embryo where it forms the endothelium of the entire intra-embryonic vascular system. That is, the angioblast in the yolk area provides the source from which arises the endothelial lining of all the primitive blood vessels of the embryo and also of all later endothelium of later blood vessels. The endothelium of all blood vessels thus traces its ancestry back to the yolk-sac angioblast.

The **local origin theory** may be divided into two schools of thought. One school espouses the idea that "mesenchyme may, in practically any region of the body, transform into vascular tissue" (McClure, '21, p. 221). Accordingly, primitive blood capillaries arise in loco from mesenchyme in various parts of the embryo, and these local vessels sprout, grow, and become united to form the continuous vascular system. The endothelium which forms the walls of all capillaries and the lining tissue of all blood vessels of larger dimensions forms directly from mesenchyme. Addition to this mesenchyme may occur by proliferation from endothelium already formed or by the conversion of mesenchyme as single cells or cellular aggregates (McClure, '21; Reagan, '17).

A second school which advocates the local origin of blood vessels differs from the view described above principally by the assumption that, while the endothelium of blood vessels appears to arise in loco from the mesenchyme, it is not a generalized type of mesenchyme but rather a "slightly modified mesenchymal cell" (Stockard, '15). Relative to this position, the following quotation from Stockard, '15, p. 323, is given:

The facts presented seem to indicate that vascular endothelium, erythrocytes and leucocytes, although all arise from mesenchyme, are really polyphyletic in origin: that is, each has a different mesenchymal anlage. To make the meaning absolutely clear, I consider the origin of the liver and pancreas cells a parallel case. Both arise from endoderm, but each is formed by a distinctly different endodermal anlage, and if one of these two anlagen is destroyed, the other is powerless to replace its product.

3. LATER DEVELOPMENT OF BLOOD VESSELS

While the capillary possessing a wall composed of thin, flattened endothelial cells is the basic or fundamental condition of all blood vessels in the body, it is only of transitory importance in the development of the arteries and veins. For, in the formation of the arteries and the veins, the primitive capillary enlarges and its endothelial wall is soon reinforced by the addition of white and elastic connective tissue fibers and smooth muscle tissue. The connective tissue and smooth muscle develop from the adjacent mesenchyme present in the area in which the capillary makes its appearance.

a. Arteries

The arteries are the system of blood vessels which convey the blood from the heart to the systemic organs. Most arteries are composed of three coats of tissue which come to surround the endothelium of the capillary, namely, an inner **tunica intima,** a middle **tunica media,** and an outer **tunica adventitia.** The tunica media is composed of smooth muscle fibers and elastic connective tissue fibers, while the other two coatings are fabricated of connective tissue fibers.

In the large arteries in the immediate vicinity of the heart, the tunica media is poorly muscularized but its elastic fibers are plentiful. However, in the more distally placed arteries, the so-called distributing arteries which include most of the arteries, the tunica media is supplied copiously with smooth muscle fibers.

b. Veins

The veins are the vascular tubes which convey the blood from the systemic organs back to the heart. The walls of the veins are more delicate than those of the arteries, and the various tunics mentioned above are thinner, especially the tunica media. The veins of the extremities form internal, pocket-shaped **valves** which prevent the blood from moving backward.

c. Capillaries

The capillaries which form the ramifying bed of blood vessels between the arteries and veins retain the primitive condition, and their walls are composed of flattened endothelial cells. The size of the arteries and the thickness of the arterial walls decrease as they approach the capillary bed, while those of the veins increase as they leave the capillary area.

4. HEMATOPOIESIS (HEMOPOIESIS)

a. Theories of Blood-cell Origin

Hematopoiesis is the name given to the process which effects the formation of blood cells. Though it is agreed that blood cells generally arise from mesenchymal cells, all students of the problem do not concur in the belief that all arise from a specific type of mesenchymal cell. For example, in the quotation given above from Stockard, '15, it is stated that one type of mesenchymal cell gives origin to the red blood cells, while leukocytes or white blood cells arise from a slightly different type of mesenchymal cell. This may be called the dualistic theory of hematopoiesis. The view held today by many in this field of development is that all blood cells arise from fixed, undifferentiated, mesenchymal cells which give origin to a mother cell, the **hemocytoblast.** From the hemocytoblast, four main stem cells arise, **lymphoblasts, monoblasts, granuloblasts,** and **erythroblasts,** each of which differentiates into the adult type of blood cell as shown in fig. 333A. Such an interpretation is the basis for the monophyletic or unitarian theory of blood cell origin. Some observers, however, believe that the **erythrocyte, granulocyte,** and the **monocyte** each have a separate stem cell. The latter view is the basis of the trialistic theory. (Consult Maximow and Bloom, '42, pp. 107–116 for discussion relative to blood-cell origin.)

b. Places of Blood-cell Origin

1) Early Embryonic Origin of Blood Cells. It long has been recognized that the yolk-sac area is a region of early blood-cell development. This is one aspect of the angioblast theory of His, referred to on page 731. In the teleost fish, *Fundulus,* Stockard ('15) reports the origin of red blood cells from two main sources:

(1) an **intermediate cell mass** or **blood string** in the vicinity of the notochord and

(2) the **blood islands** in the yolk sac.

However, the yolk-sac area appears to be the primary source for the early phases of hematopoiesis in most vertebrate embryos. In the human embryo, both red and white cells have been described as arising from **primitive hemocytoblasts** in the yolk sac by Bloom and Bartelmez ('40). These authors report the origin of primitive erythrocytes as arising primarily intra-vascularly, although some develop extra-vascularly. Definitive erythrocytes develop, according to these authors, in the entoderm and within blood vessels of the yolk sac (fig. 333B). In the 24-hr. chick embryo, the blood islands in the area vasculosa of the blastoderm show a direct conversion of mesodermal cells into primitive blood cells and the endothelium of the forming blood capillaries (fig. 333C). In the frog, blood islands appear in the mesoderm and entoderm of the ventro-lateral areas of the body of 3- to 4.5-mm. embryos. These islands are extensive, extending from the liver area caudally toward the tail-bud region.

2) Later Sites of Blood-cell Formation. As indicated previously in teleost fishes, early blood formation occurs in the region of the notochord near the developing kidney tissue, as well as in the yolk-sac area. During later development, hematopoiesis in teleost fishes is centered in the **kidney area.** The origin of blood cells from kidney tissue also is true in the amphibian tadpole (Jordan and Speidel, '23, a and b). The liver also functions in these forms to produce blood cells. In the developing shark embryo, blood cells appear to be formed *around the heart* and later in the **esophageal area** of the adult. In the adult frog, the spleen functions as a center of blood-cell formation, although in the

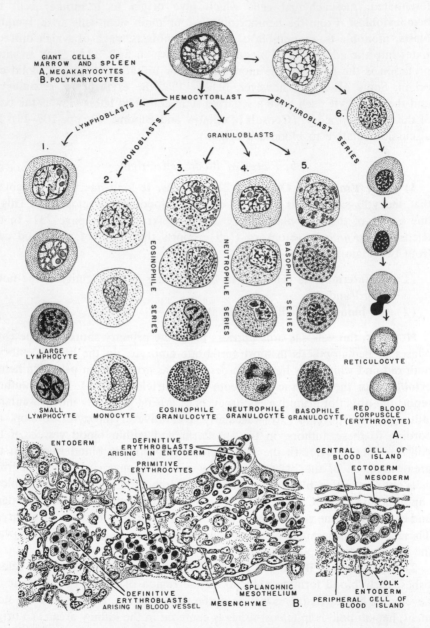

FIG. 333. Developing blood cells. (A) Diagram showing origin of different types of blood cells from the primitive hemocytoblast. (Redrawn and slightly modified from Patten, 1946. Human Embryology, Blakiston, Philadelphia.) (B) Blood-cell origin in the yolk-sac area of human embryo. (Redrawn from Bloom and Bartelmetz, 1940. Am. J. Anat. 67.) (C) Differentiation of blood cells and blood vessel endothelium in a blood island of chick embryo yolk-sac area.

terrestrial form, *Rana temporaria,* the bone marrow functions in this capacity as it does in the adults of reptiles, birds, and mammals. In the adult reptile and bird, the bone marrow seems to function in the production of all types of blood cells. In the mammal, the bone marrow possibly elaborates only erythrocytes and granular, white blood cells, while the lymphocytes probably are produced in other areas, such as the **pharyngeal and palatine tonsils** and **lymph nodes,** etc. In all vertebrates from the teleost fishes to the mammals, it is probable that scattered lymphoid tissue in various parts of the body functions in the formation of lymphocytes.

During the development of the early human embryo and later fetus, the following have been given as sites of blood-cell formation (Minot, '12; Gilmour, '41):

(a) yolk sac in embryos up to 3 mm., i.e., the end of the fourth week of pregnancy,

(b) mitosis of previously formed erythroblasts in general circulation, yolk sac, and chorion of embryos from 3 to 9 mm. in length,

(c) liver and yolk sac of 10- to 18-mm. embryos. In embryos of 470- to 546-mm. there is a gradual decrease in the liver,

(d) spleen, beginning in the 28-mm. embryo; thymus, and lymph glands in the 35-mm. and larger embryos,

(e) bone marrow during the third month and later.

3) Characteristics of Development of the Erythrocyte. Most vertebrates in the adult condition retain the nucleus in the erythrocyte or red blood cell. To this cell is given the function of carrying oxygen from the site of external respiration to the body tissues. It also is a factor in conveying carbon dioxide from the tissues to the site of external respiration. The oxygen-carrying capacity of the erythrocyte resides in the presence of the compound **hemoglobin.** Hemoglobin is a complex protein molecule, containing iron atoms. The iron atoms make it possible for the hemoglobin to convey oxygen.

In the adults of various amphibian species, there is a tendency for the red blood cell to lose its nucleus by various means (Noble, '31, pp. 181–182). This tendency toward loss of the nucleus reaches an extreme form in *Batrachoseps* where more than 90 per cent of the red blood cells have lost their nuclei. In adult mammals, the mature erythrocyte loses its nucleus (column 6, fig. 333A) but it is retained in the early embryo.

4) Characteristics of Various White Blood Cells. White blood corpuscles or leukocytes vary greatly in number and in morphological features in all vertebrates. In general, the following two major groups of white blood corpuscles may be distinguished.

a) GRANULOCYTES. Granulocytes are cells which arise from **granuloblasts** (columns 3, 4, and 5, fig. 333A). These cells are characterized by the presence of an irregularly shaped nucleus and by a cytoplasm which possesses granules of various dimensions and staining affinities.

b) LYMPHOID FORMS. Lymphoid forms are of two types, namely, **lymphocytes** and **monocytes.** These cells arise from **lymphoblasts** and **monoblasts** respectively (columns 1 and 2, fig. 333A). The **lymphocytes** are small, rounded cells with a clear cytoplasm and a large nucleus. They are found in all vertebrates and are abundant especially in fishes and amphibia. Large numbers are found in the lymph nodes in various parts of the body. **Monocytes** are similar to the lymphocytes but are much larger and have a tendency to possess an irregularly shaped nucleus. Various hematologists hold that the monocyte is a special type of blood cell, distinct from other leukocytes and of a separate developmental origin.

D. Morphogenesis of the Circulatory System

1. INTRODUCTION

The major alterations of the basic arterial and venous conditions into the morphology present in the adult or definitive body form of the species occur during the larval period, or the period of transition from primitive embryonic body form to the definitive or adult form. This fact is true not only of the circulatory system but of all other organ systems as well (Chap. 11). The pronounced changes, therefore, which occur in the revamping of the basic, generalized condition of the circulatory system during the larval period should be regarded as transformation which adapts the basic embryonic condition to conditions which must be met when the developing organism emerges into the environment of the adult.

2. TRANSFORMATION OF THE CONVERGING VEINS OF THE EARLY EMBRYONIC HEART INTO THE MAJOR VEINS WHICH ENTER THE ADULT FORM OF THE HEART

a. Alteration of the Primitive Converging Veins of the Heart in the Shark, Squalus acanthias

An early stage of the developing venous circulation of *Squalus acanthias* is shown in figure 334A. Only two veins are present, the **primitive vitelline veins.** They enter the sinal rudiment of the developing heart. Before the liver lobes form, the left vitelline vein develops a new venous sprout, the **intestinal vein,** which extends caudalward along the lateral aspect of the intestine to the developing cloacal area (fig. 334B). Here it forms a collar-like venous structure around the cloaca and continues back below the tail gut as the **caudal vein.** Meanwhile, the **anterior, posterior,** and **common cardinal veins** begin their development, and the **liver** also begins to form (fig. 334C). As the liver develops, two prominent liver lobes are elaborated (Scammon, '13), and the vitelline veins become surrounded by the developing liver trabeculae

(Chap. 13). During this process, the vitelline veins are fenestrated, and sinusoids are produced. These sinusoids connect with the right and left vitelline (hepatic) veins at the anterior end of the liver.

Posterior to the liver, the right and left vitelline veins form a collar around the duodenum as shown in figure 334C. The left portion of the duodenal collar then disappears, and the **hepatic portal vein** which receives blood from the developing stomach, pancreas, and intestine enters the liver as indicated in figure 334D.

As the above development progresses, three important changes are effected (fig. 334E):

(1) The lateral veins along the lateral body wall arise and join the common cardinal veins near the entrance of the right and left vitelline (hepatic) veins;

(2) the intestinal vein loses its connection with the caudal vein; and

(3) the postcardinal veins extend caudally and connect with the caudal vein.

Meanwhile, the mesonephric kidneys begin to develop, and new veins, in the form of irregular venous spaces, form between the two kidneys. These new veins are the **subcardinal veins.** The subcardinal veins are joined by the internal renal veins which ramify through the kidney substance from the posterior cardinal veins. They course over and around the forming renal tubules (fig. 334F, G).

Later, the two subcardinal veins extend forward and by means of an anastomosis on either side connect with the posterior cardinal veins anterior to the mesonephric kidneys. As this transformation occurs, the segment of each posterior cardinal vein atrophies between the kidney and the point where the subcardinal venous anastomosis joins the posterior cardinal vein (fig. 334G).

While the above changes evolve, the anterior cardinal veins expand greatly over the dorsal pharyngeal area, where they form sinus-like spaces. These anterior cardinal venous sinuses receive the **internal jugular veins** from the brain region and various **pharyngeal veins. Coronary veins** and **external jugular** veins also develop as shown in figure 334H.

b. Changes in the Primitive Converging Veins of the Heart in the Anuran Amphibia

1) Vitelline Veins. As in the shark embryo and in all other vertebrates, the vitelline veins of the frog or toad embryo are among the first blood vessels to be formed in the body. In frog embryos of about 3- to 4-mm. in length, the two vitelline veins begin to appear as irregular blood spaces along the ventro-lateral aspect of the midgut region, extending anteriad around the forming liver. At a point immediately anterior to the liver rudiment, these vessels fuse to form the endocardinal rudiment of the heart (fig. 332I–K).

Proceeding forward from the heart region, the two primitive subintestinal blood vessels continue forward below the rudiment of the foregut where they form the rudiments of the *ventral aorta*. They diverge and extend dorsad around the foregut to the dorsal area of the foregut. These vessels which thus pass around the foregut represent the third pair of aortal arches, i.e., the first pair of branchial aortal arches (fig. 335A). The first branchial aortal arches join the forming *dorsal aortae*. The dorsal aortae form first as irregular blood spaces, extending along the primitive gut from below the forming brain posteriad to the midgut area. Here they diverge to give origin to the vitelline arteries which ramify over the yolk substance of the midgut and there anastomose with branches of the vitelline veins.

About the time of hatching, the two vitelline veins become enmeshed in the substance of the developing liver, and the vitelline veins gradually become divided into three groups (fig. 335B):

    (a) a right and left vitelline vein between the liver and the sinus venosus of the heart,

    (b) the veins within the liver which form an irregular meshwork, and

    (c) the two vitelline veins, posterior to the liver substance.

The left vitelline vein, anterior to the liver, soon atrophies and becomes fused with the right vitelline vein as indicated in figure 335C and D. The right vitelline vein thus receives the **hepatic veins.** Within the liver substance, the two vitelline veins break up into smaller veins to form ultimately the sinusoids of the liver (fig. 335C). Posterior to the liver, the vitelline veins form the hepatic portal and intestinal veins (fig. 335C).

    2) Lateral (Ventral Abdominal) Veins. The lateral veins form first as two minute veins, which extend posteriad from the lateral ends of the sinus venosus of the heart. Eventually they unite with the iliac veins as shown in figure 335D.

FIG. 334. The developing venous system in *Squalus acanthias*. (Modified from Hochstetter, '06.)   (A) An early stage in the development of the venous system. The two primitive vitelline veins only are present. (B) Later stage in development of vitelline veins. (C) Early stage in development of hepatic portal system. A venous ring is formed around the duodenum. Anterior and posterior cardinal veins are evident. (D) Later stage in the hepatic-portal system development. Left segment of duodenal collar has disappeared. Observe that the efferent hepatic veins (V. hepaticae revehentes) represent the right and left vitelline veins between the liver lobes and the sinus venosus, whereas the afferent hepatic veins (V. hepaticae advehentes) are the vitelline veins just posterior to the liver. (E) Lateral veins make their appearance. Posterior cardinal veins join veins around the cloacal area and thus assume responsibility for venous drainage of the tail region, and the intestinal vein in consequence loses its connection with the caudal vein of the tail. (F) Subcardinal veins appear between the kidneys. (G) Subcardinal veins make connection with posterior cardinal veins. Posterior cardinal veins regress anterior to the mesonephric kidneys where the posterior cardinal and subcardinal veins anastomose. (H) Mature plan of the venous system showing the converging veins of the heart. Hepatic portal vein omitted.

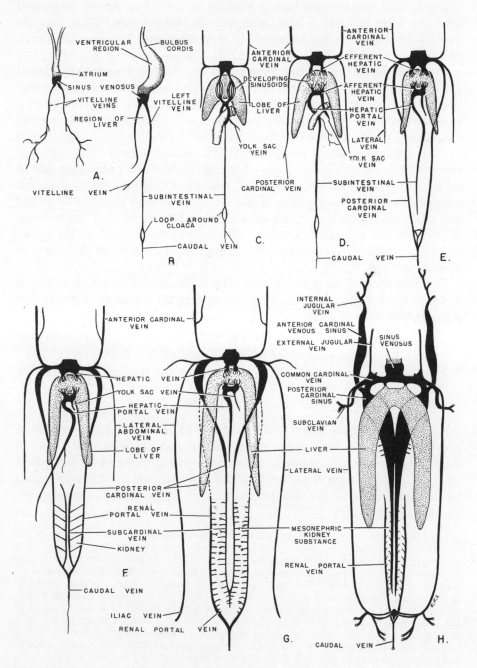

FIG. 334. (*See facing page for legend.*)

Anteriorly, the two lateral (ventral abdominal) veins lose their connection with the sinus venosus and merge together to form one ventral abdominal vein; the latter acquires a connection with the hepatic portal vein near the liver. A ventral abdominal circulation is established thus between the hepatic portal system and the iliac veins (fig. 335E, F).

3) **Formation of the Inferior Vena Cava.** The **inferior vena cava** is a vessel not found in the venous system of the developing shark. It is a blood vessel associated with and characteristic of lung breathers. As such, the inferior vena cava appears first among the vertebrates in the lungfishes (Dipnoi) and it functions to shunt the blood from the posterior regions of the body over to the right atrial portion of the heart. That is, the inferior vena cava is a vessel correlated with the division of the heart into two parts. One part is devoted to getting the non-oxygenated systemic blood into the lung region, while the other part functions to propel the aerated blood from the lungs into the head region and other parts of the body. This division of labor within the heart is not necessary in strictly gill-breathing fishes, such as the sharks and teleosts, and, in consequence, an inferior vena cava is not developed in these vertebrates.

The formation of the inferior vena cava in the anuran amphibia is shown in figure 335C–G and need not be explained further. It is to be observed that it forms from four segments:

(1) a right vitelline vein,
(2) an hepatic segment,
(3) a segment which extends posteriad from the liver to the fused sub-cardinal vein, and
(4) the subcardinal vein. (Consult figure 335E.)

4) **Formation of the Renal Portal System.** The renal portal system is inaugurated among the cartilaginous fishes (i.e., the shark group). It does not exist in cyclostomes. As shown in figure 334 relative to the developing shark embryo, it results from the formation of the subcardinal veins, accompanied by the obliteration of the anterior portions of the posterior cardinal veins.

Fig. 335. Developing venous vessels in the anuran amphibia. (B–G, redrawn and modified from Kampmeier, 1920, Anat. Rec. **19**; H, redrawn from Kampmeier, 1925, J. Morph. 41; I, redrawn from Goodrich after Kerr, 1930, Studies on the Structure and Development of Vertebrates, Macmillan, Ltd., London.) (A) Primitive plan of early, circulation in frog embryo. The relationship of the primitive venous system shown in B to the rest of the vascular system is evident. (B) Plan of venous system of 4 mm. embryo of the toad, *Bufo vulgaris.* (C) Plan of venous system of 6 mm. embryo of the toad, *Bufo vulgaris.* (D) Plan of venous system of 15 mm. embryo of the toad, *Bufo lentiginosus.* (E) Plan of venous system of 18 mm. embryo of the toad, *Bufo lentiginosus.* (F) Plan of venous system of young toad of *Bufo lentiginosus,* immediately after metamorphosis. (G) Plan of venous system of mature *Rana pipiens.* (H) Left posterior lymph hearts of an adult *Rana pipiens.* (I) Internal structure of mature frog heart.

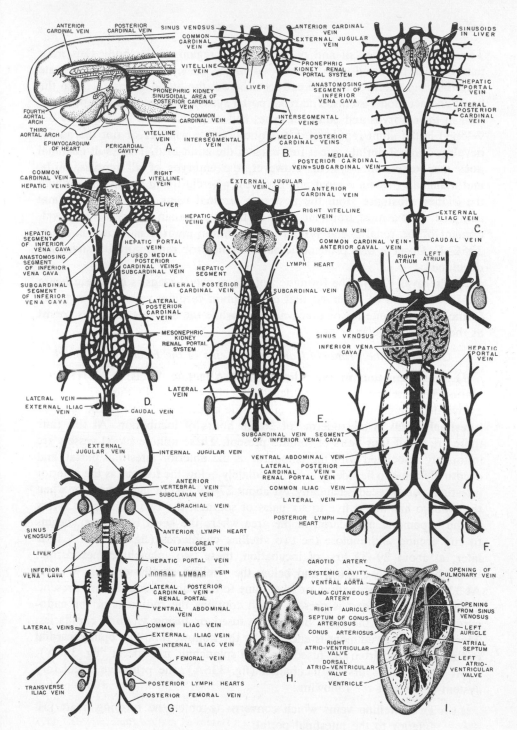

FIG. 335. (*See facing page for legend.*)

The blood from the tail and posterior trunk region of the body thus must pass through the small blood vessels within the kidney substance. Here waste materials and excess water are extracted before the blood is passed on to the heart and aeration systems. The renal portal system is developed exceptionally well in the embryos and adults of fishes and amphibia. It is inadequately developed in the adult reptile, and it is questionable whether or not the poorly developed, renal portal system functions in the adult bird. The adult mammal does not possess this system. However, the embryos of all reptiles, birds, and mammals possess a renal portal system wherein blood is shunted through the kidney substance from the posterior cardinal veins into the subcardinal complex. It is a most transient affair in the mammalian embryo. The development of the renal portal system in the anuran embryo is shown in figure 335C–E. Observe that pronephric and mesonephric renal portal systems are developed.

5) Precaval Veins. The formation of the precaval veins is shown in figure 335B–G. It is to be observed that the common cardinal veins become transformed into the anterior or precaval veins, while the anterior cardinals persist as the internal jugular veins.

c. Changes in the Primitive Converging Veins of the Heart in the Chick

1) Transformation of the Vitelline and Allantoic Veins: a) Vitelline Veins. The vitelline veins in the developing chick first make their appearance as two delicate capillaries, one on either side of the inner wall of the **anterior intestinal portal** in blastoderms of 26–28 hours of incubation. At this time there are about four pairs of somites present. These minute blood vessels are intimately associated with the entoderm of the anterior intestinal portal, and eventually come to lie side by side immediately below the foregut as the anterior intestinal portal recedes caudally. At about 27–29 hrs. of incubation, or when the embryo has about five to six pairs of somites, the two splanchnic layers of the hypomeric mesoderm, in the area where the heart is to form, begins to cup around and enclose the two vitelline capillaries (fig. 332L). A little later, at about 29–33 hrs. of incubation, these two splanchnic mesodermal layers begin to fuse above and below the vitelline capillaries (fig. 332M). At 33–38 hrs. of incubation, or when nine to ten pairs of somites are present, a simple, tubular heart is present which contains the rudiment of the **endocardium** within in the form of the two fused or fusing vitelline capillaries. This endocardial rudiment is enclosed by the hollow, tube-like **epimyocardial rudiment** derived from the fused layers of splanchnic mesoderm (fig. 336A).

At about 33–38 hrs. of incubation (fig. 336A), the primitive circulatory system consists of the following:

(1) Two vitelline veins which converge to enter the forming heart just anterior to the intestinal portal;

(2) the primitive tubular heart;

(3) two delicate capillaries, the future ventral aortae, course anteriad from the heart below the foregut. As the ventral aortae approach the anterior limits of the foregut they diverge and travel dorsad as the **mandibular aortal arches,** one on either side of the gut tube, to the dorsal region. In the dorsal area of the foregut the mandibular aortal arches become continuous with

(4) the **dorsal aortae.** These two delicate vessels lie upon the foregut on either side of the notochord, and extend caudalward into the region of the developing midgut.

During the period of 40 to 50 hours of incubation the following changes occur in the above system (fig. 336B and B'):

(1) The **rudimentary vitelline arteries** extend outward over the yolk-sac area from the dorsal aortae, forming many small capillaries.

(2) The **anterior and posterior cardinal veins** and connecting **intersegmental veins** are established and unite with the sinus venosus by means of the **common cardinal vein** (fig. 336B').

(3) The **vitelline veins** extend outward over the blastoderm and continue anteriorly around the head area as the **anterior vitelline veins.** The latter veins unite with the **circumferential blood sinus.** A complete circulation through the embryo and out over the yolk-sac area is thus effected.

During the early part of the third day of incubation the right and left vitelline veins begin to fuse in the area just posterior to the heart. This fusion forms a single vein, the **ductus venosus** (fig. 337A). The latter structure joins the sinus venosus of the heart. Posteriorly, the vitelline veins make a secondary connection with the developing **posterior vitelline or omphalomesenteric veins** which extend backward along the sides of the midgut to the area where the vitelline arteries leave the dorsal aortae. At this point each omphalomesenteric vein turns sharply laterad and courses along the pathway of a vitelline artery (fig. 336C).

At the end of the third day of incubation the ductus venosus is present as an elongated structure lying between the anterior intestinal portal and the heart. A posterior vitelline vein continues posteriad from the ductus venosus around each side of the anterior intestinal portal (fig. 336D). As observed in Chapter 13, during the third and fourth days of incubation the liver rudiment begins to form. In doing so, the trabeculae of the liver surround the ductus venosus. The immediate segment of the ductus venosus which becomes surrounded by the forming liver substance forms the **meatus venosus.** As development of the liver proceeds, two main groups of veins develop in the liver substance (fig. 337B, D): (1) An **anterior efferent group of hepatic veins** which drain blood from the liver and (2) a **posterior afferent set of hepatic**

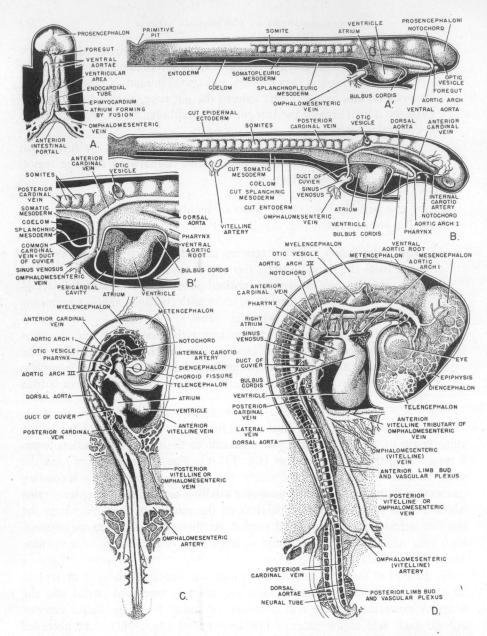

FIG. 336. Early development of the circulatory system in the chick. (A) Primitive vitelline (omphalomesenteric) veins, heart, ventral aorta, and the first or mandibular pair of aortal arches. About stage 10 of Hamburger and Hamilton, 1951, J. Morph. **88.** Approximately 33–38 hrs. of incubation. (A′) Lateral view of same. (B) Lateral view of chick circulatory system of about 45–50 hrs. of incubation. (About Hamburger and Hamilton stage 13.) (B′) Same, showing common cardinal vein (duct of Cuvier). (C) Circulatory system of chick during early part of third day of incubation. (About Hamburger and Hamilton stage 15.) (D) Circulatory system of chick embryo about 72˙ hrs. incubation.

veins, representing branches of the hepatic portal vein. The latter brings blood from the stomach and intestinal areas to the liver.

During the fifth to seventh days of incubation, the afferent and efferent sets of hepatic veins develop profuse branchings, and venous sinusoids are formed within the liver substance between these two sets of veins. Meanwhile, the meatus venosus within the liver atrophies and a complete **hepatic portal system** is established between afferent and efferent hepatic veins during the seventh and eighth days of incubation as shown in figure 337E.

While the above changes in the liver are emerging, changes in the omphalo-mesenteric veins, posterior to the liver substance, are produced as shown in figure 337A–E. By the fifth day, a new vein, the **mesenteric vein**, is formed (fig. 337D), which begins to drain blood from the developing midgut and hindgut areas. By the eighth day, the mesenteric vein is a prominent structure (fig. 337E). At this time, the blood from the yolk sac, via the omphalo-mesenteric veins, and that from the mesenteric vein must pass through the liver sinusoids en route to the efferent hepatic veins (fig. 337E).

b) ALLANTOIC VEINS. The two **allantoic** or **lateral veins** begin to develop during the third day of incubation, and, by the end of this day, two delicate blood vessels extend along the lateral body wall, reaching back toward the hindgut area (figs. 336D; 337B). During the fourth day (fig. 337C), the caudal ends of the two allantoic veins begin to ramify within the walls of the allantois. A secondary attachment to the hepatic veins within the liver is established also at this time (fig. 337C). During the late fourth day and the fifth day of incubation, the right allantoic vein degenerates, and the proximal portion of the left allantoic vein loses its connection with the common cardinal vein (fig. 337D). During the seventh and eighth days (and until the time of hatching), the passage of blood from the allantois through the liver to the vena cava inferior is as indicated in figure 337E. The portion of the allantoic vein extending anteriorly from the umbilical area to the liver persists after hatching and drains blood from the midventral portion of the body wall. It is called the **epigastric vein** (fig. 337I).

2) Formation of the Inferior Vena Cava. The formation of the inferior vena cava of the chick is shown in figure 337F–I and needs no other explanation. It is to be observed that, following the degeneration of the meso-nephric kidneys and the ascendancy of the metanephric kidney, the passage of blood by way of the renal portal system through the mesonephric kidney is abated. In the newly hatched chick, a much-weakened, renal portal system is established via the renal portal vein (fig. 337I). However, most of the blood through this vein passes directly into the common iliac vein and not through the kidney substance.

3) Development of the Precaval Veins. The precaval veins are the direct descendants of the anterior cardinal and common cardinal veins as indicated in figure 337F–I. In figure 337I, it is to be observed that the caudal ends of

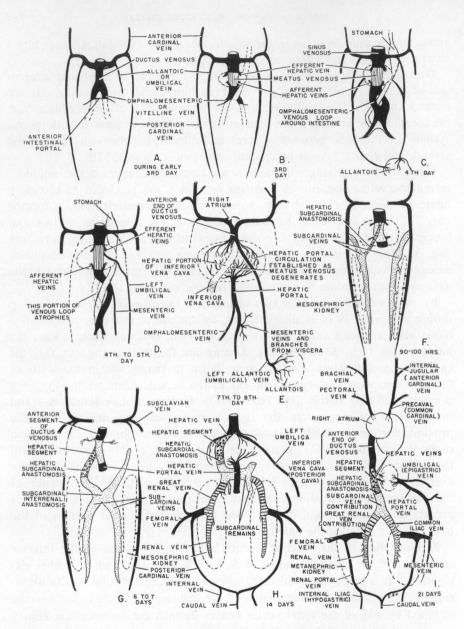

FIG. 337. Ventral views of developing allantoic, hepatic portal, and inferior caval veins in chick. (Diagrams C and D are adapted from figures in Lillie, **1930**, The Development of the Chick, Henry Holt, N. Y., after Hochstetter; diagrams F–H are adapted, considerably modified, from Miller, **1903**, Am. J. Anat. **2.**) (A) Diagram of converging veins of heart during early third day of incubation. (B) Same at end of third and early fourth days. (C) Middle fourth day. (D) End of fourth and early fifth days. (E) Seventh to eighth days. (F) Development of inferior vena cava at end of fourth and beginning of fifth day of incubation. (G) Same, 6–7 days. (H) Same, fourteenth day. (I) Same at about hatching time, 20–21 days.

the posterior cardinal system function to drain the blood from the caudal end of the body and posterior appendages, while the anterior cardinal veins and common cardinal veins function to drain the blood from the head, neck, and forelimb areas.

d. The Developing Converging Veins of the Mammalian Heart (e.g., Human)

The formation of the hepatic portal system in the human embryo is shown in figure 338G, H, and that of the inferior and superior venae cavae is shown in figure 338A–F. The general principles of venous development, described in the previous pages of this chapter, apply here, and descriptive matter is not needed to supplement the accompanying figures. It is worthy of mention, however, that two additional veins are introduced in the abdominal area of the embryo, namely, the two **supracardinal veins.** These veins persist as a part of the **vena cava inferior** and **azygos veins.** Anteriorly, the two precavae, so prominent in the lower vertebrates, including the birds, are displaced partially by the formation of an anastomosing vein from the left to the right side with the dropping out, to a considerable extent, of the proximal portion of the left precava. Thus, the common cardinal vein on the right side comes to function as the proximal portion of the single **superior or anterior vena cava,** while the common cardinal vein on the left side comes to form the **coronary sinus** of the heart, and occasionally as a variant, the **oblique vein** of the left atrium.

3. DEVELOPMENT OF THE HEART

a. General Morphology of the Primitive Heart

In the vertebrate group, two types of hearts are present, namely, *lymph hearts* (fig. 335H) and the heart of the arteriovenous system. The heart of the arteriovenous system is a centralized, well-muscularized mechanism, placed ventral to the esophageal segment of the gut in the anterior extremity of the coelomic cavity. Its function is to receive blood from the veins of the body and to propel it forward toward the anterior or head region. Fundamentally, the embryonic heart of the arteriovenous system is a *tubular affair,* composed of four segments:

(1) a thin-walled **sinus venosus** or caudal portion of the heart, connecting with a series of converging veins,
(2) the **atrium,** a segment lying anterior to the sinus,
(3) the **ventricle,** lying anterior to the atrium, and
(4) the **bulbus cordis.**

The ventricle and, to some extent, the bulbus cordis of the embryonic heart later develop the structures which act as the main propulsive mechanism of the heart, while the sinus and atrium give origin to the blood-receiving areas.

b. The Basic Histological Structure of the Primitive Embryonic Heart

Structurally, the embryonic heart is composed of two parts. An inner delicate lining, the rudiment of the **endocardium,** forms as a result of the fusion of the vitelline blood capillaries in the immediate area of the forming heart. The endocardium thus is composed of **endothelium** (fig. 332F–M). Surrounding the endocardial rudiment, there is the **epimyocardium** derived from the ventro-mesial portions of the hypomeric (splanchnopleural) mesoderm which extends ventrally from the foregut in this area (fig. 332F–M). Basically, the mesial walls of the two hypomeric areas of the mesoderm which lie below the foregut in this region constitute the **ventral mesentery** of the primitive gut. Consequently, the epimyocardium of the primitive heart may be regarded as modified ventral mesentery. That portion of the ventral mesentery which is dorsal to the forming heart forms the **dorsal mesocardium,** while that part which extends ventrally below the heart forms the **ventral mesocardium.** The latter is a transient structure, no sooner formed than obliterated in most instances. The dorsal mesocardium tends to persist for a time, more in some species than in others. Caudally, the posterior lateral areas of the **sinus venosus** project the splanchnopleural mesoderm laterally to contact the lateral somatopleural mesoderm with which the splanchnopleural mesoderm fuses. This outward extension of the caudo-lateral edges of the sinus venosus produces a bridge across the coelomic space from the lateral body wall to the sinus venosus. These bridges on either side across the primitive coelom form the **lateral mesocardia.** Through these mesocardial bridges, the common cardinal veins empty their contents into the heart.

Fig. 338. Changes in the converging veins of the heart in the mammalian embryo. (Redrawn and modified from Patten, 1946, Human Embryology, Blakiston, Philadelphia, after McClure and Butler.) (A–F) Developmental changes in converging veins of the human heart. Primitive converging veins of the heart shown in black; hepatic segment of inferior vena cava shown in white with coarse stipple; subcardinal veins shown in light stipple; supracardinal veins in white with crossed lines. (Note: the author assumes the responsibility for adding a vitelline venous segment to the anterior end of the developing inferior vena cava. As a result of observations on developing pig, cat, and opossum embryos, the author is convinced that a vitelline segment is contributed to the developing posterior vena cava in the mammal.) (A) Primitive basic condition. (B–F) Later stages as indicated. (F) Adult condition. The following contributions appear to enter into the formation of the inferior vena cava, viz., (1) a very short vitelline segment; (2) an hepatic segment; (3) an anastomosis between the hepatic segment and the subcardinal interrenal anastomosis; (4) a subcardinal-supracardinal anastomosis; (5) a right supracardinal segment caudal to the kidneys; and (6) a posterior cardinal contribution in the pelvic area. Note also that the *azygos vein* is formed from the anterior end of the right posterior cardinal vein plus the right supracardinal with its connections with the hemiazygos vein. Observe further that the *superior vena cava* is composed of the right common cardinal vein from the area of juncture with the azygos vein to the point of its entrance into the right atrium. (G–J) Formation of the hepatic portal vein in the pig. (Redrawn and slightly modified from Patten, 1948. Embryology of the Pig, Blakiston, Philadelphia.

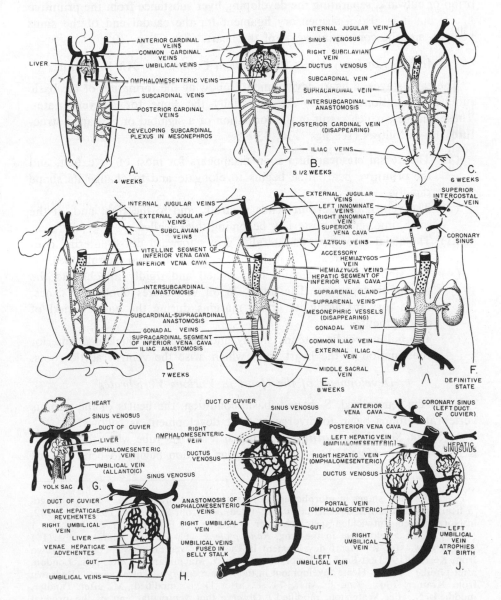

FIG. 338. (*See facing page for legend.*)

c. Importance of the Septum Transversum to the Early Heart

There is another structure which is important to the primitive embryonic heart and to its later development. This structure is the **primary septum transversum** or the **mesodermal partition** which forms across the coelomic cavity, below (ventral) to the lateral mesocardia. It forms not only a partition or bulwark, separating the developing liver substance from the primitive heart, but it is also a suspensory ligament for the caudal end of the sinus venosus and the converging veins of the heart. (See Chap. 20.)

d. Activities of Early-Heart Development Common to All Vertebrates

The early stages of heart development, following the formation of the basic rudiments mentioned above, are essentially the same for all vertebrates. These changes, which result in the formation of a sigmoid or S-shaped structure, are as follows (see figs. 336, 339):

(1) The **dorsal mesocardium** soon disappears for most of its extent, and the primitive heart tube begins to elongate and to change its shape rapidly.

(2) The **ventricular portion** bends ventrally and to the right and, at the same time, grows posteriad, becoming thick-walled.

(3) The **atrial area** expands laterally, grows forward dorso-anteriad over the ventricular area; and at the same time forms two lateral lobes.

(4) The **sinus venosus** remains thin walled and rigidly attached to the septum transversum. The latter, in all vertebrates above the fishes, bends forward along its upper margins during the early period of development.

(5) The **bulbus cordis** extends slowly and becomes a thickened anterior continuation of the heart from which arise the ventral aortic roots.

e. Development of the Heart in Various Vertebrates

From the generalized, S-shaped, basic condition, the hearts of the various vertebrate groups begin to diverge in their development as follows:

1) Shark, Squalus acanthias. Starting as a straight tube when the embryo is 5.2 mm. long (fig. 339A), the ventricular portion begins to bend toward

---

FIG. 339. Early stages in morphogenesis of various vertebrate hearts. (A–C) Stages in heart development in *Squalus acanthias*. (Redrawn from Scammon, 1911, Chap. 12, in Normentafeln Entwichlungsgeschichte der Wirbeltiere by F. Keibel, G. Fischer, Jena.) (D–F′) Heart development in the frog, *Rana pipiens*. (D–F) Left lateral views; (F′) ventral view. (G–K) Heart development in the chick, ventral views. (H–K, redrawn from Kerr, 1919, Text-Book of Embryology, vol. II, Macmillan and Co., Ltd., London, after Greil.) (L–O) Heart development in the human embryo, ventral views. (Redrawn from Kramer, 1942, Am. J. Anat. 71. L, after Davis, modified; M, after Tandler, modified; N, after Waterston, modified.) Observe that ventricular end of the original bulbus cordis, i.e. the conus portion, *contributes to the right ventricle in diagrams N and O.*

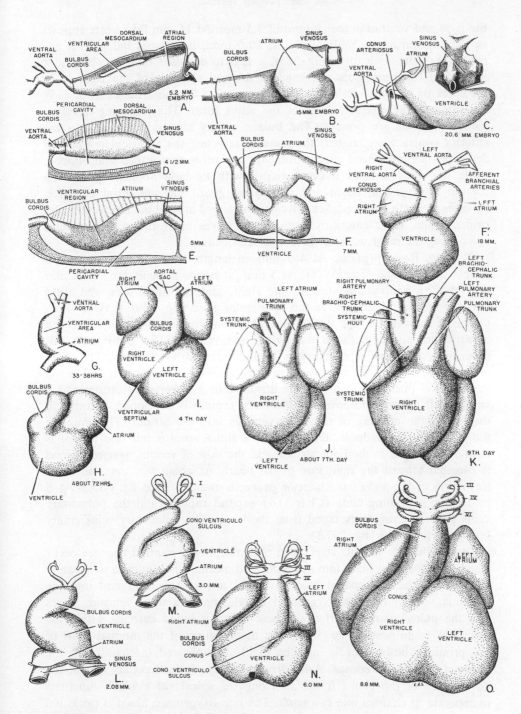

FIG. 339. (*See facing page for legend.*)

the right and ventrad in the embryo of 7.5 mm. At 15 mm., the heart appears as indicated in figure 339B, while, at 20.6 mm., it assumes the general appearance of the adult form (fig. 339C). It is to be noted that the ventricular portion of the heart does not bend as dramatically toward the right as in the chick or mammalian heart. In the embryo of 37 mm., the heart already has attained the characteristics of the adult form. The following developmental features are present. The bulbus cordis has transformed into the anterior contractile chamber, the **conus arteriosus;** the ventricular area has developed a pronounced musculature; the atrium is thin walled and bilobed, while the sinus venosus is cone shaped with its base applied against the septum transversum. Right and left valves guard the sinu-atrial entrance. A series of semilunar or pocket valves are arranged around the atrioventricular orifice, while, more anteriorly, cup-shaped valves are forming in transverse rows along the inner walls of the conus arteriosus.

2) **Frog, Rana pipiens.** At 4½ mm. in length, the heart is present as a simple straight tube (fig. 339D). At 5 mm., it begins to bend, the ventricular area moving ventrad and toward the right, and the atrial area and sinus venosus moving anteriad over the ventricular area (fig. 339E). At 7 mm., the heart has assumed the typical S-shaped condition of the adult form, and constrictions appear between the atrium and ventricle (fig. 339F). At this time, also, a median septum begins to divide the atrial chamber. The atrial septum begins as a fold from the antero-dorsal wall of the atrium and grows ventrad and posteriad to divide the atrium into a larger right atrium and a smaller left artium. Moreover, as the atrial septum is developed, it forms to the left of the opening of the sinus venosus into the atrium. Therefore, in the 8- to 10-mm. tadpole, the opening of sinus venosus into the atrium is entirely restricted to the right atrium, and the flow of venous, systemic blood is directed toward the right side of the heart. At about this time, also, the formation of the vena cava inferior proceeds rapidly. (See fig. 335.) At 8 to 10 mm., the lung buds (Chap. 14) expand rapidly, and the pulmonary veins begin to bring back blood from the lungs. The pulmonary veins empty into the left atrium (fig. 257B).

During the late tadpole stages and metamorphosis, internal changes occur which transform the heart into a complicated mechanism, designed to separate and project the oxygenated blood anteriad toward the head and into the systemic vessels; the non-oxygenated blood from the sinus venosus passes into the pulmocutaneous arteries. These different blood currents within the heart are made possible largely by the modification of the internal walls of the primitive bulbus cordis into the highly complicated mechanism of the contractile **conus arteriosus.** Aside from a series of small pocket valves, the dorsal wall of the conus forms an elongated **spiral valve** which functions to separate its channel into two parts. The non-oxygenated blood is projected dorsally to the spiral valve and into the pulmocutaneous vessels by the spiral valve, while the oxygenated blood passes ventrally to the **spiral valve** and into the arteries coursing toward the head and into the systems (fig. 335I). This condition of the conus is present also in urodeles with well-developed lungs, but, in urodeles without well-developed lungs, the spiral valve is absent and the interatrial septum may regress (Noble, '31, pp. 187–194).

3) Amniota. The heart of reptiles, birds, and mammals differs from the heart of the *Amphibia* in that a mechanism is present which separates, more or less completely, the oxygenated blood from the non-oxygenated blood. For example, the heart of birds and mammals is a four-chambered affair as an **interventricular septum** divides the primitive ventricle into two separate compartments while an **interatrial septum** separates the primitive atrium into two atria. A double heart is produced in this manner wherein the non-oxygenated blood returning from the organ systems passes through the right atrium and ventricle en route to the lungs while the oxygenated blood from the lungs journeys through the left atrium and ventricle on its way back to the organ systems. In the heart of birds and mammals, it is to be observed also, that only two arterial channels convey blood from the heart; namely, a **pulmonary arterial trunk** and a **systemic arterial trunk.** Another feature is present in the heart of the birds and mammals which serves to distinguish it from the hearts found in all lower vertebrates, in that the sinus venosus is absorbed almost entirely during embryonic development into the wall and structure of the right atrium.

Turning now to a consideration of the hearts of reptiles we find that the turtles and snakes possess a heart with two atria and a ventricular region divided rather completely into two ventricles. However, the interventricular septum is slightly incomplete in the region near the atria, and some leakage of blood between the two ventricles is possible. In the crocodilians the interventricular septum is completely developed, but a small opening, the **foramen of Panizza,** is present at the bases of the two systemic arterial trunks. This foramen arises as a secondary perforation later in development and does not represent an incompleteness of the interventricular septum. In the reptilian heart the sinus venosus retains its identity as a separate chamber of the heart. Furthermore, contrary to the conditions found in the avian and mammalian heart, **three arterial trunks convey blood away from the ventricles.** Two of these vascular trunks come from the right ventricle, and one from the left ventricle, for a *pulmonary trunk* conveys blood from the right ventricle to the lungs, while a *systemic aortic* root also carries blood from the right ventricle to the abdominal aorta. From the left ventricle, on the other hand, blood is propelled through a single aortic root to the head, forelimbs, and abdominal aorta (fig. 341H).

a) HEART OF THE CHICK. The heart arises as a simple tube during the *second day* of incubation (fig. 339G). At the end of the second day and during the *third day,* the primitive ventricle bends to the right, and the atrium begins to travel forward above the ventricle (figs. 336C; 339H'). At the end of the *third day,* the heart attains the typical sigmoid or S-shaped condition which arises as the first major step in heart development in all vertebrate embryos. During the *fourth day* of incubation, the atrial area expands into two main lobes, the beginnings of the right and left atria; the ventricular area expands greatly and thickens; and the bulbus cordis lies in the median line between the developing atria (fig. 339I). The position of the various parts of the heart on the whole assumes more nearly the adult condition.

Internally, toward the end of the fourth day, an **interatrial septum** begins to develop from the dorso-anterior area between the two atrial lobes, slightly to the left of the opening of the sinus venosus. The septum continues to form posteriad toward the narrowed **atrio-ventricular opening** between the atria and the forming ventricles. Simultaneously in the atrioventricular opening, two endocardial thickenings, the **endocardial cushions,** arise, one dorsal and one ventral. At the apex of the ventricle, an **interventricular septum** appears and grows forward toward the atrioventricular opening (fig. 340G).

During the *fifth and sixth days,* the two **endocardial cushions** grow together and separate the atrioventricular canal into two passageways by the formation of a **cushion septum.** The atrial septum grows toward the endocardial cushion area and unites with the **cushion septum.** However, the atrial septum never is completed during embryonic life, as small openings or **fenestrae,** appear in the septum permitting blood to pass through the septum. During the last week of incubation, the fenestral openings in the atrial septum become much smaller and completely close shortly after hatching. The ventricular septum, meanwhile, grows forward to unite with the cushion septum. Up to the fifth day, but one passageway leaves the heart via the developing bulbus cordis and ventral aorta. However, during the *fifth day,* beginning at the area just anterior

---

Fig. 340. Early stages in morphogenesis of various vertebrate hearts *(Continued).* (A–E) Internal changes in the developing heart of the pig. (A–D, redrawn from Patten, **1948.** Embryology of the Pig, 3d edit., Blakiston, Philadelphia.) (A) Diagram of 3.7 mm. pig embryo heart, ventral wall removed. (B) Similar diagram of 6 mm. pig heart. (C) Similar diagram of 9.4 mm. pig heart. (D) Similar diagram of dissected pig fetal heart shortly before birth. (E) Schematic drawing of dissected 18 mm. pig heart viewed from right side with walls of right atrium and right ventricle removed. Observe that the bulbus cordis has divided into two vascular trunks. (F) Dorsal aspect of the heart of an 11 wk. (60 mm.) human embryo. (Redrawn and modified from Patten, **1946.** Human Embryology, Blakiston, Philadelphia.) The *contraction wave* of the heart beat is indicated by heavy arrows. Starting at the *sinus node* situated in the dorsal wall of the right atrium, the contraction wave spreads over the atrial walls and also to the *atrioventricular node* located in the atrial septum from whence it travels distally through the ventricular tissue. (G) The developing chick heart, of about 6–7 days. Right walls removed to show developing cardiac septa. The ventricular septum is still incomplete, and the atrial septum is fenestrated. (This figure has been modified considerably from Kerr, **1919.** Text-Book of Vertebrate Embryology, vol. II, Macmillan, Ltd., London, after Greil.) (H) Adult heart of the South American lung fish, *Lepidosiren paradoxus,* right side removed. (Redrawn from Robertson, **1913.** Quart. J. Micros. Sci., **59.**)

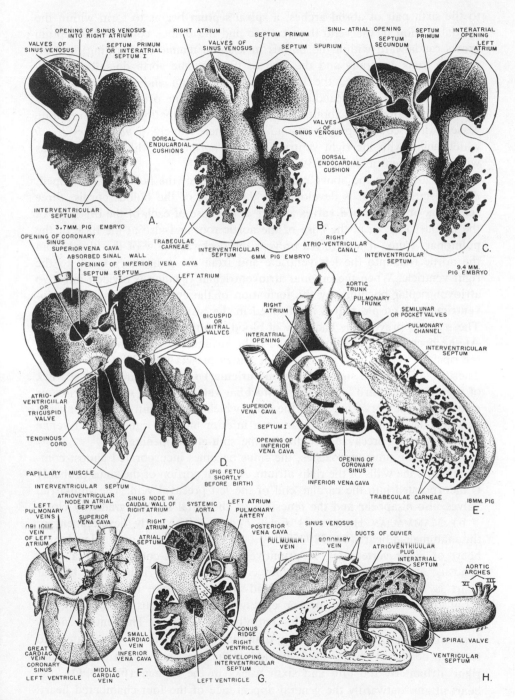

OPENING OF SINUS VENOSUS
INTO RIGHT ATRIUM

VALVES OF
SINUS VENOSUS

SEPTUM PRIMUM
OR INTERATRIAL
SEPTUM I

RIGHT ATRIUM

VALVES OF
SINUS VENOSUS

SEPTUM PRIMUM

SEPTUM
SPURIUM

SINU- ATRIAL OPENING

SEPTUM
SECUNDUM

SEPTUM
PRIMUM

INTERATRIAL
OPENING

LEFT
ATRIUM

DORSAL
ENDOCARDIAL
CUSHIONS

VALVES
OF SINUS VENOSUS

DORSAL
ENDOCARDIAL
CUSHION

INTERVENTRICULAR
SEPTUM

A.

3.7MM. PIG EMBRYO

TRABECULAE
CARNEAE

INTERVENTRICULAR
SEPTUM

6MM. PIG EMBRYO

B.

RIGHT
ATRIO-VENTRICULAR
CANAL

INTERVENTRICULAR
SEPTUM

9.4 MM.
PIG EMBRYO

C.

OPENING OF CORONARY
SINUS

SUPERIOR VENA CAVA

ABSORBED SINAL WALL

OPENING OF INFERIOR VENA CAVA

SEPTUM   SEPTUM
II   I

LEFT ATRIUM

BICUSPID
OR MITRAL
VALVES

ATRIO-
VENTRICULAR
OR TRICUSPID
VALVE

TENDINOUS
CORD

PAPILLARY MUSCLE

INTERVENTRICULAR SEPTUM

D.

(PIG FETUS
SHORTLY
BEFORE BIRTH)

RIGHT
ATRIUM

AORTIC
TRUNK

PULMONARY
TRUNK

SEMILUNAR
OR POCKET VALVES

PULMONARY
CHANNEL

INTERVENTRICULAR
SEPTUM

INTERATRIAL
OPENING

SUPERIOR
VENA CAVA

SEPTUM I

OPENING OF
INFERIOR
VENA CAVA

OPENING OF
CORONARY
SINUS

INFERIOR VENA CAVA

TRABECULAE CARNEAE

18MM. PIG

E.

LEFT
PULMONARY
VEINS

ATRIOVENTRICULAR
NODE IN ATRIAL
SEPTUM

SINUS NODE IN
CAUDAL WALL OF
RIGHT ATRIUM

SYSTEMIC
AORTA

LEFT ATRIUM

PULMONARY
ARTERY

SUPERIOR
VENA CAVA

OBLIQUE
VEIN
OF LEFT
ATRIUM

RIGHT
ATRIUM

ATRIAL
SEPTUM

POSTERIOR
VENA CAVA

PULMONARY
VEIN

SINUS VENOSUS

CORONARY
VEIN

DUCTS OF CUVIER

ATRIOVENTRICULAR
PLUG

INTERATRIAL
SEPTUM

AORTIC
ARCHES

SMALL
CARDIAC
VEIN

INFERIOR
VENA CAVA

CONUS
RIDGE

RIGHT
VENTRICLE

DEVELOPING
INTERVENTRICULAR
SEPTUM

SPIRAL VALVE

VENTRICULAR
SEPTUM

GREAT
CARDIAC
VEIN

CORONARY
SINUS

LEFT VENTRICLE

F.

MIDDLE
CARDIAC
VEIN

LEFT VENTRICLE

G.

H.

FIG. 340. *(See facing page for legend.)*

to the sixth pair of aortal arches, a **spiral septum** begins to form within the caudal portion of the ventral aortal sac and the bulbus cordis. This septum grows caudalward within the bulbus in a spiral manner, separating the pulmonary trunk ventrally and the root of the systemic aorta dorsally. It continues backward toward the interventricular septum and there unites with a similar septum at the caudal end of the bulbus. The original bulbus cordis thus becomes divided at about the *seventh day* of incubation into two separate vessels which course spirally around each other, namely, a *pulmonary trunk* which unites with the right ventricle and an *aortal root* which is continuous with the left ventricle (fig. 339J).

Coincident with the above changes, the valves of the heart are developed. As the spiral septum is developed in the region of the bulbus cordis, **three semilunar or cup-shaped valves** appear at the base of each of the divisions of the bulbus. That is, at the base of the aortic root and also at the base of the pulmonary trunk. These valves prevent the backward flow of the blood from the aortic root into the left ventricle and from the pulmonary trunk to the right ventricle. When the original atrioventricular opening is divided into two atrioventricular openings by the formation of the cushion septum, the **atrioventricular or cuspid valves** are formed in the two atrioventricular openings. These valves prevent the backflow of blood into the atria from the ventricles. At the opening of the sinus into the right atrium, the right and left sides of the opening enlarge and produce folds which project inward into the atrium. These folds form the **sinu-atrial (sinu-auricular) valves.** During the last week of incubation, a third valve, the **Eustachian valve or sinus septum,** arises as a fold from the dorsal aspect of the sinus which projects into the right atrium between the openings of the vena cava inferior and the right and left venae cavae superior (precavae). It divides the sinu-atrial opening.

As hatching time approaches, the sinus becomes incorporated almost completely into the walls of the right atrium. A small portion of the sinus probably is incorporated into the cardiac end of the left precaval vein. The sinu-atrial valves also disappear and the fenestrae of the atrial septum gradually close.

b) MAMMALIAN HEART: *1) Early Features.* The early development of the mammalian heart (fig. 339) follows the general pattern of the developing heart of lower vertebrates. A primitive tubular heart composed of a sinus venosus, atrium, ventricle and bulbus cordis is evolved. This simple tubular heart is followed by a typical sigmoid-shaped structure in which the two atrial lobes hang ventrally, one on either side of the bulbus cordis, while the ventricular region projects caudo-ventrally (fig. 339N). The sinus venosus is much smaller, relatively speaking, than that formed in lower vertebrates and tends to be placed toward the right side of the heart in relation to the future right atrium. By the fifth and sixth weeks in the human (fig. 339O), the heart attains outwardly the general appearance of the four-chambered heart.

2) Internal Partitioning. The internal divisions of the heart begin to appear in the human at about the fifth week, and in the pig at about 4 mm. or 17 days. This process is similar in the human and the pig, and while the following description pertains particularly to the pig it may be applied readily to the developing human heart. In the pig, as in the chick, a crescentic fold or septum of the atrial chamber begins to grow caudally toward the atrioventricular opening from the antero-dorsal region of the atrium. This septum forms the **septum primum or interatrial septum I** (fig. 340A). As this septum grows caudad, two thickenings, the **endocardial cushions,** one dorsal and one ventral, arise in the atrioventricular opening (fig. 340B). The endocardial cushions fuse and divide the atrioventricular canal into two openings. The septum primum ultimately joins and fuses with the endocardial cushions, but the septum as a whole is incomplete, an **interatrial opening** being present (fig. 340C). Meanwhile, the sinus venosus shifts more completely toward the right atrium, and the opening of the sinus into the right atrium also shifts dextrally. This permits an enlarged area to appear between the interatrial septum and the **valvulae venosae,** or valves of the sinus venosus guarding the sinu-atrial opening. In this area, **interatrial septum II or septum secundum,** arises as a downgrowth from the atrial roof (fig. 340C, D). This second septum eventually produces a condition as shown in figure 340D. The arrow denotes the passageway or **foramen ovale** in the septum secundum and also the outlet for the blood into the left atrium over the dorsal part of the valve of the foramen ovale (**valvula foraminis ovalis),** derived from the atrioventricular end of septum I. This condition persists until birth. The valve of the foramen ovale derived from septum I prevents the backflow of blood from the left atrium into the right atrium.

The atrioventricular valves are shown also in figure 340D, together with the fibrous attachments of these valves to the muscular columns of the left and right ventricles. The atrioventricular or **cuspid valves** arise as thickened, shelf-like growths of connective tissue, to which the tendinous cords from the papillary muscles become attached. The left and right ventricles are produced as in the chick by the upgrowth from the ventricular apex of the **interventricular septum.** In the human, the interventricular septum fuses with the endocardial cushions during the eighth to ninth weeks. The papillary muscles projecting inward into the ventricular cavities (fig. 340D) represent modifications of the trabeculae carneae (fig. 340B).

3) Fate of the Sinus Venosus. The developing superior and inferior venae cavae open into the right horn of the sinus venosus. As the right atrium enlarges it absorbs this right horn into its walls and the venae cavae obtain separate openings into the right atrium (fig. 340D). The body of the sinus venosus becomes the coronary sinus which opens into the right atrium below the opening of the inferior vena cava. The coronary veins empty into the coronary sinus. The left horn of the sinus venosus may persist as a part of the **oblique vein** of the left atrium (fig. 340F).

	f. Fate of the Segments of the Early Embryonic Heart in Various Vertebrates				
	Fishes	*Amphibia*	*Reptiles*	*Birds*	*Mammals*
Sinus venosus	Retained as separate chamber of the heart	Retained as separate chamber of the heart	Small and closely united with right atrium	Taken up almost completely within the wall of right atrium	Practically the same as in birds
Atrium	Single chamber in most fishes; in Dipnoi separated by fenestrated interatrial septum (see fig. 340H)	Divided by interatrial septum into two atria; in water-living amphibians the septum may be fenestrated	Divided by interatrial septum into two atria	Same as in reptiles	Same as in reptiles
Ventricle	Single chamber, excepting in Dipnoi where it is divided partly by interventricular septum	Single chamber	Turtles, lizards, and snakes almost completely divided by interventricular septum; in crocodilians, the ventricle is completely divided into two chambers	Interventricular septum divides primitive ventricle into two chambers	Same as in birds
Bulbus cordis	Single, anterior contractile chamber, the **conus arteriosus**. The conus is weakened in Dipnoi, and **spiral valve** is present	Develops a single contractile chamber, the **conus arteriosus**. A spiral valve incompletely divides the conus into two channels. Spiral valve may be absent in urodeles without well-developed lungs	Divides into **three aortic trunks** (fig. 341H)	Divides into **two aortic trunks** (fig. 342D, J)	Same as in birds. However, a part of the bulbus cordis may contribute to form a portion of the wall of the right ventricle

4) The Division of the Bulbus Cordis (Truncus Arteriosus and Conus).
The division of the bulbus cordis occurs synchronously with the above changes.
Two internal ridges opposite each other are formed during this process. These
ridges fuse and divide the bulbus in a spiral fashion into a dorsal aortic root
and a pulmonary trunk as indicated in figure 340E. The pulmonary trunk
opens into the right ventricle, and the aortic root opens into the left
ventricle. Three cup-shaped, **semilunar (pocket) valves** are developed from
internal ridges in the areas between the base of the aortic trunk and the left
ventricle and between the base of the pulmonary trunk and the conus portion
of the right ventricle (fig. 340E).

4. Modifications of the Aortal Arches

When the heart begins to form, its position is ventro-posteriorly to the
developing pharyngeal area. As the pharyngeal region enlarges, the heart
recedes, relatively speaking, and moves caudally. This caudal recession of the
primitive heart in relation to the pharyngeal area is greater in fishes than in
the amphibia and higher vertebrates. Therefore, the ventral aortae (and later
ventral aorta) are longer in fishes than in other vertebrates. Actually, in the
amphibia and particularly in the higher vertebrates, the primitive heart itself
tends to lie below the pharyngeal area. Consequently, the bulbus cordis or
anterior end of the primitive heart comes to lie below the midpharyngeal
region, and the aortal arches in amphibia and in higher vertebrates arise from
the anterior end of the primitive heart in bouquet fashion (figs. 341E, 342A,
E). On the other hand, in fishes, a single, elongated, ventral aorta is formed,
which extends the length of the pharyngeal area. The developing heart is
attached to its caudal end, and the aortal arches arise along its extent (fig.
341A).

The aortal arches are paired vessels which run dorsally through the substance of the visceral arches. Six pairs of these arches are formed generally
in the gnathostomous vertebrates, although some of them are transitory structures. The first, second, and fifth pairs of aortal arches are the most transitory
in all forms above the fishes.

During development the aortal arches are modified differently in the various
vertebrate groups. In fishes, a permanent, branchial mechanism is inserted
midway along the branchial visceral arches. The aortal arch of each branchial
visceral arch is broken up into an afferent vessel, passing from the ventral
aorta to the branchial (gill) structure, and an efferent vessel, leading from
the gill mechanism to the dorsal aorta (fig. 341B). In the majority of amphibia,
the first, second, and third *branchial aortal arches become involved temporarily*
in the development of gill mechanisms, although some, such as *Necturus,*
retain the gills permanently. In higher vertebrates, none of the aortal arches
are concerned with gill formation, and are, in consequence, transformed
directly into the adult form.

The transformation of the aortal arches in the shark, frog, chick, and mammal is shown in figures 341 and 342. It is important to observe that, in those vertebrates possessing lungs, the pulmonary artery grows back from the sixth aortal arch. In a sense, however, the pulmonary arteries represent a direct caudal growth from the posterior ventral aortae, particularly in reptiles, birds, and mammals (fig. 342A, B, C, E, F, G).

5. DORSAL AORTAE (AORTA) AND BRANCHES

Two dorsal aortae arise first, one on either side of the notochord and above the primitive gut tube, and their origin is synchronous with the formation of the ventral, vitelline (subintestinal) blood vessels and the heart. Posterior to the pharyngeal area, the primitive dorsal aortae soon fuse to form a secondary vessel, the *dorsal aorta,* lying below the notochord. Anteriorly, in the pharyngeal area, they remain separate, and the cephalic end of each primitive dorsal aorta grows forward into the developing forebrain area. These forward growths of the primitive dorsal aortae into the forebrain area form the anterior rudiments of the **internal carotid arteries.** The primitive dorsal aortae, therefore, give origin to a single secondary vessel, the **dorsal aorta,** which is bifurcated at its cephalic end in the region of the pharyngeal area of the gut.

Aside from the cephalic ends of the internal carotid arteries, three main sets of arteries arise from the developing dorsal aorta:

1) **Dorsal intersegmental arteries,** passing between the somites and sending a dorsal branch toward the neural tube and epaxial musculature and a lateral branch into the hypaxial musculature (fig. 343A). The lateral branches develop into *intercostal* and *lumbar arteries* of the

---

FIG. 341. Modifications of the aortal arches. In the following diagrams, the aortal arches are depicted in such a way as to represent two parts, viz. an *afferent system,* conveying the blood from the heart to the branchial (gill) region, and an *efferent system,* leading the blood away from the branchial area. The afferent system of vessels is finely stippled, whereas the efferent system is ringed with lines. With the exception of certain lateral views all diagrams have been made from the dorsal view.   (A–D) Aortal vessel changes in embryos of *Squalus acanthias.* (A and B, adapted from actual conditions described by Scammon, **1911.** See reference under Fig. 339.)   (A) Generalized, basic condition present in embryo of 15 mm. embryo.   (B) Lateral view, 20.6 mm. stage. (C and D) The afferent and efferent systems in the adult form. D should be superimposed upon C. Diagrams C and D have been separated to minimize confusion.   (E–G) Modifications of the aortal arches in the frog. The modifications of the aortal arches in the frog involve a complicated series of changes. In Fig. 335 (A) the simple tubular aortal arches are shown during the earlier phases of development. In Fig. 257 (B) a later stage is depicted. In the latter figure the aortal arches are separated into functional afferent and efferent vessels supplying the branchiae or gills. At the time of metamorphosis the vessels are reorganized, apparently, into tubular vessels according to the pattern shown in Fig. 341 (E). The transformations of the basic conditions shown in Fig. 341 (E) into the adult form are outlined in Figs. 341 (F and G).   (H) The three divisions of the bulbus cordis in the turtle.

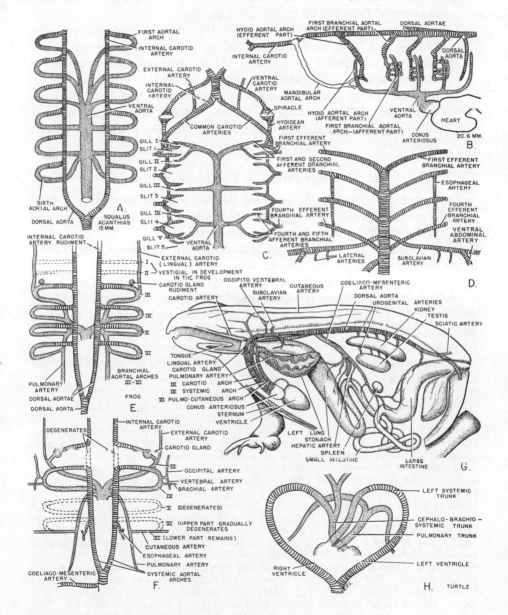

FIG. 341. (See facing page for legend.)

761

adult. The arteries to the bilateral appendages arise as modifications of the lateral branches of the intersegmental arteries (fig. 343B, C').

2) **Lateral arteries** which are not as truly segmented as are the dorsal intersegmental arteries. They pass laterally into the developing nephrotomic structures (fig. 343A). The renal and genital arteries of the adult are derived from the lateral series of arteries.

3) **Ventral arteries** much fewer in number than the above-mentioned series (fig. 343A). The vitelline arteries of the yolk-sac area are the first of these ventral arteries to develop. In the *Amniota,* the umbilical or allantoic arteries also belong to the ventral series of arteries arising from the dorsal aorta. These vessels pass to the placenta or allantoic areas. The **coeliac, superior mesenteric, inferior mesenteric,** and **umbilical arteries** are the adult derivatives of the ventral series of arteries arising from the primitive dorsal aorta.

E. Development of the Lymphatic System

The lymphatic system often is called the white blood circulatory system because red blood cells are not present normally, its blood being composed of a lymph fluid and various types of white blood cells.

Lymph vessels are present in all gnathostomous vertebrates, particularly in the bony fishes and in amphibia, reptiles, birds, and mammals. They appear to be absent in cyclostomes. The lymphatic system is highly developed in the amphibia where it possesses **lymph hearts,** which actively propel the lymphatic fluid forward. Lymph hearts are found in the tail region of bird embryos, including the chick. However, lymph flow on the whole is of a sluggish nature. Lymph vessels never join arteries but connect in various regions with the veins. In larval amphibia and in certain adult species of amphibia, these connections with the venous system may be numerous.

Fig. 342. Modifications of the aortal arches *(Continued).* (A) Generalized, basic condition of the aortal arches in the chick embryo developed during the first 3½ days of incubation. (B) Left lateral view of condition present during latter part of the third day. (C) Schematic representation of changes in aortal arches, dorsal aortae, and the aortal sac of the chick embryo after the first week and a half of incubation. Observe that each external carotid artery arises from the anterior end of a ventral aortic root plus an anastomosis with the common carotid segment. Note further that the right and left sixth aoral arches persist until approximately the twenty-first day (see diagram D). (Diagram C is based to some extent upon data supplied by Pohlman, **1920.** Anat. Rec. **18.**) (D) Dorsal view of adult condition of aortal-arch and bulbuscordis derivatives in the developing chick after hatching. (E) Generalized aortal arch condition in mammalian embryo. (F) Dorsal view of aortal arches of about 6 mm. human embryo. (G) Lateral view of same. (This figure redrawn and adapted from Patten, **1946.** Human Embryology, Blakiston, Philadelphia, after Congdon.) (H) Dorsal view of aortal arches of 14 mm. embryo. (I) Left lateral view of same. (This figure is redrawn and adapted from Patten, **1946.** Human Embryology, Blakiston, Philadelphia.) (J) Dorsal view of conditions present after birth. (See also Fig. 379.)

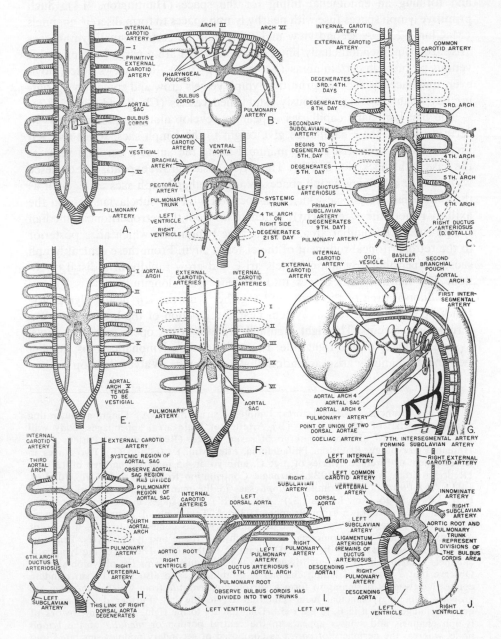

FIG. 342. (See facing page for legend.)

Two general views are held as to the origin of the lymphatic system. One view holds that lymphatic vessels develop independently of blood vessels and originate as small spaces in the mesenchyme, the mesenchymal cells flattening and forming an endothelial lining for the space (Huntington, '14). Such primitive lymph spaces fuse with nearby lymph spaces to form discrete channels (McClure, '21). A second view maintains that the certain, small **lymph sacs** arise from small endothelially lined channels which are a part of the primitive venous plexuses in certain areas (Sabin, '12, p. 709). Both views agree, however, that once formed, the primitive lymph vessels grow and spread by sprouting new channels from previously established vessels (Clark and Clark, '32).

The first lymphatic capillaries appear to develop along the main veins. In certain regions, these capillaries give origin to the lymph sacs. **Right and left** jugular **lymph sacs** arise in the mammal along the anterior cardinal veins at the base of the neck (fig. 343D). These lymph sacs grow, expand, and coalesce with smaller adjoining lymph spaces. Various other lymph sacs arise, such as the **subclavian lymph sac** which is associated with the subclavian vein in the axillary region, the **cisterna chyli** which arises from the retroperitoneal, median lymph sac in the lumbar area, and the **iliac lymph sacs** which arise posterior to the retroperitoneal rudiment of the cisterna chyli. From these central lymph sacs, the peripheral lymph channels arise and grow rapidly in a distal direction. The **thoracic duct** comes into existence as a longitudinal vessel along the middorsal area of the body and together with the **left jugular lymphatic trunk** opens into the venous system near the junction of the internal and external jugular veins. The **right jugular lymphatic trunk** opens into the venous system similarly on the right side. From these main lymphatic areas, smaller peripheral channels arise as endothelial outgrowths. **Valves** develop within.

FIG. 343. Branches of dorsal aorta; lymphatic structures. (A) Diagram illustrating various branches of dorsal aorta. (B) Arteries of brain area, appendages, body wall and umbilical cord of human embryo of seven weeks. (Redrawn from Patten, **1946.** Human Embryology, Blakiston, Philadelphia, after Mall.) (C and C') Two stages in development of forelimb arteries of pig: C, embryo of 4.5 mm.; C', embryo of 12 mm. (Redrawn from Woollard, **1922.** Carnegie Contribution to Embryology, No. 70, Vol. 14.) (D) Formation of primitive lymph sacs in the mammal (cat). (Redrawn from F. T. Lewis, **1906.** Am. J. Anat. **5.**) (E and E') Four stages in the development of a lymph node. (Redrawn from Bremer, **1936.** A Text-book of Histology, Blakiston, Philadelphia.) Diagram E, to the left. Lymphatic vessels come to surround a mass of primitive lymphoid tissue composed of mesenchymal tissue and lymphocytes. Primitive connective tissue surrounds the mass. Diagram E, to the right. The ingrowing lymphatic channels break up the lymphoidal tissue with the subsequent formation of lymph sinuses. Observe that a peripheral lymph channel is established, and also that the surrounding connective tissue is beginning to form a surrounding *capsule* from which *trabeculae* are growing into the lymphoidal mass. Diagram E', to the left. Further development of growth changes shown in E, to the right. Diagram E', to the right. A loose meshwork of lymph channels and sinuses appears in the central portion or *medulla* of the lymph node, whereas the periphery or *cortex* is composed of secondary nodules separated into compartments by the ingrowth of trabeculae from the peripheral capsule.

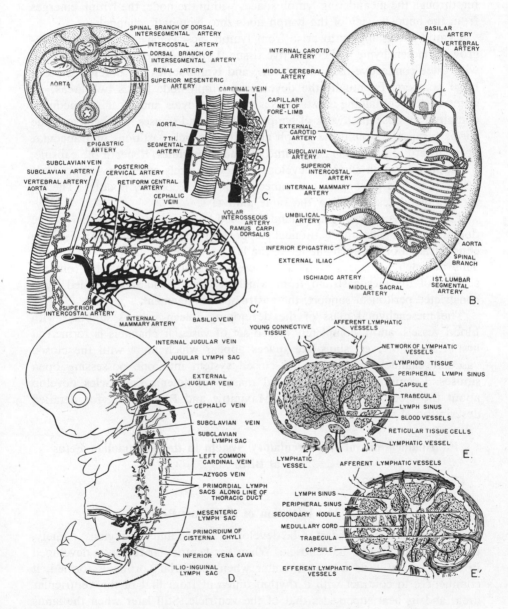

Labels in the figure:

A.
- SPINAL BRANCH OF DORSAL INTERSEGMENTAL ARTERY
- INTERCOSTAL ARTERY
- DORSAL BRANCH OF INTERSEGMENTAL ARTERY
- RENAL ARTERY
- SUPERIOR MESENTERIC ARTERY
- AORTA
- EPIGASTRIC ARTERY

C.
- CARDINAL VEIN
- AORTA
- 7TH. SEGMENTAL ARTERY

C'.
- SUBCLAVIAN VEIN
- SUBCLAVIAN ARTERY
- VERTEBRAL ARTERY
- AORTA
- POSTERIOR CERVICAL ARTERY
- RETIFORM CENTRAL ARTERY
- CEPHALIC VEIN
- CAPILLARY NET OF FORE-LIMB
- VOLAR INTEROSSEOUS ARTERY
- RAMUS CARPI DORSALIS
- SUPERIOR INTERCOSTAL ARTERY
- INTERNAL MAMMARY ARTERY
- BASILIC VEIN

B.
- BASILAR ARTERY
- VERTEBRAL ARTERY
- INTERNAL CAROTID ARTERY
- MIDDLE CEREBRAL ARTERY
- EXTERNAL CAROTID ARTERY
- SUBCLAVIAN ARTERY
- SUPERIOR INTERCOSTAL ARTERY
- INTERNAL MAMMARY ARTERY
- UMBILICAL ARTERY
- INFERIOR EPIGASTRIC
- EXTERNAL ILIAC
- ISCHIADIC ARTERY
- MIDDLE SACRAL ARTERY
- 1ST. LUMBAR SEGMENTAL ARTERY
- SPINAL BRANCH
- AORTA

D.
- INTERNAL JUGULAR VEIN
- JUGULAR LYMPH SAC
- EXTERNAL JUGULAR VEIN
- CEPHALIC VEIN
- SUBCLAVIAN VEIN
- SUBCLAVIAN LYMPH SAC
- LEFT COMMON CARDINAL VEIN
- AZYGOS VEIN
- PRIMORDIAL LYMPH SACS ALONG LINE OF THORACIC DUCT
- MESENTERIC LYMPH SAC
- PRIMORDIUM OF CISTERNA CHYLI
- INFERIOR VENA CAVA
- ILIO-INGUINAL LYMPH SAC

E.
- YOUNG CONNECTIVE TISSUE
- AFFERENT LYMPHATIC VESSELS
- NETWORK OF LYMPHATIC VESSELS
- LYMPHOID TISSUE
- PERIPHERAL LYMPH SINUS
- CAPSULE
- TRABECULA
- LYMPH SINUS
- BLOOD VESSELS
- RETICULAR TISSUE CELLS
- LYMPHATIC VESSEL
- LYMPHATIC VESSEL

E'.
- AFFERENT LYMPHATIC VESSELS
- LYMPH SINUS
- PERIPHERAL SINUS
- SECONDARY NODULE
- MEDULLARY CORD
- TRABECULA
- CAPSULE
- EFFERENT LYMPHATIC VESSELS

FIG. 343. (*See facing page for legend.*)

A characteristic feature of the lymphatic system is the development of **lymph nodes** (lymph glands) along the lymphatic vessels. A lymph node is a small, rounded structure with lymph vessels entering it at various points (fig. 343E). From these lymph vessels, a flow of lymph oozes around a meshwork of **lymphoid cords,** contained within the lymph node. After passing through the meandering lymph spaces within the node, the lymph emerges from the opposite side of the lymph node into lymphatic channels.

Lymph nodes appear to arise from lymph sacs which are invaded by ingrowing mesenchyme and connective tissue. **Lymphoblasts** become associated with these connective-tissue ingrowths, and **lymphocytes** are differentiated in large numbers. Eventually the developing lymph node forms two areas, an outer **cortex,** containing dense masses of lymphocytes and an inner **medulla,** containing a loose meshwork of lymph channels and sinuses. Connective tissue forms a **capsule** around the lymph node from which partitions or **trabeculae** grow inward to divide the cortex into **secondary nodules.** Beneath the capsule, a peripheral lymph sinus is developed. Blood vessels enter the lymph node at the hilus and pass along the trabeculae to the secondary nodules. The returning blood vessels follow the same pathways.

The **spleen** is a large lymph gland attached to the omental derivative of the dorsal mesogastrium or peritoneal support of the stomach. It arises as a concentration of mesenchyme along the left aspect of the early mesogastrium. This mesenchymal mass eventually increases in size and projects from the surface of the mesogastrium from which it later becomes suspended by a constricted peritoneal support, the **gastro-splenic ligament.**

The mesenchymal mass of the developing spleen is well supplied with blood vessels, and a completely closed set of vascular channels is formed at first. Later, however, **sinus-like spaces** appear which unite with the closed vascular channels converting the closed system into one possessing open sinuses. Lymphoid tissue forms and masses of **splenic corpuscles** develop about the blood vessels. (Consult Maximow and Bloom, '42, for detailed description of splenic structure.)

F. Modifications of the Circulatory System in the Mammalian Fetus at Birth

Consult Chap. 22.

G. The Initiation of the Heart Beat

The first parts of the heart to be developed are the anterior regions, namely, the bulbus cordis and the ventricle. When the ventricular region is developed in the chick, it starts to twitch. Later when the atrial portion is formed, it commences to contract with a rhythm different from that of the ventricular area, and its beat supersedes that of the ventricle. Still later when the sinus venosus is established, it emerges with its own contraction rhythm, and this rhythm then dominates the contraction wave which spreads forward over the heart. The area of the sinus continues to be the "pacesetter" of the heart beat throughout life, although in birds and mammals, the sinus is taken up into the posterior wall of the right atrium. In the mammal (fig. 340F), the **sinus node,** located in the right atrium, initiates, under normal conditions, each heart beat. The contraction stimulus spreads distally to the peculiar fibrous bundle, located in the atrial septum and the atrioventricular area. This bundle is known as the **atrioventricular node,** and its fibers descend into the muscles of the ventricular area, conveying the heart beat to the ventricles.

Though fibers from the autonomic nervous system reach the heart in the region of the right atrium and stimuli from these nerves may greatly affect the rhythm of the heart beat, the essential control of the beat lies within the heart's own nodal system (fig. 340F).

Bibliography

Bloom, W. and Bartelmez, G. W. **1940.** Hematopoiesis in young human embryos. Am. J. Anat. **67**:21.

Clark, E. R. and Clark, E. L. **1932.** Am. J. Anat. **51**:49.

Gilmour, J. R. **1941.** Normal haemopoiesis in intra-uterine and neonatal life. J. Path. & Bact. **52**:25.

Hochstetter, F. **1906.** Chap. IV in Handbuch der vergleichenden und experimentellen Entwickelungslehre der Wirbeltiere by O. Hertwig. Gustav Fischer, Jena.

Huntington, G. S. **1914.** Development of lymphatic system in amniotes. Am. J. Anat. **16**:127.

Jordan, H. E. and Speidel, C. C. **1923a.** Blood cell formation and destruction in relation to the mechanism of thyroid accelerated metamorphoses in the larval frog. J. Exper. Med. **38**:529.

———— and ————. **1923b.** Studies on lymphocytes. I. Effects of splenectomy, experimental hemorrhage and a hemolytic toxin in the frog. Am. J. Anat. **32**:155.

Kampmeier, O. E. **1920.** The changes of the systemic venous plan during development and the relation of the lymph hearts to them in *Anura.* Anat. Rec. **19**:83.

Maximow, A. A. and Bloom, W. **1942.** A Textbook of Histology. Saunders, Philadelphia.

McClure, C. F. W. **1921.** The endothelial problem. Anat. Rec. **22**:219.

Miller, A. M. **1903.** The development of the postcaval vein in birds. Am. J. Anat. **2**:283.

Minot, C. S. **1912.** Chap. 18, Vol. II, p. 498, The origin of the angioblast and the development of the blood in Human Embryology by Keibel, F. and Mall, F. P. J. B. Lippincott Co., Philadelphia.

Noble, G. K. **1931.** The Biology of the Amphibia. McGraw-Hill, New York and London.

Reagan, F. P. **1917.** Experimental studies on the origin of vascular endothelium and of erythrocytes. Am. J. Anat. **21**:39.

Sabin, F. R. **1912.** Chap. 18, Vol. II, p. 709, Development of the lymphatic system in human embryology by Keibel, F. and Mall, F. P. J. B. Lippincott Co., Philadelphia.

Scammon, R. E. **1913.** The development of the elasmobranch liver. Am. J. Anat. **14**:333.

Stockard, C. R. **1915.** The origin of blood and vascular endothelium in embryos without a circulation of the blood and in normal embryos. Am. J. Anat. **18**:227.

18

The Excretory and Reproductive Systems

A. Introduction
  1. Developmental relationships
  2. Functions of the excretory and reproductive systems
  3. Basic embryonic tissues which contribute to the urogenital structures
B. Development of the excretory system
  1. General description
    a. Types of kidneys formed during embryonic development
    b. Types of nephrons or renal units produced in developing vertebrate embryos
  2. Functional kidneys during embryonic development
    a. Pronephros
    b. Mesonephros
    c. Metanephros and opisthonephros
  3. Development and importance of the pronephric kidney
    a. General considerations
    b. Shark, *Squalus acanthias*
    c. Frog
    d. Chick
    e. Mammal (human)
  4. Development of the mesonephric kidney
    a. *Squalus acanthias*
    b. Frog
    c. Chick
    d. Mammal
  5. Development of the metanephric kidney
    a. Chick
      1) Metanephric duct and metanephrogenous tissue
      2) Formation of the metanephric renal units
    b. Mammal (human)
      1) Formation of the pelvis, calyces, collecting ducts, and nephric units
      2) Formation of the capsule
      3) Changes in position of the developing kidney
  6. Urinary ducts and urinary bladders
    a. Types of urinary ducts
    b. Urinary bladders
    c. Cloaca

768

A. Introduction

1. Developmental Relationships

The excretory and reproductive systems often are grouped together as the **urogenital system.** This inclusive term is applied to these two systems because they are associated anatomically in the adult form and, during development, show marked interrelationships and dependencies.

An important relationship, shared by the developing reproductive and excretory systems, involves the caudal end or cloaca of the developing digestive tube. It is this area of the differentiating metenteron which affords an outlet to the external environment for the urogenital ducts in the majority of the vertebrate species. This fact will become obvious later.

2. Functions of the Excretory and Reproductive Systems

The functions of the reproductive systems of the male and female are discussed in Chapters 1 to 4 and 22.

The excretory system is most important in the maintenance of life, and is an important feature in the flow of fluids through the body as described in the introduction to Chapter 17. Food substances and water pass into the body through the walls of the digestive tract, and oxygen is admitted through the respiratory surfaces. The veins convey these substances to the heart and arteries (with the exception of fishes and some amphibia where oxygen passes directly into the arterial system), and the heart and arteries propel them to the tissues. Here the food substances and water are utilized, and excess

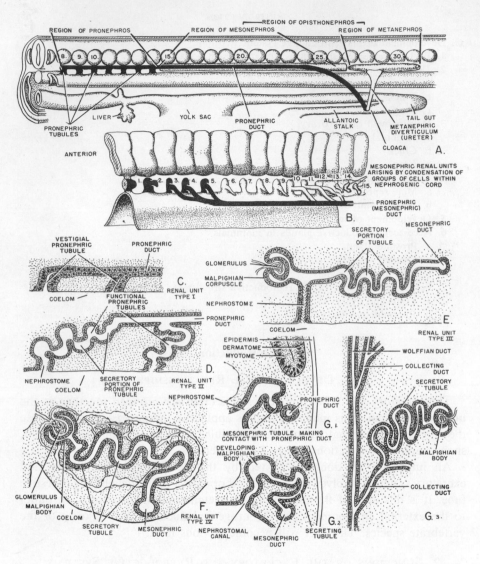

FIG. 344. Regions of kidney origin within the vertebrate group; types of renal units formed. (A) The regions in the body where the different types of vertebrate kidneys arise. *The pronephric tubules and the pronephric duct are shown in black to emphasize the fact that this part of the developing renal system is a fundamental and necessary primordium without which later kidney development is distorted.* (B) Differentiation of the anterior portion of the nephrotomic plate and the common method of origin of the pronephric duct. In the anterior region (toward the left in the figure) the nephrotomic plate segments into individual nephrotomes from each of which a renal tubule arises (see tubules 1 to 5). Tubules 6–9 is a vestigial area of tubule development. The anterior mesonephric region indicated by tubules 10 to 15, etc. In the anterior mesonephric area, e.g., tubules 10 and 11, the individual tubules show a tendency to arise segmentally, but in more posterior mesonephric regions, e.g., tubules 12 to 15, etc., the tubules arise through condensation of cellular masses within the *nephrogenic cord*. Hence, primitive

(Continued on facing page.)

770

salts, wastes, and water are the by-products. The veins, lymphatics, and arteries convey these substances to the areas of elimination as follows:

(1) Carbon dioxide and water are residues of carbohydrate metabolism. The carbon dioxide and some of the excess water in the body are discharged through the respiratory surfaces.

(2) The products of protein breakdown together with excess water and mineral salts are conveyed mainly to the kidneys and are eliminated there.

Exceptional areas exist for the elimination of some of the above-mentioned materials. For example, a certain amount of salts, nitrogenous wastes, and

---

FIG. 344—(Continued)

segmentation is lost. The pronephric duct is formed through coalescence of the outer distal portions of the pronephric tubules (see tubules 3, 4, and 5). The coalesced portion thus formed grows caudally to join the cloaca. The mesonephric tubules, however, appropriate the pronephric duct in a secondary manner, growing outward to join this duct (see tubules 10 to 12). The pronephric duct, after this appropriation, becomes the *mesonephric or Wolffian duct.*

FIGS. 344C–F are diagrams of different types of renal units (nephrons) which appear in developing vertebrate kidneys.

(C) This diagram represents a form of renal unit which we may designate as Type I. It is a vestigial tubule which may or may not become canalized. Its chief function is to initiate the formation of the pronephric duct. It is found in the pronephric kidneys of elasmobranch fishes, reptiles, birds, and mammals and, to some extent, in the anterior portion of the mesonephric kidneys of these groups.

(D) This diagram represents a renal unit found typically in the pronephric kidneys of larval forms such as that of the frog tadpole. It is designated as Type II. It possesses a ciliated nephrostome connecting with the coelomic cavity and a secretory portion which joins the pronephric duct.

(E) This diagram is given to represent the typical form of renal unit found in the earlier phases of mesonephric kidney development of lower vertebrates. It is called Type III. It is found also in the pronephric kidney of *Hypogeophis* (Gymnophiona) (see Brauer, '02). With some modifications it may represent a type of renal unit found in the adult kidney of the urodele, *Necturus maculosus* (see fig. 345D).

(F) The *Type IV* renal unit is similar to Type III but lacks the ciliated nephrostomal connection with the coelomic cavity. It is the later renal unit of the mesonephric kidney of most fishes and amphibia and the typical renal unit found in the mesonephric kidney of reptile, bird, and mammalian embryos. With some elaboration it would represent the nephron (renal unit) found in the metanephric kidney of reptiles, birds, and mammals.

G.1., G.2., G.3., stages in development of the mesonephric tubule in the embryo of *Squalus acanthias.* G.1. and G.2. the tubule arises from the nephrotome in a segmental fashion and appropriates the pronephric duct. G.3. a later mesonephric tubule. In the latter tubule the nephrostomal connection with the coelomic cavity is lost. Observe that the tubule empties into the collecting duct, an outgrowth of the mesonephric duct. The early primitive segmental condition is lost and many tubules are formed in each body segment.

water pass off through the sweat glands of mammals; water and possibly small quantities of salts and wastes find riddance through the tongue's surface and oral cavity of dogs; and the salt-excretory glands in the gills of teleost fishes remove excess salt materials from the blood, together with small amounts of nitrogenous substances. On the whole, however, the kidneys function to eliminate most of the nitrogenous residues and excess water, together with salt ions of various kinds, particularly those of chloride, sulfate, sodium, and potassium. The dispatch of salt ions by the kidneys is all important in maintaining the correct salt balance in the blood stream.

3. Basic Embryonic Tissues Which Contribute to the Urogenital Structures

The basic, embryonic, cellular areas which contribute to the formation of the excretory and reproductive structures are as follows:

(1) the **nephrotomic plate (intermediate-cell-mass mesoderm)** (fig. 344A).
(2) the adjacent **coelomic tissue,** underlying the nephrotomic plate during its development,
(3) the **entodermal lining** and **surrounding mesoderm** at the caudal end of the digestive tube, and
(4) the **ectoderm** of the integumentary areas where the urogenital openings occur.
(5) **primordial germ cells.**

B. Development of the Excretory System

1. General Description

The excretory system is composed of the following:

(1) a series of excretory units, known as **nephric units** or **nephrons,**
(2) the **kidney,** a structure in which the nephrons are grouped together,
(3) a series of **collecting ducts** from a particular region of the kidney, which join the nephric units on the one hand and a **main excretory duct** on the other, and
(4) the **cloaca** (or its derivative, the urinary bladder) and a passageway to the external surface of the body (figs. 345A, B, D; 348G, D).

a. Types of Kidneys Formed During Embryonic Development

The kidney in Greek is called **nephros** and in Latin, **ren.** The words **nephric** and **renal** are adjectives, pertaining to the kidney but differing etymologically. By adding a prefix to the word nephros, various types of kidneys are denoted as follows:

(1) **Holonephros** is a word that was introduced by Price (1896) and designates a kidney derived from the entire nephrotomic plate in which a single nephron (nephric unit) arises from each **nephrotome.** (The

word **nephrotome** is applied to each segmented mass or bridge of mesoderm, developed within the nephrotomic plate, which connects the somite to the unsegmented lateral plate mesoderm or hypomere. See figure 344B.) The early development of the kidney tubules in the hagfish, *Polistotrema (Bdellostoma) stouti* (Price, 1896), and in the elasmobranch fish, *Squalus acanthias* (Scammon, '11), tends to simulate holonephric conditions.

(2) **Pronephros, mesonephros, metanephros,** and **opisthonephros** are terms for types of kidneys. Actually, during the development of all gnathostomous vertebrates, the nephrotomic plate on either side produces not one holonephros but instead three types of kidneys which are adapted to three different developmental and functional conditions. These kidneys develop antero-posteriorly in three general regions of the nephrotomic plate (fig. 344A). The most anteriorly developed kidney is called the **pronephros;** the kidney which develops from the midregion of the nephrotomic plate is the **mesonephros;** and that which arises from the caudal end of the nephrotomic material is the **metanephros.** Kerr ('19) attaches the name **opisthonephros** to the kidney which arises posterior to the pronephros in the late larvae of fishes and amphibia. The opisthonephric kidney takes its origin from the entire caudal portion of the nephrotomic plate. It therefore represents the nephrogenic tissue of the posterior part of the embryonic mesonephric kidney plus the nephrogenic material which enters into the formation of the metanephric kidney of reptiles, birds and mammals.

b. Types of Nephrons or Renal Units Produced in Developing Vertebrate Embryos

Four main types of renal units are produced during kidney development in various vertebrate species. Consult figure 344C–F.

2. FUNCTIONAL KIDNEYS DURING EMBRYONIC DEVELOPMENT

During embryonic development, the following types of **functional kidneys** occur in the gnathostomous vertebrates.

a. Pronephros

The pronephric kidney is functional in all species producing free-living larval forms. In these larvae it operates not only to remove waste materials but is essential also in the removal of excess water, thus preventing edema (Howland, '16, '21; Swingle, '19). Free-living larvae are found in teleost, ganoid and lung-fishes, and in the amphibia.

b. Mesonephros

In all free-living larvae the pronephros is succeeded by the mesonephros during the larval period. The decline of the pronephros and the ascendancy of the mesonephros is well illustrated in figure 335B–E relative to the developing venous system in anuran larvae. The mesonephric kidney also functions in the embryos of elasmobranch fishes, reptiles, birds, and mammals. In the mammals its efficiency as a renal organ appears to be correlated with the degree of intimacy existing between the extra-embryonic and maternal tissues in the placenta. When this relationship is intimate (fig. 373D) as in rats, mice, humans, etc., the mesonephric kidneys are less developed, and therefore probably less functional, than in species such as the pig. In the pig the placental relationship between embryonic and maternal tissue is not so close as in the species mentioned above (fig. 373B), and the mesonephric kidneys are very large and well developed.

c. Metanephros and Opisthonephros

As indicated on p. 773 the metanephros is the kidney of the adult form of reptiles, birds, and mammals, while the opisthonephros is the mature kidney in fishes and amphibians. As the definitive or adult form of the body is achieved in both of these groups, the mature form of the kidney assumes the renal responsibilities.

3. DEVELOPMENT AND IMPORTANCE OF THE PRONEPHRIC KIDNEY

a. General Considerations

Observation and experimentation upon the developing urinary and genital systems of gnathostomous vertebrates suggest that the **pronephric kidney,** and particularly its duct, the **pronephric duct,** are most important in the later development of the excretory and reproductive systems (Gruenwald, '37, '39, '41). The pronephric kidney therefore may be regarded as fulfilling two important functions in the gnathostomous vertebrates, namely:

(1) It operates as an early renal organ in free-living larval species, and
(2) It is a necessary precursor in the development of the reproductive system and the later excretory system.

The pronephric kidney develops from the anterior portion of the nephrotomic plate at about the level of the developing heart and stomach region (fig. 344A and B). This area of the nephrotomic plate becomes segmented into separate **nephrotomes** (fig. 344A and B). During the differentiation of each nephrotome in the pronephric area, the connection between the nephrotome and the dermo-myotome disappears, and a small dorso-lateral outgrowth from the middle portion of the nephrotome occurs (fig. 344B, 1 and 2). This cylindrical outgrowth proceeds dorso-laterally toward the developing skin and then turns posteriad and grows caudally (fig. 344B, 3). In the next posterior nephrotome, it meets a similar rudimentary tubule with which it unites (fig. 344B, 3 and 4). The area of union formed by these combined tubules grows caudalward to the next nephrotome to unite with its tubule (fig. 344B, 5), etc. As a result, the fused portions of the pronephric tubules give origin to the pronephric or segmental duct (fig. 344B).

The above method of origin of the pronephric duct has been described for elasmobranch fishes, reptiles, birds, and mammals. A different method of pronephric duct origin occurs in the amphibia and teleosts where the pronephric duct apparently arises by a longitudinal splitting of the nephrotomic plate (Field, 1891; Goodrich, '30). The pronephric duct, once formed, continues to grow caudalward above the nephrotomic plate until it reaches the caudal end of the plate. In this area, the growing end of the pronephric duct turns ventrally and joins the cloaca (figs. 344A; 346F).

The entire pronephric portion of the nephrotomic plate is never realized in the formation of pronephric tubules. The number of tubules actually formed varies greatly and is confined generally to a limited number of nephrotomes in the middle or posterior pronephric area.

b. Shark, Squalus acanthias

In *Squalus acanthias,* a considerable nephrotomic area, overlying the caudal portion of the developing heart in segments 5–11, may produce suggestive indications of pronephric tubule formation. However, generally only three to five pronephric tubules are definitely formed. The distal ends of these tubules unite to form the pronephric or segmental duct and the latter grows caudalward to join the cloaca. The pronephric tubules are aberrant and soon disappear, but the pronephric duct remains and when joined by the mesonephric tubules it becomes known as the **Wolffian or mesonephric duct** (fig. 347A).

c. Frog

In the frog, *Rana sylvatica,* Field (1891) describes the origin of the pronephric kidney from a thickening and outgrowth of the somatopleuric layer of the nephrotomic plate in segments 2–4. Three tubules arise from this thickened area, one tubule in segment two, another in segment three, and a third in segment four.

A cross section of the developing second pronephric tubule at a time when the neural tube is wholly closed and a short while before hatching is shown in figure 346A. At about the time of hatching the second pronephric tubule is well advanced, as indicated in figure 346B, and the fully developed first pronephric tubule of an embryo (larva) of about 8 mm. is shown in figure 346C. The entire pronephric kidney of one side consisting of three tubules viewed from the ventral aspect at the 8 mm. stage is presented in figure 346E. The general plan of the pronephric kidney at the 18 mm. stage is pictured in figure 346F. Figure 346D lies in plane A–D of figure 346F.

Contrary to the manner of origin of the pronephric duct from the distal ends of the pronephric tubules in the embryo of *Squalus acanthias,* Field describes the origin of this duct in the frog from a thickening of the somato-pleuric layer of the nephrotomic plate in segments 4–9. This somatopleuric thickening separates, becomes canalized, and grows caudally to join the dorsal area of the cloaca, a union which is accomplished at about the time of hatching (fig. 258F'). The pronephric tubules in their development unite with the cephalic end of this duct.

As the development of the pronephric kidney advances it is to be observed that one large **glomus** is formed, projecting into the restricted coelomic chamber or **nephrocoel** which is shut off partly from the common peritoneal cavity by the expanding lungs (fig. 346D). Each ciliated nephrostome opens into this nephrocoelic chamber (fig. 346F). (*Note:* Reference may be made to figure 335A–C which shows the well-developed **renal portal system** inserted into postcardinal vein in relation to the pronephric kidney. The postcardinal vein breaks up into a series of small capillaries which ramify among the coiling pronephric tubules (see figure 346C) to be gathered up again into the posterior cardinal vein as it opens into the common cardinal vein.)

d. Chick

The pronephric tubules of the pronephric kidney of the chick are rudi-mentary, occupying a region of the nephrotomic plate, from the fifth to the sixteenth somites. However, all of the tubules do not appear simultaneously.

The pronephros begins to form at about the stage of 12 to 13 pairs of somites (stage 11, Hamburger and Hamilton, '51, or at about 40 to 45 hrs. of incubation), and small aberrant tubules are formed (fig. 345E) which grow caudally to give origin to the pronephric duct as indicated in figure 344A.

FIG. 345. Developing kidney tubules. (A & B) General structure of adult human kidney. (A) This diagram represents a single renal unit in relation to blood vessels, collecting duct and the minor calyx. Arrows denote direction of excretional flow. The position of A in drawing B is shown by the elongated oblong in B. (A is redrawn, some-what modified, from Glendening, 1930, The Human Body, Knopf, Inc., N. Y.) (B) Human kidney, part of wall removed, exposing pelvis and other general structures. (Re-drawn from Maximow and Bloom, 1942, A Textbook of Histology, Saunders, Phila-delphia, after Brauer.) (C) Including C-1 to C-6. Stages in the development of a mesonephric renal unit in the frog, *Rana sylvatica* (C to C-6 redrawn from Hall, 1904, Bull. Mus. Comp. Zool. at Harvard College, vol. 45). C represents a section through a developing mesonephric tubule showing cellular condensation in relation to pronephric (mesonephric) duct. C-1 to C-6 are diagrammatic figures of a developing renal unit from right side of body. The somatic or lateral portion of the tubule is shaded by lines, the splanchnic portion is unshaded. (D) Diagrammatic representation of a section through pelvic kidney of *Necturus maculosus*. (Redrawn and modified from Chase, 1923, J. Morph., **37**.) A tubule of the ventral series is shown with a peritoneal canal and ciliated nephrostome which opens into the coelomic cavity. A tubule of the dorsal series also is depicted. The latter type of tubule lacks a ciliated nephrostome opening into the coelom. (E) Pronephric tubule in the chick. Section passes through somite 11 of embryo of 16–17 somites. (F) Section through mesonephric kidney of 96 hr. chick embryo, partly sche-matized. (G) Schematized section through mesonephric kidney of six to seven day chick.

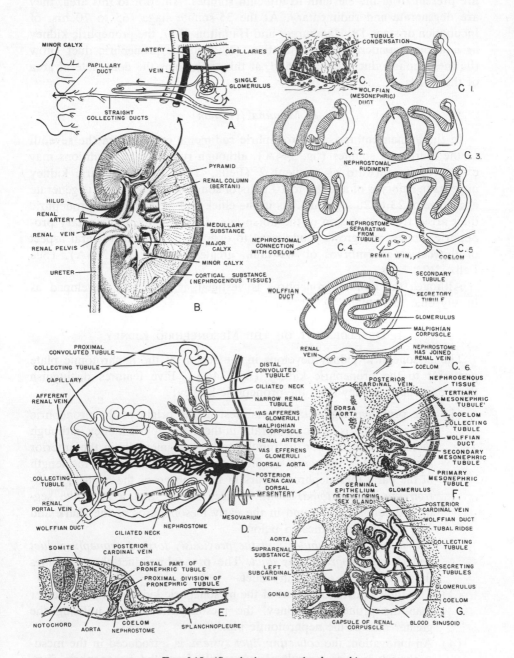

FIG. 345. (*See facing page for legend.*)

At the 16- to 21-somite stage, the pronephric kidney is well developed, but not all the tubules are present. At the 21-somite stage, pronephric tubules are present from the eleventh to fifteenth somites. Anterior to this area, they are degenerate and rudimentary. At the 35-somite stage (65 to 70 hrs. of incubation or stage 18, Hamburger and Hamilton, '51), the pronephric kidney as a whole is undergoing degeneration, although the pronephric duct (now the mesonephric duct) remains and, at this time, joins the dorso-lateral area of the cloaca.

e. Mammal (Human)

In the human embryo, the pronephric rudiments extend from the seventh to the fourteenth somites (fig. 344A), although rudimentary conditions may extend as far forward as segment 2 (Felix, '12). The pronephric kidney appears in embryos of about 9 to 10 pairs of somites, and begins to degenerate at a stage of 23 to 28 segments. As in the chick and the shark, the pronephric duct arises from the fusion of the dorso-lateral ends of the rudimentary pronephric tubules and grows caudalward to open into the ventro-lateral aspect of the cloaca in embryos of 4.2 mm., greatest length (fig. 344A). (See Felix, '12.)

Although the human pronephros is vestigial, it is as well developed as in any other mammalia.

4. Development of the Mesonephric Kidney

The mesonephric kidney develops in the region of the nephrotomic plate posterior to the pronephric kidney (fig. 344A). Five features distinguish the mesonephric kidney from the pronephric kidney:

(1) The primitive segmentation manifest in the origin of the pronephric kidney tubules is lacking generally in the mesonephric kidney, although there is a tendency for the tubules to arise segmentally in the anterior region. Also, a segmental origin of the tubules throughout the length of the early mesonephros occurs in the embryo of the hagfish, *Polistrotrema (Bdellostoma) stouti* (Price, 1896), and a primitive segmental condition is found in the early mesonephros of the shark and frog embryos as indicated below.

(2) *The mesonephric tubules join the previously formed pronephric duct and thus appropriate this duct.* The pronephric duct then becomes the mesonephric (Wolffian) duct.

(3) The antero-posterior extent of the mesonephric kidney is much greater than the pronephric kidney, the mesonephric kidney utilizing the greater part of the nephrotomic plate.

(4) An innovation, the *collecting duct system,* is introduced in the mesonephric kidney as a result of outgrowths from the mesonephric duct.

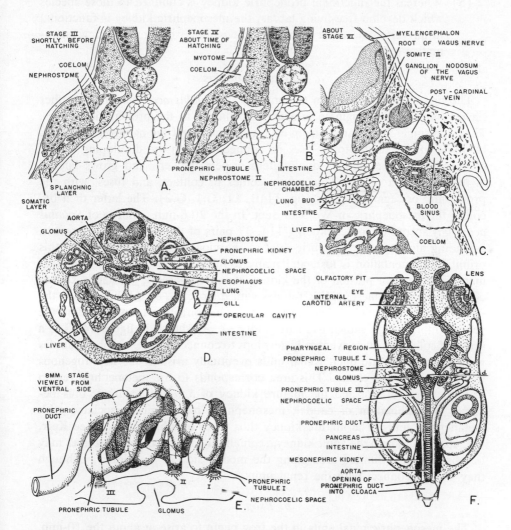

FIG. 346. The developing pronephric kidney in the frog, *Rana sylvatica* (A–C and E, redrawn from Field, 1891, Bull. Mus. Comp. Zool. at Harvard College, vol. 21. E considerably modified). (A) Transverse section through developing second pronephric tubule of frog embryo at a time when the neural tube is completely closed, two gill fundaments are present and the otic vesicle is a shallow depression. (B) Same tubule at about the time of hatching. (C) Section through first pronephric tubule at 8 mm. stage. (D) Transverse section through second pronephric tubule, see line d, fig. 346F, of 18 mm. *Rana pipiens* tadpole. (E) Entire pronephric kidney of one side of 8 mm. *R. sylvatica* embryo. (F) Schematic reconstruction of 18 mm. *R. pipiens* tadpole looking down from dorsal area upon the pronephric kidneys and the developing mesonephric kidneys.

The renal units empty their products into these collecting ducts in the mature form of the kidney.

(5) Whereas the functional pronephric kidney is confined to those species which develop free-living larvae, the mesonephric kidney is functional in all vertebrate embryos with the possible exception of a few mammalian species.

a. Squalus acanthias

The mesonephric tubules in the embryo of *Squalus acanthias* and in other elasmobranch fishes originate in a manner similar to the pronephric tubules. That is, a single tubule arises from each nephrotome of the nephrotomic plate. In doing so, the nephrotome loses its connection with the developing somite or dermo-myotome, and its dorso-lateral aspect thickens and grows laterad in the form of a tubule. This tubule comes in contact, and fuses, with the pronephric or segmental duct (fig. 344B, 11; G.1, G.2). The latter then becomes the mesonephric or Wolffian duct. In the 20.6-mm. embryo of *Squalus acanthias* according to Scammon ('11), 37 pairs of these tubules are present, extending along the mesonephric duct to the cloaca (fig. 347A). Later, this primitive segmentation is lost, and many tubules are developed in each segment. The anterior portion of the kidney soon degenerates; the nephrostomal connections of the mesonephric tubules with the coelom established during the development of the tubules are lost; and the mesonephric tubules assume the general morphology shown in figure 344G.3). As shown in figure 344G.3, a series of collecting ducts eventually develops to connect the mesonephric tubules with the mesonephric duct. Renal units eventually arise in the nephrogenous tissue overlying the cloaca. This area corresponds to the metanephric region of higher vertebrates, and the mature kidney of *Squalus acanthias* thus becomes a combination of caudal, mesonephric, renal units, associated with metanephric units. The mature kidney thus is an **opisthonephros.** (See Kerr, '19, also p. 773). In the adult kidney, segmentally arranged **nephrostomes** may be observed in a limited area along the medial side of the kidney, although they do not connect with the renal units.

b. Frog

The mesonephric renal units in the frog begin to arise at about the 10-mm. stage. As in the shark embryo, the early origin of the mesonephric renal units is segmental. An intermediate zone of the nephrotomic plate between the developing mesonephros and the pronephric kidney does not develop renal units. Coincident with this fact those units which arise more posteriorly in the nephrotomic plate are developed better than those which arise anteriorly.

The renal units arise as cellular condensations of mesodermal cells within the cellular mass of the nephrotomic plate (fig. 345C-1). These cellular condensations elongate, become canalized, and assume a union with the mesonephric duct as shown in figure 345C-1 to C-5. A nephrostomal connection with the coelomic cavity also appears, but the nephrostomal segment soon acquires a secondary connection with a renal vein (fig. 345C, 4–6). The veins thus come to drain the coelomic cavity directly. (In the water-abiding urodele, *Necturus maculosus,* the nephrostomal connection remains in contact with some of the renal units, even in the adult. See figure 345D.)

As the mesonephric kidney of the frog continues to develop, many new mesonephric renal units are added, and several units appear in each body segment. In consequence the primitive segmental arrangement of the renal units is lost, particularly in the caudal region of the nephrotomic plate where the kidney is developed most highly. Collecting ducts develop as evaginations of the mesonephric duct and the renal units discharge their contents into these collecting ducts.

Caudally situated nephrotomic material, comparable to the metanephric area of the kidney of higher vertebrates, is incorporated along with the mesonephric kidney as in the shark embryo. The adult form of the kidney, therefore, may be regarded as an opisthonephros, composed of mesonephric and metanephric renal units.

c. Chick

The mesonephros of the chick develops from the nephrotomic plate in the region between the somites 13 and 30. The nephrotomic plate in the chick embryo increases its substance rapidly through cell proliferation posterior to the area of pronephric-kidney origin. The original nephrotomic plate in this way becomes converted into an elongated mass or cord of cells called the **nephrogenic cord.** The mesonephric tubules arise as condensations within this cord of nephrogenous tissue. The renal unit emerges initially as a rounded mass of epithelial cells as in the frog. These epithelial masses elongate. They acquire a Malpighian body at one end, while the other end unites with the mesonephric duct. Some of the anterior tubules may have coelomic connections, similar to the pronephric tubules, but as this portion of the mesonephric kidney degenerates, these nephrostomal structures have little functional significance.

As development progresses, the nephrotomic substance increases greatly through proliferation of its constituent cells, and several renal units arise in each body segment (fig. 345F). To aid this process, the mesonephric duct forms collecting ducts which extend outward into the region of the developing renal units, and a group of these units joins each collecting duct (fig. 345G). The mature form of the mesonephric tubule of the chick consists of a glandular (secretory) segment which connects with either the mesonephric or the collecting duct on the one hand and with a Malpighian body and its glomerulus on the other (fig. 345G). The mesonephric kidney of the chick is a prominent excretory organ from the fifth to the eleventh day. During the developmental period from 8 to 10 days its tubular system is exceedingly complex compared to that shown in figure 345G. After this period, it begins to degenerate, and its function is taken over by the developing metanephric kidney.

d. Mammal

As in the chick, the mesonephric kidney in many mammalian embryos is a prominent excretory structure. However, in the rat, mouse, and certain other mammals its function as an excretory organ is dubious, probably resulting from the fact that the placental connection in these forms is sufficiently intimate to assume excretory functions. In the 10-mm. pig (figs. 261, 262), it is a prominent structure, filling a considerable part of the coelomic cavity on either side. In the human embryo, the condition is intermediate between that of the pig and rat. It possibly functions as an excretory structure in the human embryo.

The renal unit or mesonephric tubule which is evolved within the nephrogenic cord is similar to that of the bird. It develops from a condensed mass of epithelium within the nephrotomic plate (nephrogenic cord). This condensed, S-shaped mass elongates, becomes canalized, and joins the mesonephric duct. The mesial end of the tubule, in the meantime, develops a Malpighian body with its glomerules and vascular connections. The glandular tube is a highly coiled affair and is associated intimately with the veins as indicated in figure 344F. Collecting ducts, arising as evaginations of the mesonephric duct similar to those in the chick mesonephros, are formed.

5. DEVELOPMENT OF THE METANEPHRIC KIDNEY

The metanephric kidney is the later embryonic and adult form of the renal organ in reptiles, birds, and mammals. As observed above, the mesonephric kidney involves three structures:

(1) the urinary or Wolffian duct,
(2) a series of collecting ducts which evaginate from the mesonephric or Wolffian duct to connect with the renal units, and
(3) the nephrons or renal units.

These same relationships are present in the developing metanephric kidney.

FIG. 347. Urogenital system relationships in various vertebrates.   (A) Reconstruction of 20.6 mm. embryo of *Squalus acanthias*. (Redrawn from Scammon, 1911, Chap. 12, Normentafeln Entwichlungsgeschichte der Wirbeltiere, by F. Keibel, G. Fischer, Jena.) (B) Left side view of dissection of male pickerel, *Esox lucius,* showing reproductive and urinary ducts and absence of a cloaca. (Redrawn from Goodrich, 1930, Studies on the Structure and Development of Vertebrates, Macmillan and Co., Limited, London.) (C) Male reproductive system, ventral aspect, of the pigeon. (Redrawn from Parker, 1906, Zootomy, Macmillan and Co., Limited, London, The Macmillan Co., N. Y.)

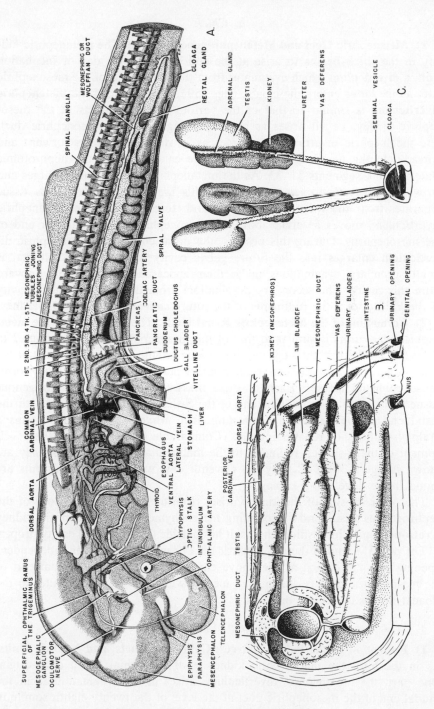

SPINAL GANGLIA
MESONEPHRIC OR WOLFFIAN DUCT
CLOACA
RECTAL GLAND
ADRENAL GLAND
TESTIS
KIDNEY
URETER
VAS DEFERENS
SEMINAL VESICLE
CLOACA
SPINAL CORD
A.
C.
DORSAL AORTA
1ST. 2ND. 3RD. 4TH. 5TH. MESONEPHRIC TUBULES JOINING MESONEPHRIC DUCT
PANCREAS
COELIAC ARTERY
PANCREATIC DUCT
DUODENUM
DUCTUS CHOLEDOCHUS
GALL BLADDER
VITELLINE DUCT
SPIRAL VALVE
COMMON CARDINAL VEIN
THYROID
ESOPHAGUS
VENTRAL AORTA
LATERAL VEIN
STOMACH
LIVER
HYPOPHYSIS
OPTIC STALK
INFUNDIBULUM
OPHTHALMIC ARTERY
POSTERIOR CARDINAL VEIN
DORSAL AORTA
TESTIS
KIDNEY (MESONEPHROS)
AIR BLADDER
MESONEPHRIC DUCT
VAS DEFERENS
URINARY BLADDER
INTESTINE
URINARY OPENING
GENITAL OPENING
ANUS
B.
MESONEPHRIC DUCT
SUPERFICIAL OPHTHALMIC RAMUS OF THE TRIGEMINUS
MESOCEPHALIC GANGLION
OCULOMOTOR NERVE
EPIPHYSIS
PARAPHYSIS
MESENCEPHALON
TELENCEPHALON

FIG. 347. (See facing page for legend.)

783

a. Chick

1) Metanephric Duct and Metanephrogenous Tissue. The metanephric kidney in the chick begins to arise at the end of the fourth day of incubation from a **diverticulum** which evaginates from the caudal end of the mesonephric duct as the latter enters the cloaca (fig. 259). The origin of the **metanephric diverticulum** is similar to that of the various collecting ducts of the mesonephric kidney, i.e., it arises as an outpushing from the mesonephric duct. The metanephric diverticulum enlarges as its distal end grows forward and dorsad into the nephrogenous tissue of the caudal end of the nephrotomic plate in trunk segments 31–33. As the metanephric diverticulum enlarges and grows into the nephrogenous tissue in this area, the nephrogenous tissue separates from the mesonephric tissue and, together with the metanephric diverticulum, moves anteriad above the mesonephros to the anterior end of the mesonephros. During this process, the distal end of the metanephric diverticulum enlarges into the future pelvic cavity of the kidney. Numerous small secondary evaginations make their appearance and extend outward from this cavity. The secondary evaginations from the primary pelvic cavity of the kidney form the rudiments of the future **collecting ducts** of the kidney.

2) Formation of the Metanephric Renal Units. The formation of the metanephric renal units is similar to that of the mesonephric units. At about 7 to 8 days of incubation, the nephrogenous tissue around the terminal ends of the collecting-duct evaginations from the primary pelvic cavity of the kidney forms dense epithelial masses. Each of these masses of condensed nephrogenous tissue assumes an S shape. One end of the S-shaped rudiment unites with the distal end of the developing collecting duct, while the other end forms a Malpighian body or renal corpuscle. (Comparable stages involving the development of the S-shaped rudiment in the mammalian metanephric kidney are shown in figure 348A–C.) By the eleventh day, well-formed renal units are found in the developing kidney.

The outer capsule of the kidney arises from the peripheral portions of the nephrogenous tissue and surrounding mesenchyme. The metanephric kidney is **retroperitoneal** in position, that is, it lies outside the peritoneal cavity proper.

The posterior end of the metanephric duct or **ureter** acquires an independent opening into the cloaca as the above changes occur, for the caudal end of the mesonephric duct is drawn into, merges with, and thus contributes to the cloacal wall as the cloaca enlarges.

b. Mammal (Human)

1) Formation of the Pelvis, Calyces, Collecting Ducts, and Nephric Units. As in the bird, the metanephric kidney of the mammal has a dual origin. One part, the metanephric diverticulum, arises as an evagination from the caudal end of the mesonephric duct at the level of the twenty-eighth somite in the 5- to 6-mm. human embryo (fig. 348H). This evagination extends dorsally

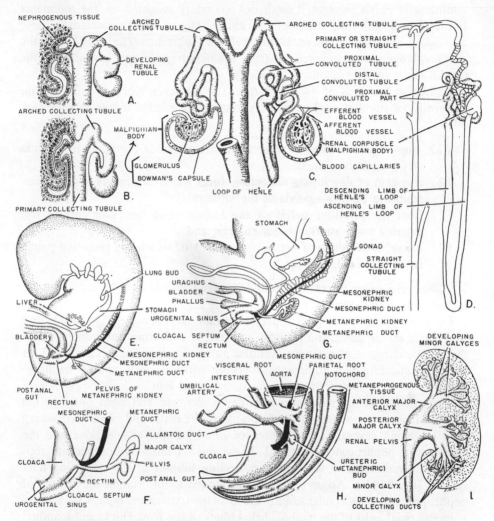

FIG. 348. The developing metanephric kidney. (A) Condensation of rudiment of renal tubule in relation to rudiment of arched collecting tubule. (B) Renal tubular rudiment has united with arched collecting tubule. (C) Later stage in differentiation of renal unit. (D) Final stage in development of renal unit. (E) Developing mesonephric and metanephric kidney of human embryo of about 5 weeks. (F & G) Mesonephric and metanephric conditions in human embryo of 8 mm. or about sixth week of development. (H) Diagram showing origin of metanephric uteric bud from caudal end of mesonephric duct in human embryo approximating 5.3 mm. greatest length. (Redrawn from Felix, 1912, in Chap. 19, Human Embryology, by F. Keibel and F. P. Mall, Lippincott, Philadelphia.) (I) Differentiation of kidney pelvis in human embryo of 20 mm. length or about seven weeks of gestation.

into the caudal end of the **nephrotomic plate** (nephrogenic cord). (See figure 348E.) The metanephric diverticulum enlarges at its distal end and thus forms the rudiment of the pelvis of the kidney as in the chick (fig. 348F). As the rudimentary pelvis enlarges, it sends out secondary evaginations, the rudiments of the future collecting ducts of the kidney (fig. 348I). Surrounding these secondary diverticula, there is the cellular substance (fig. 348I) of the **metanephrogenous tissue,** derived from the nephrogenic cord posterior to the caudal limits of the mesonephric kidney.

In human embryos of 14 to 15 mm. (about seven weeks), four definite primordia of the metanephric urinary system are established as follows (fig. 348I):

(1) **Nephrogenous tissue** is present which surrounds beginning diverticula of the collecting ducts;

(2) a system of **developing collecting ducts** which represents evaginations from the primitive pelvis of the kidney;

(3) from the **primitive pelvis** of the kidney arise the rudiments of the **anterior and posterior major calyces;** and

(4) the **primitive ureter** (metanephric duct) of which the primitive pelvis is the distal enlargement.

(The word calyx refers to a rounded, distal division of the pelvis of the kidney. The plural form of calyx is calyces.)

From each major calyx, secondary or **minor calyces** arise (fig. 348I), and from each minor calyx, the **primary or straight collecting ducts** emerge into the surrounding, nephrogenous, cellular mass. Each primary calyx and its straight collecting-duct rudiments, together with the surrounding nephrogenous cells, form the rudiment of the future **renal lobe.**

The straight collecting ducts continue to elongate and push out into the surrounding nephrogenous tissue. In doing so, the distal end of each collecting duct sends out several (usually three or four) smaller evaginations into the surrounding nephrogenous material. These smaller terminal evaginations represent the rudiments of the **arched collecting tubules** of the collecting duct system (fig. 348A). Around each of the arched-tubule rudiments, masses of nephrogenous tissue condense into the S-shaped structure typical of the developing renal units of the mesonephric kidney of the frog, chick, and mammal and in the metanephric kidney of the chick. A sigmoid-shaped concentration of nephrogenous cells fuses with each arched collecting tubule and elongates distally, differentiating into the parts of the typical, mammalian, metanephric tubule (fig. 348A–D).

As the kidney continues to develop, the original primary or straight collecting ducts branch repeatedly, forming about 12 generations by the fifth month of human fetal existence. As these branches arise, the pelvis of the kidney and the calyces enlarge considerably, and some of the collecting ducts are drawn into and are taken up into the walls of the expanding calyces. In the fully formed kidney, about 20 of these large straight collecting ducts open into the papillary ducts at the apex of the **renal lobe or pyramid** into a minor calyx (fig. 345A, B) (Felix, '12). The outer peripheral portion of the kidney, containing the glomeruli and various parts of the renal units (nephrons), forms the cortex of the kidney, while the inner portion, in which lie the straight collecting and papillary ducts, forms the medulla (fig. 345B).

2) Formation of the Capsule. The metanephrogenous tissue around the developing pelvis and collecting ducts of the kidney becomes divided into **inner and outer zones.** The inner zone cells differentiate into the renal units, whereas the outer zone cells form the interstitial connective tissue and outer, connective-tissue capsule of the kidney.

3) Changes in Position of the Developing Kidney. The early developing kidney is located in the pelvic area at the caudal end of the mesonephric kidney. As the mesonephric kidney declines in size and moves caudally, the metanephric kidney pushes anteriorly and takes its final retroperitoneal position at birth in the region of the first lumbar area. (Cf. figs. 3B–F; 348E–G.)

6. Urinary Ducts and Urinary Bladders

a. Types of Urinary Ducts

The following two types of urinary ducts were mentioned above:

(1) The **pronephric duct,** which later becomes the **mesonephric duct,** is the functional urinary duct in the larval embryonic form of fishes, amphibia, reptiles, birds, and mammals. It continues to be the main urinary duct in adult fishes and amphibia, particularly in the female. (See (2) below.)

(2) A second type of urinary duct represents an outgrowth of the mesonephric duct. Examples of this type are: (a) the **metanephric duct** and its branches in the kidneys of reptiles, birds, and mammals, (b) the **collecting ducts** in the mesonephric kidney of all vertebrates, and (c) the **adult urinary ducts** in the posterior kidney region of certain male fishes, such as are present in the shark, *Squalus acanthias,* and in the salamander, *Triton taeniatus.*

b. Urinary Bladders

During the development of the urinary system in the mammal, the ventral portion of the cloacal area and its allantoic diverticulum become separated from the dorsal cloacal or rectal area by the caudal growth of a fold of tissue, known as the urorectal fold or **cloacal septum.** The cloacal septum eventually divides the cloaca into a ventral **bladder and urogenital sinus region,** and a dorsal primitive **rectum** (fig. 348E–G). As this development proceeds, the proximal portions of the mesonephric and metanephric ducts are taken up into the wall of the caudal bladder region, and a considerable amount of mesoderm is contributed to the entodermal lining of the developing bladder. This mesodermal area presumably forms a part of the lining tissue of the bladder (fig. 349A, B). The metanephric duct or **ureter,** in the meantime, shifts its position anteriad and becomes united with the dorso-posterior portion of the bladder, while the point of entrance of the mesonephric duct migrates posteriad to empty into the anterior end of the dorsal region of the urogenital sinus (figs. 348F, G; 349A, B).

In turtles and in some lizards, the adult relationships of the urinary bladder and rectum are established in a somewhat similar manner to that of the mammals, although the caudal migration of the cloacal septum is not extensive. Also, the cloaca is retained.

The urinary bladder (or bladders) of some teleost and ganoid fishes arise as swellings and evaginations of the caudal ends of the mesonephric ducts (fig. 347B). A distinct urinary bladder is absent in elasmobranch fishes and in birds, but is present in amphibia as a ventral diverticulum of the cloaca.

c. Cloaca

A cloaca into which open the urogenital ducts and the intestine is a common basic condition of the vertebrate embryo. It is retained in the definitive or adult body form of elasmobranch fishes and to a considerable extent in dipnoan fishes. It is present also in the adults of amphibia, reptiles, birds (fig. 347C), and protothcrian mammals. A cloaca is dispensed with in the adult stage of teleost (fig. 347B) and ganoid fishes, and also in the adult stage of higher mammals (fig. 349A–D).

C. Development of the Reproductive System

The general features of the adult condition of the reproductive system are described in Chapters 1 and 2. For most vertebrates, the reproductive system consists of the reproductive glands, the **ovaries** or **testes,** and the **genital ducts.**

FIG. 349. Differentiation of the caudal urogenital structures in the human embryo. (A) Later stage in differentiation of the cloaca; the rectal area is being separated from the ventrally placed urogenital sinus by the cloacal (urorectal) membrane. Condition of sixth week (about 12 mm.) embryo. (B) Rectal and urogenital areas completely separated. Müllerian and mesonephric ducts present. Metanephric duct has moved forward into the posterodorsal area of the developing bladder. The Müllerian ducts have fused at their caudal ends to form the uterovaginal rudiment. This condition is present at about 8 weeks. (C) Male fetus of about 5 months. Testis beginning to pass into developing scrotal sac. (See also fig. 3.) (D) Female fetus of about 5 months. (E to K) Stages in development of external genitalia. (E) Indifferent condition (about 7 weeks). (F) Male about tenth week. (G) Male about 3 months. (H) Male close of fetal life. (I) Female about tenth week. (J) Female about 3 months. (K) Female close of fetal life. (L & M) Stages in development of the broad ligament and separation of the recto-uterine pouch above from the vesico-uterine pouch below.

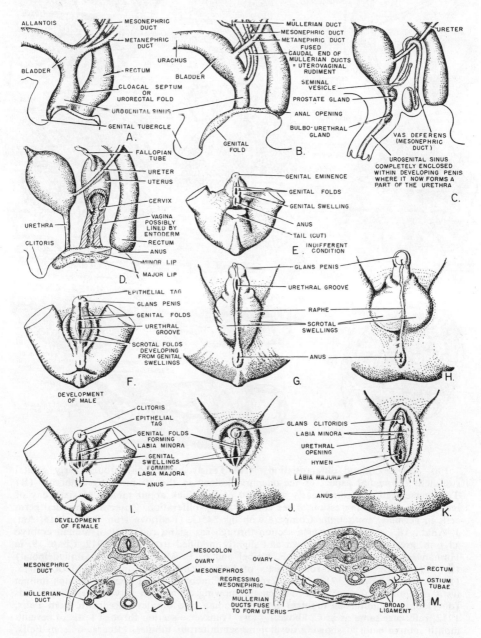

FIG. 349. *(See facing page for legend.)*

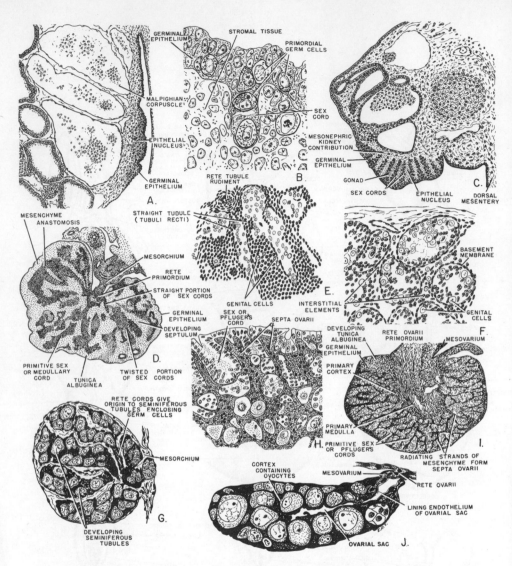

FIG. 350. Sex gland differentiation. (A) Transverse section through early genital rudiment on medial aspect of mesonephric kidney in the 10 mm. pig embryo. (B) Transverse section through early sex gland of the chick about middle of sixth day of incubation showing ingression of sex cord of first proliferation. Observe primordial germ cells in germinal epithelium. Compare with fig. 345G. (Redrawn from Swift, 1915, Am. J. Anat., **18**.) (C) Transverse section through sex gland rudiment of human embryo 11 mm. greatest length. (Redrawn and slightly modified from Felix, 1912, Chap. 19, in Human Embryology, vol. II, by F. Keibel and F. P. Mall, Lippincott, Philadelphia.) (D) Transverse section through testis of human embryo 70 mm. head-foot length. (Redrawn from Felix, 1912. For reference see C above.) (E) Section through human testis of embryo 70 mm. head-foot length, showing connection between testicular cords (developing seminiferous tubules) and developing rete tubules. (Redrawn from Felix, 1912, reference same as in C, above.) (F) Transverse section through testis of seventh month human embryo showing developing seminiferous tubules. (Redrawn from Felix,

(Continued on facing page.)

790

1. Early Developmental Features; the Indifferent Gonad

The gonads or reproductive glands are associated intimately with the developing mesonephric kidneys. The typical site of origin is the area between the dorsal mesentery and the anterior portion of the mesonephric kidney (figs. 345F, G; 350C). As development progresses, it tends to move laterad and in doing so becomes located along the mesial aspect of the developing mesonephric ridge (figs. 3A; 345G).

The reproductive gland arises as an elongated fold, the **genital ridge or genital fold.** The extent of this fold, in general, is longer than the actual site from which the rudimentary **gonad or reproductive gland** arises, and it may extend for a considerable distance along the mesonephric kidney. Felix ('06) designates three general areas of the primitive genital ridge:

(1) a **gonal portion,** from which the sex gland arises,

(2) a **progonal** area in front of the gonal area, which gives origin to the anterior suspensory ligament of the gonad, and

(3) an **epigonal** area behind, which continues caudally as a peritoneal support along the mesonephric kidney (fig. 3A).

The rudimentary structural parts of the early genital ridge in the gonal area, viewed in transverse section, consist of the following (fig. 350A–C):

(1) primitive **germ cells** (origin of the germ cells discussed in Chapter 3, see figure 60),

(2) the **germinal (coelomic) epithelium** and the primitive sex cords and cells proliferated therefrom, and

(3) **contributions from mesonephric tissue,** forming in most vertebrates the rete tissue of the urogenital union together with the primitive mesenchyme of the gonad.

The first stages in the development of the gonad consist of a thickening of the germinal (coelomic) epithelium and of a rapid and copious proliferation of cells from its inner surface. The primitive (primordial) germ cells become associated with the thickened germinal epithelium and its proliferated cells, and migrate inward into the substance of the gonad with the cells of the germinal epithelium (fig. 350B).

As a result of the activities of the germinal epithelium, a mass of cells, the

---

FIG. 350—*(Continued)*

1912, reference same as in C, above.) (G) Differentiating testis in the wood frog, *Rana sylvatica.* (Redrawn from Witschi, 1931, Sex and Internal Secretions, edited by Allen et al., Williams and Wilkins, Baltimore.) (H) Ingrowth of sex cords from germinal epithelium of ovary of 6 weeks old rabbit. (Redrawn from Brambell, 1930, The Development of Sex in Vertebrates, Macmillan, N. Y.) (I) Section through differentiating ovary in the opossum, 63 mm. pouch young. (J) Differentiating ovary in the wood frog, *Rana sylvatica.* (Redrawn from Witschi, 1931, reference same as G, above.)

so-called **epithelial nucleus** (Felix, '12), is deposited in the genital ridge between the coelomic (germinal) epithelium and the Malpighian (renal) corpuscles of the mesonephric kidney (fig. 350C). As the epithelial nucleus increases in quantity, the genital ridge bulges outward from the general surface of the mesonephric kidney, and, at the same time, the nuclear cells push into the mesonephric substance against the renal corpuscles (figs. 345G; 350A–C).

During the early stages of the proliferative activities of the germinal epithelium in most vertebrates, cellular cords, the **sex or medullary cords,** appear to arise from the germinal epithelium (fig. 350B). These cords of cells are composed as indicated above of epithelial and germ cells. However, in the mouse and in the human, the proliferative activity of the germinal epithelium is such that the cellular nucleus of the genital ridge arises without a visible, dramatic ingrowth of cellular cords from the germinal epithelium (Brambell, '27; Felix, '12). Still, the cellular sex cords or elongated masses of cells do appear as secondary developments somewhat later in the genital ridges of the mouse and human (fig. 350C).

The early gonad up to this stage of development represents an **indifferent, bipotential condition,** having the structural basis for differentiation either into the testis or ovary (see figs. 350C; 351C-3). The indifferent condition in the human sex gland is present when the embryo is about 11 to 14 mm. long, i.e., at about the sixth or seventh week; in the chick, it occurs during the sixth day of incubation; and in the frog, it is present during the larval period.

2. DEVELOPMENT OF THE TESTIS

a. Mammal (Human)

As the indifferent gonad begins to differentiate into the testis, the following behavior is evident:

(1) The germinal epithelium becomes a distinct flattened membrane, separated from the primitive **tunica albuginea.** Unlike the conditions in the developing ovary, the germinal epithelium quickly loses its germinative character and forms the relatively inactive, superficial membrane of the sex gland (fig. 350D). (The tunica albuginea eventually becomes a connective tissue layer below the coelomic (germinal) epithelium of the male and female sex glands.)

(2) The **primitive sex or medullary cords** of the indifferent gonad grow more pronounced, and they possibly may segregate lengthwise into separate, elongated cellular masses (fig. 350D).

(3) These elongated cellular masses or **primitive seminiferous tubules** become remodeled directly into the later seminiferous tubules. In doing so, their distal ends (i.e., the ends toward the primitive tunica albuginea of the sex gland) appear twisted and show anastomoses with neighboring seminiferous tubules, while their proximal ends assume

a straightened condition and project inward toward the area connecting the sex gland with the mesonephric kidney (fig. 350D).

(4) In the area between the inner ends of the developing seminiferous tubules and the Malpighian corpuscles of the mesonephric tubules, a condensation of cellular material occurs which forms the **rete primordium** (fig. 350D). From the rete primordium the future **rete tubules** are developed.

(5) As the rete tubules form, they unite with the inner straightened portions of the seminiferous tubules (the developing **tubuli recti**) and distally with the renal corpuscles (Malpighian bodies) of the mesonephric tubules (fig. 350E). The appropriated mesonephric tubules form to a considerable degree the **efferent ductules** of the epididymis.

(6) While the foregoing processes ensue, the sex gland gradually becomes separated as a body distinct from the mesonephric kidney and appears suspended from the kidney by a special peritoneal support, the **mesorchium.** Within the mesorchium are found blood vessels, lymphatics, and the efferent ductules of epididymis (fig. 350D).

(7) Coincident with these changes, mesenchyme between the developing seminiferous tubules forms a coating of connective tissue around each tubule. This connective tissue membrane gives origin to the *basement membrane* of the seminiferous tubule. Within the tubules, **epithelial elements, primitive germ cells,** and **sustentacular elements** (Chap. 3) or *Sertoli* cells appear. The Sertoli cells extend from the connective-tissue wall of the tubule inward between the epithelial and genitaloid cells. The genital cells lie close to the surrounding connective-tissue or basement membrane (figs. 8; 350F).

(8) Between the developing seminiferous tubules, the various cells, blood vessels, etc., of the **interstitial tissue** begin to appear (fig. 350F; see Chap. 1).

(9) Accompanying the foregoing transformations, the primitive tunica albuginea, which originally appeared as a narrow area, containing a few scattered cells between the germinal epithelium and the sex cords, becomes thickened and develops into a tough, connective-tissue layer, surrounding the testicular structures and separating the latter from the covering coelomic epithelium. This appearance of the tunica albuginea is one of the characteristic features of testicular development. Extending from the tunica albuginea inward between small groups of seminiferous tubules as far as the rete area or **mediastinum,** connective-tissue partitions are formed. These partitions are the **septula.** Each septulum comes to surround a small group of seminiferous tubules and thus divides the testis into compartments or **lobules** (fig. 7). Within each lobule, several seminiferous tubules are found, with the **tubuli contorti** or twisted portion of the tubules lying distally within

the compartment and the **tubuli recti** lying proximally toward the rete testis and mediastinum.

The formation of the rete-testis canals and of the **urogenital union** in general has been the subject of much controversy. In the elasmobranch fishes, Brachet ('21) considered the rete-testis canals to be formed by the nephrostomial canals of the anterior mesonephric tubules which unite with the developing seminiferous tubules. In the frog, Witschi ('21) believed a condensation of cells in the hilus of the testis formed the rudiments of the rete tubules and that these rudiments unite with the mediastinal ends of the seminiferous tubules on the one hand and with the renal corpuscles of the mesonephric tubules on the other, forming the urogenital union. In the chick, it is possible that the rete tubules arise as outgrowths from the renal corpuscles (Lillie, '30, p. 394). In the human, Felix ('12) concluded that the rete tubules arise from a **rete rudiment** in the testicular hilus, but de Winiwarter ('10) considered them as outgrowths from the renal (Malpighian) corpuscles of the mesonephric tubules.

b. Chick

The development of the testis in the chick closely resembles that described above for the mammal. The sex or medullary cords arise during the fifth and sixth days of incubation from the germinal epithelium (fig. 350B). For a detailed description, consult Swift, '16, and Lillie, '30.

c. Frog

The main essentials of testicular development in the frog follow the pattern described above. However, because the gonadal rudiment of the frog differs slightly from that described for the mammal, certain features are presented here.

The germinal epithelium of the primitive gonad of the anuran is thin, and the primitive germ cells lie, together with various epithelial elements, below the germinal epithelium. In the center of this primitive gonad is the slit-like primitive gonadal cavity. This cavity is surrounded by the germ cells, epithelial cells and germinal epithelium. This condition may be regarded as the indifferent stage of gonadal development.

In the differentiation of the testis, cellular strands, the rudiments of the future rete tubules, grow down into the primitive gonadal cavity from the mesonephric kidney. In the male, these mesonephric strands are thick and grow rapidly. The primitive germ cells and epithelial cells eventually grow inward across the primitive gonadal cavity and become clustered about the mesonephric strands (fig. 350G).

At first the germ cells and epithelial elements form cellular nests associated with the mesonephric strands. Later, the cellular nests and associated cells from the mesonephric strands elongate into the primitive seminiferous tubules.

These seminiferous tubules develop lumina and unite directly with the rete tubules which arise, in the meantime, from cells of the mesonephric strands. The distal ends of the rete tubules join with the Malpighian corpuscles of certain mesonephric tubules. The mesonephric tubules thus united to the rete tubules are, of course, joined to the mesonephric duct. In consequence, these mesonephric tubules become the *efferent ductules or vasa efferentia of the testis* (Witschi, '21, '29).

3. DEVELOPMENT OF THE OVARY

a. Mammal

1) Formation of Primary Cortex and Medulla. The early phases of differentiation of the ovary varies in different mammalian species. Two features, however, are constant—features that serve to distinguish the differentiating ovary from the testis. One of these features consists of the fact that the ovary is *more retarded in its development than the testis;* the testicular features appear sooner in the male embryo than do ovarian features in the female embryo. This is a negative difference, but nevertheless, it serves to distinguish the two sexes. Another constant and positive feature, however, is that the germinal epithelium in the ovary retains its **proliferative activity,** while, in the differentiating testis, this activity is lost in the early stages of differentiation.

In the cat and rabbit (de Winiwarter, '00, '09), and in the calf and opossum, the first stage of ovarian differentiation is indicated by a second proliferation of sex cords (Pflüger's cords) from the germinal epithelium (fig. 350H and I). The earlier sex or medullary cords thus are pushed inward toward the hilus of the ovary, and a definite compact **primary cortex** is established, containing cords of epithelial and germ cells. The medullary cords become broken up in the meantime and are pressed inward in the direction of the forming **primary medulla** of the ovary. Some of the germ cells of the medullary cords undergo the earlier stages of meiosis but soon degenerate.

Synchronized with the foregoing changes in the peripheral area of the ovary are transformations within the hilar region, that is, the area of the ovary nearest to the mesonephric kidney. A conspicuous feature of these changes is the ingrowth of mesenchyme and differentiating connective tissue from the mesonephric kidney. Three morphogenetic phenomena accompany this ingrowth:

(1) Blood vessels grow into the ovary from the mesonephric kidney to form a primitive vascular plexus within the developing medulla.

(2) A concentration of mesenchymal cells appears in the area between the developing ovary and the mesonephric kidney. This concentration of mesenchyme is the **rete blastema,** or the rudiment of the **rete ovarii.**

(3) From the region of the rete blastema radiating columns of mesenchyme and differentiating connective tissue fibers extend outward through

the medullary zone into the cortical zone of the ovary. These columns establish the **septa ovarii.** The septa ovarii branch distally, dividing the cortical zone into columns and compartmental areas of germ and epithelial cells.

The proliferation of sex cords (Pflüger's cords) may continue from the germinal epithelium for an extensive period in certain mammals, such as the cat. De Winiwarter and Sainmont ('09) noted three successive periods, although Kingsbury ('38) was unable to find a clear-cut distinction between the first and second proliferation. In the developing opossum, active proliferation from the germinal epithelium may be observed up to a time just previous to the fourth month, following birth (Nelsen and Swain, '42).

At an early stage of development, the primitive ovary in transverse section presents the following features (fig. 350I):

(1) an outer **proliferating germinal epithelium;**

(2) a primitive **tunica albuginea** beneath the germinal epithelium, composed of epithelial and germ cells together with some connective tissue elements contributed by the ovarian septa;

(3) the **primitive cortex,** a compact layer within the primitive tunica albuginea, composed of masses of germ cells, egg cords, and epithelial elements, together with strands of differentiating mesenchymal cells. The mesenchymal strands from the ovarian septa segregate the egg cords into separate areas of germ cells and epithelial elements;

(4) internally, near the **mesovarium** or the peritoneal support of the ovary, is the **primitive medulla** composed of epithelial cells, mesenchyme, blood vessels, and some oocytes and oogonia;

(5) in the region of the mesovarium is a compact cellular mass, the rudiment of the **rete ovarii,** the homologue of the rudiment of rete testis in the male. The fundament of the rete ovarii continues rudimentary, but a framework of connective tissue is established in this area of the ovary similar to that of the mediastium in the testis, and

(6) from the area of the rete ovarii, **radiating strands of mesenchymal** cells, extend peripherally through the medulla and into the cortex, and thus establish the *septa ovarii,* i.e., septa of the ovary. Certain relatively large "interstitial cells" appear in the septula areas.

2) Formation of the secondary cortex and medulla. During later stages in ovarian development the following changes are effected:

(1) The primitive tunica albuginea becomes converted into a relatively thick **secondary tunica albuginea** lying between the germinal epithelium and the cells of the cortical zone. It contains connective-tissue fibrils and fibers of larger dimension, together with mesenchyme and connective tissue cells. The changes in the developing tunica albuginea

are associated with an ingrowth of cells from the ovarian septa into the albuginean tunic.

(2) The primitive cortex transforms into a thick **secondary cortex,** containing many oocytes, some of which are surrounded by epithelial cells. The complex of an oocyte enclosed by epithelial cells forms a **primitive egg follicle,** which in mammals is called a primary **Graafian follicle.** The complete development of the Graafian follicle, however, does not occur until sexual maturity, although earlier stages may be produced previous to this period.

(3) A **secondary medulla** is formed containing a connective tissue network, enclosing blood vessels. From these blood vessels branches extend into the cortex. Some genitaloid cells may be found in the medulla.

(4) The rete blastema remains as a compact mass of cells, sharply delimited from surrounding cells. It comes to lie in the area between the ovary and the mesovarium, and forms the **rete ovarii.**

The development of the human ovary differs somewhat from the account given above in that active proliferation of cortical cords from the germinal epithelium is problematical. The proliferation of cells in the developing human ovary appears more gradual, and the egg cords of the primary cortex are developed in a gradual manner from cells lying below the germinal epithelium of the undifferentiated gonad (Felix, '12, p. 904).

b. Chick

The pattern of ovarian development in the chick follows that of the mammal, and a cortex and a medulla are established. One clear distinction in the ovarian development in the chick compared with that in the mammal occurs, however, for the right sex-gland rudiment remains vestigial in the chick while the left rudiment develops rapidly into the ovary. Thus it is, that sex differences can be distinguished in developing chicks by macroscopic examination of the sex glands during the latter part of the second week of incubation. The enlarged appearance of the left ovary in the female chick becomes noticeable at this time.

c. Frog

The developing ovary in the frog differs primarily from the developing testis in two ways:

(1) The **germ cells and accompanying epithelial cells** remain peripherally near the germinal epithelium, where they multiply and increase in number; some of them enlarge during the formative stages of the oocyte.

(2) The **mesonephric rete cords,** which in the testis are much thickened, appear slender in the developing ovary and fuse to form the lining

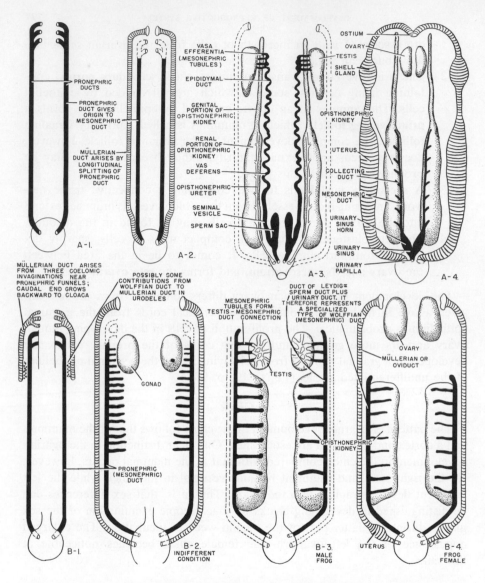

FIG. 351. Development of the reproductive and urinary ducts in vertebrates. (A-1 to A-4) Development of the reproductive ducts in *Squalus acanthias*. In A-2 the origin of the ostial funnel or coelomic opening of the oviduct is presented as a derivative of the opening of one or more pronephric tubules into the coelomic cavity. In fig. A-3, the urinary or opisthonephric duct is independent of the mesonephric (pronephric) duct which now is the vas deferens. The opisthonephric duct appears to take its origin as an evagination from the caudal end of the original pronephric duct. (B-1 to B-4) Development of the reproductive ducts in the frog. B-1 is adapted from data given by Hall, 1904, Bull. Mus. Comp. Zool. at Harvard College, vol. 45. (C-1 to C-7) Development of the reproductive and urinary ducts in mammals. The Müllerian duct arises as an invagination of the coelomic epithelium at the anterior end of the mesonephric kidney. (See fig. 351D.) Once its formation is initiated, it grows caudalward along the pronephric

(Continued on facing page.)

798

tissue of the **ovarian sac** or enlarged space within the ovary (fig. 350J). The ovary of the fully developed frog (and amphibian ovaries in general) is saccular (Chap. 2).

4. DEVELOPMENT OF THE REPRODUCTIVE DUCTS

Most vertebrate embryos, with the exception of those of teleost and certain other fishes, develop two sets of ducts, one set of which later functions as reproductive ducts. These ducts are the mesonephric, **Wolffian** or male ducts and the **Müllerian** or female ducts. In the elasmobranch fishes, the Müllerian duct arises by a longitudinal division of the mesonephric duct (fig. 351A). In the Amphibia, the Müllerian duct takes its origin independently. Anteriorly it arises as a peritoneal invagination of the coelomic epithelium, in the region of the cephalic end of the mesonephros. Posteriorly, this peritoneal invagination, as it grows caudally, appears to receive, in some urodeles, contributions from the mesonephric duct (fig. 351B). In the Amniota the Müllerian duct arises independently by a tubular invagination of the coelomic epithelium at the anterior end of the mesonephric kidney (fig.

Fig. 351—(*Continued*)

(mesonephric) duct to join the cloaca (see fig. 351, C-2). The metanephric duct or ureter arises as an evagination of the caudal end of the pronephric (mesonephric) duct (see fig. 344A). C-2 is a drawing of the urogenital system of a 26 mm. pig embryo viewed from the ventral aspect. Note extent of Müllerian duct growth caudalward. C-3 represents a generalized indifferent condition of the urogenital system of the mammal. C-4 and C-5 are diagrams of later stages in the development of the female (C-4) and the male (C-5). These conditions pertain particularly to human embryos. However, by a division of the uterus simplex into a bicornate or duplex condition it may be applied readily to other mammals. (C-6) Later arrangement of reproductive ducts and the associated ovaries in the human female after the descent of the ovaries. Observe origin of various ligaments. (In this connection see also fig. 3.) (C-7) Later development of the reproductive duct-testis complex in the human male, during descent of the testis into the scrotum. Observe origin of testicular ligaments. (See also fig. 3.) (D) Transverse section through anterior end of the mesonephric kidney of 10 mm. pig embryo presenting the Müllerian duct invagination of the coelomic epithelium covering the mesonephros. E–N are diagrams showing the adult excretory and reproductive duct relationships in various fishes. The urinary ducts are shown in black. (Redrawn and modified from Goodrich, 1930, Studies on the Structure and Development of Vertebrates, Macmillan and Co., Limited, London, after various authors.)

It will be observed that in the male ganoid fish, *Acipenser,* the vasa efferentia extend from a longitudinal testis duct through the anterior or genital part of the kidney to the Wolffian (mesonephric) duct. The Wolffian duct thus becomes a duct of Leydig as in the frog. However, in teleosts, and in *Protopterus* and *Polypterus,* a separate genital duct which opens into the caudal end of the mesonephric duct is evolved. Hence, the Wolffian (mesonephric) duct in these forms functions as a urinary duct only. The separation of the genital duct from the urinary duct, with the exception of the urogenital sinus region at the posterior end, is a fundamental characteristic of most vertebrate male reproductive systems, including many amphibia. In female fishes, fig. 351, I–N, as in other vertebrates, the reproductive duct is always distinct from the urinary duct. The exact homologies of the reproductive duct in forms such as *Lepisosteus* (Lepidosteus) and teleosts (fig. 351, L–N) with the Müllerian duct in other vertebates is not clear.

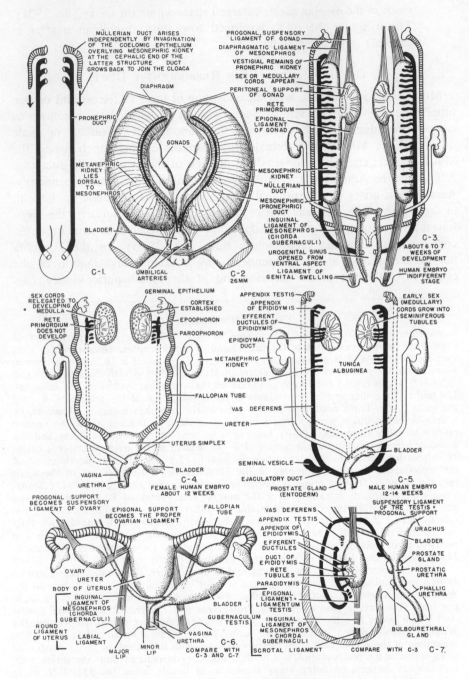

FIG. 351—(Continued)

See legend on pp. 798 and 799.

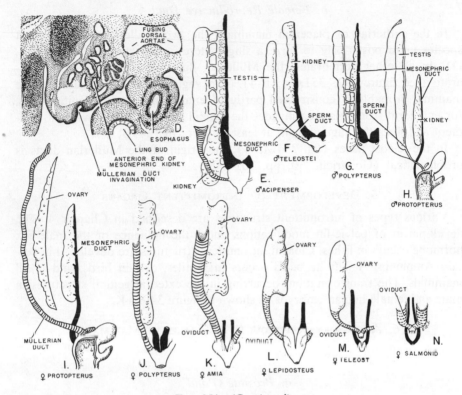

FIG. 351—(*Continued*)

See legend on pp. 798 and 799.

351C). The blind caudal end of the invagination grows posteriorly along the side of the mesonephric duct to join the cloaca (fig. 351C-2).

a. Male Reproductive Duct

The developing gonad of the males of Amphibia, reptiles, birds, and mammals, together with the elasmobranch and ganoid fishes, appropriates the mesonephric duct for genital purposes. In this appropriation, the rete tubules of the testis unite with certain of the mesonephric tubules. The latter form the **vasa efferentia** or **efferent ductules** of the epididymis (fig. 351A–C). In teleosts, dipnoan fishes, and *Polypterus,* the marginal testicular duct becomes modified into a vas deferens which conveys the genital products to the urogenital sinus (fig. 351F–H).

In all vertebrates and in some mammals (Chap. 1), the testis remains within the abdominal cavity. However, in most mammals and in the flatfishes, there is a posterior descent of the testis (figs. 3 and 5) into a compartment posterior to the abdominal cavity proper.

b. Female Reproductive Duct

In the eutherian or placental mammals, the two Müllerian ducts in most species unite posteriorly to form a single uterovaginal complex (fig. 349B, D). In all other vertebrates, the Müllerian ducts or oviducts remain separate (see figures 33; 351A-4, B-4). The vagina of the eutherian female mammal probably is constructed partly of entoderm from urogenital sinus, for entoderm from this area invades the caudal end of the uterovaginal rudiment and lines the vaginal wall, at least in part (fig. 349B, D).

In the teleost fishes (fig. 351M, N), the origin of the Müllerian ducts is problematical (Goodrich, '30, pp. 701–705).

5. DEVELOPMENT OF INTROMITTENT ORGANS

Various types of intromittent structures are described in Chapter 4. The development of pelvic-fin modifications under the influence of the male sex hormone occurs in fishes. Cloacal intromittent structures are developed in certain Amphibia. A definite penis occurs in reptiles, certain birds, and in all mammals. The transformation, occurring in the external genital structures in male and female human embryos, is shown in figure 349E–K.

6. ACCESSORY REPRODUCTIVE GLANDS IN MAMMALS

Refer to figures 2 and 349C.

a. Prostate Gland

The prostate gland arises as entodermal outgrowths from the membranous urethra near the entrance of the genital ducts. The surrounding mesenchyme provides the connective tissue and muscle. The **paraurethral glands** or ducts of Skene in the female represent minute homologues of the prostate gland.

b. Seminal Vesicles

The seminal vesicles arise as saccular outgrowths from the mesonephric ducts.

c. Bulbourethral Glands

The bulbourethral (Cowper's) glands in the male arise as outgrowths from the entoderm of the **cavernous urethra.** The **vestibular glands** or glands of Bartholin are the female homologues of the bulbourethral glands.

7. PERITONEAL SUPPORTS FOR THE REPRODUCTIVE STRUCTURES

a. Testis and Ovary

The testis and ovary are pendent structures in all vertebrates and they are supported by peritoneal extensions from the dorso-lateral region of the coelomic cavity. The support of the testis is the **mesorchium** and that of the ovary is the **mesovarium.** However, supports other than those mentioned in the preceding sentence are concerned with the support of the testis and ovary during development. Figures 3A, B and 351C-3 demonstrate an anterior ligamentous, **progonal support** for the developing sex gland, whereas caudally there is a posterior, **epigonal support** continuing posterially to join the **inguinal ligament** of the mesonephros. In the developing mammal the progonal support merges with the diaphragmatic ligament of the mesonephros. Caudally the inguinal ligament of the mesonephros joins a ligamentous area in the genital swelling, known as the **scrotal ligament** in the male and the **labial ligament** in the female. Consult fig. 351C-6 and C-7 for later history.

b. Reproductive Ducts

The **male reproductive duct** (vas deferens, Wolffian duct) lies close to the kidney structures in the retroperitoneal space in most vertebrates other than those mammals with descended testes (see Chap. 1). The male reproductive duct, therefore, assumes a retroperitoneal position and is not suspended extensively within the coelomic cavity. On the other hand, the **female reproductive duct** (oviduct) is a pendant, twisted structure and is supported by a well-developed peritoneal support, the **mesotubarium.** In mammals, due to the fact that the reproductive ducts tend to join posteriorly, the mesotubarial supports, along the caudal region of the reproductive ducts, aid in dividing the pelvic region of the coelomic cavity into two general regions, viz., a dorsal or **rectal recess,** and a ventral, **urinary recess** (fig. 349L, M).

In the mammals, the mesotubarial support of the Fallopian tube is known as the **mesosalpinx.** The mesosalpinx is continuous with the broad, shelf-like, lateral support of the uterus, known as the **broad ligament.** The broad ligament is developed from the mesotubarium together with the remains of the mesonephric kidney substance (349L, M). The **round ligament** of the mammalian uterus and the **ovarian ligament** arise from a basic rudiment comparable to the **gubernaculum testis** in the male (see figs. 3; 351C-3, C-6, C-7).

Bibliography

Brachet, A. **1921.** Traité d'Embryologie des Vertébrés. Paris.

Brambell, F. W. R. **1927.** The development and morphology of the gonads of the mouse. Part I. The morphogenesis of the indifferent gonad and the ovary. Proc. Roy. Soc., London, sB. **101**:391.

Brauer, A. **1902.** Beiträge zur Kenntniss der Entwicklung und Anatomie der Gymnophionen. III. Die Entwicklung der Excretionsorgane. Zool. Jahrbücher, Abt. Anatomie und Ontogenie. **16**:1.

de Winiwarter, H. **1900.** Recherches sur l'ovogénèse et l'organogénèse de l'ovaire des mammifères (lapin et homme). Arch. biol., Paris. **17**:33.

————. **1910.** Contribution a l'étude de l'ovaire humain. Arch biol., Paris. **25**:683.

———— and Sainmont, G. **1909.** Nouvelles recherches sur l'ovogénèse et l'organogénèse de l'ovaire des mammifères (chat). Arch biol., Paris. **24**:1.

Felix, W. **1906.** Chap. 2, Part III, in Vergleichenden und Experimentellen Entwickelungslehre der Wirbeltiere by O. Hertwig. Gustav Fischer, Jena.

————. **1912.** Chap. **19** in Human Embryology by F. Keibel and F. P. Mall. J. B. Lippincott Co., Philadelphia.

Field, H. H. **1891.** The development of the pronephros and segmental duct in *Amphibia.* Bull. Mus. Comp. Zool. at Harvard College. **21**:201.

Goodrich, E. S. **1930.** Studies on the Structure and Development of Vertebrates. Macmillan and Co., London.

Gruenwald, P. **1937.** Zur Entwicklungsmechanik des urogenitalsystems beim Huhn. Arch. f. Entwicklngsmech. d. Organ. **136**:786.

————. **1939.** The mechanism of kidney development in human embryos as revealed by an early stage in the agenesis of the ureteric buds. Anat. Rec. **75**:237.

————. **1941.** The relation of the growing Müllerian duct to the Wolffian duct and its importance for the genesis of malformations. Anat. Rec. **81**:1.

Hamburger, V. and Hamilton, H. L. A series of normal stages in the development of the chick embryo. J. Morph. **88**:49.

Howland, R. B. **1916.** On the effect of removal of the pronephros of the amphibian embryo. Proc. Nat. Acad. Sc. **2**:231.

————. **1921.** Experiments on the effect of removal of the pronephros of *Amblystoma punctatum.* J. Exper. Zool. **32**:355.

Kerr, J. G. **1919.** Textbook of Embryology, Vol. II, Vertebrata with the Exception of Mammalia. Macmillan Co., Ltd., London.

Kingsbury, B. F. **1938.** The postpartum formation of egg cells in the cat. J. Morphol. **63**:397.

Lillie, F. R. **1930.** The Development of the Chick. Henry Holt & Co., New York.

Nelsen, O. E. and Swain, E. **1942.** The prepubertal origin of germ cells in the ovary of the opossum *(Didelphys virginiana).* J. Morphol. **71**:335.

Price, G. C. **1896.** Development of the excretory organs of a myxinoid, *Bdellostoma stouti* Lochington. Zool. Jahrb. Anat. u. Ontogenic. **10**:205.

Scammon, R. E. **1911.** Normal plates of the development of *Squalus acanthias.* Chap. 12 in Normentafeln zur Entwicklungsgeschichte der Wirbeltiere von F. Keibel. G. Fischer, Jena.

Swift, C. H. **1916.** Origin of the sex cords and definitive spermatogonia in the male chick. Am. J. Anat. **20**:375.

Swingle, W. W. **1919.** On the experimental production of edema by nephrectomy. J. Gen. Physiol. **1**:509.

Witschi, E. **1921.** Development of gonads and transformation of sex in the frog. Am. Nat. **55**:529.

————. **1929.** Studies on sex differentiation and sex determination in amphibians. I. Development and sexual differentiation of the gonads of *Rana sylvatica.* J. Exper. Zool. **52**:235.

19

The Nervous System

A. Introduction
  1. Definition
  2. Structural and functional features
    a. The morphological and functional unit of the nervous system
    b. The reflex arc
    c. Structural divisions of the vertebrate nervous system
    d. The supporting tissue
B. Basic developmental features
  1. The embryonic origin of nervous tissues
  2. The structural fundaments of the nervous system
    a. The elongated hollow tube
    b. The neural crest cells
    c. Special sense placodes
  3. The histogenesis of nervous tissue
    a. The formation of neurons
      1) General cytoplasmic changes
      2) Nuclear changes
      3) Growth and development of nerve-cell processes
    b. The development of the supporting tissue of the neural tube
    c. Early histogenesis of the neural tube
    d. Early histogenesis of the peripheral nervous system
C. Morphogenesis of the central nervous system
  1. Development of the spinal cord
    a. Internal changes in the cord
    b. Enlargements of the spinal cord
    c. Enveloping membranes of the cord
  2. Development of the brain
    a. The development of specialized areas and outgrowths of the brain
      1) The formation of the five-part brain
      2) The cavities of the primitive five-part brain and spinal cord
    b. The formation of cervical and pontine flexures
    c. Later development of the five-part brain
D. Development of the peripheral nervous system
  1. Structural divisions of the peripheral nervous system
  2. The cerebrospinal system
  3. General structure and function of the spinal nerves
  4. The origin, development and functions of the cranial nerves
    O. Terminal

A. Introduction

1. Definition

The nervous system serves to integrate the various parts of the animal into a functional whole, and also to relate the animal with its environment. It consequently is specialized to detect changes in the environment (irritability) and to conduct (transmit) the impulses aroused by the environmental change to distant parts of the organism. The environmental change provides the **stimulus,** the protoplasmic property of irritability **detects** the stimulus, and **transmission** of impulses thus aroused makes it possible for the animal to **respond** once the impulse reaches the **responding mechanism.** This series of events is illustrated well in less complex animal forms such as an ameba. In this organism, the stimulus aroused by an irritating environmental change is transmitted directly to other parts of the cell, and the ameba responds by a contraction of its protoplasm away from the source of irritation. On the other hand, the complex structure of the vertebrate animal necessitates an association of untold numbers of cells, some of which are specialized in the **detection** of stimuli, and others **transmit** impulses to a **coordinating center,** from whence still other cells convey the impulses to specialized **effector** (responding) **structures** (fig. 352A).

2. Structural and Functional Features

a. The Morphological and Functional Unit of the Nervous System

There are two opposing views regarding the morphological and functional unit of the nervous system. One view, widely championed, postulates that this unit is a specialized cell called the **neuron.** The neuron is a distinct cellular entity, having a cell body containing a nucleus and a central mass of cytoplasm from which extend cytoplasmic processes of various lengths (fig. 352B). The nervous system is made up of many neurons in physiological contact with each other at specialized functional junctions known as the **synapses** (fig. 352A). The synapse represents an area of functional contact specialized in the conduction of impulses from one neuron to another. However, it is not an area of morphological fusion between neurons. Each neuron, according to this view, originates from a separate embryonic cell or **neuroblast** of ectodermal origin, and each develops a **definite polarity,** i.e. impulses normally pass in one direction to the cell body and from thence distad to the area of synapse.

A contrary, older view is the **reticular** or **nerve-net** theory. This theory assumes that the nerve cells and their processes are a continuous mass of protoplasm or syncytium in which the "cell bodies" are local aggregations of a nucleus and a cytoplasmic mass. The entire controversy between this and the neuron theory revolves around the "synapse area." The **neuron doctrine** assumes a distinct morphological separation at the synapse, but the **reticular theory** postulates a direct morphological continuity. We shall assume that the neuron doctrine is correct.

b. The Reflex Arc

While the neuron, in a strict sense, represents the functional unit of the nervous system, in reality, chains of physiologically related neurons form the functional reflex mechanism of the vertebrate nervous system. The functional

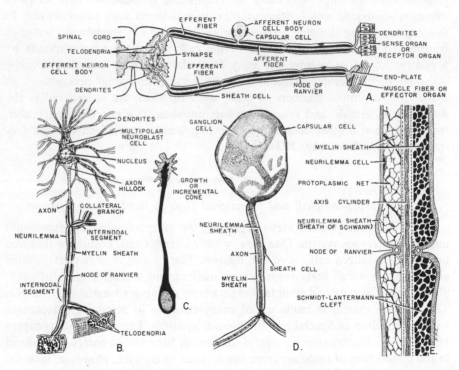

FIG. 352. Neuron structure and relationships. (A) Structural components of a simple reflex arc. (B) Diagrammatic representation of a motor neuron. (Redrawn from Ranson, 1939, The Anatomy of the Nervous System, Philadelphia, Saunders, after Barker.) (C) Developing nerve fiber (process) of young neuroblast. Observe *growth* or *incremental cone* at distal end of growing process. (Redrawn from Ranson, 1939, The Anatomy of the Nervous System, Philadelphia, Saunders, after Cajal, Prentiss-Arey.) (D) Neuron from spinal ganglion of a dog showing ganglion cell body with its surrounding *capsular cells* and *capsule. Observe that the capsular cells and capsule are continuous with sheath cell and neurilemma.* (Redrawn, somewhat modified, from Ranson, 1939, The Anatomy of the Nervous System, Philadelphia, Saunders.) (E) Longitudinal section of myelinated nerve fiber. (Redrawn from Ranson, 1939, The Anatomy of the Nervous System, Philadelphia, Saunders, after Nemiloff, Maximow-Bloom.)

reflex mechanism is an arrangement of neurons known as the **reflex arc.** Theoretically, a simple type of reflex arc would possess (fig. 352A):

(1) a sense receiving structure, the **receptor;**

(2) the **sensory neuron,** whose long **afferent** or **sensory fiber** contacts the sensory receptor, while its **efferent** fiber or **axon** continues from the body of the neuron to the central nervous system. Within the central nervous system the **terminal fibers (telodendria)** of the efferent fiber of the sensory neuron forms a **synapse** with

(3) the **dendrites** of an **efferent neuron.** From the efferent or motor neuron a **motor fiber** (axon) leaves the central nervous system and continues to

(4) the **effector organ.**

Functionally, however, even the simplest type of reflex arc may not be as elementary as this. More probably, a system of one or more **association neurons** placed between the sensory and motor neurons exists in most instances.

c. Structural Divisions of the Vertebrate Nervous System

The nervous system of vertebrate animals consists of

(1) the **central nervous system,** a tubular structure composed of a coordinated assembly of association neurons and their processes. The central nervous system is integrated with

(2) the **peripheral nervous system** constructed of a series of sensory and motor neurons which connect the central nervous system with distal parts of the body. Through the medium of various types of **sense receptors** the central nervous system is made aware of changes in the external and internal environment of the body.

d. The Supporting Tissue

In addition to the irritable cellular neurons, the nervous system contains connective or supporting tissue. However, unlike most of the other organ systems of the body, the supporting tissue of the nervous system is derived mainly from an ectodermal source. Small amounts of connective tissue of mesodermal origin parallel the various blood capillaries which ramify through nervous tissue, but the chief supporting tissue of the brain and spinal cord is the **neuroglia** of ectodermal origin. The neuroglia consists of two main cellular types, the **ependymal cells** and the cells of the **neuroglia proper.**

The ependymal cells (fig. 353A) form a single layer of columnar epithelium which lines the lumen of the neural tube. From the inner aspect or base of each ependymal cell a process extends peripherad toward the external surface of the neural tube (fig. 353F–H). Later the peripheral process may be lost. During the earlier stages of their development the ependymal cells are ciliated on the aspect facing the neurocoel (fig. 353A).

The cells of the neuroglia proper lie within the substance of the nerve tube between the neuron-cell bodies of the *gray matter* and also between the nerve fibers of the *white matter* (fig. 353H). Conspicuous among the neuroglia cells are the **protoplasmic astrocytes** (fig. 353D) which reside mainly among the neurons of the gray matter and the **fibrous astrocytes** (fig. 353B) found in the white matter. The processes of the fibrous astrocytes are longer and finer than those of the protoplasmic astrocytes, and they may attach to blood vessels (fig. 353B). Two other cellular types of neuroglia, the **oligodendroglia** and the **microglia** cells, also are present (fig. 353C and E). The microglia cells presumably are of mesodermal origin (Ranson, '39, p. 57).

B. Basic Developmental Features

1. THE EMBRYONIC ORIGIN OF NERVOUS TISSUES

The ectoderm of the late gastrula is composed of two general organ-forming areas, namely, **neural plate** and **epidermal** areas (fig. 192A). Both of these **primitive ectodermal** areas are concerned with the development of the future nervous system and associated sensory structures. From the neural plate region arises the **primitive neural tube** (Chap. 10), the **basic rudiment of the central nervous system,** whereas the **line of union** between the neural plate and the epidermal areas gives origin to the **ganglionic** or **neural crest cells** which contribute much to the formation of the **peripheral nervous system.** As observed in Chapters 9 and 10, the determination of the **neural plate material** and the **formation of the neural tube** are phenomena dependent upon the inductive powers of the underlying notochord and somitic mesoderm in the Amphibia. Presumably the same basic conditions obtain in other vertebrate embryos.

FIG. 353. Structure of the developing neural tube. (A) Ciliated *ependymal cells* from ependymal layer of the fourth ventricle of a cat. (Redrawn from Maximow and Bloom, 1942, A Textbook of Histology, Philadelphia, Saunders, after Rubaschkin.) (B–E) Various types of *neuroglia cells*. (Redrawn from Ranson, 1939, The Anatomy of the Nervous System, Philadelphia, Saunders, after Rio Hortega.) (F) Transverse section of neural tube of three-day chick embryo. The *spongioblasts* are stained black after the method of Golgi. (Redrawn from Maximow and Bloom, 1942. See reference under A, after Cajal.) (G) Transverse section of part of spinal cord of 15 mm. pig embryo showing structural details. This section was constructed from several sections. The part of the section to the left reveals the neuroglial support of the developing neuroblasts. (Redrawn from Hardesty, 1904, Am. J. Anat., 3.) (H) Transverse section, constructed from sections, of part of the spinal cord of 55 mm. pig embryo showing neuroglial support for developing neuron cells. (Redrawn from Hardesty, 1904, Am. J. Anat., 3.) (I) Transverse section of spinal cord of newborn mouse depicting spongioblasts which are moving peripherally from the central canal. These spongioblasts are in the process of transforming into stellate neuroglia cells or *astrocytes.* (J) Transverse section of 9 mm. pig embryo portraying *ependymal, mantle,* and *marginal layers, external* and *internal limiting membranes,* and blood vessels growing into the nerve substance. (Redrawn from Hardesty, 1904, Am. J. Anat., 3.) (K) Transverse section of spinal cord of 20 mm. opossum embryo indicating general structure of the spinal cord. Observe dorsal root of spinal nerve growing into nerve cord at the right of the section.

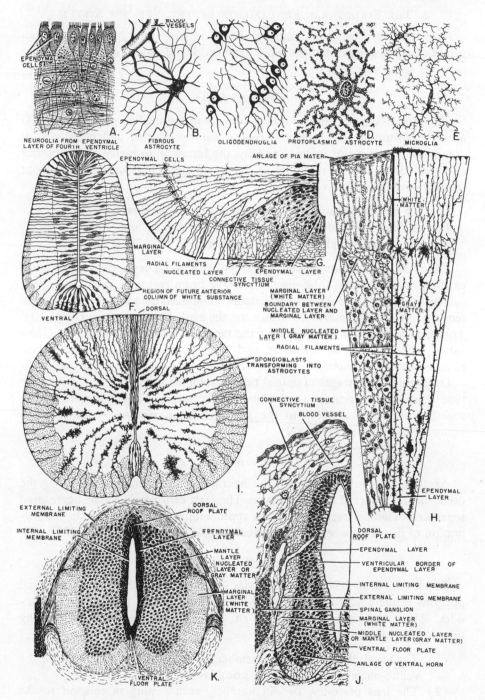

 A. NEUROGLIA FROM EPENDYMAL LAYER OF FOURTH VENTRICLE
EPENDYMAL CELLS

B. FIBROUS ASTROCYTE
BLOOD VESSELS

C. OLIGODENDROGLIA

D. PROTOPLASMIC ASTROCYTE

E. MICROGLIA

F.
EPENDYMAL CELLS
MARGINAL LAYER
RADIAL FILAMENTS
NUCLEATED LAYER
CONNECTIVE TISSUE SYNCYTIUM
REGION OF FUTURE ANTERIOR COLUMN OF WHITE SUBSTANCE
VENTRAL
DORSAL

G.
ANLAGE OF PIA MATER
EPENDYMAL LAYER

H.
WHITE MATTER
MARGINAL LAYER (WHITE MATTER)
BOUNDARY BETWEEN NUCLEATED LAYER AND MARGINAL LAYER
MIDDLE NUCLEATED LAYER (GRAY MATTER)
RADIAL FILAMENTS
GRAY MATTER
EPENDYMAL LAYER

I.
SPONGIOBLASTS TRANSFORMING INTO ASTROCYTES
CONNECTIVE TISSUE SYNCYTIUM
BLOOD VESSEL

K.
EXTERNAL LIMITING MEMBRANE
INTERNAL LIMITING MEMBRANE
DORSAL ROOF PLATE
EPENDYMAL LAYER
MANTLE LAYER NUCLEATED LAYER OR GRAY MATTER
MARGINAL LAYER (WHITE MATTER)
VENTRAL FLOOR PLATE

J.
DORSAL ROOF PLATE
EPENDYMAL LAYER
VENTRICULAR BORDER OF EPENDYMAL LAYER
INTERNAL LIMITING MEMBRANE
EXTERNAL LIMITING MEMBRANE
SPINAL GANGLION
MARGINAL LAYER (WHITE MATTER)
MIDDLE NUCLEATED LAYER OR MANTLE LAYER (GRAY MATTER)
VENTRAL FLOOR PLATE
ANLAGE OF VENTRAL HORN

Fig. 353. (See facing page for legend.)

811

2. THE STRUCTURAL FUNDAMENTS OF THE NERVOUS SYSTEM

The early nervous system shortly after the neural tube is formed is composed of an elongated, **hollow tube,** aggregations of **neural crest cells,** and a series of **sense placodes.**

a. The Elongated Hollow Tube

The primitive neural tube, located dorsally in the median plane (fig. 217G and H), forms the basis for the **central nervous system** and potentially is composed of two major regions, namely, the future **brain region** at its anterior end and posteriorly the rudiment of the **spinal cord.** The future brain region quickly develops three regions, viz.:

(1) the **prosencephalon,** or the rudiment of the **forebrain;**

(2) the **mesencephalon,** or future **mid-brain** region, and

(3) the **rhombencephalon,** or **hindbrain** region (fig. 354D and E).

The rhombencephalon passes imperceptibly into the developing spinal cord, or the primitive neural tube posterior to the brain region.

The cephalic end of the primitive neural tube from the time of its formation tends to present a primary neural flexure, the **cephalic flexure** (see Chap. 10). This flexure occurs in the region of the **mesencephalon.** It is slight in teleost fishes, more marked in amphibia, and pronounced in elasmobranch fishes, reptiles, birds and mammals (fig. 354E and F).

During the early stages of neural tube development, the anterior end of the tube tends to form primitive segments or **neuromeres.** These neuromeres fuse together as they contribute to the primitive brain regions as indicated in figure 354A–D (see Hill, 1900).

b. The Neural Crest Cells

As the neural tube is formed, the neural crest cells come to lie along the dorso-lateral aspect of the neural tube. The crest cells soon become aggregated together in clumps, each aggregation representing the initial stage in the formation of the various **cranial and spinal ganglia** (see figures 347A; 357B–F).

c. Special Sense Placodes

The *special sense placodes* are a series of epithelial thickenings of the lateral portions of the epidermal tube overlying the future head region. These placodes, which represent contributions of the epidermal tube to the forming nervous system, are as follows:

(1) The **nasal placodes,** two in number, each arising on either side of the ventro-anterior region of the primitive head.

(2) The **lens placodes,** two in number, each arising in relation to the **optic outpushing** of the diencephalic portion of the forebrain.

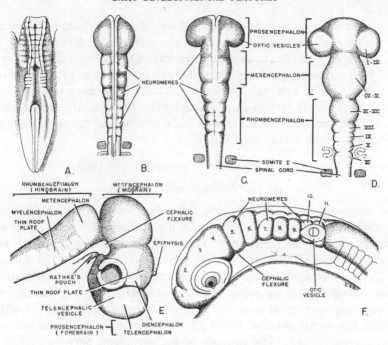

FIG. 354. Early development of the brain in the chick and teleost fish showing the tendency to form neural segments or *neuromeres*. (All figures redrawn from Hill, 1900, Zool. Jahrbücher, abt. Anat. u. Ontogenie 13.) (A) Dorsal view of developing brain of chick embryo of 4 pairs of somites. (B) Dorsal view of primitive brain or encephalon of chick embryo of 7 pairs of somites. (C) Dorsal view of brain of chick embryo with 11 pairs of somites. (D) Dorsal view of developing brain of chick embryo with 14 pairs of somites. (E) Lateral view of brain of chick embryo about 75 to 80 hours of incubation. In the foregoing illustrations, observe that the neuromeres gradually fuse to form parts of primitive five-part brain shown in E. (F) Brain, lateral view, *Salmo fario*, 33 somites, 22 days old. Segments 1–3 represent the prosencephalon, 4 and 5 the mesencephalon, 6 the anterior part of the rhombencephalon, and 7–11 to the posterior region of the rhombencephalon. Observe that the cephalic flexure is present slightly at this time. A little later in the 36 day embryo it is more pronounced.

(3) The **acoustic placodes,** two in number, taking their origin from the dorso-lateral portion of the epidermal tube overlying the middle portion of the hindbrain.

In water-dwelling vertebrates, other placodes arise in the head region associated with the **lateral-line system.** The *lateral line placodes* probably represent an extension of the acoustic placodal system in lower vertebrates. Hence, the general term **acoustico-lateral or neuromast system** (see Goodrich, '30, p. 732) may be applied to this general system of sensory structures.

(4) **Taste-bud placodes.** The taste buds are distributed variously in different vertebrate species. In man, cat and in other mammals they are located on the tongue, particularly its posterior part (fig. 285E) on the

soft palate, and in the pharyngeal area. In fishes, taste buds are found generally over the buccal cavity and pharynx, and also on the outer surface of the head and branchial region. In some teleosts they may be distributed generally over the external surface of the body (fig. 356C). The external distribution of taste buds over the head region occurs also in certain aquatic amphibia. Consequently, the distribution of the epithelial thickenings which give origin to the taste buds varies greatly in different vertebrates.

3. THE HISTOGENESIS OF NERVOUS TISSUE

a. The Formation of Neurons

The neurons of the central nerve tube arise from primitive neuroblasts. The primitive neuroblasts in turn take their origin from the cells of the **ependymal zone** of the nerve tube. The ependymal zone is the layer, two to three cells in thickness, which lines the lumen or neurocoel of the developing tube. Cell proliferation occurs within this zone, and the primitive neuroblasts migrate outward into the more lateral areas. After leaving the immediate confines of the ependymal zone, the neuroblasts presumably begin to differentiate into the many peculiar forms of the neurons to be found within the central nervous system. The neurons of the peripheral nervous system arise from cells which migrate from the central nerve tube, and from cells of the neural crests and certain sense placodes.

1) General Cytoplasmic Changes. The basic physiological functions of **irritability** and **conductivity** found in living protoplasm is developed to a high degree in the neuron or essential cellular entity of the nervous system. In consequence, the morphological changes which the simple epithelial cell of the forming neural tube assumes during its differentiation into a neuron is in harmony with these basic functions. One of the morphological changes in the developing neuroblast is the formation of coagulated threads of cytoplasmic material embedded in a more liquid cytoplasm. These threads are known as **neurofibrils,** while the more liquid, less-differentiated parts of the cytoplasm are called the **neuroplasm.** Accompanying the changes which produce the neurofibrils is the formation of another characteristic of neurons, namely, **processes or cytoplasmic extensions** from the body of the cell (fig. 352B). These processes are of two general types, the **dendrites** and the **axon (neuraxis** or **axis cylinder).** Several dendrites are generally present but only one axon is developed. The exact function of the dendrites has been questioned but the possibility is conceded that they function as "the chief receptive organelles of the neuron" (Maximow and Bloom, '42, p. 190), whereas the axon is believed to convey the nerve impulse away from the cell body to the **terminal arborizations** or **teledendria** (fig. 352A). The teledendria make physiologic contact (i.e., they synapse) with the dendrites of other neurons or they form a specialized relationship with **effector cells** such as glandular cells or muscle fibers (fig. 352A). The neurofibrils extend into the cell processes. The precise relationship of the neurofibrils to conduction and transmission of nervous impulses is unknown. (*Note:* The formation of the sheaths surrounding the nerve fiber is described on page 819.)

2) Nuclear Changes. Associated with the changes in the cytoplasm mentioned above are alterations of the nucleus. One of the striking features of nuclear change is that it enlarges, and becomes vesicular, though the basichromatin remains small in quantity. The nucleolus experiences profound changes, and is converted from a homogeneously staining body into a vacuolated structure in which the desoxyribose nucleic acid is irregularly localized along the edges. Contemporaneous with the nuclcolar changes there is a "marked production of Nissl substance in the cytoplasm" (Lavelle, '51, p. 466). Accompanying the changes in the nucleus is its loss of mitotic activity, although a centrosome is present in the cytoplasm. All neuroblasts, however, do not lose their power of division; only those which start to differentiate into neurons. During embryonic life many potential neurons remain in the neuroblast stage and these continue to proliferate and give origin to other neuroblasts. Shortly after birth or hatching this proliferative activity apparently ceases, and the undifferentiated neuroblasts then proceed to differentiate into neurons.

3) Growth and Development of Nerve-cell Processes. The early neuroblasts of the central nerve tube are at first **apolar,** that is, that do not have distinct processes. These apolar cells presumably transform in **unipolar** and **bipolar** varieties of **neuroblasts.** The unipolar cells have one main process, the axon, and the bipolar cells have two processes, an axon and a dendrite. From these two primitive cell types **multipolar neurons** arise having several dendrites and one axon (fig. 352B).

As the nerve-cell process begins to develop, a small cytoplasmic extension from the cell body occurs. To quote directly from Harrison ('07), p. 118, who was the first to study growing nerve-cell processes in the living cell: "These observations show beyond question that the nerve fiber develops by the outflowing of protoplasm from the central cells. This protoplasm retains its amoeboid activity at its distal end, the result being that it is drawn out into a long thread which becomes the axis cylinder. No other cells or living structures take part in the process. The development of the nerve fiber is thus brought about by means of one of the very primitive properties of living protoplasm, amoeboid movement, which, though probably common to some extent to all cells of the embryo, is especially accentuated in the nerve cells at this period of development." The distal end of a growing nerve fiber has a slight enlargement, the "growth cone" or "growth club" (fig. 352C). The conclusions of Harrison on growing nerve fibers in tissue culture were substantiated by Speidel ('33) in his observations of growing nerve fibers in the tadpole's tail.

Many different shapes of cells are produced during the histogenesis of the neural tube. However, two main morphological types of cells may be considered:

(1) One type of neuron possesses a short axon or axis cylinder. This type of neuron lies entirely within the gray substance of the neural tube.

(2) In a second type of neuron a long fiber or axis cylinder is developed and this fiber leaves the gray substance and traverses along the white substance of the cord or within the fiber tracts of the forming brain. In many instances, the cell body of the second type of neuron lies within the gray matter of the spinal cord, but its axis cylinder passes out of the nerve tube as the **efferent** or **motor fiber** of a spinal or cranial nerve (fig. 355F and I).

b. The Development of the Supporting Tissue of the Neural Tube

The potential connective tissue cell of the neural tube is the **spongioblast.** Spongioblasts are of ectodermal origin and differentiate into two main types of cells: (1) **Ependymal cells,** and (2) **neuroglia cells.**

Spongioblasts together with primitive neuroblasts lie at first within the ependymal zone of the neural canal particularly close to the lumen. Cilia are developed on the free surface of each spongioblast lining the neurocoel. From the opposite end of the cell, that is, the end facing the periphery of the tube, an elongated process extends peripherad to the outer surface of the neural tube. In this way a slender framework of fibers extends radially across the neural tube, from the lumen to the periphery (fig. 353F–H). A spongioblast which retains a relationship with the lumen and at the same time possesses a fiber extending peripherad is known as an **ependymal cell.** The **ependymal cells** thus are those cells whose bodies and nuclei lie next to the lumen of the developing spinal cord and brain but possess processes which radiate outward toward the periphery of the cord (fig. 353A and F). The peripheral fiber or extension may be lost in the later ependymal cell together with its cilia.

In fishes and amphibians the supporting elements of the central nerve tube retain the primitive arrangement outlined above (see Ariens-Kappers, '36, p. 46). However, in reptiles, birds and mammals, the radial pattern of many of the primitive spongioblasts is lost, and these spongioblasts transform into **neuroglia cells,** losing their connection with the lumen and with the external limiting membrane of the tube (fig. 353I).

c. Early Histogenetic Zones of the Neural Tube

The neural plate of the late gastrula is a thickened area of cells of about 3 to 4 cells in thickness. As the neural plate is transformed into the neural tube the majority of the neural plate cells become aggregated within the lateral walls of the tube. The lateral walls of the developing neural tube in consequence are thicker than the dorsal and ventral regions. As already observed in Chapter 10, this discrepancy in the thickness of the walls of the tube is due (in the amphibia) to the inductive influence of the somite which comes to lie along the lateral regions of the primitive tube. In the 9-mm. pig embryo, the neural tube in transverse section begins to present three general zones (fig. 353J), viz.:

(1) an **ependymal layer** of columnar cells lining the lumen,

(2) a relatively thick nucleated **mantle layer** occupying the middle zone of the neural tube, and

(3) a **marginal layer** without nuclei extending along the lateral margins of the tube.

The *ependymal layer of cells* lies against the **internal limiting membrane** of the tube, and consists of differentiating spongioblasts as indicated above. The **mantle layer** contains many neuroblasts and in consequence is referred to as the middle nucleated zone. It forms the future gray matter of the neural tube. The outer or marginal zone in its earlier phases of development is a meshwork of neuroglia and ependymal cell processes. Later, however, the processes of neurons come to lie among the fibrous processes of the neuroglia and ependymal cells as the nerve cell fibers extend along the spinal cord. The **external limiting membrane** lies around the outer edge of the marginal layer, and thus forms the outer boundary of the tube. In figure 353H is shown the relationships of the ependymal, mantle and marginal layers of the spinal cord of a 55-mm. pig embryo together with the ependymal and neuroglia cells. The arrangement of the ependymal, mantle and marginal layers in the spinal cord of a 22-mm. opossum embryo is shown in figure 353K.

d. Early Histogenesis of the Peripheral Nervous System

The formation of the cerebrospinal series of nerves which comprise the peripheral nervous system involves cells located within the neural crest materials and also within the mantle layer (gray matter) of the neural tube. One feature of the development of the spinal nerves is their basic *metamerism,* for a pair of spinal nerves innervates the somites of each primitive segment or metamere.

The neuroblasts of each spinal nerve arise in two areas, viz.:

(1) the **neural crest material** which forms segmental masses along the lateral sides of the neural tube, and

(2) **cells within the ventral portions of the gray matter of the tube.**

In the development of a spinal nerve bipolar neuroblasts appear within the neural crest material. Each bipolar neuroblast sends a process distad toward the dorso-lateral portion of the neural tube and a second process lateroventrad toward the body wall tissues, or toward the viscera. Later these bipolar elements become unipolar and form the **dorsal root ganglion cells.**

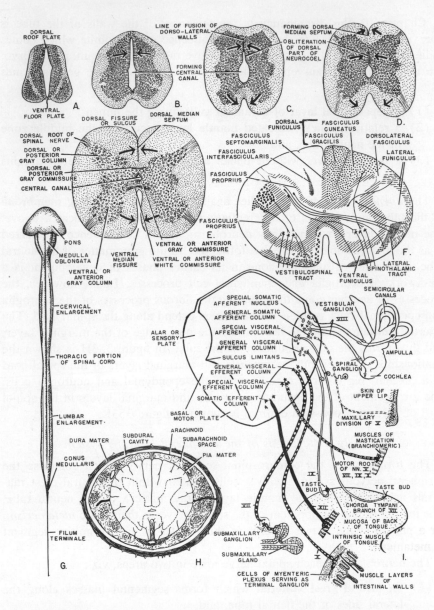

FIG. 355. Development of general structural features of the spinal cord; the nuclei of origin and nuclei of termination of cranial nerves associated with the myelencephalon. (A–E) The formation of the central canal, dorsal median septum, dorsal median sulcus, and ventral median fissure in pig embryos. Arrows in the dorsal part of the developing nerve cord show obliteration of the dorsal part of the primary neurocoel by medial growth of the lateral walls of the spinal cord. By this expansive, medial growth, the *dorsal median septum* and the *dorsal sulcus* (fissure) are formed. Observe that the *central canal* is developed from the ventral remains of the primary neurocoel after the obliteration of the dorsal portion of the primary neurocoel has been effected. In diagrams C–E, the

818

Within the ventral gray matter of the spinal cord, fusiform bipolar cells arise which send processes at intervals out into the marginal layers and from thence outward through the external limiting membrane of the tube at the levels corresponding to the developing dorsal root ganglia. The groups of processes which thus emerge from the neural tube below a single dorsal root ganglion soon unite with the ventrolateral processes of the dorsal root ganglion cells to form the **ventral root** of the spinal nerve. Within the neural tube the cell bodies of the ventral root fibers soon form multipolar neuron cells.

As development proceeds, the cell bodies of the neurons within the dorsal root ganglia become encased by **capsular cells** which develop from some of the neural crest cells (fig. 352D). The capsular cells in consequence are of ectodermal origin and they are continuous with the **neurilemma sheath.** The cells of the neurilemma sheath also arise from certain neural crest cells and from cells within the neural tube. These cells migrate distad as **sheath cells** along with the growing nerve fiber. The **neurilemma** or **sheath of Schwann** arises as an outward growth from the cytoplasm of the **sheath cells;** the neurilemma sheath thus appears in the form of a delicate tube surrounding the nerve fiber (axis cylinder) of the neuron (352D). Later on, a secondary substance appears between the nerve fiber (axis cylinder) and the neurilemma in many nerve fibers. This substance is of a fatty nature and forms the *myelin (medullary) sheath* (fig. 352E). Myelin deposition by sheath cells depends primarily upon an axis cylinder stimulus and not upon the sheath cells, for it is only a particular type of nerve fiber, the *myelin-emergent fiber,* which possesses the ability to form myelin (Speidel, '33). In the peripheral nerve fibers, the neurilemma at certain intervals dips inward toward the axis cylinder, forming the **node of Ranvier.** The area between two nodes is known as an **internodal segment** (fig. 352B). One sheath cell is present in each internodal segment. The nerve fibers of the peripheral nervous system with respect to

---

FIG. 355—*Continued*

arrows drawn in the ventral portions of the nerve tube indicate the ventro-medial expansion of lateral portions of the developing nerve tube with the subsequent formation of the *ventral median fissure.* In E the dorsal, ventral, and lateral *columns* or *funiculi* of white matter are shown. (F) Diagram depicting some of the principal fiber tracts of the spinal cord of man. Ascending tracts on the right; descending tracts on the left. (Redrawn from Ranson, 1939. For reference see G.) (G) Ventral view of human spinal cord, nerves removed, showing cervical and lumbar enlargements. (Redrawn from Ranson, 1939, The Anatomy of the Nervous System, Philadelphia, Saunders.) (H) Diagram revealing the relation of the meninges, i.e., the protective membranes of the central nervous system, to the spinal cord. (Redrawn from Ranson, 1939. For reference see G.) (I) Schematic diagram of transverse section through myelencephalon (medulla), portraying dorso-ventral position of *nuclei of origin* in motor plate and the nuclei of *termination* in alar plate of cranial nerves associated with the myelencephalon.

their sheath-like coverings are of two kinds, viz., **myelinated** fibers with neurilemma and **unmyelinated** (Remak's) fibers with a **thin neurilemma.** The latter are found especially among the sympathetic nerve fibers of the cerebrospinal series. (See Ranson, '39, p. 51.)

It may be observed here, parenthetically, that the myelinated fibers of the brain and spinal cord differ from the myelinated fibers of the peripheral nervous system in that the sheaths are formed by an investment of neuroglia fibers and nuclei and not by a neurilemma sheath. Many naked axons also are present in the central nervous system.

C. Morphogenesis of the Central Nervous System

1. DEVELOPMENT OF THE SPINAL CORD

a. Internal Changes in the Cord

During the early development of the spinal cord described above the following areas are evident:

(1) the ependymal layer,
(2) the mantle layer, and
(3) the marginal layer.

The further development of these areas results in the formation of a thin **dorsal roof plate** and a **ventral floor plate** mainly from the ependymal layer (fig. 353J and K). Somewhat later the neural cavity of the cord is reduced by the apposition and fusion of the dorso-lateral walls of the lumen immediately under the dorsal plate, leaving a rounded **central canal** below located near the floor plate (fig. 355A–E). Synchronized with these events the lateral walls of the neural tube expand greatly as the mass of cells and fibers increases. During this expansion, the two dorsal parts of the lateral walls move dorsad and mediad and in this way come to lie apposed together in the median plane above the central canal. This apposition forms the **dorsal median septum** (fig. 355D and E). The dorsal roof plate becomes obliterated during this process. Ventrally, also, the lateral portions of the neural tube move toward the mid-ventral line below the central canal. However, the two sides do not become closely apposed, and as a result the **ventral median fissure** is formed (fig. 355D and E).

During the growth and expansion of the two lateral walls of the neural tube, the neuroblasts of the nucleated mantle layer in the **dorsal** or **alar plate** of the spinal cord increase greatly in number and form the **dorsal (or posterior) gray column** (fig. 355A–E). The developing neuroblasts of the dorsal gray column become associated with the dorsal root fibers of the spinal nerves. Ventrally, the neuroblasts of the mantle layer increase in number in the basal plate area of the spinal cord and form a **ventral (anterior) gray column.** The ventral root fibers of the spinal nerves emerge from the ventral gray column. In the region of the central canal the mantle layer forms the **dorsal and ventral gray commissures** which extend across the nerve cord joining the gray columns in the lateral walls of the cord. Somewhat later, a **lateral gray column** on either side may be formed between the dorsal and ventral gray columns.

As the above growth and development of the mantle layer is achieved, the marginal zone of the spinal cord also increases in size as nerve fibers from the developing neurons in the gray columns and in the spinal ganglia of the dorsal roots grow into the marginal layer between the neuroglia elements. Moreover, nerve fibers from developing neuroblasts in the brain grow posteriad in the marginal layer of the cord. As the growth and expansion of the dorsal and ventral gray columns toward the periphery of the spinal cord occurs, the marginal layer becomes divided into definite regions or columns known as **funiculi.** The **dorsal funiculus,** for example, lies between the dorsal median septum and the dorsal gray column while the **ventral funiculus** is bounded by the ventral median fissure and the ventral gray column. The **lateral funiculus** lies laterally between the dorsal and ventral gray columns (fig. 355F). Below the ventral gray commissure, fibers cross from one side of the cord to the other, forming the **ventral white commissure.**

Eventually the nerve fibers of each funiculus become segregated into **fiber tracts.** As a result, the dorsal funiculus becomes subdivided into the two fiber-tract bundles, the **fasciculus gracilis** near the dorsal medial septum and the **fasciculus cuneatus** near the dorsal gray column. Other fiber tracts are shown in figure 355F. (Consult Ranson, '39, p. 110.)

b. Enlargements of the Spinal Cord

The spinal cord in many tetrapoda tends to show two enlarged areas, viz. (fig. 355G):

(1) The **brachial (cervical) enlargement** in the area of origin of the brachial nerves;

(2) The **lumbar (sacral) enlargement** in the area of origin of the lumbosacral plexus.

Posteriorly the cord tapers toward a point, and anteriorly, in the region of the first spinal nerve, it swells to become continuous with the myelencephalon.

c. Enveloping Membranes of the Cord

Immediately surrounding the spinal cord is a delicate membrane, the **pia mater,** presumably developed from neural crest cells. More lateral is the **arachnoid layer,** developed probably from neural crest cells and mesenchyme. Between the pia mater and the arachnoid is the **subarachnoid space** containing blood vessels, connective tissue fibers, and a lymph-like fluid. Outside of the arachnoid layer is a cavity, the **subdural cavity.** The external boundary of the subdural cavity is formed by the **dura mater.** The latter is a tough connective tissue membrane of mesenchymal origin (fig. 355H).

2. DEVELOPMENT OF THE BRAIN

a. The Development of Specialized Areas and Outgrowths of the Brain

1) The Formation of the Five-part Brain. The primitive vertebrate brain from its earliest stages of development begins to show certain enlargements, sacculations and outpushings. Furthermore, it possesses two main areas which are **non-nervous** and membranous in character, namely, the **thin roof plate** of the rhombencephalon and the **thin roof plate** of the posterior portion (diencephalon) of the prosencephalon (figs. 354E; 356A). These thin roof plates ultimately form a part of the *tela chorioidea.* Vascular tufts, the *chorioid plexi,* also project from these roof plates into the third and fourth ventricles.

The anterior region of the primitive brain known as the prosencephalon or **forebrain** soon divides into the anterior **telencephalon** and a more posterior **diencephalon** (fig. 354C–E). The telencephalon gives origin to two lateral outgrowths or pouches, the **telencephalic vesicles** (figs. 354E; 357E). The telencephalic vesicles represent the rudiments of the **cerebral lobes.** From the diencephalon, four or five evaginations occur, namely, a mid-dorsal evagination, the **epiphysis** or rudiment of the **pineal body** (fig. 356A), and in front of the epiphysis a second mid-dorsal evagination occurs normally in most vertebrates, namely, the **paraphysis** (see Chapter 21); two ventro-lateral outgrowths, the **optic vesicles** (fig. 354B–D) from which later arise the optic nerves, retina, etc., and a mid-ventral evagination, the **infundibulum.** The infundibulum unites with Rathke's pouch (figs. 354E; 356A), a structure which arises from the stomodaeum. Rathke's pouch ultimately differentiates into the anterior lobe of the pituitary body (see Chapter 21).

The **mesencephalon,** unlike the fore- and hind-brain regions, does not divide. However, from the mesencephalic roof or **tectum** dorsal swellings occur which appear to be associated with visual and auditory reflexes. In fishes and amphibia, two swellings occur, the so-called **optic lobes** or **corpora bigemina.** In reptiles, birds and mammals four swellings arise in the tectum, the **corpora quadrigemina.** (fig. 357H–O).

The rhombencephalon divides into an anterior **metencephalon** and posterior medulla or **myelencephalon** (fig. 354E and G). Two **cerebellar outpushings** arise from the roof of the metencephalon.

The primitive five-part brain forms the basic embryonic condition for later brain development in all vertebrates.

2) The Cavities of the Primitive Five-part Brain and Spinal Cord. As previously observed, the brain and spinal cord are hollow structures, and its generalized cavity is called the neural cavity or **neurocoel** (fig. 357A). From the primitive neurocoel, special cavities in the brain arise, as follows (see figure 357A):

(1) The telencephalon is made up of the anterior part of the prosencephalon and two **telencephalic vesicles.** Each vesicle ultimately gives origin to a **cerebral lobe.** The cavities of the telencephalic vesicles are known as the **first and second ventricles.**

(2) The cavity of the posterior, median portion of the telencephalon and that of the diencephalon form the **third ventricle.**

(3) The roof of the original mesencephalon may give origin to hollow, shallow outpushings, but the cavity of the mesencephalon itself becomes a narrow passageway and is known as the **cerebral aqueduct** or the **aqueduct of Sylvius.**

(4) The cavity of the rhombencephalon is called the **fourth ventricle.**

b. The Formation of Cervical and Pontine Flexures

In addition to the primary or cephalic flexure previously described (p. 812) other flexures may appear in the developing vertebrate brain, especially in higher vertebrates. The **cervical flexure** develops at the anterior portion of the spinal cord, as it joins the myelencephalon. It involves the caudal portion of the **myelencephalon,** and the anterior part of the cord. It bends the entire brain region ventrally (see figure 357D and E). The latter flexure is absent in fishes, is present to a slight degree in the early neural tube of the amphibia, and is pronounced in reptiles, birds and mammals. The third or **pontine flexure** of the brain bends the brain dorsally. It arises in the mid-region of the rhombencephalon, in the area between the myelencephalon and the metencephalon. It appears later in development than the cephalic and cervical flexures, and is found only in higher vertebrates.

c. Later Development of the Five-part Brain

The various fundamental regions of the five-part brain develop differently in different vertebrates. Figure 357B–G and H–O illustrates the changes of the regions of the primitive five-part brain in the shark, frog, bird, dog, and human. For detailed discussion of the function of the various parts of the brain of the vertebrate, see Ranson, '39.

D. Development of the Peripheral Nervous System

1. STRUCTURAL DIVISIONS OF THE PERIPHERAL NERVOUS SYSTEM

The peripheral nervous system integrates the peripheral areas of the body with the central nervous system. It is composed of two main parts,

(1) the **cerebrospinal system** of nerves and

(2) the **autonomic system.** The latter is associated intimately with the cerebrospinal system.

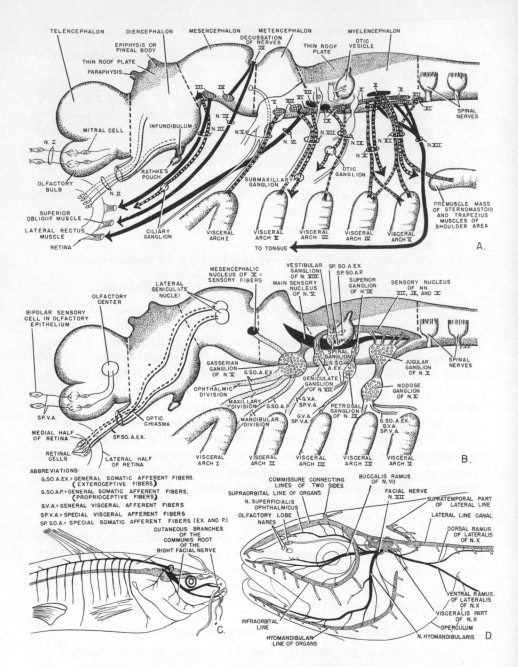

FIG. 356. The cranial nerves; nuclei of origin and termination; functional components. (*Note:* The accompanying figures illustrate the *nuclei of origin* and *nuclei of termination* of the various cranial nerves. They are generalized figures and should be regarded only as approximate representations. This must be true, for the position of the respective nuclei within the brain "varies greatly in different orders of vertebrates" [Ranson]. This variation presumably is the result of a developmental principle known as *neurobiotaxis*. This principle postulates that the dendrites of a neuron together with the cell body move

824

toward the source from whence the neuron receives its stimulation. That is, the dendrites grow, and the neuron cell body as a whole moves, toward the particular nerve fiber tract from which the impulses are received. As these impulses and fiber tracts vary slightly with the particular environmental conditions under which the different animal groups live, the location of the nuclei within the brain correspondingly will vary to a degree within the respective vertebrate groups. It is· to be observed, also, that the nuclei of origin of the afferent fibers of the cranial nerves, and of the cerebrospinal nerves in general, are located outside of the central nerve tube, with the exception of the neuron cell bodies of the second or optic nerve which are located in the retina, an extension of the forebrain, and the mesencephalic nucleus of the fifth nerve. The nuclei of origin of the efferent fibers are placed within the latero-basal areas of the nerve tube (fig. 355I).)

(A) The nuclei of origin of the various motor components of the cranial nerves here are shown to be located within fairly definite regions along the antero-posterior axis of the vertebrate brain. Reference may be made to Fig. 355I, for the dorso-ventral distribution of these nuclei.

The following symbols are used:

1. Somatic motor fibers are shown in solid black.
2. Special visceral motor fibers are indicated in black with white circles.
3. General visceral motor fibers are black with white markings.

Nuclei of origin within the brain are as follows:

III—black = Edinger-Westphal nucleus, origin of general visceral efferent fibers of Oculomotor Nerve

III—cross lines = nucleus of origin of somatic motor fibers of Oculomotor Nerve

IV—cross lines = nucleus of origin of somatic motor fibers of Trochlear Nerve

V—cross hatched = special visceral motor nucleus origin of special visceral motor fibers of Mandibular division of Trigeminal Nerve

VI—cross lines = nucleus of origin of somatic motor fibers of Abducent Nerve

VII—cross hatched = special visceral motor nucleus of Facial Nerve

VII—black = superior salivatory nucleus (?), origin of general visceral motor fibers of Facial Nerve

IX—cross hatched = origin of special visceral motor fibers of Glossopharyngeal Nerve (this nucleus represents the anterior portion of *nucleus ambiguus* of Vagus Nerve)

IX—solid black = inferior salivatory nucleus (?), origin of general visceral motor fibers of Glossopharyngeal Nerve

X—cross hatched = nucleus ambiguus or origin of special visceral motor fibers of Vagus Nerve

X—solid black = dorsal motor nucleus, origin of general visceral motor fibers of Vagus Nerve

XI—cross hatched = probable nucleus of origin of special visceral motor fibers of Spinal Accessory Nerve

XII—cross lines = nucleus of origin of somatic motor fibers of Hypoglossal Nerve

(B) Sensory nuclei or nuclei of termination of fifth, seventh, ninth, and tenth cranial nerves, shown along the antero-posterior axis of the vertebrate brain. (The dorso-ventral distribution of these nuclei is presented in Fig. 355I.) The nuclei of termination of the eighth cranial nerve has been omitted. (Figs. A and B are schematized from data supplied by Ranson, 1939, The Anatomy of the Nervous System, Philadelphia, Saunders.)

(C) Cutaneous taste-bud branches of the right Facial Nerve in the fish, *Ameiurus.* (Redrawn from Johnston, 1906, The Nervous System of Vertebrata, Philadelphia, Blakiston, after Herrick.)

(D) Head of the pollack, *Pollachius virens,* revealing seventh and tenth cranial nerve distribution to lateral line system of the head. (Redrawn from Kingsley, 1912, Comparative Anatomy of Vertebrates, Philadelphia, Blakiston, after Cole.)

2. The Cerebrospinal System

The **cerebrospinal system** of nerves is composed of the cranial and spinal nerves. Two sets of neurons enter into the composition of the cranial and spinal nerves, viz.:

(1) **afferent neurons,** whose fibers receive stimuli from certain receptor organs and convey the impulses to the central nervous system, and

(2) **efferent neurons,** with fibers which convey the impulses from the central nervous system to the peripheral areas. The central nervous system with its multitudes of association neurons thus acts to correlate the incoming impulses from afferent neurons and to shunt them into the correct outgoing pathways through the fibers of the efferent neurons (see figure 358A).

Most of the *afferent or sensory neurons* are located in ganglia outside of the central nerve tube, within the dorsal root ganglia of the spinal nerves and in the ganglia of the cranial nerves in close association with the brain (fig. 356B). On the other hand, the cell bodies of the **somatic efferent or motor fibers** are found within the gray matter of the central nerve tube, and the cell bodies of the **visceral efferent or motor fibers** are located within the gray matter of the central nerve tube and also in peripheral (autonomic) ganglia.

3. General Structure and Function of the Spinal Nerves

In each of the spinal nerves the nerve fibers are of **four functional varieties,** namely, **visceral sensory** (afferent); **visceral motor** (efferent); **somatic sensory** (afferent); and **somatic motor** (efferent). The visceral components are distributed to the glands, smooth muscles, etc., of the viscera located within the thoracic and abdominal cavities, together with the blood vessels of the general body areas. The somatic components innervate the body wall tissues including the skin and its appendages. A spinal nerve and its component fibers in the trunk region is shown in figure 358A, and figure 358B shows this distribution in the region of the brachial plexus.

A typical spinal nerve is composed of the following general parts:

(1) The **dorsal** or **sensory root** with its ganglion, and
(2) the **ventral** or **motor root.**
(3) Each spinal nerve divides into
(4) a **dorsal ramus,** and
(5) a **ventral ramus.** The ventral ramus may divide into
(6) a **lateral branch** and
(7) a **ventral branch.** Connecting with the spinal nerve also are
(8) the **gray and white rami** of the autonomic nervous system.

As the peripheral nerve fibers grow distad they become grouped together to form peripheral nerves. Each nerve in consequence is an association of bundles or fasicles of fibers surrounded and held together by connective tissue. Most of the peripheral nerve fibers are myelinated. The connective tissue which surrounds a nerve is called the **perineurium** and that which penetrates inward between the fibers is the **endoneurium** (fig. 358C).

4. THE ORIGIN, DEVELOPMENT AND FUNCTIONS OF THE CRANIAL NERVES

Consult diagrams, figures 356A and B, also 355I.

O. TERMINAL

The **nervus terminalis** is a little understood nerve closely associated with the olfactory nerve. It was discovered by F. Pinkus in 1894, in the dipnoan fish, *Protopterus,* after the other cranial nerves were described. In consequence it does not have a numerical designation. (Consult Larsell, '18, for references and discussion.)

I. OLFACTORY

Arises from bipolar cells located in olfactory epithelium. These cells give origin to fibers which grow into the olfactory bulb to synapse with olfactory-bulb neurons (fig. 356B).

Summary of functional components: **Special visceral afferent fibers.**

II. OPTIC

The optic nerve arises from neurons located in the retina of the eye. They grow mediad along the lumen of the optic stalk to form the optic nerve. In mammals part of the fibers from the median half of each retina **decussate,** i.e., cross over, and follow the fibers from the lateral half of the retina of the other eye into the brain (fig. 356B). In birds, however, decussation of the optic nerve fibers is complete, as it is in reptiles and fishes, and probably also in amphibians.

Summary of functional components: **Special somatic afferent fibers,** cell bodies in the retina. In fishes, there are **efferent fibers** in the optic nerve controlling, possibly, movements of retinal elements (Arey, '16, and Arey and Smith, '37).

III. OCULOMOTOR

The third cranial nerve is composed mainly of **somatic motor fibers** which originate from neuroblasts in the **anterior basal area** of the mesencephalon. These fibers grow latero-ventrad from the mesencephalic wall to innervate the premuscle masses of the inferior oblique, inferior, medial and superior rectus muscles of the eyeball (fig. 356A).

Summary of functional components: (1) **Somatic motor fibers** controlling eye muscles indicated, (2) **general somatic afferent (sensory) fibers,** i.e. pro-

prioceptive fibers for eye muscle tissue, (3) **general visceral efferent fibers.**
The neuron bodies of the visceral efferent fibers are located in the Edinger-
Westphal nucleus of mesencephalon. The fibers from these neurons form the
preganglionic fibers which terminate in the ciliary ganglion. The postganglionic fibers from cell bodies in ciliary ganglion innervate the intrinsic
(smooth) muscles of the ciliary body and iris.

IV. TROCHLEAR

The fourth cranial nerve arises from neuroblasts in the posterior ventral
floor of the mesencephalon near the ventral commissure. The fibers grow
dorsad and somewhat posteriad within the wall of the mesencephalon to the
mid-dorsal line where they emerge to the outside and decussate (i.e. cross),
the nerve from one side passing laterad toward the eye of the opposite side
where it innervates the developing premuscle mass of the superior oblique
muscle (fig. 356A).

Summary of functional components: (1) **Somatic motor fibers** controlling
superior oblique muscle, (2) **general somatic afferent (sensory) fibers,** i.e.
proprioceptive fibers from eye muscle tissue.

V. TRIGEMINAL

The trigeminal nerve is a complex association of sensory and motor fibers
(fig. 356A, B). It has the following divisions:

A. Ophthalmicus or Deep Profundus

Composed of **somatic sensory fibers** to the snout region. Fibers originate
from neuroblasts in the dorso-anterior part of the neural crest cells which give
origin to the Gasserian (semilunar) ganglion. This portion of the semilunar
ganglion probably should be regarded as a separate and distinct ganglion.
One fiber from each bipolar neuroblast grows anteriad toward the snout while
the other fiber enters the wall of the metencephalon. These neurons later
become unipolar.

Summary of functional components: **General somatic afferent (sensory)
fibers.**

B. Maxillaris

The maxillary ramus of the fifth cranial nerve is composed of **somatic
sensory fibers** from the upper jaw and snout and mucous membranes in these
areas. The fibers arise from neuroblasts within the neural crest material which
forms the central mass of the semilunar ganglion. One fiber from each bipolar
neuroblast grows anteriad toward the snout while the other fiber grows mediad
to enter the wall of the metencephalon along with fibers from the ophthalmic
and mandibular divisions. These neurons later become unipolar.

Summary of functional components: **General somatic afferent (sensory)
fibers.**

C. Mandibularis

The mandibular ramus is composed of **general sensory (afferent) fibers** with cell bodies lying in the **mesencephalic nucleus** of the fifth nerve (see figure 356A). Associated with these sensory fibers are **motor fibers** (generally spoken of as **special visceral motor fibers**) distributed to the **muscles of mastication.** The latter muscles arise from mesoderm associated with the first or mandibular visceral arch. During development the motor fibers arise from a localized mass of neuroblasts lying in the pons of the metencephalon (see figure 356A), and they emerge from the ventro-lateral aspect of the pons and grow out toward the mandibular arch. Later they become associated with the sensory fibers observed above.

Summary of functional components: (1) **General somatic afferent (sensory) fibers,** of the proprioceptive variety, originating in mesencephalic nucleus of the fifth nerve (fig. 356A, B), (2) **special visceral efferent (motor) fibers** to muscles of mastication from motor nucleus noted above.

VI. ABDUCENS

The word abducens means to lead away, or draw aside. It is applied to the sixth cranial nerve because it innervates the **lateral rectus** muscle of the eyeball whose function is to pull the eye away or outward from the median line. It is composed almost entirely of **somatic efferent (motor) fibers** whose origin is within a nucleus lying in the caudo-ventral area of the pons (fig. 356A). In the embryo, neuroblasts in this area grow outward from the ventro-lateral wall of the pons and forward into the developing premuscle mass of the external (lateral) rectus muscle.

Summary of functional components: (1) **Somatic efferent fibers,** (2) **general somatic afferent fibers,** i.e. proprioceptive fibers from the external rectus muscle.

VII. FACIAL

In higher vertebrates this nerve is composed largely of **motor fibers** of the **special visceral variety** innervating the musculature derived from the hyoid visceral arch. As indicated previously (Chap. 16) the muscle tissue of this arch forms the facial (mimetic) and *platysma* musculature of mammals and the posterior belly of digastric and stylohyoid muscles. In fishes muscle tissue is restricted to the region of the hyoid arch and is concerned with movements of this arch. The motor fibers distributed to the hyoid arch of fishes are located in the **hyomandibular branch** of the facial nerve (see figure 357I). Aside from these special visceral motor fibers, sensory fibers are present whose cell bodies lie within the **geniculate ganglion** of the facial nerve. The sensory fibers which innervate some of the taste buds on the anterior two-thirds of the tongue in mammals are **special visceral afferent fibers** coursing in the **chorda tympani nerve,** whereas those along the pathway of the facial nerve are

general visceral sensory fibers providing deep sensibility to the general area of distribution of the facial nerve. The special visceral afferent fibers to the taste bud system are prominent elements in the seventh cranial nerve of many fishes (fig. 356C). In fishes also, the seventh cranial nerve contains **lateral-line components** distributed to the **lateral-line organs of the head** (fig. 356D).

The **special motor fibers** of the facial nerve arise from neuroblasts located in the pons as indicated in figure 356A, and the **general visceral motor fibers** take origin from cell bodies in the nucleus salvatorius superior.

Summary of components: (1) **Special visceral efferent (motor) fibers** to musculature arising in area of hyoid arch, (2) in mammals, **preganglionic general visceral efferent fibers** by way of chorda tympani nerve to submaxillary ganglion; and from thence, postganglionic fibers to submaxillary and sublingual salivary glands. (3) **Special visceral afferent fibers** to taste buds on anterior portion of tongue by way of chorda tympani nerve; in fishes, special visceral afferent fibers arc extensive. (4) **General visceral afferent fibers.** (5) In fishes, **lateral-line components to head region** are present.

VIII. ACOUSTIC

The acoustic nerve contains **special somatic sensory components** which receive sensations from the **special sense organs** derived from the **otic vesicle.** The otic vesicle differentiates into two major structures, viz.: (1) one related to **balance or equilibration,** and (2) the other concerned with **hearing or the detection of wave motions** aroused in the external medium. This differentiation is obscure in fishes. However, in those vertebrates which dwell in water other hearing devices may be used aside from those which may involve the developing ear vesicle. One aspect of the mechanism which enables water-dwelling vertebrates to detect pressure or wave motions of low frequency in the surrounding watery medium is the **lateral line system** associated with the fifth, seventh, ninth and tenth cranial nerves.

In accordance with the differentiation of the otic vesicle into two sense-perceiving organs, the sensory neurons of the acoustic ganglion of the eighth cranial nerve become segregated into two ganglia, namely, (1) **the vestibular ganglion** containing bipolar neurons which transmit proprioceptive stimuli through the vestibular nerve from the organ of equilibration composed of the *utricle, saccule* and *semicircular canals,* and (2) the **spiral ganglion** containing bipolar neurons which transmit somatic sensations from the **spiral or hearing organ** (fig. 361H).

Summary of functional components: (1) **Special somatic afferent fibers** of proprioceptive variety associated with equilibration, (2) **special somatic afferent fibers** of exteroceptive variety, associated with hearing.

IX. GLOSSOPHARYNGEAL

The glossopharyngeal nerve is associated with the third visceral arch and nearby areas of the pharynx. It has two major components; one of these components is **motor,** innervating the musculature derived from the embryonic third visceral arch, while the other component is **sensory.** The sensory components are derived from neuron bodies within the **superior** and **petrosal ganglia** (fig. 356B). Aside from receiving **general sense impulses** from the pharyngeal area, many of these sensory components are associated with the **taste buds** on the caudal portion of the tongue. The latter components thus are **special sensory components.**

The **visceral motor (efferent) components** to the musculature derived from the third visceral arch arise from neuroblasts located in the ventro-lateral floor of the anterior part of the **myelencephalon** (fig. 356A). The sensory components take origin from neural crest cells located in the region of the third visceral arch. Fibers from these neuroblasts grow mediad into the nerve tube, and latero-ventrad toward the third visceral arch region.

Summary of functional components: (1) **General visceral afferent fibers** with cell bodies in petrosal ganglion whose peripheral fibers terminate in the posterior tongue region and in the pharyngeal area, (2) **special visceral afferent fibers** with cell bodies in petrosal ganglion whose peripheral fibers contact the taste buds in the posterior third of the tongue, (3) **special visceral efferent fibers** to musculature derived from the third visceral arch. In mammals, this musculature is the **stylopharyngeus muscle,** (4) in mammals: **general visceral efferent fibers,** composed of preganglionic fibers from neurons in inferior salivatory nucleus located probably in the region between the pons and medulla pass to the otic ganglion. Postganglionic fibers from otic ganglion innervate the parotid gland. (5) In fishes: **lateral-line components** are present and distributed to posterior head region. In mammals, some **general somatic afferent fibers** from cell bodies in the superior ganglion appear to innervate cutaneous areas in the ear region.

X. Vagus

The tenth cranial or vagus nerve is composed of several functional components. It is a prominent nerve associated with the **autonomic nervous system** as indicated below. In addition to these autonomic components, the functional components of the tenth cranial nerve are related to the visceral arches caudal to the third visceral arch. The tenth cranial nerve thus supplies several visceral arches. In consequence, it must be regarded as a composite nerve, arising from **extensive motor nuclei,** the **dorsal motor nucleus** and the **nucleus ambiguus** in the ventro-lateral area of the myelencephalon (fig. 356A). The tenth nerve has two main ganglia, the **jugular** and **nodose ganglia.** The motor fibers arise from neuroblasts in the nuclei mentioned above and grow out laterally to the visceral arch area, and the sensory components take origin from neuroblasts of neural crest origin which become aggregated in the jugular and nodose ganglia.

Summary of functional components: (1) **Special visceral afferent fibers**

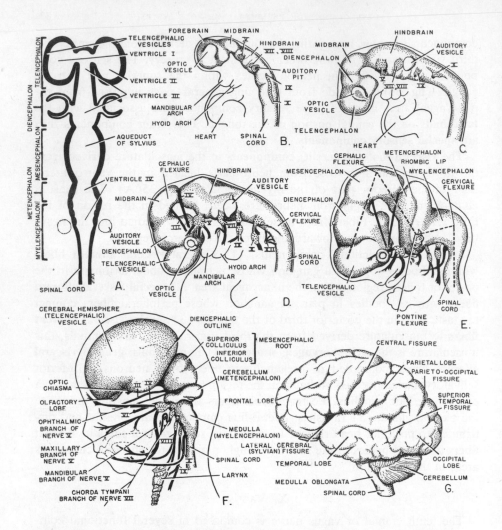

Fig. 357. External morphological development of various vertebrate brains. (A) Diagram showing the fundamental regional cavities of the primitive five-part vertebrate brain. (B–G) External morphological changes of the developing human brain and cranial nerves. (Redrawn, somewhat modified, from Patten, 1946, Human Embryology, Philadelphia, Blakiston, adapted primarily from Streeter and reconstructions in Carnegie Collection.) (B) 20 somite embryo, probably 3½ weeks. (C) 4 mm. embryo, about 4 weeks. (D) 8 mm. embryo, about 5⅓ weeks. (E) 17 mm. embryo, about 7 weeks. (F) 50–60 mm. embryo, about 11 weeks. The brain now begins to assume the configuration shown by the chick at hatching (see Fig. 347L and M). Roman numerals III, IV, V, VI, VII, IX, X, XI and XII indicate cranial nerves. See Fig. 356A and B for functional components of the cranial nerves at this time. (G) Lateral view of brain at about the ninth month. (H, I, and I′) Adult form of the brain of *Squalus acanthias*. It is to be observed that the brain of *Squalus acanthias* loses the marked cephalic flexure (see Fig. 347A) present in the early embryo, and assumes a straightened form during the later stages of its development. (H and I ventral and dorsal views, respectively, drawn from dissected specimens; I′ redrawn and slightly modified from Norris and Hughes, 1919, J. Comp. Neurol., 31.) (J and K) Ventral and dorsal

whose cell bodies lie in nodose ganglion with peripheral terminations in taste buds of pharyngeal area, (2) **general visceral afferent fibers** whose cell bodies lie in nodose ganglion, with peripheral distribution to pharynx, esophagus, trachea, thoracic and abdominal viscera, (3) **general somatic afferent fibers** with cell bodies in jugular ganglion and peripheral distribution to external ear region, (4) **special visceral efferent fibers** to striated musculature of pharyngeal area; cell bodies lie in nucleus ambiguus, (5) **general visceral efferent fibers.** Preganglionic cell bodies in dorsal motor nucleus; terminate in sympathetic ganglia associated with thoracic and abdominal viscera, (6) in fishes: a prominent **lateral line component** is present which is distributed along the lateral body wall.

The **special visceral motor fibers** of the vagus are associated with musculature arising from the caudal visceral arches.

XI. Spinal Accessory

The spinal accessory nerve arises in close association with the vagus. It is composed mainly of motor fibers and distributed to musculature derived from premuscle masses in the caudal branchial area (fig. 356A). They may be regarded as **special visceral motor** fibers.

Summary of functional components: (1) **Special visceral efferent fibers** whose cell bodies lie in nucleus ambiguus and in anterior part of spinal cord and distributed to trapezius, and sternocleidomastoid, muscles and striated muscles of pharynx and larynx, (2) **general visceral efferent fibers** associated with vagus nerve, with cell bodies in dorsal motor nucleus of vagus.

XII. Hypoglossal Nerve

The twelfth cranial nerve is a somatic motor nerve composed mainly of efferent fibers distributed to the hypobranchial or tongue region. These fibers arise from neuroblasts in an extensive nuclear region from the anterior cervical area along the floor of the myelencephalon near the midventral line (fig. 356A). In lower vertebrates these fibers innervate certain of the anterior trunk myotomes whose muscle fibers travel ventrad into the hypobranchial area. In higher vertebrates the hypoglossal nerve fibers innervate the tongue and associated muscles.

Fig. 357—*Continued*

views, respectively, of the adult form of the brain in the frog, *Rana catesbiana.* Like the developing brain in *Squalus,* the brain of the developing frog loses its pronounced cephalic flexure as development proceeds. (L and M) Ventral and dorsal views, respectively, of the adult form of brain in the chick shortly before hatching. The *cervical, pontine,* and *cephalic flexures* are partly retained in developing brain of chick, and in this respect it resembles the developing mammalian brain. Compare these diagrams with Figs. 354E, 259. (N and O) Ventral and dorsal views, respectively, of the adult brain of the dog. (Redrawn from models.)

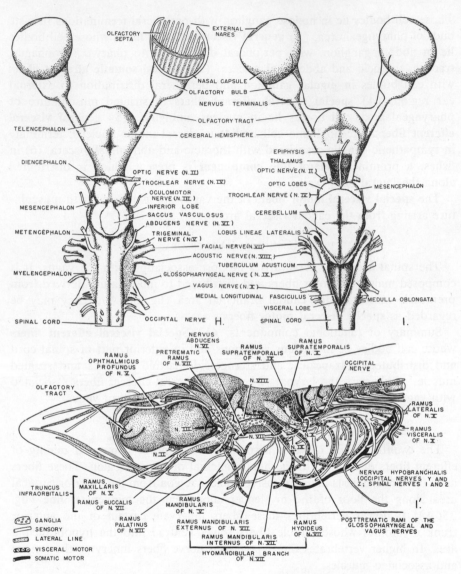

Fig. 357—*Continued*   For legend see p. 832.

Summary of functional components: (1) **Somatic motor fibers;** (2) **somatic sensory,** i.e., proprioceptive fibers, from tongue musculature.

5. The Origin and Development of the Autonomic System

a. Definition of the Autonomic Nervous System

The autonomic nervous system is that part of the peripheral nervous system which supplies the various glands of the body together with the musculature

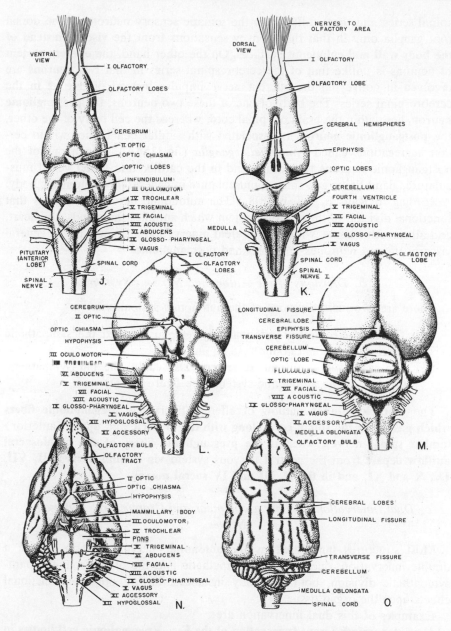

VENTRAL VIEW
I OLFACTORY
OLFACTORY LOBES
CEREBRUM
II OPTIC
OPTIC CHIASMA
OPTIC LOBES
INFUNDIBULUM
III OCULOMOTOR
IV TROCHLEAR
V TRIGEMINAL
VII FACIAL
VIII ACOUSTIC
VI ABDUCENS
IX GLOSSO-PHARYNGEAL
X VAGUS
PITUITARY (ANTERIOR LOBE)
SPINAL CORD
SPINAL NERVE I
J.

DORSAL VIEW
NERVES TO OLFACTORY AREA
I OLFACTORY
OLFACTORY LOBE
CEREBRAL HEMISPHERES
EPIPHYSIS
OPTIC LOBES
CEREBELLUM
FOURTH VENTRICLE
V TRIGEMINAL
VII FACIAL
VIII ACOUSTIC
IX GLOSSO-PHARYNGEAL
X VAGUS
MEDULLA
SPINAL CORD
SPINAL NERVE I
K.

I OLFACTORY
OLFACTORY LOBES
CEREBRUM
II OPTIC
OPTIC CHIASMA
HYPOPHYSIS
III OCULO MOTOR
IV TROCHLEAR
VI ABDUCENS
V TRIGEMINAL
VII FACIAL
VIII ACOUSTIC
IX GLOSSO-PHARYNGEAL
X VAGUS
XII HYPOGLOSSAL
XI ACCESSORY
OLFACTORY BULB
OLFACTORY TRACT
L.

OLFACTORY LOBE
LONGITUDINAL FISSURE
CEREBRAL LOBE
EPIPHYSIS
TRANSVERSE FISSURE
CEREBELLUM
OPTIC LOBE
FLOCCULUS
V TRIGEMINAL
VII FACIAL
VIII ACOUSTIC
IX GLOSSO-PHARYNGEAL
X VAGUS
XI ACCESSORY
MEDULLA OBLONGATA
OLFACTORY BULB
M.

II OPTIC
OPTIC CHIASMA
HYPOPHYSIS
MAMMILLARY BODY
III OCULOMOTOR
IV TROCHLEAR
PONS
V TRIGEMINAL
VI ABDUCENS
VII FACIAL
VIII ACOUSTIC
IX GLOSSO-PHARYNGEAL
X VAGUS
XI ACCESSORY
XII HYPOGLOSSAL
N.

CEREBRAL LOBES
LONGITUDINAL FISSURE
TRANSVERSE FISSURE
CEREBELLUM
MEDULLA OBLONGATA
SPINAL CORD
O.

FIG. 357—*Continued*   For legend see p. 832.

of the heart, blood vessels, digestive, urinary and reproductive organs, and other involuntary musculature. It differs from the cerebrospinal nerve series in its **efferent system** of **neurons,** and not in the afferent system. The latter is composed of ordinary afferent neurons located in the ganglia of the cerebrospinal series and these differ from the somatic sensory neurons of the dorsal root ganglia only in that they convey sensations from the **viscera instead of the body wall and cutaneous surfaces.** On the other hand, the efferent system of neurons is unlike that of the cerebrospinal series in that **two neurons** are involved in conveying the efferent nerve impulse instead of **one** as in the cerebrospinal series. The body of one of these two neurons, the **preganglionic neuron,** lies within the brain or spinal cord, whereas the cell body of the other, the **postganglionic neuron,** is associated with similar cell bodies within certain aggregations called *sympathetic ganglia* (fig. 358A). The axons of the postganglionic neurons run to and end in the cardiac and blood vessel musculature, gland tissue and smooth musculature in general throughout the body. According to Ranson, '18, p. 308, "The autonomic nervous system is that functional division of the nervous system which supplies the glands, the heart, and all smooth muscle, with their efferent innervation and includes all general visceral efferent neurones both pre- and postganglionic."

b. Divisions of the Autonomic Nervous System

There are two main divisions of the autonomic system, viz.:

(1) **The thoracicolumbar autonomic system,** also called the sympathetic division of the autonomic system, and

(2) **The craniosacral autonomic system,** also called the parasympathetic division of the autonomic system (see figure 358D).

The **thoracicolumbar outflow** of efferent fibers has **preganglionic fibers which pass from the spinal cord along with the thoracic and upper** (anterior) **lumbar spinal nerves,** whereas the **preganglionic fibers of the craniosacral outflow** depart from the central nervous system **via cranial nerves III, VII, IX, X and XI, and in the II, III and IV sacral nerves.**

c. Dual Innervation by Thoracicolumbar and Craniosacral Autonomic Nerves

Most structures innervated by the autonomic nervous system receive a double innervation, one from the sympathetic and the other from the parasympathetic division, both, in many instances, having opposite functional effects upon the organ tissue.

Examples of this dual innervation are:

1) **Autonomic Efferent Innervation of the Eye. Preganglionic cell bodies** in oculomotor nucleus, fibers passing with nerve III to **ciliary ganglion.** Postganglionic cell bodies in ciliary ganglion; **postganglionic fibers** by way of short ciliary nerves to ciliary muscle and circular muscle fibers of iris. **Function: Accommodation of eye and decrease in diameter of pupil.** The foregoing innervation is a part of the cranio-sacral autonomic outflow. A parallel inner-

vation to the iris of the eye occurs through the thoracicolumbar autonomic system as follows:

Cell bodies of **preganglionic neurons** in intermedio-lateral column of spinal cord, from which preganglionic fibers pass to **superior cervical ganglion** of autonomic nervous system. Cell bodies of **postganglionic fibers** lie in the superior cervical ganglion and fibers pass from this ganglion along the internal carotid plexus to the ophthalmic division of the fifth nerve, and from thence along the long ciliary and nasociliary nerves to iris. **Function: dilation of the pupil.**

2) Autonomic Efferent Innervation of the Heart. Preganglionic cell bodies in dorsal motor nucleus of vagus in myelencephalon. Fibers pass by way of vagus nerve to terminal (intrinsic) ganglia of the heart. **Postganglionic cell bodies** in terminal ganglia of heart; **postganglionic fibers** pass to heart muscle. **Function: slows the heart beat.** The foregoing represents the craniosacral autonomic or parasympathetic innervation. The corresponding sympathetic innervation is as follows:

Preganglionic cell bodies in intermedio-lateral column of spinal cord; preganglionic fibers pass to superior, middle and inferior cervical ganglia of sympathetic ganglion series. **Postganglionic cell bodies** in cervical ganglia from which **postganglionic fibers** pass via cardiac nerves to cardiac musculature. **Function: acceleration of heart beat.**

d. Ganglia of the Autonomic System and Their Origin

The ganglia of the autonomic nervous system represent aggregations of the cell bodies of **postganglionic neurons;** the cell bodies of the **preganglionic neurons** lie always within the central nervous system. These autonomic ganglia arise from two sources; viz.:

1) The **neural crest material** of the dorsal root ganglion of the spinal nerves and the neural crest material associated with certain cranial nerves, and
2) from **cells of the neural tube** which migrate from the tube along the forming ventral or efferent nerve roots of the spinal nerves (Kuntz and Batson, '20).

These migrating neural cells become aggregated to form three sets of ganglia as follows:

1) The sympathetic **chain ganglia** lying on either side of the vertebral column.
2) The **collateral** or **subvertebral ganglia** located between the chain ganglia and the viscera. Examples of collateral ganglia are the **coeliac, superior mesenteric** and **inferior mesenteric** ganglia.
3) The **terminal** or **intrinsic ganglia** lie near or within the organ tissue such as the **ciliary** and **submaxillary ganglia.**

Fig. 358. General structural features of spinal nerves, and of nerve fibers terminating in muscle tissue.   (A) Diagrammatic representation of a spinal nerve in the region of the mammalian diaphragm showing functional components. Three facts are evident relative to the components of a typical spinal nerve, viz., (1) The somatic efferent motor neuron lies within the central nerve tube; its fiber extends peripherad to the effector organ. One neuron therefore is involved in the somatic efferent system (see Fig. 352A). (2) Unlike the somatic efferent system, the visceral efferent (motor) system is composed of a chain of *two neurons,* a *preganglionic neuron* whose cell body lies within the central nerve tube, and a *postganglionic neuron* whose cell body lies in one of the peripheral ganglia. (3) The somatic afferent (sensory) and visceral afferent (sensory) fibers both possess but one neuron whose cell body lies within the dorsal root ganglion. The *somatic afferent fiber* connects with a sense or receptor organ lying somewhere between the viscera and the external surface (i.e., cutaneous surface) of the body, whereas the *visceral afferent fiber* contacts the structural makeup of the visceral structures.   (B) A spinal nerve in the region of the brachial plexus. The main difference between this type of nerve and the typical spinal nerve resides in the fact that the ventral ramus proceeds into the limb and not into the body wall. Before proceeding into the limb it inosculates with the ventral rami of other nerves to form the *brachial plexus.*   (C) Portion of a transverse section of the sciatic nerve of a newborn showing groups of nerve fibers joined together into bundles. Each nerve-fiber bundle is surrounded by connective tissue, the *perineurium,* and is partly divided by septa of connective tissue, the *endoneurium.* External to the perineurium is the *epineurium,* or the connective tissue which holds the entire nerve together (Redrawn from Maximow and Bloom, 1942, A Textbook of Histology, W. B. Saunders Co., Philadelphia, after Schaffer.)   (D) Diagram of the autonomic efferent system of neurons and ganglia. The *parasympathetic (craniosacral) outflow* is shown in heavy black lines with white spaces; the *sympathetic (thoracicolumbar) outflow* is represented by ordinary black lines. (Adapted from Ranson, 1939, The Anatomy of the Nervous System, Philadelphia, Saunders, after Meyer and Gottlieb.)

    G. cerv. sup. = superior cervical ganglion
    G. stellatum = inferior cervical or stellate ganglion
    G. mes. sup. = superior mesenteric ganglion
    G. mes. inf. = inferior mesenteric ganglion
    G. pelv. = pelvic ganglion

Neurohumoral substances are produced at the terminal (effector) tips of the various autonomic nerve fibers. A substance similar to *adrenalin* appears to be produced at the tips of the *sympathetic nerves proper,* whereas in the case of the *parasympathetic fibers* the substance is *acetylcholine.* These humoral substances stimulate the effector structures. (E, F, and G) Nerve endings associated with muscle tissue.   (E) Effector (motor) nerve endings associated with cardiac or smooth muscle. Sympathetic motor endings terminate in small swellings. This figure portrays sympathetic motor endings on a smooth muscle cell of an artery of the rabbit's eye. (Redrawn from Maximow and Bloom, 1942, A Textbook of Histology, Philadelphia, Saunders, after Retzius.)   (F) Another example of the termination of sympathetic nerve fiber endings on smooth muscle fibers. In this instance the bronchial musculature is the effector organ. (Redrawn from Maximow and Bloom, 1942, A Textbook of Histology, Philadelphia, Saunders, after Larsell & Dow.) (G and G') Nerve endings in striated muscle. (G redrawn from Ranson, 1939, The Anatomy of the Nervous System, Philadelphia, Saunders, after Huber & De Witt; G' redrawn from Maximow and Bloom, 1942, A Textbook of Histology, Philadelphia, Saunders, after Boeke.)   (G) Represents a *neuromuscular end organ* of a *sensory nerve* fiber terminating within a *muscle spindle* in striated muscle from a dog. These muscle spindles are in the form of a connective tissue capsule which invests spindle-shaped bundles of muscle fibers. Within this capsule, large myelinated nerve fibers terminate in non-myelinated branches which spiral around the muscle fibers or end in flattened discs.   (G') Represents a somatic motor (efferent) nerve fiber terminating in a *motor plate* within a striated muscle fiber. The *motor plate* is composed of an irregular mass of sarcoplasm below the sarcolemma of the muscle fiber. This motor plate receives the *naked terminal ramifications* of the nerve fiber.

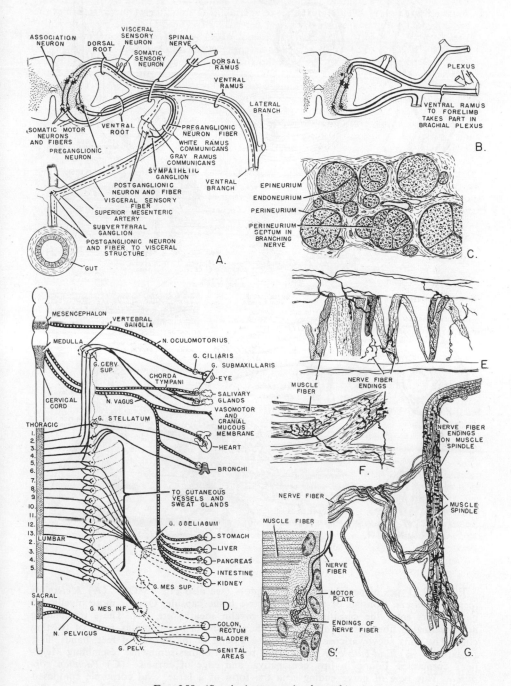

FIG. 358. *(See facing page for legend.)*

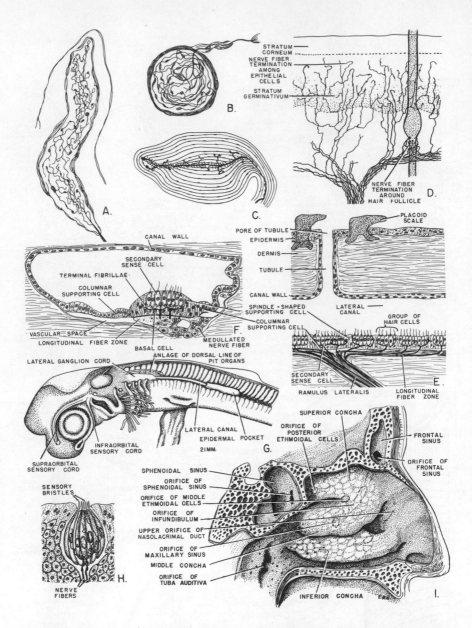

FIG. 359. Types of peripheral sense receptors (see also Fig. 358G). (A) *Meissner's tactile corpuscle.* Consists of a thin connective tissue capsule. One or more myelinated nerve fibers enter the capsule, where the myelin sheaths are lost. These terminating non-myelinated fibers break up into branches which form a complex mass of twisting coils. The coils show varicose enlargements. Found in the dermis of feet, hands, lips, forearms. (B) *End-bulb of Krause.* Small rounded bodies somewhat resembling Meissner's corpuscles. Found in lips, conjunctiva, and edge of cornea. (C) *Pacinian corpuscle.* This type of nerve ending is in the form of a large, oval corpuscle composed of concentric layers of connective tissue. The central axis of the corpuscle receives the

840

The general arrangement of these ganglia and the autonomic nerve fibers to the spinal nerve series is shown in figure 358A. It is to be observed that only **two neurons,** a preganglionic and a postganglionic, are involved in the efferent chain regardless of the number of ganglia traversed.

E. The Sense or Receptor Organs

1. DEFINITION

The sense organs are the sentinels of the nervous system. Endowed particularly with that property of living matter known as **irritability,** they are able to detect changes in the environment and to transmit the stimulus thus aroused to afferent nerve fibers. However, the perceptive ability of all sense organs is not the same, for specific types of sense receptors are developed specialized in the detection of particular environmental changes.

There are two general areas of sensory reception, viz.: (1) **The somatic sensory area,** and (2) the **visceral sensory area.** The location of somatic and visceral areas in the myelencephalon are shown in figure 355I.

The **somatic sensory organs** are associated with the general cutaneous surface of the body and also in tissues within the body wall. Consequently, this area may be divided for convenience into two general fields, namely, (1)

FIG. 359—*Continued*

terminal ends of one or more unmyelinated fibers, and also, in addition, the terminal end of a myelinated fiber which loses its myelin as it enters the axial core of the corpuscle. Side branches arise from the central core of nerve fibers. Found in deeper parts of dermis, and also in association with tendons, joints, intermuscular areas as well as in the mesenteries of the peritoneal cavity, and the linings of the pleural and pericardial cavities. (D) *Nerve endings in skin and hair follicles.* As the myelinated fibers enter the skin they break up into smaller myelinated fibers. After many divisions the myelin sheaths are lost, and finally the neurilemma also disappears. The *free nerve endings* enter the epidermis and after other divisions form a network of terminal fibers among the epidermal cells. Below the stratum germinativum of the skin, some of the fibers terminate in small, leaf-like enlargements around the hair-follicles below the level of the sebaceous glands. (A–D, redrawn and somewhat modified from Ranson, 1939, The Anatomy of the Nervous System, Philadelphia, Saunders.) (E) Part of longitudinal section of the lateral line canal of a *Mustelus* "pup" at the level of the first dorsal fin. Observe termination of nerve fibers among groups of sensory *hair cells.* The lateral line canal communicates with the surface at intervals by means of small tubules. (Redrawn and modified from Johnson, 1917, J. Comp. Neurol., 28.) (F) Transverse section of lateral line canal, higher magnification, showing termination of nerve endings among the secondary sense (hair) cells. (Redrawn from Johnson, 1917, J. Comp. Neurol., 28.) (G) The lateral line sensory cord is shown growing posteriad within the epidermal pocket of a 21 mm. embryo of *Squalus.* (Redrawn from Johnson, 1917, J. Comp. Neurol., 28.) (H) Taste bud of human. (Redrawn from Neal and Rand, 1939, Chordate Anatomy, Philadelphia, Blakiston.) (I) Sagittal section through human nasal cavity depicting nasal conchae (turbinates) and various openings leading off from the lateral wall of the nasal cavity. *The olfactory area of the mucous membrane extends over the superior concha and medially over the upper part of the nasal septum.* Observe opening of eustachian tube (tuba auditiva).

The **exteroceptive** or **general cutaneous field,** having sense organs detecting stimuli at or near the surface of the body, and (2) the **proprioceptive field,** with sense organs located in the body-wall tissues, such as striated muscles, tendons, joints and the equilibration structures of the internal ear.

The **visceral sensory organs** receive stimuli from the **interoceptive field,** that is, the visceral structures of the body.

2. SOMATIC SENSE ORGANS

a. Special Somatic Sense Organs

The visual organs, the ear, and in water-living vertebrates the lateral-line system, are sense organs of the special variety.

b. General Somatic Sense Organs

These structures are in the form of free nerve endings, terminating among cells and around the roots of hairs, or they are present as encapsulated nerve endings such as the **corpuscles of Meissner,** end **bulbs of Krause,** and **Pacinian corpuscles** (fig. 359A–D).

3. VISCERAL SENSE ORGANS

a. Special Visceral Sense Organs

The taste buds of various sorts, located generally on the tongue, mucous surface of the buccal cavity and pharynx and in some fishes on the external body surface are specialized visceral sense organs (fig. 285E).

In most craniates the paired olfactory organs are exteroceptive in function, although, possibly, olfactory organs may be regarded as primitively interoceptive. The olfactory organ is regarded generally as a special visceral sense organ.

b. General Visceral Sense Organs

General visceral sense organs are located among the viscera of the body. They represent free-nerve endings lying in the walls of the digestive tract and other viscera. They respond to mechanical stimuli.

4. THE LATERAL-LINE SYSTEM

The lateral-line organs are a specialized series of organs located in the cutaneous areas of the body. They are found in fishes and water-living amphibia. A sense organ of the lateral-line system is composed of a patch of **hair cells** or **neuromasts,** columnar in shape, possessing cilia-like extensions at the free end (fig. 359E). Basally the hair cells are associated with the terminal fibrillae of sensory nerves. The hair cells are supported by elongated, sustentacular elements. In cyclostomous fishes the neuromasts are exposed to the surface, but in Gnathostomes they lie embedded within a canal system lying deep within the dermis (fig. 359F). The **pit organs, ampullae,** etc., located over the head region of fishes belong to the lateral-line system. They are highly specialized structures. A developmental stage of the lateral-line canal in *Squalus acanthias* are shown in figure 359G.

5. THE TASTE-BUD SYSTEM

The taste-bud system of vertebrates is most variable in its distribution. In mammals the taste buds are scattered over the tongue (fig. 285E), and upon the larynx, pharynx and soft palate. The taste buds on the anterior portion of the tongue are supplied by the **chorda tympani branch** of the **facial** nerve, the posterior lingual taste buds by the **glossopharyngeal,** and those in the region of the pharynx by the **vagus.** In most fishes the taste buds are spread over the inner surfaces of the pharynx and extensively over the buccal cavity. In some fishes and amphibia they appear also over the external surface of the head, and in some teleosts they are found over much of the body surface (see figure 356C).

Taste buds consist of groups of specialized columnar epithelial cells, known as **hair cells,** surrounded and supported by **sustentacular cells.** Each hair cell has a sensory bristle protruding to the surface, whereas basally it is in contact with dendritic terminalizations of sensory nerves (fig. 359H).

6. THE DEVELOPMENT OF THE OLFACTORY ORGAN

The senses of smell and taste are much alike. Both detect chemical substances dissolved in fluid. The olfactory epithelium of the vertebrate group is of the simple columnar variety containing **neurosensory cells** (fig. 356A) supported by non-nervous epithelial elements. Each neurosensory cell at its free surface terminates in a series of cilia-like structures, and at its basal end is prolonged into a neurite (nerve fiber) which passes into the olfactory bulb where it breaks up into a number of **telodendria.** The **olfactory area** of the human nasal passageway is shown in figure 359I (see legend).

a. Development of the Olfactory Organs in Squalus acanthias

The two olfactory sacs in *Squalus* develop as invaginations of a thickened **olfactory placode** on either side of the antero-ventral aspect of the head near the oral invagination. They remain as blind sacs, extensively folded internally and closely associated with the olfactory bulbs of the brain (fig. 357H).

b. Development of the Olfactory Organs in the Frog

The olfactory organs in the frog arise from two placodes, one on either side of the head immediately in front of the developing eyes. These placodes invaginate, and push downward and posteriad toward the developing oral cavity. At about the 10 to 12 mm. stage they perforate into the anterior end of the oral cavity. The walls of the olfactory inpushing become folded to form the complicated nasal passageway of the adult frog. The external opening of each passageway is called an **external naris** while the opening into the buccal cavity is known as the **choana** (fig. 257B).

c. Development of the Olfactory Organs in the Chick

The development of the olfactory organ in the chick embryo resembles the development of this structure in the mammal, described below.

d. Development of the Olfactory Organs in the Mammalian Embryo

As in other vertebrates, the olfactory areas of the olfactory organs of mammals develop from olfactory placodes located one on either side on the ventrolateral aspect of the primitive head region (fig. 256). The olfactory placodes sink inward to form the olfactory pits, and each pit expands laterally and distally. The lateral external margin of each olfactory pit is called the **lateral nasal process,** and that of the median external margin is called the **median nasal process.** The median and lateral nasal processes come in contact with the **maxillary process** of the upper jaw.

As the olfactory pit grows posteriad it comes to open into the roof of the primitive oral cavity as the **primitive choana** (figs. 288A and 256) posteriomedially to the junction of the maxillary and median nasal processes. Later, as each **palatal process** grows mediad from the maxillary processes, the nasal pit and the upper oral area become separated from the oral cavity below by the formation of the **secondary palate** (fig. 289D–F). Meanwhile, the **median nasal septum** (fig. 288A) grows ventrad and posteriad from the **fronto-nasal process** and unites with the secondary palate in the median line (fig. 288B). Two nasal passageways thus are established leading posteriorly (fig. 288D) to open into the pharyngeal area as the **secondary choanae** (fig. 289F). The epithelium of the original nasal placode and pit comes to lie in the dorso-medial and dorso-lateral areas of this nasal passageway along either side of the nasal septum (fig. 359I). The olfactory epithelium gives origin to bipolar cells, one pole developing cilia-like processes which lie exposed to the surface of the epithelium while the other pole develops an elongated fiber which grows dorsad and posteriad to enter the forming olfactory bulb of the telencephalon (fig. 356A).

7. THE EYE

a. General Structure of the Eye

The general structure of the eye is shown in figure 360A.

b. Development of the Eye

The early stages of the development of all vertebrate eyes tend to follow certain generalized steps, and the following description of the developing eye of the chick presents the principles involved. The eye of the chick begins to develop as lateral outgrowths from the caudal end of the prosencephalon (future diencephalon) (fig. 354B–D). These outgrowths, the **primary optic evaginations,** begin to appear early on the second day of incubation, even before the neural tube is closed. At about the 12 somite stage, which exists at about 38 hours of incubation, the primary optic vesicles begin to constrict proximally in the area near the brain, and distally they come into conatct with the overlying epidermis (fig. 360B). At 16 somites, or about 45 to 49 hrs. of incubation, the primary optic vesicle has differentiated into a proximal constricted **optic stalk** and a distal **primary optic vesicle** (fig. 360C). At the 22 somite stage (about 50 hrs. of incubation), the optic vesicle begins to invaginate and the overlying ectoderm starts to thicken preparatory to formation of the lens (fig. 360D). At 55 hrs. of incubation, invagination of the optic vesicle is completed, and the two-layered or **secondary optic vesicle** is formed. The lens rudiment at this time is an invaginated vesicle still retaining a small, open duct to the external surface. The following features of eye development in the 55 hr. chick are present:

(1) The lens vesicle is almost completely formed.

(2) The secondary optic vesicle is in the form of a cup, whose inner layer forms the **retinal rudiment,** and its outer layer the **rudiment of the pigmented coat** of the eye.

(3) The ventral or lower edge of the optic stalk also is invaginated to form the **choroid fissure,** which continues the invagination of the optic cup back into the region of the ventral area of the optic stalk (fig. 360E).

In the 72 to 75 hr. chick (about 40 pairs of somites) the two-layered optic cup presents an outer **thinner layer,** the rudiment of the pigmented coat, and an inner, thicker **retinal layer.** The lens vesicle at this time is completely free from the overlying ectoderm and its inner (medial) wall is thicker than the external wall. The medial thicker wall is the rudiment of the **body of the lens** and the outer thinner wall is the **anterior epithelium** of the lens (fig. 360F). At 96 to 100 hrs. of incubation the developing lens of the eye has undergone marked changes from the condition present at 72 to 75 hrs. of incubation. The medial wall of the lens vesicle has thickened greatly and lens fibers are evident, while the lateral wall of the vesicle forms a relatively thin epithelial membrane (fig. 360G). The mesoderm below the ectoderm also forms a thin, internal epithelial membrane which lines the developing cornea. At this time the lips of the optic cup show the first indications of two distinct areas, viz.: a **retinal or optic part,** the **pars optica retinae,** which forms the **visual portion** of the adult retina, and a **pars caeca retinae** lying distally in the region of the lens (fig. 360G). The pars caeca does not develop visual cells. At the eighth to ninth days of incubation, the pars caeca shows the beginning stages of **ciliary body formation,** and the development of the **iris** (fig. 360H). The mesenchyme overlying the iris forms the condensed stromal tissue, but the **sphincter** and

dilator muscles of the iris develop from the pigmented layer of the pars caeca. Two definite layers are present in the retina, viz.: **inner marginal and outer mantle layers.** The rudiment of the **sclerotic** coat of the eye is present, and in front of the developing iris the mesenchyme of the sclerotic coat continues below the external ectoderm forming the rudiment of the **cornea.** The massive **vitreous body** is present and a delicate membrane separates the vitreous body from the optic cup. It is probable that the vitreous body forms from contributions of the optic cup and the lens vesicle. At this time, also, the rudiments of the upper and lower eyelids are present as folds of the integument surrounding the outer edges of the corneal zone of the eye (fig. 360H).

c. Special Aspects of Eye Development

The foregoing description of the developing eye of the chick presents the common or general features of eye development. The data given below describe certain features of the later development of the vertebrate eye, particularly that of the mammal and the bird.

1) The Choroid Fissure, Hyaloid Artery, Pecten, etc. The choroid fissure is the trough-like continuation of the invaginated area of the optic cup into the optic stalk, and it permits a ready entrance into the optic cup. Mesenchyme extends along the fissure and invades the optic cup and its developing vitreous body. The central artery of the retina in the developing eye of the pig and human also grows inward with the mesenchyme; in the region of the optic cup it is called the **hyaloid artery** (fig. 360I). The hyaloid artery gives origin to a mass of capillaries which surround but do not enter the developing lens. This vascularization of the peripheral lens area persists until a short while before the time of birth but regresses rapidly as birth approaches. The hyaloid artery also regresses completely, leaving in its previous course a **lymph space** known as the **hyaloid canal** of the vitreous body (fig. 360A).

The choroid fissure eventually closes, including the portion which extends into the region of the optic cup. In the region of the optic stalk it persists for a while as a small canal containing mesenchyme and the **central artery** of the retina. As the retina develops, the nerve fibers of the forming optic nerve converge toward the optic stalk and grow inward toward the brain along the

---

Fig. 360. Diagrams illustrating the development of the eye.   (A) General structural features of the adult mammalian eye. (Redrawn from Morris' Human Anatomy, 1943, Philadelphia, Blakiston.)   (B–H) Development of the eye of the chick. Ages indicated on the figures. Diagram E' represents the developing eye viewed from the ventral aspect showing the *choroid fissure* into which small capillaries are beginning to course forward into the optic cup. Mesenchyme also invades the choroid fissure. In diagram H the *pecten* has been slightly schematized.   (I) Sagittal section through the developing eye of an 18 mm. pig embryo. Observe the *hyaloid artery* coursing from the optic nerve area across the vitreous chamber to the lens.   (I') Later stage in differentiation of the retina. The rods and cones lie in the outermost area of the retina.

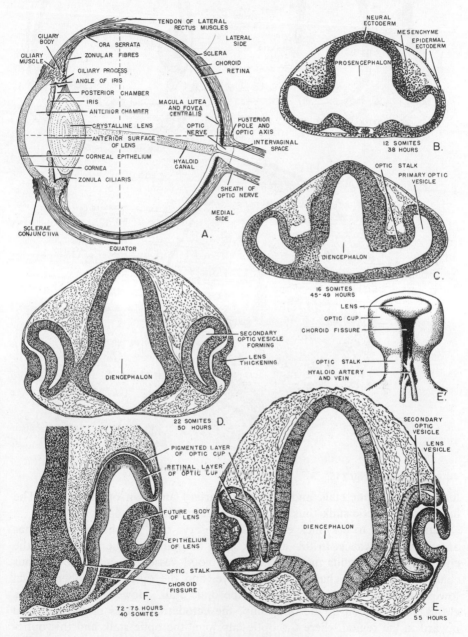

FIG. 360. *(See facing page for legend.)*

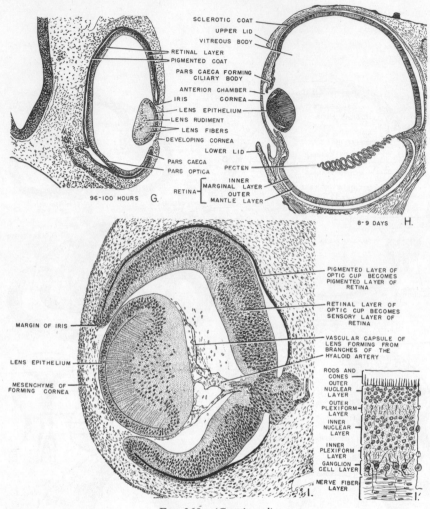

SCLEROTIC COAT
UPPER LID
VITREOUS BODY
RETINAL LAYER
PIGMENTED COAT
PARS CAECA FORMING
CILIARY BODY
ANTERIOR CHAMBER
IRIS   CORNEA
LENS EPITHELIUM
LENS RUDIMENT
LENS FIBERS
DEVELOPING CORNEA
LOWER LID
PARS CAECA
PARS OPTICA   PECTEN
INNER
MARGINAL LAYER
RETINA   OUTER
MANTLE LAYER

96-100 HOURS   G.

8-9 DAYS   H.

PIGMENTED LAYER OF
OPTIC CUP BECOMES
PIGMENTED LAYER OF
RETINA

RETINAL LAYER OF
OPTIC CUP BECOMES
SENSORY LAYER OF
RETINA

VASCULAR CAPSULE OF
LENS FORMING FROM
BRANCHES OF THE
HYALOID ARTERY

MARGIN OF IRIS

LENS EPITHELIUM

MESENCHYME OF
FORMING CORNEA

RODS AND
CONES
OUTER
NUCLEAR
LAYER
OUTER
PLEXIFORM
LAYER
INNER
NUCLEAR
LAYER
INNER
PLEXIFORM
LAYER
GANGLION
CELL LAYER
NERVE FIBER
LAYER

Fig. 360—(*Continued*)

For legend see p. 846.

lumen of the optic stalk and the central artery and vein of the retina. The lumen of the optic stalk thus becomes converted into the optic nerve.

Turning now to the chick embryo, we observe that the choroid fissure has an added significance. In this embryo, as in the mammal, the presence of the choroid fissure permits mesenchyme and blood vessels to enter the vitreous chamber (optic-cup chamber) of the eye, and the optic nerve fibers travel toward the brain along the lumen of the optic stalk. However, as the fissure closes in the region of the optic cup, the ectodermal edges of the cup fold inward in the region where the optic cup joins the optic stalk and this optic-cup fold comes to enclose the inward migrating mesenchyme and blood vessels. Thus it happens that in addition to the entrance of mesenchyme and blood vessels into the vitreous chamber the pigmented and nervous layers of the pars optica retinae fold inward around and enclose the blood vessels and mesenchyme. This forward projection of ectodermal and mesodermal tissues into the vitreous chamber toward the lens forms the **pecten** of the bird's eye (fig. 360H). From the seventh to the eleventh days the rudiment of the pecten increases greatly in length, and becomes very narrow, folded, and comb-shaped. Shortly before hatching, the number of folds increases to about 18, and the structure as a whole is highly pigmented and vascularized. The pecten appears to increase the vascular supply to the vitreous chamber, and also, it is possible that the pecten may act in some way to increase the visual powers of the retina. In the reptiles a similar, but less complex projection, the **vascular papillary cone,** is developed, and in the eye of teleost fishes the **falciform process** may be homologous with the papillary cone of reptiles and pecten of birds.

2) The Formation of the Lens. The early formation of the lens vesicle from the overlying ectoderm appears to be dependent upon inductive influences emanating from the optic vesicle in some species, e.g., *Bombinator,* but in others, e.g., *Rana esculenta,* the lens vesicle appears to form independently. (See Werber, '16, and Spemann, '38, Chapter 3.) The inner wall of the lens vesicle differentiates into elongated slender cells of the lens. The nuclei remain near the center of these slender cells, and the cells gradually transform into the transparent lens fibers. The outer, lateral wall of the lens vesicle forms a layer of low columnar cells, the lens epithelium (fig. 360H and I).

3) The Choroid and Sclerotic Coat of the Eyeball; the Cornea. The developing optic cup is at all times surrounded by mesenchyme. This mesenchyme condenses around the pigmented layer of the optic cup to form two distinct layers, namely, (1) An **inner vascular coat** immediately surrounding the pigmented layer, and (2) an **outer white fibrous thick connective tissue layer.** The inner vascular coat forms the soft, vascular **choroid coat** of the eyeball, whereas the fibrous layer develops the hardened **sclera** or sclerotic coat. The sclerotic coat in reality is the skeletal investment of the eyeball, upon which the extrinsic muscles of the eye insert, and from which internally the ciliary muscles or muscles of accommodation take their origin (fig. 360A). Also, the muscles of the iris indirectly are dependent upon the sclera for their efficiency. The choroid coat is the main source of blood supply for the eyeball as a whole. It is highly pigmented and absorbs excess light rays from the retina. In many vertebrates, including various mammals such as the cat, dog, cow, deer, ferret, etc., the inner layer of the choroid coat near the retina develops a light reflecting surface, the **tapetum lucidum.** In the cat and other carnivores, this reflecting surface appears to be due to crystals of **guanine,** while in the cow it is due, probably, to connective tissue fibers which glisten and thus reflect the light.

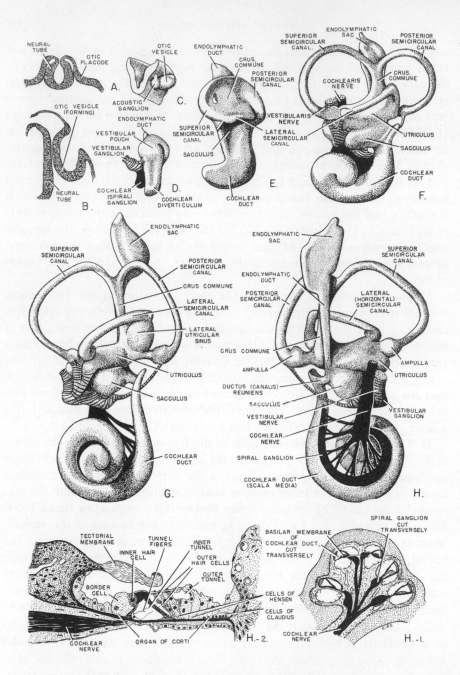

FIG. 361. Development of the ear. (A) Chick embryo of ten somites, about 33–38 hours of incubation. Transverse section through developing rhombencephalon at the level of the *otic placodes* which are beginning to sink inward below the surrounding ectoderm (epidermis). (B) The otic vesicles are forming in this 19 somite (about 48 hours of incubation) chick embryo. Slight constriction of otic vesicle near its junction with the ectoderm. (C) Left otic vesicle of 4.3 mm. human embryo. The small

acoustic ganglion lies to the left in the figure. The neural tube (rhombencephalic portion) has not closed dorsally. (D) Left otic vesicle of 9 mm. human embryo viewed from lateral aspect. The differentiating acoustic ganglion is shown to the left. It is now dividing into vestibular and spiral ganglia. The cochlear diverticulum is shown extending ventrally. (E) Later differentiation (11 mm. human embryo) of left otic vesicle, lateral view. (F) 20 mm. human embryo, left, lateral view of differentiating otic vesicle. (G) 30 mm. human embryo, left, lateral view of differentiating otic vesicle. (H) 30 mm. human embryo, left, median view of differentiating otic vesicle. (H-1) Semischematic plan of cochlear duct and spiral ganglion of 4 month human embryo. (H-2) High-powered view of basilar membrane (lamina spiralis membranacea) shown in Fig. 361H-1, portraying the spiral organ of Corti. (I-1) Three-dimensional schematic drawing of the human ear composed of the *external ear,* the *middle ear,* and the *inner ear.* The external ear is composed of the *pinna and external auditory meatus.* The middle ear is made up of the middle ear cavity or cavity of the *tympanum* with its auditory ossicles, the *malleus, incus,* and *stapes.* The external tympanic membrane is stretched across the entrance of the external auditory meatus into the middle ear cavity whereas the *internal* tympanic membrane covers the *fenestra rotunda (fenestra cochlea).* The internal ear located within the petrous bone communicates with the middle ear directly by means of the *fenestra ovalis (fenestra vestibuli)* and indirectly by means of the fenestra rotunda. The stapes is inserted in the fenestra ovalis and the malleus is joined to the external tympanic membrane. By means of the stapedial articulation with the incus and the latter's association with the malleus, the three auditory ossicles thus extend across the middle ear cavity from the external tympanic membrane to the fenestra ovalis.

The structural parts of the inner ear are made up of the *membranous labyrinth,* the *semicircular canals, utriculus, sacculus,* and the *cochlear duct* (fig. 361F and G). Surrounding the membranous labyrinth is the other structural part of the ear, the *bony labyrinth,* which conforms to the general shape of the membranous labyrinth. A fluid, the *endolymph,* is contained within the membranous labyrinth, whereas perilymph lies in the space between the membranous labyrinth and the bony labyrinth.

The development of the membranous labyrinth is shown in Fig. 361A–H, and the formation of the pinna and external auditory meatus is depicted in Figs. 328A and B, and 329A. It is to be observed that swellings upon the hyoid and mandibular visceral arches contribute to the formation of the pinna, and that the external auditory meatus develops from the invaginating *hyomandibular cleft* (branchial groove) between these two arches. The origin of the auditory ossicles is shown in Fig. 319C-1 and C-2. Fig. 361I-2 shows the early relationship of these ossicles within the mesenchymal substance of the developing middle ear cavity. During the formation of the middle ear cavity spaces form around the developing ossicles. These spaces then coalesce to form the rudiments of the middle ear cavity or cavity of the *tympanum.* This rudimentary tympanic cavity later unites with the distal end of the *first branchial pouch.* The proximal portion of the first branchial pouch forms the *eustachian tube* which connects the pharyngeal area with the middle ear cavity. The extent to which the middle ear cavity eventually comes to be lined with entoderm from the expanded distal end of the eustachian tube (first branchial pouch) is problematical. The external tympanic membrane is developed from the ectoderm of the external auditory meatus ·(hyomandibular cleft invagination) and the lining of the middle ear cavity. Between these two membranes is a layer of mesenchyme which transforms into connective tissue. The malleus remains attached to the external tympanic membrane. (I-2) Schematic diagram of an early stage in development of the auditory ossicles and tympanic cavity in the human embryo. Observe that the first branchial pouch is expanding into the area around the forming auditory ossicles where spaces, shown in black, are beginning to appear within the mesenchyme surrounding the developing ossicles. (J) Diagram of the ear in the frog. Unlike the condition in the frogs a tympanic cavity is almost entirely absent in urodeles. (K) Diagram of the ear of a reptile comparable to conditions found in the snakes. It is to be observed that an external tympanic membrane or external ear opening is absent. Observe that the ear ossicle is composed of stapedial and extrastapedial segments. (L) Diagram of the ear of the chick. The ear "ossicle" is composed of two parts, viz., a

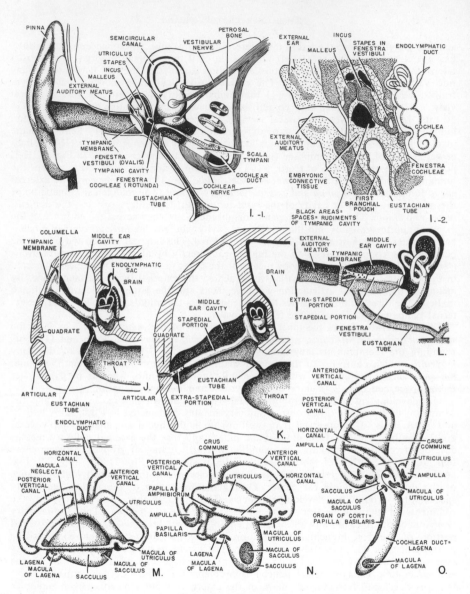

FIG. 361—*Continued*

bony stapedial portion which articulates with the fenestra vestibuli and a distal cartilaginous extrastapedial segment which connects with the external tympanic membrane.
The eustachian tube connects with the same tube on the contralateral side to form a
common opening into the dorsal pharyngeal area. The external ear opening is protected
by feathers. The ear of lizards resembles that of the bird, a short external auditory
meatus being present, protected externally in many instances by scales. In the frog, *Rana
cavitympanum* of Siam, the tympanic membrane similarly has moved inward and an
external auditory meatus is present. (M) The right membranous labyrinth of the shark,
Squalus acanthias. (Redrawn from Adams and Eddy, 1949, Comparative Anatomy, New
York, Wiley & Sons. (N) The right membranous labyrinth of the frog, *Rana.* (O)
The right membranous labyrinth of the pigeon, *Columba.*

The **cornea** of the eyeball is formed mainly from the mesenchyme of the sclerotic coat which extends forward in front of the developing anterior chamber of the eye (fig. 360H). The overlying skin forms the **corneal epithelium.**

4) Contributions of the Pars Caeca. The pars caeca or non-nervous part of the primitive optic cup gives origin to the smooth muscle tissues of the iris. These muscles are derived probably from the pigmented layer of the original optic vesicle. The **zonula ciliaris** or suspensory ligament of the lens also is derived from this source.

5) The Origin of the Ciliary Muscles. The smooth muscle tissue of the **ciliary muscle** together with the connective tissue of the ciliary bodies, and the stromal tissue of the iris, are derived from the mesenchyme of the primitive choroid coat which overlies the pars caeca of the optic cup.

6) Accessory Structures of the Eye. The **upper** and **lower eyelids** develop as folds of the integument about the eyeball and circumscribing the corneal area (fig. 360H). In the chick these folds are apparent on the seventh day of incubation, and in the human embryo at about the seventh week. In mammals the eyelids normally fuse after their formation, and in many they do not reopen until some time after birth. In the dog the eyelids reopen at about 10 to 15 days after birth, while in the human and guinea pig they reopen before birth. Complete fusion of the eyelids does not occur in the chick. A third or rudimentary eye structure, the **plica semilunaris,** is present at the inner angle of the human eye. This structure may represent the **nictitating membrane** in the cat and dog, and possibly also the nictitating membrane of the chick. The real homology of the plica semilunaris with these structures, however, is questionable.

Accessory **eye glands** arise in land vertebrates. The **lacrimal** glands arise as epidermal ingrowths from the inner aspect of the developing upper (man, cat, dog) or lower (urodeles) eyelid. The lacrimal gland is developed typically in mammals. The racemose **harderian** gland arises as a solid ingrowth of epidermal cells at the inner angle of the nictitating membrane. The secretion of the harderian gland found in reptiles, birds, and also in certain mammals is oily while that of the lacrimal gland is watery. The **tarsal** (Meibomian) glands of the human eyelid arise as epithelial invaginations

The **naso-lacrimal duct** in mammals arises from the **naso-lacrimal groove** formed in the area of the lateral nasal and maxillary processes; it extends from the nasal sac to the angle of the eye (fig. 256). During the formation of the face this groove sinks inward and forms a duct which establishes a definite connection with the inner edges of each eyelid. It opens into the nasal chamber.

8. STRUCTURE AND DEVELOPMENT OF THE EAR

a. Structure

The functions of **hearing** and **equilibration** (balance) in the gnathostomous vertebrate group involve the structure known as the **membranous labyrinth** of the **inner ear.** The latter structure is composed of a central saccular area to which are attached a complex of ducts and canals (fig. 361H). It is located within a protective encasement of cartilage or bone which conforms to the general shape of the membranous labyrinth (fig. 361I). However, the labyrinth **fits loosely** within its protective case, and a space, filled with fluid, the **perilymph,** intervenes between the walls of the membranous labyrinth and the walls of the **cartilaginous or bony labyrinth** which surrounds the membranous labyrinth. Within the membranous labyrinth is a fluid, the **endolymph.** The function of equilibration is concerned mainly with movements or lack of movement, i.e., inertia, of the **endolymph,** while the function of hearing entails wave movements in the **perilymph** which in turn are transferred to a portion of the endolymphatic fluid.

The membranous labyrinth is composed of a saccular region divided into two compartments, the **utriculus** and **sacculus** connected by a narrow passageway. To the utriculus and sacculus the following ducts and canals are attached (see figure 361H, M, N, and O).

1) Three semicircular canals, which, throughout the jawed vertebrate group, adhere to the following pattern: (a) a horizontal canal, (b) a posterior vertical canal, and (c) an anterior vertical canal. Each of these canals is expanded at one end to form an enlargement known as the **ampulla.**

2) An endolymphatic duct, generally connected to the sacculus near the connecting passageway between the sacculus and utriculus. The distal end of the endolymphatic duct is enlarged to form the **endolymphatic sac.**

3) A Cochlear Duct or Lagena. The lagena is an evagination of the sacculus. It is abortive in lower vertebrates but greatly extended in mammals.

All of the semicircular canals are attached to the utriculus. The anterior and posterior vertical canals generally attach at one end of the utriculus to a common chamber, the **crus commune,** before joining the utriculus.

The internal lining of the membranous labyrinth possesses, in restricted areas, specialized sensory epithelial cells, known as **neuromast cells,** associated with branches of the acoustic cranial nerve. In the utriculus and sacculus these areas of sensory epithelium are called **maculae.** A single macula is found in the utriculus and another in the sacculus. A gelatinous membrane is associated with each macula and concretions or **otoliths** may be present in the jelly of this membrane. Within each ampulla of the semicircular canals a sensory area of epithelium is present known as a **crista,** with the cilia-like projections from the ends of the cells embedded in a gelatinous mass. The functions of the maculae presumably present sensations which tell the animal how much the body is tilted up and down in one plane, i.e., **static equilibrium,** whereas the semicircular canals offer sensations which enable the animal to detect its position when it is moving up and down or around in a series of different planes. That is, the semicircular canals probably are concerned with **dynamic equilibrium.**

The endolymphatic duct appears to lack specialized sensory areas. In the elasmobranch fishes, the endolymphatic ducts open by means of small pores at the top of the head. The endolymphatic-sac area of the duct may be absent in some fishes, but in many teleosts, reptiles, and amphibia the endolymphatic sac is greatly enlarged. In the frog group, the endolymphatic sac is most extensive, protruding itself into the brain and spinal cord areas.

Sensory patches of epithelium are present in the lagena. In reptiles, birds and mammals, the lagena is extended considerably. In birds and mammals the lagena is called the **cochlear duct,** and it contains an extensive area of sensory epithelium known as the **organ of Corti.**

In tetrapod vertebrates a **middle ear** containing a specialized ossicle or ossicles, is added to the hearing mechanism (fig. 361I, J, K and L), and in reptiles, birds and mammals an **external meatus** or specialized structure for receiving sound waves is found. The external auditory meatus in mammals is supplemented by the addition of an external ear or **pinna,** a funnel-shaped structure for collecting sound waves (fig. 361I).

b. Development of the Internal Ear

The internal ear arises from the otic placode which sinks inward to form the otic vesicle. The otic vesicle gradually transforms into the shape and structure of the internal ear peculiar to the species. The transformation of the otic vesicle in the human embryo is shown in figure 361C–H.

c. Development of the Middle Ear

The development of the middle ear results from an evagination of the pharyngeal wall which primarily involves the region of the first branchial pouch. This evagination unites distally with spaces forming around the ossicles. The opening into the pharynx is retained, and the narrow passageway between the pharynx and the middle ear cavity containing the ossicle or ossicles of the ear is called the **eustachian duct or tube.**

d. Development of the External Auditory Meatus and Pinna

The external auditory meatus forms from an epidermal invagination in the area of the first visceral groove, that is the region between the mandibular and hyoid visceral arches. The pinna of the external ear in mammals arises from swellings on the mandibular and hyoid arches. These swellings enlarge and fuse to form the complicated form of the pinna (figs. 328 and 329).

F. Nerve fiber-effector organ relationships

(Consult figure 358F–G.)

Bibliography

Arey, L. B. **1916.** The function of the efferent fibers of the optic nerve of fishes. Jour. Comp. Neurol. **26**:213.

———— and Smith, H. V. **1937.** Anat. Rec. 67 (suppl. 4).

Ariens-Kappers, C. U., Huber G. C. and Crosby, E. C. **1936.** The Comparative Anatomy of the Nervous System of Vertebrates, including Man. Vols. I and II. Macmillan, New York.

Goodrich, E. S. **1930.** Studies on the structure and development of vertebrates. Macmillan and Co., Ltd., London.

Harrison, R. G. **1907.** Observations on the living developing nerve fiber. Anat. Rec. **1**:116.

Hill, C. **1900.** Developmental history of the primary segments of the vertebrate head. Zool. Jahrb. Anat. **13**:393.

Kuntz, A. and Batson, O. V. **1920.** Experimental observations on the histogenesis of the sympathetic trunks in the chick. J. Comp. Neurol. **32**:335.

Larsell, Olof. **1918.** Studies on the nervus terminalis: Mammals. Jour. Comp. Neurol. **30**:3.

Lavelle, A. **1951.** Nucleolar changes and development of Nissl substance in the cerebral cortex of fetal guinea pigs. J. Comp. Neurol. **94**:453.

Maximow, A. A. and Bloom, W. **1942.** A Textbook of Histology, 4th Edition. Saunders, Philadelphia.

Ranson, S. W. **1918.** An introduction to a series of studies on the sympathetic nervous system. Jour. Comp. Neurol. **29**:305.

————. **1939.** The Anatomy of the Nervous System. Saunders, Philadelphia.

Speidel, C. C. **1933.** Studies of living nerves: II. Activities of ameboid growth cones, sheath cells, and myelin segments, as revealed by prolonged observation of individual nerve fibers in frog tadpoles. Am. J. Anat. **52**:1.

Spemann, H. **1938.** Embryonic Development and Induction. Yale University Press, New Haven, Conn.

Werber, E. I. **1916.** On the blastolytic origin of the 'independent' lenses of some teratophthalmic embryos and its significance for the normal development of the lens in vertebrates. J. Exp. Zool. **21**:347.

20

The Development of the Coelomic Cavities

A. Introduction

1. DEFINITIONS

The **coelomic cavities** are the spaces which come to surround the various viscera of the body such as the **pericardial cavity** around the heart, the **pleural**

cavities surrounding the lungs, and the **peritoneal cavity** in which lie the stomach, intestines, reproductive organs, etc. These coelomic spaces and recesses arise from a generalized basic condition known as the **primitive splanchnocoelic coelom.** The primitive splanchnocoelic coelom is the elongated cavity which extends throughout the trunk region beginning just anterior to the heart and continuing posteriorly to the base of the tail. It encloses the developing heart and the developing mesenteron (gut) from the esophageal region posteriorly to the anal region.

2. Origin of the Primitive Splanchnocoelic Coelom

As observed previously (Chapter 10) the elongated mesodermal masses lying along either side of the developing neural tube, notochord, and enteric tube have a tendency to hollow out to form a cavity within. That is, like the neural, gut, and epidermal areas of the late gastrula, the two mesodermal masses tend to **assume the form of tubes.**

In the case of *Amphioxus,* each individual somite forms a cavity, the **myocoel.** These myocoels merge on either side in their ventral halves to form an elongated splanchnocoel below the horizontal septum (see page 506). Later the two splanchnocoels fuse below the developing gut to form the single splanchnocoelic coelom which comes to surround the gut. In the vertebrate group, however, the two elongated splanchnocoels on either side of the developing gut tube and heart form directly in the hypomeric (lateral plate) area of the mesodermal masses without a process of secondary fusion as in *Amphioxus.* In the upper part of each mesodermal mass, that is in the **epimere,** and to some extent also in the **mesomere** (nephrotomic plate) in the vertebrate group as in *Amphioxus,* there is a tendency for the coelomic spaces to appear in segmental fashion within the primitive somites and within the anterior portion of the mesomere. These individual spaces within the somites are called **myocoels,** and the spaces which arise in the segmented portion of the nephrotome are called the **nephrocoels.**

In young shark embryos, such as the 3–4 mm. embryo of *Squalus acanthias,* and in amphibian embryos of the early post-gastrular period, the myocoelic and nephrocoelic portions of the coelom are continuous dorso-ventrally with the splanchnocoelic coelom (fig. 217G and H). (Actually, during the early stages of coelomic development within the mesodermal masses, in the shark and amphibian embryos, the coelom within the epimere and nephrotomic portions of the mesoderm is continuous antero-posteriorly and it is only after the appearance of the primitive somites and segmentation within the nephrotome that they become discontinuous.) On the other hand, in the embryos of higher vertebrates, the respective myocoels within the somites appear later in development, and in consequence they are always separated from the splanchnocoel. Similarly, the nephrocoelic coelom also arises later and only the separate nephrocoels which develop within the pronephric tubules and certain types of mesonephric tubules make contact with the splanchnocoelic portion of the coelom.

In all vertebrates (see figures 254, 332F–M) the formation of the primitive, generalized **coelomic cavity proper** or generalized **splanchnocoelic portion of the coelom** is formed by the fusion around the developing heart and gut structures of the two elongated splanchnocoels present in the hypomeric portions of the mesodermal masses as described below.

B. Early Divisions of the Primitive Splanchnocoelic Coelom

1. FORMATION OF PRIMITIVE SUSPENSORY STRUCTURES

The splanchnic walls of the early coelomic cavities (splanchnocoels) within the two hypomeres become apposed around the structures, lying in the median plane (fig. 254). In the region of the heart, this apposition gives rise to the **dorsal and ventral mesocardia** and to the **epimyocardium** of the heart itself (fig. 254A, B) and, in the region of the stomach and intestine, it produces the dorsal and ventral mesenteries of the gut tube and various ligaments, connecting one organ with another. The mesenchyme which arises from the two splanchnic layers also gives origin to the muscles and connective tissues of the gut and its evaginated structures (fig. 311A, B). The ventral mesocardium disappears in all vertebrates (Chap. 17). The dorsal mesocardium may persist for a while but eventually disappears entirely or almost entirely (Chap. 17). The **dorsal mesentery** is present constantly in reptiles and mammals but may be perforated and reduced in the intestinal area in other vertebrate classes, so that little of the dorsal mesentery remains to suspend the intestine in certain cases as, for example, in the shark. The dorsal mesentery above the stomach, the **mesogastrium,** and also the **ventral mesentery** in the immediate region between the stomach and liver and between the liver and the ventral body wall persist in all vertebrates. As a rule, however, the ventral mesentery disappears caudal to the liver with the exception of dipnoan and anguilliform fishes and the ganoid fish, *Lepisosteus*. In these forms the ventral mesentery tends to persist throughout the peritoneal cavity. It follows, therefore, that the two bilaterally developed, splanchnocoelic cavities tend to merge into one cavity or generalized splanchnocoel with a partial retention in certain areas of the splanchnic layers of the two hypomeres which act as suspensory ligamentous structures for the viscera.

2. FORMATION OF THE PRIMITIVE TRANSVERSE DIVISION OF THE BODY AND THE PRIMARY PERICARDIAL AND PERITONEAL DIVISIONS OF THE COELOM

The primitive splanchnocoelic coelom soon becomes divided into the pericardial coelom, surrounding the heart, and the peritoneal or abdominal coelom, surrounding the digestive viscera, by the formation of the **lateral mesocardia**

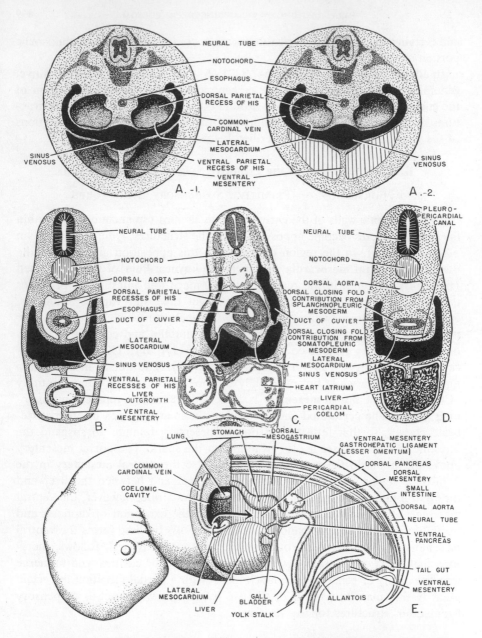

FIG. 362. The lateral mesocardia form the initial division of the embryonic coelom. (A-1 and A-2) represent idealized sections through the vertebrate embryonic body in a plane between the caudal limits of the sinus venosus and the anterior extremity of the potential liver region of the embryo. (A-1) Diagram of the initial stage of separation of the pericardial and peritoneal coelomic cavities in many vertebrates. *Two dorsal and two ventral recesses or passageways above and below the lateral mesocardia and lateral horns of the sinus venosus* are evident. These passageways communicate with the pericardial and peritoneal divisions of the primitive coelom. (A-2) Separation of primitive

and the **primitive septum transversum** which develop in relation to the converging veins of the sinus venosus and the ventro-cephalic growth of the liver rudiment. In other words, **a ventral partition is established across the primitive splanchnocoelic coelom** in a plane which separates the caudal end of the heart (i.e., sinus venosus) from the anterior limits of the liver. This **primitive transverse partition** partially separates the primitive splanchnocoelic coelom into two main divisions:

(1) a cephalic compartment, the **pericardial cavity,** around the heart and

---

FIG. 362—*Continued*

coelom into anterior pericardial and posterior peritoneal areas in early human embryo. The precocious development of the caudal wall of the parietal pericardium obliterates the ventral recesses shown in A-1 previous to septum transversum formation and the outgrowth of the liver rudiment. Communication between pericardial and peritoneal coelomic divisions is possible *only through the dorsal parietal recesses* (dorsal pericardio-peritoneal canals). (B) Schematic diagram representing the initial division by the lateral mesocardia of the primitive coelomic cavity into anterior pericardial and posterior peritoneal divisions in an embryo of *Squalus acanthias* 10 mm. long. The liver outgrowth has been extended forward slightly for diagrammatic purposes. (C) Initial division, by the lateral mesocardia, of the primitive coelom in the 72 hr. chick embryo. Due to the depressed condition of the anterior end of the body much of the heart appears in the section below the sinus venosus and lateral mesocardia. However, if the embryo were straightened and the atrium, etc., of the heart pushed forward, the structural conditions would appear much the same as in B. The dorsal parietal recesses appear on either side of the esophagus. (D) Semidiagrammatic section through caudal end of sinus venosus of 22 mm. shark embryo. The *dorsal closing folds* are developing on either side of the esophagus, thus closing the dorsal recesses. The liver rudiment is expanding within the substance of the ventral mesentery caudal to the heart to form the *liver-septum transversum complex*. The latter structure obliterates the ventral recesses below the lateral mesocardia. (E) Diagrammatic representation of the forward and ventral growth of the developing liver within the substance of the ventral mesentery to form the *liver-septum transversum complex*. (See fig. 363D.) Observe: ventral parietal recesses are obliterated by the forward growth of this complex of tissues. The arrow denotes the passageway from the pericardial coelom into the peritoneal coelom through the dorsal parietal recesses (dorsal pericardioperitoneal canals). (F) Early stage in development of human heart and septum transversum showing ingrowth of somatopleural mesoderm between the previously formed caudal wall of the parietal pericardial membrane (see A-2) and the entoderm of the anterior intestinal portal. (Redrawn from Davis, 1927, Carnegie Inst. Public 380, Cont. to Embryology, 107.) (G) Later stage of human heart development. Mesodermal partition (septum transversum) is present as a thickened mass of tissue below the developing sinus venosus and between the caudal wall of the parietal pericardium and the gut entoderm. (Redrawn from Davis, see fig. 362F, for reference.) (H) Lateral dissection of fifth week human embryo to show ingrowth of liver tissue into thickened septum transversum. (Redrawn from Patten, 1946, Human Embryology, Blakiston, Philadelphia.) Arrow denotes passageway (dorsal parietal recess; pericardioperitoneal canal; pleural canal) between pericardial and peritoneal coelomic cavities. (I-1) Sagittal section through 15 mm. pig embryo showing thickened anterior face of liver. This thickened anterior face of the liver later separates from the liver as the *primary septum transversum* (peritoneo-pericardial membrane). (I-2) Higher powered drawing to show condition of anterior face of liver shown in fig. 362, I-1. (J) Transverse section through thorax and pulmonary area of the body of a bird to show position of dorsal *pulmonary diaphragm*. (Redrawn from Goodrich, 1930, Studies on the Structure and Development of Vertebrates, Macmillan Co., Limited, London.) Observe position of liver lobes in relation to the heart. Compare with fig. 294, G-4 & G-5.

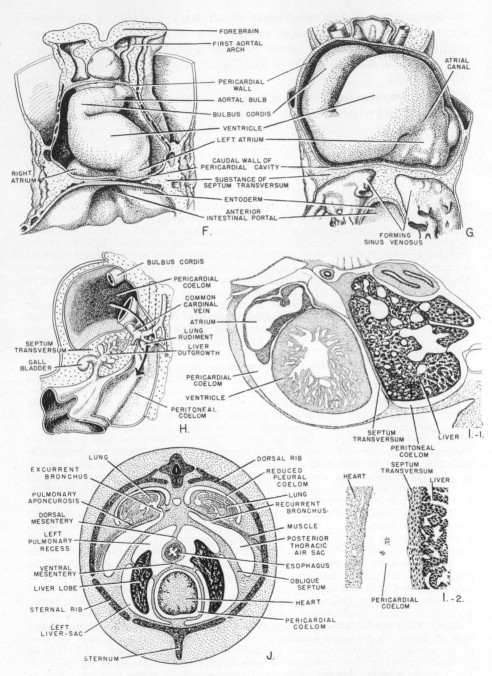

FIG. 362—(Continued)

See legend on p. 860.

(2) a larger caudal compartment, the **peritoneal cavity,** around the digestive viscera and urogenital structures.

This primary division of the early coelomic cavity is accomplished by the formation of:

1) The **lateral mesocardia,** and
2) the **primary (primitive) septum transversum.**

The two lateral mesocardia are formed previous to the development of the primitive septum transversum. Eventually the lateral mesocardia fuse in part to the dorsal edge of the transverse septum and become a part of it. The lateral mesocardia thus, in reality, represent the initial stage in the division of the general coelomic cavity. In consequence we shall consider the lateral mesocardia as important structures which enter into the formation of the primary transverse division of the embryonic body, but they should not be confused with the primitive septum transversum in a strict sense.

a. Lateral Mesocardia

The lateral mesocardia (fig. 362A-1, A-2) are formed as follows:
A lateral bulging or growth from the splanchnopleure at the caudal limits of the developing sinus venosus extends dorso-laterad on each side to meet a somewhat similar though smaller growth mediad of the somatopleural mesoderm. These growths form a bridge on each side across the coelomic cavity, extending dorso-laterad from the posterior lateral edges of the ventrally situated sinus venosus to the somatic wall. The area of union of this bridge on either side with the lateral body wall is the **lateral mesocardium.** The lateral mesocardia, in other words, represent the areas of juncture between the lateral body walls and the lateral extensions of the sinus venosus. The common cardinal veins or ducts of Cuvier join these right and left lateral extensions or horns of the sinus venosus in the substance of the lateral mesocardia. Anterior to the lateral mesocardia is the pericardial coelom, while posterior to them is the peritoneal coelom. The two passageways dorsal to the lateral mesocardia, on either side, are called the **dorsal parietal recesses of His,** while those ventral to the lateral mesocardia and on either side of the ventral mesentery and developing liver constitute the **ventral parietal recesses of His** (fig. 362A).

b. Formation of the Liver-Septum Transversum Complex

1) Formation of Liver-Septum Complex through Modification of the Ventral Mesentery by Liver Outgrowth. As the liver rudiment in the shark, chick, pig, etc., grows ventrally and forward between the two splanchnopleural layers of the ventral mesentery, it expands the ventral mesentery laterally as the liver substance forms within the mesenchyme between the two splanchnic layers. The expanding liver substance eventually reaches the ventral and lateral

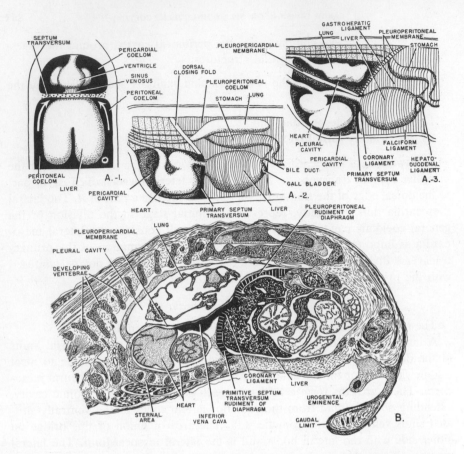

Fig. 363 (A-1, 2, 3). Diagrams showing the invasion of the peritoneal coelom around the liver and relations of septum transversum and diaphragm to the liver. (A-1) The peritoneal invasion separates the liver substance away from the lateral body wall and also from the anterior face of the liver itself. The separated, thickened, anterior face of the liver (see fig. 362, I-1 and I-2) forms the *primary septum transversum* (peritoneo-pericardial membrane). (A-2) The relation of the liver and other viscera to the *secondary* septum transversum formed by the addition of the *dorsal closing folds* (see fig. 362D) to the primary septum transversum. (A-3) This is a diagrammatic representation of conditions shown in B. Observe position of various ligaments associated with the liver. (B) Sagittal section through opossum embryo presenting relation of the liver to diaphragm. The ventral part of the diaphragm is the remodeled primary septum transversum. Observe that the inferior vena cava perforates the diaphragm. The area of attachment of the liver to the diaphragm is the *coronary ligament*. (The preparation from which this drawing was made was loaned to the author by Dr. J. A. McClain.) (C) Pericardioperitoneal opening below the esophagus in the shark, *Squalus acanthias*. (See also fig. 362D.) (D) Schematic diagram, dorsal view, of initial stage of developing pleural cavities in the mammal showing the anterior and posterior lateral body folds. The anterior lateral body fold gives origin to the pulmonary ridge or rudiment of the pleuropericardial membrane and the posterior lateral body fold forms most of the *pleuroperitoneal membrane*. Cf. fig. 362E. (E–H) Schematic diagrams showing later stages in separation of pleural cavities in the mammal, viewed from the dorsal aspect. Observe that the pleuroperitoneal membrane is formed from two rudiments, viz., *the posterior lateral body fold* and *a very small splanchnopleuric contribution* (fig. 363F).

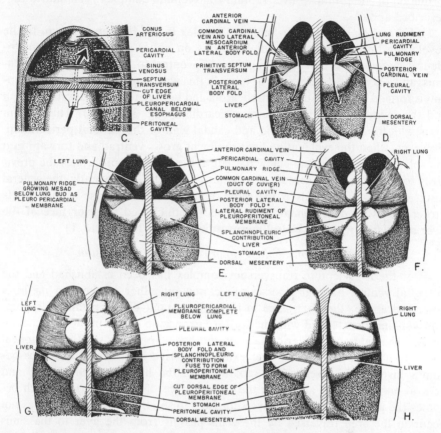

FIG. 363—(Continued)

See legend on p. 864.

body wall, where it fuses with the somatopleure from the body wall. Since the lateral expansion of the developing liver is more rapid than its forward growth, the anterior face of the liver gradually becomes flattened in the area just below (ventral to) the lateral mesocardia and immediately posterior to the sinus venosus of the heart. The mesenteric tissue, covering the anterior face of the liver, then fuses with the more dorsally located, lateral mesocardia. A transverse division across the body is completed in this manner below the lateral mesocardia, and the ventral parietal recesses in consequence are closed. Passage from the pericardial cavity to the peritoneal (abdominal) cavity is now possible only by way of the pericardioperitoneal canals (dorsal parietal recesses) (fig. 362E).

Although liver-rudiment development in the embryo of the frog and in the embryos of other amphibians is precocious the essential procedure in the formation of the primitive liver-septum transversum complex is similar to that described above.

2) Formation of the Liver-Septum Complex in the Human Embryo. In the developing human embryo, medial growths on either side from the somatopleural mesoderm occur in the region caudoventral to the forming sinus venosus, and below the developing gut tube. In this way ,a primitive transverse septum is formed below the lateral mesocardia and between the entoderm of the gut and the caudal wall of the parietal pericardium (fig. 362F, G). This septum fuses with the lateral mesocardia and caudal wall of the parietal pericardium. However, when the evaginating liver rudiment grows ventrad and forward into the splanchnopleural tissue below the gut, it ultimately appropriates the previously formed transverse septum as its anterior aspect. Consequently, the general result of the two methods is the same, namely, the transverse septum in its earlier stages of development appears as the thickened **anterior face of the liver associated with the lateral mesocardia** (figs. 261A; 362H, I).

c. Formation of the Primary Septum Transversum

After the liver-septum transversum complex has been established and the potential ventral parietal recesses are closed by either of the two methods described above, the next stage in the development of the primitive septum transversum is correlated with the forward expansion of the peritoneal coelom around the sides and anterior face of the liver. In doing so, the peritoneal coelom on either side of the liver extends anteriad and mesiad and thus becomes involved in a secondary separation of the liver from the lateral and ventral body wall and also from the anterior face of the liver itself which becomes the **primary septum transversum** (fig. 363A, B). A separation does not occur in the area traversed by the veins passing from the liver to the sinus venosus or slightly dorsal to this area. Here the liver remains attached directly to the septum transversum and is suspended literally from it. This attaching tissue forms the **coronary ligament** of the liver. The ingrowth of the two coelomic areas on either side of and ventral to the liver, by apposition of the coelomic epithelium in the median plane, forms a secondary ventral mesentery of the liver. This secondary ventral mesentery or **falciform ligament** ties the liver to the mid-ventral area of the body wall and to the septum transversum. (*Note:* The terms *primary septum transversum* and *peritoneopericardial membrane* are synonymous.)

C. Coelomic Changes in Fishes, Amphibians, Reptiles, and Birds

1. In Fishes

In the adult shark, and fishes in general, the fully developed adult form of the septum transversum forms a complete partition between the pericardial cavity and the peritoneal cavity. In fishes the pericardial cavity in the adult fish, as in the embryo, extends laterally and ventrally to the body wall in a fashion similar to that of the peritoneal cavity. Also, the heart continues to lie posterioventrally to the pharyngeal region in a manner very similar to that of the basic, embryonic body plan (fig. 294G–I).

In the formation of the adult, piscine, septum transversum from the primary transverse septum two membranous partitions are developed which close the dorsal parietal recesses or the openings above the lateral mesocardia. These partitions are called the **dorsal closing folds** and they arise as follows:

The splanchnopleural tissue on either side of the foregut, just anterior to the stomach rudiment and above the primitive septum transversum, forms a thin fold of tissue. This fold grows laterad and ventrad and fuses ultimately with the lateral mesocardium and the somatopleuric tissue, which overlies the common cardinal vein, as this vein travels caudo-ventrally along the body wall to reach the lateral mesocardium and the sinus venosus. As a result of this splanchnopleuric and somatopleuric fusion of tissues with the dorsal edge of the primary septum transversum a **dorsal closing fold** is formed on either side of the esophagus, and the two dorsal parietal recesses are obliterated, separating completely the pericardial cavity from the peritoneal cavity (fig. 362D). However, a small pericardioperitoneal opening may be left below the esophagus in the shark.

The **secondary septum transversum** thus formed is a thickened transverse partition, composed of two walls, an **anterior pericardial wall** and a **posterior peritoneal wall,** with a loose tissue layer between these two coelomic membranes. The liver is suspended from the peritoneal or caudal aspect of the septum transversum in the region of the **coronary ligament,** while the posterior end of the sinus venosus is apposed against the anterior or pericardial face of the transverse septum. The common cardinal and other converging veins of the heart utilize the substance of the septum transversum as a support on their way to the sinus venosus. The hepatic veins (the right and left, embryonic vitelline veins) pass through the coronary ligament on their journey to the sinus venosus.

2. In Amphibians, Reptiles, and Birds

The conversion of the primary septum transversum in amphibians, reptiles, and birds into the secondary or adult septum transversum occurs essentially as described above. A **dorsal closing fold,** obliterating the **dorsal parietal recess** on either side of the gut, is developed, although, in reptiles and birds, the inward growth and contribution of somatopleuric tissue overlying the common cardinal ridge is more important than in fishes in effecting this closure.

However, one must keep in mind an important fact, namely, that, in amphibia, reptiles and birds, there is an extensive *caudal migration of the heart, septum transversum, and liver complex from their original cephalic position just posterior to the pharyngeal area.* This caudal migration produces a condition in which the *primary septum transversum and the dorsal membranes, formed by the dorsal closing folds,* are inclined to a great degree, with the ventral end of the **primary septum transversum** considerably more posterior in position than the dorsal edge of the **dorsal membranes.** Consequently, a secondary recess or pocket is formed on either side anterior and dorsal to the septum transversum. This secondary recess occurs on either side of the gut, and, into each of these recesses, a **lung** extends in many reptiles and in those amphibia which possess lungs. In this pocket also lie certain of the air sacs of birds. Thus, the general cavity back of the **pericardioperitoneal membrane or secondary septum transversum** (i.e., the primary septum transversum plus the two dorsal membranes, formed by the dorsal closing folds) is known as the **pleuroperitoneal cavity** in amphibia and many reptiles. In birds (see below), the respiratory part of the lung becomes enclosed dorsally near the vertebrae within a separate **pleural cavity,** separated from the peritoneal cavity by the **dorsal diaphragm** (fig. 362J). The thin air sacs of the bird's lung (Chap. 14) project from the lung through the dorsal diaphragm into the peritoneal cavity and also into certain of the bones. In the turtle group, among the reptiles, a dorsal diaphragm is developed below each lung, segregating the lungs partly within dorsal cavities, thus simulating the bird condition.

D. Formation of the Coelomic Cavities in Mammals

In the mammalia, a pronounced caudal migration of the heart, liver, and developing diaphragm occurs. Also, as in birds, a further morphogenetic feature is present which results in the development of a pleural cavity for each lung in addition to the peritoneal and pericardial cavities present in fishes, amphibians, and reptiles. Thus it is that the development of two partitioning membranes on either side of the gut tube, the **pleuropericardial membranes,** which correspond to the dorsal closing membranes mentioned above, together with two additional membranes, the **pleuroperitoneal membranes,** are necessary to effect the division of the primitive splanchnocoelic coelom into the four main coelomic cavities in the *Mammalia.*

1. FORMATION OF THE PLEUROPERICARDIAL MEMBRANE

It so happens that the anterior cardinal vein develops slightly in advance of the posterior cardinal vein. As a result the common cardinal vein, which develops from the caudal end of the primitive anterior cardinal vein, travels along the lateral body wall in an inclined plane to reach the area of the lateral mesocardium and sinus venosus of the heart. This inclined pathway of the common cardinal vein is characteristic of the vertebrate embryo. As the common cardinal vein increases in size, a lateral ridge or elongated bulge is formed along the lateral body wall. This ridge projects inward into the coelomic cavity and inclines caudo-ventrally to reach the dorsal edge of the area of the primitive septum transversum (fig. 363D).

In the mammals, the mesonephric folds (ridges), in which the mesonephric kidneys develop, are large and project downward into the coelomic cavity. The anterior ends of the mesonephric ridges continue along the lateral body wall on either side and follow an inclined plane antero-ventrally to the dorsal edge of the primitive septum transversum (fig. 363D). Two **lateral body folds or ridges,** which incline toward and fuse with the dorsal edge of the primitive septum transversum, are produced in this manner on either side. These folds are an **anterior lateral body fold or ridge,** overlying the common cardinal vein, and a **posterior lateral body fold,** which represents the antero-ventral continuation of the mesonephric ridge as it inclines ventrally to join the lateral edge of the primitive septum transversum (fig. 363D). A V-shaped pocket is formed between these two ridges. This pocket represents the **primitive pleural cavity or pocket.** The apex of this V-shaped pocket unites with the primitive septum transversum. As the lung buds grow out posteriorly below the foregut, each projects into a pleural pocket (fig. 363F).

The formation of the pleuropericardial membrane is effected by an ingrowth of tissue along the edge of the anterior, lateral body fold, the fold that overlies the common cardinal vein. This ingrowing tissue forms a secondary ridge, known as the **pulmonary ridge,** which continues to grow mesad below the developing lung until it reaches the splanchnopleure of the esophagus with which it fuses. A pleuropericardial membrane, in this way, is established which separates the pericardial cavity below from the pleural cavity above (fig. 363E–G). The pleuropericardial membranes probably are homologous with the dorsal closing folds of the secondary septum transversum of the vertebrates below the mammals.

2. DEVELOPMENT OF THE PLEUROPERITONEAL MEMBRANE

As mentioned previously, the cephalic end of the mesonephric ridge projects forward and ventrad along the lateral body wall to unite with the primitive septum transversum to form the posterior, lateral body fold. The medial growth of this **posterior, lateral body fold** and ultimate fusion with a small splanchnopleural outgrowth, the **splanchnopleural fold,** forms a second partitioning membrane, the **pleuroperitoneal membrane,** which separates the pleural cavity from the general peritoneal cavity (fig. 363E–H). Contributions of the somatic mesoderm to the lateral body-fold tissue are significant in the formation of the pleuroperitoneal membrane. It is to be noted that the primitive pleural cavities of the mammalian embryo are small and dorsally placed, one on either side of the gut and dorsal to the pericardial cavity. Their later expansion is described below. To summarize the partitioning process of the primitive coelom in mammals, we find that the following membranes are formed:

(1) the primary septum transversum,
(2) the two dorsal closing folds or pleuropericardial membranes, and
(3) two pleuroperitoneal membranes.

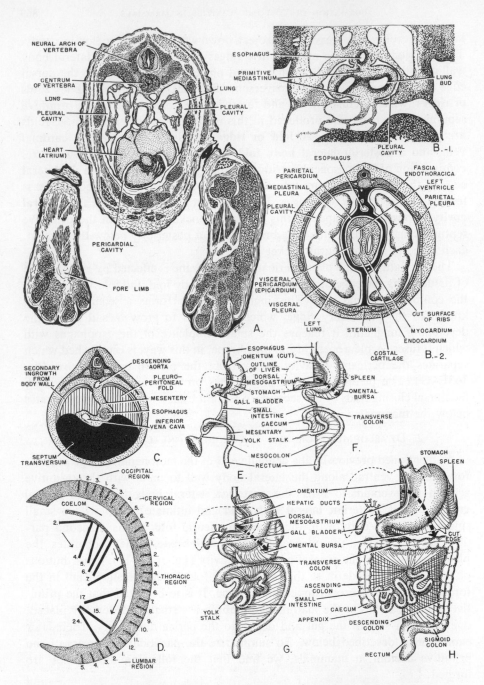

FIG. 364 (A). Transverse section of the thoracic area of opossum embryo showing the separation of the parietal pericardium from the lateral body walls by expanding pleural sacs. (The preparation from which this drawing was made was loaned to the author by Dr. J. A. McClain.) (B-1) Transverse section through lung buds and pleural

E. Development of Independent Pericardial Walls

1. The Arrangement of the Parietal Pericardial Wall in Fishes

The parietal pericardium of the fish embryo is fused with the lateral body wall. The caudal area of the sinus venosus is associated intimately with the anterior wall of the septum transversum. This condition is a primary one in all vertebrate embryos. It is retained in the adult fish.

2. Formation of an Independent Parietal Pericardial Wall in the Chick

In the chick, **two main processes occur** in development which separate the septum transversum from the liver, and also the parietal pericardial membrane from the lateral body walls. These processes are:

(a) The peritoneal cavity on either side of the liver grows forward and separates the cardiac or anterior face of the liver from the posterior face of the septum transversum, with the exception of the area where the veins from the hepatic region perforate the septum. This process frees the septum transversum from the liver surface and permits it to function as a part of the pericardial sac as indicated in figure 294G-4; G-5.

(b) The extending peritoneal coelom not only separates the liver from the posterior face of the septum transversum, but it continues anteriad followed by the liver lobes along the ventral and lateral aspects of the body wall and splits the membranous pericardium away from the lateral body wall. Ventrally, a median septum unites the pericardium with the body wall (fig. 362J).

3. Formation of the Independent Parietal Pericardial Wall in Amphibians and Reptiles

A somewhat similar process to that described for the chick obtains in reptiles and, to a modified extent, in amphibia.

Fig. 364—*Continued*

cavities of a 10 mm. pig embryo showing position of the *primitive mediastinum*. (B-2) Later mediastinal area development portraying adult position (black area) of the mediastinum. (Based on the cat.) Observe that fig. 364 (A) is an intermediate condition between figs. 364 (B-1) and 364 (B-2). (C) Probable origin of parts of the mammalian diaphragm. (D) The caudal migration of the septum transversum and developing diaphragm during development. 2-position = embryo of 2 mm.; 24-position = 24 mm. embryo. (Redrawn from F. P. Mall, 1910, Chap. 13, Vol. 1, Manual of Human Embryology, Lippincott, Philadelphia.) (E–H) Development of the mesenteries and omental bursa or lesser peritoneal cavity in the human. The cross-lined areas in H show areas of the mesentery which fuses with the body wall. The arrows in F–H denote development of the lesser peritoneal cavity.

4. Separation of the Parietal Pericardial Wall in Mammals

On the other hand, in the mammals, it is the pleural cavities, i.e., the pleural divisions of the splanchnocoelic coelom, which extend ventrally around the heart and thus separate the parietal pericardium from the thoracic body wall (fig. 364A and B). Posteriorly, they separate the pericardium from the anterior face of the developing diaphragm (fig. 363B). The secondary condition of the mediastinum thus is established which extends dorsoventrally between the two pleural sacs (fig. 364B-2). It is to be observed that the medial walls of the pleural sacs fuse with the lateral walls of the pericardium by means of the connective tissue which forms between these two layers.

F. The Mammalian Diaphragm

The mammalian diaphragm is a musculotendinous structure, innervated by the phrenic nerve and developed from tissues around the gut, primary septum transversum, the two pleuroperitoneal membranes, and possibly also by contributions from the body wall. Study figure 364C. The exact origin of the voluntary musculature of the diaphragm is in doubt, but it is assumed to come from the cervical myotomes in the region of origin of the phrenic nerve, together with some invasion of muscle substance from the lateral body wall posterior to the cervical area. Successive caudal positions of the septum transversum and developing diaphragm, assumed during its recession in the body, are shown in figure 364D.

G. The Pulmonary Diaphragm or Aponeurosis of the Chick

The **pulmonary diaphragm** in the chick is a composite structure formed of two membranes which develop in a horizontal position in the dorsal region of the thoracic area below the lungs. Each of these two membranes fuses with the median mesentery and the lateral body wall and thus forms a partition separating the **pleural cavities** above from the peritoneal cavity below (fig. 362J). The development of this partitioning membrane is as follows:

In the four- to five-day chick as the lung buds grow out dorso-posteriad each lung bud pushes into a mass of mesenchyme which is continuous from the splanchnopleure around the esophagus to the dorsal region of the liver. This connecting bridge of mesenchyme is the **pleuro-peritoneal membrane** and it extends from the region of the esophagus across the lower part of the lung bud tissue to the liver lobe on each side. The mesenchymal connection of this membrane with the liver then spreads laterally to unite with the lateral body wall. As a result, the pleural cavity above is shut off from the peritoneal cavity below. A continual growth dorsoposteriad of the pleuro-peritoneal membrane, and subsequent fusion with the dorsal body wall tissues, separates the pleural cavity completely from the peritoneal cavity. However, certain canals remain in this membrane for the passage of the air sacs (see Chapter 14) of the lungs. Striated musculature from the lateral body wall grows into the pleuro-peritoneal membrane on either side and converts it into a muscular structure. These two muscular partitions thus form the **pulmonary diaphragm.**

H. The Omental Bursa

In all gnathostomous vertebrates, the mesogastrium is prone to form a primitive pocket, associated with the rotation of the stomach to the right. This pocket is quite prevalent in most gnathostomous embryos from the elasmobranch fishes to the mammals and is known as the primitive **omental bursa.** In mammals, the omental bursa is highly developed, and it gives rise to the **lesser peritoneal cavity,** retaining its connection with the **greater peritoneal cavity** by means of the **foramen of Winslow.** The lesser peritoneal cavity in the cat is extensive, filling the entire inside of the omental sac. In the human, however, the distal part of the lesser peritoneal cavity is reduced by the fusion of the omental layers. Though a rudimentary omental bursa is formed in the early embryonic condition of elasmobranch fishes (sharks), it soon disappears, so that, in the adult fish, the omental bursa is nonexistent. Figure 364E–H presents various stages in the development of the omental bursa in the human embryo.

I. The Formation of Various Ligaments in the Stomach-Liver Region

Ligaments are those specializations of the peritoneal tissue which unite various organs with each other or with the body wall.

1. The Gastro-hepatic and Hepato-duodenal Ligaments. These structures are derivatives of the ventral mesentery between the stomach-duodenal area and the liver. The gastro-hepatic ligament ties the stomach and liver together while the hepato-duodenal ligament unites the duodenum with the liver.

2. The Coronary Ligament of the Liver. This is the tissue which unites the liver with the caudal face of the septum transversum and in mammals with the later developed diaphragm. Its development is described on page 866.

3. The Falciform Ligament of the Liver. This unites the liver in the median plane to the ventral body wall and to the septum transversum or diaphragm.

4. The Gastro-splenic Ligament suspends the spleen from the stomach and it represents a modification of the mesogastrium (see Chapter 17).

(*Note:* Ligamentous structures associated with the reproductive organs are described in Chapter 18.)

Bibliography

Goodrich, E. S. **1930.** Chap. XII in Studies on the Structure and Development of Vertebrates. Macmillan and Co., London.

Mall, F. P. **1910.** Chap. 13, Vol. I, Manual of Human Embryology, Lippincott, Philadelphia.

21

The Developing Endocrine Glands and Their Possible Relation to Definitive Body Formation and the Differentiation of Sex

A. Introduction

The **endocrine glands** are those glands which produce **hormonal secretions.** The term **hormone** is derived from a Greek word meaning to *stimulate* or to *stir up.* Selye in 1948 (p. 11) defined hormones as *"physiologic, organic compounds produced by certain cells for the sole purpose of directing the activities of distant parts of the same organism."*

The endocrine organs may be separated into two main groups:

(1) **purely endocrine glands,** and
(2) **mixed endo-exocrine glands.**

Purely endocrine glands have as their sole function the production of hormones. Under this heading are included the pituitary (hypophysis), thyroid, parathyroid, pineal, adrenal (suprarenal), and thymus glands.

Mixed endo-exocrine glands are exemplified by the pancreas, liver, duodenum, and reproductive organs. Parts of these organs are purely exocrine, e.g., the pancreas where **pancreatic juice** is produced by the acinous cells but which elaborates, at the same time, **insulin** from the **islets of Langerhans.** The liver elaborates the exocrine secretion, **bile,** which is discharged through the bile ducts and, concurrently, manufactures the **antipernicious-anemia factor** which is dispensed into the blood stream directly. The duodenum produces **digestive substances** and also **secretin.** Secretin is elaborated by the epithelial lining cells of this area, and it stimulates the pancreas to secrete its pancreatic juice.

Relative to their secretory activities all **endocrine glands** have this physio-morphological feature in common: *They discharge the hormonal or endocrine substance directly into the blood stream without the mediation of a duct system.* Endocrine glands, therefore, are distinguished by this process from **exocrine glands,** which exude the secretory product into a duct system from whence the secretion passes to the site of activity.

B. Morphological Features and Embryological Origin of the Endocrine Glands

1. PANCREAS

The **islets of Langerhans** are small masses of cells or islands scattered among the acini (alveoli) of the general pancreatic tissue. The pancreatic islets appear to arise as specialized buds from the same entodermal cords which give origin to the alveoli. The islets separate early from the entodermal cords and produce isolated cellular cords. Blood capillaries form a meshwork within these cords of cells (figs. 295G; 365A). Their secretion, **insulin,** is concerned with sugar metabolism and prevents the malfunction known as **diabetes.**

Pancreatic islets are found extensively in the vertebrates and generally are

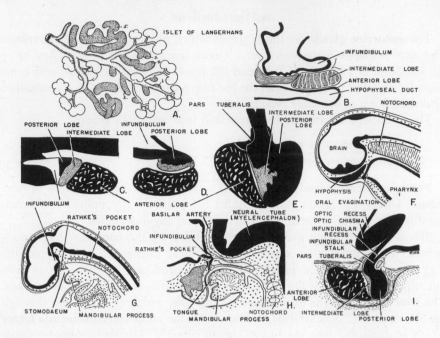

FIG. 365. The pancreatic islets and pituitary gland. (A) Origin of islet tissue from developing pancreatic ducts and acini. 1 = young bud; 5 = older bud. (Modified from Arey, '46, *Developmental Anatomy,* Philadelphia, Saunders.) (B–E) Diagrams of pituitary gland conditions in *Petromyzon* (B), *Rana* (C), Reptile (D), and Man(E). (Modified from Neal and Rand, 1939, *Chordate Anatomy,* Philadelphia, Blakiston.) (F) Origin of Rathke's pouch material from inner layer of epidermal ectoderm in early tadpole of *Rana.* (G–I) Developmental stages of hypophysis in human embryo.

associated with the pancreas. In some teleost fishes, the two glands are separated although both are derived from the entoderm. The pancreatic islets are classified as belonging to the **solid, non-storage type** of endocrine gland.

2. PITUITARY GLAND (HYPOPHYSIS CEREBRI)

Previous to the latter part of the last century, the function of the pituitary gland was presumed to be one of **mucous secretion,** hence the name **pituitary** from the Latin, *pituita,* a nasal secretion. It was so regarded by Vesalius in 1543. The English anatomist, Willis, believed that the pituitary gland secreted the cerebrospinal fluid.

The pituitary gland (fig. 365E and I) is composed of three main parts as follows:

a. Anterior Lobe

The **anterior lobe** (pars anterior) is composed of two subdivisions:

(1) a large anterior lobe **(pars distalis),** and
(2) a smaller glandular mass **(pars tuberalis).**

b. Posterior Lobe

The **posterior lobe** (lobus nervosus, pars neuralis) is derived from the distal part of the infundibulum.

c. Pars Intermedia

The **pars intermedia** or intermediate lobe is associated closely with the posterior lobe but has the same embryonic origin as the pars distalis and pars tuberalis of the anterior lobe.

In *Petromyzon fluviatilis,* the hypophysis is a flat, tube-like organ attached to the **infundibular evagination** of the floor of the diencephalon. The anterior lobe is represented by the hypophyseal duct which ends blindly below the infundibulum. From this duct are proliferated the cells of the intermediate lobe (fig. 365B). The pituitary gland shows great similarity, in all higher vertebrates, being composed of three main parts, viz., pars anterior, pars intermedia, and pars posterior (fig. 365C–E). However, in the chicken, whale, manatee, and armadillo, the intermediate lobe is missing (Selye, '48).

The pars anterior and the pars intermedia of the pituitary gland develop from Rathke's pouch as evaginations of the middorsal area of the stomodaeal pocket, although in the frog Rathke's pouch develops precociously from the so-called neural ectoderm above the stomodaeal invagination (fig. 365F–I). Rathke's pouch gradually comes into contact with the ventrally directed infundibular evagination from the diencephalon. The distal part of the infundibular evagination forms the pars neuralis, while Rathke's pouch differentiates into the pars distalis, pars intermedia, and pars tuberalis.

3. THYROID GLAND

The thyroid gland (fig. 366B) was described first in 1656 by Thomas Wharton, the English anatomist, who called it the thyroid gland because of its association with the thyroid or shield-shaped cartilage of the larynx.

After about 50 years of work by many observers on the thyroid gland and its activities, the crystalline form of the secretory principle of the thyroid gland was isolated by Kendall in 1919, and he called it **thyroxine.** This compound contained 65 per cent of iodine by weight and its empirical formula was subsequently determined as $C_{15}H_{11}O_4NI_4$.

One of the thyroid's functions is to govern carbohydrate metabolism, and, in general, the gland controls the basal metabolism of the animal together with growth processes. In man and the cat, the thyroid gland is in the form of two lateral lobes, located on the ventro-lateral aspect of the thyroid cartilage of the larynx, the two lobes being joined by an **isthmus.** In birds, there are two glands, both being located within the thoracic cavity; in fishes, including the Cyclostomes, the thyroid is an unpaired structure and is to be found generally between and near the posterior ends of the lower jaws. The gland, therefore, is a constant feature of all vertebrates.

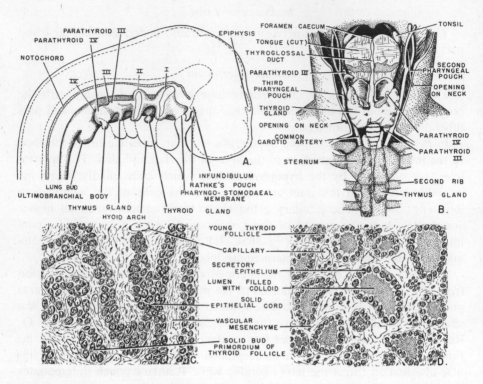

Fig. 366. Thyroid, parathyroid, and thymus glands in human embryo. (A) The loci of origin of thyroid, parathyroid, thymus, and ultimobranchial bodies. (B) Late stage (somewhat abnormal) of thyroid, parathyroid, and thymus gland development in human. (C) Early stage of thyroid follicle differentiation. (D) Later stage of thyroid follicle differentiation.

In the embryos of all vertebrates the thyroid gland appears as a pharyngeal derivative. In the human as in fishes and amphibia (Lynn and Wachowski, '51), it arises as a midventral outpocketing of the anterior pharyngeal floor. In the human embryo, this outpocketing occurs between the first and second branchial pouches at about the end of the fourth week of development (fig. 366A). Its point of origin is observable during later development as a small indentation, the **foramen caecum,** in the region between the **root** and **body** of the tongue (fig. 285). It is a bilobed evagination which soon loses its connection with the pharyngeal floor and migrates caudally to the laryngeal area where it differentiates into a double-lobed structure, connected by a narrow bridge of thyroid tissue, the isthmus. Occasionally, a persistent thyroglossal duct, connecting the foramen caecum with the thyroid gland, remains (fig. 366B). While the thyroid rudiment migrates posteriad, the **post-branchial (ultimobranchial) bodies,** which take their origin from the caudal margin of the fourth branchial pouch, become incorporated within the thyroid tissue.

The significance of this incorporation is unknown, and evidence of functional thyroid tissue, being derived from the post-branchial body cells, is lacking.

When the cellular masses of the developing thyroid gland reach the site of the future thyroid gland, the cells multiply and break up into cellular strands, surrounded by mesenchyme and blood vessels (fig. 366C). These strands in turn break up into small, rounded, bud-like masses of epithelial cells, the young thyroid follicles (fig. 366D). During the third month of development in the human, colloidal substance begins to appear within the young thyroid follicles. The colloid increases during the fourth month, and the surrounding cells of the follicle appear as a single layer of low columnar cells. Each thyroid follicle as a whole assumes the typical appearance of a functioning structure. Blood capillaries ramify profusely between the respective follicles.

The colloidal substance within each thyroid follicle presumably represents stored thyroid secretion, and the thyroid gland is regarded, therefore, as a "storage type" of endocrine gland. The theory relative to thyroid gland function is set forth that the follicle cells may secrete directly into the capillaries and, hence, into the blood stream, or the secretion may be stored as colloid within the follicles. Later this reserve secretion in the form of colloid may be resorbed by the cells in times of extreme activity and passed on into the region of the capillaries. In certain instances, e.g., dog and rat, individual thyroid follicles may be lined with stratified squamous epithelium (Selye, '48, p. 695).

In the larvae of the cyclostome, *Petromyzon,* the so-called **endostyle** is lined with rows of mucus-secreting cells, alternating with ciliated cells. This endostylar organ becomes transformed into the thyroid gland upon metamorphosis. A localization of iodine in certain of the endostylar cells in the larva has been demonstrated (Lynn and Wachowski, '51, p. 146).

4. PARATHYROID GLANDS

The parathyroid glands in man are four, small, rounded bodies, located along the dorsal (posterior) median edges of the two thyroid lobes of the thyroid gland (fig. 366B). Unlike the storage type of endocrine gland, such as the thyroid gland with its follicles, the parathyroids contain no follicles and, therefore, represent the solid type of endocrine gland. Blood capillaries ramify through its substance which is composed of closely packed masses of polyhedral epithelial cells, arranged in small cords or in irregular clumps. Two main cell types are present in mammals, the **chief or principal cells** with a clear cytoplasm and the **oxyphil cells** whose granules stain readily with acid stains. The chief cells are common to all vertebrate parathyroids and thus may represent the essential cellular type of the parathyroid gland (Selye, '48, p. 540).

The removal of the parathyroid glands results in a reduction of the calcium content of the blood, muscular tetany, convulsions, and ultimate death. The parathyroid glands in some way regulate calcium metabolism to keep the calcium content in the blood stream at its proper level.

Parathyroid structures may be present in fish (Selye, '48), but it is generally believed that true parathyroid tissue is confined to the *Tetrapoda*. Two parathyroid glands on each side are found in most urodeles and other amphibia, and in reptiles. The birds have relatively large parathyroid glands, attached to the two thyroid glands located in the thoracic cavity. All mammals possess parathyroid glands which, in some instances, are located internally within the thyroid gland as well as externally. Accessory parathyroid glands, apart from the two parathyroids attached to the thyroid gland, are found in rats and mice and, consequently, may not be disturbed if the thyroid gland is removed in these rodents.

The parathyroid glands arise in the human embryo from proliferations of the dorso-lateral walls of the third and fourth branchial pouches (fig. 366A). The parathyroids which arise from the third pair of pouches are known as parathyroids III, while those from the fourth pair of branchial pouches are called parathyroids IV. Parathyroids III arise in close proximity to the thymus-gland rudiments (fig. 366A). However, it is to be observed that the thymus rudiments arise from the ventral aspect of the third pair of pouches. The parathyroid-III rudiments move caudally with the thymus gland rudiments and come to lie in relation to the lateral lobes of the thyroid, posterior to parathyroids IV which take their origin in close relation to the post-branchial (ultimobranchial) bodies (fig. 366A and B).

Parathyroids IV appear to be a constant feature of all *Tetrapoda*. In those species having but two parathyroids, it is probable that their origin is from the fourth branchial pouches.

5. Thymus Gland

The thymus gland or "throat sweetbread" (the pancreas is referred to commonly as the "stomach sweetbread") lies in the anterior portion of the thoracic cavity and posterior neck region (fig. 366B). In some cases, it may extend well along in the neck region toward the thyroid gland. In the thoracic area, it lies between the two pleural sacs, that is, within the mediastinum, and reaches as far caudally as the heart. Histologically, it is composed of two parts:

(1) a **cortex** and
(2) a **medulla.**

The cortex contains masses of **thymocytes** or lymphocyte-like cells, while the medulla contains thymocytes, reticular cells, and the so-called **Hassall's corpuscles,** composed of stratified, squamous, epithelial cells.

In man, the thymus gland arises from the ventral portion of the third branchial pouches during the sixth week. These epithelial derivatives of the third branchial pouch become solid masses of cells which migrate posteriad into the anterior thoracic area.

The thymus gland is found in all vertebrates, but its morphology is most variable. In birds, it is situated in the neck region in the form of isolated, irregular nodules. The bursa of Fabricius, previously mentioned (Chap. 13) as an evagination in the cloacal-proctodaeal region of the chick, is a "thymus-like organ" (Selye, '48, p. 681). Thymus glands in reptiles are located in the neck region, and, in amphibians the two thymus glands lie near the angle of the jaws. In fishes several small, thymus-gland nodules arise from the dorsal portions of the gill pouches and come to lie dorsal to the gill slits in the adult.

The function of the thymus gland is not clear. It appears to have some relationship to sexual maturity. (For thorough discussion, see Selye, '48, Chap. IX.)

6. Pineal Body

The pineal gland appears to have been first described by Galen, the Greek scientist and physician (130–ca.200 A.D.), who believed it to function in relation to the art of thinking. Descartes (1596-1650) considered it to be the "seat of the soul."

During development, two fingerlike outgrowths of the thin roof of the dienoephalon of the brain occur in many vertebrates, namely, an anterior **paraphysis** or parietal organ, and a more posteriorly situated **epiphysis.** In certain Cyclostomes *(Petromyzon),* the posterior pineal body or **epiphysis** is associated with the formation of a dorsal or **pineal eye,** while the anterior pineal organ or **paraphysis** forms a rudimentary eyelike structure. In *Sphenodon* and in certain other lizards, the paraphysis or anterior pineal evagination develops an eyelike organ. Also, in various Amphibia (frogs; Ambystoma) rudimentary optic structures arise from the fused epiphyseal and paraphyseal diverticula. In consequence, we may assume that a primary function in some vertebrates of the dorsal, median pineal organs is to produce a dorsal, light-perceiving organ. In certain extinct vertebrates, a fully developed median dorsal eye appears to have been formed in this area.

On the other hand, the epiphysis (fig. 366A) in some reptiles, in birds and in mammals has been interpreted as a glandular organ. Various investigators have suggested different metabolic functions. However, an endocrine or essential secretory function remains to be demonstrated. (Consult Selye, '48, p. 595.)

Many types of cells enter into the structure of the pineal gland. Among these are the **chief cells,** which are large and possess a clear cytoplasm. Nerve cells and neuroglial elements also are present. Various other cell types possessing granules of various kinds in the cytoplasm are recognized.

7. ADRENAL (SUPRARENAL) GLANDS

The adrenal bodies are associated, as the name implies, with the renal organs or kidneys. In fishes, definite adrenal bodies are not present, but cellular aggregates, corresponding to the adrenal cells of higher vertebrates, are present and associated with the major blood vessels.

In man and other mammals, the adrenal body is composed of:

(1) an outer, yellow-colored **cortex** and
(2) an inner **medullary area.**

The medulla contains the **chromaffin** cells—cells which have a pronounced affinity for chromium salts, such as potassium dichromate, which stain them reddish brown and produce the so-called **"chromaffin reaction."**

The hormone, secreted by the medulla, is **adrenaline** *(epinephrine)*. It has marked metabolic and vasoconstrictor effects. The smooth muscle tissue of the **arrector pili** muscles associated with the hairs in mammals contract and raise the hair as a result of adrenaline stimulation.

The morbid state, known as Addison's disease and named after the English physician, Thomas Addison, who first described this fatal illness, arises from decreased function of the adrenal cortex. Various types of hormones have been discovered which arise from the cortical layer of the adrenal body, and a large number of steroid substances have been isolated from this area of the adrenal gland (Selye, '48, p. 89). In fishes, the cortical cell groups are isolated from those of the medulla, and, in the elasmobranch fishes, the cortex forms a separate organ. Its removal may be effected without injury to the medulla but with resulting debility, ending in death.

Embryologically, the adrenal cortex and medulla take their origin from two distinct sources. The cortex arises as a proliferation of the dorsal root of the dorsal mesentery in the area near the anterior portion of the mesonephric kidney and liver on either side (fig. 367A, B). These two proliferations give origin to two cortical masses, each lying along the anterior mesial edge of the mesonephric kidney. Further growth of these masses produces two rounded bodies, the adrenals (suprarenals), lying between the anterior portions of the mesonephric kidneys (figs. 3A and B; 367B) and later in relation to the antero-mesial portion of the metanephric kidneys (fig. 3B–E). After the cortical masses are established, the **chromaffin cells** invade them from the medial side (fig. 367C). The potential chromaffin cells migrate from the sympathetic ganglia in this area. Upon reaching the site of the developing adrenal gland they move inward between the cortical cells to the center of the gland where they give origin to the medulla. With the diverse embryological origins of the cortex and the medulla, it is seen readily why two separate glandular structures are present in lower vertebrates.

In man and other mammals, a later developed secondary cortex is laid down around the primary cortex. The primary cortex, characteristic of fetal

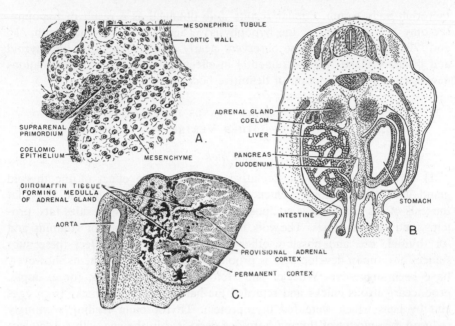

FIG. 367. Differentiation of the adrenal (suprarenal) body. (A) Early stage in prolif-eration of adrenal cortical primordium from coelomic epithelium. (B) Later stage of cortex, forming rounded masses associated with cephalic ends of mesonephros. The anterior end of the mesonephros lies between the adrenal body and lateral wall of the coelom. (Compare fig. 3H and B.) (C) Cells from sympathetic ganglia penetrating medial side of primitive cortical tissue of adrenal body to form chromaffin cells of adrenal medulla.

life, then comes to form the "inner cortical zone" or **androgenic zone** (Howard, '39).

8. GONADS

The developing gonads were described in Chapter 18, and their hormonal functions were outlined in Chapters 1 and 2.

C. Possible Influence of Endocrine Secretions on the Development of Definitive Body Form

1. THYROID AND PITUITARY GLANDS AND ANURAN METAMORPHOSIS

One of the earlier studies in this field of development was that by Guder-natsch ('12 and '14) which showed that mammalian thyroid gland fed to anuran, and urodele larvae stimulated growth, differentiation, and metamor-phosis. In a later series of studies by Allen (see Allen, '25, for references and review) and by Hoskins ('18 and '19), it was demonstrated that the removal of the thyroid gland in young tadpoles of Rana and Bufo prevents metamorphosis from the larval form into that of definitive body form (i.e., the adult body form). Similar results were obtained as a result of hypophy-sectomy (i.e., removal of the hypophysis). (See Allen, '29, and Smith, '16 and '20.) The work of these observers clearly demonstrates that the thyroid and pituitary glands are instrumental in effecting the radical transformations necessary in the assumption of definitive body form in the *Anura*.

2. THYROID AND PITUITARY GLANDS IN RELATION TO THE DEVELOPMENT OF OTHER VERTEBRATE EMBRYOS

a. Chick

1) Thyroid Gland. Studies relative to the possible effect of the thyroid gland upon the developing chick embryo are complicated by the fact that the yolk of the chick egg is composed of many other factors besides fats, proteins, and carbohydrates. The yolk is a veritable storehouse for vitamins and for thyroid, sex, and possibly other hormones. Just what effect these substances have upon development is problematical. Some experiments, however, have been suggestive. Wheeler and Hoffman ('48, a and b), for example, produced goitrous chicks and retarded the hatching time of chicks from eggs laid by hens which were fed thyroprotein. Thyroprotein feeding seemingly reduced the amount of thyroid hormone deposited in the egg with subsequent deleterious effects upon the developing chicks. In normal development, the thyroid gland of the chick starts to develop during the third day and produces follicles which contain colloid by the tenth and eleventh days of incubation. Furthermore, Hopkins ('35) showed that thyroids from chick embryos of 10 days of incubation hastened metamorphosis in frog larvae. From days 8 to 14 the chick embryo undergoes the general changes which transform it from the larval form which is present during incubation days 6 to 8 into the definitive body form present at the beginning of the third week of incubation.

The foregoing evidence, therefore, while it does not demonstrate that thyroid secretion actually is being released by the developing thyroid gland into the chick's blood stream, does suggest that the thyroid gland may be a factor in chick development and differentiation. If the chick's thyroid gland is secreting the thyroid hormone into the chick's blood stream during the second week of the incubation period, it is evident that the developing chick during the period when it is assuming the definitive body form has two sources of thyroid hormone to draw upon:

(1) that contained within the yolk of the egg and
(2) that produced by its own thyroid gland.

2) Pituitary Gland. Relative to the development of the pituitary gland in the chick, Rahn ('39) showed that the anterior lobe develops both acidophilic and basophilic cells by the tenth day of incubation. Also, Chen, Oldham, and Geiling ('40) demonstrated that the pituitary of chicks from eggs incubated for five days possessed a melanophore expanding principle when administered to hypophysectomized frogs.

This general evidence, relative to the developing pituitary gland in the chick, suggests that the cells of the pituitary gland may be active functionally during the latter part of the first week and during the second week of incubation. If so, the pituitary gland may be a factor in inducing the rapid growth and changes which occur during the second week of incubation. It suggests further, that a possible release of a thyrotrophic principle may be responsible for the presence of colloid within the developing thyroid follicles during the second week of incubation.

b. Mammal

As in the chick, the developing embryo of the placental mammal is in contact with hormones from extraneous sources. Hormones are present in the amniotic fluid, while the placenta is the seat of origin of certain sex and gonadotrophic hormones. Also, the maternal blood stream, which comes in contact with embryonic placental tissues, is supplied with pituitary, thyroid, adrenal, and other hormonal substances. This general hormonal environment of the developing mammalian embryo complicates the problem of drawing actual conclusions relative to the effect of the embryo's developing endocrine system upon the differentiation of its own organ systems and growth. Nevertheless, there is circumstantial evidence, relating to possible activities of the developing, embryonic, endocrine glands upon development.

1) Thyroid Gland. Colloid storage within the follicles of the developing, human, thyroid gland is evident at 3 to 4 months. In the pig embryo, Rankin ('41) detected thyroxine and other iodine-containing substances in the thyroid at the 90-mm. stage, and Hall and Kaan ('42) were able to induce metamorphic effects in amphibian larvae from thyroids obtained from the fetal rat at 18 days. The foregoing studies suggest that the thyroid gland is able to function in the fetal mammal at an early stage of development. (For further references, consult Moore, '50.)

2) Pituitary Gland. Similarly, in the pituitary gland, granulations within the cells of the anterior lobe are present in the human embryo during the third and fourth months (Cooper, '25). Comparable conditions are found in the pituitary of the pig from 50 to 170 mm. in length (Rumph and Smith, '26).

c. Fishes

The relationship between the thyroid and pituitary glands in the development of fishes is problematical. There is evidence in favor of a positive influence of endostylar cells and of the cells of the developing thyroid gland in the transformation of the ammocoetes larva of the cyclostome, *Petromyzon*, into the definitive or adult body form. Similar evidence suggests a thyroid activity relationship in the transformation of the larvae of the trout and the bony eel. However, this evidence is not indisputable, and more study is necessary before definite conclusions are possible. (Consult Lynn and Wachowski, '51, for discussion and references.)

3. GENERAL CONCLUSIONS RELATIVE TO THE INFLUENCE OF THE THYROID AND PITUITARY GLANDS IN VERTEBRATE EMBRYOLOGY

These conclusions are:

(a) Positive activities of the thyroid and pituitary glands are demonstrated in the transformation of the larval form into the definitive or adult form in the Anura.

(b) Suggestive evidence in favor of such an interpretation has been accumulated in fishes.

(c) Circumstantial evidence, relative to the possible activities of the thyroid and pituitary glands during the period when the embryos of the chick and mammal are transforming into the adult form, is present. With the evidence at hand, however, it is impossible to conclude definitely that these glands are a contributing factor to a change in body form (metamorphosis) in chick and mammalian embryos (fig. 256).

D. Possible Correlation of the Endocrine Glands with Sex Differentiation

1. DIFFERENTIATION OF SEX

a. General Sex Features in the Animal Kingdom

Many animal groups are **hermaphroditic,** that is, both sexes occur in the same individual. Flatworms, roundworms, oligochaetous annelids, leeches, many mollusks, and certain fishes are representatives of this condition, whereas most vertebrates, insects, and echinoderms are bisexual. If one examines the developing gonads in insects or vertebrates, it is evident that, fundamentally, the potentialities for both sexes exist in the same individual. As observed previously (Chap. 18), the early gonad is bipotential in most vertebrates, and two sets of reproductive ducts are formed. As sex is differentiated, the gonadal cortex and the Müllerian duct assume dominance in the female, while the gonadal medulla and Wolffian duct become functional if the animal is a male. Generality, therefore, gives way to specificity. Conditions thus are established in the developing reproductive system, similar to the generalized conditions to be found in other systems. If we take into consideration the fact that in a large number of animals both sexes are present in a functional state in one individual and in many bisexual species both sexes are present in a rudimentary condition in the early embryo, we arrive at the conclusion *that both sexes are fundamentally present in a large majority of animal species.* Sex, therefore, tends to be an hermaphroditic matter among many species of animals. The problem of sex differentiation, consequently, resolves itself into this: Why do both sexes emerge in the adult condition in a large number of animals, whereas in the development of many other animal species, only one of the two sex possibilities becomes functional?

b. Chromosomal, Sex-determining Mechanisms

A considerable body of information has been obtained which demonstrates a fundamental relationship between certain chromosomes and sex determination. The general topography of chromosomal sex-determining mechanisms has been established for a large number of species. A pair of homologous chromosomes, the so-called sex chromosomes, apparently have become specialized in carrying the genic substances directly concerned with sex determination. In many species, the members of this pair of sex-determining chromosomes appear to be identical throughout the extent of the chromosomes in one of the sexes. In the other sex, on the other hand, the two sex-determining chromosomes are not identical. When two identical chromosomes are present in a particular sex, that sex is referred to as the **homogametic sex,** for the reason that all of the gametes derived from this condition will possess identical sex chromosomes. However, that sex which possesses the two dissimilar chromosomes is called the **heterogametic sex** for it produces unlike gametes, Often the heterogametic condition is represented by one chromosome only, the other chromosome being absent. If under the above circumstances the normally appearing chromosome is called X, and the deleted, diminutive or strangely appearing chromosome is called Y, while the chromosome which is absent be designated as O, we arrive at the following formula:

XX = the homogametic sex and either XY or XO = the heterogametic sex. In many (probably in most) animal species *the male is the heterogametic sex* (fig. 368A–C).

In some animal groups, however, such as the butterflies, the moths, possibly the reptiles, the birds, some fishes, and probably urodele amphibia, the female is the heterogametic sex, and the male is homogametic. In these particular groups, many authors prefer to use the designation ZZ for the homogametic sex (i.e., the male) and ZO or ZW for the female or heterogametic sex. The sex-determining mechanism in these groups, according to this arrangement, will be ZZ:ZW or ZZ:ZO (fig. 368D).

In endeavoring to explain the action of these chromosomal mechanisms, one of the underlying assumptions is that the genic composition of the chromosomes actively determines the sex. For example, in cases where the female sex is homogametic it is assumed that the X-chromosome contains genes which are female determining; when two (or more) X's are present, the female sex is determined automatically. When, however, one X-chromosome is present, the determining mechanism works toward male determination. In those species where the female sex is the heterogametic sex it may be assumed that the Z-chromosome (or X-chromosome, depending upon one's preference) contains genes which are male determining. When only one of these Z-chromo-

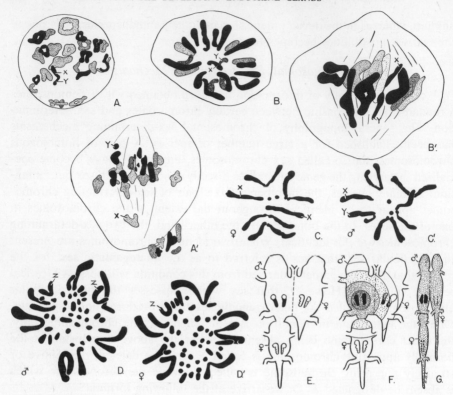

FIG. 368. The sex chromosomes in man, opossum, chick, and *Drosophila;* parabiotic experiments in *Amphibia*. (A) Late primary spermatocyte in human. (A') First maturation spindle in human spermatocyte. (Redrawn from Painter, '23, J. Exper. Zool., 37.) (B) Dividing spermatogonium in opossum testis. (B') First maturation spindle in spermatocyte of opossum. (Redrawn from Painter, '22, J. Exper. Zool., 35.) (C) Sex chromosomes in female *Drosophila*. (C') Sex chromosomes in male *Drosophila*. (Redrawn from Morgan, Embryology and Genetics, 1934, Columbia University Press, N. Y., after Dobzhansky.) (D) Sex chromosomes in common fowl, male. (D') Sex chromosomes in common fowl, female. (Redrawn from Bridges, 1939, Chap. 3, *Sex and Internal Secretions,* edited by Allen et al., Baltimore, Williams and Wilkins, after Sokolow, Tiniakow, and Trofimov.) (E–G) Diagrams illustrating the spreading of gonadal substances in frogs, toads, and salamanders. In toads, E, the gonadal influences (antagonisms) are evident only when the gonads actually are in contact. In the frogs, F, the range of influence is wider but its effect falls off peripherally. Figure G represents the condition in newts and salamanders. It is evident that in this group, some substance is carried in the blood stream which suppresses the gonads in the two females as indicated in the diagram. (Redrawn and modified slightly from Witschi, 1939, Chap. 4, *Sex and Internal Secretions,* edited by Allen et al., Baltimore, Williams and Wilkins.)

somes is present the developmental forces swing in the direction of the female sex. Sex, from this point of view, is determined by a genic balance, a balance which in turn is governed by the quality of certain genes as well as the quantitative presence of genes. (For detailed discussion consult Bridges, '39, and White, '48.)

c. Possible Influence of the Sex Field in Sex Determination

Two gonadal sex fields, the **cortical field** and the **medullary field,** are present in the early vertebrate gonad in amphibians, reptiles, birds, and mammals. This condition is true also of many fishes. Sex differentiation primarily is a question as to which one of these fields will assume dominance. During development in various instances, sex differentiation is clearly the result of only partial dominance on the part of one sex field, the other field emerging partly or almost completely. As a result, various types of intersexes may appear. For example, in the male toad, **Bidder's organ** at the anterior part of the testis represents a suppressed cortical or ovarian field, held in abeyance by the developing testis. Surgical removal of the two testes permits the cortical field or Bidder's organ to become free from its suppressed state. As a result, functional ovaries are developed, and the animal reverses its sex, becoming a functional female (Witschi, '39).

One of the classical examples which demonstrates the dependence of the developing sex field upon surrounding environmental factors is the **freemartin.** The freemartin appears in cattle when twins of the opposite sex develop in such a manner that an anastomosis or union of some of the fetal blood vessels occurs (Lillie, '17). Under these circumstances the female twin always experiences a transformation in the direction of maleness in the gonad and sex ducts. In those instances of freemartin development where the cortical field of the developing ovary is suppressed and the medullary area is hypertrophic, a partial or fairly well-developed testis may be formed. Under these conditions it is presumed that some substance is elaborated within the medullary field of the developing gonad of the male twin which enhances the development of the similar field in the freemartin ovary and suppresses, at the same time, the cortical field. The development of fully differentiated gametes (i.e., sperm) in the freemartin "testis" has not been demonstrated, but, on the whole, the more normally developed freemartin testis shows conditions at the time of birth which are comparable to a similar gonad of the normal male at about the same age, with the questionable presence or absence of very young germ cells. Gametogenesis in the developing testis of the bull occurs after birth. Consequently, the development of gametes in the freemartin of cattle cannot be ascertained because the freemartin gonad remains in the position of the normal ovary and does not descend into the scrotum as it does in the male (Willier, '21). A scrotal residence (Chap. 1) is necessary for spermatogenesis in all males, possessing the scrotal condition.

A particularly interesting case of intersexuality, resulting from the lack of complete supremacy on the part of one sex field, is shown in the fowl described by Hartman and Hamilton ('22). A brief résumé of its behavior and anatomy, as described by the authors, is presented herewith.

The bird was hatched as a robust chick and developed into an apparently normal Rhode Island Red pullet. The following spring the comb and wattles began to enlarge, and the bird after a few abortive attempts, learned to give the genuine crow of a rooster. . . . It was often seen scratching on the ground and calling the flock to an alleged morsel of food, and though it was never seen to tread hens it would strut and make advances after the manner of cocks. . . . The female behavior of the bird was as follows. For years it would sing like a laying hen. On two occasions it adopted incubator chicks, caring for them day and night and clucking like a normal hen. . . . On one occasion it dropped an egg, which though small and elongated, showed the bird to be in possession of functional ovary and oviduct.

Its internal anatomy demonstrated the presence of a left ovotestis and a right testis. An oviduct was present on the left side and a vas deferens on both sides. The right testis contained tubules, and within the tubules were ripe sperm. The ovotestis on the left side contained a cortex studded "with oocytes of every size up to a diameter of 20 mm." and "not unlike the ovary of a normal hen approaching the laying season" (Hartman and Hamilton, '22). Seminiferous tubules also were present in the ovotestis which was filled with sperm.

An interesting example of complete sex reversal was produced experimentally in the axolotl, *Siredon (Ambystoma) mexicanum,* by Humphrey ('41). In doing so, Humphrey orthotopically implanted an embryonic testis of *Ambystoma tigrinum* into an axolotl embryo of similar age. After the ovary on the opposite side of the host (i.e., the young axolotl) had changed to a testis, the implanted testis was removed. Somewhat later, the sexually reversed female axolotl was bred with other females with success. The F_1 and F_2 generations suggest that the female axolotl is heterogametic whereas the male is homogametic, with a possible XY or ZW condition in the female and an XX (or ZZ) arrangement in the male. It is interesting to observe that Humphrey obtained YY (or WW) females which were fertile.

Many other studies have been made along the lines of experimental transformation of sex. Of these, the careful studies of Witschi ('39) are illuminating. The method, employed by Witschi, was to join two embryos of opposite sex before the period of sex differentiation. In his studies, he used toad, frog, and urodele embryos. Three different results were obtained, in which the medulla or developing testicular rudiment tended to dominate and suppress the cortex or developing female sex field. For example, in toads, it was evident that the medulla suppressed the cortex only if the two fields came into actual contact; in frogs, the effect of suppression was inversely proportional to the distance of the two sex fields from each other; on the other hand, in urodeles, the substance produced by the medulla evidently circulated in the blood stream and produced its effects at a distance (fig. 368E–G). Witschi postulated the presence of two, not readily diffusible, "activator" substances, **cortexin,** formed by the cortex, and **medullarin,** elaborated by the medulla, to account for the results in the toad and frog embryos, and, in urodeles, he assumed a hormonal substance to be present.

The foregoing examples and many others (Witschi, '39) suggest the following interpretations relative to sex determination and differentiation:

(1) The germ cell, regardless of its genetic constitution, develops into an egg or a sperm, depending upon whether it lies in a developing cortex or in a developing medulla. That is, the influence of the sex field governs the direction of germ-cell differentiation (fig. 22).

(2) The sex field is a powerful factor in determining sex. A factor (or factors) which enables an elevation to partial or complete dominance on the part of one sex field, which under normal conditions is suppressed, may result in the partial or complete reversal of sex.

(3) Differentiation of sex is dependent upon an interplay between the genes of the sex chromosomes and the bio-chemical forces present in the gonadal sex field. This interplay may be considered to work as follows: (a) If the male-sex field or medulla in a particular species is stronger than the female field or cortex, that is, if it is able to compete for substrate substances more vigorously and successfully and to produce diffusible hormonal substance more plentifully, it will suppress the female sex field. Under these conditions, the chromosomal sex-determining mechanism is established in such a way that the male is the heterogametic sex, composed of XY or XO chromosomal combinations, and the female is XX, *the genes of the extra X chromosome being necessary to override the male tendency present normally in the male sex field.* (b) On the other hand, if the female sex field or cortex is stronger physiologically, then the female is the heterogametic sex (XO or ZW), *the homozygous condition of the sex chromosomes in the male being necessary to suppress the natural tendencies toward supremacy of the stronger female sex field.* (c) It may be that the general characteristics and strength of the sex field are controlled by genes present in certain autosomal chromosomes, whereas the specific role which the particular sex field takes normally in sex differentiation is controlled by the genes in the sex chromosomes.

2. Influence of Hormones on the Differentiation of Sex

The possible effects of hormones upon sex differentiation, particularly upon the development of the accessory ducts, have been studied with great interest since F. R. Lillie's ('17) description of freemartin development in cattle. He tentatively made the assumption that the male fetal associate of the freemartin produces a **hormonal substance** which, through the medium of vascular anastomoses within the placentae of the two fetuses, brings about a partial suppression of the developing ovary and effects, in part, a sex reversal in the developing reproductive organs of the female. The female member of this heterosexual relationship, therefore, is more or less changed in the direction of the male; hence, the common name freemartin.

It should be mentioned in this connection that in the marmoset, *Oedipomidas geoffroyi,* similar anastomoses between the placental blood vessels of heterosexual twins fail to produce the freemartin condition, both twins being normal. Species differences in the response to hormones or other sex-modifying substances therefore occur (Wislocki, '32).

The studies made in an endeavor to ascertain the influences which sex hormones play in the development of the reproductive system and in sexual differentiation have produced the following general results.

Developing ovaries and testes and the reproductive ducts of birds, frogs, and urodeles may show various degrees of sex reversal when the developing young are exposed to hormones or other humeral substances of the opposite sex. There is some evidence to the effect that sex reversal by sex hormones is accomplished more readily and completely from the homogametic sex to the heterogametic sex, suggesting, possibly, that the sex field of the heterogametic sex is the stronger and more resistant. The reproductive ducts are more responsive to change than are the gonads (Burns, '38, '39a; Domm, '39; Mintz, Foote, and Witschi, '45; Puckett, '40; Willier, '39; and Witschi, '39).

In mammals, the gonads (ovary and testis) appear quite immune to the presence of sex hormones, whereas the reproductive ducts respond partially to the sex hormone of the opposite sex. The caudal parts of the genital passages are more sensitive to change than are the more anterior portions (Burns, '39b, '42; Greene, Burrill, and Ivy, '42; and Moore, '41, '50).

Castration experiments before and shortly after birth in mammals produce the following effects:

(1) Removal of the testis results in retardation and suppression of the male duct system, while it allows the female duct system to develop.

(2) Removal of the ovary does not affect the female duct system until the time of puberty.

(See LaVelle, '51, and Moore, '50, for extensive references and discussion.)

The general conclusions to be drawn from the above experiments, relative to the differentiation of the reproductive ducts, are as follows:

(1) The reproductive ducts are responsive to sex hormones after they are formed in the embryo.

(2) The male duct system normally responds to humeral substances, elaborated by the developing testis soon after it is formed.

(3) The female duct system probably is not dependent upon hormonal secretion for its development until about the time of sexual maturity.

(4) The developing ovary, unlike the developing testis, probably under normal conditions does not elaborate sex hormones in large amounts until about the time of sexual maturity.

3. GENERAL SUMMARY OF THE FACTORS INVOLVED IN SEX DIFFERENTIATION IN THE VERTEBRATE GROUP

The sex glands (gonads) and the reproductive ducts appear to arise independently of each other.

The primitive gonad is composed of two main parts:

(1) the primordial germ cells and
(2) cellular structures which act as supporting and enveloping structures for the germ cells.

The presence of the primitive germ cells probably is a primary requisite for the development of a functional reproductive gland (see p. 121).

In the differentiation of the gonad, two basic sex fields or territories appear to be involved in *Tetrapoda* and probably also in most fishes. These territories are:

(1) the medulla or testis-forming territory and
(2) the cortex or ovary-forming area.

The sex fields may be controlled by the genes in the autosomal chromosomes, and there probably is a tendency for one or the other of these fields to be functionally stronger than the other. The heterogametic (XY, XO, ZW or ZO) conditions of the sex chromosomes appear to be associated with the stronger sex field, and the homogametic (i.e., XX or ZZ) combination is associated with the weaker sex field.

During development, presumably, there is a **struggle for supremacy** through competition for substrate substances (see Dalcq, '49) by these two sex fields and, under normal conditions, the sex chromosomal mechanism determines which of the two sex fields shall be suppressed and which shall rise to domination. The sex chromosomes thus control the direction of sex differentiation, whereas the field or territory elaborates the power of differentiation.

Disturbing influences may upset the sex-determining mechanism set forth above, and various degrees of hermaphroditism may arise in the same individual in proportion to the degree of escape permitted the normally suppressed sex field.

The sex ducts arise in association with the pronephric kidney and its duct, the pronephric (mesonephric) duct. The Müllerian or female duct arises by a longitudinal splitting of the original pronephric (mesonephric) ducts (e.g., in elasmobranchs) or by an independent caudal growth of a small invagination of the coelomic epithelium at the anterior end of the mesonephric kidney (e.g., reptiles, birds, and mammals). This independent caudal growth is dependent, however, upon the pre-existence of the mesonephric duct (Chap. 18). In the urodeles, the Müllerian duct appears to arise partly from an independent origin and in part from contributions of the mesonephric duct.

Two sets of primitive ducts thus are established in the majority of vertebrates in each sex, the **Müllerian or female duct** and the **mesonephric (pronephric) or male duct.**

During later normal development, the **Müllerian duct** is developed in the female, while, in the male, the **mesonephric duct** is retained and elaborated as the functional, male reproductive duct.

The male duct system is dependent upon secretions from the developing testis for its realization during the later embryonic period and during postnatal development, whereas the female duct develops independently of the ovary up to the time of sexual maturity when its behavior is altered greatly by the presence of the ovarian hormones.

Bibliography

Allen, B. M. **1929.** The influence of the thyroid gland and hypophysis upon growth and development of amphibian larvae. Quart. Rev. Biol. **4**:325.

————. **1925.** The effects of extirpation of the thyroid and pituitary glands upon the limb development of anurans. J. Exper. Zool. **42**:13.

Brahms, S. **1932.** The development of the hypophysis in the cat *(Felis domestica).* Am. J. Anat. **50**:251.

Bridges, C. B. **1939.** Chap. II, Cytological and genetic basis of sex. Sex and Internal Secretions, 2nd Edition. Edited by Allen, et al., Williams & Wilkins, Baltimore.

Burns, R. K., Jr. **1938.** The effects of crystalline sex hormones on sex differentiation in *Amblystoma.* I. Estrone. Anat. Rec. **71**:447.

————. **1939a.** The effects of crystalline sex hormones on sex differentiation in *Amblystoma.* II. Testosterone propionate. Anat. Rec. **73**:73.

————. **1939b.** Sex differentiation during the early pouch stages of the opossum *(Didelphys virginiana)* and a comparison of the anatomical changes induced by male and female sex hormones. J. Morphol. **65**:497.

————. **1942.** Hormones and experimental modification of sex in the opossum. Biol. Symp. **9**:125.

Chen, G., Oldham, F. K., and Geiling, E. M. K. **1940.** Appearance of the melanophore-expanding hormone of the pituitary gland in the developing chick embryo. Proc. Soc. Exper. Biol. & Med. **45**:810.

Cooper, E. R. A. **1925.** The histology of the more important human endocrine organs at various ages. Oxford University Press, Inc., New York.

Dalcq, A. M. **1949.** The concept of physiological competition (Spiegelman) and the interpretation of vertebrate morphogenesis. Exp. Cell Research, Supplement 1, Bonnier, Stockholm and Academic Press, New York.

Domm, L. V. **1939.** Chap. V. Modifications in sex and secondary sexual characters in birds in Sex and Internal Secretions by Allen, et al., 2d ed., The Williams & Wilkins Co., Baltimore.

Greene, R. R., Burrill, M. W., and Ivy, A. C. **1942.** Experimental intersexuality. The relative sensitivity of male and female rat embryos to administered estrogens and androgens. Physiol. Zoöl. **15**:1.

Gudernatsch, J. F. **1912.** Feeding experiments on tadpoles. I. The influence of specific organs given as food on growth and differentiation. A contribution to the knowledge of organs with internal secretion. Arch. f. Entwicklngsmech. d. Organ. **35**:457.

————. **1914.** Feeding experiments on tadpoles. II. A further contribution to the knowledge of organs with internal secretion. Am. Jour. Anat. **15**:431.

Hall, A. R., and Kaan, H. W. **1942.** Anatomical and physiological studies on the thyroid gland of the albino rat. Anat. Rec. **84**:221.

Hartman, C. G., and Hamilton, W. F. 1922. A case of true hermaphroditism in the fowl, with remarks upon secondary sex characters. J. Exper. Zool. 36:185.

Hopkins, M. L. 1935. Development of the thyroid gland in the chick embryo. J. Morphol. 58:585.

Hoskins, E. R. and M. M. 1918. Further experiments with thyroidectomy in *Amphibia*. Proc. Soc. Exper. Biol. & Med. 15:102.

———. 1919. Growth and development of *Amphibia* as affected by thyroidectomy. J. Exper. Zool. 29:1.

Howard, E. 1939. Effects of castration on the seminal vesicles as influenced by age, considered in relation to the degree of development of the adrenal X zone. Am. J. Anat. 65:105.

LaVelle, F. W. 1951. A study of hormonal factors in the early sex development of the golden hamster. Contrib. to Embryol. Carnegie Inst., Washington, Publ. 34:223.

Lillie, F. R. 1917. The free-martin; a study of the action of sex hormones in the fetal life of cattle. J. Exper. Zool. 23:371.

Lynn, W. G., and Wachowski, H. E. 1951. The thyroid gland and its functions in cold-blooded vertebrates. Quart. Rev. Biol. 26:123.

Mintz, B., Foote, C. L., and Witschi, E. 1945. Quantitative studies on response of sex characters of differentiated *Rana clamitans* larvae to injected androgens and estrogens. Endocrinology. 37:286.

Moore, C. R. 1941. On the role of sex hormones in sex differentiation in the opossum (*Didelphys virginiana*). Physiol. Zoöl. 14:1.

———. 1950. The role of the fetal endocrine glands in development. J. Clin. Endocrinol. 10:942.

Puckett, W. O. 1940. Some effects of crystalline sex hormones on the differentiation of the gonads of an undifferentiated race of *Rana catesbiana* tadpoles. J. Exper. Zool. 84:39.

Rahn, H. 1939. The development of the chick pituitary with special reference to the cellular differentiation of the pars buccalis. J. Morph. 64:483.

Rankin, R. M. 1941. Changes in the content of iodine compounds and in the histological structure of the thyroid gland of the pig during fetal life .Anat. Rec. 80:123.

Rumph, P., and Smith, P. E. 1926. The first occurrence of secretory products and of a specific structural differentiation in the thyroid and anterior pituitary during the development of the pig foetus. Anat. Rec. 33:289.

Selye, H. 1948. Textbook of Endocrinology. Université de Montreal, Montreal, Canada.

Smith, P. E. 1916. The effect of hypophysectomy in the early embryo upon growth and development of the frog. Anat. Rec. 11:57.

———. 1920. The pigmentary growth and endocrine disturbances induced in the anuran tadpole by the early ablation of the pars buccalis of the hypophysis. Am. Anat. Memoirs. 11, The Wistar Institute of Anatomy and Biology, Philadelphia.

Wheeler, R. S., and Hoffman, E. 1948a. Goitrous chicks from thyroprotein-fed hens. Endocrinology. 42:326.

——— and ———. 1948b. Influence of quantitative thyroprotein treatment of hens on length of incubation period and thyroid size of chicks. Endocrinology. 43:430.

White, M. J. D. 1948. Animal Cytology and Evolution, Chap. XI. Cambridge University Press, London.

Willier, B. E. 1921. Structures and homologies of free-martin gonads. J. Exper. Zool. 33:63.

———. 1939. Chap. III. The embryonic development of sex in Sex and Internal Secretions by Allen, et al., 2d ed., The Williams & Wilkins Co., Baltimore.

Wislocki, G. B. 1932. Placentation in the marmoset (*Oedipomidas geoffroyi*) with remarks on twinning in monkeys. Anat. Rec. 52:381.

Witschi, E. 1939. Chap. IV. Modification of the development of sex in lower vertebrates and in mammals in Sex and Internal Secretions by Allen, et al., 2d ed., The Williams & Wilkins Co., Baltimore.

PART V

The Care of the Developing Embryo

The care of the developing embryo necessitates the formation of various types of embryonic membranes, and in many species, the retention of the developing embryo within either maternal or paternal body structures (Chap. 22).

22

Care and Nourishment of the Developing Young

A. Introduction
  1. Care in relation to the number of young produced
  2. General environmental conditions necessary for development
  3. Types of enveloping or protective membranes
  4. Types of food sources
  5. Mechanisms for oxygen supply and carbon dioxide removal
  6. Oviparity, ovoviviparity, and viviparity
B. Formation and importance of the protective embryonic membranes
  1. The egg membranes
    a. Primary and secondary egg membranes
    b. Tertiary egg membranes
      1) Mammals
      2) Birds
        a) Formation of the chalaziferous layer
        b) Deposition of the middle dense layer of albumen
        c) Formation of the inner liquid layer of albuminous material and the chalazae
        d) Deposition of the outer liquid albuminous layer
        e) Formation of the egg membranes and egg shell
      3) Reptiles
      4) Amphibians
      5) Fishes
  2. The extra-embryonic membranes
    a. Yolk sac
    b. Amnion
    c. Chorion (serosa)
    d. Allantois
    e. Yolk stalk, allantoic stalk, belly stalk, and umbilical cord
  3. The reproductive duct as a protective embryonic membrane
  4. Uncommon or specialized structures as protective mechanisms
C. Special adaptations of the extra-embryonic membranes for uterine existence
  1. Implantation
    a. Definition
    b. Types of implantation
  2. The placenta and placentation
    a. Definition
    b. Types of embryonic tissues involved in placentation

899

A. Introduction

1. CARE IN RELATION TO THE NUMBER OF YOUNG PRODUCED

In this chapter, we shall consider the methods by which developing embryos of different vertebrate species are cared for and nourished during development. The amount of care given to the developing egg varies greatly. However, one primary rule appears to govern the reproductive habits of the species, namely, the *species must survive*. This survival is accomplished by two principal methods:

(1) by the production of enormous numbers of developing young, given no protective care, with the result that few survive to the adult or reproductive stage, and

(2) by the formation of fewer developing individuals with greater amounts of protective care.

Generally speaking, the fewer the individual embryos produced, the greater the care.

Examples of the method of species survival without parental care are evident in the codfish, *Gadus,* which spawns about 8 to 10 millions of eggs during a particular breeding period or in the ling, *Molva,* which discharges from 14 to 60 millions of eggs at one time. In these instances, the species survive by the sheer number of developing young produced. On the other hand, the shark, bird, and mammal substitute an extreme care of the developing egg, with the result that the number of eggs produced at each breeding period is reduced enormously, compared with that of the cod or ling.

2. General Environmental Conditions Necessary for Development

Regardless of whether or not there is specialized care of the developing young, the following conditions, concerned with the nutrition and care of the young, are necessary in the development of all vertebrate embryos:

(a) All embryos develop within a fluid or "embryonic lake" made possible by the presence of certain, enveloping membranes;

(b) a favorable temperature is required, particularly in warm-blooded species;

(c) food material including water must be supplied;

(d) oxygen is necessary to the developing embryo, and

(e) the removal of carbon dioxide and other wastes is imperative.

3. Types of Enveloping or Protective Membranes

Many types of protective membranes are produced in the vertebrate group for the purpose of caring for the developing young. These membranous and other types of protective envelopes may be classified as follows:

a. Egg membranes.
b. Extra-embryonic membranes.
c. The uterine portion of the oviduct.
d. Uncommon or specialized structures.

The **egg membranes** are those membranes produced around the egg during its formation in the ovary or during the journey down the oviduct. They are classified generally into three categories:

(1) **Primary egg membranes** are the membranes which are produced by the surface layer of the egg as it develops in the ovary, e.g., the vitelline membrane;

(2) **secondary egg membranes** are the membranes contributed to the egg by the activities of the surrounding follicle cells of the ovary, e.g., the zona pellucida of mammals, possibly also the chorion of some fish eggs; and

(3) **tertiary egg membranes** are the membranes contributed to the egg as it passes down the oviduct, such as the albuminous layers of frog and chicken eggs.

The **extra-embryonic membranes** are those membranes constructed of embryonic tissues which extend out of and beyond the strict confines of the embryonic body. As such they represent specialized embryonic tissues adapted to fulfill certain definite functions necessary to the embryo. The extra-embryonic membranes are:

(1) The **yolk sac,** found in most species. The yolk sac is developed as an extension of the primitive gut.

(2) The **amnion,** representing a sac-like structure which surrounds the embryo. It is found only in the *Amniota,* that is, the reptiles, birds, and mammals.

(3) The **allantois.** This structure arises as an outpushing from the mid-ventral area of the hindgut, and is found only in reptiles, birds, and mammals.

(4) **Pharyngeal diverticula.** The pharyngeal diverticula are found in certain species of fish and in amphibians. The external gill filaments of the shark embryo mentioned in Chapter 14 are an example of this type of extra-embryonic membrane. Also in certain species of Amphibia elaborate *pharyngeal placentae* are evolved which function in a respiratory capacity.

The **uterine portion of the oviduct** functions, of course, as a capsule to protect the developing egg in all ovoviviparous and viviparous species.

Uncommon, specialized structures for the protection of the developing embryo are formed in many species of fishes and Amphibia. These structures are described more explicitly on p. 915.

4. TYPES OF FOOD SOURCES

There are two main types of food sources for vertebrate embryos, namely, **endogenous** and **exogenous** sources. The endogenous form of food supply is found in all amphibian species, in the lung-fishes, Amphioxus, etc., where nourishment necessary for development is incorporated directly **within the developing embryonic cells** from the beginning cleavages of the egg. On the other hand, in the exogenous type of food supply the nourishment necessary for development lies **outside of the developing embryonic tissues.** This type of food storage is found in elasmobranch and teleost fishes, reptiles, birds, and mammals. Two categories are to be observed, as follows:

(1) In the majority of fishes, and in all reptiles, birds, and prototherian mammals, the food is stored within the egg. The developing embryo which lies upon this food source utilizes a specialized type of extra-embryonic tissue to digest and assimilate the food materials.

(2) In some fishes and in the metatherian and eutherian mammals, most, or practically all, of the food elements come directly from the maternal (and, in some instances in fishes, from paternal) tissues as the embryo develops. Here also, a specialization of extra-embryonic tissue is necessary to táp the supply of food.

5. MECHANISMS FOR OXYGEN SUPPLY AND CARBON DIOXIDE REMOVAL

Two types of oxygen supply and carbon dioxide removal mechanisms are encountered. In the majority of fishes and in the larger number of Amphibia, the surface of the developing egg functions as a respiratory membrane. In some fishes, and in rare instances in the Amphibia, special diverticula of the pharyngeal area are developed to care for this function. On the other hand, in all reptiles, birds, and mammals, the allantoic diverticulum from the hind-gut assumes respiratory responsibilities.

6. OVIPARITY, OVOVIVIPARITY, AND VIVIPARITY

The word **oviparous** is derived from two Latin words, namely, *ovum,* egg, and *parere,* to bring forth. Oviparous animals thus produce eggs from which the young are hatched after the egg is laid or spawned. Among the vertebrates, oviparous species include most of the fishes, amphibia, reptiles, birds, and prototherian mammals. **Ovoviviparity** is a condition in which the egg is retained within the confines of the reproductive duct or other specialized areas where it hatches, and the young are brought forth or born alive. The greater portion of the embryo's nourishment is derived from the nutritive materials within the egg, while oxygen uptake, together with fluid substances and the elimination of carbon dioxide, is effected through the oviducal wall and its blood vessels. Ovoviviparous species include certain sharks, teleosts, certain urodele and anuran amphibia, and various reptiles. In **viviparity** (Latin, *vivus,* alive) the new individual is brought forth alive. In viviparity the developing embryo obtains some or all of its nourishment through the wall of the uterus or other specialized structure. Viviparous forms are found among the sharks, teleosts, and reptiles, together with all species of metatherian and eutherian mammals.

B. Formation and Importance of the Protective Embryonic Membranes

1. THE EGG MEMBRANES

a. Primary and Secondary Egg Membranes

The formation of the primary and secondary egg membranes were described in Chapter 3. The importance of these membranes formed around the egg, while it develops in the ovary, is considerable. The so-called **fertilization membrane,** produced, for example, in *Amphioxus,* the **zona radiata** and **chorion** of fishes, the **vitelline membrane** of amphibians, reptiles, and birds, or the **zona pellucida** of mammals are important structures. All these membranes form the first or *primary protective coating* around the embryo. Between the embryo and this primary embryonic membrane is a fluid-filled area, the **perivitelline space.** The perivitelline fluid is favorable to the embryo. Thus, the surrounding fertilization, vitelline, or zona membranes act as an insulating wall between the outside environment and this early perivitelline pond of the embryo. All vertebrate embryos, from the fishes to the mammals, are protected normally by the **primary embryonic membrane** during the period of cleavage, and, in many fishes and amphibians this membrane functions until the time when the embryo hatches and assumes a free-living existence.

b. Tertiary Egg Membranes

1) Mammals. The lengths of the Fallopian tubes of different mammalian species vary considerably. In the mouse, rabbit, human, and sow, the Fallopian tubes vary in length, not only from species to species but also from individual to individual within the species. Yet, the time of passage of the egg through this region of the reproductive duct approximately, for all four species, is from 3 to 3½ days. On the other hand, the length of the uterine tube of the opossum may be from 5 to 10 times that of the mouse, yet the time consumed in egg transport in the former species is about 19 to 24 hours. Moreover, in the sow and mouse, evidence has been accumulated which tends to show that egg transport through the middle portion of the uterine tube is slower than that of the portion near the infundibulum or of the part near the uterus (Anderson, '27; Lewis and Wright, '35). In the *Monotremata,* Flynn and Hill ('39, p. 540) conclude that "passage through the tube must be fairly rapid." In all these instances, the rate of egg travel through the uterine tube appears to be dependent upon necessary developmental changes within the cleaving egg and functional changes within the uterus and the uterine tube. In other words, the rate of egg propulsion through the Fallopian tube varies with the species. The time consumed in transit is not related to the length of the tube, but is correlated with changes in the uterus, preparatory to receiving the egg at a proper developmental stage.

The deposition of protective enveloping coats around the egg during egg passage through the Fallopian tube is encountered in certain mammals. In the monotremes, a rather dense, albuminous coat is deposited around the egg in the upper two thirds of the Fallopian tube, and a clearer, more fluid secretion is deposited around the egg by the glandular cells in the posterior third of the tube (Flynn and Hill, '39). A leathery shell is formed around the egg and these albuminous coats in the posterior segment or uterus. In the opossum, a dense albuminous coating forms around the egg during its passage down the upper part of the Fallopian tube, while a thin much tougher membrane is added around the outside of the albuminous material in the tube's lower part. In the rabbit, a thick albuminous coating is deposited around the egg as it passes downward within the Fallopian (uterine) tube. Therefore, formation of protective egg envelopes may be regarded as a specific function of the Fallopian tube during egg passage in some mammals.

The reactions of the developing egg within the uterine portion (uterus) of the reproductive duct in the higher mammals are dramatic events in which the embryo develops special contacts with the uterine wall. In some cases, the embryo becomes entirely enclosed within the tissues of the uterus. These phenomena are considered on pages 914, 920.

2) Birds. The passage of the hen's egg down the oviduct has been studied at various times from the time of Aristotle to the present. In its transportation, the "naked yellow" or ovum becomes surrounded by an intricate association of fibers, albuminous substance, membranes, and calcareous shell which form a system of protective envelopes. As the egg of the hen passes posteriad in the oviduct, it rotates slowly under the influence of muscular contractions and the spiral arrangement of longitudinal folds of the mucous membrane lining the oviduct. This rotation aids in the deposition of the membranes and albuminous layers.

a) FORMATION OF THE CHALAZIFEROUS LAYER. The first coating of albumen is deposited around the egg as it passes through the **posterior portion of the infundibulum** (fig. 157). It is in the form of a sheet of mucin-like fibers in the meshes of which is a dense albuminous substance. This capsule of albumen is applied closely to the vitelline membrane of the ovum, and it represents the **membrana chalazifera, or chalaziferous layer** (fig. 369A). (See Romanoff and Romanoff, '49, pp. 137, 219.)

b) DEPOSITION OF THE MIDDLE DENSE LAYER OF ALBUMEN. The egg soon leaves the infundibular area of the oviduct and enters the **albumen-secreting region** where a dense layer of albuminous material, the **albuminous sac,** is deposited together with mucin fibers, the albumen being enmeshed in the latter (fig. 369A).

c) FORMATION OF THE INNER LIQUID LAYER OF ALBUMINOUS MATERIAL AND THE CHALAZAE. As the egg continues its journey posteriad, it is rotated upon the spirally arranged folds of the oviduct. This rotation twists the mucin-like fibers in the inner portion of the dense albuminous layer, and it is believed that this twisting motion squeezes the more fluid albumen out of the mucin meshwork where it becomes deposited immediately around the chalaziferous layer to form the **inner liquid layer of albumen.** At the same time, some of the mucin fibers become twisted in opposite directions at the *upper and lower ends of the egg* as the latter is rotated along the spiral folds of the oviduct. These twisted fibers form a bundle at the anterior and posterior ends of the egg and become attached firmly to the chalaziferous layer, reaching outward into the dense albumen. These two bundles of twisted mucin fibers form the **chalazae,** one chalaza being tied to the chalaziferous layer at the lower end of the egg (i.e., the end occupying the more posterior position in the oviduct) and the other lying attached to the chalaziferous layer at the upper end of the egg (fig. 369A).

d) DEPOSITION OF THE OUTER LIQUID ALBUMINOUS LAYER. As a result of the resection experiments of Asmundson and Burmester ('36), one is led to conclude that a considerable amount of the outer, watery, albuminous layer which comes to surround the middle dense layer of albumen is deposited in the anterior part (i.e., the ovarian end) of the albumen-secreting portion of the oviduct (figs. 157; 369A). Some of the watery material is added in the isthmus and in the uterus (Romanoff and Romanoff, '49, p. 220).

e) FORMATION OF THE EGG MEMBRANES AND EGG SHELL. As the egg reaches the isthmus, the **shell membranes** are formed around the albuminous material. In the upper part of the isthmus, the thin **inner membrane** is formed, while the thick, coarse, **outer membrane** is deposited in the posterior parts of the isthmus. These two membranes of the egg expand considerably coincident with the passage of a watery albuminous material through their meshwork into the outer, liquid, albuminous layer while the egg passes through the lower part of the isthmus, and also during the first part of the egg's occupancy of the uterus. As a result, the volume of the albumen is increased rapidly and considerably in this general area.

During the latter part of the period of the egg's residence within the uterus, **calcareous concretions or mammillae** are deposited upon the external face of the coarse, outer, egg membrane (fig. 369B). Each conical concretion or **mammilla** is embedded in the outer egg membrane. The broader distal end of the mammila faces outward while the pointed proximal end is attached to the egg membrane (fig. 369B). Small pores appear between the various mammillae. External to the mammillary layer, a **spongy layer of collagenous fibers** is formed. This spongy layer gradually becomes impregnated with calcium salts which lie within the spaces between the spongy fibers and between the mammillary and spongy layers. The calcified spongy layer and associated mammillary concretions form the egg shell. The calcium probably is secreted in the form of bicarbonate which later changes to calcium carbonate. Some calcium chloride and phosphate, together with a calcium-protein substance also are formed. The colored pigments of the egg shell in colored eggs are

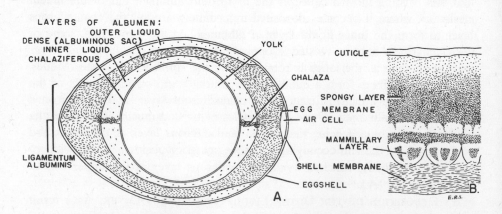

FIG. 369. Structure of the hen's egg. (A and B redrawn from Romanoff and Romanoff, 1949. Wiley & Sons, Inc., N. Y.) (A) General structure of newly laid hen's egg (after Romanoff). (B) Detailed structure of egg shell (after von Nathusius).

ooporphyrin pigments, derived probably from the hemoglobin of worn-out red blood cells. A thin **cuticle** or protective film is applied to the surface of the calcified spongy layer just before the egg is laid (fig. 369B).

The rate of transport of the egg through the oviduct of the hen is interesting. Once the egg has entered the infundibulum, it takes but 20 minutes to complete its passage through this area. The infundibular region constitutes five per cent of the length of the oviduct. In the albumen-secreting region where it accumulates most of its albumen, the egg spends about four hours. This segment forms about 60 per cent of the total oviducal length. The passage through the isthmus requires approximately one hour. This region forms 15 per cent of the total length of the oviduct. The last or uterine segment is about the same length as that of the isthmus, but the egg spends about 80 per cent of its passage time or about 19 hours in this portion. The rate of passage, therefore, in the more anterior portion of the oviduct is rapid, somewhat slower in the isthmus, and very slow in the uterus (Romanoff and Romanoff, '49).

3) Reptiles. Egg passage through the oviduct and deposition of the tertiary egg membranes in reptiles probably resembles very closely that of the bird with the exception that in a considerable number of reptiles the young develop in the uterus and are discharged in a free-living condition (see p. 83). Also, the eggs of modern reptiles have a thick leathery shell instead of the brittle calcareous shell of bird's eggs.

4) Amphibians. In the frog, egg transport down the glandular portion of the oviduct appears to be effected mainly by the propelling force of the beating cilia, possessed by certain of the cells lining the oviduct. This ciliary action possibly is aided by some peristaltic action of the oviducal musculature. The cilia are found on the cells which line the longitudinal ridges which run "more or less the length of the oviduct" (Noble, '31, p. 282). As the egg moves downward (posteriad), it is covered by mucus or similar gelatinous material. In the common frog, *Rana pipiens,* three gelatinous layers are deposited around the egg during its oviducal passage.

Passage of the egg through the oviduct in other *Amphibia* probably resembles that of the frog.

In many *Amphibia* (e.g., frogs), the caudal portion of the oviduct is expanded to form a special compartment, called the **uterus,** where the eggs remain for a period before discharge to the outside. In some urodeles, the eggs are retained in the oviduct, and the young are born in the larval or fully metamorphosed state (see p. 189).

5) Fishes. Internal egg transport in fishes presents a variety of conditions. In many teleosts, the ovary, when egg formation is completed, becomes a large egg sac, directly connected with the short oviduct. At the time of spawning, a general contraction of the ovarian tissues occurs, and the eggs are expelled into the oviduct and from there to the outside. The contraction of the ovarian tissues, together with a peristaltic behavior of the oviducal musculature, affords the mechanism necessary to transport the eggs to the external environment. Egg membranes are not deposited around the egg as it passes through the oviduct in teleost fishes.

In the elasmobranch fishes, however, **glandular and uterine portions** of the oviduct are present, and the large egg is transported through the upper glandular region of the oviduct in a manner similar, presumably, to that in the hen. Surrounding membranes of albuminous materials, and an outer chitinoid "shell" are produced in the glandular area. These membranes vary with the species and some are complicated as indicated in figure 380A. In many elasmobranch fishes and also in the so-called viviparous teleost fishes, the egg is retained in the uterine portion of the oviduct. Here the young develop and, when discharged to the outside, are able to fend for themselves. In these forms, the uterus is adapted to the function of providing the embryo with an environment suitable for its development.

In the cyclostomatous fishes, an oviduct is not present, and egg transport resolves itself into a discharge of eggs into the coelomic cavity from which the eggs pass through openings into the cavity of the urogenital sinus. Ovarian membranes only are present around the cyclostome egg. These membranes may be complex as in the hagfish, *Polistotrema (Bdellostoma),* (fig. 162).

2. The Extra-embryonic Membranes

The extra-embryonic membranes as indicated previously are those membranes produced from the embryonic tissues. These membranes are the *yolk sac, amnion, chorion (serosa)* and *allantois.* In a strict sense, the *periderm* (see Chapter 12) probably should be included as an extra-embryonic membrane for it is elaborated at the surface area of the epidermis and functions to protect and presumably to regulate the possible entrance of substances from the surrounding environment.

a. Yolk Sac

A yolk sac is present in all reptiles, in birds and mammals, and in those fishes which have megalecithal eggs, that is, having a large amount of yolk substance stored within the egg. Two types of yolk sacs are found among the vertebrates, viz.:

(1) a yolk sac whose walls are composed of entoderm, mesoderm and ectoderm in the form of closely associated layers. This type of yolk sac is found in the embryos of the hagfishes, *Polistotrema (Bdellostoma) stouti* and *Myxine glutinosa,* in most elasmobranch fishes, and in teleosts (fig. 370A). Some of the amphibia with a large quantity of yolk in the egg such as *Necturus maculosus,* also approach this condition.

(2) a second type of yolk sac is found in reptiles, birds and mammals. In these instances the wall of the yolk sac is composed mainly of ento-

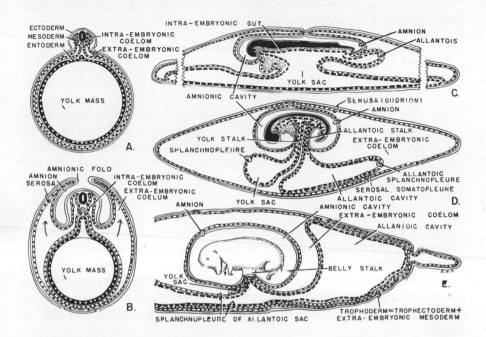

FIG. 370. Diagrams of extra-embryonic membranes.   (A) Transverse section of yolk sac and developing body in teleost and elasmobranch fishes showing relation of body layers to the yolk mass.   (B) Transverse section of yolk sac and forming serosa (chorion) in reptiles, birds, and prototherian mammals.   (C-E) Diagrams showing extra-embryonic membranes in the pig.   (C) Conditions in 16-17 somite pig, age approximately 16 days. The ends of the diagram have been omitted in part, because of length of embryonic vesicle. (D) Conditions in embryo of 5 mm. or about 17-18 days of age.   (E) The extra-embryonic membranes in embryo of about 4-5 weeks of age.

derm and mesoderm, i.e., the splanchnopleure, as the extra-embryonic coelom tends to separate the splanchnopleure from the somatopleure in these forms (fig. 370B).

b. Amnion

The amnion is a specialized sac which comes to encompass the embryo in reptiles, birds and mammals (fig. 370B–E). Because of its restriction to these vertebrates, the reptiles, birds and mammals are grouped together as the *Amniota,* the fishes and amphibia being designated as the *Anamniota.*

Eggs which are spawned into the surrounding water, as in fishes and amphibia, are cradled or cushioned by the surrounding fluid, and the embryo is free to develop without undue pressure from any side. In the *Amniota,* however, this watery environment must be established artificially and hence the amnion is formed to accommodate and enclose the fluid of this individualized embryonic "swimming" pool.

The amnion arises generally in two ways, as follows, although intermediate forms are found among certain mammals (see Mossman, '37).

(1) By a **dorsal folding of the somatopleure,** in which anterior, lateral, and posterior amnionic folds project dorsad and fuse (see figures 238B; 242C and G; 370B–E). This method is found in reptiles, birds, prototherian mammals, the opossum, pig, rabbit, etc.

(2) The second main method is by **cavitation,** i.e., a cavity develops within the cells forming the inner cell mass of the early embryo (fig. 372A and B). Found in human, mouse, rat, etc. In the monkey, the formation of the amnion is somewhat intermediate between the folding and cavitation methods.

c. Chorion (Serosa)

The formation of the amnion by the folding method also results in the development of the chorion or serosa, in that it separates the somatopleure from the splanchnopleure of the yolk sac (fig. 370B and C). However, in those forms which utilize the hollowing out or cavitation method of amnion formation as in the human, the chorion forms directly by the attachment of extra-embryonic mesoderm to the inner aspect of the trophectoderm (fig. 372 A and B).

d. Allantois

In most fishes and amphibia, external respiration of the developing embryo is possible by a direct interchange of oxygen and carbon dioxide across the perivitelline fluid and primary embryonic membranes into the surrounding watery medium. However, in eggs which are deposited on dry land, such as those of birds, reptiles, and prototherian mammals, a specialized embryonic structure, the **allantois,** is formed to permit external respiration to occur. The allantoic diverticulum arises as a mid-ventral outpushing of the caudal end of the hindgut (fig. 370C). The allantois is a hollow, sac-like structure composed of entoderm on the inside and splanchnopleuric mesoderm externally. As it extends outward, blood vessels develop in the mesoderm. It eventually comes in contact with the chorion with which it fuses to form the **chorio-allantoic membrane** (fig. 370D and E). The chorio-allantoic membrane in reptiles and birds contacts the surface membranes of the shell (fig. 299E).

In the higher mammals an allantoic diverticulum also is formed. In this group of vertebrates, the allantois not only serves the function of external respiration but also is the main instrument in nutrition. In the human embryo, the entodermal evagination from the hindgut forming the allantoic diverticulum is small, and blood vessels develop precociously within the mesoderm of the body stalk (see figure 372B). These blood vessels course distad to the developing chorion and its villi where external respiration is accomplished.

However, in the pig and many other mammals, the allantoic diverticulum is a large, spacious structure (see figure 370D and E).

Respiratory devices thus arise as diverticula from two general areas of the vertebrate body, viz.:

(1) the **pharyngeal area** (see Chapter 14) and
(2) the **hindgut area.**

e. Yolk Stalk, Allantoic Stalk, Belly Stalk, and Umbilical Cord

As the embryo increases in size (see figures 370C–E; 372B–D), the yolk-sac connection with the mid-gut area of the embryo becomes relatively smaller. The constricted area of entoderm and mesoderm which connects the yolk sac with the midgut is called the **vitelline duct** or **yolk stalk.** Similarly, the constricted area of the allantois which connects the allantoic diverticulum with the hindgut area is called the **allantoic stalk.** As the embryo continues to enlarge, the yolk stalk and allantoic stalk are brought closer together and their mesoderms fuse. The closely associated yolk and allantoic stalks form the **belly stalk** in the area where they attach to the belly (ventral) wall of the embryo (fig. 370E). The narrowing ring-like area between the ventral body

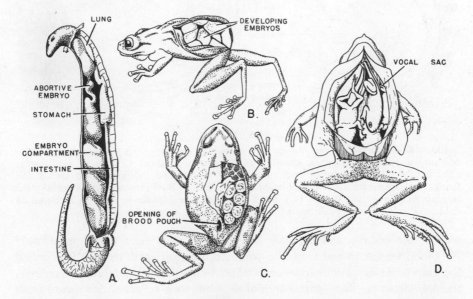

FIG. 371. Brood compartments for care of young. (A) Pregnant female of the lizard, *Chalcides tridactylus (Seps chalcides)*, showing uterine compartments containing developing eggs. (Redrawn from Needham, 1942, Biochemistry and Morphogenesis, Cambridge University Press, London.) (B) Dorsal brood pouch in the anuran, *Gastrotheca pygmaea*. (C) Dorsal brood pouch in *Gastrotheca marsupiata*. Observe small dorsal opening of pouch. (D) Dissection of vocal (brood) pouch in male of *Rhinoderma darwinii*. (B–D, redrawn from Noble, 1931, The Biology of the Amphibia, McGraw-Hill, N. Y.)

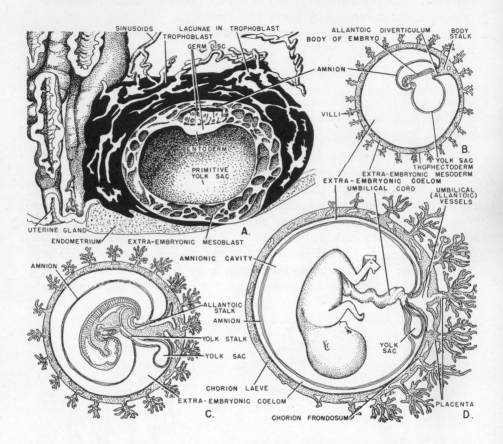

FIG. 372. Extra-embryonic membranes in human embryo. (A) Diagrammatic representation of extra-embryonic membranes in embryo of about 12 days of age, shortly after enclosure within uterine endometrium. (Redrawn and modified from Hertig and Rock, 1941, Carnegie Contr. to Embryology, vol. 29.) (B) Extra-embryonic membranes in embryo of about 16 days. (C) Extra-embryonic membranes in embryo of about 28 days. (D) Extra-embryonic membranes in embryo of about 12 weeks.

wall of the embryo and the yolk and allantoic stalk tissues is a passageway for blood vessels to and from the yolk and allantoic stalk tissues. It is called the *umbilical ring, umbilicus* or *omphalos*. As the embryo continues to enlarge, the amnion in the mid-ventral area of the embryo is reflected downward from the umbilical ring or **umbilicus** over the yolk-stalk and allantoic-stalk tissues and thus eventually encloses the yolk and allantoic stalks (figs. 370E; 372C and D). This entire structural complex composed of amnionic tissue, together with enteric and allantoic diverticula and splanchnopleuric mesoderm, is called the **umbilical cord** (fig. 372D).

In the human embryo, that portion of the mesoderm which connects the

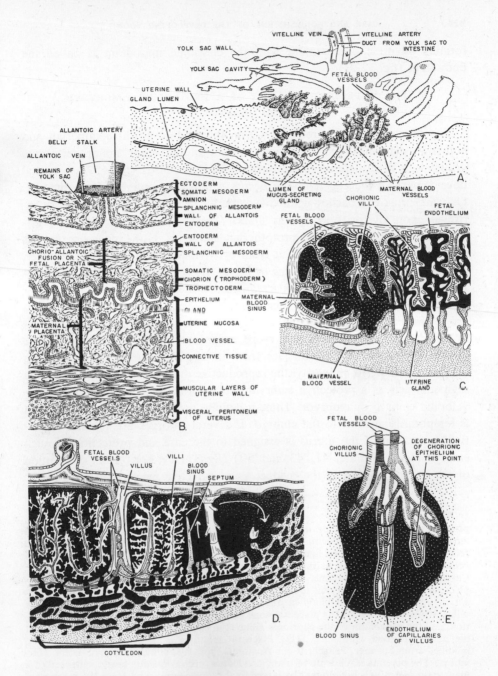

FIG. 373. Placental relationships. (A) Placenta of *Mustelus laevis*. This is a yolk-sac placenta, and the yolk sac tissues burrow into the wall of the uterus, invading the uterine glands. It does not erode the endometrium, however, and therefore resembles the placental conditions in the pig, shown in fig. 373B. It is essentially an epithelio-chorial type of placenta. (Redrawn from Needham, 1942, Biochemistry and Morphogenesis, Cambridge University Press, London.) (B) Placental relationships in the pig. The

913

forming allantoic diverticulum with the chorionic mesoderm is called the **body stalk** (fig. 372B).

3. THE REPRODUCTIVE DUCT AS A PROTECTIVE EMBRYONIC MEMBRANE

The developing egg is retained within the oviduct in all metatherian and eutherian mammals and in various species in the other major vertebrate groups with the exception of the birds. Even in the birds (fig. 157), a partial development of the egg normally occurs within the confines of the oviduct. Oviparity thus encroaches upon ovoviviparity in birds, and ovoviviparity infringes upon viviparity in certain sharks *(Squalus acanthias),* reptiles (various snakes and lizards), and prototherian mammals. However, oviparity has this feature which distinguishes it from ovoviviparity and viviparity, namely, *the new individual always hatches or leaves the confinement of the egg membranes outside the protective environment of the reproductive duct (or other protective structures).* On the other hand, ovoviviparous and viviparous forms are released from the egg membranes and thus "hatch out" within the oviduct or other covering structure. The more viviparous the particular species, the sooner the new individual hatches from its egg membranes. In most cases of ovoviviparity and viviparity, the reproductive duct (specifically, the uterine segment) acts as a protective embryonic membrane which surrounds the developing embryo or embryos. Thus, a definite area of the reproductive duct is temporarily allotted to the embryo. If several embryos are present, a particular segment of the uterus is assigned to the care and protection of each embryo (see TeWinkle, '41, '43, and '50) (fig. 371A). For further description of the uterine portion of the oviduct as a protective mechanism see p. 919.

FIG. 373—*Continued*

placenta is of the *epitheliochorial variety,* i.e., the epithelium of the chorionic tissue comes into contact with the epithelium of the uterus without erosion of either. (C) Placental relationships in the dog. This figure represents a small area at the edge of the *zonary placenta* shown in fig. 378D, as indicated. (Redrawn and modified from Mossman, 1937, Carnegie Institute Publications, vol. 26, Contributions to Embryology, No. 158.) This placenta is a dual type, in that the edge of the placenta resembles somewhat the *hemochorial type,* i.e., maternal blood in direct contact with the chorionic epithelium of the villus, while the center of the placental zone is of the endotheliochorial type of placentation, i.e., the epithelium of the chorionic villus is in contact with the endothelial lining of the maternal blood capillaries. (D) Placental relationship in human. (Redrawn and modified from Spanner, Zeitschrift für Anatomie, vol. 105, Julius Springer, Berlin, Germany.) The placenta is made up of many cotyledons, each *cotyledon* being composed of a main *stem villus,* which contains the larger fetal blood vessels, and from the large stem villus smaller *branching villi* extend out into the surrounding maternal blood. Imperfectly developed *septa* separate the various cotyledons. This type of placentation is of the hemochorial variety, i.e. the chorionic epithelium is in contact with the maternal blood. (E) Diagram illustrating the *hemoendothelial type of placentation* in the late gestation period of the rabbit. Here the chorionic epithelium is eroded and the capillaries of the chorionic villi lie within the maternal blood.

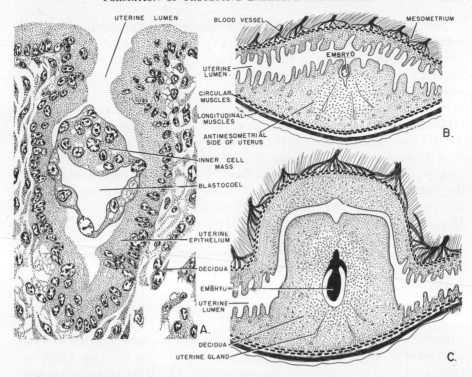

FIG. 374. Placentation in the mouse. (A) Blastocyst within fold of the uterine mucosa. (B) Longitudinal section of uterine site of placentation showing mesometrial and antimesometrial aspects. (C) Later stage of conditions shown in B. Observe that placentation of the embryo is in the antimesometrial side of the uterus. The placenta is probably of the hemochorial relationship at first becoming hemoendothelial later as in the rabbit. (See Mossman, '37.) (A–C, redrawn from Snell, 1941, The Early Embryology of the Mouse, Blakiston, Philadelphia.)

4. UNCOMMON OR SPECIALIZED STRUCTURES AS PROTECTIVE MECHANISMS

Many structures other than the oviduct are used by various vertebrate species to accommodate and protect the developing egg. In the teleost, *Heterandria formosa,* the eggs are retained within the ovary (Scrimshaw, '44). Although a typical, teleostean, oil droplet is present in the egg which measures 0.39 mm. in diameter, it is not utilized until late in development, and most of the nourishment is afforded by a vascular sac which partly encloses the embryo. In the teleost, *Gambusia affinis,* the egg also develops in the ovarian follicle, but, in this case, most of the nourishment is derived from yolk which is contained within the egg. In the sea horses, *Hippocampus,* and in the pipefishes, *Syngnathus,* the eggs are transferred to a pouch, formed by folds of skin located in the ventral body wall of the male. Here the embryos develop (fig. 106). Many teleost fish are "mouth breeders," that is, they carry the eggs for various periods in the buccal cavity.

The amphibia show an array of protective devices for young. The marsupial frogs are most interesting. In *Gastrotheca (Nototrema) pygmaea,* the "maternal purse," formed by cutaneous folds, spreads over the dorsal area of the trunk, and an elongated opening in the middorsal line permits passage into the sac (fig. 371B). In *Gastrotheca marsupiata,* the opening of the dorsal brood pouch is located in the sacral area (fig. 371C). The brood pouch of *Gastrotheca ovifera* is similar to that of *G. marsupiata* (Noble, '31, pp. 60, 510). In some forms, such as *G. weinlandii,* the skin of the back is covered by calcareous dermal plates and in such species Noble says the young are "enclosed within a veritable coat of mail!" Lastly, mention may be made of the little Chilean frog, *Rhinoderma darwinii.* In this instance the male frog carries the few eggs and young, through metamorphosis, in his vocal pouches (fig. 370D). (See Noble, '31, pp. 71 and 507.)

C. Special Adaptations of the Extra-embryonic Membranes for Uterine Existence

1. IMPLANTATION

a. Definition

Implantation **is the process whereby the embryo becomes attached to a nutritional substrate.** The term is applied generally to those embryos which become associated intimately with the uterine wall. This is the common usage of the term. However, it is well to point out that the embryos of teleost and elasmobranch fishes as well as those of reptiles, birds and prototherian mammals become attached to the yolk substrate of the egg. Moreover, this attachment entails the elaboration of an extra-blastular or extra-embryonic tissue (i.e., the periblast tissue) of a syncytial nature similar to that present where embryos attach intimately to the uterine wall in the higher mammals. Most vertebrate embryos thus rely upon a process of implantation for nutritional support.

b. Types of Implantation

When implantation occurs in such a way that the embryo remains within the lumen of the uterus while the extra-embryonic membranes make a superficial attachment to the uterine mucosa, it is called **central or superficial implantation.** This type of implantation is found in all cases of implantation in lower vertebrates. In the marsupial mammals it is present in *Perameles* and *Dasyurus,* and among the eutherian mammals in the pig, cow, rabbit, sheep, dog, cat, etc. In the mouse and rat the early blastocyst comes to lie between the uterine epithelial folds in an antimesometrial position. These folds soon enclose the blastocyst almost completely (fig. 374A–C). This type of implantation is called **eccentric implantation** and it borders upon the complete interstitial variety. In still other mammals, such as the guinea pig, man, chimpanzee, the embryo burrows into the uterine mucosa below the epithelium and in this way becomes surrounded completely by the endometrial tissue of the uterus. This condition is known as **complete interstitial implantation** (fig. 375A–C).

2. The Placenta and Placentation

a. Definition

The process of implantation implies an interaction and attachment between the extra-embryonic membranes and the uterine wall. This area of attachment between maternal and embryonic tissues is called the **placenta,** and the word **placentation** denotes the general process effecting this attachment. The word placenta is derived from the Greek and it means a *flat cake*. It received this name because the human placenta is a flat, rounded mass shaped more or less like a pancake. The placenta may be defined as **the association between embryonic and uterine tissues for the purpose of physiological exchange of materials.** It is evident that this is a restricted definition applicable only to uterine types of implantation.

b. Types of Embryonic Tissues Involved in Placentation

In all vertebrate embryos it is the extraembryonic somatopleure (extraembryonic ectoderm plus extraembryonic somatopleuric mesoderm) which contacts the uterine mucosa during placentation. In those species which possess a **yolk-sac placenta,** for example, in the dogfish, *Mustelus laevis, the midgut extension of the splanchnopleure* which surrounds the yolk unites with the extraembryonic somatopleure to form the embryonic contact (fig. 373A). On the other hand, in the **chorio-allantoic placenta** of the lizard, *Chalcides tridactylus,* and in the chorio-allantoic placenta of all eutherian mammals, *it is the allantoic evagination of the hindgut* which contacts the extraembryonic somatopleure (called the chorion in higher vertebrata) and unites with it to form the embryonic part of the placenta (fig. 373B). However, in all of these instances *the epithelium of the extraembryonic somatopleure* makes the direct contact with the maternal tissue. Certain exceptions to this general rule apparently exist, for in the rabbit during the later stages of gestation, the epithelium of the chorion may disappear in certain areas, permitting exposure of the fetal blood vessels to the maternal blood (fig. 373E).

c. Types of Placental Relationships in the Eutherian Mammals

1) Epitheliochorial Type. If the epithelium of the uterus is not destroyed, and the embryonic tissue merely forms an intimate contact with the uterine epithelium, the placenta is called an **epitheliochorial placenta,** e.g., pig (fig. 373B). Under these conditions the placental area is large and *diffuse* (see figure 378A). (The placenta of the dogfish, *Mustelus laevis* (fig. 373A) is essentially of this type.)

2) Endotheliochorial Variety. If the epithelium of the uterus is eroded, and the embryonic tissue (i.e., chorionic epithelium) comes in contact with the endothelium of the maternal blood vessels, the attachment is called an **endotheliochorial placenta** (e.g., dog, cat, and other *Carnivora,* figure 373C). As the placental attachment becomes more intimate the placental area becomes restricted. Compare figure 378A and B with C, D and E.

3) Endotheliochorial Plus Syndesmochorial Placenta. In the Ungulata (cows, sheep, goats) the placenta is an extensive affair similar to that of the pig. However, the attachment between embryonic and maternal tissues occurs in certain areas known as **cotyledons** (fig. 378B). In parts of these cotyledons the association of maternal and embryonic tissue is of the **endotheliochorial variety,** but in other areas of the cotyledons only the epithelium of the uterus disappears, leaving the chorionic epithelium of the extra-embryonic tissue in contact with the connective tissue of the uterine wall. A condition where the chorionic epithelium makes contact with the connective tissues of the uterine wall is called a **syndesmochorial relationship.**

4) Hemochorial Placenta. In the rodents, primates (including man), shrews, moles, and bats the endothelium of the maternal blood vessels is destroyed by the erosive activity of the embryonic tissues, and the chorionic epithelium of the embryonic portion of the placenta comes directly in contact with the maternal blood (fig. 373D). This type of association is known as a **hemochorial placenta.**

5) Hemoendothelial Placenta. In the rabbit, the initial contact of the fetal tissues with the uterine epithelium forms an **epitheliochorial relationship.** Still later it becomes, after erosion of maternal tissue, a **hemochorial condition,** and finally, during the latter phases of pregnancy, even the chorionic epithelium disappears, leaving the endothelium of the embryonic blood vessels in contact with the maternal blood (fig. 373E). This type of association is the most intimate placental contact known and it is called a **hemoendothelial relationship.**

3. IMPLANTATION OF THE HUMAN EMBRYO

a. Preparation for Implantation

In all cases of uterine care of the developing egg, the uterus must be prepared for the event. This preparation is induced by the activities of the ovarian hormones (see Chapter 2 and figures 53 and 59). Implantation of the embryo occurs in the early **luteal phase** of the reproductive cycle when the endometrial mucosa is in an optimum condition for the reception of the developing egg.

b. Implantation

As indicated above, p. 904, the process of egg transport down the Fallopian tube occurs at a rate which permits the developing egg (embryo) and the uterine tissue to prepare themselves for the implantation event. About three to three and one-half days elapse during the passage of the egg through the

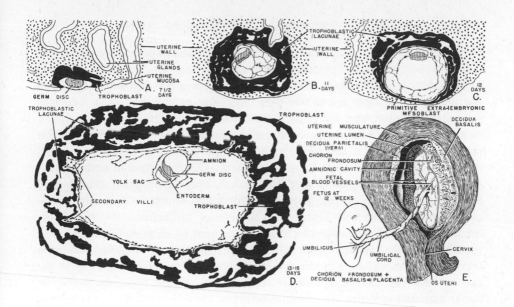

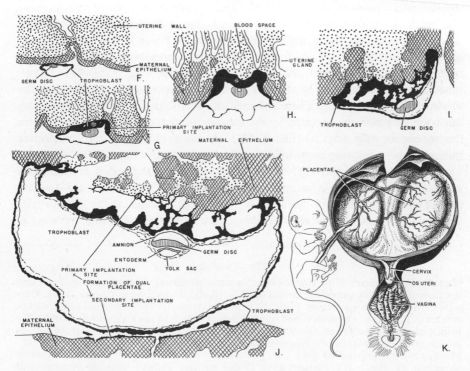

FIG. 375. *Implantation in human and monkey.* Trophoblastic ectoderm shown in complete black in the following diagrams. (A) Human about 7½ days. Blastocyst almost completely inside of the endometrium. (B) Human about 11 days. Blastocyst within endometrium. Trophoblast enlarging. (C) Human about 12 days. (D) Condition of human embryonic vesicle at about 13–15 days. Observe enormous thickening of tropho-

Fallopian tube. As a result, when the developing human egg reaches the uterus it is in the early blastula (blastocyst) condition (Chap. 6). The **zona pellucida** or secondary egg membrane is still intact. The blastocyst remains free within the uterus presumably for about four days. During this period, it becomes separated from the zona pellucida (i.e., it hatches) and the blastocoelic cavity of the blastocyst (blastula) subsequently enlarges greatly. The implantation site for man (and also monkeys) under normal conditions is the mid-dorsal or mid-ventral area of the uterus (Mossman, '37). The human embryo presumably begins to implant about 7 to 8 days after fertilization (Hertig and Rock, '45). In doing so that pole of the blastocyst which contains the developing germ disc becomes attached to the uterine epithelium. As this occurs the uterine epithelium becomes eroded in the area of immediate contact with the blastocyst, and the epithelial cells of the trophoblast layer of the blastocyst increase in number. As a result, the trophoblast tissue enlarges greatly in the contact area (fig. 375A, F and G). During this process a change occurs in the trophoblast cells for the external cells fuse together to form a **syncytium,** the so-called **syntrophoblast,** while the inner trophoblast cells remain cellular and form the **cytotrophoblast** (fig. 376A). The syntrophoblast presumably acts as the invading tissue. (*Note:* the trophoblast tissue in figures 372A and in 375 is shown in black.) As the syntrophoblast increases in quantity it comes to enclose irregular spaces, the **trophoblastic lacunae** (fig. 375B–D). Simultaneously localized areas of the syntrophoblast extend outward to form the **primary villi** (fig. 376A). These primary villi at first lack a mesenchymal core, but soon they become invaded by the mesoderm of the somatopleure to form the **secondary villi** (figs. 372B; 376B). At about 11 days, the developing human embryo is completely inside of the uterine wall (fig. 375B). At 12 to 15 days (fig. 375C and D), the syntrophoblast has expanded considerably and secondary villi begin to appear around the inner portions of the trophoblast (figs. 375D; 376B). Meanwhile (fig. 375D), some of the endometrial tissue close to the invading chorionic vesicle, including blood vessels, is

---

FIG. 375—*Continued*

blast tissue, the presence of trophoblastic lacunae containing endometrial residues, and the formation of the secondary chorionic villi. (A–D, redrawn from Corner, 1944, Ourselves Unborn, Yale University Press, New Haven, Conn.) (E) Placental relationships at about 12 weeks. (Redrawn and modified from De Lee and Greenhill, 1943, The Principles and Practice of Obstetrics, Saunders, Philadelphia.) (F) Early stage in implantation of the monkey, *Macaca mulatta,* blastocyst about 9 days of age. (G) Monkey blastocyst about 10 days. (H) Monkey blastocyst about 10 days. (I) Monkey blastocyst 11 days. (J) Blastocyst of 13-day monkey embryo showing primary and secondary implantation sites. (F–J redrawn from Wislocki and Streeter, 1938, Carnegie Instit. Contributions to Embryology, Vol. 27, Contributions to Embryology, No. 160.) (K) Placentae of *Lasiopyga callitrichus.* Observe that umbilical cord and its blood vessels attach to the primary placental disc, while blood vessels are given off from the primary disc to the secondary disc. (Redrawn from Wislocki, 1929. Carnegie Contributions to Embryology, Vol. 20, Contributions to Embryology, No. 111.)

broken down to form liquefied areas, the **embryotroph.** It is possible that this liquefied material is assimilated by the syntrophoblast and passed inward to the developing germ disc. If this histological material thus is utilized it forms a source of nutrition, and it may be called **histotrophic nutrition.**

c. Formation of the Placenta

As the developing chorionic vesicle grows within the endometrium of the uterus, the uterine mucosa expands over the growing vesicle (fig. 377A and B). That part of the endometrial tissue overlying the chorionic vesicle is called the **decidua capsularis** (fig. 377A), and the portion of the endometrial lining of the uterus not concerned with the enclosure of the chorionic vesicle is called the **decidua vera** or **decidua parietalis.** The part of the endometrium lying between the muscle tissue of the uterine wall and the enlarging villi (fig. 372C and D) of the chorionic vesicle is the **decidua basalis** (fig. 377A).

At first chorionic villi are developed over the entire chorionic vesicle (fig. 372B), but as development goes on the villi in relation to the decidua parietalis are resorbed gradually to form a smooth area of the chorion, the **chorion laeve** (fig. 372D). Finally, only those villi in relation to the decidua basalis remain (fig. 372D). The villi within the decidua basalis enlarge and become the

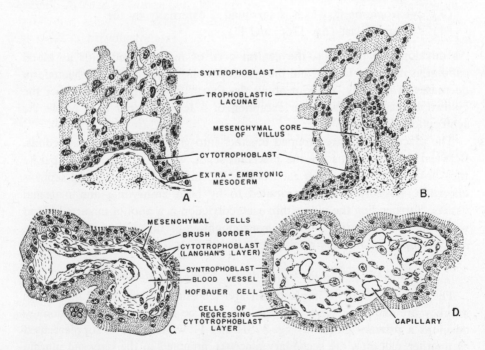

FIG. 376. Structure of villi in human chorionic vesicle. (A) Primary villus. (B) Secondary villus. (C) Villus from chorion at about 4 weeks. (D) Villus at about 14 weeks. Observe gradual disappearance of cytotrophoblast.

main villi for physiological interchange of materials between the embryo and the maternal tissues. This portion of the chorionic vesicle with the enlarged chorionic villi is known as the **chorion frondosum** (fig. 372D). The villi of the chorion frondosum and the tissue of the decidua basalis together form the **placenta.** The embryonic mesodermal tissues of the placenta are continuous with mesoderm of the **umbilical cord,** and the embryonic blood vessels of the placenta are directly continuous with the blood vessels of the umbilical cord (fig. 372D). The placental area thus is a dual structure composed of the decidua basalis or **maternal placenta** (placenta materna) and the **chorion frondosum** or fetal placenta (placenta fetalis) (fig. 375E). The placental area gradually expands during the early months of pregnancy until at about the fifth month when it reaches its greatest relative size or about one-half the internal aspect of the uterus.

The early chorionic villi of about the fourth week of pregnancy are composed of four constituent parts, viz.:

(1) blood capillaries which course within
(2) the mesenchymal cells of the mesodermal core. Surrounding the internal core of mesenchyme is the trophectodermal layer composed of an inner
(3) cytotrophoblast, which is surrounded externally by the
(4) syntrophoblast (fig. 376C and D).

As development proceeds, the central core of mesenchyme with its blood capillaries increases in size, and the cytotrophoblast layer of the trophectoderm decreases in quantity, until, at about the fourth month, little remains of the cytotrophoblast layer with the exception of a few scattered cells below the syntrophoblast (fig. 376D).

The placental villi are grouped together into groups known as **cotyledons.** Between the cotyledons are the **placental septa,** which incompletely separate the various cotyledons from each other. The origin of the placental septa is uncertain, possibly being contributed to by both embryonic and maternal tissues. Surrounding the villi within each cotyledon is a pool of maternal blood which bathes the surfaces of the syntrophoblast of the villi. A hemochorial relationship is in this way established (fig. 373D).

4. IMPLANTATION IN THE RHESUS MONKEY, *Macaca mulatta*

The various stages of implantation and placental formation of the rhesus monkey are shown in figure 375F–K. It is to be observed that the monkey develops a **primary placenta** (fig. 375H and I) which later is supplemented by another placenta, the **secondary placenta,** attached to the opposite uterine wall (fig. 375J and K). Also, the embryo of the rhesus monkey, unlike the human embryo, does not bury itself within the uterine mucosa, and the cho-

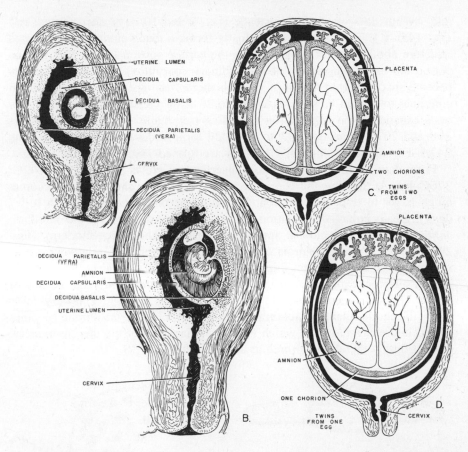

FIG. 377. Human placentation. (A) Condition at about 4 weeks. (B) About six weeks. Villi disappearing on one side, while those of chorion frondosum are enlarging. (A and B redrawn from Corner, 1944, Ourselves Unborn, Yale University Press, New Haven, Conn.) (C) Placental relationships in dizygotic (i.e. two fertilized eggs) twins implanted close together. Observe two chorionic vesicles, and two placentae. (D) Placental relationships in monozygotic (one fertilized egg) twins. Observe one chorionic vesicle, two amnions, and one placenta. (C and D redrawn from Dodds, 1938, The Essentials of Human Embryology, John Wiley & Sons, New York.)

rionic vesicle remains within the lumen of the uterus (see Wislocki and Streeter, '38).

5. IMPLANTATION OF THE PIG EMBRYO

As in the human the passage of the cleaving egg of the pig through the Fallopian tube is slow, consuming about 3½ days. When the egg reaches the uterus it still is surrounded by the zona pellucida and developmentally is in an advanced state of cleavage or early blastocyst formation (fig. 145H). It remains free in the uterine horn for about 6 to 7 days. During this period the blastocyst enlarges and elongates at a rapid pace, particularly during the sixth and seventh days of uterine existence (i.e., 9 and 10 days after copulation) (fig. 145I–L). The blastocyst eventually forms a much elongated attenuated structure about 1 meter long. During the earlier portion of the free uterine period the many blastocysts of the ordinary conceptual process in the sow become spaced within the horn of each uterus, an intriguing process which continues to remain baffling. From 10 to 13 days after copulation the blastocysts experience the gastrulation processes (see figure 145M–R; and figures 208 and 209); from days 13 to 15 body form is developed gradually (fig. 242A–F) and the amnion and chorion are formed (fig. 242G).

From days 14 to 17 the allantoic diverticulum grows rapidly (figs. 242G; 370C–D). At this time the chorionic vesicle as a whole shortens and becomes much larger in transverse section. The yolk sac of the embryo of 16 to 17 days is greatly enlarged in relation to the size of the embryo, and the entoderm at its distal end lies closely apposed against the chorionic ectoderm (figs. 242F; 370C). As the allantoic cavity expands, the yolk sac, relatively speaking, contracts, and a relationship is established similar to that in figure 370D. As the allantois expands its mesoderm comes in contact with the mesoderm of the chorionic membrane and fuses with it (fig. 370E). This new layer forms the **chorio-allantoic membrane.** The chorio-allantoic membrane becomes folded into elongated folds which fit into similar folds of the uterine mucosa. A relationship thereby is formed as shown in figure 373B.

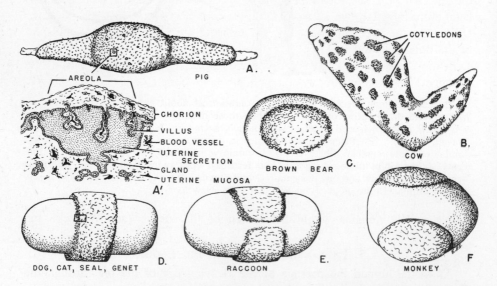

FIG. 378. External appearance of chorionic vesicles in various mammals. (A) Pig. This placental type is called *diffuse*. (A′) Enlarged drawing of small cotyledon or areola. (B) Cow. Observe large cotyledons. This type of placenta is called *cotyledonary*. (C) Brown bear. Special zonary placenta. (D) Dog, etc. Zonary placenta. (E) Raccoon, incomplete zonary placenta. (A, B–E, redrawn and modified from Hamilton, Boyd and Mossman, 1947, Human Embryology, Williams and Wilkins, Baltimore.)

In certain areas of the chorion, specialized structures or **areolae,** containing small villi, appear to slightly invade the uterine glands (fig. 378A'). However, the epithelium is not destroyed, and at all times the maternal and fetal aspects of the greatly expanded placental area (see figure 378A) may be separated without injury either to the chorionic or to the uterine epithelium.

6. FATE OF THE EMBRYONIC MEMBRANES

a. Yolk Sac

The yolk sac of teleost and elasmobranch fishes is withdrawn gradually toward the ventral body wall and intestine. The contribution of the yolk sac differs considerably in the two groups. In the teleost fishes, the somatopleuric portion of the yolk sac contributes much to the body wall while the splanchnopleuric tissues of the yolk sac form a considerable part of the latero-ventral region of the intestine. In the elasmobranch fishes, the somatopleuric layer of the yolk sac forms only a small area of the ventral body wall in the anterior trunk region, and the splanchnopleuric tissue of the yolk sac is withdrawn inward toward the duodenal area. This withdrawal of the splanchnopleuric tissue is a complex affair, for as the external yolk sac is withdrawn an internal yolk sac is developed as an evagination from the yolk stalk (vitelline duct) near the duodenum (fig. 296A). While the external yolk sac gets smaller the internal yolk sac increases in size, and after the external yolk sac has been entirely withdrawn a considerable part of the internal yolk sac remains. Ultimately the splanchnopleure of the internal yolk sac forms a small area of the duodenal wall.

In the chick the yolk sac is still large as hatching approaches. During the eighteenth and nineteenth days the yolk sac containing a considerable amount of yolk is withdrawn into the body cavity through the **umbilicus.** Here the yolk is absorbed rapidly and the yolk sac tissues are taken up into the wall of the intestine about 5 or 6 days after hatching.

The yolk sac of the higher mammals does not contain yolk substance. One of its main functions is the formation of the first blood cells (see Chapter 17). The yolk stalk and yolk sac increase somewhat in size during the early phases of development. Ultimately the yolk stalk becomes greatly elongated and separates from the yolk sac. The proximal portion of the yolk stalk is taken up into the wall of the intestine. In the human embryo, the area of yolk stalk inclusion into the intestinal wall is about 18 to 24 inches proximal to the ilio-caecal area.

b. Amnion and Allantois

The amnion and allantois of the Amniota function until birth. During parturition the amnion generally ruptures, but may remain intact around the offspring. For example, in a litter of six puppies, half of the amnions may be ruptured and half may be intact. The intact amnion must then be ruptured or the puppy will suffocate. In the human the **after-birth** consists of the following:

(a) the maternal membranes—decidua vera, decidua basalis, and decidua capsularis (vera), and

(b) the fetal membranes—chorion frondosum, chorion laeve, amnion, yolk sac, allantois, and umbilical cord.

D. Functions of the Placenta

The functions of the placenta are many, and the more intimate the contact with the maternal tissue the functions appear to increase. The various functions of the placenta may be listed as follows:

(1) Food materials pass from the maternal blood stream to the blood stream of the embryo.

(2) Waste materials pass from the embryo's circulatory system to the blood stream of the mother.

(3) Serves as the external respiratory mechanism for the embryo.

(4) It functions to elaborate two ovarian hormones, **estrogen** and **progesterone** (see Chapter 2) together with **chorionic follicle-stimulating and luteinizing hormones.** The production of estrogen and progesterone helps maintain pregnancy (see Chapter 2) and at the same time brings about the development of the mammary glands.

(5) The placenta and after-birth tissues form a source of nourishment to the female of many mammals, for it is generally eaten by the mother.

E. Tests for Pregnancy

The elaboration of chorionic follicle-stimulating and luteinizing hormones by the placenta in increasing amounts during the first part of pregnancy and their excretion by the kidneys makes possible certain tests for the detection of pregnancy (see Engle, '39).

1. ASCHHEIM-ZONDEK TEST

Aschheim and Zondek were the first investigators to detect gonad-stimulating principles in the urine of pregnant women. The excretion of these substances in pregnancy urine begins during the second week, about the fifteenth day, rises sharply to the thirtieth day and then gradually falls to the ninetieth day (Siegler and Fein, '39). This secretion probably is elaborated by the trophoblast of the developing chorion during the second week of pregnancy and later by the epithelium of the chorionic portion of the placenta. The presence of these gonad-stimulating substances in the urine provokes reproductive changes in the ovaries of common laboratory animals when injected with the urine. Aschheim and Zondek were the first to use this method for detecting pregnancy. The method consists of the injection of small amounts of pregnancy urine into mice and rats and, later, observing the appearance of hemorrhagic conditions of the follicles within the ovaries. A modification of the Aschheim-Zondek or A-Z test used by Kupperman, Greenblatt, and Noback, '43, consists of the injection of 1.5 cc. of a morning sample of urine into the lower portion of the abdomen of immature rats. The animal is killed with ether after two hours and pronounced hyperemic conditions of the ovary are observed as a positive test.

2. FRIEDMAN MODIFICATION OF THE ASCHHEIM-ZONDEK TEST

In this test 10 cc. of the suspected urine is injected into the marginal vein of the rabbit's ear. In about 12 to 24 hours a positive test is denoted by ovulation points (blood points) on the ovarian surface and by hemorrhagic conditions within the follicles. This test is as accurate as the original A-Z test and works in almost 98 to 99 per cent of the cases.

3. TOAD TEST

When the "clawed toad" of South Africa, *Xenopus laevis,* is injected with pregnancy urine, the animal ovulates within a few hours and the eggs are easily detected.

4. FROG TEST

Wiltberger and Miller, '48, advocate the following test. Five cc. of a first morning (overnight) sample of urine is carefully injected subcutaneously into the dorsal or lateral lymph sacs of a male frog. Two or more frogs are used. Each frog is then placed in a clean, dry, glass jar with perforated lid. After 2 to 4 hours at ordinary room temperature, any urine that is voided by the frogs is examined microscopically. If urine is not present, the frog is seized by the hand while still in the jar. This treatment usually results in urination. Sperm in the urine denotes a positive test.

F. The Developing Circulatory System in Relation to Nutrition, etc.

All of the developing systems undergo gradual alterations which are integrated with, and contribute to, the ever-changing demands involved in the welfare of the embryo. However, the circulatory system is the one system which must assume the burden of transport of food materials, oxygen, and water to the developing systems. Synchronously it transports deleterious substances to the areas of elimination. While assuming this burden it also must evolve its own development to bring about the structure of the adult form of the circulatory system.

A striking example of the dual burden carried by the developing circulatory system is presented in the changes which go on a short time before and after birth (mammals) or hatching (reptiles and birds). The placental area in mammals and the chorio-allantoic structures in reptiles and birds act as respiratory

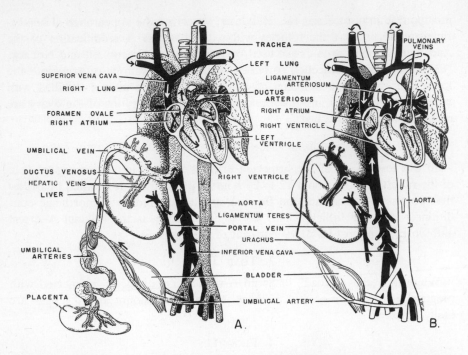

FIG. 379. Diagrams of probable fetal and postpartum circulations through the heart in the mammal.   (A) Fetal circulation. Oxygenated blood passes through umbilical vein, to liver. Passing through the liver by means of the ductus venosus it gathers blood from the liver veins and empties into the inferior vena cava through the hepatic vein. Within the inferior vena cava it mixes with non-oxygenated blood from the posterior part of the body. Reaching the right atrium it passes across the atrium through the foramen ovale and into the left atrium and from thence into left ventricle. The blood from the superior vena cava crosses to one side of the blood current from the inferior vena cava in the right atrium on its way to right ventricle. Most of the blood from the right ventricle courses through the ductus arteriosus into the descending aorta. A small amount goes to the lungs via the pulmonary arteries.   (B) Circulation after birth. Observe there is no passage of blood from the right atrium into the left atrium. The blood in the left atrium is returning oxygenated blood from the lungs. The ductus arteriosus has atrophied. (See text.) (A redrawn and modified from Windle, 1940, Physiology of the Fetus, Saunders, Philadelphia. B adapted from A.)

and excretory regions before birth and hatching. The circulatory system therefore must accommodate these areas in the fulfillment of the respiratory and excretory functions. However, at the same time the developing heart and immediate blood vessels in relation to the heart also must look forward, as it were, to the requirements of the period after birth (mammals) or after hatching (reptiles and birds). A diagram of the circulation of the blood through the heart previous to birth in the mammalian heart is shown in figure 379A, and figure 379B delineates the pathway of the blood after birth. Before birth the valve-like arrangement of the interatrial septa, I and II, permits the oxygenated blood from the placenta to flow from the right atrium into the left atrium. From the left atrium the blood passes into the left ventricle and from thence out through the aortic root to supply heart tissues, head region and systemic structures in general. On the other hand, the blood from the superior vena cava flows through the right atrium to the right ventricle, and from there it is propelled out into the proximal portion of the pulmonary artery, and through the ductus arteriosus (Botalli) (left sixth aortal arch) to the systemic aorta. The unaerated blood from the right ventricle

Fig. 380. Care of young.   (A) Egg capsule of *Scyllium canicula* (dogfish) containing developing egg fastened on seaweed by means of terminal tendrils. (Redrawn from Kyle, 1926, The Biology of Fishes, Sidgwick and Jackson, Ltd., London, after Varges. (B) Male bowfin *(Amia)* guarding young. (Redrawn from Dean, 1896, Quart. J. Micros. Sci. **38.**)   (C) Scarlet tanager feeding young. (Redrawn from photo by A. A. Allen, in Pennsylvania Bird-Life, pub. by Pa. Game Commission, Harrisburg, Pa.)   (D) Opossum, suckling young.   (E) Female hedgehog *(Erinaceus europeus)* guarding young. (Redrawn from Figuier, 1870, Mammalia, D. Appleton and Co., New York.)

in this way is mixed with aerated blood within the descending aorta. Some circulation to and from the capillary bed within the lungs also occurs at this period.

At birth and after, the change in the place of oxygenation of the blood from the placental area to the lungs with the stoppage of the blood flow through the umbilical vessels, necessitates the changes shown in figure 379B. The closure, normally, of the foramen ovale in interatrial septum II, together with the shrinkage of the ductus arteriosus to form the **ligamentum arteriosum** accommodates this change in direction of blood flow. The alterations which effect the stoppage of blood flow through the foramen ovale and ductus arteriosus are functional and they actually precede the morphological closure changes. The foramen ovale is functionally closed by the apposition of Septum I and Septum II. This apposition is effected by the equalization of the blood pressures in the right and left atria. However, the structural closure of the foramen ovale is produced by the growing together and gradual fusion of the two interatrial septa. The process is variable in different human individuals, and failure to attain complete structural closure of the foramen ovale occurs in about 20 to 25 per cent of the cases. Functionally, this failure to close may not be noticeable. On the other hand, in the heart of the kitten, failure to develop a complete morphological closure by 6 to 8 weeks after birth is rare.

The morphological closure of the ductus arteriosus also is gradual. This does not interfere with the relative normal functioning of the lungs for the opening up of the capillary bed within the lungs together with the concomitant voluminous flow of blood through the pulmonary arteries to the lungs, associated with the pressure exerted at the distal end of the ductus arteriosus by the blood within the descending aorta, aids the functional closure of the ductus arteriosus. In some individuals, the ductus arteriosus may remain open, to some degree, even in the adult.

G. Post-hatching and Post-partum Care of the Young (fig. 380)

Although care of the young after hatching or after birth is beyond the province of this work, it should be observed that such care is characteristic of birds and mammals, and is present in certain instances in fishes and amphibia (fig. 380B). In the marsupial mammals, the early post-partum care of the young in the marsupial pouch of the mother is closely related to the pre-hatching or pre-partum care of the young in other animal groups. In the opossum, for example (fig. 380D), the utterly helpless young are firmly attached to the nipples of the mother for about 50 days (McCrady, '38). This attachment in reality constitutes a kind of "oral placenta." From this viewpoint, the care of the developing embryo in marsupial mammals may be divided into two phases, namely, a **uterine phase** and an **early post-partum**

phase. The first phase in the North American opossum consumes about 13 days, and the latter about 50 days. After the young become free from their nipple attachment they spend about 40 days in and out of the marsupium.

Bibliography

Anderson, D. H. **1927.** The rate of passage of the mammalian ovum through various portions of the Fallopian tube. Am. J. Physiol. **82**:557.

Asmundson, V. S. and Burmester, B. R. **1936.** The secretory activity of the parts of the hen's oviduct. J. Exper. Zool. **72**:225.

Eigenmann, C. H. **1892.** On the viviparous fishes of the Pacific coast of North America. Bull. U. S. Fish Commission, Vol. **12**:381.

Engle, E. T. **1939.** Gonadotropic substances of blood, urine, and other body fluids. Chapter 18, Sex and Internal Secretions. Ed. by Allen, et al., Williams & Wilkins, Baltimore.

Flynn, T. T. and Hill, J. P. **1939.** Part IV: Growth of the ovarian ovum, maturation, fertilization, and early cleavage. Trans. Zool. Soc. London. 24 Part **6**:445.

Hertig, A. T. and Rock, J. **1945.** Two human ova of the pre-villous stage, having a developmental age of about seven and nine days respectively. Carnegie Inst. Publ. No. 557, Contrib. to Embryol. **31**:65.

Hisaw, F. L. and Albert, A. **1947.** Observations on reproduction of the spiny dogfish, *Squalus acanthias*. Biol. Bull. **92**:187.

Kerr, J. G. **1919.** Textbook of Embryology, Vol. II, The Macmillan Co., London.

Kupperman, H. S., Greenblatt, R. B., and Noback, C. R. **1943.** A two- and six-hour pregnancy test. J. Clinical Endocrinol. **3**:548.

Lewis, W. H. and Wright, E. S. **1935.** On the early development of the mouse egg Carnegie Inst. Publ. Contrib. to Embryol. **25**:113.

McCrady, E., Jr. **1938.** The embryology of the opossum, The American Anatomical Memoirs, No. 16. The Wistar Institute of Anatomy and Biology, Philadelphia.

Mossman, H. W. **1937.** Comparative morphogenesis of the fetal membranes and accessory uterine structures. Carnegie Inst. Publ. No. 479. Contrib. to Embryol. **26**:129.

Noble, G. K. **1931.** The Biology of the Amphibia, McGraw-Hill Book Co., New York.

Romanoff, A. L. and Romanoff, A. J. **1949.** The Avian Egg. John Wiley and Sons, New York.

Scrimshaw, N. S. **1944.** Embryonic growth in the viviparous poeliciid, *Heterandria formosa*. Biol. Bull. **87**:37.

Siegler, S. L. and Fein, M. J. **1939.** Studies in artificial ovulation with the hormone of pregnant mares' serum. Am. J. Obst. & Gynec. **38**:1021.

TeWinkle, L. E. **1941.** Structures concerned with yolk absorption in *Squalus acanthias*. Biol. Bull. **81**:292.

⸻. **1943.** Observations on later phases of embryonic nutrition in *Squalus acanthias*. J. Morph. **73**:177.

⸻. **1950.** Notes on ovulation, ova, and early development in the smooth dogfish, *Mustelus canis*. Biol. Bull. **99**:474.

Wiltberger, P. B. and Miller, D. F. **1948.** The male frog, *Rana pipiens,* as a new test animal for early pregnancy. Science. **107**:198.

Index

Page references in *italic* type refer to illustrations in text; those followed by t refer to tables.

A

A-Z test, for pregnancy, 927
Abomasum, of cow or sheep, 623
Acetylocholine, *838*
Acids, role of in egg activation, 218
Acipenser, reproductive and urinary ducts of, *799*
   A. fulvescens, xvii
   A. sturio, cleavage in, 308, *309*
Acoustico-lateral system, 813
Acraniata, xv
Acroblast, 126, 150
  in guinea pig sperm, 150
  in human sperm, 150
  multiple, in grasshopper, *150*
Acrodont tooth, 607
Acrosome, 148
  formation of, 150
  role of in egg-sperm contact, 232
  shapes and positions of, *143*
Activation, of egg (*see also* Egg, activation of)
   acids in, 217
   artificial, 217
    in *Arbacia*, 218
    role of temperature in, 219
   by strichnine, 218
   complete, 212
   fertilizin in, 225
   in hypertonic sea water, 217, 218
   membrane formation during, 218
   partial, 212, 217
  of sperm, during fertilization, 212
Addison, Thomas, 882
Addison's disease, 882
Adelmann, H. B., 716
Adipose glands, 665
Adipose tissue, 658
  formation of, 664
Adrenal glands, 882
  differentiation of, *883*
  role of secretions of in color change, 594
  structure of, 882
Adrenalin (Adrenaline), *838*
Adrenaline (Adrenalin), 882
Aerial adaptations, of muscles, 708
After-birth, in human, 926

Aftershaft, of feather, 571, 578
Agglutination, of egg during fertilization, and sperm secretions, 230
  of sperm, 225
Agglutinin factor, 225
Air-bladder evagination, of pharynx, dorsal, 601
  dorso-lateral, 601
Air sacs, cellular composition of, 649
  formation of in chick embryo, 646
  in bird group, 644
  interclavicular, 647
  intermediate, anterior, 647
  posterior, 647
Alar plate, 820
Albumen, deposition of in birds, middle dense layer of, 905
  outer liquid layer of, 905
Albumen-secreting region, in oviduct of bird, 905
Albuminous layer, of rabbit and opossum eggs, 303
Albuminous sac, of bird's egg, 905
Allanson, M., 46
Allantoic stalk, 911
Allantoic veins (*see* Veins, allantoic)
Allantois, 902, 908, 910
  fate of, 925
Allen, B. M., 883, 884
Alligator, ventricles of heart of, *704*
Alligator mississippiensis, xviii
  egg, characteristics of, 204t
  fertilization, site of, 204t
  sperm entrance into egg, place of, 204t
Allophores, 591
Alveolar ducts, 650
Alveolar sacs, 650
Alveolus (Alveoli), of lung, structure of, 650
  of jaw, 611
Ambystoma, effect of primordial germ cells on gonad maturation in, 121
  fate of pre-chordal plate mesoderm in, 525
  pineal organ of, 881
  spermatheca of, *190*
Ambystoma maculatum, equatorial plane of cleavage in, 283

933

Estrous cycle, factors controlling, 96
  follicular phase of, 92
  in mammals, 92
  luteal phase of, 92
Estrus, definition of, 93
  relation of to activity of oviduct during
    egg transport, 200
  relation of to ovulation, 95
Eustachian duct (see Eustachian tube)
Eustachian tube, *841, 851, 855*
Eustachian valve, of chick heart, 756
Eutheria, xx
Evagination, scrotal, 11
Evans, H. M., 41
"Ex ovo omnia," 53, *54*
Excretory duct, main, of kidney, 772
Excretory system, 768
  development of, 772
  functions of, 769
Exoccipital center, of ossification, 695
Exocrine glands, 875
Exogastrulation, 449
Exogenous sources, of food for embryo,
  902
Exoskeleton, 668
Extension, in gastrulation, definition of,
  398
External auditory meatus, 855
External naris, 844
Exteroceptive field, 842
Extodermal expansion, definition of, 395
  (*see also* Epiboly)
Extra-embryonic coelom, 909
Extra-embryonic membranes, 901
  diagrams of, *909*
  in human embryo, *912*
Eycleshymer, A. C., *306, 308, 473*
Eye, accessory structures of, 853
  development of, 844
    special aspects of, 846
  extrinsic muscles of, development of,
    716
  general structure of, 844
Eyelids, 853

F

Fabricius, bursa of, 602, 881
Falciform ligament, 866
  of liver, 873
Falciform process, of teleost fish eye, 849
Fallopian tube, in rabbit, behavior in sperm
  transport, 193
Fankhauser, G., 160, *270*
Fascia deep, 556
  spermatic, external, 13
    internal, 13
    middle, 13

Fascia deep—*(Continued)*
  superficial, 556
  perineal, 12
Fasciculus (Fasciculi), definition of, 701
  or muscle fiber bundles, 701
Fasciculus cuneatus, 821
Fasciculus gracilis, 821
Fat, brown, 664, 665
  types of, 664
  white, 664
Fat droplets, origin of, 157
Feather(s), after shaft, formation of, 571,
  578
  contour, 571
    development of, 575
      early phase of, 575
      secondary phase of, 575
    development of, *577*
      in chick, *572*
  down, 573
    later, development of, 578
  filoplumous, development of, 578
  general structure of, 571
  nestling down, development of, 573
Feather follicle, 571
Feather vane, formation of, 576
Felis (see Cat, *Felis)*
Felix, W., 778, *785, 787, 791, 792, 794, 797*
Fenestra cochlea, *851*
Fenestra ovalis, *851*
Fenestra rotunda, *851*
Fenestra vestibuli, *851*
Fenestrae, of atrial septum of chick heart,
  754
Ferret, pituitary ablation of, 39
Ferret, *Putorius vulgaris,* effect of light
  upon reproductive activities, 44,
  45
Fertilization, 211
  areas of, 189
  behavior of gametes during, 221
  changes in physiological activities at, 243
  definition, 113, 211
  dry, 232
  external, and reproductive duct, 17
  fusion of gametes at, 234
  in *Echidna, 254, 255*
  in *Gambusia affinis,* 199
  in hen's egg, *252*
  in *Heterandria formosa,* 199
  in ovary, 197
  in *Styela* (Cynthia) *partita, 224, 245*
  internal, general features of, 189
    reproductive duct in, 18
    sperm transport in, 189
  metabolic change at, 243
  movements of ooplasmic substances dur-
    ing *Styela, 264*

G